Encyclopedia of

INFANT AND EARLY CHILDHOOD DEVELOPMENT

ENCYCLOPEDIA OF INFANT AND EARLY CHILDHOOD DEVELOPMENT

EDITORS-IN-CHIEF

MARSHALL M. HAITH
and
JANETTE B. BENSON
Department of Psychology, University of Denver,
Denver, Colorado, USA

ELSEVIER

AMSTERDAM • BOSTON • HEIDELBERG • LONDON • NEW YORK • OXFORD
PARIS • SAN DIEGO • SAN FRANCISCO • SINGAPORE • SYDNEY • TOKYO
Academic Press is an imprint of Elsevier

ACADEMIC
PRESS

Academic Press is an imprint of Elsevier
The Boulevard, Langford Lane, Kidlington, Oxford OX5 1GB, UK
525 B Street, Suite 1900, San Diego, CA 92101-4495, USA

First edition 2008

British Library Cataloguing in Publication Data
A catalogue record for this book is available from the British Library

Library of Congress Catalog Number: 2007930619

ISBN: 978-0-12-370460-3

For information on all Elsevier publications
visit our website at books.elsevier.com

PRINTED AND BOUND IN CANADA
07 08 09 10 11 10 9 8 7 6 5 4 3 2 1

EDITORS-IN-CHIEF

Marshall M. Haith received his M.A. and Ph.D. degrees from U.C.L.A. and then carried out postdoctoral work at Yale University from 1964–1966. He served as Assistant Professor and Lecturer at Harvard University from 1966–1972 and then moved to the University of Denver as Professor of Psychology, where he has conducted research on infant and children's perception and cognition, funded by NIH, NIMH, NSF, The MacArthur Foundation, The March of Dimes, and The Grant Foundation. He has been Head of the Developmental Area, Chair of Psychology, and Director of University Research at the University of Denver and is currently John Evans Professor Emeritus of Psychology and Clinical Professor of Psychiatry at the University of Colorado Health Sciences Center.

Dr. Haith has served as consultant for Children's Television Workshop (Sesame Street), Bilingual Children's Television, Time-Life, and several other organizations. He has received several personal awards, including University Lecturer and the John Evans Professor Award from the University of Denver, a Guggenheim Fellowship for serving as Visiting Professor at the University of Paris and University of Geneva, a NSF fellowship at the Center for Advanced Study in the Behavioral Sciences (Stanford), the G. Stanley Hall Award from the American Psychological Association, a Research Scientist Award from NIH (17 years), and the Distinguished Scientific Contribution Award from the Society for Research in Child Development.

Janette B. Benson earned graduate degrees at Clark University in Worcester, MA in 1980 and 1983. She came to the University of Denver in 1983 as an institutional postdoctoral fellow and then was awarded an individual NRSA postdoctoral fellowship. She has received research funding form federal (NICHD; NSF) and private (March of Dimes, MacArthur Foundation) grants, leading initially to a research Assistant Professor position and then an Assistant Professorship in Psychology at the University of Denver in 1987, where she remains today as Associate Professor of Psychology and as Director of the undergraduate Psychology program and Area Head of the Developmental Ph.D. program and Director of University Assessment. Dr. Benson has received various awards for her scholarship and teaching, including the 1993 United Methodist Church University Teacher Scholar of the Year and in 2000 the CASE Colorado Professor of the Year. Dr. Benson was selected by the American Psychological Association as the 1995–1996 Esther Katz Rosen endowed Child Policy Fellow and AAAS Congressional Science Fellow, spending a year in the United States Senate working on Child and Education Policy. In 1999, Dr. Benson was selected as a Carnegie Scholar and attended two summer institutes sponsored by the Carnegie Foundation program for the Advancement for the Scholarship of Teaching and Learning in Palo Alto, CA. In 2001, Dr. Benson was awarded a Susan and Donald Sturm Professorship for Excellence in Teaching. Dr. Benson has authored and co-authored numerous chapters and research articles on infant and early childhood development in addition to co-editing two books.

EDITORIAL BOARD

Richard Aslin is the William R. Kenan Professor of Brain and Cognitive Sciences at the University of Rochester and is also the director of the Rochester Center for Brain Imaging. His research has been directed to basic aspects of sensory and perceptual development in the visual and speech domains, but more recently has focused on mechanisms of statistical learning in vision and language and the underlying brain mechanisms that support it. He has published over 100 journal articles and book chapters and his research has been supported by NIH, NSF, ONR, and the Packard and McDonnell Foundations. In addition to service on grant review panels at NIH and NSF, he is currently the editor of the journal *Infancy*. In 1981 he received the Boyd R. McCandless award from APA (Division 7), in 1982 the Early Career award from APA (developmental), in 1988 a fellowship from the John Simon Guggenheim foundation, and in 2006 was elected to the American Academy of Arts and Sciences.

Warren O. Eaton is Professor of Psychology at the University of Manitoba in Winnipeg, Canada, where he has spent his entire academic career. He is a fellow of the Canadian Psychological Association, and has served as the editor of one of its journals, the *Canadian Journal of Behavioural Science*. His current research interests center on child-to-child variation in developmental timing and how such variation may contribute to later outcomes.

Robert Newcomb Emde is Professor of Psychiatry, Emeritus, at the University of Colorado School of Medicine. His research over the years has focused on early socio-emotional development, infant mental health and preventive interventions in early childhood. He is currently Honorary President of the World Association of Infant Mental Health and serves on the Board of Directors of Zero To Three.

Hill Goldsmith is Fluno Bascom Professor and Leona Tyler Professor of Psychology at the University of Wisconsin–Madison. He works closely with Wisconsin faculty in the Center for Affective Science, and he is the coordinator of the Social and Affective Processes Group at the Waisman Center on Mental Retardation and Human Development. Among other honors, Goldsmith has received an National Institute of Mental Health MERIT award, a Research Career Development Award from the National Institute of Child Health and Human Development, the James Shields Memorial Award for Twin Research from the Behavior Genetics Association, and various awards from his university. He is a Fellow of AAAS and a Charter Fellow of the Association for Psychological Science. Goldsmith has also served the National Institutes of Health in several capacities. His editorial duties have included a term as Associate Editor of one journal and membership on the editorial boards of the five most important journals in his field. His administrative duties have included service as department chair at the University of Wisconsin.

Richard B. Johnston Jr. is Professor of Pediatrics and Associate Dean for Research Development at the University of Colorado School of Medicine and Associate Executive Vice President of Academic Affairs at the National Jewish Medical & Research Center. He is the former President of the American Pediatric Society and former Chairman of the International Pediatric Research Foundation. He is board certified in pediatrics and infectious disease. He has previously acted as the Chief of Immunology in the Department of Pediatrics at Yale University School of Medicine, been the Medical Director of the March of Dimes Birth Defects Foundation, Physician-in-Chief at the Children's Hospital of Philadelphia and Chair of the Department of Pediatrics at the University Pennsylvania School of Medicine. He is editor of "Current Opinion in Pediatrics" and has formerly served on the editorial board for a host of journals in pediatrics and infectious disease. He has published over 80 scientific articles and reviews and has been cited over 200 times for his articles on tissue injury in inflammation, granulomatous disease, and his New England Journal of Medicine article on immunology, monocytes, and macrophages.

FOREWORD

This is an impressive collection of what we have learned about infant and child behavior by the researchers who have contributed to this knowledge. Research on infant development has dramatically changed our perceptions of the infant and young child. This wonderful resource brings together like a mosaic all that we have learned about the infant and child's behavior. In the 1950s, it was believed that newborn babies couldn't see or hear. Infants were seen as lumps of clay that were molded by their experience with parents, and as a result, parents took all the credit or blame for how their offspring turned out. Now we know differently.

The infant contributes to the process of attaching to his/her parents, toward shaping their image of him, toward shaping the family as a system, and toward shaping the culture around him. Even before birth, the fetus is influenced by the intrauterine environment as well as genetics. His behavior at birth shapes the parent's nurturing to him, from which nature and nurture interact in complex ways to shape the child.

Geneticists are now challenged to couch their findings in ways that acknowledge the complexity of the interrelation between nature and nurture. The cognitivists, inheritors of Piaget, must now recognize that cognitive development is encased in emotional development, and fueled by passionately attached parents. As we move into the era of brain research, the map of infant and child behavior laid out in these volumes will challenge researchers to better understand the brain, as the basis for the complex behaviors documented here. No more a lump of clay, we now recognize the child as a major contributor to his own brain's development.

This wonderful reference will be a valuable resource for all of those interested in child development, be they students, researchers, clinicians, or passionate parents.

T. Berry Brazelton, M.D.
Professor of Pediatrics, Emeritus Harvard Medical School
Creator, Neonatal Behavioral Assessment Scale (NBAS)
Founder, Brazelton Touchpoints Center

PREFACE

Encyclopedias are wonderful resources. Where else can you find, in one place, coverage of such a broad range of topics, each pursued in depth, for a particular field such as human development in the first three years of life? Textbooks have their place but only whet one's appetite for particular topics for the serious reader. Journal articles are the lifeblood of science, but are aimed only to researchers in specialized fields and often only address one aspect of an issue. Encyclopedias fill the gap.

In this encyclopedia readers will find overviews and summaries of current knowledge about early human development from almost every perspective imaginable. For much of human history, interest in early development was the province of pedagogy, medicine, and philosophy. Times have changed. Our culling of potential topics for inclusion in this work from textbooks, journals, specialty books, and other sources brought home the realization that early human development is now of central interest for a broad array of the social and biological sciences, medicine, and even the humanities. Although the 'center of gravity' of these volumes is psychology and its disciplines (sensation, perception, action, cognition, language, personality, social, clinical), the fields of embryology, immunology, genetics, psychiatry, anthropology, kinesiology, pediatrics, nutrition, education, neuroscience, toxicology and health science also have their say as well as the disciplines of parenting, art, music, philosophy, public policy, and more.

Quality was a key focus for us and the publisher in our attempts to bring forth the authoritative work in the field. We started with an Editorial Advisory Board consisting of major contributors to the field of human development – editors of major journals, presidents of our professional societies, authors of highly visible books and journal articles. The Board nominated experts in topic areas, many of them pioneers and leaders in their fields, whom we were successful in recruiting partly as a consequence of Board members' reputations for leadership and excellence. The result is articles of exceptional quality, written to be accessible to a broad readership, that are current, imaginative and highly readable.

Interest in and opinion about early human development is woven through human history. One can find pronouncements about the import of breast feeding (usually made by men), for example, at least as far back as the Greek and Roman eras, repeated through the ages to the current day. Even earlier, the Bible provided advice about nutrition during pregnancy and rearing practices. But the science of human development can be traced back little more than 100 years, and one can not help but be impressed by the methodologies and technology that are documented in these volumes for learning about infants and toddlers – including methods for studying the role of genetics, the growth of the brain, what infants know about their world, and much more. Scientific advances lean heavily on methods and technology, and few areas have matched the growth of knowledge about human development over the last few decades. The reader will be introduced not only to current knowledge in this field but also to how that knowledge is acquired and the promise of these methods and technology for future discoveries.

CONTENTS

Several strands run through this work. Of course, the nature-nurture debate is one, but no one seriously stands at one or the other end of this controversy any more. Although advances in genetics and behavior genetics have been breathtaking, even the genetics work has documented the role of environment in development and, as Brazelton notes in his foreword, researchers acknowledge that experience can change the wiring of the brain as well as how actively the genes are expressed. There is increasing appreciation that the child develops in a transactional context, with the child's effect on the parents and others playing no small role in his or her own development.

There has been increasing interest in brain development, partly fostered by the decade of the Brain in the 1990s, as we have learned more about the role of early experience in shaping the brain and consequently, personality, emotion, and intelligence. The 'brainy baby' movement has rightly aroused interest in infants' surprising capabilities, but the full picture of how abilities develop is being fleshed out as researchers learn as much about what infants can not do, as they learn about what infants can do. Parents wait for verifiable information about how advances may promote effective parenting.

An increasing appreciation that development begins in the womb rather than at birth has taken place both in the fields of psychology and medicine. Prenatal and newborn screening tools are now available that identify infants at genetic or developmental risk. In some cases remedial steps can be taken to foster optimal development; in others ethical issues may be involved when it is discovered that a fetus will face life challenges if brought to term. These advances raise issues that currently divide much of public opinion. Technological progress in the field of human development, as in other domains, sometimes makes options available that create as much dilemma as opportunity.

As globalization increases and with more access to electronic communication, we become ever more aware of circumstances around the world that affect early human development and the fate of parents. We encouraged authors to include international information wherever possible. Discussion of international trends in such areas as infant mortality, disease, nutrition, obesity, and health care are no less than riveting and often heartbreaking. There is so much more to do.

The central focus of the articles is on typical development. However, considerable attention is also paid to psychological and medical pathology in our attempt to provide readers with a complete picture of the state of knowledge about the field. We also asked authors to tell a complete story in their articles, assuming that readers will come to this work with a particular topic in mind, rather than reading the Encyclopedia whole or many articles at one time. As a result, there is some overlap between articles at the edges; one can think of partly overlapping circles of content, which was a design principle inasmuch as nature does not neatly carve topics in human development into discrete slices for our convenience. At the end of each article, readers will find suggestions for further readings that will permit them to take off in one neighboring direction or another, as well as web sites where they can garner additional information of interest.

AUDIENCE

Articles have been prepared for a broad readership, including advanced undergraduates, graduate students, professionals in allied fields, parents, and even researchers for their own disciplines. We plan to use several of these articles as readings for our own seminars.

A project of this scale involves many actors. We are very appreciative for the advice and review efforts of members of the Editorial Advisory Board as well as the efforts of our authors to abide by the guidelines that we set out for them. Nikki Levy, the publisher at Elsevier for this work, has been a constant source of wise advice, consolation and balance. Her vision and encouragement made this project possible. Barbara Makinster, also from Elsevier, provided many valuable suggestions for us. Finally, the Production team in England played a central role in communicating with authors and helping to keep the records straight. It is difficult to communicate all the complexities of a project this vast; let us just say that we are thankful for the resource base that Elsevier provided. Finally, we thank our families and colleagues for their patience over the past few years, and we promise to ban the words "encyclopedia project" from our vocabulary, for at least a while.

Marshall M. Haith
and
Janette B. Benson
Department of Psychology, University of Denver
Denver, Colorado, USA

HOW TO USE THE ENCYCLOPEDIA

The Encyclopedia of Infant and Early Childhood Development is intended for use by students, research professionals, and interested others. Articles have been chosen to reflect major disciplines in the study of infant and early child development, common topics of research by academics in this domain, and areas of public interest and concern. Each article serves as a comprehensive overview of a given area, providing both breadth of coverage for students, and depth of coverage for research professionals. We have designed the encyclopedia with the following features for maximum accessibility for all readers.

Articles in the encyclopedia are arranged alphabetically by subject in the Contents list. The index is located in volume 3. Some topics are covered in a multitude of articles from differing perspectives, while other topics may have only one entry. We encourage use of the index for access to a subject area, rather than use of the Contents list alone, so that a reader has a full notion of the coverage of that topic. The influence of the family on an infant, for example, may be covered under separate articles on Family Dynamics, Birth Order, Siblings and Sibling Rivalry, Family Influences, and Parenting Styles and Their Effects. A reader searching under F for family in the Contents list would easily find one of these articles but would miss the others.

Each article contains a glossary, cross-references to other related encyclopedia articles, and suggested readings where applicable, and relevant websites for additional information. The glossary contains terms that may be unfamiliar to the reader, with each term defined *in the context of its use in that article*. Thus, a term may appear in the glossary for another article defined in a slightly different manner or with a subtle nuance specific to that article. For clarity, we have allowed these differences in definition to remain so that each article is fully understandable on its own.

Each article has been cross-referenced to other related articles in the encyclopedia at the close of each article. We encourage readers to use the cross-references to locate other encyclopedia articles that will provide more detailed information about a subject.

The suggested readings include recent secondary sources to aid the reader in locating more detailed or technical information. Review articles and research articles that are considered of primary importance to the understanding of a given subject area are also listed. These suggested readings are not intended to provide a full reference listing of all material covered in the context of a given article, but are provided as next steps for a reader looking for additional information.

CONTRIBUTORS

B Ackerson
University of Illinois at Urbana–Champaign, Urbana, IL, USA

D Adams
National Institutes of Health, Bethesda, MD, USA

K E Adolph
New York University, New York City, NY, USA

A Ahuja
National Jewish Hospital, Denver, CO, USA

N Akhtar
University of California, Santa Cruz, Santa Cruz, CA, USA

A Almas
University of Toronto, Toronto, ON, Canada

S Al'Otaiba
Florida State University, Tallahassee, FL, USA

H Als
Harvard Medical School, Boston, MA, USA

K M Andrews
McGill University, Montreal, QC, Canada

M E Arterberry
Colby College, Waterville, ME, USA

J B Asendorpf
Humboldt-Universität zu Berlin, Berlin, Germany

D H Ashmead
Vanderbilt University Medical Center, Nashville, TN, USA

R N Aslin
University of Rochester, Rochester, NY, USA

J W Astington
University of Toronto, Toronto, ON, Canada

J Atkinson
University College London, London, UK

L E Bahrick
Florida International University, Miami, FL, USA

D B Bailey
RTI International, Research Triangle Park, NC, USA

L A Baker
University of Southern California, Los Angeles, CA, USA

A Balasubramanian
University of California, Riverside, Riverside, CA, USA

R Barr
University of British Columbia, Vancouver, BC, Canada

P J Bauer
Emory University, Atlanta, GA, USA

A Baxter
University of South Alabama, Mobile, AL, USA

A Belden
Washington University School of Medicine, St. Louis, MO, USA

D Benoit
University of Toronto, Toronto, ON, Canada;
The Hospital for Sick Children, Toronto, ON, Canada

D Bergen
Miami University, Oxford, OH, USA

K Bernard
University of Delaware, Newark, DE, USA

B I Bertenthal
Indiana University, Bloomington, IN, USA

J Bhagwat
Cornell University, Ithaca, NY, USA

N Bhullar
Widener University, Chester, PA, USA

A E Bigelow
St. Francis Xavier University, Antigonish, NS, Canada

M M Black
University of Maryland, Baltimore, MD, USA

E Blass
University of Massachusetts, Amherst, MA, USA

N J Blum
University of Pennsylvania School of Medicine, Philadelphia, PA, USA

C A Boeving
Yale University School of Medicine, New Haven, CT, USA

C F Bolling
Cincinnati Children's Hospital Medical Center, Cincinnati, OH, USA

M H Bornstein
National Institutes of Health, Bethesda, MD, USA

L Bosch
Universitat de Barcelona, Barcelona, Spain

O Braddick
University of Oxford, Oxford, UK

J Brooks-Gunn
Columbia University, New York, NY, USA

R T Brouillette
McGill University, Montreal, QC, Canada

A W Burks
Duke University Medical Center, Durham, NC, USA

S C Butler
Harvard Medical School, Boston, MA, USA

J P Byrnes
Temple University, Philadelphia, PA, USA

M L Campbell
Kennedy Krieger Institute, Baltimore, MD, USA

R L Canfield
Cornell University, Ithaca, NY, USA

S M Carlson
Institute of Child Development, Minneapolis, MN, USA

A S Carter
University of Massachusetts Boston, Boston, MA, USA

M Casasola
Cornell University, Ithaca, NY, USA

L M Casper
University of Southern California, Los Angeles, CA, USA

I Chatoor
Children's National Medical Center, Washington, DC, USA

A I Chin
University of California, Los Angeles, Los Angeles, CA, USA

R Clark
University of Wisconsin, Madison, WI, USA

A Clarke-Stewart
University of California, Irvine, Irvine, CA, USA

C M Connor
Florida State University, Tallahassee, FL, USA

J Coolbear
University of Toronto, Toronto, ON, Canada;
The Hospital for Sick Children, Toronto, ON, Canada

M L Courage
Memorial University, St. John's, NL, Canada

M J Cox
University of North Carolina, Chapel, NC, USA

A Crawford
University of Toronto, Toronto, ON, Canada;
Mount Sinai Hospital, Toronto, ON, Canada

E M Cummings
University of Notre Dame, Notre Dame, IN, USA

L A Dack
University of Toronto, Toronto, ON, Canada

M W Daehler
University of Massachusetts, Amherst, MA, USA

S R Daniels
University of Colorado Health Sciences Center, Denver, CO, USA

R B David
St. Mary's Hospital, Richmond, VA, USA

G Dawson
University of Washington, Seattle, WA, USA

L F DiLalla
Southern Illinois University School of Medicine, Carbondale, IL, USA

J A DiPietro
Johns Hopkins University, Baltimore, MD, USA

B M D'Onofrio
Indiana University, Bloomington, IN, USA

R L Doty
University of Pennsylvania School of Medicine, Philadelphia, PA, USA

M Dozier
University of Delaware, Newark, DE, USA

W O Eaton
University of Manitoba, Winnipeg, MB, Canada

C Edwards
University of Nebraska–Lincoln, Lincoln, NE, USA

K K Elam
Southern Illinois University School of Medicine, Carbondale, IL, USA

R R Espinal
University of Chicago, Chicago, IL, USA

R S Everhart
Syracuse University, Syracuse, NY, USA

D Fair
Washington University School of Medicine, St. Louis, MO, USA

F Farzin
University of California, Davis, Davis, CA, USA

D J Fidler
Colorado State University, Fort Collins, CO, USA

T Field
University of Miami School of Medicine, Miami, FL, USA

B H Fiese
Syracuse University, Syracuse, NY, USA

K W Fischer
Harvard Graduate School of Education, Cambridge, MA, USA

H E Fitzgerald
Michigan State University, East Lansing, MI, USA

D R Fleisher
University of Missouri School of Medicine, Columbia, MO, USA

M J Flory
New York State Institute for Basic Research, Staten Island, NY, USA

B Forsyth
Yale University School of Medicine, New Haven, CT, USA

S Fowler
University of Kansas, Lawrence, KS, USA

R C Fretts
Harvard Vanguard Medical Associates, Wellesley, MA, USA

J J Gallagher
University of North Carolina at Chapel Hill, Chapel Hill, NC, USA

J M Gardner
New York State Institute for Basic Research, Staten Island, NY, USA

J-L Gariépy
The University of North Carolina at Chapel Hill, Chapel Hill, NC, USA

M A Gartstein
Washington State University, Pullman, WA, USA

M Gauvain
University of California at Riverside, Riverside, CA, USA

D R Gemmill
California Sudden Infant Death Syndrome Advisory Council, Escondido, CA, USA

I R Gizer
Emory University, Atlanta, GA, USA

M M Gleason
Tulane University Health Sciences Center, New Orleans, LA, USA

M M Gleason
Brown University School of Medicine, Providence, RI, USA

R L Gómez
The University of Arizona, Tucson, AZ, USA

L Godoy
University of Massachusetts Boston, Boston, MA, USA

W A Goldberg
University of California, Irvine, CA, USA

E C Goldfield
Harvard University, Boston, MA, USA

S Goldin-Meadow
University of Chicago, Chicago, IL, USA

H H Goldsmith
University of Wisconsin–Madison, Madison, WI, USA

C Golomb
University of Massachusetts Boston, Boston, MA, USA

E L Grigorenko
Yale University, New Haven, CT, USA

J E Grusec
University of Toronto, Toronto, ON, Canada

L M Gutman
University of London, London, UK

M de Haan
University College London Institute of Child Health, London, UK

J W Hagen
University of Michigan, Ann Arbor, MI, USA

R J Hagerman
University of California, Davis, Medical Center, Sacramento, CA, USA

N Halfon
University of California, Los Angeles, Los Angeles, CA, USA

G S Halford
Griffith University, Brisbane, QLD, Australia

J Harel
University of Haifa, Haifa, Israel

K M Harrington
Emory University, Atlanta, GA, USA

H Hayne
University of Otago, Dunedin, New Zealand

L J Heffner
Boston Medical Center, Boston, MA, USA

N Heilbron
University of North Carolina, Chapel, NC, USA

R W Hendershot
University of Colorado at Denver Health Sciences Center, Denver, CO, USA

M Hernandez-Reif
University of Miami School of Medicine, Miami, FL, USA

K Herold
University of California, Santa Cruz, Santa Cruz, CA, USA

A H Hindman
University of Michigan, Ann Arbor, MI, USA

J A Hofheimer
University of North Carolina at Chapel Hill, Chapel Hill, NC, USA

C von Hofsten
Uppsala University, Uppsala, Sweden

G Hollich
Purdue University, West Lafayette, IN, USA

J R Hollister
University of Colorado at Denver and Health Sciences Center, Denver, CO, USA

A H Hoon
Kennedy Krieger Institute, Baltimore, MD, USA

N Howe
Concordia University, Montréal, QC, Canada

C Howes
University of California, Los Angeles, Los Angeles, CA, USA

A Hupbach
University of Arizona, Tucson, AZ, USA

J S Hyde
University of Wisconsin, Madison, WI, USA

J Isen
University of Southern California, Los Angeles, CA, USA

J S Jameson
Coloradoes State University, Fort Collins, CO, USA

T Jirikowic
University of Washington, Seattle, WA, USA

R Jochem
University of California, Davis, Davis, CA, USA

M H Johnson
University of London, London, UK

S P Johnson
New York University, New York, NY, USA

T R B Johnson
The University of Michigan, Ann Arbor, MI, USA

M V Johnston
Kennedy Krieger Institute, Baltimore, MD, USA

J Jones-Branch
University of Nebraska–Lincoln, Lincoln, NE, USA

T A Jusko
University of Washington, Seattle, WA, USA

J Kagan
Harvard University, Cambridge, MA, USA

J Kapala
McGill University Health Centre, Montréal, QC, Canada

B Z Karmel
New York State Institute for Basic Research, Staten Island, NY, USA

T G Keens
Keck School of Medicine of the University of Southern California, Los Angeles, CA, USA

D J Kelly
The University of Sheffield, Sheffield, UK

S King
University of Washington, Seattle, WA, USA

P Kitchen
University of Southern California, Los Angeles, CA, USA

J Koontz
University of California, Riverside, Riverside, CA, USA

C B Kopp
Los Angeles, CA, USA

C D Kouros
University of Notre Dame, Notre Dame, IN, USA

L L LaGasse
Warren Alpert Medical School of Brown University, Providence, RI, USA

F G Lamb-Parker
Columbia University, New York, NY, USA

M Lampl
Emory University, Atlanta, GA, USA

A L Lathrop
University of Rochester, Rochester, NY, USA

R A Lawrence
University of Rochester School of Medicine and Dentistry, Rochester, NY, USA

M S Leidy
University of California, Riverside, CA, USA

E M Lennon
New York State Institute for Basic Research, Staten Island, NY, USA

T A Lenzi
Vanderbilt University Medical Center, Nashville, TN, USA

S E Lerman
University of California, Los Angeles, Los Angeles, CA, USA

B M Lester
Warren Alpert Medical School of Brown University, Providence, RI, USA

H Liang
King's College London, London, UK

K Libertus
Duke University, Durham, NC, USA

E Lieven
Max Planck Institute for Evolutionary Anthropology, Leipzig, Germany

B Lozoff
University of Michigan, Ann Arbor, MI, USA

J S Lu
David Geffen School of Medicine at UCLA, Los Angeles, CA, USA

M C Lu
David Geffen School of Medicine at UCLA, Los Angeles, CA, USA

J Luby
Washington University School of Medicine, St. Louis, MO, USA

R Lucas-Thompson
University of California, Irvine, Irvine, CA, USA

L E Lurye
New York University, New York, NY, USA

M Macaoay
Children's National Medical Center, Washington, DC, USA

S C Mangelsdorf
University of Illinois at Urbana–Champaign, Champaign, IL, USA

M Martinos
University College London Institute of Child Health, London, UK

D Matthews
University of Manchester, Manchester, UK

K McCrink
Yale University, New Haven, CT, USA

M McIlreavy
University of Georgia, Athens, GA, USA

L M McKelvey
University of Arkansas for Medical Sciences, Little Rock, AR, USA

G W McRoberts
Haskins Laboratories, New Haven, CT, USA

A N Meltzoff
University of Washington, Seattle, WA, USA

D Messinger
University of Miami, Coral Gables, FL, USA

S Meyer
University of California Davis, Davis, CA, USA

L J Miller
Sensory Processing Disorder Foundation, Greenwood Village, CO, USA

M A Miller
University of California, Riverside, CA, USA

W R Mills-Koonce
University of North Carolina, Chapel, NC, USA

K Minde
Montreal Children's Hospital, Montreal, QC, Canada

J L Miner
University of California, Irvine, Irvine, CA, USA

K L Morris
University of California, Riverside, Riverside, CA, USA

F J Morrison
University of Michigan, Ann Arbor, MI, USA

M C Moulson
Massachusetts Institute of Technology, Cambridge, MA, USA

M E Msall
University of Chicago, Chicago, IL, USA

M Muenke
National Institutes of Health, Bethesda, MD, USA

P Y Mullineaux
Southern Illinois University School of Medicine, Carbondale, IL, USA

J P Murray
Kansas State University, Manhattan, KS, USA

A D Murray
Kansas State University, Manhattan, KS, USA

L Nadel
University of Arizona, Tucson, AZ, USA

A Needham
Duke University, Durham, NC, USA

C A Nelson
Harvard Medical School, Boston, MA, USA

L M Oakes
University of California, Davis, Davis, CA, USA

H Carmichael Olson
University of Washington, Seattle, WA, USA

M Y Ono
University of California, Davis Medical Center, Sacramento, CA, USA

C W Oppenheimer
University of North Carolina at Chapel Hill, Chapel Hill, NC, USA

T Ostler
University of Illinois at Urbana–Champaign, Urbana, IL, USA

K P Palmer
University of Arkansas for Medical Sciences, Little Rock, AR, USA

R Panneton
Virginia Tech, Blacksburg, VA, USA

R D Parke
University of California, Riverside, Riverside, CA, USA

O Pascalis
The University of Sheffield, Sheffield, UK

D L Paulhus
University of British Columbia, Vancouver, BC, Canada

F S Pedroso
Universidade Federal de Santa Maria, Santa Maria, Brazil

J L Petersen
University of Wisconsin, Madison, WI, USA

S L Pillsbury
Richmond, VA, USA

J Pinkston
University of Kansas, Lawrence, KS, USA

F Pons
Universitat de Barcelona, Barcelona, Spain

G Posada
Purdue University, West Lafayette, IN, USA

A Pressel
University of North Carolina, Chapel, NC, USA

H H Raikes
University of Nebraska–Lincoln, Lincoln, NE, USA

J T Rapp
St. Cloud State University, St. Cloud, MN, USA

H E Recchia
Concordia University, Montréal, QC, Canada

M Regalado
University of California, Los Angeles, Los Angeles, CA, USA

J M Retrouvey
McGill University Health Centre, Montréal, QC, Canada

C A Reynolds
University of California, Riverside, Riverside, CA, USA

J E Richards
University of South Carolina, Columbia, SC, USA

J Richmond
Harvard University, Boston, MA, USA

J Robinson
University of Connecticut–Storrs, Storrs, CT, USA

M K Rothbart
University of Oregon, Eugene, OR, USA

D N Ruble
New York University, New York, NY, USA

J A Rudolph
Children's Hospital Medical Center, Cincinnati, OH, USA

P A Rufo
Children's Hospital Boston, Boston, MA, USA

S Russ
University of California, Los Angeles, Los Angeles, CA, USA

A Sadeh
Tel Aviv University, Tel Aviv, Israel

R C Schaaf
Thomas Jefferson University, Philadelphia, PA, USA

A Scher
University of Haifa, Haifa, Israel

B L Schlaggar
Washington University School of Medicine, St. Louis, MO, USA

T J Schofield
University of California, Riverside, Riverside, CA, USA

E K Scholnick
University of Maryland, College Park, MD, USA

S Schwartz
McGill University Health Centre, Montréal, QC, Canada

D C Schwebel
University of Alabama at Birmingham, Birmingham, AL, USA

N Sebastián-Gallés
Universitat de Barcelona, Barcelona, Spain

R Seifer
Brown University, Providence, RI, USA

M Shah
University of Pennsylvania School of Medicine, Philadelphia, PA, USA

E Simonoff
King's College London, London, UK

D P Sladen
Vanderbilt University Medical Center, Nashville, TN, USA

D L Smith
The Children's Hospital, Denver, CO, USA

K A Snyder
University of Denver, Denver, CO, USA

J B Soep
University of Colorado at Denver and Health Sciences Center, Denver, CO, USA

K C Soska
New York University, New York, NY, USA

M M Stalets
Washington University School of Medicine, St. Louis, MO, USA

L Sterling
University of Washington, Seattle, WA, USA

M Sumaroka
National Institutes of Health, Bethesda, MD, USA

H N Switzky
Northern Illinois University, DeKalb, IL, USA

D E Szwedo
University of Virginia, Charlottesville, VA, USA

A Taddio
The Hospital for Sick Children, Toronto, ON, Canada and University of Toronto, ON, Canada

B Taubman
University of Pennsylvania School of Medicine, Philadelphia, PA, USA

D M Teti
The Pennsylvania State University, University Park, PA, USA

A M Tharpe
Vanderbilt University Medical Center, Nashville, TN, USA

C R Thomann
University of Massachusetts, Boston, MA, USA

R A Thompson
University of California Davis, Davis, CA, USA

N Tolani
Columbia University, New York, NY, USA

M Tomasello
Max Planck Institute for Evolutionary Anthropology, Leipzig, Germany

C M Torrence
University of Denver, Denver, CO, USA

N Towe-Goodman
The Pennsylvania State University, University Park, PA, USA

S E Trehub
University of Toronto at Mississauga, Mississauga, ON, Canada

R E Tremblay
University of Montréal, Montreal, QC, Canada

E Tronick
University of Massachusetts, Boston, Boston, MA, USA

A Tullos
The University of Texas, Austin, TX, USA

C D Vallotton
Harvard Graduate School of Education, Cambridge, MA, USA

I D Waldman
Emory University, Atlanta, GA, USA

J S Wallerstein
The Judith Wallerstein Center for the Family in Transition, Corte Madera, CA, USA

S E Watamura
University of Denver, Denver, CO, USA

N Wentworth
Lake Forest College, Lake Forest, IL, USA

R A Williamson
University of Washington, Seattle, WA, USA

K Willoughby
University of Toronto, Toronto, ON, Canada

M A Winter
Syracuse University, Syracuse, NY, USA

M S Wong
University of Illinois at Urbana–Champaign, Champaign, IL, USA

J D Woolley
The University of Texas, Austin, TX, USA

K Wynn
Yale University, New Haven, CT, USA

P D Zeanah
Tulane University Health Sciences Center, New Orleans, LA, USA

C H Zeanah
Tulane University Health Sciences Center, New Orleans, LA, USA

P D Zelazo
Institute of Child Development, Minneapolis, MN, USA

P Zelkowitz
McGill University, Montreal, QC, Canada

C Zera
Brigham and Women's Hospital, Boston, MA, USA

D Zlotnik
National Institutes of Health, Bethesda, MD, USA

K M Zosuls
New York University, New York, NY, USA

CONTENTS

VOLUME 1

A

B

VOLUME 2

G

H

I

L

VOLUME 3

R

S

T

V

Gender: Awareness, Identity, and Stereotyping

K M Zosuls, L E Lurye, and D N Ruble, New York University, New York, NY, USA

Glossary

Collective identity – Refers to the self as a member of a collective group, such as gender or race. See also social identity.

Gender awareness – Although the term 'awareness' is often used more generally, in this article, this term specifically refers to children's ability to distinguish the sexes.

Gender constancy – Proposed by Lawrence Kohlberg to refer to children's understanding that gender is not changeable. The development of gender constancy includes three stages: (1) accurate identification of sex category membership for oneself and others (basic gender identity); (2) stability of sex category membership over time (gender stability); and (3) consistency of sex category membership across superficial transformations in appearance or context (gender consistency).

Gender development – Refers to the processes involved in the development of the components of gender, including concepts and beliefs about gender, gender identity, or self-perception as a member of a gender group, gender-related preferences, and gender-related behaviors. Developmental processes are generally described as cognitive, socialization, or biological.

Habituation methodologies – A type of looking time method in which infants are first presented with a stimulus until they lose interest in it or 'habituate' to it and are then presented with a pair of stimuli. The pair of stimuli contains one stimulus similar to and one stimulus different from the habituation stimulus. The time infants spend looking at each stimulus is measured. These studies presume that differences in looking time between the familiar and novel stimulus represent an awareness of differences between the two stimuli.

Looking time methods (preferential looking methods) – Methods used in studies with infants who are still too young to effectively express their knowledge verbally and who have other infancy-related performance limitations (e.g., cognitive, motor) that do not allow for the use of methods in which children have to perform tasks or answer questions. These methods typically involve showing infants pairs of stimuli and measuring the time that infants spend looking at each one of the stimuli.

Sequential touching paradigm – An unstructured task in which children are given a set of objects from two different categories (e.g., male and female dolls) and categorization is inferred if a child touches objects from a single category in succession more than would be expected from chance. It is thought that such spontaneous behaviors indicate attention to categorical contrasts.

Social identity – Although defined in various ways, key elements include: (1) refers to aspects of the self-concept that are defined in terms of or in relation to other people and groups, (2) socially constructed and interpersonally significant categories, and (3) certain values and emotional significance are attached to these role or category memberships. Social identity is a broader concept than collective identity in that it can refer to the self as fulfilling a role or the self as a member of a collective group (i.e., collective identity).

Violation of expectancy paradigm – A looking time method in which children's looking times are measured in response to mismatched stimuli or impossible events compared to properly matched or possible events. Longer looking times to mismatched stimuli/impossible events are thought to indicate that an event is perceived as novel, surprising, or incongruous, suggesting that it is unexpected.

Introduction

Psychologists have long been intrigued with the processes involved in the development of the 'gendered' self. Children grow up in a world ubiquitous with social categories and by the time that they are toddlers, they learn to label others and themselves according to their gender. By the time they enter elementary school, children know a wide range of gender stereotypes. Children also develop sex-typed behaviors at an early age, and such behaviors tend to increase during early childhood. Because the development of gender-related knowledge and sex-typed behavior appear to coincide, the relationship between these two facets of gender development remains an area of active study. During early childhood, it has been suggested by some researchers that attainment of gender identity has important implications for the adoption and maintenance of sex-typed behavior. However, as children become older, develop more complex identities, and become embedded in more complex social worlds, it is believed that the influence of gender identity may expand and become important for self-evaluation and psychological wellbeing. Although the role of biological factors will be discussed, the focus of this article is on gender identity as a social construct and the processes involved in children's developing understanding of themselves as girls or boys. In this article, we focus on children's emerging understanding of three major aspects of gender development – identity, awareness, and stereotypes – from the perspective that gender development is best understood as resulting from a combination of social, biological, and cognitive factors. Central to our point of view is the idea that children play an active role in their gender development and continually construct and revise their understanding of what it means to be a boy or girl.

Gender Knowledge in Infants and Toddlers

In this section, we examine the first indications of children's awareness of gender category distinctions. These signs involve both simple perceptual distinctions in infancy and more advanced abilities of toddlers to categorize themselves and others as boys and girls and show evidence of gender stereotype knowledge.

Perceptual Distinction

Evidence from a number of studies using habituation and preferential looking methodologies supports the idea that infants are able to perceptually discriminate between men and women well before gender differentiated behavior is observed. Infants as young as 3–4 months can distinguish males and females using facial features and 6-month-old infants can distinguish the voices of women and men. By 9 months of age, most infants are able to discriminate between pictures of men and women and use hair and clothing information as gender cues. By 12 months of age, infants also demonstrate intermodal gender knowledge; that is, infants are able to recognize the associations between male and female faces and voices, showing that they can form associations across sensory modalities. In a study by Diane Poulin-Dubois and colleagues that investigated this ability, 1-, 9-, and 12-month-old infants were presented with pairs of male and female photographs and either a male or a female voice saying, "Hi baby! Look at me! Here I am. Look at me!" The oldest group of infants was most consistent in looking for a longer period of time when the picture matched the voice, especially in the case of female faces. This greater ability to match female faces and voices might be due to infants' greater amount of exposure to, and therefore expertise in processing, female compared to male faces and voices. Taken together, these studies suggest that by the time children reach their first birthday, they have in place the perceptual categories of gender.

Active Categorization

The ability to perceptually distinguish males from females sets the stage for the development of more advanced knowledge about gender. In the second year of life, children begin to categorize people as men and women and boys and girls spontaneously in their everyday lives. In other words, in addition to recognizing that males and females look different, children use this knowledge to actively categorize people as males and females. A study using a sequential touching paradigm in which observers coded the order in which infants touched a set of male and female dolls found that although at 18 months of age some children appeared to categorize males and females, categorization increased sharply between 18 and 22 months of age. Although the authors of this study interpreted this behavior to indicate that in the months before children turn 2 years, they increasingly attend to and use gender categories, this conclusion is open to interpretation.

Most studies investigating children's ability to categorize males and females have used either nonverbal or verbal gender-labeling paradigms. Studies using different procedures have led to different conclusions about when children are first able to actively categorize males and females. Studies assessing gender labeling in very young children have most typically used nonverbal measures that involve pointing to a picture of a male or female in response to an experimenter's question, or sorting such pictures into boxes designated for either males or females. Most of these studies have concluded that children are generally not successful at gender labeling until they are about 28–30 months old. Nevertheless, research using different procedures, particularly preferential looking techniques and measures of children's vocabularies, suggests a different conclusion. For example, our own research has found that while at 17 months of age only a minority of children have spontaneously (i.e., without prompts or cues) and flexibly (i.e., across contexts) used a gender label, by 21–22 months of age, a majority of children have produced at least one gender label, with most children having produced multiple labels. Other studies examining children's word usage have found that children begin to overgeneralize the labels mommy and daddy to other females and males starting at about 18 months of age, and that by 24 months of age, both boys and girls appear to have learned more same-gender-typed words (e.g., beads, fire truck, girl, boy) than other-gender-typed words. These studies all suggest that although young children might not have a sophisticated understanding of gender, by the age of 2 years, children have some understanding of gender as a social category and have begun to divide their social worlds into males and females.

Aside from categorizing other males and females, children also learn to categorize themselves into a gender group. Studies assessing children's self-labeling have typically used the same nonverbal pointing and sorting procedures just discussed and results from these studies have led to similar conclusions for self-labeling. That is, children appear to reliably self-label when they are approximately 28–30 months old. However, some evidence suggests that children are able to verbally self-label by the time that they are 2 years old. Such self-labeling is of particular interest, because it appears to represent a primitive or 'basic' gender identity. In other words, once children achieve a basic gender identity not only do they recognize that there are two gender groups, but also that they are a member of one of them. This understanding is thought by some researchers to have motivational significance for subsequent gender development, as discussed in a later section.

Gender Stereotype Knowledge

Given children's increased understanding of gender during the second year, it is not surprising that studies using a variety of paradigms suggest that infants' knowledge of attributes stereotypically associated with gender categories increases substantially during the second year. For example, in a study by Lisa Serbin and colleagues that used an adaptation of the preferential looking paradigm, researchers found that at 18 and 24 months of age, girls were able to match male and female faces and voices to gender-stereotyped toys (i.e., dolls and vehicles). Another looking time study by some of the same researchers found that both boys and girls made associations between male and female faces and masculine and feminine items

at 18 and 24 months of age, although these associations were only significant for masculine items. Interestingly, these associations were found for both conventionally stereotyped items, such as a fire hat and a tiara, and metaphorically stereotyped items, such as a fir tree and a heart. The metaphoric associations are particularly interesting, as they suggest that gender knowledge can be acquired not only through direct teaching and observation of certain items, but also through inferring associations between gender and certain physical (e.g., angularity, size) and more abstract and internal qualities (e.g., gentleness, love). Nevertheless, as with some of the other looking-time studies we have described, these interpretations are open to debate. For instance, it is not clear why associations were only significant for male items and why items such as hearts, which commonly adorn girls' clothing and accessories, would have been considered metaphoric rather than conventional objects commonly associated with females. There are myriad challenges involved with studying infants because of their limited language, cognitive, and motor skills; thus, it is the task of researchers to find creative ways of studying infants' knowledge. As with any field of research, it is necessary to replicate findings using multiple research methods.

Gender Knowledge in Early Childhood

Even though 2–3-year-olds are able to categorize males and females, their understanding of gender is still rudimentary. From the ages of approximately 3–6 years, children develop a better understanding of gender as an unchangeable, enduring social category and their knowledge of gender stereotypes increases. At the same time, children are likely to develop a more complex sense of themselves as members of a gender category.

Gender Constancy

According to Kohlberg, achieving gender constancy is a critical milestone in gender development. The idea of gender constancy is analogous to Piaget's concept of conservation of physical properties in that gender constancy refers to understanding that gender is an invariant human property that is stable across time and superficial changes in appearance. Kohlberg outlined three developmental stages that children achieve in order to have gender constancy. The first stage, gender identity, is children's basic awareness that they are either boys or girls. The second stage, gender stability, refers to the recognition that gender identity does not change over time. The third stage, gender consistency, represents the achievement of gender constancy and refers to the understanding that gender is not changed by transformations in gender-typed appearances, activities, and traits. In other words, once children achieve gender constancy, at about age 6–7 years, they understand that they are either a girl or a boy (gender identity), that they will grow up to be an adult of the same gender (i.e., a woman or a man) (gender stability), and that their gender will not be changed if they do things such as put on opposite sex-typed clothes (gender consistency). Numerous studies, including cross-cultural evidence, have confirmed the order of the stages, though the exact ages at which the highest level is reached vary greatly depending on methodology.

Rigidity and Flexibility of Identity

As children grow older and develop more sophisticated knowledge about gender, their gender-related self-concepts and gender-related behaviors are also likely to be impacted. In fact, researchers have found evidence to support the idea that children progress through a developmental pattern in their gender concepts that can be described as a sequence of three phases: (1) beginning awareness (construction/information processing), (2) rigidity (consolidation/schema confirmation), and (3) flexibility (integration/schema development). While these stages are characterized by a quantitative increase in gender knowledge, they are also characterized by a qualitative change in knowledge and possibly behavior, particularly in terms of how rigidly or flexibly children classify attributes and behaviors as appropriate for 'both' sexes. For instance, a child who has a rigid concept of femininity might think that only girls can wear pink and she might also become adamant about wearing pink dresses everyday. An older child with a more flexible concept of femininity would be more likely to think that both boys and girls can wear pink; thus, this knowledge might be associated with more flexible behaviors.

It appears that children tend to enter a short-lived period of rigidity in terms of gender stereotype knowledge between the ages of about 4 and 6 years, followed by increasing levels of flexibility over the next several years. The increase of flexibility beginning at about age 7 or 8 years is consistent with other areas of cognitive and social cognitive development, such as higher classification abilities, a full understanding of gender constancy, and a better understanding of people in terms of psychological traits. For instance, research has shown that the ability to understand that the same object or person can belong to two categories simultaneously is related to more egalitarian responding on gender stereotyping measures. Both multiple classification ability and full gender constancy understanding emerge in the early elementary school years at around the time when children become more flexible. Also, prior to the age of 7–8 years, children's self and other descriptions typically refer to concrete, observable characteristics and social relationships (e.g., "I am a girl. My best friend is Mary. I like to dance"). By the age of 8 years, children's self and other descriptions consist of statements that reflect a view of people as having more abstract, psychological characteristics that direct behavior. These descriptions also become more evaluative in terms of comparisons with others. Thus, as children become older, their gender identities may take on meaning beyond superficial, physical characteristics and become imbued with meaning linked with stable psychological characteristics. In general, more research is needed to investigate the concepts of rigidity and flexibility with respect to the ways in which children think and feel about themselves as girls or boys, both in terms of normative developmental patterns and individual differences.

Although general cognitive and social cognitive factors might play an important role in the development of identification with a gender category, it is important to remember that the social context is also likely to play an important role in the timing of various phases of gender development and the degree to which certain phenomena, such as gender rigidity, are observed. For instance, children might be more likely to develop a basic gender identity at an earlier age and show an early and intense degree of gender rigidity if they grow up in a highly sex-typed environment with parents who adhere to 'traditional' gender roles and attitudes.

Multidimensionality of Identity

The bulk of research on children's early gender identity has focused on Kohlberg's stages. However, more recently, researchers have begun to investigate aspects other than knowledge about one's own gender (i.e., gender identity, stability, and consistency) and turned to focus on children's self-perceptions of similarity to other members of one's gender group and to the evaluative meaning of gender identity. Within the gender identity and racial/ethnic identity literatures, theorists have begun to investigate identity as a multidimensional construct, with dimensions that tap into a range of factors having to do with an individual's unique, subjective experience as a member of a social category. David Perry and colleagues have proposed a multidimensional model of gender identity that focuses on children's feelings about themselves as girls or boys. In addition, Robert Sellers and colleagues developed a multidimensional model of racial identity to study African American identity, and researchers interested in other social and collective identities, such as gender, have begun to adapt this model to their own research in order to investigate identity with greater depth and precision. Although these models are most applicable to middle childhood and beyond, little is known about how and when these other aspects of identity develop. As a result, the gender development literature lacks a certain degree of continuity in terms of identity development from early through middle childhood. The following two sections will review these multidimensional models in light of what is known from the existing literature to suggest possible developmental patterns.

Perry's model

As will be discussed in the following section, by the time that children are in elementary school, they know a broad range of gender stereotypes. Therefore, starting at a young age, children can assess the degree to which they are typical of their gender using a number of different dimensions (e.g., toy and activity preferences, playmate preferences, academic and professional aspirations). How do feelings of being typical for one's gender interact with factors such as pressure to conform to gender stereotypes and general feelings about one's gender group, to affect adjustment outcomes, such as self-worth and self-perceived social competence?

In order to address this question, Perry and colleagues proposed a multidimensional model of gender identity that, in addition to knowledge of gender identity, includes three components: (1) feelings of psychological typicality or compatibility with one's gender; (2) feelings of pressure from parents, peers, and self for conformity to gender stereotypes; and (3) intergroup gender attitudes (i.e., the degree to which one feel's one's own gender group is superior). Their research has found that while perceived gender typicality and contentedness is positively related to psychological adjustment, the felt pressure to conform to gender stereotypes is negatively related to adjustment. These dimensions have primarily been studied among children in middle childhood through adolescence; therefore the developmental course of these dimensions is unclear.

It has been suggested that while felt pressure to conform might develop in preschool, feelings of perceived typicality might not emerge until children are slightly older and engage in social comparison. Social comparison processes serve to help children self socialize (i.e., learn and adopt the social rules of a given culture or environment) and are oriented toward (1) determining how one is supposed to behave and (2) evaluating how good one is at a certain behavior. Although research on social comparison has typically focused on the academic domain, findings might nevertheless help to illuminate processes involved in gender self-socialization. After all, children certainly engage in social comparison to learn a host of social norms and behaviors, including those related to gender. The degree to which children perceive that they meet standards for 'appropriate' behavior for their gender group is likely to affect feelings of typicality.

There is considerable evidence showing that the seeking out and use of social comparison information for self-evaluations of competence increases during the early years of elementary school. However, it is not until about age 7 years that children reliably use social comparison information for competence-related self-assessments. These findings also suggest that beginning at about age 7 years, pressures to conform might take on new meaning and importance to the self, consequently children might feel more pressure to conform to gender stereotypes. It is also possible that these processes might emerge slightly earlier in the case of gender self-socialization, given that children possess most of the prerequisite cognitive skills (e.g., recognition that people have different characteristics and capacities, recognition of the relative characteristics or skills of different people), strategies (e.g., choosing relevant others to compare oneself to), and motivation necessary for social comparison during the preschool years. However, the actual use of social comparison information might depend on other factors, such as the concreteness of the category, the stability of relevant characteristics, perceived relevance of information to one's own stable characteristics, and social pressures. While a given child might not begin to think of 'smartness' or intelligence as a stable trait until age 7 or 8 years, he or she might recognize the stability of gender slightly earlier, at about age 6 years, when he or she achieves gender constancy and sees gender as an enduring characteristic. In fact, research from the gender constancy literature supports the idea that social comparison processes are associated with high levels of gender constancy. In a study by Diane Ruble and colleagues, 4–6-year-old children divided into high- and low-gender constancy groups watched a commercial for a gender-neutral toy that had either two boys or two girls playing with the toy or did not see a commercial (control group). Only high-constancy children who saw opposite-sex children playing with the toy avoided spending time with the toy in a subsequent play session and expressed that the toy would be more appropriate for an opposite sex child. Furthermore, since gender is so salient early in life, children might also be more motivated to use social comparison information at earlier ages in their gender-related self-socialization as a way to learn how to behave 'like a girl' or 'like a boy'. Thus, it remains to be investigated when gender-related social comparison processes and feelings about gender typicality emerge and whether these two processes are related.

Given that feelings of gender typicality have important implications for psychological adjustment, it would be important for future research to further investigate the sources of these perceptions and their impact on feelings of typicality starting at earlier ages. More research is also needed to understand better exactly what factors are important to making children feel typical for their own gender. For instance, certain domains, such as appearance, might be particularly important to feeling typical, whereas others, such as personality traits, might be less so. Furthermore, the importance of certain domains might vary across gender, age, social contexts, and other dimensions of gender identity.

Sellers' model

As children become older, they also begin to identify with other social categories and develop more complex self-concepts. As a result, social group membership alone is not enough to predict the consequences that will stem from that membership. It is also important to consider factors such as the importance of gender identity to one's self-concept and the degree to which gender identity is salient to a given child in a given situation. Sellers and colleagues have developed a multidimensional model of racial identity with four components (salience, centrality, ideology, regard) that are useful dimensions along which to study gender identity. Although some of these dimensions are more applicable to older children, some components, such as salience, are likely to be important at an early age.

Category salience, the concept that individuals may be more 'ready' to perceive and process information relevant to certain categories, has been a prominent concept in the cognitive schema literature. This literature suggests that the chronic or momentary salience of a category such as gender in a given context or for a given person can affect related behaviors and attitudes. For instance, salience of gender to the self-concept might be affected by environmental factors such as whether a person is the minority sex in a given situation. For example, boys are more likely to mention their maleness when asked to describe themselves when they come from households in which females are the majority and girls are more likely to mention their femaleness when they come from households in which males are the majority. Developmental level might also affect gender salience. In one study, gender salience was higher for children at higher levels of constancy. However, once children are slightly older and better able to use other information, such as personality characteristics, in person perception, gender salience might decrease in self and other perceptions.

The salience of a social category can also activate related stereotypes. Thus when gender is made salient in certain domains, such as academic contexts, negative stereotypes (e.g., girls are not good at math) can potentially affect performance and behavioral outcomes. At very young ages, gender is often particularly salient in children's bedrooms, toy stores, and preschools. The activation of gender stereotypes, such as 'girls play with dolls' might limit the range of activities that children engage in, possibly depriving them of other experiences that would allow for the development of a wider range of abilities and interests.

Another potentially important dimension of gender identity is centrality, or the importance of and degree to which individuals define themselves in terms of their gender. The centrality of gender identity in terms of its role in early gender development has not received much attention in the literature, however recent research from our laboratory has found that centrality is an important consequence of the attainment of constancy in children 3–5 years of age. That is, at the point at which children learn that gender is an unchanging part of their self-concept, it becomes a central aspect of their identity. Contrast, a social learning approach might suggest that as children internalize socialization pressures to behave in gender-consistent ways and their self-regulatory processes maintain that behavior, gender consequently assumes greater centrality in the self-concept. Furthermore, given that children acquire other identities, such as racial or ethnic identities at an early age, it would be important for future research to investigate the relative importance of multiple identities to children's early self-concepts.

Although the third dimension proposed by Sellers' model is ideology, which refers to an individual's beliefs, opinions, and attitudes about one's group, an analogous dimension in the case of children's gender identities is 'knowledge'. For the purposes of this article, knowledge refers to knowledge of gender stereotypes, the status of one's gender group, and discrimination against one's gender group. Although a wealth of research has investigated children's gender-stereotype knowledge, less is known about children's perceptions of gender-based status differences and discrimination. Young children attribute greater power to males, in the sense of viewing them as stronger, faster, and more aggressive, but it is not clear that such beliefs reflect perceptions of higher status for males. Research is still needed to understand how and when knowledge of status differences and discrimination emerge and how these forms of gender knowledge affect children's perceptions and evaluations of themselves as girls and boys.

Finally, independent of salience, centrality, and knowledge, children might differ in their regard, or their evaluation, of their gender. In other words, children may vary in the degree to which they like being a boy or girl and or feel proud of their gender group membership. What is it that children like or value about being a boy or girl? Unfortunately, little developmental research is available. However, work with adults suggests that while males might be more likely to be positively valued in terms of competence and leadership attributes, females might be more likely to be esteemed for general moral and interpersonal qualities such as goodness and nurturance. This stereotype of females as 'better' than men is consistent with research on sexism among adults, which shows that an important component of modern sexism, often embraced by both men and women, is the idea that women have a greater capacity for warmth, nurturance, and other related 'good' qualities. This type of sexism has been termed benevolent sexism by Peter Glick, Susan Fiske, and colleagues. Although such stereotypes are complimentary, they might actually perpetuate stereotypes of women that restrict their roles in society and prevent them from being seen as suitable for higher-status roles associated with men.

Young children might also evaluate boys and girls on the dimensions of power and valence, such that boys are associated with power-related adjectives (e.g., strong, fast, hit) but when asked for generalized attitudes about girls and boys, girls are seen as more 'good'. Thus, the elementary school corollary of benevolent sexism might be the idea that girls are 'sugar and spice and everything nice' while boys are 'naughty'. In other words, although 'naughtiness' has a negative connotation, certain behavior in this category (e.g., aggression) might be overlooked in boys (e.g., 'boys will be boys') because they are seen as gender appropriate while girls might be judged particularly harshly for engaging in certain behaviors that are not seen as compatible with a 'sugar and spice' image. Nevertheless, studies have shown that overall, elementary school aged children tend to rate their own sex more positively in terms of positive traits (e.g., smart) than the other sex. In the end, differential regard of males and females may depend on which attributes are salient or important to an individual child. This is likely to vary as a function of age and context.

Gender-Stereotype Knowledge

By the time that children are 3 years old, it is clear that they know gender stereotypes from a variety of domains, including toys and household objects. For example, children as young as 3 years understand that dolls and domestic tools (e.g., broom, iron) are associated with females, whereas balls, hammers, and cars are associated with males. Stereotype knowledge appears to increase rapidly between 3 and 5 years, reaching a ceiling for certain domains, such as clothing, by 5 years. Preschool- and kindergarten-aged children also negatively evaluate gender role violations, such as wearing opposite sex-typed clothing. Several studies have shown that appearance violations tend to be judged as particularly serious for boys, possibly because appearance stereotypes are especially central to the way in which girls are defined and perceived. Thus, to look 'like a girl' is almost tantamount to being a girl. In contrast, when thinking of boys, children seem to be more likely to perceive boys in terms of activities and traits (e.g., 'rough'). Nevertheless, the consequences of norm violations for girls in terms of activities and traits might be less severe, possibly because boys' activities are often seen as more desirable, especially when compared to more sedentary activities and household chores traditionally associated with girls. The harsher consequences of gender deviance among boys might also be related to perceived status differences, with worse consequences for the higher-status group (i.e., boys) engaging in behavior associated with the lower-status group (i.e., girls). More research is needed, however, to assess young children's understanding of gender-related status differences and how such understanding might be related to perceptions of norm violations.

Occupational stereotypes are learned by children around kindergarten and children as young as 6 years old rate stereotypically masculine jobs, such as a doctor, auto mechanic, and business executive as higher status than stereotypically feminine jobs, such as nurse, fashion model, and teacher, and this knowledge appears to increase with age. In order to investigate whether children judged male and female stereotyped jobs as differing in status simply because they were associated with males and females, Lynn Liben and colleagues conducted an experiment in which children were presented with novel jobs, such as a 'Higgler', paired with either a man or a woman performing the job. Children ages 11–12 years, but not younger children (ages 6–8 years) rated the jobs portrayed with men as higher status. The same study also found that although boys and girls did not differ in their interest in conventionally masculine jobs, boys reported significantly lower interest than girls in conventionally feminine jobs. Given how early children begin to develop stereotypes about occupations and show a preference for jobs stereotyped for their own gender, it follows that an awareness of occupational stereotypes might begin to shape children's interests, goals, and activities at an early age. Children are likely to learn occupational stereotypes through a variety of sources at very young ages, including through stereotyped portrayals of men and women in children's books, television, and other media, and through their everyday experiences with men and women in traditional roles. These stereotypes might be further reinforced through pretend play in which children act out different roles along gender lines, such as those of 'doctor' and 'nurse'.

Structure of Gender Stereotypes

Since even very young children learn gender stereotypes from numerous domains, it is important to consider the structure of gender stereotypes. Researchers have had a tendency to study gender stereotypes with a low degree of specificity, using standardized measures that tend to focus on certain stereotype domains, such as activities. This approach allows for only a limited understanding of the relative influence of various stereotypes on children's self and other judgments and behaviors.

Carol Martin and colleagues have proposed a model in which children's gender stereotypes are comprised of multiple components. In order to test their model, they conducted a series of studies in which they investigated the degree to which children would rely on a stereotype from one domain to predict that a person would also possess a stereotype from the same or a different domain (i.e., toys, appearance, personality, occupation). They found that 4-6-year-old children were consistently able to make stereotyped inferences within the domain of toys, but only for target children presented as having interests stereotyped for their own sex. This result suggests that children appear to first learn gender-stereotype associations for their own sex. This finding is consistent with schematic processing views, which posit that once children know their own sex (i.e., "I am a girl", gender identity), they become motivated to attend to and learn own-sex relevant information. In a study looking at between-domain associations (e.g., the degree to which a target child of an unspecified sex who is aggressive is also interested in playing with trucks) in 6-, 8-, and 10-year-olds, the researchers found that although 6-year-olds were only able to make cross-domain inferences for own-sex stereotyped characteristics, 8- and 10-year-olds were able to make inferences for both masculine and feminine stereotypes. Stereotypic judgments were also more extreme among the older children. Nevertheless, as children grow older, they are also likely to show increased flexibility in their application of stereotypes in that they are more likely to assign specific stereotypes to both sexes rather than endorse that a stereotyped characteristic is 'only' true for one sex. Thus, although older children are able to recognize that both males and females can have certain traits, they might still be prone to make spontaneous stereotyped judgments.

Studies such as this that have assessed stereotypes in ways that go beyond just asking children which gender category is associated with which objects or attributes suggest that stereotype knowledge continues to develop through early and middle childhood. In order to reconcile the ability of young children to pass certain types of measures and not others better, researchers have distinguished between vertical and horizontal stereotypic associations. While vertical associations refer to the ability to associate a male or female label to an attribute (e.g., girls play with dolls), horizontal associations refer to the ability to infer that a male or female described as having some attribute will also possess another related attribute (e.g., girls who play with trucks also play with airplanes). It appears that children younger than 8 years are limited in their ability to make horizontal associations, especially for the opposite sex. A possible reason for this is that young children tend to rely more on categorical rather than individuating information to make inferences about others. Thus, for example, if young children are presented with a girl who plays with trucks and asked what toy she would like to play with (e.g., a doll or an airplane), they would be more likely to use categorical information (i.e., the child's female gender) rather than individuating information (i.e., the child's counter-stereotypic interest) to make the inference. One implication of young children's reliance on categorical information is that children might

be more likely to stereotype more often and more rigidly until they are better able to use other information, especially when the information runs counter to their stereotypic beliefs.

Implications of Gender Knowledge

One of the most important reasons for understanding the development of children's gender-related knowledge is to understand the origins of other aspects of children's gender development, such as sex-typed behaviors, same-sex peer preferences, and children's evaluations of themselves and others, all of which have numerous implications for children's social, psychological, and achievement outcomes better.

Sex-Typed Behaviors

Although there is debate about the role of gender knowledge in the development of sex-typed behaviors (particularly in relation to socialization and biological factors), there is evidence that suggests that gender-related knowledge and gender identity play a role in the development of sex-typed preferences.

The best way to investigate such a relationship is with longitudinal studies; however, to date only three known studies have investigated the relationship between gender-category knowledge and sex-typed behaviors using longitudinal designs. Although the results of one study were mixed, two studies suggest a directional effect of gender labeling on gender-typed behavior. In a study by Beverly Fagot and Mary Leinbach, children were tested once a month beginning at 18 months of age until they passed a gender-labeling pointing task or reached 30 months of age without having done so. The children were also observed at home when they first entered the study and twice a week in playgroups over the remainder of the study. At 18 months of age, there were no significant differences in play between the boys and girls who would become early and late labelers (i.e., those who did and did not pass the gender-labeling task by 27 months of age, respectively). However, early-labeling children showed more of an increase in gender-typical toy play from 18 to 27 months, relative to children who had not yet passed the gender-labeling task. A recent study from our own laboratory found a similar relationship between gender labeling and play at even earlier ages. We found that children who had verbally self-labeled by 21 months (e.g., "me a girl") and children who had more gender labels in their vocabularies were more likely to show an increase in their sex-typed play from 17 to 21 months of age. However, more research using other measures of gender category knowledge, gender identity, and more frequent behavioral measures between the ages of approximately 17–36 months is needed. Also, as Eleanor Maccoby has suggested other aspects of gender identity, such as the notion of thinking about oneself as part of a collective group of girls or boys (e.g., "We are girls" vs. "I am a girl") are also like to emerge as children begin to play and relate to one another on a more interactive level.

Gender Segregation

Another important aspect of the social context in which children construct their gender identities is peer relationships. One of the most pervasive phenomena of early gender development is sex segregation. Starting between the ages of 2 and 3 years, children begin to show a preference for same-sex playmates. By preschool, children spend little time with other-sex peers. Many potential explanations have been offered for sex segregation, including preferences based on behavioral similarity (e.g., boys might be more attracted to playing with boys because they are more likely to engage in rough and tumble play) and more general gender-based cognitions or beliefs that they are more similar to own-sex peers. By about age 5 years, boys' and girls' play groups also differ on a number of dimensions, including group size, activities, and proximity to adults. Play in same-sex peer groups also tends to exaggerate sex differences in play styles, whereas both sexes adjust their behavior somewhat when playing with opposite-sex peers. Given that young children spend the majority of their time with same-sex peers, the differences seemingly inherent in such experiences are likely to have a major impact on the development of individual children's sex-typed attributes and self-perceptions as girls or boys. For instance, researchers have posited that play with sex-typed toys and same-sex peers leads girls and boys to have very different experiences that contribute to the development of sex differences in interests, interpersonal styles, and skills.

Although a wealth of research has studied gender segregation, more research is needed to investigate the ways in which gender identity and gender knowledge relate to preferences for same-sex peers and the ways in which experiences in same-sex play groups affect various dimensions of gender identity. Gender segregation begins at about the same age as gender categorization skills, and a direct examination of a possible connection would be of great interest.

Self-Perception

The content of gender stereotypes might have important implications for the ways in which boys and girls conceptualize gender and the way in which they perceive others and themselves as members of a gender category. For instance, although some have argued that exposing children to gender stereotypes, such as dressing girls in pink and boys in blue, might be important to the development of a secure gender identity, this argument presumes that children cannot be socialized to conceptualize gender categories in ways that differ from traditional stereotypes. Although superficial perceptual differences play an important role in children's early gender category understanding, other cues, such as gender labels paired with biological knowledge about genital differences can be equally, if not more, influential in children's early gender concepts. For instance, research by Sandra Bem has demonstrated that children as young as 3 years with genital knowledge are more likely to demonstrate gender constancy than children who do not have this kind of anatomical knowledge. Conceptions of gender that are less reliant on stereotypes might ultimately allow children to establish a gender identity without rigidly adhering to stereotyped behaviors and beliefs. Nevertheless, most children grow up in highly stereotyped environments and a certain degree of gender conformity might be beneficial, especially if children do not feel too much pressure to conform to gender stereotypes. Research has shown that children who feel gender typical and who experience little pressure for gender conformity are less distressed than other children. For instance, girls who are particularly feminine in their dress yet do not perceive pressure to adhere to appearance norms might be perceived more positively by others and might also perceive themselves positively as girls.

However, despite the potentially beneficial aspects of conforming to gender stereotypes, stereotypes might also result in attributes and concerns that could ultimately threaten wellbeing. For instance, a recent study found that a considerable proportion of girls as young as 5-years-old desired to be thinner and that perceived peer desire for thinness predicted decreases in girls' appearance satisfaction and self-esteem in early elementary school aged children. This finding highlights the idea that early stereotype knowledge and concepts about important, defining qualities of males and females are in place at an early age and can also begin to affect values, self-perceptions, and behaviors surprisingly early in life. Ultimately, it might be most adaptive for children to feel comfortable with themselves as girls or boys, yet not base their feelings of typicality on rigidly stereotyped conceptions of males and females.

Theoretical Perspectives

It is likely that multiple processes account for the development of gender-related knowledge and sex-typed behaviors. Although most current research and theorizing in gender development has become increasingly integrative in terms of considering the ways in which cognitive, social, and biological factors work together to affect gender identity and gender-related behaviors, there is still some debate over the relative influence of cognitive, socialization, and biological processes, particularly at the earliest stages of development. In this section, we review some of the dominant perspectives on processes in early gender development.

Cognitive and Socialization Perspectives: Infancy and Toddlerhood

The question of when children become aware of their gender group membership lies at the heart of research on early gender identity development largely because of theories stemming from Kohlberg's cognitive developmental theory of gender development. These theorists consider gender identity, or the awareness of oneself as a girl or a boy, to hold implications for the development of sex-typed behaviors.

Kohlberg's theory emphasizes that gender development involves an active construction of gender identity. According to this perspective, gender identity development is initiated by children within the context of a sex-typed social environment and driven by a motivation to adapt to that environment and maintain a positive self-image. Thus, underlying children's gender identity construction is a motivation to bring their self-perceptions and behaviors in line with their developing knowledge about gender (e.g., "I am a girl. Girls play with dolls. I'll play with dolls."). This idea stands in contrast to the theoretical writings of Kohlberg's contemporary, Walter Mischel. Rooted in behavioral learning approaches popular in the 1950s and 1960s, Mischel's social learning approach posited that children first learn sex-typed behaviors from models in the social environment. According to social learning theorists, cognitive processes of identity formation only begin once children have already begun to learn sex-typed behaviors and are rewarded for them (e.g., "I have been rewarded for doing girl things, I must be a girl"). Although this theory has recently been modified by Albert Bandura and colleagues to put more emphasis on cognitive information processing, contemporary social learning approaches still stress that sex-typed behavior precedes the emergence of gender identity. In contrast, like Kohlberg, contemporary cognitive constructivist theorists believe that developmental changes in the understanding of gender are crucial to the development of children's gendered behavior and thinking.

The processes underlying early gender development and the developmental sequence of the earliest emergence of gender identity and gender differentiated behaviors remains an area of active debate and research. Much of the debate concerning the influence of basic gender identity and gender labeling on the development of gender-typed behaviors is based on the assumption that gender-typed behavior emerges prior to labeling. In fact,

few studies have looked at children's early gender-typed behaviors and preferences. Because sex differences and children's understanding of gender categories appear to emerge around the same age ranges, researchers need to closely examine the extent to which gender identity influences the development of early gender-typed behaviors.

Cognitive and Socialization Perspectives: Early Childhood

Social cognitive theory

Social cognitive theory proposes that the same processes, such as modeling and reinforcement, continue to influence sex-typing in similar ways as children become older. Through such experiences, children develop outcome expectancies and self-efficacy beliefs that serve to motivate and regulate gender role conduct. As children mature, their social worlds expand beyond the home and limited peer contexts and they are exposed to a greater prevalence of male and female exemplars and social agents who teach and encourage sex-typed behaviors and attributes. According to social cognitive theory, as a result of this exposure and a greater ability to organize and abstract social information, children's gender role learning increases. As children's cognitive and verbal skills improve, parents are likely to broaden the scope of their gender socialization through their conversations and interactions with their children. At the same time, peers are thought to act as powerful socializing agents through modeling, social sanctions, and serving as comparative references for the appraisal of personal efficacy. In school, teachers may treat boys and girls differently and encourage gender-stereotyped behaviors. Teachers might also convey different expectancies for girls and boys that affect girls' and boys' self-efficacy appraisals and valuations of different skills. Finally, daily experiences in our culture of exposure to stereotypical media representations of males and females and the segregation of jobs along gender lines, ensure that children are provided with multiple sources of gender role models.

Cognitive constructivist theories

Cognitive constructivist theories place greater emphasis on how gender knowledge continues to influence the development of sex-typing. Although, Kohlberg's cognitive developmental theory is unclear about the extent of gender knowledge that is required for organizing children's behavior, contemporary cognitive constructivist theorists agree that all levels of gender understanding, including basic gender identity, have motivational importance, but that different types of understanding might elicit different kinds or degrees of motivation. For instance, basic gender identity, might be associated with greater levels of information seeking about gender-related things (e.g., what attributes are associated with, or are important to, making a girl a girl) while more sophisticated levels of understanding (e.g., gender stability) might be associated with motivation to adhere to gender norms. Thus, at each level of gender knowledge, children are socializing themselves in terms of gender and the outcome of this self-socialization may vary at different points of identity development.

Gender schema theories

Gender schema theories address the ways in which children represent and process gender-related knowledge. Schemas are viewed as dynamic knowledge structures that change in response to situations and age-related changes in person perception and that have content that varies with social experiences and other individual level and cultural level differences. As organizers of gender development, gender schemas are thought to provide an important link between gender cognitions and gender-related behaviors. According to this perspective, once children identify themselves as girls or boys, they selectively attend to, and remember, own-sex relevant information and are motivated to use this information to shape their own behaviors and make gender-related inferences and judgments.

Social categorization perspectives

Researchers have recently become increasingly focused on the group context of gender development and the contextual variability of gender identity. While gender-category knowledge and gender-stereotype knowledge might be important prerequisites to stereotyped judgments and behaviors, it is also necessary to recognize that stereotypes are activated within contexts that can make gender either more or less salient. For instance, a study by Rebecca Bigler found that when gender was made salient in a classroom using the physical space (e.g., girls' and boys' bulletin boards) and through teachers' communications and instructions (e.g., "All the boys should be sitting down"), but without the use of stereotypes or the encouragement of competition between boys and girls, children in this 'gender' classroom were more likely to endorse gender stereotypes than children in a control classroom.

Theorists have also come to increasingly refer to gender as a collective identity, or the self as a member of a collective group (e.g., girls or boys). Although very young children may be able to label themselves and others according to gender, it may take some more time before they develop a sense of themselves as members of a collective gender group. Theorists such as Fabio Sani and Mark Bennett have posited that once children attain a more developed sense of themselves as a member of a gender group, they come to define themselves through their relationship with other group members and

in relation to the gender 'out-group'. Furthermore, they suggest that social contexts can change the salience of comparison groups and result in flexible stereotyping. For instance, in a Scottish study using 6- and 7-year-olds, children selected cards to describe their own group (girls or boys) after they had either used the same procedure to describe opposite-sex peers (boys or girls) or same-sex adults (women or men). Cards that were selected to describe the children's in-groups depended on which comparison out-group was first presented. For instance, when the comparison group was girls, the most frequent adjectives boys selected to describe boys were 'strong' and 'brave'. In contrast, when the comparison group was men, boys most frequently described boys as 'honest' and 'happy'. These results provided some support for self-categorization theory, which posits that stereotypes are inherently comparative and depend on the inter-group context.

Biological Perspectives

Biological approaches typically emphasize the role of hormones in the sexual differentiation of the brain and behavior. Research on nonhuman species has found that exposure to androgens early in development causes masculinization of sex-typed sexual, cognitive, and social behaviors in females. Although it is not ethically possible to experimentally manipulate hormones in humans, evidence from 'natural experiments' in which children were prenatally exposed to abnormal hormone levels has contributed much to our knowledge of the important role of biological factors in gender development.

The most extensively studied natural experiment is the case of girls with congenital adrenal hyperplasia (CAH), a genetic disease in which the fetus is exposed to high levels of androgens early in gestation. The external genitals of females with CAH are masculinized to varying degrees, but they have ovaries and a uterus and are fertile. Most girls are diagnosed at birth and treated with cortisol to reduce androgen excess and have surgery to feminize their genitalia. Research has found that girls with CAH as young as 3 years play more with boys' toys than comparison girls. Greater preferences for boys' toys have also been related to the degree of prenatal androgen excess. In later childhood and adolescence, girls with CAH report being more interested in male compared to female sex-typed occupations and report being more interested in male sex-typed activities and male playmates than control girls. Nevertheless, girls with CAH tend to have a typical female gender identity, although degree of identification might be reduced compared to typical females. A possible explanation for identifying with their gender while having other-sex interests is that girls with CAH might have different beliefs from normal girls about what is integral to being a girl. It would be interesting for future research to explore the content of the gender identities of girls with CAH and the ways in which parents might talk to them about gender identity compared to parents of non-CAH girls.

Research and case studies involving other special populations, such as boys with complete androgen insensitivity syndrome (CAIS) and boys without a penis (due to accidents or a rare congenital defect called cloacal exstrophy) also suggest that biology plays a role in the development of gender-differentiated activities and interests. Nevertheless, gender identity outcomes are variable across and within various disorders, suggesting the influence of both biological and social factors in the development of gender identity.

Studies investigating the influence of normal variations in prenatal hormones measured indirectly from umbilical cord blood, amniotic fluid, or mother's blood have shown some associations between testosterone levels and traits that show sex differences. For instance, higher levels of testosterone in mothers' blood during the second trimester of pregnancy, has been associated with greater levels of male typical activities in 3.5-year-old girls. However, many studies have yielded nonsignificant results and more research is needed to interpret significant findings and understand the processes through which hormones affect sex differentiations in behavior at various stages in development.

Although it is tempting to interpret biological correlates of sex differences as evidence for the 'innateness' and inevitability for sex differences, it is important to keep in mind that biological factors do not imply determinism. Just as hormones can affect behaviors, behaviors can exert a reciprocal influence on hormones. Boys and girls are raised in environments that reinforce and perpetuate sex differentiation across development. Thus, while certain sex differences may be rooted in biology, because of the various processes discussed in this article, they are likely to become part of what children come to associate with males and females and become integrated into children's gender identities.

Conclusion

From an early age, children notice differences between males and females and begin to develop a gender identity. As they become older, this identity becomes multifaceted and imbued with evaluative meaning. Children also learn many gender stereotypes and this knowledge can influence their conceptions of gender, their thoughts and feelings about themselves as girls or boys, and their behaviors. However, the processes involved in the earliest stages of gender development remain a subject of active debate, making continued exploration of the unique and joint

affects of biological, cognitive, and social learning factors necessary. Furthermore, future research needs to bridge the gap between theories of gender identity in early and middle childhood by, for example, investigating the relationship between attainment of gender constancy stages and the development of other dimensions of gender identity (e.g., centrality, evaluation, salience). It should also be noted that the overwhelming majority of research on early gender development has been conducted with white, middle class children and more research is needed to investigate the ways in which cultural and contextual factors might affect gender development. Clearly the field of gender development has the potential to remain an active and exciting area of research in child development, with many new discoveries for years to come.

See also: Friends and Peers; Self Knowledge; Social and Emotional Development Theories; Social Interaction.

Suggested Readings

Bigler RS (1995) The role of classification skill in moderating environmental influences on children's gender stereotyping: A study of the functional use of gender in the classroom. *Child Development* 66: 1072–1087.

Bussey K and Bandura A (1999) Social cognitive theory of gender development and differentiation. *Psychological Review* 106: 676–713.

Egan SK and Perry DG (2001) Gender identity: A multidimensional analysis with implications for psychological adjustment. *Developmental Psychology* 37: 451–463.

Kohlberg L (1966) A cognitive-developmental analysis of children's sex-role concepts and attitudes. In: Maccoby EE (ed.) *The Development of Sex Differences*, pp. 82–173. Stanford: Stanford University Press.

Martin CL, Ruble DN, and Szkrybalo J (2002) Cognitive theories of early gender development. *Psychological Bulletin* 128: 903–933.

Miller CF, Trautner HM, and Ruble DN (2006) The role of gender stereotypes in children's preferences and behavior. In: Tamis-LeMonda C and Balter L (eds.) *Child Psychology: A Handbook of Contemporary Issues.* Philadelphia: Psychology Press.

Mischel W (1966) A social learning view of sex differences in behavior. In: Maccoby EE (ed.) *The Development of Sex Differences*, pp. 56–81. Stanford: Stanford University Press.

Poulin-Dubois D, Serbin LA, Kenyon B, and Derbyshire A (1994) Infants' intermodal knowledge about gender. *Developmental Psychology* 30: 436–442.

Ruble DN and Frey KS (1991) Changing patterns of comparative behavior as skills are acquired: A functional model of self-evaluation. In: Suls J and Wills TA (eds.) *Social Comparison: Contemporary Theory and Research.* Hillsdale, NJ: Erlbaum.

Ruble DN, Alvarez JM, Bachman M, *et al.* (2004) The development of a sense of "we": The emergence and implications of children's collective identity. In: Bennett M and Sani F (eds.) *The Development of the Social Self.* East Sussex, England: Psychology Press.

Ruble DN, Martin CL, and Berenbaum S (2006) Gender development. In: Kuhn D and Siegler R (eds.) *Handbook of Child Psychology: Cognition, Perception and Language,* 6th edn. New York: Wiley.

Genetic Disorders: Sex-Linked

J Isen and L A Baker, University of Southern California, Los Angeles, CA, USA

Glossary

Autosome – Any chromosome other than the sex Chromosomes (X and Y). Humans have 22 pairs of homologous autosomes.

Diploid – Cells containing two sets of chromosomes, usually one from the mother and one from the father. Somatic cells in humans are diploid.

Haploid – Cells containing only one chromosome from a homologous pair, as in the case of human gametes. Males are also haploid with respect to the X chromosome, while females are diploid.

Heterozygotic – The presence of two different alleles on homologous chromosomes at a given locus. This is contrasted with the homozygotic state of possessing two identical alleles at a given locus.

Imprinting – A phenomenon in which the expression of a given allele depends on whether the allele was inherited from the mother or father.

Proband – An individual affected with a disorder under investigation, and from whom other family members are identified for study. Also called 'index case'.

Sex-influenced – A trait influenced by different processes in males and females, usually as a function of different hormonal exposure in the two sexes.

Sex-limited – Different sets of genes influence a trait in males and females.

Sex-linked – A trait controlled by one or more genes on the X or Y chromosome.

X-inactivation – The process in females whereby one X chromosome is randomly inactivated in each cell line, resulting in genetic mosaicism.

Introduction

Many heritable disorders affect one particular sex much more frequently. This sex difference in prevalence may suggest that the genetic mechanisms are either 'sex-linked' (influenced by one or more genes on the X or Y chromosome) or 'sex-limited' (different genes affecting males and females). A skewed sex ratio is especially salient for developmental disorders such as autism and language/speech disabilities, as well as childhood aggression. The prevalence is invariably higher in males, indicating that a sex-linked, sex-influenced, or sex-limited process may account for the etiology of these complex disorders.

Sex-linkage occurs when a trait is controlled by genetic loci on either the X or Y chromosome. However, there are few traits or disorders known to be directly influenced by Y-linked genes, so these will not be discussed here. The expressive effect of a given allele can span anywhere from recessive (an allelic effect is completely masked in the presence of another allele on the homologous X chromosome) to dominant (one allele is always expressed independently of the homologous allele). Some alleles can also act in a semi-dominant (additive) manner, such that a heterozygous combination of two different alleles leads to a quantitatively intermediate phenotypic expression (e.g., medium height) compared to the phenotypes produced by the two homozygous combinations (short or tall). The dominant–recessive nature of X-linked gene action determines whether males or females are more affected at the phenotypic level. For X-linked traits that are recessive or semi-dominant, males will typically show a higher prevalence. Since most single-gene disorders (sex-linked or otherwise) are recessive, the bulk of affected cases will be male.

A gross disparity in prevalence indicates the possibility that a genetic disorder may be sex-linked, although there are alternative interpretations. Sex-limiting or sex-influencing factors, such as testosterone exposure, may instead explain sex differences in prevalence. Autosomal genes may account for some disorders, although these alleles may function differently in males and females due to interactions with other X-linked genes. In general, the mere existence of sex differences in prevalence or mean trait levels does not necessarily imply sex-linkage. Nor does the fact that sex chromosomes are implicated for a disorder guarantee that the disorder is sex-linked.

Sex-linkage, sex-limitation, and sex-influenced models are described in detail here, followed by a review of several known sex-linked disorders as well as syndromes caused by sex chromosome abnormalities. Finally, we turn to autism as an example demonstrating how one can evaluate evidence for sex-linkage and sex-limitation.

Theoretical Background

In general, males suffer a poorer developmental outcome than females. There are higher rates of prenatal disturbances, birth complications, and childhood disorders in males. This phenomenon is mirrored by a male–female sex ratio that progressively declines from conception to adulthood. Male embryos greatly outnumber females at conception. Not surprisingly, the male–female ratio of fetal deaths is immense, reportedly reaching 2:1 within some populations. Nonetheless, the male–female ratio among live births lingers around 1.05, which is small but still significantly greater than 1. It is only with further male attrition during childhood that gender parity is finally reached by adulthood; males who survive gestation and infancy manifest much higher levels of developmental disorders than females. These skewed sex ratios support the argument that males, due to genetic disadvantages, are more sensitive to environmental perturbation than females. That is, they experience greater difficulty overcoming early developmental challenges.

What accounts for this increased male frailty? While the ultimate source of this phenomenon is linked to Darwinian sexual selection, the actual genetic mechanism is poorly understood. There are at least two competing explanations: sex-linkage and hormonal sex-limitation. Briefly stated, both mechanisms will result in a sexually divergent prevalence for a disorder. However, sex-linkage models assume that the genetic etiology of a disorder is the same across sex, whereas sex-limitation asserts that the causes are essentially different between the sexes.

Sex-Linked vs. Sex-Limited Traits

Sex-linkage exists when traits are influenced by alleles located on the X chromosome. The phenotypic prevalence for a sex-linked trait differs between the sexes as a result of the unique karyotype (46, XY) of males, and, less perceptibly, due to the mosaicism of the female cell line (i.e., different X-chromosomes being expressed in different cells). For females who carry two X chromosomes (see **Figure 1**), full phenotypic expression of a trait only occurs in the homozygous condition (in which both alleles are present). If females are heterozygous for an X-linked gene, the process of X-inactivation guarantees that a given allele will be expressed in only a proportion of developing cells. (One X chromosome is randomly inactivated during development, ensuring that females do not possess twice as many gene products as males.) For males, genes on the sex chromosomes generally operate in a haploid (single chromosome) state. Alleles on their single X chromosome will have a higher likelihood of being expressed (i.e., higher penetrance) due to their hemizygotic (XY) status. Moreover, the expressivity of an allele will be especially enhanced in males if traits are X-linked recessive.

All sex-linked traits stem from genetic variation on the X chromosome. Interestingly, sex-linked traits are not confined to reproductive-related processes, but instead

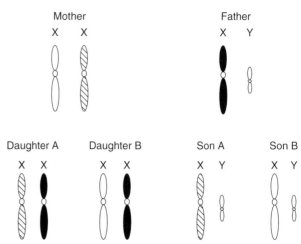

Figure 1 Diagram representing the transmission of sex chromosomes from parents to offspring (via the gametes). Mothers transmit one of their two X chromosomes to each child. Fathers can pass either an X chromosome or a Y chromosome to their offspring. In the former case, the product would be XX (female). In the latter case, the child would be XY (male). Note that daughters receive an identical copy of the X chromosome from their father. (Maternal transmission is more complicated, however, since sections of the mother's two X chromosomes recombine during gamete formation, so that the maternal X chromosome received by each offspring is effectively different than what is received by any other sibling.)

exert influences on a wide array of domains. This contrasts with the Y chromosome, which is solely involved with sex determination and male fertility. Although a condition known as hairy ears syndrome was thought to be Y-linked, more recent evidence has cast doubt on that speculation. The most significant gene on the Y chromosome is the SRY gene, which determines testes formation and appears to be structurally invariant in humans.

Sex-limitation occurs when genes are only expressed in one sex or the other (e.g., breast development in females; beard growth in males). Genes may also be sex-influenced, where the same genes are expressed differently in males and females. Although many genetics textbooks typically distinguish between sex-limited and sex-influenced traits, many studies in practice refer to both of these effects as sex-limited, indicating that the underpinnings of a disorder are fundamentally different between the sexes. These effects may result from different hormonal environments, socialization processes, or other environmental factors which may lead to different relative effects of (autosomal) genes in the two sexes. For example, a disorder might be heritable in males but more environmentally caused in females. Furthermore, sex-limitation occurs if different sets of genes are operating between the sexes. This contrasts with sex-linkage, in which the etiology is the same for males and females. For example, if color blindness is a recessive sex-linked condition, then color-blind females should possess a double dose of the same allele that colorblind males possess. However, if color blindness were a sex-limited trait, we would find that males are generally colorblind for different and perhaps nongenetic reasons (e.g., greater frequency of head injury).

The distinction between sex-linked, sex-limited, and sex-influenced mechanisms is a recurring theme, and will be discussed with regard to a potentially sex-linked developmental disorder. For theoretical purposes here, we place these mechanisms in the context of the broad developmental process.

The higher male morbidity in early childhood is often thought to reflect a sex-linked genetic mechanism. Since females have a second ('backup') copy of the X chromosome, the risk associated with a deleterious mutation is considerably lower. The diploid state of females leads to greater stability during development. It is true that some X-linked mutations can severely disrupt development in females, as in the case of Rett syndrome. However, for most conditions, the effect of a deleterious mutation is more debilitating in males (and, in the case of Rett syndrome, spontaneously aborts the male fetus with few exceptions).

An alternative to the sex-linkage model is that the hormonal milieu differs between the sexes. This often takes a sex-limited form, since testosterone exposure in early infancy overlaps little between males and females. Such theories claim that testosterone suppresses immune functions and stifles language-related abilities. Norman Geschwind, for example, hypothesized that prenatal testosterone is tied to a constellation of quirks and disorders that are more often observed in boys: immune diseases, left-handedness, and reading disabilities. Although this hypothesis has not been well supported, a similar and more compelling theory has been applied to autism. The presence of a Y chromosome should dramatically increase susceptibility to the disorder, since the fetus' testes are a major source of testosterone in the uterus.

These two mechanisms, sex-linkage and sex-limitation, do not necessarily have to be mutually exclusive. However, the former is more directly genetic, while the latter may operate through hormonally mediated channels. Additionally, sex-linkage is not generally concerned with the domain of sexual development and differentiation, whereas sex-limitation is tied to sexually dimorphic processes. They each entail unique predictions, which can be compared when information about the biological relatives of affected individuals is available. It is difficult to distinguish these two mechanisms in the absence of genetically informative data, as both may lead to a similar level of sexual divergence in prevalence.

Known Sex-Linked Disorders

It is considerably easier to determine the genetic mechanism when a disorder is controlled by allelic variation at a single genetic locus. There are several well-known disorders that are inherited in a Mendelian fashion, meaning that they are transmitted by a single allele, which can behave as recessive or dominant. This type of transmission can be contrasted to a multifactorial polygenic process, in which the effects of multiple genetic loci additively increase vulnerability to a disorder.

Most alleles are not completely dominant or recessive, but rather possess an intermediate level of expressivity. However, it is convenient to describe sex-linked traits using the classic Mendelian approach. Some sex-linked disorders are indeed purely recessive (e.g., color blindness), while other disorders such as fragile X syndrome are less so. When the inheritance of a recessive sex-linked gene is involved, prevalence will be much higher in males. Conversely, for genes that are best described as dominant, prevalence may be higher in females. This is because females can receive a mutation from either their mother or father, and therefore the chance of inheriting a disorder may be twice that of males (who can only inherit an X-linked mutation from their mother); note that this is more of a technical possibility than an actual phenomenon.

Consistent with most autosomal-linked diseases, sex-linked Mendelian disorders are typically recessive. As mentioned before, X-linked disorders are not necessarily tied to sexual development, but affect domains as wide-scoping as color vision, blood clotting, and neuronal growth. The sex-linked nature of these disorders was demonstrated prior to the availability of molecular genetic tools. This is because sex-linked recessive traits have specific inheritance patterns. At the pedigree level, transmission of the disorder must pass from mother to son. Furthermore, a female carrier will transmit the disorder to half of her male offspring.

At the population level, one should observe that the prevalence of affected females is the square of the proportion of males who are affected. (The odds are squared to reflect the fact that females require a homozygous combination of mutations to manifest the disorder.) This prediction assumes that affected males have equal mating success relative to female carriers. If the condition is lethal in childhood or renders affected males sick and undesirable, such males will be less likely to produce children compared to female carriers. Girls would therefore be less likely to inherit the allele from their father, and the proportion of females affected will be less than the square of males. This caveat does not apply to sex-linked color blindness since it does not affect mating success or mortality, but would be relevant to developmental disorders.

Color vision deficiency, or color blindness, is a relatively common disorder that interferes with perception of red and green hues. It reportedly occurs in about

8% of white males and in about 0.7% of white females. This pattern in prevalence remarkably coincides with quantitative predictions of a recessive condition; the proportion of affected females is the square of the proportion of affected males. Another notable X-linked recessive disorder is androgen insensitivity syndrome. It is unique among the sex-linked disorders in that it has powerful implications for our understanding of sexual development. A single genetic mutation renders the androgen receptor severely compromised or missing. Although an affected fetus might produce normal amounts of testosterone, the lack of binding sites for androgen prevents masculine sexual differentiation. Affected individuals are almost always genotypic males who appear phenotypically indistinguishable from females. Other recessive conditions include Lesch–Nyhan syndrome and hemophilia, but these are extremely rare.

A few sex-linked disorders are influenced by genes that are not recessive. Fragile X syndrome is the most prominent to fall under this category. Due to the semi-dominant nature of the alleles leading to this disorder (i.e., variations in the *FMR1* gene), female carriers often exhibit less severe symptoms. The deleterious forms of the *FMR1* gene frequently cause mental retardation in males but milder learning difficulties in females. Fragile X syndrome is the most common form of inherited mental retardation. (Down syndrome, which is more prevalent, is not hereditary.) It is thought that the prevalence is twice as high in males, although ascertainment in females is less straightforward. The detection rate in females is probably lower, since they are usually able to live independently.

Fragile X syndrome has a very complex inheritance that defies simple Mendelian descriptions. A mutation of the *FMR1* gene leads to a variety of physical anomalies and cognitive defects. Moreover, the defective gene itself (an expansion in a repeating triplet nucleotide sequence) becomes more deleterious across generations, since the expansion increases in each transmission. Production of the FMR1 protein is severely curtailed in individuals with fragile X syndrome, and the effect worsens across generations. Since the FMR1 protein is necessary for normal brain function, affected individuals will present with intellectual disabilities. Such individuals often exhibit social impairment and autistic behavior. Thus, fragile X syndrome is interesting in that it contains features that closely parallel pervasive developmental disorders.

Rett syndrome is a pervasive developmental disorder which is transmitted in a dominant X-linked fashion. Unlike fragile X syndrome, the mutation is highly penetrant. In other words, the mutation is extremely potent and will invariably be expressed if present. Rett syndrome is caused by a mutation of the *MECP2* gene. Due to its dominant and debilitating nature, most cases of Rett syndrome are sporadic in which the *MECP2* mutation spontaneously arises in a parent's gonad.

Nearly all cases of Rett syndrome are female, although a few male cases have been reported. The sex difference in prevalence can be interpreted as reflecting a much higher lethality in male fetuses. This is supported by observations that affected females have fewer male siblings than would be expected. The male lethality of this disorder portends the debilitating consequences experienced by its female survivors. In general, development appears to follow a normal trajectory until 1–2 years of age. At that point, intellectual growth is suddenly stunted and psychomotor abilities begin declining. Affected individuals are relegated to a life of profound mental retardation.

At least one X-linked gene has also been shown to affect impulsive and aggressive behavior in humans. Specifically, monoamine oxidase A (MAO-A) is an enzyme (found in the human brain) controlled by a single gene on the X chromosome, and is involved in the metabolism of neurotransmitters serotonin (5-HT), norepinephrine (NE), and dopamine (DA). In a large Dutch pedigree, Han Brunner's group found a point mutation in the *MAO-A* gene that was associated with abnormal aggressiveness in adult males. Further support for the role of MAO-A on aggression comes from Jean Shih's studies of knockout mice (i.e., an inbred strain bred to be missing the normal MAO-A allele), which exhibit elevated levels of aggressive and violent behavior. In children, MAO-A mutations have been shown to confer a greater risk of aggression and violence, but only in those who experienced elevated levels of physical maltreatment by their parents. Adverse environments, therefore, may enhance the effects of some X-linked genes.

Sex Chromosome Abnormalities

Some genetic disorders are not caused by mutations, but rather stem from the failure of sex chromosomes to properly separate during gamete formation – a process called nondysjunction. This will lead to numerical abnormalities, in which individuals have more than two sex chromosomes (either X or Y) or lack one copy. In addition, a chromosome may be present but functionally faulty. Unlike those with autosomal abnormalities (i.e., Down syndrome), affected individuals usually do not suffer global mental retardation. Instead, sex chromosome abnormalities often lead to learning disabilities and difficulty in specific cognitive domains. The most common types of cases are XYY syndrome, Klinefelter syndrome, and Turner syndrome (TS).

XYY males possess a trisomy of the sex chromosomes instead of the normal two. Most XYY males appear physically normal (aside from taller stature) and do not experience unusual deficits. However, there may be an increased risk of learning disorders and language problems. Additionally, there was early speculation that XYY males are more prone to aggression and criminal behavior, but this view was made obsolete in 1976. A study by Herman Witkin and colleagues showed that higher rates of XYY males in prison populations could be explained by lower intelligence rather than higher aggression or violence.

Some males possess an extra copy of the X chromosome. These XXY males exhibit Klinefelter syndrome. Unlike males with the XYY karyotype, Klinefelter males are usually sterile and often possess a variety of physical anomalies. Klinefelter boys tend to exhibit selective deficits in reading and language skills. Arithmetic skills may also be compromised, but visuospatial skills are remarkably intact. This often results in a large discrepancy between verbal intelligence quotients (IQ) and performance IQ.

One conclusion is that boys with sex chromosome abnormalities manifest a cognitive profile exaggerative of typical males. That is, delayed language skills tend to be coupled with normal visuospatial abilities. This observation is useful because it may shed light on disorders that are genetically more elusive (i.e., dyslexia, autism, stuttering). Interestingly, TS girls exhibit the opposite profile.

Girls with TS have only one intact X chromosome. Their second copy is a nonfunctional stub or is altogether missing. In over two-thirds of cases, it is the X-chromosome of paternal origin that is missing. The girls possess extremely short stature and a variety of medical problems. However, their condition often goes unnoticed until adolescence, when it is found that they are not developing secondary sexual characteristics. In terms of academic performance, they generally have verbal skills in the normal range but show deficits in spatial skills and mathematical problem solving.

This cognitive profile has attracted interest because it refutes hypotheses that superior visuospatial skills are X-linked recessive. However, females with TS also experience gonadal dysgenesis, which causes the ovaries to degenerate and thwart all secretion of hormones. Perhaps optimal spatial intelligence results from the interaction of sex steroids with genetic loci on the X chromosome. In 2003, a group led by Judith Ross evaluated that possibility by experimentally treating TS girls with androgen replacement. Surprisingly, girls who received androgen did not show increases in spatial cognition, but did show improvement in working memory.

Finally, some investigators have drawn a link between autism and TS, noting that the risk of autism is 200-fold in females with TS. Autism is present only among TS girls who inherited an intact X chromosome from their mother; no cases of autism are observed among those who possess a paternally derived X chromosome. David Skuse and colleagues have argued that genetic imprinting (i.e., different gene expression depending on which parent transmitted it) might explain the male vulnerability to autism, insomuch that superior social–emotional processing is associated with an X chromosome of paternal origin.

Blueprint for Evaluating Potential Sex-Linked Disorders

When a disorder is controlled by a single mutation, it is rather straightforward to determine whether sex-linkage is at work, based on patterns of transmission across generations and associations with measured polymorphisms on the X-chromosome. For complex polygenic disorders, however, it is necessary to carefully weigh evidence of sex-linkage and sex-limitation in order to discover the underlying biological process. For example, if family pedigree data supports evidence for sex-linkage, then an intensive hunt for relevant loci on the X chromosome will be warranted. However, if sex-limitation is demonstrated, then hormonal and/or environmental influences should be explored. This is because there are two major routes by which genetic differences between the sexes are manifested at the phenotypic level: (1) an X-linked route and (2) an 'indirect' hormonal route.

The second route is described as 'indirect' because the disorder is influenced by an epigenetic mechanism in which sex steroids alter transcription of genes. For example, substances produced by the gonads (androgen and estrogen) might interact with genes carried on the autosomes. If liability for the disorder can be shown to correlate with androgen levels (prenatal or otherwise), then sex-linkage is unlikely a source of the gender skew in prevalence. A sex-influenced steroid pathway is essentially different from a sex-linked genetic mechanism.

These two models can be tested at the molecular level (i.e., genetic linkage studies) as well as at the latent or phenotypic level (i.e., family transmission studies). Evidence for sex-linkage occurs when a disorder is associated with specific polymorphisms on chromosome X. The genetic signature of affected individuals is compared to that of unaffected individuals. Sex-linkage is demonstrated if a specific marker on the X chromosome can successfully discriminate the two groups. Sometimes, however, when stratifying a sample by gender, it is found that the genetic loci associated with the disorder in males are different from the trait loci in females. This would be an example of sex-limitation, since the genes contributing to the disorder in males would be different from those influencing females.

When working with pedigree data, sex-linkage can be demonstrated if transmission of risk tends to run from mother to son but not from father to son. Also, since daughters inherit the same X chromosome from their father, sisters will share on average 75% of their alleles identical by descent. Therefore, symptoms of a sex-linked disorder should be most similar among sister–sister and father–daughter pairs. Sibling resemblance should weaken among brother–brother and opposite-sex pairs. Finally, the genetic loading of risk should be higher in families with affected females than in those with male-only cases. Since females require a higher genetic dosage to manifest a sex-linked disorder, a higher prevalence of the disorder should be observed in the biological (particularly paternal) relatives of female probands.

Autism: An Illustrative Example

These predictions can be used to evaluate the sex-linked status of candidate disorders. Autism serves as a good example to illustrate the methods for detecting sex-linked effects, as the male–female ratio is 4:1. This has led investigators to propose that X-linked mutations may increase vulnerability, although testosterone-related individual differences have also been endorsed as a potential source of the sex difference in prevalence. It should be noted, however, that autism is considered a complex disorder with genetic heterogeneity, such that several different genes (including several autosomal ones) may account for different forms of autism. Still, the sex difference in prevalence has led investigators to consider sex-linkage as one potential etiological source of autism.

Sex differences in prevalence are not necessarily the product of genotypic differences between the sexes. However, autism appears a strong candidate as a sex-linked genetic disorder because it is unlikely that environmental influences would lead to systematic gender bias. Autism emerges too early in life to be caused by gender-specific socialization patterns. Indeed it would seem bizarre that parents could treat infant boys in such a fundamentally different way that would cause them to develop severe impairments in communication and social skills.

Evidence for sex-linkage is based on autistic features in boys with fragile X syndrome. A substantial proportion of fragile X boys suffer social anxiety, repetitive/stereotyped behaviors, and language disturbances such as echolalia. However, the deficits observed in these boys may qualitatively differ from those with pure autism. Also, the amount of FMR1 protein is not related to the degree of autistic behavior in fragile X boys. This suggests that X-linked mutations affecting the *FMR1* gene are not directly responsible for the high prevalence of autism.

The absence of gender effects on familial risk also runs contrary to sex-linkage. In 2000, Andrew Pickles and colleagues reported that the prevalence of broadly defined autism is no higher in the biological relatives of female probands than in the relatives of male probands. This indicates that the genetic threshold necessary for manifestation of autism is not higher in females, thereby undermining a key argument for sex-linkage. Furthermore, among parents of male probands, the rate of autism is actually lower in mothers than in fathers. This result departs from the sex-linked expectation that risk is primarily transmitted from mother to son.

Molecular studies, however, have met with more success. In a genetic linkage study, a group led by Hugh Gurling explored a region of the X chromosome involved in the encoding of MeCP2 and FMRP. (Mutations of the *MECP2* and *FMR1* gene cause Rett syndrome and fragile X syndrome, respectively.) Genetic markers in this region produced a likelihood ratio of approximately 100:1 that autism is X-linked. Similarly, Merlin Butler and colleagues observed a highly skewed X-inactivation pattern in a significant portion of autistic females. The control group was composed of unaffected sisters, who showed a much more random (and typical) pattern of X-inactivation. (Skewed X-inactivation is comparable to the male [haploid] disadvantage of 'putting all your eggs in one basket'.) The interpretation, then, is that random inactivation buffers females from the deleterious effect of any single allele.

It should be noted that molecular evidence in favor of sex-linkage for some forms of autism has emerged quite recently. Previous genome-wide searches had consistently pointed to autosomal linkage. In fact, even sex-limited expression of autosomal genes had been implicated. A group led by Stan Nelson, for example, discovered a linkage site on chromosome 17 among families possessing at least two children with broadly defined autism. However, linkage was specific to families possessing male-only cases of autism. No significant linkage sites were found for the remaining families who possessed female cases. This suggests that the genes influencing autism may differ between the sexes, although it does not imply that the overall magnitude of genetic influence is different. Indeed, twin studies demonstrate that the heritability is equally high for males and females.

Equal heritability in the face of a marked sexual divergence in prevalence may occur in the presence of sex-specific hormonal thresholds. For example, the 'extreme male brain' theory of Simon Baron-Cohen describes a neurodevelopmental trajectory that is typified by high androgen levels. Elevated exposure to testosterone should lead to enhanced growth of the brain's right hemisphere at the expense of left hemisphere development. As a result of these mean differences in prenatal testosterone, males will normally develop an asymmetry favoring the right hemisphere. This bias is reflected in males' superior functioning in right hemisphere-specialized tasks, such as mental rotation. The drawback is that language skills are delayed. As a result, female infants begin verbally interacting at a younger age and are more effective at gesture-based communication, two skills that autistic children generally lack.

According to this theory, the traits that contribute to autism are an extreme magnification of the same characteristics that typical males possess to a greater degree than typical females (e.g., fiddling with objects instead of chatting on the telephone, systematizing instead of empathizing). One extension of this argument is that intellectual impairment in autistic males should follow a more normal distribution within a more typical range. Autistic females, in contrast, should adhere to a more deviant IQ distribution. Cognitive development in autistic females should be more qualitatively deviant because autism is essentially the unfolding of a masculine developmental process.

There is a general consensus that autistic females possess lower IQs than their male counterparts. In fact, the sex ratio in autism is least distorted among those with the lowest levels of intellectual functioning. As one approaches the higher-functioning end of the spectrum, the sex ratio climbs to 9:1. This contrasts with the pattern observed for fragile X syndrome, in which mental retardation is proportionately more common among males than among females. This suggests that a sex-linked model is inferior to a sex-limited or sex-influenced interpretation.

Evidence for a sex-influenced hormonal mechanism comes from females who possess an autosomal-recessive condition known as congenital adrenal hyperplasia. Females with this disease are often exposed to abnormally high levels of testosterone during early development. Consistent with the 'extreme male brain' theory, they score as high as male controls (and significantly higher than female controls) on a self-report autism questionnaire. Furthermore, the digit length ratio of autistic children tends to cluster at the very masculine end of the spectrum. (The length of the index finger in relation to the ring finger is sexually dimorphic; low ratios serve as a putative index of increased fetal testosterone.) Interestingly, the digit length ratio is similarly low in the fathers of autistic children, indicating that genetic risk may be transmitted from father to son.

Concluding Remarks

The sex distribution of a disorder may provide important clues concerning its genetic origins. Indeed, understanding the source of the disparity in prevalence is tantamount to identifying the etiological roots of the disorder. Therefore, it is important to discern the various genetic mechanisms that might lead to a systematically higher prevalence in one gender. Sex-linkage is one of several processes that might account for the greater male vulnerability to developmental disorders.

The evidence regarding autism as a sex-linked disorder, however, is mixed. The gender skew in prevalence may stem from a combination of sex-influenced, sex-limited, and sex-linked processes. This ambiguity reflects the fact that the genetic and environmental factors contributing to autism are diverse. As with any polygenic disorder, each predisposing gene (X-linked or otherwise) probably exerts only a small effect on overall risk. Heterogeneity further complicates matters, since it is unlikely that the same mechanisms account for the entire spectrum (i.e., Asperger syndrome, autism with speech, autism without speech).

All sex-linked disorders that have hitherto been established involve mutations at a single genetic locus. However, as clinicians continue to refine the diagnostic categories, it is likely that X-linked alleles will emerge as significant risk factors for polygenic disorders. Single-gene disorders and sex chromosomal abnormalities provide an ideal starting base from which to search for genetic loci involved in the pathology of more complex disorders.

See also: Autism Spectrum Disorders; Behavior Genetics; Endocrine System; Fragile X Syndrome; Genetic Disorders: Single Gene; Genetics and Inheritance; Intellectual Disabilities; Nature vs. Nurture; Screening, Newborn and Maternal Well-being; Screening, Prenatal.

Suggested Readings

Baron-Cohen S and Hammer J (1997) Is autism an extreme form of the 'male brain'? *Advances in Infancy Research* 11: 193–217.

Brunner HG, Nelen MR, van Zandvoort P, *et al.* (1993) X-linked borderline mental retardation with prominent behavioral disturbance: phenotype, genetic localization, and evidence for disturbed monoamine metabolism. *American Journal of Human Genetics* 52: 1032–1039.

Pickles A, Starr E, Kazak S, *et al.* (2000) Variable expression of the autism broader phenotype: Findings from extended pedigrees. *Journal of Child Psychology and Psychiatry* 41: 491–502.

Ross J, Roeltgen D, Stefanatos G, *et al.* (2003) Androgen-responsive aspects of cognition in girls with Turner syndrome. *Journal of Clinical Endocrinology and Metabolism* 88: 292–296.

Skuse DH (2005) X-linked genes and mental functioning. *Human Molecular Genetics* 14: R27–R32.

Stone JL, Merriman B, Cantor RM, *et al.* (2004) Evidence for sex-specific risk alleles in autism spectrum disorder. *American Journal of Human Genetics* 75: 1117–1123.

Talebizadeh Z, Bittel D, Veatch O, Kibiryeva N, and Butler M (2005) Brief report: Non-random X chromosome inactivation in females with autism. *Journal of Autism and Developmental Disorders* 35: 675–681.

Vincent JB, Melmer G, Bolton PF, *et al.* (2005) Genetic linkage analysis of the X chromosome in autism, with emphasis on the fragile X region. *Psychiatric Genetics* 15: 83–90.

Witkin H, Mednick S, and Schulsinger F (1976) Criminality in XYY and XXY men. *Science* 193: 547–555.

Relevant Website

http://www.ncbi.nlm.nih.gov – Online Mendelian Inheritance in Man (OMIM).

Genetic Disorders: Single Gene

E L Grigorenko, Yale University, New Haven, CT, USA

Glossary

Developmental science – Studies of complex systemic changes in human occurring over life-span.
Epigenetics – Studies of changes in gene functioning (silencing and transcription initiation) that occur without changes in the genes themselves.
Genetics – Studies of heredity investigating how genes are transmitted from generation to generation.
Genomics – Studies of the whole genome and how it functions as a complex system of interacting genes in an environment.
Proteomics – Studies of proteins and their functions.

Introduction

We refer to development as a complex process of realization of biological mechanisms uniquely defining a human being. These biological mechanisms cannot unfold in a vacuum; they unfurl in the environments defined by 'humanness', that is, in the human habitat. The idea that both internal forces hidden in an individual, as well as the external characteristics of the habitat, guide the development of a human being has been central to social and behavioral sciences since their very emergence. Relevant challenges and debates have not really been about whether either matters, but rather about what constitutes internal and external forces of development and how their various elements interact with each other. One of the charges of developmental sciences is to define these internal and external 'black boxes' and to understand, as much as possible, direct, indirect, and interactive mechanisms of their functioning.

The objective of this article is to sample from the modern body of knowledge on the content and function of one of the many internal forces guiding development – the human genome. With amazingly rapid developments in genetics and genomics, the genetic 'draw' of the internal forces black box is gradually being filled by a summary of the roughly 24 500 genes carried by individuals from the moment of conception. Genetics and genomics are on their way to characterizing every individual in terms of his or her genetic 'script', but scientists today understand that it is environments, in their infinite variability, that guide the interpretation of the genetic script by its carrier into the actual performance, which is always a unique realization of the inherited genetic script. Yet, understanding what these genes do and whether or not their functions are modifiable by environment is a very important task that is greatly relevant to both developmental and health sciences.

The article is structured into three parts. First, a number of concepts that capture the vocabulary used throughout the article are introduced. Second, a general description of single-gene disorders (SGDs), depicting their common and specific features, and introduces a number of examples of such disorders are provided. Third, comments on selected common characteristics of SGDs that might be of interest to developmentalists in the context of understanding genetic forces of development are made.

Concepts and Definitions

Broadly defined, genes are sources of information that define growth patterns and functions of human cells; genes are units of inheritance forming the bases of heredity. Genes are contained in a complex chemical known as deoxyribonucleic acid (DNA). This complex polymer is made of simpler chemicals referred to as nucleotides. Nucleotides are basic constituents of DNA; they are organic molecules that consist of a nitrogenous base (adenine (A), guanine (G), thymine (T), or cytosine (C)), a phosphate molecule, and a sugar molecule. Thousands of nucleotides link together in a long chain forming DNA in such a way that C matches with G and A matches with T to establish a base pair (bp). Because of this selective pairing of nucleotides, although DNA is usually double-stranded, it is enough to know the sequence of nucleotides on one DNA strand to reproduce a complementary sequence on the other DNA strand. Each human has ~3 billion bp of DNA, which together form the human genome. Within an organism, DNA is contained in cell nuclei and organized into chromosomes. Chromosomes enfold both genes and intergenetic DNA. Genetic DNA (i.e., DNA that forms genes) is presented by segments that contain the information necessary to manufacture a functional ribonucleic acid (RNA) needed for subsequent synthesis of proteins. Genes themselves are complex structures that contain, chiefly:

1. regions determining specifics of the RNA product to be produced (so-called promoter regions);
2. transcribed regions establishing the content of the RNA product (so-called exons);

3. noncoding intra-exonic pieces of DNA that are not transcribed (so-called introns); and
4. other functional sequence regions (e.g., 3′ UTR). Functionally, genes can be 'working' (i.e., expressed) or 'not working' (i.e., silent, not expressed). Expressed genes can produce different gene products, which result in protein synthesis or in regulation of other genes.

The human genome is characterized by the presence of 46 chromosomes – 22 pairs of autosomal (nonsex) chromosomes and two sex chromosomes. Chromosomes 1–22 are identical for males and females, whereas sex chromosomes differ. Sex chromosomes are defined as X and Y; males are '46, XY' and females are '46, XX'. Each pair of autosomal chromosomes is formed by a maternal and a paternal chromosome; thus, each individual has two copies of the same gene – one inherited from the mother and one from the father. Paternal and maternal chromosomes essentially carry the same information: each chromosome contains the same set of genes, but their nucleotide sequences can vary slightly (by less than 1%). The pairwise relationships between the two chromosomes and genes harbored by chromosomes determine various patterns of genetic transmission.

Decoding DNA for the sake of revealing its bp constitution is referred to as 'sequencing'. The first draft of the human genome became available with the completion of the Human Genome Project in 2003. Now various gaps in this draft have been closed and pieces of the genomes of many individuals from different ethnic backgrounds have been sequenced. From the rapidly accumulated mass of human DNA sequences completed to date, it is evident that two unrelated individuals have, on average, one different nucleotide per 1000 bp. Although when considered across the whole human genome these differences amount to 3 million per person, when two people are compared with each other, the differences amount to only ∼0.1%. The places in the genome where these differences occur are referred to as polymorphic sites (or loci) and the differences themselves are referred to as polymorphisms (or variants). When people differ at particular sites, they are said to have different alleles at those sites. There are two main types of polymorphisms: (1) those for which only two types of different alleles can be observed, called di-allelic polymorphisms; and (2) those for which multiple different alleles can be observed in the population, called multi-allelic polymorphisms. The chief examples of di-allelic polymorphisms are single nucleotide changes called SNPs (pronounced 'snips', or single nucleotide polymorphisms). An illustration of an SNP is when, at a particular site, a certain percentage (e.g., 60%) of the population will have a T nucleotide and the remaining percentage (e.g., 40%) will have a C nucleotide. The chief examples of multi-allelic polymorphisms are DNA variants involving multiple nucleotides, so-called STRPs (pronounced 'es-ti-ar-piz', or short tandem repeat polymorphisms). For this type of polymorphism, multiple alternative alleles exist in the general population in which each allele is characterized by a particular frequency. To establish what particular allele an individual carries at a particular polymorphic site, this individual's DNA needs to be genotyped or sequenced. Both genotyping and sequencing, among other techniques, are widely used in studies of the genetic bases of human disorders. If a person has the same alleles at a given site, this person is referred to as homozygous for that allele; if the alleles differ, the person is referred to as heterozygous.

DNA polymorphisms arise as a result of mutations. Mutations change a so-called wild (i.e., original) type of allele into a mutant type. Generally, mutations are subdivided into functional (i.e., resulting in some kind of a change) and nonfunctional (i.e., not leading to any registrable change) types. Functional mutations, in turn, can be advantageous (e.g., leading to particular advantages such as the human ability to speak) or detrimental. The focus of this article is on detrimental mutations that form the genetic bases for SGDs. Mutations are either newly acquired (i.e., happening in a given individual *de novo* or anew) or heritable. Yet, the presence of a mutation in an individual (i.e., the mutation is structurally present in the DNA sequence) does not guarantee this mutation will play a role in development because of internal, so-called epigenetic processes that regulate the function of the genome in a human being. Thus, genetic does not mean deterministic; it means probabilistic. Mutant genes might code for an abnormal protein; these abnormalities can be either structural (i.e., an abnormal protein will be synthesized) or functional (i.e., more or less of a particular protein than needed will be synthesized).

Genetics refers to studies of heredity (i.e., how genes are transmitted from generation to generation), whereas genomics refers to studies of the whole genome and how it functions as a system in an environment (i.e., how the inherited genes are expressed within a particular individual). Proteomics is the study of proteins and their functions. Collectively, all three disciplines contribute to understanding the genetic bases of human disorders in general and SGDs in particular.

Single-Gene Genetic Disorders

The Centers for Disease Control and Prevention (CDC) of the Department of Health and Human Services (DHHS) defines SGDs as a group of conditions caused by a deleterious change (mutation) in one specific gene. The CDC recognizes more than 6000 SGDs. Each specific SGD tends to be rare (i.e., its prevalence in the general population is typically <0.01–0.001%). Examples of very rare SGDs are severe hydroxylase deficiencies, inborn conditions caused by genetic alterations in the *CYP11B* gene on chromosome 8, which are characterized by dehydration, occasional vomiting, poor feeding, failure to gain weight, and intermittent fever. These deficiencies are seen in fewer than 200 000 individuals in the US (i.e., less than 0.001% of the population). The incidence of hyperphenylalaninemia, an inborn metabolic disorder (see below) is higher, affecting 1 in 15 000 newborns, with a wide range of prevalence in different populations around the world (e.g., 0.001% in the US, 0.003% in Ireland, and 0.0001% in Finland). When considered as a group, however, SGDs may be seen in 1 in 300 individual births. Thus, collectively, although rare individually, these conditions constitute a substantial number of pediatric illnesses.

SGDs can be subdivided into three types: (1) Mendelian disorders; (2) repeat expansion disorders; and (3) disorders involving epigenetic mechanisms. In the literature at large, SGDs are also referred to as monogenetic disorders; these terms can be used interchangeably.

Mendelian Single-Gene Disorders

A large number of SGDs conform, in their patterns of inheritance, to laws discovered by Gregor Mendel and are thus referred to as Mendelian. Mendelian SGDs are transmitted in families. These families are typically ascertained through an individual with a disorder, who is referred to as a 'proband'. The family of a disordered individual is referred to as a nuclear family if it includes only first-degree relatives (i.e., parents and siblings) or extended family (or kindred) if it includes other types of relatives. Families are typically represented graphically by pedigrees; these representations use conventional symbols to illustrate males and females, disordered or nondisordered individuals, types of relationships among relatives, and probands.

There are five basic patterns of single-gene inheritance, two of which describe modes of transmission of mutant genes located on autosomal chromosomes 1–22 (autosomal dominant and recessive patterns of inheritance) and three of which describe modes of transmission of mutant genes located on sex chromosomes (two for X chromosome, X-linked dominant and X-linked recessive, and one for Y chromosome, Y-linked).

Under an autosomal-dominant pattern of inheritance, the disorder usually appears in every generation. In such families, every affected child has an affected parent and each child has a 50% chance of inheriting the disease from the affected parent and, if affected themselves, passing the mutant gene to their children. In this pattern of inheritance, only one copy of the mutant gene is needed for the manifestation of the disorder. It is important to mention that autosomal-dominant conditions are also characterized by incomplete penetrance (i.e., the probability of expressing a phenotype given a genotype); penetrance of autosomal dominant SGDs is low compared with other types of inheritance. Correspondingly, although only one mutated gene (either maternal or paternal) is required for the disorder, a substantially smaller proportion of the individuals compared with the carriers of the mutant allele will develop the disease. An example of a SGD transmitted in the autosomal dominant fashion is Marfan syndrome (MFS), a disorder of the connective tissue. This disorder was first described by French pediatrician Antoine Marfan in the late nineteenth century in a 5-year-old girl named Gabrielle. MFS is characterized by less than normal stiffness of tendons, ligaments, blood vessel walls, cartilage, heart valves, and many other structures supported by connective tissue because of abnormal biochemistry. Data from research studies indicate that the estimated prevalence of MFS is 1 in 5000 with no predilection for either sex. Although the penetrance of MFS is high, its degree of severity varies dramatically, so that the presentation ranges from few (if any) symptoms to life-threatening heart problems. The syndrome cannot be diagnosed by a single test and requires a sophisticated scoring system. Phenotypically, people with MFS present with disproportionately long limbs and fingers, a relatively tall stature, and predisposition to cardiovascular abnormalities. The chief mechanism for the development of MFS is a mutation in the gene *FBN1* (located on the long arm (q) of chromosome 15, 15q21.1) encoding the production of the protein fibrillin, one of the components of microfibrils, constituting connective tissue. Today, scientists have identified more than 600 different mutations associated with MFS. The overwhelming majority of these mutations (~75%) are familial, that is, transmitted in families, but there are also cases in which the syndrome is cased by *de-novo* mutations in *FBN1*. Also, ~10% of individuals with MFS do not have any detectable mutations in *FBN1*; thus, it is possible that the syndrome can be caused by some other genetic mechanism, likely involving two other genes whose proteins interact with the protein encoded by *FBN1*, *TGFBR1,* and *TGFBR2*, which code for receptors of the transforming growth factor-beta (TGFβ). To manage MFS, doctors might encourage patients to restrict physical activity, reduce emotional stress, monitor cardiovascular functioning, and take possible preventive measures such as β-blocker medication for aortic protection and prophylactic surgery (e.g., replacement of the aortic root). Correspondingly, children diagnosed with MFS are recommended to avoid highly demanding isometric exercise and competitive or contact sports, but to remain active by engaging in specific aerobic exercise and eating healthy diets to prevent obesity.

For a disorder to be inherited in the autosomal recessive mode of inheritance, a person needs to have two copies of the mutated gene. Often a proband with a recessive disorder has unaffected parents, each of which has a copy of the mutant. If both parents are carriers (i.e., they have one copy of the mutated gene, but not the phenotype), they have a 25% chance of having a child affected by the disorder. This distinctive pedigree pattern, in which there are mutant genes for recessive disorders, is 'horizontal', meaning that the disorder is observed more often within a generation (i.e., within a sibship) than across generations (i.e., between parents and offspring). A well-known example of an autosomal recessive disorder is hyperphenylalaninemia (HPA), also referred to as phenylketonuria (PKU). The first systematic description of a case of HPA was done by Norwegian physician Ivar Følling in the 1930s. HPA is a genetic disorder of metabolism caused chiefly by the lack of or malfunctioning of the enzyme phenylalanine hydroxylase (PAH); this enzyme converts dietary phenylalanine, which is present in dairy products, into tyrosine. The production of the PAH enzyme is controlled by the gene *PAH*, situated on the long arm of chromosome 12 (12q23.2). Scientists have reported somewhere in the neighborhood of 450 mutations in the gene that vary in origin and create a range of severity in the manifestation of HPA. HPA presents an example of a disorder whose molecular basis is well understood and can be interfered with therapeutically to prevent associated mental retardation. In its untreated form, HPA can result in severe neurological and functional disability. Studies have shown that dietary restrictions aimed at maintaining the plasma concentration of phenylalanine (and, consequently, the cerebral tissue) within safe limits of nontoxic concentration (120–360 mmol/L) have made remarkable improvements in the lives of people carrying two copies of the mutant gene. Although if diagnosed early (prenatally) and treated attentively for life, the presentation of mental retardation can be avoided, HPA has been associated with other outcomes, including structural and functional changes in the brain, abnormalities of visual function, and emotional and behavioral difficulties, which require professional attention.

If a mutant gene of which only one copy is required for manifestation of the disorder is located on X chromosome, the mode of transmission is referred to as X-linked dominant. In pedigrees with this pattern of inheritance, males are affected more often than females. The chance of transmitting the mutant allele also differs for men and women; because all sons of an affected male will receive his Y chromosome, all of them will be unaffected, and because all daughters of an affected male will received his mutant X chromosome, all daughters will be affected. In turn, because she has two X chromosomes, a woman with an X-linked dominant condition has only a 50% chance of transmitting her mutant X chromosome. Thus, half of her sons and half of her daughters, on average, are expected to be affected. As an example of this pattern of transmission, consider Aicardi syndrome, named for the French

neurologist who systematically described the syndrome in the 1960s. This syndrome is lethal for males and thus is observed only in females. Its frequency is very low and is estimated at 300–500 cases worldwide. Phenotypically, this syndrome is characterized by the partial or complete absence of the corpus callosum, the structure that links the two hemispheres of the brain. The onset of the syndrome unfolds at the age of 3–5 months and presents through infantile spasms (a form of seizures), brain microcephaly and deviant structure, lesions of the retina of the eye, and mental retardation. There is a substantial amount of variation in the severity of the syndrome, both anatomically (i.e., the number and severity of abnormalities) and behaviorally (i.e., the extent of mental retardation). The genetic causes of Aicardi syndrome are unknown.

The X-linked recessive mode of transmission requires two copies of the mutant gene on X chromosome. Similar to the X-linked dominant mode, males are affected more often than females and risk of transmission is different for males and females. Because males have only one copy of X chromosome, they cannot transmit the disorder to their sons, but they can transmit the disorder to their daughters. Affected women will transmit the mutant X chromosome to all their children. In addition, women can be carriers of these disorders – even if they have no phenotypic manifestation, they have a 50% chance of transmitting the mutant X chromosome to their children. If this happens, all their sons will be affected and some of their daughters might be affected as well, provided they receive the second copy of the mutant chromosome from their fathers. An example of this type of disorder is muscular dystrophy of Duchenne type (MDD), named after the French neurologist Guillaume Duchenne, who first described a case of MDD. The estimated prevalence of MDD is 1 in 3500 male births. It is a disorder that presents with rapidly worsening muscle weakness and a loss of muscle mass (wasting) that starts in the lower limbs (legs and pelvis) and spreads to the whole body. MDD usually onsets before the age of 6 years and can manifest its first symptoms as early as infancy. By mid-childhood (age 10 years or so), walking might require braces, and by late childhood (age 12 years or so) confinement to a wheelchair might be necessary. MDD can also present through many other symptoms (e.g., breathing and bone disorders). The disorder is caused by mutant versions of the *DMD* gene (located in the short arm (p) of chromosome X, Xp21), which codes for the protein dystrophin, an essential cell membrane protein in muscle cells. A distinct feature of the *DMD* gene is that it is the largest and most complex known gene in the human genome. Studies show that this gene is characterized by large numbers of mutations, deletions, and duplications of genetic material. There is no known cure for MDD, but there is a significant ongoing effort to develop state-of-the-art pharmacological treatments as well as attempts at gene therapy.

Finally, the last type of Mendelian transmission is exemplified by Y-linked disorders caused by mutations on Y chromosome. Although Y chromosome is very small and home to relatively few genes (compared with other chromosomes), it is far from being the genetic 'badlands' it was once considered. Clearly, this type of inheritance is relevant to males only; females do not have Y chromosome and, thus, cannot transmit or manifest a disorder. Y-linked disorders are rare and there are few examples of them. One such example is a late-onset sensorineural deafness. In addition, Y chromosome contains a number of genes involved in spermatogenesis; mutations in these genes have been reported to lead to genetic disorders of infertility.

Repeat Expansions Single-Gene Disorders

The 24 500 genes and DNA between them form ~3 billion DNA bp. Of note is that a large portion of these bp are composed of recurring motifs of repetitive DNA (e.g., STRPs, see above; repetitive DNA sequences in specific parts of the human chromosomes, the telomeres and centromeres, and heterogeneous DNA regions). These recurring motifs can occur both within and outside genes. When inside genes, they can disrupt the function of these genes. These repetitive motifs are heritable and transmitted from generation to generation. They form another, non-Mendelian type of mechanism for SGD. Fragile X syndrome is an example of one such non-Mendelian SGD.

Fragile X syndrome is a genetic condition associated with a variety of developmental problems ranging from learning difficulties to mental retardation. The symptoms are variable and can include anxiety, hyperactive behavior (e.g., fidgeting and excessive physical movements), impulsivity, problems with social interactions and communication, and seizures. The syndrome's incidence is ~1 in 4000 boys and 1 in 8000 girls, with greater severity of symptoms in males. Many males also have characteristic physical features of fragile X syndrome that strengthen with age (long and narrow face, high-arched palate, high-pitched speech, large ears, prominent jaw and forehead, unusually flexible fingers, enlarged testicles). The heritable nature of the syndrome and its connection with sex was first noted in the 1940s, but the nature of the disorder was established only in the late 1970s. The syndrome is caused by mutation in the gene known as *FMR1* (located on the long arm of chromosome X, at Xq27.3), which codes for production of a protein called fragile X mental retardation 1, or FMRP. FMRP is ubiquitous in the human body and observed in higher amounts in the brain and testes; it is hypothesized that in the brain FMRP is involved in the regulation of synaptic plasticity by binding and transporting a number of essential neuronal RNAs. The *FMR1* gene has a region containing a repetitive motif composed of repeated sequences of three nucleotides, CGG. In most people, the number of repeats varies from a low of six to a high of 54 and the repeats appear are interrupted by a different three-base motif, AGG. In people with fragile X syndrome, the repeat is observed from 200 to more than 1000 times. The result of this expansion is that it results in the disruption of the 3′ region (3′ UTR) of the gene, which inactivates its proper translation or silences it. This alteration, in turn, results in the disruption of production, so that FMRP protein is deficient, not sufficiently present, or absent. Malfunction, shortage, or loss of the FMRP protein is what leads to the development and manifestation of fragile X syndrome. If the repeat is observed 55 to 200 times, the situation is referred to as a permutation expansion. Carriers of such a variant of the *FMR1* gene do not demonstrate typical fragile X features or behaviors. However, they are at risk for the development of a disorder called fragile X associated tremor/ataxia (FXTAS). FXTAS is a progressive disorder of movement (ataxia), tremors, memory loss, reduced sensation in the lower extremities, and mental and behavioral changes. Women who carry 35–200 copies of the repeat are also at risk for premature ovarian failure, which can result in infertility. The repeat is inherited with an X-linked dominant pattern. However, inheriting the permutation does not necessarily lead to inheriting the disorder. What is characteristic of fragile X syndrome is that a mother who carries a permutation and does not present any symptoms of the syndrome might have a child with fragile X syndrome. This is possible because the permutation in the *FMR1* gene can expand to more than 200 CGG repeats in cells that develop into eggs. All the mothers of males with fragile X syndrome have been reported to be carriers, thus it is possible that new mutations are very rare or only occur in males. The permutation appears to be passing through the maternal germline, gradually expanding until a critical level has been reached and the expanded repeat has been inherited by the male child manifesting the syndrome.

Since the identification of the molecular mechanism of fragile X, scientists have associated various DNA repeated sequences with a number of disorders. In fact, today there are more than 40 neurological, common neurodegenerative, or neuromuscular disorders associated with DNA repeat (especially trinucleotide repeat) instability. The signature characteristic of these disorders is in the instability of the number of DNA repeated motifs, which might result in the expansion of the number of the repeats over a threshold that, in turn, might trigger molecular pathological effects leading to manifestation of a disorder.

Single-Gene Disorders Involving Epigenetic Mechanisms

The last category of SGDs briefly described in this article includes disorders involving so-called epigenetic mechanisms (i.e., mechanisms that produce genetic changes without changes in genotype). To illustrate this category of SGDs, consider Rett syndrome.

Rett syndrome is a postnatal developmental disorder presented in initially normally developing children through loss of acquired motor and language skills, slowed brain and head growth, gait abnormalities, and seizures. The disorder was initially described in the late 1960s by Austrian pediatrician Andres Rett. The syndrome occurs almost exclusively in women, with estimated prevalence of 1 in 10 000–15 000 newborns. The overwhelming majority (more than 99%) of cases of Rett syndrome appear to occur in individuals with no family background for the disorder, although the literature contains descriptions of a few families with more than one affected individual. Based on the patterns of genetic transmission in these families, it was incorrectly suggested that Rett syndrome demonstrated an X-linked dominant pattern of inheritance that caused prenatal lethality in males. Yet, the investigation of these families and sporadic cases of Rett syndrome led to the identification of the gene, located on the long arm of chromosome X (Xq28) and known as *MECP2*. This gene codes for a protein called methyl cytosine binding protein 2 (MeCP2), which regulates other genes through use of biochemical switches that can either silence or activate a gene (i.e., trigger or shut down production of specific proteins). Various mutations (more than 2000 known today) in *MECP2* explain ∼95% of cases of classic Rett syndrome. Mutations in another gene located on chromosome X, *CDKL5* (Xp22.13), have also been reported to be associated with phenotypes similar to that of Rett syndrome and usually referred to as atypical cases of Rett syndrome. Of interest is that proteins produced by *MECP2* and *CDKL5* have been shown to interact. The identification of both genes as the foundation of Rett syndrome has led to a series of investigations of molecular functions of these genes. There is now a substantial body of research indicating that MeCP2 epigenetically regulates genes that are involved in neuronal maturation. It appears that its regulation is not global, but specific, that is, targeted at certain genes. Among such targets of MeCP2 is, for example, the gene that encodes brain-derived neurotrophic factor (BDNF). Levels of BDNF were found to be differentially informative in postmortem studies of brains from patients with Rett syndrome. It is the targets regulated by MeCP2 that are thought to contribute to Rett syndrome pathogenesis. The disruption of regulation by MeCP2 might set off a chain of molecular events controlled by the proteins produced by gene-targets of MeCP2 that leads to the manifestation of Rett syndrome.

Single-Gene Disorders and Developmental Sciences

Several comments can be made.

The first set of comments pertains to the realization that rare SGDs are, actually, quite common when considered collectively. Specifically, although the general population risk for a newborn to have a SGD has been estimated at 1%, family history drastically changes risks for children of individuals from such families (for up to 25% for recessive and 50% for dominant conditions). Thus, conditions that can be very infrequent in the general population might be quite frequent in particular families. Correspondingly, knowledge of SGDs is very important for developmentalists working with families at higher risk for rare developmental disorders. Besides, as stated earlier, although each individual condition can be rare or very rare, collectively, SGDs form a large group of children with special needs. This group of children requires professionals working with them to have knowledge of their conditions and to use special developmental and pedagogical practices.

Second, understandably, families with a child with a SGD and practitioners who work with individuals with SGDs often ask what the future holds. The answer to this question varies, of course, depending on a particular SGD. However, the general thought here is related to the status of research linking genes and phenotypes (disorders). One of the fundamental realizations since the 1980s pertains to the rarity (if not absence) of absolutely deterministic outcomes involving the human genome. Whereas genetics typically leads to an identification of a particular gene controlling the manifestation of a particular disorder, genomics provides knowledge on how this gene interacts with other genes, which it might regulate or cowork with within a pathway or which can be regulated by it, and proteomics unravels complex patterns of associations between proteins produced by this gene. Consider the illustration from the studies of MFS. As indicated earlier, selected manifestations of MFS appear to be caused by mutations in *TGFBR1* and/or *TGFBR2*, the genes coding for receptors of the TGFβ. Mouse models of MFS have indicated the presence of increased TGFβ-signaling in aortic aneurysm; this rise in signaling can be prevented by TGFβ-antagonists [e.g., TGFβ-neutralizing antibody or an angiotensin II type 1 receptor (AT1) blocker]. For example, researchers have shown that the administration of losartan, an AT1 antagonist, to a mouse model of MFS prevents aortic aneurysm in this mouse. This basic work has direct implications for clinical outcomes, creating new hope of reversing cardiac symptomatology for MFS patients. Thus, the initial identification of the *FBN1* gene as the basis for the majority of cases of MFS (a genetics finding) leads to understanding the pathways in which this gene is involved and identification of other 'players' in this pathway (a genomics finding), which, in turn, leads to understanding proteins interactive within these pathways (a proteomics finding). And the hope is that all this knowledge can lead to clinical discoveries essential to remediation and treatment of both symptomatology and syndromatology of SGDs. Thus, the message communicated through research studies of SGDs is that the more the field understands about SGDs, the more it departs from the initial simplistic notion of deterministic deleterious mutations that initially dominated the field. Rapidly developing molecular medicine presents individuals with SGDs and their families with high levels of hope.

Third, as is evident from the discussion earlier, genetic heterogeneity of SGD is rather impressive. The presentation of genetic heterogeneity is twofold. First, although the majority of cases of a particular disorder are typically explained by a single gene, often there are other genes in the pathway in which the protein synthesized by the gene in question operates and the disorder might be caused by mutations in these other pathway-related genes (consider the example of MFS). Second, within a single gene there are often multiple mutations that can result in the manifestation of a disorder. Consider an example of cystic fibrosis (CF) – a recessive disorder of progressive damage to the respiratory and digestive systems. In the US, the incidence of CF is 1 in 3200 in Caucasian American newborns, 1 in 15 000 African American newborns, and 1 in 31 000 Asian American newborns, but the estimated carrier frequency is much higher across all groups. CF is caused by mutations in the *CFTR* gene (located on the long arm of chromosome 7 at 7q31.2) coding for a protein called the cystic fibrosis transmembrance conductance regulator, whose function is to form channels across the membranes of cells that produce mucus, sweat, saliva, tears, and digestive enzymes for the transport of charged particles in and out of such cells. These mutations either change the coding sequence or delete a small amount of DNA, thus altering the coding instruction for the CFTR protein. As a result, the production, structure, or stability of the membrane channels can be altered, preventing them from functioning properly and leading to symptoms of CF. As of today, more than 1000 mutations in the *CFTR* gene are known. Among these mutations, 23 are common and account for more than 90% of detectable mutations. In other words, heterogeneity of mutations is remarkable and this heterogeneity is associated with the presentation and severity of CF. Thus, it is important to consider a range of variability in ways the same disorder can be manifested in different children.

Fourth, frequencies of deleterious disorder-related mutations differ substantially in individuals from various ethnic backgrounds. For example, Tay-Sachs disease (TSD) is an autosomal-recessive disorder of lysosomal storage caused by a deficiency of hexosaminidase A and characterized by developmental delay followed by substantial worsening of conditions (paralysis, seizures, blindness) and subsequent death in early childhood; this disorder is caused by mutations in *HEXA* gene, situated on the long arm of chromosome 15, 15q24.1. The carrier frequency of TSD is 1 in 300, but it ranges substantially for different ethnic subgroups (e.g., 1 in 30 in the Ashkenazi Jewish population and 1 in 52–92 in individuals of Irish background).

These first four remarks lead to the fifth comment, which considers the issue of genetic screening for SGDs.

As we rapidly expand our knowledge of how the human genome operates, we come across a number of ethically charged issues, one of which is genetic screening, which is characterized by both remarkable benefits and frightening downfalls. For example, as a result of prenatal screening of Ashkenazi Jews for TSD begun in the 1970s, today the incidence of TSD has decreased by more than 90% in this population. Obviously, this is a tremendous success on par with the success of immunization. Yet, there are examples of failed screening policies. At the same time TSD screening was launched, 12 US states and the District of Columbia instituted mandatory sickle cell screening programs for African Americans because of high rates of disease-related mutations in this population (in the general US population, 1 in 3700 Americans but 1 in 500 African Americans have some form of sickle-cell diseases). Today, 44 US states, the District of Columbia, Puerto Rico, and the US Virgin Islands test all newborns for sickle-cell anemia (sickle-cell disease is the generic name for a group of disorders affecting hemoglobin, red blood cell molecules delivering oxygen to body cells, with common features of anemia, repeated infections, and periodic episodes of pain). This is a recessive disorder caused by the *HBB* gene, located on the short arm of chromosome 11 (11p15.4); in the remaining six states the tests are available but not mandatory. The result was stigmatization of carriers, denial of health and life insurance and employment opportunities, and a variety of other limitations (e.g., denial of acceptance into the US Air Force Academy).

Although this happened 30 years ago, this history emphasizes the importance of public education, privacy protection policies, autonomy of any screening institution, and laws against discrimination based on genetic disorders. In addition to these issues, characteristics of SGDs raised in the earlier comments are directly linked to questions such as:

1. Who do we screen? Do we screen all fetuses or newborns or only those whose families have histories of SGDs?
2. Do we screen families and babies of all ethnic backgrounds or only of those backgrounds where frequencies of particular SGDs are elevated? Does that mean that there should be different, ethnicity-specific screening tools?
3. Given genetic heterogeneity of SGDs, do we screen only for the dominant gene or for all genes associated with particular SGDs? And how many mutations in each gene should screening include?
4. Finally, what are the purposes of genetic screening in the context of SGDs? These and many other questions are at the heart of discussions of SGDs.

The final remark pertains to the fact that the role of the environment in the development and manifestation of various SGDs has been neglected. Little is known about phenotypic variation in presentation of specific SGDs in patients with the same mutations living in different physical and cultural environments. Accumulation of data on the variability in manifestation of the same genetic syndrome (especially when attributed to the same mutations) in different environmental conditions may be of considerable importance for understanding the pathogenesis and prognosis of monogenetic disorders. And these environmental conditions should be defined broadly, ranging from climatic conditions, to cultural and religious practices, to specific dietary and leisure/stress-avoidance and remediation practices.

In summary, the term SGD might be misleading in that it is associated, at least superficially, with an image of a straightforward, deterministic chain linking 'the' mutation in 'the' gene to 'the' disorder. It turns out that there is a considerable amount of clinical variability in the disorder (often there are many disorders under a collective umbrella of a particular SGD). It also turns out that the disorder in question is characterized by a considerable amount of genetic heterogeneity, both from the point of view of what gene causes that disorder and what particular mutant allele within the gene is responsible for that disorder. In fact, if anything, the chain linking the human genome and disorders is not deterministic, but probabilistic. And this means that this chain can be broken by interventions, both biochemical (pharmaceutical) and environmental (developmental and pedagogical). Developmentalists just have to find ways of breaking these chains.

Acknowledgments

Preparation of this article was supported by Grants R21 TW006764 (PI: Grigorenko) from the Fogarty Program as administered by the National Institutes of Health, Department of Health and Human Services, and R01 DC007665 as administered by the National Institute of Deafness and Communication Disorders (PI: Grigorenko).

See also: ADHD: Genetic Influences; Behavior Genetics; Endocrine System; Fragile X Syndrome; Genetic Disorders: Sex Linked; Genetics and Inheritance; Screening, Prenatal.

Relevant Websites

http://www.cdc.gov – Centers for Disease Control and Prevention, Single Gene Disorders and Disability (SGDD).
http://ghr.nlm.nih.gov – Genetics Home Reference, Cystic fibrosis.
http://ghr.nlm.nih.gov – Genetics Home Reference, Sickle cell disease.
http://www.ornl.gov – Oak Ridge National Laboratory, Human Genome Project Information.

Genetics and Inheritance

A Balasubramanian, J Koontz, and C A Reynolds, University of California, Riverside, Riverside, CA, USA

Glossary

Chromosome – A coiled double-stranded assembly of deoxyribonucleic acid (DNA) that contains multiple genes and is located in the cell nucleus.
DNA marker – A polymorphic segment of DNA that may or may not code for a protein.
Endophenotype – An intermediate trait associated with a behavior or disorder that may be more proximate to gene action.
Gene – The fundamental unit of inheritance made of DNA that governs observed physical and behavioral features. Variations in the form of a gene are called alleles.
Genotype – The combination of alleles at a particular chromosomal locus.

Heritability – The contribution of genes to individual differences in a trait; amount of trait variance accounted for in a population by genetic influences.
Phenotype – An observable trait or characteristic.
QTL (quantitative trait loci) – A gene or DNA segment that contributes to a complex phenotype.

Introduction

The nature vs. nurture debate has ended: genes and environments both influence behaviors and disorders in infancy and childhood. The hunt for specific gene candidates for behavioral traits and the environments under which gene expression may be modified is of current focus. In this article, genetic transmission, single-gene traits, complex traits, and methods to locate candidate genes such as linkage and association are outlined. Approaches that disentangle genetic and environmental influences are highlighted emphasizing the research methods and findings for a variety of psychologically relevant traits. Emerging research considering the interaction between genes and environments will clarify the complex etiologies of intellectual abilities and disabilities, temperament, and behavioral syndromes and disorders in childhood.

Genetic Transmission

Gregor Mendel (1822–1884), an Augustinian friar, discovered the fundamental element of inheritance, what we now call a 'gene', and generalizations regarding inheritance, known subsequently as the laws of segregation and independent assortment. Mendel studied multiple varieties of *Pisum sativum*, the garden pea plant, which is self-pollinating, and considered several either–or traits, including plant height (tall, short), pea shape (smooth, wrinkled), and pea color (yellow, green). From breeding experiments, Mendel determined that first-generation hybrid crosses (F1 generation) resembled only one parent. For example, the resultant offspring of a tall plant crossed with a short plant resulted in a tall plant. Indeed, tall height, smooth pea shape, and yellow pea color dominated over the recessive traits, short height, wrinkled pea shape, and green pea color, respectively. In the second generation (F2 generation), the hybrid offspring from the first generation were allowed to self-pollinate and recessive traits were again visible in 25% of the offspring; thus, the ratio of dominant traits to recessive traits exhibited was 3:1. The resulting offspring in subsequent generations (F3 and so on) led Mendel to make additional observations. The first was that plants with recessive traits only produced recessive types; for example, short pea plants crossed with short pea plants only produced short pea plants. Second among the plants exhibiting dominant traits only one-third were 'pure', that is, invariably producing plants with the dominant characteristics (tall plants only), and two-thirds were not pure types but hybrids, producing offspring which carried both dominant and recessive elements. Mendel concluded that each parent contributes equivalently to their offspring, forming pairs of inherited elements (genes) for each character. The law of segregation follows such that during the formation of germ cells or gametes (sperm and egg in humans) the pairs of genes must segregate so that at fertilization the full complement of genes are united. Mendel also studied the inheritance of combinations of traits and observed independence of inheritance, for example, tall plants produced yellow or green peas equally often as did short plants. The law of independent assortment thus states that the

inheritance of a pair of genes determining one trait is independent of simultaneous inheritance of pairs of genes for other traits.

Genes

Genes control heritable physical and behavioral features in humans and other organisms. The word gene refers to both the physical and functional aspects of a segment of deoxyribonucleic acid (DNA), which contains instructions for the making of a protein. The DNA molecule is double-stranded and helical in structure with complementary strands held together by hydrogen bonds formed between base pairs, also called nucleotides: adenine (A) with thymine (T) and cytosine (C) to guanine (G). The sequence of the base pairs of a gene provides the specific instructions for the making of a protein. The sequence of DNA for a particular gene may vary resulting in differing forms of a gene, called alleles.

Genes are located on chromosomes in the nucleus of all cells. Humans possess 23 pairs of chromosomes in all cell nuclei, except germ cells in which it is necessary for procreation to contain half that number; thus, sperm and egg cells carry only 23 chromosomes. When sperm and egg unite, the fertilized egg will then contain the appropriate 46 chromosomes or 23 pairs. Chromosomes 1–22 are called autosomal chromosomes, while the 23rd pair includes the sex chromosomes, X and Y. Females have two X chromosomes while males have one X and one Y chromosome; mothers provide an X chromosome only while fathers provide an X or a Y chromosome to their resulting offspring.

Meiosis

Meiosis describes the process of cell division for reproductive cells that will result in sperm or egg cells with half the number of chromosomes. This is in contrast to the cell division that takes place in nongerm cells called mitosis, which results in daughter cells that are identical. **Figure 1** represents meiosis in females and males. Reproductive cells contain 23 pairs of chromosomes prior to meiosis, with one set maternally derived and the other set paternally derived. During the first stage of meiosis, each homologous pair of chromosomes line up (maternal chromosome 1 with paternal chromosome 1, and so on), duplicate themselves, and then between homologous chromosomes an exchange of DNA segments of equal length at the identical location occurs, called crossing-over or recombination. In the second phase of meiosis the reproductive cell divides twice more to produce four germ cells with half the complement of 23 chromosomes. In females, one reproductive cell undergoing meiosis results in one viable egg cell and three cells that are not functional, whereas in males a single reproductive cell

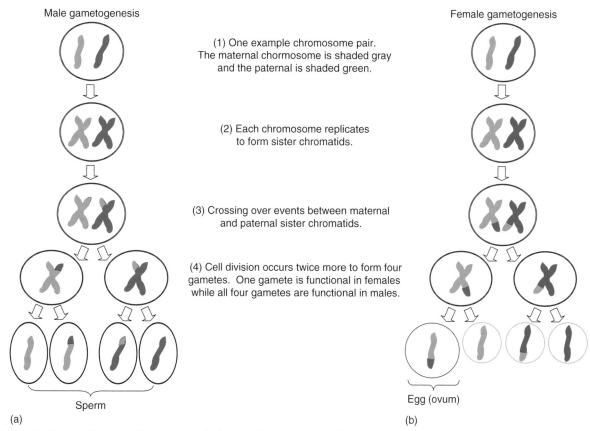

Male gametogenesis

(1) One example chromosome pair. The maternal chormosome is shaded gray and the paternal is shaded green.

(2) Each chromosome replicates to form sister chromatids.

(3) Crossing over events between maternal and paternal sister chromatids.

(4) Cell division occurs twice more to form four gametes. One gamete is functional in females while all four gametes are functional in males.

Female gametogenesis

Sperm

Egg (ovum)

(a)

(b)

Figure 1   Meiosis. The formation of germ cells (gametes) in (a) males and (b) females. Reproduced from Hetherington *et al.* (2003) *Child Psycology*. McGraw-Hill, with permission from McGraw-Hill.

undergoing meiosis results in four sperm cells. The resulting chromosomes in the germ cells, egg and sperm, contain DNA from maternally and paternally derived chromosomes due to crossing-over in the first phase of meiosis, ensuring added genetic variation. The segments of DNA that are exchanged during the crossing-over process is random for any meiotic division, thus it is next to impossible to recreate the exact combination of genes in germ cells produced in a single individual.

Gene Expression

As alluded to in Mendel's work, an expressed trait or phenotype is due to a combination of alleles, or forms of genes at a particular chromosomal location. If the alleles are identical in sequence, then genotype is said to be homozygous; if they differ the genotype is heterozygous. In the case of a heterozygous genotype, one set of allele instructions may dominate over the other set of instructions in expression of the protein, for example, gene expression for smooth pea coat completely dominates overexpression of wrinkled pea coat in the pea plant. A completely recessive trait, therefore, is one that is not expressed such as the wrinkled pea coat. In the case of

only two possible alleles one's genotype can be homozygous dominant, heterozygous dominant, or homozygous recessive at that locus. If neither allele was dominant over the other, they would be considered to act in an additive or co-dominant manner in their contribution to the expressed phenotype. In humans, one example of complete dominance is brown *vs.* blue eye color. If an individual inherits the allele coding for brown eyes and the allele coding for blue eyes, brown eye color will be expressed, that is, they are heterozygous dominant. Thus, only one copy of the dominant allele is needed for the expression of brown eyes. If inheriting two blue alleles, that is, homozygous recessive, blue eye color may be expressed (assuming a homozygous recessive blue–blue genotype for the green–blue gene).

The actual mechanics of gene expression are complex and involve multiple stages. Key steps are generally described here. First, the DNA sequence is transcribed into messenger ribonucleic acid (mRNA). RNA is single stranded and has four nucleotides: A, U, C, and G. Thus, T in DNA is replaced with U in RNA. Sequences of three nucleotides are called codons and indicate amino acids, which are building blocks of proteins. For example, an mRNA sequence of CAG codes for the amino acid GLN, or glutamine. Other three-letter codons may indicate start or stop synthesizing a chain of amino acids or polypeptide chains. After DNA is transcribed into mRNA, modifications may occur including RNA splicing in which noncoding regions of the RNA, introns, are cut out and the remaining exons (protein-coding regions) are united resulting in an unbroken RNA strand. Translation of the fully mature mRNA occurs in the cytoplasm of the cell by ribosomes, the location in the cell where proteins are synthesized with instructions contained in the three-letter codons of the mature mRNA. Protein expression is influenced by multiple factors, including the physiological state of a particular cell to an individual's developmental level.

Single Gene and Chromosomal Disorders

Mendelian principles of gene transmission can be applied to parent–offspring transmission in humans, and indeed they have been invaluable to uncovering the etiology of disorders that occur as a result of rare alleles or DNA mutations. Family pedigrees are examined for systematic patterns to examine the emergence of a disorder from the maternal or paternal line.

Single-Gene Autosomal Traits

Infant and childhood disorders may be a result of rare recessive alleles for genes located on autosomal chromosomes. Phenylketonuria (PKU) is a rare genetic disorder caused by a single recessive gene on chromosome 12 that occurs in an average of 15 000 newborns per year. These newborns lack phenylalanine hydroxylase, an enzyme necessary for the metabolism of the amino acid phenylalanine. The buildup of phenylalanine can be toxic leading to brain damage and severe mental retardation. If detected at birth, the detrimental effects of PKU can be lessened with a diet lacking in phenylalanine. Following this diet from birth till early childhood can lessen the intellectual deficits.

Single-gene autosomal-dominant disorders are rarer. Autosomal dominant disorders, have less than favorable outcomes and are less likely to be passed on from one generation to another since many of the traits associated with these disorders tend to decrease an individual's likelihood of procreating. A notable exception is Huntington's disease (HD), a rare neurodegenerative disease that typically emerges in middle-to-late adulthood and is characterized by involuntary movements, changes in personality, and memory problems. The mutation for HD is located on chromosome 4: an unstable expansion of a CAG triplet repeat. The greater the number of unstable expanded triplets, the earlier this disorder is expressed. Approximately 10% of cases are diagnosed in individuals under the age of 20 years.

Sex-Linked Disorders

Some single-gene disorders are transmitted through the inheritance of the sex chromosomes, usually X-linked recessive alleles. Expression of a sex-linked disorder occurs most often in males given the greater number of genes on the X than Y chromosome; thus, only one copy of the recessive allele is necessary for expression of the disorder in males. Females are usually carriers for the disorder and can pass the recessive allele to male offspring. Males with an X-linked disorder will have normal sons, since the recessive allele on the X chromosome will only be passed to their female offspring. Fragile X syndrome is a common sex-linked disorder that is one of the leading causes of mental retardation. This disorder is characterized by cognitive deficits and mild abnormal facial traits including an elongated face with a prominent jaw, broad forehead, and large ears. Individuals may also depict behaviors characteristic of attention deficit hyperactiviy disorder (ADHD) and autism. Fragile X syndrome is caused by an expanded triplet repeat of CGG on the X chromosome. This expanded triplet repeat sequence causes the chromosome to look 'fragile', appearing as if it could physically break. This mutation interferes with transcription of a crucial RNA binding protein. The repeated sequence expands as it passes from one generation to another, increasing chances of expression in successive generations. Fragile X syndrome is more likely to be expressed in males than females. The full mutation is present in 1 in 3600–4000 male births, and in 1 in 4000–6000 female births. The disorder can be partially expressed in females in a 'mosaic' manner due to random inactivation of one of the two X chromosomes in each cell.

Chromosomal Disorders

Beyond single genes, there are chromosomal disorders that affect behavioral phenotypes. Down syndrome, also known as trisomy 21, is a rare condition in which individuals are born with an extra copy of chromosome 21 due to errors occurring during meiosis. In 2006, 1 in 733 newborns was born with Down syndrome. Down syndrome is the most common form of mental retardation; however, cognitive impairments can range dramatically but are typically moderate to mild. Physical characteristics of Down syndrome are many and include heart defects, delayed skeletal maturation, stunted height, poor muscle tone (hypotonia), and a shorter lifespan. Environmental factors may increase the likelihood of trisomy 21 nondisjunction, including older maternal age (age 35 years and older) and possibly behavioral health factors such as smoking in the case of younger mothers (age 35 years and younger).

Chromosomal aberrations are also observed for the sex chromosomes. Females with only one X chromosome have a disorder called Turner's syndrome, which occurs in 1 in 2500 females. Stunted height and underdeveloped ovaries are features. Though of average intelligence, some females with Turner's syndrome are lacking in social skills, prompting researchers to propose that sociability may be X-linked. Furthermore, parent of origin may matter; the paternal X chromosome may mediate sociability and better social interaction skills as opposed to the maternal X chromosome.

Klinfelter syndrome (KS) is a disorder resulting in males having an extra X chromosome, that is, XXY. Males with KS have an increased risk of learning disabilities, developmental delays, behavioral problems, and infertility due to the underdevelopment of the testes. One in 500 males are born with KS. When females receive an extra X chromosome, this can result in triple X or 47, XXX. Physical and behavioral features vary but may include increased height and risk of cognitive disabilities, particularly involving speech and language. One in 1000 girls is born with triple X.

Genomic Imprinting

The manifestation of particular behavioral characteristics or symptoms of disorders can be affected by which parent provided the naturally occurring allele or rare mutation, a process called genomic imprinting. Methylation, the formation of methyl groups consisting of C and G, can lead to the silencing or expression of an allele; thus, methylation can alter protein formation. Genomic imprinting may occur for spina bifida and some forms of cancers. It is also implicated in some chromosomal disorders. For example, Prader–Willi syndrome (PWS) and Angelman's syndrome are two disorders that arise from spontaneous deletions on chromosome 15; however, the expression of either disorder depends upon which parent the offspring receives the imprinted mutation from. PWS is expressed in individuals who receive the mutation from the father, while Angelman's syndrome is expressed in individuals who receive the mutation from the mother. Obesity and irrepressible appetite characterize PWS and 1 in 12 000–15 000 newborns are diagnosed with PWS. Angelman's syndrome is characterized by normal growth, but poor coordination (ataxia) and muscle tone (hypotonia), severe mental retardation, and absence of speech. One in 10 000–20 000 individuals are born with Angelman's syndrome. Factors that impact the occurrence of methylation during gamete formation are being investigated.

Locating Genes

Linkage and association analyses help geneticists hunt for genes that may be causative or associated with a disorder. Linkage analyses take advantage of violations of Mendel's law of independent assortment to find chromosomal locations where a causative gene may lie. During recombination that occurs in meiosis, segments of DNA are swapped between maternal and paternal homologous chromosomes, and indeed this process is random between meiotic events. However, the closer two genes or DNA gene markers are to one another on a chromosome the more likely they will be inherited jointly and not be split by a recombination event. Through the employment of large family pedigrees, linkage studies are used to trace the co-occurrence of particular DNA marker alleles and disorders. Ideally the DNA marker may lie in the causative gene itself or be positioned close to the causative gene. As a result of linkage studies, geneticists located the form of the gene that causes HD on chromosome 4.

While linkage studies are particularly useful in locating DNA markers, which may be near or within the potential disease-causing gene, association studies examine known genes and whether they are associated with the disease trait. The known genes may be those close to a DNA marker identified in a linkage study, or known genes that are of interest given the proteins that they code for. Polymorphisms such as single-nucleotide polymorphisms (SNPs), ideally in exons or coding regions, are identified and used in the association analyses. SNP alleles of unrelated healthy persons may be compared to a group that exhibits a disease to see if a particular allele occurs more frequently in the disease group than by chance (a case-control design). While association studies have the statistical power to detect modest effects, this approach is more likely to identify genes that do not represent true association when using unrelated cases and controls because the cases may come from different subpopulations with different gene frequencies than controls (called population stratification). However, a growing number of researchers are having more success with this technique by searching for genetic markers in family-based designs where lineage is known. For example, analyses of parents and offspring test whether offspring exhibiting a disorder may be more likely to inherit a particular allele; affected and unaffected siblings may also be used in these analyses.

Complex Traits and Disorders

Many behavioral phenotypes in infancy and childhood are complex and reflect the influence of multiple genes and environments. For example, temperament and cognitive abilities demonstrate rich variation in the population. Unlike single-gene traits, environments and genes involved in complex traits or disorders may increase (or decrease) trait values or risk of expression but may not be necessary for the emergence of the trait or disorder. The designs used to investigate the relative influence of genetic vs. environmental effects on complex behavioral traits – twin and adoption designs – take advantage of naturally occurring 'experiments' of nature or nurture.

Comparing relatives who vary in genetic relatedness or who share varying degrees of their rearing environment provide a metric for calculating the relative influence of anonymous genetic and environmental factors.

Heritability. Every observed trait, or phenotype (P), is thought to result from the effects of genes (G) and the environment (E). Geneticists use certain statistical techniques to quantify genetic effects, with the heritability estimate derived from a comparison of correlations between individuals who vary in either genetic relatedness or extent to which environments are shared. Heritability is an estimate of how much trait variance is accounted for in the population by genetic factors. Thus, heritability reflects the extent to which differences in a population are due to genetic differences; estimates can vary according to population, time, and geographical contexts. Narrow-sense heritability refers to genetic variance that is explained by additive genetic effects (no dominance) and is notated as h^2_N or a^2. Broad-sense heritability refers to all sources of genetic variance including additive effects (a^2), dominance (d^2), and any other gene–gene interaction effects. Remaining differences between individuals in a population may be due to shared environmental effects (c^2) and nonshared environmental effects (e^2). In the typical behavioral genetic models estimates of heritability and environmental effects completely describe individual differences in traits; thus, when summed together they account for 100% of the trait variability.

Environmentality. Environment refers to all nongenetic factors. Shared environmental effects such as being reared in the same home, attending the same schools, and other neighborhood or regional effects make relatives more similar to one another. In contrast, the unique experiences of individuals by definition are not shared with one another and make relatives dissimilar from one another. Thus, the environmentality estimates c^2 and e^2 index the extent to which shared and nonshared environmental effects, respectively, influence individual differences in a phenotype.

Behavioral Genetic Designs and Methods

Twin designs. Geneticists have conducted twin studies since Sir Francis Galton (1822–1911), a cousin of Charles Darwin, advocated their use in determining the influence of nature vs. nurture, though he did not distinguish between types of twins. Monozygotic (MZ) twins are commonly referred to as identical twins. They share 100% of their genes in common. This type of twinning occurs when one egg is fertilized with one sperm, and then the resulting zygote divides and separates into two genetically identical cells. MZ twinning is typically viewed as a chance event and is not believed to be heritable, though some evidence for familial effects on identical multiple

births has emerged from large-scale Nordic studies. Environmental factors may include advancing maternal age.

Dizygotic (DZ) twins are commonly referred to as fraternal twins. This type of twinning occurs when two eggs are matured and released, and each egg is then fertilized by a separate sperm. These twins are expected to be no more genetically similar than typical siblings, and on average share about 50% of their segregating genes. They may be of the same or opposite sex. This type of twinning appears to be moderately heritable, with a greater maternal lineage effect noted in some studies. The chance of fraternal twins increases with maternal age.

Comparison of twin siblings may offer clues to the importance of genetic and environmental influences for behavioral phenotypes. For example, examining MZ twins who are discordant for a disease like schizophrenia, can help to explain on environmental factors that may lead to only one twin of an identical pair to have schizophrenia. Studying similarity or concordance of MZ vs. DZ twins is the most common method to estimate the extent of genetic effects. Because MZ twins share 100% of their genes in common while DZ twins share 50% of their segregating genes, MZ twins would be expected to be twice as similar than DZ when genes act in an additive fashion to influence a trait (e.g., no dominance) and shared environmental effects are not present. For example, if DZ twin similarity is greater than would be expected, that is, their correlation is greater than half the MZ correlation, then shared environmental effects are suspected to be present. If the DZ correlation is less than half the MZ correlation then dominance may be present because MZ twins are genetically identical, including any dominance effects, whereas 25% of the dominance effects are in common for DZ twins. In twins-reared-together designs, dominance and shared environmental effects cannot be estimated simultaneously thus researchers choose which to consider based on patterns of twin similarity.

Equal environments as well as random mating of parents are two key assumptions that are required to estimate heritability and environmentality estimates using twins. A third is that the twins are representative of the population. The equal-environments assumption (EEA) poses that there are no differences between MZ and DZ twins reared together in the shared environmental influences that affect their phenotypic similarity. Existing research indicates a high degree of support for the EEA for most psychological and psychiatric traits. The random-mating assumption stipulates that mates or spouses do not select one another based on (heritable) phenotypes of interest. Random mating is most certainly untrue for cognitive abilities and attitudes, with a high degree of spouse similarity present from the time of marriage. However, there is markedly little spouse similarity for most personality traits. The presence of nonrandom mating may result in inflated estimates of the shared environment if not accounted for in the statistical analyses. Infant and child twins do appear to be similar to the general population for the majority of behavioral phenotypes. It is common for twins to experience more difficult births and be physically smaller than singletons at birth. With respect to behavioral traits, twins may have greater tendency to show language delays, but approximately after 8 years of age they tend to be similar to singletons.

Adoption designs. In a typical family, parents and offspring are genetically similar and they share home, neighborhood, and regional environments. In the adopted family any similarities between the adopted offspring and the biological parent can be attributed to genetic causes, while similarities between the adoptive siblings, for example, can be thought of as due to environmental causes. Combined twin and adoption designs are even more powerful in disentangling environmental and genetic effects. Because twins are the same age, one can be sure that differences between the siblings are not due to being in different developmental periods. One variant of this design is to consider identical twins that have been reared apart, because they have identical genes but have different rearing environments. Even more powerful is to also include identical twin reared together as well as fraternal twins reared apart and together to maximize the information about heritable and rearing environmental effects.

Primary assumptions of the adoption design include no selective placement and that adoptive families do not systematically differ from the general population of families. The absence of selective placement refers to the assumption that were no selection criteria that adoptive parents match or are similar to biological parents for a particular trait or traits of interest. For traits such as physical characteristics, religious affiliation, and ethnicity there is evidence of selective placement. However, there is only nominal evidence for selective placement for behaviorally relevant traits such as education or intelligence. Where selective placement exists, statistical adjustments can be made to estimates of genetic and environmental influence, described further below. Adoptive parents are scrutinized prior to adoption to verify, for example, the absence of severe economic hardship and mental illness. To a large degree, adoptive parents represent the general population of parents; however, traits related to socioeconomic status (SES) and particularly mental health may be limited in range. A related concern is whether biological parents (and indeed the children they give up for adoption) differ from the general population. While some studies find differences in terms of levels of antisocial behavior and alcohol-use disorders, for example, differences are not routinely found across studies. The additional inclusion of intact nuclear families to adoption designs is sometimes used as a reference group given concerns regarding representativeness and when information on biological parents is limited.

Gene–Environment Relationships

Although genes and environments may be correlated or interact, these are routinely estimated as separate effects in twin and adoption designs. However, it is possible in some cases to directly test for gene–environment (GE) relationships, ideally with measured candidate genes and measured features of the environment.

GE correlation. Individuals with particular genotypes that lead to high trait values may be in environments that also facilitate high trait values whereas those with genotypes that lead to low trait values may find themselves in or chose environments that lead to low trait values. For example, parents transmit genes to their offspring and provide an environment as well. For example, parents with genes that increase sociability may provide environments with more social opportunities for their children, thus leading to higher sociability, while parents with genes leading to lower sociability may provide fewer social opportunities to their children who are less sociable, etc. This is referred to as a passive GE correlation because the parents provide both genes and environments to their children. An active GE correlation arises, for example, when a person due to their genetic propensities chooses environments that foster their capabilities or characteristics. A small but emerging research literature using longitudinal twin designs or extended family kinships of twins, for example, twins and their offspring, suggests that GE correlation may be identifiable for cognitive and antisocial traits. Though theoretically important, relatively few data are available to establish how important GE correlations may be in practice for behavioral traits.

GE interaction. Individuals with particular genotypes may be sensitive to particular environments; thus the expression of the phenotype may depend on the interplay between the particular genes and particular environments. For example, hypothetically children with allele A on gene W may be more likely to show high anxiety in novel situations but low anxiety in familiar situations than children with allele B who show equal levels of anxiety in both situations. GE interaction has been well documented in nonhuman organisms but less well established in human studies. However, with measured candidate genes or measured environmental factors, studies have begun to test this occurrence more frequently. Empirical examples of testing for GE interaction are noted below by topic.

Locating Candidate Genes for Complex Traits

For complex traits no single gene is causative but many genes may contribute in small measures. Variations of linkage and association methods may be employed to locate genes contributing to complex traits called quantitative trait loci (QTLs). As in linkage analysis for single-gene traits, in QTL linkage analysis the goal is to identify a narrow enough chromosomal region where a QTL may lie. One of the DNA markers used in the analysis may be the QTL itself or nearby it. Already known genes nearby the QTL region may be considered in subsequent association analyses that test for how much of the heritable variance may be due to the gene candidates.

Genetic and Environmental Contribution to Common Traits and Disorders

While some disorders in childhood are caused by single-gene mutations or chromosomal abnormalities, most disorders and traits are considered complex and are determined by multiple genes and environmental factors. Indeed, most behavioral traits show moderate genetic and environmental influence, though the rearing environment seems to be of small consequence in general (see **Figure 2**). The current task is to identify measurable environmental factors and locate gene candidates that are at least partly responsible for different traits and disorders. Current research on a variety of childhood traits is described in greater detail below.

Cognitive ability. Twin and adoption studies have shown consistently that the heritability of general intelligence is moderate in early childhood at about 40% and continues to gain in importance through adulthood peaking at about 80% until late old-age where it drops to approximately 60%. Specific cognitive abilities, such as verbal ability, spatial ability, memory, etc., are also moderately heritable though to a somewhat lesser degree than general cognitive ability. Controversy has surrounded intelligence research for over a century because of the societal and political implications of assigning to individuals a score or set of scores to indicate their cognitive ability, that

is, intelligence quotient (IQ) scores, which is predictive of school success and to a lesser degree occupational success. Embedded in this debate has been the assumption that the family environment must surely be more important than adoption or twin studies have suggested.

Studies of humans and animals have shown the importance of rearing environment in fostering or stunting intellectual growth. Some environmental aspects that cause variability in intelligence are enriched versus impoverished rearing environment (number of books and toys in the home, etc.), nutrition, quality of schools, and other life experiences. Twin and adoption studies suggest that shared or rearing environmental effects account for about 20% of individual differences in early to mid-childhood but tend to decrease to nominal levels by late adolescence. This pattern of decrease is also true for specific cognitive abilities. The decrease in shared environmental effects with age has been hypothesized to occur for a few possible reasons, including the increasing control that older children may gain over their own environment whereby they may choose particular environmental niches that suit their intellectual propensities (e.g., choosing particular classes in school, taking on hobbies, or taking part in after-school activities), an example of an active GE correlation. There is evidence for GE interaction where SES may moderate the strength of genetic influences: heritability for childhood intelligence increases as family affluence increases.

In addition to IQ tests as direct measures of ability, there is an emerging focus on possible endophenotypes. Endophenotypes for IQ would be those traits that may be closer to the neural or neuroanatomical underpinnings of ability and perhaps 'closer' to where gene action occurs. Electroencephalogram (EEG) studies have also shown heritability for multiple measures in children including coherence (a measure of interconnectivity in the brain) ranging from approximately 40% to 75% depending on location, and for alpha peak frequency (a measure of synaptic activity) at approximately 79%. Brain volume measures in adults have shown high heritability estimates (between 80% and 90%) using magnetic resonance imaging (MRI) of such structures as gray matter, white matter, cerebellar, total brain, and intracranial volume. IQ is moderately correlated with brain volume measures in adults, approximately 0.30–0.40.

Genes for intelligence are likely to be many in number and individually contributing only a small degree to individual differences. Possible QTLs for intelligence may reside in regions on chromosomes 2 and 6 that overlap with regions linked to autism, dyslexia, and reading disability. Candidate genes that code for receptors and neurotransmitters or are otherwise involved in learning and memory pathways are of particular focus in association studies. While multiple associations have been reported few have been replicated. An exception is the *CHRM2* gene that codes for cholinergic muscarinic receptor M2

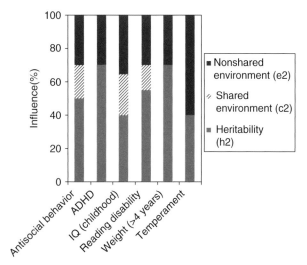

Figure 2 The relative influence of genetic and environmental factors on childhood traits. ADHD, attention deficit hyperactivity disorder; IQ, Intelligence quotient.

and may be involved in neuronal and synaptic processes important to learning and memory.

Mental retardation. As discussed above, there are rare genetic mutations and chromosomal aberrations that can result in mental retardation such as PKU, fragile X syndrome, and Down syndrome. Multiple environmental factors may lead to severe retardation including prenatal exposure to teratogens, birth trauma, and nutritional deficiencies. On the whole, heritability of severe mental retardation is relatively low. Mild retardation, where IQs range anywhere from 50 to 75 depending on criteria used, most likely represents the continuum of intelligence found in the general population (IQ of 100 is average). Thus, it is more heritable than severe retardation at approximately 50%. The search for genes for mild retardation overlaps considerably with the search for genes for general intelligence.

Learning disabilities. Many children exhibit a learning disability that is unexplained by typical causes (e.g., head injury, mental retardation). Children who exhibit learning disorders have at minimum average intelligence and their disorder is not caused by a primary physical disability (visual, hearing, or motor), an emotional disturbance, or social or cultural conditions. Learning disorders may result in impairments in math ability (dyscalculia), writing (dysgraphia), speech (specific learning impairment or SLI), and problems with reading and comprehension (dyslexia) and affect up to 5–10% of school-aged children with boys being twice as likely to be diagnosed as girls. Genetic research has focused primarily on reading disability traits or dyslexia diagnoses. Twin studies in the UK and US suggest a moderate heritable component of 40–70% and shared environmental effects ranging from 20% to 45% across reading disability traits. Replicated linkage analyses suggest potential regions of interest on chromosomes 1, 2, 6, 15, and 18. Two gene candidates on the short arm of chromosome 6 have become of interest: the doublecortin domain containing 2 (*DCDC2*) gene and *KIAA0319*, both involved in migration of neurons in prenatal development.

Temperament. Temperament in infancy and early childhood is thought to influence the presence of behavioral tendencies and serve as a precursor to personality traits expressed later in life. The consistency of temperament in an infant or young child can best be characterized on a range of dimensions that include: activity level, attention and persistence, social skills and reactivity in social situations, and level of emotions. Temperament is theorized to be biologically driven though heritability varies across traits and studies from 20% to 60% with consistently greater similarity observed for MZ than DZ twins. Thus, genetic factors only have a moderate influence on temperament characteristics. Shared environmental factors appear unimportant to individual differences in temperament, however. Nonshared environmental factors make up the remaining variation at a minimum of 40%. Hence,

not only genetics within family members but also the diversity of environmental factors across development influence temperament and eventually personality. Candidate genes of particular interest include those that are involved in the neurotransmitter systems such as dopamine, which is involved in the production of motor behaviors as well as active in a neural reward system that leads to emergence or extinction of behaviors, and serotonin, which plays a role in sleep–wake cycles, hunger, and mood amongst other domains. The dopamine D4 receptor gene (*DRD4*) has been associated with activity levels and novelty seeking, which are significant dimensions related to ADHD. Polymorphisms in the *DRD4* and serotonin transporter promoter (*5-HTTLPR*) genes have been implicated in negative emotionality and stranger anxiety/fearfulness in infants. However, these findings are preliminary and more studies must be conducted to validate the influence of these specific genes on temperament.

Autism. Autism is part of the spectrum of autistic disorders including Aspeberger's syndrome (AS) and pervasive developmental disorder – not otherwise specified (PDD-nos). Autism spectrum disorders (ASD) are discussed more fully elsewhere in this work; we only comment briefly on the emerging literature that considers autism-associated traits in population-based samples of twins. Those with ASD may exhibit varying degrees of impairments in social interactions and communication as well as demonstrate repetitive stereotyped behaviors. Twin studies have begun to consider particular symptom dimensions in the range that they occur in the general population, including social sensitivity or responsiveness, communication difficulties, and recurrent stereotyped behaviors, and suggest that these features may be strongly heritable in childhood and even adolescence, as high as 80%. Moreover, the genetic factors influencing social vs. nonsocial features may be somewhat distinct. Linkage and association analyses have yet to follow from these general population twin studies but have been proceeding in family studies with members who have autism or ASD; gene regions or candidates that have been implicated in language impairment or in neuron and synapse development have been of particular interest.

ADHD. ADHD typically emerges during the early school years, where a child exhibits an inability to pay attention for sustained periods, hyperactivity, and impulsive behavior. It affects more boys than girls, with about 5.4% of boys and 1.6% of girls having been diagnosed at some point between the ages of 5 and 17 years old. Awareness of the disorder has increased in recent years and diagnosis rates have increased as well, and it is now being recognized as persisting into adolescence and adulthood. ADHD may increase the risk of exhibiting later antisocial behavior and drug and alcohol use. It often co-occurs with learning disorders described above. Few studies have found significant shared environmental contributions, and if they do so they usually account for less than 10% of the variance. ADHD is moderately to strongly heritable with estimates ranging from 60% to 80%, if based on information garnered from parents but 10–20% lower if based on teacher reports and interviews. Some research indicates the etiological factors may be different for boys than girls; antisocial behavior is more likely to be present in boys with ADHD than girls and girls with ADHD may have more apparent intellectual deficits. Multiple-gene association studies suggest involvement of the dopamine neurotransmitter pathway, which is implicated in attention and motor activity. Gene candidates include the dopamine D4 receptor (*DRD4*), the dopamine transporter (*DAT1*), and the dopamine D5 receptor (*DRD5*) genes.

Antisocial traits. It has been divisive to consider genetic factors for antisocial behavior, by designation a social construct. However, any observed heritability may reflect underlying traits that increase risk, for example, temperament. Antisocial behaviors in childhood include rule breaking, physical aggression toward people and animals, vandalism, dishonesty, theft, and resistance toward authority. The *Diagnostic and Statistical Manual of Mental Disorders*, 4th edn. (DSM-IV) describes two disorders that represent excessive problems: conduct disorder (CD) and oppositional defiant disorder (ODD). An ODD diagnosis is a precursor to CD, with a CD diagnosis requiring the presence of more symptoms. ODD is found in about 6–11% of school-aged children while CD affects about 1–4% of children 9 years and older. More boys than girls are diagnosed with ODD and CD. The heritability of antisocial traits, including the ODD and CD disorders, is about 50% using parent-based information but may be lower if using child-based information. Shared environmental effects explain about 20% of the variation in antisocial behaviors in childhood. ODD and CD diagnoses though varying in age of emergence and severity appear to share a common genetic etiology. Similarly, antisocial traits and later criminal behavior share common genetic and environmental factors, with nonviolent criminality showing evidence of genetic influence but not violent or alcohol-involved offenses.

GE interactions may be important to antisocial behaviors and criminal offending. In adoption studies, risk of criminal behavior in adopted-away offspring is increased if the biological parents exhibited criminal behavior and further amplified if both the biological and adoptive parents displayed criminal behavior. Adoptive parents' criminal behavior did not increase the risk of criminal offending in adoptees of noncriminal biological parents. Moreover, measured environmental factors such as childhood maltreatment may transact with known genes in the emergence of antisocial traits: physical abuse in combination with the monoamine oxidase A (MAOA) allele that expresses high monoamine oxidase A may lead to a 'lower' susceptibility to exhibit antisocial behaviors compared to the MAOA allele expressing lower monoamine

oxidase A. MAOA is ubiquitously involved in the degradation of the neurotransmitters dopamine, serotonin, and norephinephrine. Dopamine is implicated in antisocial behaviors as well: one of the candidate genes associated with ADHD has also been associated with antisocial traits, *DRD4*.

Childhood obesity. Childhood obesity is a growing problem in developed countries. About 15.5% of US children meet the American Obesity Association's criteria. Children are at higher risk of obesity if they have obese parents. Twin and adoptions suggest that the heritability of body weight is about 60–80% in childhood; contributions from the shared environment begin to wane after the first year of life. Thus, the primary environmental factors in childhood are attributed to unique personal environments. Environmental factors in childhood weight gain are poor diet, low activity levels, increased television watching, and other recent societal changes that promote increased sedentary behavior (e.g., video games). Aside from rare single-gene or chromosomal disorders, a search continues to find gene candidates for obesity traits and how they might interact with dietary environment factors. Gene candidates of particular interest include those associated with metabolic syndrome (e.g., *ENPP1*), insulin resistance (e.g., *CART*), and consumption behaviors, including the dopamine and serotonin pathways (e.g., dopamine D2 receptor, *DRD2*).

The Human Genome Project

In 1990, a joint collaboration between the National Institutes of Health (NIH) and the US Department of Energy (DOE) proposed the execution and completion of the Human Genome Project (HGP). A $3 billion fund was allotted and a 15-year time frame was set to complete the entire project. However, competition between the publicly funded endeavor, which ultimately included thousands of researchers in the US and six other nations, with private researchers, principally at Celera Genomics, helped to spur its essential completion 2 years earlier than expected on 14 April 2003 and resulted in a $0.3 billion savings. The aims of the HGP were to sequence the 3.1 billion nucleotide base pairs and uncover all genes located on the 24 human chromosomes, to store as well as dispense the enormous amounts of information and data generated, to produce new laboratory and computational procedures for analysis, and to evaluate moral, legal, and societal concerns that may result.

Findings from the Human Genome Project

The entire human genome was sequenced through the examination of DNA from a handful of individuals. While the public HGP collected biological samples from several male and female individuals, the sequencing efforts considered the DNA from only a few of these donors. The private Celera Genomics project used the DNA of five individuals, including both males and females of various Caucasian, African American, Hispanic, or Asian ancestries. Thus, the sequenced human genome is really a 'template' human genome since it is based upon the identification of common variations in the nucleotide base pairs in fewer than 10 individuals. It is evident that 99.9% of nucleotide base pair sequences are the same in all human beings with only 0.1% of human genome showing variation. Much of the variation is due to SNPs, which are found approximately every 100–300 base pairs. Surprisingly only 20 000–25 000 genes may be responsible for functions related to protein coding and expression; however, many of these genes appear to code for multiple rather than single proteins. Up to 97% of the human genome is thought to be replete with noncoding DNA regions including introns and intergenic regions of DNA, sometimes referred to as 'junk DNA'. However, it is becoming clearer that the label 'junk' is a misnomer. About half of the noncoding DNA consists of repetitive base pair sequences whose functions are yet unidentified, but may have been evolutionarily important at some point in time. It is also thought to include parts of older genes thought to be difficult to remove from the human genome, since they withstand removal generation after generation. Finally, regulatory DNA sequences appear to be present that affect gene transcription or expression. In addition to a smaller quantity of genes than expected, humans share close to 96% of the same genes in common with chimpanzees. The initial aims of the project have been fulfilled, leading to other issues that the researchers must answer. The goal is to understand how genes function and interact with one another.

Moral, Ethical, and Legal Implications

The impetus of the HGP on ensuing research may provide an unprecedented opportunity to screen for, and identify, a variety of inherited disorders and diseases as well as identify specific genetic mechanisms that impact complex behavioral and physical traits. More effective prevention and treatments efforts for inherited diseases may be developed in the future due to increased understanding of gene function and expression leading to efficient drug development and newer treatment options. For instance, based on the presence and or expression of particular genes, a customized medicinal regimen could be prescribed for a patient.

Yet, moral, ethical, and legal dilemmas also stem from this advancement in the field of genetics. The implications of stem cell research and cloning have raised such concerns in recent years. Ethical quandaries could arise in the future concerning the reemergence of eugenics and the privacy/storage of genetic information. For example, should parents have the opportunity to choose what traits their unborn fetus expresses later in life – that is, eye color, height, or intellectual capacity? For example, if an unborn fetus merely presents with a genetic propensity for a particular trait, that is, expression of the trait is not certain, will parents (or society) feel compelled to intervene or abort the pregnancy because they could be born with a less than 'perfect' set of genes?

Researchers and policy makers are debating whether genetic information should be kept private or become public knowledge. If made widely available, each person's genetic information could be stored in a database and could play an ever more crucial role in the criminal justice system. DNA evidence could play a more substantive role in linking criminals with various types of crimes. In contrast, public knowledge of a person's genetic information could hamper an individual's opportunities. For instance, a person may live his life around a minor genetic flaw. Indeed, larger-scale impacts could result: persons may face discrimination as a result of minor gene defects or even on the basis of typically occurring alleles or genotypes. For example, denials of employment opportunities or insurance coverage could result from carrying specific genes – even if these 'defective' genes are never expressed. Legal safeguards regarding dissemination of genetic information and insurance coverage vary widely by country. At this point, these and other moral, ethical, and legal dilemmas are yet to be fully debated or resolved.

Conclusions and Future Directions

Most common behavioral traits and disorders in childhood show a moderate-to-strong genetic basis and small if present effect of the shared environment. This should not be construed as evidence for genetic determinism of behavior. Indeed, even single-gene traits such as PKU are amenable to environmental intervention. Importantly the field of behavioral genetics has moved from presenting estimates of the relative influence of anonymous genes and environments on behavior to incorporating measured genes and environments.

While the sequencing of the human genome has increased the pace of genetic research in behavioral domains, gaps in knowledge are considerable. For example, what functions do nontranscribed intronic and intergenic stretches of DNA serve? A multitude of hypotheses exists including that these stretches of DNA have an important influence on or regulate gene expression. A better understanding of the role(s) of so-called 'junk' DNA will lead to an improved understanding of gene function.

Increased knowledge of gene function and gene–gene interactions will illuminate biological pathways for behavioral traits. The crucial task is to uncover neural pathways and endophenotypes through which genes ply their influence and the environmental contexts under which genes are expressed. Emerging research on GE interplay suggests that both genetic susceptibility and environmental contexts are important. Genes and environmental factors are likely to be of small effect individually for most behavioral traits; thus the multifaceted pathways from small accumulating effects leading to complex behavior will long be of interest.

See also: ADHD: Genetic Influences; Autism Spectrum Disorders; Behavior Genetics; Down Syndrome; Family Influences; Fragile X Syndrome; Genetic Disorders: Sex Linked; Genetic Disorders: Single Gene; Intellectual Disabilities; Learning Disabilities; Maternal Age and Pregnancy; Nature vs. Nurture; Obesity; Temperament; Twins.

Suggested Readings

Boomsma D, Busjahn A, and Peltonen L (2002) Classical twin studies and beyond. *Nature Review Genetics* 3: 872–882.
Bouchard TJ (2004) Genetic influence on human psychological traits. *Current Directions in Psychological Science* 13: 148–151.
Carey G (2003) *Human Genetics for the Social Sciences.* Thousand Oaks, CA: SAGE.
Gottesman II and Hanson DR (2005) Human development: Biological and genetic processes. *Annual Review of Psychology* 56: 263–286.
Hetherington *et al.* (2003) *Child Psycology.* McGraw-Hill.
Mendel's, Paper in English, Experiments in Plant, Hybridization (1865) by Gregor Mendel. http://www.mendelweb.org/Mendel.html.
Morgan RM (2006) *The Genetics Revolution: History, Fears, and Future of a Life-Altering Science,* 1st edn. Westport, CT: Greenwood Press.
Nervous System, How genetic disorders are inherited. http://www.mayoclinic.com/health/genetic-disorders/DS00549.
Palladino MA (2006) *Understanding the Human Genome Project. CT The Benjamin Cummings Special Topics in Biology Series,* 2nd edn. San Francisco: PB Pearson/Benjamin Cummings.
Plomin R (2003) *Behavioral Genetics in the Postgenomic Era.* Washington, DC: American Psychological Association.
Plomin R, DeFries JC, McClearn GE, and McGuffin P (2001) *Behavioral Genetics.* New York: Worth Publishers.
Posthuma D and de Geus EJC (2006) Progress in the molecular-genetic study of intelligence. *Current Directions in Psychological Science* 15: 151–155.
Rutter MJ (2006) *Genes and Behaviour: Nature–Nurture Interplay.* Oxford, UK: Blackwell Publishing.

Relevant Websites

http://genomics.energy.gov – Genome programs of the US Department of Energy Office of Science.
http://www.hdsa.org – Huntington's Disease, Society of America.
http://www.ncbi.nlm.nih.gov – National Center for Biotechnology Information; Genomic Biology, Human Genome Resources.
http://www.nichd.nih.gov – National Institute of Child Health and Human Development, Child Development and Behavior (CDB) Branch.
http://health.nih.gov – US Department of Health and Human Services, National Institutes of Health, Child Behavior Disorders.

Grammar

D Matthews, University of Manchester, Manchester, UK
M Tomasello, Max Planck Institute for Evolutionary Anthropology, Leipzig, Germany

Glossary

Agreement – Words are said to agree when they share a relevant feature (such as number, person, or gender). For example, with respect to the sentence 'The cats are wet' we can say that the words 'cats' and 'are' agree in number (plural as opposed to singular).
Argument – A noun phrase bearing a specific grammatical relation to a verb. For example, the arguments of the verb 'to kick' might be 'John' and 'the ball'. These arguments may be identified either in terms of grammatical relations (as a subject and direct object) or semantic roles (as agent and patient).
Auxiliary – In English, words such as 'have' in 'I have eaten', 'do' in 'They do not know' or 'can' in 'He can help'. Auxiliaries precede a main verb (such as eat, "know", or help in the above examples) and have verb like properties in that they may mark person, number, and tense. In English auxiliaries can invert with the subject of a sentence to form a question (e.g., Can he help? Do they know?).
Case – Some words are marked for case. For example, the pronoun 'I' is said to be in the

nominative case and the pronoun 'me' is in the accusative case. The words refer to the same person but in different roles. Nominative case is used, for example, when the person is the agent of an action ('I am eating') whereas accusative case would be used if the person was the patient of an action ('The monster ate me'). Many languages rely heavily on case markings to express such things as who did what to whom (nominative, accusative), who received something (dative), who possesses something (genitive), where something came from (ablative), is going to (allative), or is currently located (locative), the means with which something is done (instrumental), and so on.

Construction – A grammatical construction is an abstract pattern made up of smaller linguistic units such as words and inflectional morphemes. Constructions may exist at the whole utterance level, for example, the passive construction, or they may describe fragments of utterances, for example, the noun phrase construction, or the plural construction.

Distribution – The range of environments in which a word or grammatical item may occur. For example, English nouns (e.g., dog) are often found after determiners (the dog, a dog) and before a plural suffix (dog-s).

Lexicon – The lexicon is the vocabulary of a language or a person who speaks that language.

Morphology – The form or structure of words. Words can be analyzed as being made up of one or several morphemes. For example, the word 'dogs' is made up of two morphemes: 'dog' and 's'. The sufffix -s is an inflectional morpheme, also referred to as a 'bound morpheme' because the -s cannot occur on its own but must be bound to a word.

Phrase – Sentences and clauses can be understood as being made up of phrases. For example, 'The dog quickly ate my favorite dinner' could be analyzed into three phrases: a noun phrase (the dog) a verb phrase (quickly ate) and another noun phrase (my favorite dinner). These phrases could be made up of different numbers of constituent words ('my favorite dinner', might be replaced by 'my dinner' or just 'it') but they would still play the same role in the sentence. The clustering of words into phrases that then make up sentences is sometimes referred to as the constituent structure of language.

Semantic roles: agent/patient – Also called thematic roles, these are semantic categories (e.g., agent, patient, theme, instrument, location) that describe the relationship between an argument (generally expressed as a noun phrase) and a predicate (often a verb). For example, the sentence 'John ate the apple in the park' has three thematic roles (the agent: John, the patient: the apple and the location: the park).

Semantics – The meanings of words and larger linguistic structures, such as sentences.

Syntax – The ordering of words or phrases into larger structures, particularly sentences. Syntax and morphology are often subsumed under the more general title of grammar.

Introduction

Infants begin to communicate with others about the world in the months immediately preceding their first birthdays. Typically their first means of communication is pointing and other nonlinguistic gestures. In the months immediately following their first birthdays, infants begin to learn conventional means of communication in the form of linguistic symbols. One-year-olds use linguistic symbols initially as single-unit expressions that convey what, to an adult, are complex meanings (so-called holophrases); for example, "Airplane" may mean, "There is an airplane" and "Apple!" may mean "I want an apple."

The fundamental question is how young children proceed from these single-unit holophrases to more complex forms of linguistic competence in which they comprehend and produce multiunit linguistic utterances, in other words, how they develop grammatical competence with a language. How we answer this question depends heavily on what we think grammatical competence amounts to. This is a matter of great controversy and two main theoretical views have been debated ever since the 1960s.

One view, the generative grammar view, began with the work of Noam Chomsky, who argued that the essence of human language lies in our possession of recursive procedures (abstract rules of grammar), which allow us to generate countless utterances from a finite lexicon (the store of the words we know). Many people who ascribe to the generative view argue that children must have innate knowledge of the rules of grammar since they would be impossible to learn. Indeed, Chomsky originally proposed that there must be a universal grammar that all children would have innately and that they would apply to the language they hear around them. What the universal rules of this grammar would be is currently unclear. However, it is important to bear in mind that any innate knowledge of language, if it exists at all, could only provide a starting point. There are more than 6000 different languages in the world – each with its own set of grammatical conventions – and so to acquire the specific grammatical conventions of specific languages, much will have to be learned.

Another view takes this need to learn each language's idiosyncrasies seriously and proposes that there is no innate grammar. Instead all of grammar – from the most regular of structures (e.g., 'The cat drank the milk') to the most peculiar of idioms (e.g., 'The more the merrier') – is learned. This usage-based view argues that we do not only store words (that are combined with abstract rules) but rather we store linguistic units of all sizes in memory – words and whole utterances alike. On this view, children are able to learn about grammar by forming generalizations over the examples of complex utterances that they have heard and remembered. The result is that all words, whole utterances, and generalizations are stored as symbolic associations of sound and meaning, often referred to as 'constructions'.

Taking this usage-based view, a key theoretical device we will use to trace out the development of grammar is the 'grammatical construction', which is basically a combinatorial pattern of smaller linguistic units. Constructions may be very simple, as in the English plural used to designate multiple entities of the same kind. This construction prototypically consists of a referential word (noun) plus an ending, or 'inflection', written as (-s) (e.g., boy + s > boys). But constructions may also be very complex, as in the English ditransitive construction which, prototypically, consists of a pattern of the following type: noun phrase + verb + noun phrase + noun phrase, as in "The boy gave the girl a gift," for indicating transfer of possession (see **Table 1**).

One key question for developmental psycholinguists concerns how abstractly children's early constructions are represented. The fact that children sometimes make creative errors (e.g., saying 'mouses') would seem to imply some kind of abstractness in the cognitive representation of early linguistic constructions (in this example 'any noun can combine with (-s) to form a plural'). But the question is precisely what degree of abstractness is involved and how this changes over developmental time. As documented below, grammatical development seems to be characterized by a gradual move from more concrete and local constructions/representations to more abstract and general constructions/representations during the preschool period. Again, though, this is a matter of debate and some would argue that evidence for early abstractions is a sign that children have innate principles that guide their acquisition of grammar.

Below we trace the developmental path children follow when moving from holophrases to abstract constructions. We then consider the development of some key grammatical devices, namely, word order and case marking and discuss the level of abstraction that children manifest in their comprehension and production of word order. Next, we discuss the development of inflectional morphology. We then describe a handful of the various abstract constructions children master. Finally, we return

to the theoretical issues discussed in this introduction and consider some of the learning processes that are likely to underlie grammatical development.

From Holophrases to Abstract Constructions

Children produce their earliest multiword utterances to talk about many of the same things they communicated prelinguistically or with holophrases. They talk about the existence and recurrence of objects, people's action on objects, and the location or properties of objects, and people. This talk may take the form of statements (declaratives e.g., 'There's a plane!'), requests (imperatives e.g., 'Give it to me!'), questions (e.g., 'Where did it go?'), and performatives (e.g., 'Hello'). The grammatical constructions underlying these multiword utterances can come in the form of word combinations, pivot schemas, item-based constructions, and abstract constructions.

Word Combinations

Beginning at around 18 months of age, many children combine two words or holophrases in situations in which they both are relevant (e.g., "all-gone apple" to announce the loss or consumption of an apple, "Daddy coffee" to describe Daddy's coffee or "Boomboom plane" to describe the noise of a plane). In these word combinations both words have roughly equivalent status. For example, a child has learned to name a ball and a table and then spies a ball on a table and says, "Ball table." Utterances of this type include both 'successive single-word utterances' (with a pause between them) and 'word combinations' or 'expressions' (under a single intonational contour). The defining feature of word combinations or expressions is that they partition the experiential scene into multiple symbolizable units – in a way that holophrases obviously (by definition) do not – and they are totally concrete in the sense that they are comprised only of concrete pieces of language, not abstract categories (e.g., noun, verb).

Pivot Schemas

Beginning at around 8 months of age, many of children's multiword productions show a more systematic pattern and the first signs of linguistic abstraction. Often there is one word or phrase that seems to structure the utterance in the sense that it determines the speech act function of the utterance as a whole (often with help from an intonational contour), with the other linguistic item(s) simply filling in variable slot(s). Thus, in many of these early utterances one event-word is used with a wide variety of object labels (e.g., "More milk," "More grapes," "More

Table 1 Early grammatical constructions

Construction	Example/comments
Identificationals	*It's a dog.* Almost always take one of three simple forms: *It's a/the X.* *That's* *a/the. This's a/the X.*
Attributives	*There's a plane.* Often take one of two forms: *Here's a/the X. There's a/the X.*
Possessives	*(It's) X's. That's X's/my __. This is X's/your __.*
Intransitives (unergatives and unaccustaives)	*He smiled* (unergative: an actor does something) *It broke* (unaccusative: something happens to something) In the development of English unergatives such as *sleep* and *swim* predominate. The main verbs young children use in the this construction are: *go, come, stop, break, fall, open, play, jump, sit, sing, sleep, cry, swim, run, laugh, hurt,* and *see.*
Transtives	*She pushed me, I want grapes* Used early on by children to talk about both physical and psychological activities. The main verbs young children use in this construction are: *get, have, want, take, find, put, bring, drop, make, open, break, cut, do, eat, play, read, draw, ride, throw, push, help, why see, say,* and *hurt.*
Datives (ditransitives)	*John read the book for Mary* (for dative) *John read the book to Mary* (to dative) *John read Mary the book* (double object dative) Used for talking about the transfer of things between people. Some verbs are choosey about which of the dative constructions they will enter into. The main verbs young children use in these constructions are: *get, give, show, make, read, bring, buy, take, tell, find,* and *send.*
Locatives	Prepositions: *X up, X down, X in, X out, on X, off X* Verb + particle constructions: *pick X up, wipe X off,* and *get X down* Used to express spatial relationships in utterance-level constructions. Children produce two-argument locative constructions early on, for example, *Draw star on me* and *Peoples on there boat,* produced by a 20-month-old. By 3 years of age most children are able to talk about locative events with three participants, for example, *He put the pen on the desk.*
Resultatives	*He wiped the table clean* Used to indicate both an action and the result of that action. Around 2 years of age children learn various combinations of 'causing verb + resulting effect' such as *pull + up* and *eat + all gone.* Later, some children produce novel resultatives e.g. *And the monster would eat you in pieces* and *I'll capture his whole head off.*
Causatives	*He killed the deer* (lexical causative verb has causal meaning). *He made her giggle* (phrasal or periphrastic causative). Phrasal causatives supply a way of causativizing an intransitive verb that cannot be used transitively. For example, instead of saying *Don't laugh me* we can say *Don't make me laugh.* *Make* is thus the direct causation matrix verb in English, but the most frequent such verb for young English learners is *let,* as in *Let her do it.* Another common matrix verb is *help,* as in *Help her get in there.* It is unknown whether young children see any common pattern among the utterances in which these three different matrix verbs are used.
Passives	*Bill was shot by John.* *He got hurt.* Used to change the perspective from the agent of an action to the patient and what happened to it. Thus, *Bill was shot by John* takes the perspective of Bill and what happened to him, rather than focusing on John's act of shooting. English-speaking children typically do not spontaneously produce full passives until 4 or 5 years of age, although they produce truncated passives (often with *get*) and adjectival passives much earlier (e.g., *He got hurt*). Children tend to begin with stative participles (e.g., *Pumpkin stuck*), then use some participles ambiguously between stative and active readings (e.g., *Do you want yours cut?*), then finally use the active participles characteristic of the full passive (e.g., *The spinach was cooked by Mommy*). Older preschoolers occasionally create truncated passives with verbs that in adult English do not passivize, for example, *It was bandaided, He will be died and I won't have a brother anymore,* indicating some productivity with the construction.
Questions	*What did he buy?* (Object Wh question) *Who bought the house?* (Subject Wh question) *Did he buy a house?* (Yes–no question) In contrast to the above English examples, many languages form questions by using characteristic intonation (*He bought a <u>house</u>?*) or by the replacement of a content word with a question word (*He bought a <u>what</u>?*).

Continued

Table 1 Continued

Construction	Example/comments
Complex constructions	*I want to go* (infinitival complement construction) *I think it will fall over* (sentential complement construction) *That's the doggy I bought* (relative clause construction) *You do this and I'll do that* (conjoined clause construction). Complex constructions contain multiple predicates (e.g., 'want' and 'go' in the first example). Children generally start to produce complex constructions between the ages of 2 and 3 years, starting off with constructions they hear frequently and are motivated to use, such as the infinitival 'I want to X'.
Modals	*I have to go* (modal verb have used in deontic sense) *It might be there* (model verb might used in epistemic sense) Modality and negation are used in conjunction with argument structure constructions to talk about such things as what must, might, or should not be the case. Children are very quick to learn this using modal verbs (*can, might, could, should, must,* and so on) and negation in some form (e.g., *can't*) from early on to say what people have to or ought to do (deontic sense) and later in the epistemic sense.
Negation constructions	*I don't want to.* Negation often emerges with the ubiquitous '*no*' before a statement (e.g., *No Mummy do it*) and later with sentence internal negative markers, with or without auxiliaries (e.g., *I no want that* or *I didn't caught it*).

Please note that examples are given in italics and comments in Roman.

juice") or, more rarely, something like a pronoun or other general expression is the constant element (e.g., 'It's __' or 'Where's __'). Following Martin Braine, we may call these pivot schemas.

Item-Based and Abstract Constructions

Pivot schemas are a clear illustration of early linguistic abstraction and systematicity. However, although the order of slot and pivot may be fixed, this cannot be taken as a sign of a productive syntactic symbol: the order of the words is not used to mean anything. So, although young children are using their early pivot schemas to partition scenes conceptually with different words, they are not using syntactic symbols – such as word order or case marking – to indicate the different roles being played by different participants in that scene. The first signs of syntactic symbol use emerge with 'item-based constructions'. For example, if a child systematically differentiates the meaning of 'Kate pushed Jenny' from the meaning of 'Jenny pushed Kate', then we might take this as evidence of an item-based construction at least as abstract as (PUSHER pushed PUSHEE), where the order of the words is crucial to the meaning of the utterance. In this case the slot before the verb is for the pusher, whereas the one after the verb is for the pushee. Children who have grasped this function of word order can now use grammar to express 'who did what to whom'.

Using Grammar to Say Who Did What to Whom

One of the key advantages that grammatical development brings is the ability to mark agent–patient relations, the 'who did what to whom' of a sentence. Put simply, when there are several noun phrases in a sentence, agent–patient relations tell us the role each of these plays. So in the example 'Jenny pushed Kate' we need to know that role of Jenny is the pusher (or more generally, the 'agent') and Kate is the pushee (the 'patient'). The two major devices that languages use to mark agent–patient relations (also known as thematic roles) are (1) word order (as in our English example) and (2) morphological marking (e.g., case marking on nouns and agreement marking between nouns and verbs).

Word Order

In their spontaneous speech young English-speaking children use canonical word order (often referred to as SVO order – subject verb object) from very early in development. However, one key question of current theoretical debate concerns just how abstract this early knowledge of word order is. That is, do children understand the function of word order at an entirely abstract level from the outset (either in terms of marking abstract thematic roles such as agent and patient or in terms of abstract syntactic roles such as subject and object), or is this understanding first based on specific lexical items?

Several studies have revealed that children respond to word order better when the specific words used in test sentences are ones whose typical word order patterns they are already familiar with. For example, when given lots of animal toys, children barely 2 years of age respond appropriately to requests that they "Make the bunny push the horse" (reversible transitives) that depend crucially on a knowledge of canonical English word order and its function in marking agent–patient relations. However, if 2-year-olds are taught a new verb, 'dacking', to describe a novel canonical transitive action they do not perform so consistently. So, when asked to 'Make Cookie Monster dack Big Bird', 3-year-olds are consistently able to make Cookie Monster perform the dacking action on Big Bird, but many young 2-year-olds are not. This task is also made considerably harder for children if word order cues conflict with animacy cues. Thus if children are asked to 'Make the pencil kick the horse,' they are sometimes susceptible to picking up the toy horse and making it kick the pencil.

Children's production of word order also seems to be affected by the familiarity and frequency of the verb they are using. For example, in the 'weird word order' paradigm, developed by Nameera Akhtar, an adult describes a novel transitive scene by using a novel verb in an ungrammatical word order (e.g., saying "Ernie Bert dacking" to describe Ernie performing some novel action on Bert). The child is then asked to describe scenes with other characters performing this same novel action. The idea is to test whether children will adopt the adult's weird word order or prefer to use the novel verb in the canonical order of their language. Generally speaking, English-speaking 4-year-olds prefer to use canonical word order but 2-year-olds are just as likely to adopt the weird word orders as they are to switch to using a novel verb in canonical order. In contrast, with familiar verbs even 2-year-olds prefer to switch to canonical English order. Furthermore, 2-year-olds never copy a weird word order with pronouns even when novel verbs are used (i.e., they might say 'Ernie Bert dacked' but are unlikely to say 'He him dacked'). This suggests that 2-year-olds knowledge of word order may be based on words that they know well (e.g., high-frequency verbs and pronouns).

In contrast to the above findings, recent studies have suggested that even 2-year-olds show some abstract understanding of word order when undemanding comprehension tests are used. For example, when 2-year-olds are simultaneously shown two screens showing identical scenes except for their agent–patient relations (e.g., Screen 1: A dog acting on a lion; Screen 2: A lion acting on a dog) and are simply asked to 'Point to the lion weefing the dog', they point to the right scene (where the lion was the agent) at a rate above chance and do so even when novel verbs are used. Similar results have been found when children's eye movements are measured instead of their pointing gestures: the 'preferential looking' technique developed by Hirsh-Pasek and Golinkoff. In one study conducted by Cynthia Fisher and colleagues, children were shown two screens. In the first, a boy spun a girl around on a chair. In the second, a girl bent a boy over by pushing on his shoulder. After hearing test sentences like 'The girl is gorping the boy' 21-month-olds looked longer at the screen in which the girl was the agent than at the screen where the boy was acting on the girl.

When we take the results of these diverse methods together the picture that emerges is one where

English-speaking children are beginning to formulate abstract knowledge of the function of word order around their second birthday. However, this early knowledge of word order starts off as weak and is open to being abandoned if other orders are modeled by an adult or if other cues, such as animacy, compete with it. At this point, then, knowledge of word order shows up in above chance performance in preferential looking tasks using highly prototypical transitives. Over the next months and years, however, it will grow in strength and abstractness and show up in tasks requiring more active behavioral decision-making and language production.

One reason it takes time for this knowledge to become robust is that understanding of word order most probably starts out as a collection of various production and comprehension heuristics, which later coalesce into a full-blown understanding, for example, of English SVO word order. When comprehending an SVO utterance a child might simply know that the first noun phrase is generally the agent, or that the noun phrase following the verb is the patient. Other heuristics for English might be based on pronouns (I-me, he-him, they-them, we-us, etc.), whose roles are not only indicated with word order but also with case marking (e.g., the agent of a transitive action is expressed with a nominative pronoun 'I/he/she', whereas the patient is expressed with an accusative 'me/him/her'). We now turn to an investigation of the development of case marking – which is much more important in some other languages than it is in English.

Case and Agreement

In many languages agent–patient relations are marked not with word order, but morphologically with case or agreement. For example, in Polish the sentence 'The giraffe is chasing the monkey' can be expressed as follows: *Żyraf-a goni małp-ę (Giraffe + Nominative_marker chases monkey + Accurate_marker)*.

The ending -*a* on *zyrafa* indicates the nominative case (it marks the agent) and -*ę* on *małpę* marks the accusative case (it marks the patient). So one could just a well say *Małp-ę goni Żyraf-a* (Monkey-Acc chases Giraffe-Nom) and this would still mean 'the giraffe is chasing the monkey', since it is the case marking that does all the work in Polish not word order (although word order may be used to pragmatic effect). Case marking is used in this way in many languages ranging from slavic languages like Polish, to uralic languages like Finnish, innuit languages like Inuktitut and turkic languages like Turkish.

In the 1960s and 1970s, a number of investigators speculated that word order should be easier than case and agreement for children to learn as a syntactic device because canonical ordering is so fundamental to so many sensory-motor and cognitive activities. However, cross-linguistic research has since exploded this 'word order myth'.

That is, cross-linguistic research has demonstrated that in their spontaneous speech, children learning many different languages – regardless of whether their language relies mainly on word order, case marking, or some combination of both – generally conform to adult usage and appear to mark agent–patient relations equally early and appropriately. If anything, children learning languages that mark agent–patient relations clearly and simply with morphological (case) markers, comprehend agent–patient marking earlier than children learning word order languages such as English. This is evidenced by the fact that some children learning case-marking languages over-generalize case markers in ways indicating productive control while they are still only 2 years old.

In comprehension experiments, it is clearly the case that children learning morphologically rich languages, in which word order plays only a minor role in indicating agent–patient relations, comprehend the syntactic marking of agent–patient relations as early or earlier than children learning word order languages such as English. But it should be noted that in neither comprehension nor production do we have the kind of novel word studies that could provide the most definitive evidence of children's productive knowledge of case marking. The few novel verb studies we have of case marking show a gradual developmental pattern of increasing productivity, just as with word order marking in English and similar languages.

For English, most of the discussion of case marking has centered around pronoun case errors, such as 'Me do it' and 'Him going'. About 50% of English-speaking children make such errors, most typically in the 2–4 year age range, with much variability across children. The most robust phenomenon is that children most often substitute accusative forms for nominative forms ("Me do it") but very seldom do the reverse ("Billy hit I"). This might be due to the fact that sequences like "me do it" do occur in English as fragments of well-formed sentences like "Let me do it" whereas "hit I" is a very unlikely sequence (**Table 2**).

The particular pronouns that English-speaking children over-generalize proportionally most often are the accusative forms 'me' and 'her' (and not the nominative forms 'I' and 'she'). In his work on children's errors, Matthew Rispoli has attributed this to the morphophonetic structure of the English personal pronoun paradigm: *Nominative* I/she/he/they; *Accusative* me/her/him/them; *Genitive* my/her/his/their.

It is easily seen that 'he/him/his' and 'they/them/their' each has a common phonetic core (*h*- and *th*-, respectively) whereas 'I/me/my' and 'she/her/her' do not. And indeed, the errors that are made most often are ones in which children in these latter two cases use the forms that have a common initial phoneme ('me/my' and 'her/her') to substitute for the odd-man-out ('I' and 'she'), with the 'her-for-she' error having the overall highest rate (perhaps because 'her' occurs as both the accusative and genitive form; the so-called 'double-cell' effect). The overall idea is thus that children are making retrieval errors based on both semantic and phonological factors.

Combining Word Order, Case, and Other Cues: Coalition and Competition

In all languages there are multiple potential cues indicating agent–patient relations. For example, in many languages both word order and case marking are at least potentially available, even though one of them might most typically be used for other functions (e.g., in many morphologically rich languages, word order is used primarily for pragmatic functions such as topicalization). In addition, in attempting to comprehend adult utterances children might also attend to information that is not directly encoded in the language; for example, they may use animacy to infer that, in an utterance containing the lexical items 'man', 'ball', and 'kick', the most likely interpretation is that the man kicked the ball, regardless of how those items are syntactically combined.

In an extensive investigation of language acquisition in a number of different languages, Dan Slobin identified some of the different comprehension strategies that children use to establish agent–patient relations, depending on the types of problems their particular language presents to them. A central discovery of this research, is that children can more easily master grammatical forms expressed in 'local cues' such as bound morphology (infections attached to words – see 'Glossary') as opposed to more distributed cues such as word order and some forms of agreement. This accounts, for example, for the fact that Turkish-speaking children master the expression of agent–patient relations at a significantly earlier age than do English-speaking children. In addition, however, it turns out that Turkish is especially 'child friendly', even among languages that rely heavily on local morphological cues. This is because Turkish nominal grammatical morphemes are:

- postposed (they come at the ends of words), syllabic, and stressed, which makes them perceptually more 'salient';
- obligatory and employ almost perfect one-to-one mapping of form to function (no fusional morphemes or homophones with several meanings), which makes them more 'predictable';

Table 2   The English personal pronoun paradigm

Nominative	I	she	he	they
Accusative	me	her	him	them
Genitive	my	her	his	their

- bound to the noun, rather than freestanding, which makes them more 'local'; and
- invariably regular across different nominals and pro-nominals, which makes them readily 'generalizable'.

All of these factors coalesce to make Turkish agent–patient relations especially easy to learn, and their identification is a major step in discovering the basic processes of language acquisition that are employed by children in general.

A central methodological problem, however, is that in natural languages many grammatical markers occur together naturally, and so it is difficult to evaluate their contributions separately. One solution to this problem is to pit cues, like word order, case, and animacy against each other in what are called competition experiments. Elizabeth Bates, Brian MacWhinney, and collaborators conducted an extensive set of these experiments in order to establish which cues children use to comprehend agent–patient relations in a number of different languages. The basic paradigm is to ask children to pick up some toys from a table and act out utterances that indicate agent–patient relations in different ways – sometimes in semi-grammatical utterances with conflicting cues. For example, an English-speaking child might be presented with the utterance "The spoon kicked the horse." In this case, the cue of word order is put in competition with the most likely real-world scenario in which animate beings more often kick inanimate things than the reverse (the animacy cue). From an early age, young English-speaking children most often make the spoon 'kick' the horse, whereas Italian-speaking children are more likely to ignore word order and make the horse kick the spoon. This is because word order is quite variable in Italian, and so, since there is no case marking (and in this example agreement is no help because both the horse and the spoon are third-person singular), animacy is the most reliable cue available. German-speaking children gradually learn to ignore both word order and semantic plausibility (animacy) and simply look for nominative and accusative marking on 'the horse' and 'the spoon' (e.g., the spoon in nominative case is 'der Loeffle' but in accusative case it is 'den Leoffle').

Inflectional Morphology

As we have seen in the above discussion of case, many languages mark grammatical functions with inflectional morphemes (e.g., the -a and -ę inflections that are added to nouns mark nominative and accusative case in Polish). In English, inflectional morphology is used to mark, for example, plurality (with the inflection (-s)) and the past tense (with the inflection (-ed)). In comparison to most of the world's languages, English is relatively impoverished when it comes to inflections. Yet the acquisition of the English plural and past tense has long been the subject of intense scrutiny and heated debate. The reason for this is that inflectional morphology had become a sort of test case for different accounts of how we learn and use linguistic generalizations in general.

The basic phenomenon under investigation is the fact that children generally start using inflectional morphology in an adult-like way. (This is presumably because they are learning each inflected word by rote.) But after a while they begin to produce the odd over-generalization, for example, saying 'mouses' and 'goed'. After a prolonged period of producing occasional over-generalizations children begin to use adult-like forms almost exclusively (although adults sometimes over-generalize, especially when under communicative pressure). This developmental trajectory of early accurate use followed by a period of errors followed by renewed accurate use is referred to as a U-shaped developmental curve. There are two main schools of explanation for this U-shape curve and for how we as adults use inflections.

Single-mechanism accounts propose that children store examples of individual inflections (e.g., dogs, cats, mice) and generalizations (e.g., noun + s marks plurality) in one and the same system. Indeed in single-mechanism connectionist models, first proposed by David Rumelhart and James McClelland, generalizations are simply the outcome of individual exemplars overlapping in representational space. Other single-mechanism accounts, such as that of Joan Bybee, propose that children learn and store enormous numbers of concrete examples and they extract two types of schema from these. Source-oriented schemas are generalizations about how an inflected form is composed of a stem and an inflection (e.g., to make a plural, take a noun stem and add -s). Such schemas explain errors of over-generalization like 'mans' and 'comed'. Product-oriented schemas are generalizations about properties of inflected forms (e.g., 'plurals tend to end with -s'). These schemas explain why children have difficulty marking the plural of nouns, like dress, that already end in-s in the singular. These difficulties lead to errors of omission, for example, saying things like 'one dress, two dress' instead of 'two dresses'.

Dual mechanism accounts of inflection, put forward by Gary Marcus, Steven Pinker, and colleagues, propose that irregularly inflected words (e.g., mice) are stored in an associative memory much like the one proposed by single mechanism theorists, whereas regularly inflected words (e.g., houses) are computed by a distinct default rule (e.g., 'add -s' for English plurals) that combines a symbol for a stem with a symbol for a suffix. While this model makes roughly similar predictions about the acquisition of morphology in English as might a schema model, it does not appear to work for languages with more complex morphology, such as Polish or Finnish, where there is not one default inflection but rather several semiregular inflections that are predictable on a phonological and/or semantic basis.

Delays in the acquisition of inflectional morphology have been taken as a key diagnostic marker of language learning difficulties, sometimes called specific language impairment (SLI). Proponents of dual mechanism models argue that this impairment reflects a specific difficulty with processing linguistic rules (as opposed to storing words). Other theorists point to four main different reasons for why inflectional morphemes might be particularly hard to acquire. First, inflectional morphemes are typically phonologically reduced, unstressed, and monosyllabic – that is, they are not very salient. Second, in some though by no means all cases, inflectional morphology carries little concrete semantic weight, for example, the English third person -s agreement marker (e.g., He runs) is in most cases almost totally semantically redundant. Third, many grammatical morphemes are pluri-functional (e.g., in English the inflection -s on a noun can mark either plurality or possession – as in 'the dog's bone'). Fourth, in some languages, the form of an inflection can change dramatically depending on which word it is combining with. For example, in Russian the form of the plural inflection depends on the gender and phonological form of the noun.

Abstract Constructions

During the preschool years, English-speaking children begin to be productive with a variety of abstract constructions. We focus here on the earliest grammatical developments at the whole utterance level, what are often called argument structure constructions. However, much development is also going on at the subsentence and suprasentence level. For example, children are learning about the major internal constituents of utterance-level constructions. Most especially, they construct nominal constructions (noun phrases) in order to make reference to things in various ways ('Bill, my father, the man who fell down') and verbal constructions (verb phrases) in order predicate for something about those things ('is nice, sleeps, hit the ball').

Table 1 presents the main grammatical constructions that have been studied with respect to the acquisition of English. Many of the constructions have equivalents in other languages, although these might not be acquired at the same rate. For example, children acquiring certain non-Indo-European languages typically produce passive sentences quite early in development. This result has been obtained for children learning Inuktitut, K'iche' Mayan, Sesotho, and Zulu. This is presumably because in these languages: (1) passives are very common in child-directed speech; and/or (2) passive utterances are actually simpler than active voice constructions (e.g., in terms of agreement).

The most abstract constructions that English-speaking children use early in development have mostly been studied from an adult perspective of grammar. As mentioned in the introduction, differing views of what adult grammar amounts to lead to differences in how people propose children develop and use grammar. For example, in some generative linguistic analyses, English questions are formed by subject-auxiliary inversion (sometimes with do-support) and Wh-movement. Put simply, this account assumes that to produce a question, the child takes a simple declarative (e.g., "John bought a house") and moves, rearranges, or inserts grammatical items to yield the question form (e.g., "Did John buy a house?" or "What did John buy?"). This account assumes that children have highly abstract representations of both declaratives and questions. However, others argue this is an unlikely explanation of early question formation for two main reasons. First, some English-speaking children use Wh-question constructions before they produce any other word combinations (i.e., before they produce the declaratives that questions are supposed to be derived from). Second, several studies of children's early questions give us no reason to suppose that these constructions are represented at a completely abstract level from the beginning. Instead most children start off with a handful of questions, at first only using 'what' and 'where', which are often pronounced as one indistinguishable wh-word (as in "Wuh dis?" for "What's this" and "Wuh dis one go" for "Where does this one go?"). Later on, questions, whether produced correctly or incorrectly, appear to be based on specific combinations of wh-words and auxiliaries.

Learning Processes

The Debate: Can Children Learn Grammar?

The question of learning processes has long divided the field of language acquisition. Those who, after Noam Chomsky, take a generativist view of language generally argue that children cannot learn language by simply creatively copying what they hear around them for two reasons. First, it is argued that children do not hear enough relevant, well-formed examples to form correct generalizations about complex structures that are heard relatively rarely (e.g., questions like 'Can the boys who can run jump?'). This is called the 'poverty of the stimulus argument'. The second argument states that, even if there were enough examples in the input of a relevant grammatical principle, there would be no way to constrain how children would generalize from the input. Children could hypothesize overly general grammars (e.g., saying 'I died him' for 'I killed him') and would have no way of knowing they were incorrect since there is very little explicit negative feedback from parents to instruct them not to do this. This is called the 'no negative evidence problem'.

If one accepts the arguments that grammar cannot be learned then the obvious solution is to propose that all children are born with substantial innate grammatical knowledge. Since any given child could end up learning one of over 6000 of the world's languages, this innate knowledge would have to apply to all languages (it would have to be a universal grammar) and children would need to adapt this universally applicable knowledge to whichever language environment they happen to be born into. This solution faces two major problems. The first concerns what a universal grammar would look like given that all the world's languages each have their own different grammatical conventions. The second concerns how children would connect any innate, language-general knowledge up to the specific language(s) they happen to be learning. There is currently no satisfactory solution to either of these problems.

On the other side of the debate, people have argued that grammar is not impossible to learn and therefore it need not be innate. Below we outline some of the mechanisms that children could use to learn about grammar. It is worth bearing in mind that, since so many grammatical conventions are specific to individual languages, it seems children would need these mechanisms no matter which theory we adopt.

Learning Mechanisms

Since language is such a complex phenomenon, it would be unsurprising if children drew on many sources of information and learning mechanisms to get going. We assume that, from very early on, children have a whole host of the prerequisites for learning grammar. These would include, on the one hand, partitioning their experience of the world into categories of entities, events, goals, etc., and, on the other, processing the speech stream into recurrent patterns to discover the phonetic regularities of the ambient language. Some of these prerequisite developments will put children in a particularly good position to learn grammar. For example, Peter Jusczyk and his colleagues have shown that infants are sensitive to prosodic information, such as the intonation contour of speech, stress patterns, pauses, and durational differences. Since these prosodic properties of speech often correlate with its grammatical organization (e.g., there are often pauses at phrase boundaries), we can assume that children are hearing language in a way that will make its structure easier to identify. Of course at some point, this understanding of language form must be linked to an understanding of its function – what we use it to talk about. We will focus here on the learning skills that are needed to bring experience of the world and experience of the speech stream together to form of a conventional spoken language with the power of expression that grammar provides.

Intention Reading and Cultural Learning

Because natural languages are conventional, the most fundamental process of language acquisition is the ability to do things the way that other people do them. This depends on a complex form of imitative learning in which children must understand other people's communicative intentions and imitatively learn how they are expressed. To understand other people's communicative intentions we basically have to know that when people are talking to us they are intending to change our thoughts or intentions (e.g., to tell us about something or get us to do something). Children's ability to read and learn the expression of communicative intentions can be seen most clearly in word learning studies in which young children have to identify the adult's intended referent in a wide variety of situations in which word and referent are not both present simultaneously.

In human linguistic communication the most fundamental unit of intentional action is the utterance as a relatively complete and coherent expression of a communicative intention, and so the most fundamental unit of language learning is stored exemplars of utterances. This is what children do in learning holophrases and other concrete and relatively fixed linguistic expressions (e.g., Thank You, Don't mention it). But as they are attempting to comprehend the communicative intention underlying an utterance, children are also attempting to comprehend the functional roles being played by its various components. This is a kind of 'blame assignment' procedure in which the attempt is to determine the functional role of a constituent in the communicative intention as a whole – what we have called segmenting communicative intentions. Identifying the functional roles of the components of utterances is only possible if the child has some (perhaps imperfect) understanding of the adult's overall communicative intention, because understanding the functional role of X means understanding how X contributes to some larger communicative structure. This is the basic process by means of which children learn the communicative functions of particular words, phrases, and other utterance constituents and, with help from pattern-finding skills, categories of these.

Schematization and Analogy

Young children hear and use – on a numbingly regular basis – the same utterances repeated over and over but with systematic variation, for example, as instantiated in item-based constructions such as 'Where's the X?, I wanna X, Let's X, Can you X?, Gimme X, I'm Xing it'. Forming schemas of this type means imitatively learning the recurrent concrete pieces of language for concrete functions, as well as forming a relatively abstract slot designating a relatively abstract function. This process is called 'schematization', and its roots may be observed in various primates who schematize everything from food processing skills to arbitrary sequences in the laboratory. In grammatical development, schematization yields what we have called item-based constructions, which can be seen as a combination of constant item(s) plus slot(s), where slots represent functional categories for the child.

Key factors that are likely to affect the formation of slots relative to constant items are 'token' and 'type frequency'. Consider the following sample of three sentences: (1) Where's the dog? (2) Where's daddy? (3) Where's your spoon?

'Token frequency' refers to the frequency with which a specific form is heard in a sample. In the above sample the token frequency of 'where's' is three and the token frequency of 'dog' is one. Token frequency should predict the selection of a constant item in a schema. This is simply because the more often a word occurs, the more easily it can be picked out as a constant. 'Type frequency' refers to the frequency with which different items of the same type (e.g., nouns referring to sought things) are heard. In the above sample the type frequency of 'sought after objects' is three. Type frequency should predict where slots are formed in relation to constant items. That is, one needs to witness a certain amount of variability before or after a constant item in order to realize that different forms can slot in around it. This variability, however, cannot be completely random. Rather the variables will all bear a common relation to the constant item (i.e., they will be of one type). Slot formation is therefore an instance of category formation.

In order to move from item-based constructions to abstract constructions, children need to form schemas that have no concrete items in common. We will refer to the learning process that achieves this as 'analogy', a form of schematization that places heavy emphasis on commonalities in relational structure. For example, despite the different number of words in the sentences (1) and (2) below, the two may be functionally aligned in that they both encode the roles of agent, action and patient. Drawing an analogy between the two would thus give an abstract transitive construction, perhaps of the form agent-causes motion-patient):

1. I kicked the ball.
2. Daddy threw it.

As is the case for schematization, the coherence of the category of variables that enters into each role (e.g., agent) is proposed to affect the ease of analogizing. This means that analogies will be formed more easily if certain items always tend to fill certain roles (e.g., if the patient role is predominantly filled by nouns denoting inanimate objects and the agent role is predominantly filled by first and second person pronouns in both constructions).

The key skill involved in analogy formation is the ability to focus on detecting similarities in relational structure. This is central to the acquisition of grammar because surface similarities between utterances often need to glossed over in order to form complex, abstract constructions. To actually use abstract constructions, though, children need to fill abstract slots with concrete words and this requires selecting words from relevant categories. For example, in the transitive construction (subject verb object) the verb slot can be filled with any word that falls into the category of transitive verbs. We now consider how children cluster words into these categories.

Constructing Lexical Categories: Functionally Based Distributional Analysis

In order to cluster words and morphemes into categories, such as 'noun', 'pronoun', 'verb', 'adjective' children must draw upon information about the word's 'distribution' and its 'function'. The term distribution simply refers to the types of neighborhood a word tends to inhabit. For example, English nouns (e.g., dog) are often found after determiners (the dog, a dog) and before a plural suffix (dog -s). So children might form rough categories by clustering together words that often share the same distribution. They could also notice functional regularities pertaining to a given class of words (e.g., that nouns tend to denote entities whereas verbs tend denote actions). However, neither distributional nor functional cues used alone would be likely to yield a very satisfactory taxonomy. Studies that have used distributional analyses to categorize English words have typically only correctly classified a certain percentage of words, mostly only nouns and verbs. Functional analysis, on the other hand, does not explain children's early use of words such as the nonobject nouns 'breakfast' and 'night' and dual category words such as 'kiss' and 'hug', which may be used as nouns or verbs (a kiss vs. to kiss). Rather it would seem that only a combination of formal and functional cues would work and these would have to be understood in the context of each word's role in the wider communicative attempt – the whole construction or discourse turn. We refer to this combination of distributional and functional cues as 'functionally based distributional analysis', which be seen as the identification of items in a category on the grounds that they occur in the same formal contexts and perform the same communicative function within an utterance.

It is important to emphasize that this same process of functionally based distributional analysis also operates on units of language larger than words. For example, what is typically called a noun phrase may be constituted by anything from a proper name to a pronoun to a common noun with a determiner and a relative clause hanging off it. But for many syntactic purposes these may all be treated as the same kind of unit. How can this be, given their very different surface forms? The only reasonable answer is that they are treated as units of the same type because they all do the same job in utterances: they identify a referent playing some role in the scene being depicted. Indeed, given the very different form of the different nominals involved, it is difficult to even think of an alternative to this functionally based account.

Mechanisms for Constraining Generalization

As noted above, one theoretically very important question for language acquisition concerns how children restrain from adopting an overly general grammar. Children do occasionally produce sentences like 'She falled me down' or 'Don't giggle me' that are not adult-like but appear to have been formed on an analogical basis. In the two examples given the child has used an intransitive verb in the SVO transitive frame productively.

There are several mechanisms that may explain why these errors are not overly abundant and are gradually replaced with more conventional forms.

The first reason is that children appear to be very conservative learners. Naturalistic studies show that a vast proportion of children's spontaneous speech is either a direct copy or a rehash of chunks of speech they have heard addressed to them. To the extent that children repeat what adults say to them more or less verbatim, they will of course sound highly conventional in their language use.

Still, the above examples show that children do go beyond the speech they hear and combine words in a creative, sometimes unconventional, manner. Children very rarely receive direct feedback about their errors (parents do not generally say 'darling you really ought not to use intransitive verbs in the transitive construction'). However there is mounting evidence for indirect feedback. One example of this would be a recast. After hearing 'The magician disappeared the rabbit' a parent might reply by reformulating 'He made the rabbit disappear, did he?'. The pragmatic implication of such recasts is that the child's form was not conventional and the supplied alternative would be preferable.

Once children have a set of alternatives to express any given scene then they are in a far better position to recover for over-generalization errors. This is because these conventional forms will strengthen with experience and will become preferred to unlikely over-generalizations. For example, children might learn that the verb 'disappear' can appear in the periphrastic causative construction (e.g., The magician made the rabbit disappear). At the same time they will also be noticing properties of the verb 'disappear', for example, that it persistently appears in the intransitive construction ('It disappeared') but never in the transitive ('I disappeared it'). Consequently, when faced with the task of expressing that someone caused something to disappear, over-generalization to the transitive is now less likely and the new alternative form will become preferred.

The above example illustrates how over-generalization can be avoided by learning about linguistic structures in ever increasing detail and forming ever more accurate generalizations. One such late-developing generalization is the discovery of semantically governed verb classes. The idea here is that some verbs, such as those denoting a manner of motion (walk, drive, etc.), can alternate between transitive and intransitive constructions. Other verbs, such as those denoting motion in a specific direction (enter, leave, etc.) cannot take a direct object and thus only appear in the intransitive construction. Learning that the ability of a verb to alternate between constructions can be predicted from the narrow semantic class it enters into could thus also help children not to over-generalize. When this has been tested experimentally, children do not appear to use verb classes to avoid over-generalization until they are 4 years old. This would predict the U-shaped developmental curve whereby, early on, conservatism is the most likely explanation of a lack of over-generalization errors and then, as more experience with language is accrued, over-generalizations become a possibility but are gradually avoided by forming more accurate and detailed generalizations over time.

Conclusions

Above we have outlined the path that grammatical development typically takes and we have debated both the level of abstraction of children's early grammatical knowledge and the different theoretical accounts of development. To decide these debates and to be precise about how grammar actually develops, we need greater theoretical clarity and new empirical work. Those who argue grammar is not learnable must articulate what they propose children know innately and how this combines with the children's experience of particular languages in a way that yields the developments we observe. Those who argue that children could plausibly learn grammar need to test the learning mechanisms they propose in detailed studies with specific linguistic items and structures in a sufficient variety of languages.

See also: Categorization Skills and Concepts; Developmental Disabilities: Cognitive; Language Development: Overview; Language Acquisition Theories; Learning; Literacy; Pragmatic Development; Preverbal Development and Speech Perception; Semantic Development; Speech Perception; Theory of Mind.

Suggested Readings

Bates E and MacWhinney B (1989) Functionalism and the competition model. In: MacWhinney B and Bates E (eds.) *The Cross-Linguistic Study of Sentence Processing.* Cambridge: Cambridge University Press.

Bybee J (1995) Regular morphology and the lexicon. *Language and Cognitive Processes* 10: 425–455.

Clark EV (2003) *First Language Acquisition.* Cambridge: Cambridge University Press.

Hoff E (2005) *Language Development,* 3rd edn. Belmont, CA: Wadsworth/Thompson.

Marcus G, Pinker S, Ullman M, Hollander M, Rosen T, and Xu F (1992) Over-regularization in language acquisition. *Monographs of the Society for Research in Child Development* 57(4), 1–182.

O'Grady W (1997) *Syntactic Development.* Chicago, IL: The University of Chicago Press.

Pinker S (1989) *Learnability and Cognition: The Acquisition of Verb-Argument Structure.* Cambridge, MA: Harvard University Press.

Rumelhart D and McClelland J (1986) On learning the past tenses of English verbs. In: Rumelhart D, McClelland J, and Group TP (eds.) *Parallel Distributed Processing: Explorations in the Microstructure of Cognition.* Cambridge, MA: MIT Press.

Slobin DI (ed.) (1985–1992) *The Crosslinguistic Study of Language Acquisition,* vol 3. Hillsdale, NJ: Erlbaum.

Tomasello M (2003) *Constructing a Language: A Usage-Based Theory of Language Acquisition.* Cambridge, MA: Harvard University Press.

Relevant Website

http://childes.psy.cmu.edu – A database of child and caregiver speech with software tools for analysis can be found at the Child Language Data Exchange System.

Habituation and Novelty

K A Snyder and C M Torrence, University of Denver, Denver, CO, USA

Glossary

Declarative memory – A memory system involving structures within the medial temporal lobe (i.e., the hippocampus and adjacent entorhinal, perirhinal, and parahippocampal cortices) and midline diencephalon that is thought to support the conscious recollection of facts and events.

Dishabituation – Full or partial recovery of the orienting response that is typically observed in response to the presentation of a new or novel stimulus following habituation to a repeated stimulus.

Event-related potentials (ERPs) – Reflect the synchronous firing of neuronal populations in response to a discrete event (such as the presentation of a stimulus). They are recorded from electrodes placed on the scalp, are derived from the electroencephalogram, and provide good temporal resolution of ongoing cognitive processes.

Explicit memory – The form of memory that supports our ability to deliberately retrieve or consciously recollect, facts, events, and prior experiences.

Habituation – The decline in orienting (or responding) that is observed when a stimulus is repeated.

Implicit memory – A form of memory typically observed in terms of a facilitation or change in behavior resulting from involuntary retrieval of prior experience. Implicit memory usually occurs in the absence of conscious awareness of prior experience.

Medial temporal lobe (MTL) – The region of the brain thought to be critical for learning and memory, consisting of the hippocampus and adjacent entorhinal, perirhinal, and parahippocampal cortices.

Novelty preference – The tendency of infants to look (or orient) longer at a new or novel stimulus compared to a familiar stimulus.

Orienting reflex (OR) – The cessation and redirection of ongoing behavior that results from a sudden, unexpected, or novel event in the environment. The OR involves behavioral and physiological changes such as postural adjustments (i.e., head turning, fixating the eyes), reductions in motor activity, and autonomic responses such as vasodilation and heart rate deceleration.

Repetition suppression – The reduction in neural activity that occurs in response to a repeated stimulus. Repetition suppression occurs when the population of neurons responding to a particular stimulus decreases as the stimulus is repeated, resulting in an overall reduction of neural activity elicited by the repeated stimulus.

Introduction

Habituation and novelty paradigms have been used for more than 50 years to study perceptual and mnemonic processes in the human infant. In the first part of this article we provide a brief history and description of the different types of habituation and novelty procedures, critique the major theories and models of infant habituation and novelty preferences, and summarize major developmental trends and debates. In the second part of the article we review more recent advances in our understanding of habituation and novelty preferences using the methods of neuroscience that are now available, and provide a critical review of the debate over what kind of memory supports infant performance in these tasks.

Habituation and Novelty

Developmental psychologists have long been concerned with questions of how the mind develops. How do children acquire knowledge about the world and the ability to think, learn, remember, communicate, and feel? Research in this important domain, however, is significantly constrained by the limited behavioral repertoire of infants and young children. The typical 6-month-old, for example, can barely sit up by herself, much less understand, and follow instructions or verbally report thoughts and feelings. A significant breakthrough came when Robert Fantz in 1964 discovered that infants' looking behavior was sensitive to effects of prior experience. Specifically, Fantz discovered that infants' look less at a repeated pattern (i.e., habituation) and more at a novel pattern (i.e., the novelty preference) over time. This discovery provided researchers with an important window into early learning and memory. Methods that rely on infants' looking behavior to study cognitive development are commonly known as preferential-looking paradigms.

In the time since that seminal paper, preferential-looking methods have become ubiquitous in the field of developmental psychology and now inform most of our knowledge about cognitive development during the infancy period. A critical issue for the field of developmental psychology, however, and our understanding of infant development concerns the interpretation of infants' looking behavior. Although the empirical phenomenon itself is generally undisputed, the meaning of infants' looking behavior has always been the subject of controversy because it determines the kinds of knowledge and abilities we ascribe to young infants.

The Use of Habituation and Novelty Paradigms in the Study of Development

There are two basic types of preferential-looking procedures: the habituation–dishabituation procedure and the visual-paired comparison (VPC). These procedures both rely on the infant's inherent 'preference' for viewing novel stimuli to provide evidence for learning, memory, or discrimination. Otherwise, the procedures differ in several important respects.

The Habituation–Dishabituation Procedure

In the habituation–dishabituation procedure, a stimulus is repeated or presented for a long enough period of time until a significant decline in orienting toward the stimulus is observed. This decline in orienting is termed 'habituation'. Following habituation, the now familiar stimulus and a novel stimulus are presented one at a time, and the length of time that the infant orients toward each is recorded. If the orienting response to the novel stimulus recovers to initial levels, 'dishabituation' is said to occur.

Variants of the habituation–dishabituation procedure use different criteria to establish habituation. For example,

in a 'fixed-criterion' habituation procedure, a stimulus is presented until orienting declines to a prespecified level (e.g., visual fixation declines to 3 s or less on any given trial). In a 'fixed-level' procedure, a stimulus is presented until the infant accumulates a specific amount of exposure (e.g., the infant looks at the stimulus for a total of 2 min). In the most widely used variant of the habituation procedure, habituation is 'infant-controlled': the stimulus is presented until orienting declines to some proportion of the infant's initial levels of looking (e.g., habituation is achieved when the average of the infant's last two looks is less than one-half of the average of her three longest looks). The advantage of the infant-controlled habituation procedure is that it takes into account individual differences in (1) look duration (i.e., short vs. long lookers) and (2) encoding, since one infant may require more time to encode a stimulus than another infant. This increases the likelihood that infants who reach criterion for habituation have actually encoded the stimulus, and that infants who encode the stimulus quickly do not become bored and fussy before criterion is reached.

The Visual-Paired Comparison Procedure

The VPC procedure also consists of two phases: an encoding phase and a test phase. In the encoding phase, two identical stimuli are presented side-by-side for either a fixed period of time (e.g., 30 s), or until the infant accumulates a fixed amount of looking. The length of exposure to the familiar stimulus during the encoding phase of the VPC is typically shorter than in the habituation procedure (i.e., 5–30 s vs. 1–2 min), although some researchers have used long encoding times (e.g., 1–2 min) in the VPC. Since the encoding phase of the VPC consists of relatively brief and fixed levels of accumulated looking, rather than a decline in orienting, it is typically referred to as 'familiarization' and not habituation. The test phase consists of two trials. In each trial, the familiar stimulus and a novel stimulus are presented side-by-side for a fixed period of time and the amount of time the infant looks at each is recorded. The left–right location of the novel stimulus is counterbalanced across the test trials to control for side biases in infant looking. The traditional dependent measure examined in the VPC is the 'novelty score', which is computed as the proportion of looking to the novel stimulus across both test trials combined. Greater fixation of the novel compared to the familiar stimulus (i.e., novelty preference) is inferred to reflect memory for the familiar stimulus (**Figure 1**).

Differences between Habituation–Dishabituation and Visual-Paired Comparison

The habituation–dishabituation and VPC procedures differ in several important respects. First, the amount of time

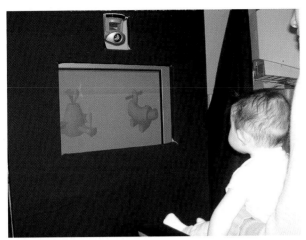

Figure 1 Six-month-old infant participating in the visual-paired comparison.

the infant views the repeated stimulus during the encoding phase is typically much longer in the habituation—dishabituation procedure than in the VPC, although some researchers have used lengthy familiarization periods in the VPC. This raises the possibility that infants may form a more robust representation of the repeated stimulus in a habituation procedure than in the VPC. Second, individual infants typically differ in the amount of time they view the familiar stimulus in a habituation procedure (due to the fact that it is infant controlled), whereas the amount of initial exposure to the familiar stimulus is controlled, and hence the same for all infants, in the VPC. Third, the familiar and novel stimuli are presented simultaneously during the test phase of the VPC procedure, whereas they are presented on different trials in the habituation—dishabituation procedure. Due to this difference in the test phases of the procedures, the VPC is considered an easier test of memory since the infant may actively compare the familiar and novel stimuli simultaneously, providing perceptual support for the comparison process. In the habituation—dishabituation procedure, however, the infant must compare each stimulus with an internal representation of the familiar stimulus, and it is a matter of debate whether the infant is actually comparing the novel stimulus with the familiar stimulus on trials in which the familiar stimulus is not present.

Thus, despite the fact that both paradigms rely on the same dependent measure (i.e., proportion of looking to a novel stimulus compared to a familiar stimulus) to provide evidence for memory, it is not clear whether the VPC and habituation—dishabituation paradigms engage the exact same cognitive processes given their procedural differences.

Limitations of Habituation–Dishabituation and Novelty Procedures

One important limitation of these procedures for the study of infant memory is that a lack of preference does not necessarily reflect forgetting since (1) null findings are inconclusive and (2) 'memory' and 'interest' are confounded in preferential-looking procedures: infants must both remember the familiar stimulus and prefer to look at the novel stimulus in order to show a novelty preference. It is possible, therefore, that null preferences might result from something other than a change in the representation of the familiar stimulus. For instance, null preferences following a delay may result from renewed interest in the familiar stimulus rather than forgetting, and age-related differences in performance may result from changes to the effect of memory on visual attention rather than memory development.

Another important limitation of these procedures is that different values of certain parameters, such as intertrial interval, may be optimal for producing habituation with infants of different ages, or encoding in the VPC under different stimulus conditions, such that spurious trends may result when using the same intertrial interval with infants of different ages, or the same familiarization periods with stimuli differing in complexity. Thus, our use of these procedures to study change across development is limited, in part, by our lack of knowledge regarding the relation between procedural parameters, stimulus conditions, and infant variables.

Major Theories of Habituation and Novelty

In general, the decrement in orienting to a repeated stimulus observed during the habituation—dishabituation and VPC procedures is considered to reflect two cognitive processes: (1) encoding (i.e., the formation of an internal representation of the repeated stimulus) and (2) a comparison of current input with an internal representation. Longer looking to a novel stimulus following habituation or familiarization is typically inferred to reflect both (1) memory for the familiar stimulus and (2) detection of the difference between the familiar and novel stimulus (i.e., discrimination). There are two major theories that attempt to explain the component processes involved in the habituation of an infant's visual attention during initial exposure and novelty preferences at test: the comparator model and optimal level theory.

The comparator model

The comparator model was proposed by E. N. Sokolov in 1963 to explain the reduction (or disappearance) of the orienting reflex (OR) with stimulus repetition or exposure. Pavlov first described the OR during his studies of classical conditioning in dogs. In what likely seemed an experimental nuisance, Pavlov noted that his subjects would fail to exhibit a conditioned response if an unexpected event occurred. Instead, the dogs would immediately orient toward and investigate this change in the environment.

The orienting response involves behavioral, physiological, and postural changes such as turning the head and fixating the eyes on the stimulus, reductions in motor activity, and autonomic responses such as vasodilation and heart rate deceleration, etc.

The concept of OR was subsequently developed by Sokolov in 1963 in his book *Perception and the Conditioned Reflex*. Sokolov viewed the OR as an adaptive response to the environment that serves to facilitate perception and learning. According to Sokolov, orienting results in the allocation of attentional resources that facilitate and promote stimulus processing by amplifying the effects of stimulation on the sense organs. When an organism orients toward a stimulus, a neuronal representation of the stimulus is constructed and stored in the cortex. Subsequent stimuli are then compared to this neuronal model. Discrepancies between existing representations and current input result in behavioral and physiological changes that amplify perception and processing of the current input. Matches, in contrast, result in behavioral and physiological changes that diminish perception and processing, and habituation of the orienting response occurs. In this way, habituation of the orienting response functions to simultaneously free the limited attentional resources of an organism from objects and events that are constant and nonthreatening in the environment, and promote the processing and evaluation of changes in the environment.

Sokolov's theory of the OR remains the most influential model of habituation today, although it has been modified and criticized over the years. For example, several researchers have argued that the stored representations to which current input is compared must not be exact copies of previously encountered stimuli, but looser representations. Otherwise, conceptual habituation or habituation to a category of stimuli (e.g., cats) could not occur. The model has also been criticized on the grounds that it does not explain certain phenomena such as why some infants never seem to habituate, or why infants continue to look at highly familiar stimuli, like a mother's face. Finally, Sokolov's assertion that the memory trace is stored in the cortex has been challenged on the grounds that lower organisms, and decorticate 'preparations' also habituate, as well as one report of habituation in an anencephalic infant.

Optimal level theory/discrepancy hypothesis

According to optimal level theories of habituation and the discrepancy hypothesis, as a stimulus loses its novelty, the infant's response should first increase and then decrease. As in the comparator model, new sensory information is compared with existing representations. In contrast to the comparator model, however, discrepancies between existing representations and new sensory information may cause the organism to either approach or withdrawal from the stimulus. Small discrepancies are thought to produce low levels of arousal, resulting in an approach response. Large discrepancies, however, are thought to produce high levels of arousal, resulting in a withdrawal response. According to optimal level theories, therefore, visual fixation is an inverted U-shaped function based on the degree of discrepancy between an existing representation and a new stimulus. In addition, optimal level theories involve an implicit motivational/interest aspect of visual attention, whereas comparator models do not.

The discrepancy hypothesis has been criticized on the grounds that the assumption that test displays can be ordered in terms of discrepancy from the infants' point of view is impossible to prove, and that evidence in support of optimal level theories is mixed. Although visual fixation to a repeated stimulus during a habituation procedure is often observed to first increase and then decrease with more exposure, many studies have shown that infants' visual fixations are an increasing function of discrepancy, rather than an inverted U-shaped function. Comparator models, however, do not readily explain the inverted U-shaped function observed in many habituation studies.

Major Developmental Trends

Although infants both habituate and show novelty preferences from birth, their performance in habituation and novelty tasks changes dramatically during the first year of life. For instance, older infants habituate more quickly than younger ones, suggesting that they encode stimuli faster. Older infants are also able to encode more complex stimuli, and discriminate smaller discrepancies between familiar and novel stimuli than younger ones. In addition, older infants appear to be able to store information in memory over longer periods of time, as evidenced by exhibiting novelty preferences over increasing delays between study and test, and form representations that are flexible across changes in the environment.

Since habituation and novelty paradigms rely on indirect measures to examine memory and discrimination, however, it is important to make a distinction between performance (i.e., whether infants' 'looking behavior' discriminates novel and familiar stimuli) and competence (i.e., whether infants' 'remember' the familiar stimulus). That is, it is possible that infants remember the familiar stimulus but fail to look longer at a novel stimulus under certain conditions. In addition, the dependent measure chosen for analysis may influence whether novelty preferences are found. In a study conducted by Adele Diamond in 1995, for example, 4-, 6-, and 9-month-old infants were habituated to three dimensional objects and then tested in the VPC. When the conventional dependent measure (i.e., novelty score) was analyzed, the infants' memory appeared to improve with age: 4-month-olds showed novelty preferences at only the shortest delay (i.e., 10 s), 6-month-olds showed novelty preferences at delays of

10 s and 1 min, and 9-month-olds showed novelty preferences at all delays tested (i.e., up to 10 min). In contrast, when the 'longest individual fixation' to each of the familiar and novel stimulus was used as the dependent measure, 4- and 6-month-olds looked longer at the novel stimulus at all delays tested. Thus, the dependent measure chosen for analysis can affect conclusions about infant memory development, especially when infant performance is considered to reflect infant competence.

In addition to age-related changes in infants' performance in habituation and novelty tasks, stimulus properties and procedural variables are also known to affect infants' performance in these tasks. For instance, stimulus complexity affects the rate at which infants habituate, as well as the size of their novelty preference at test. In general, there is an inverse relation between stimulus 'complexity' and rate of habituation: infants habituate slower to more complex stimuli. In addition, the degree of 'physical discrepancy' between the familiar stimulus and the novel stimulus (typically defined in terms of a change to one dimension, such as form, color, or orientation, of a multi-dimensional stimulus) has been found to affect the size of the novelty preference at test: the greater the 'physical discrepancy', the larger the novelty preference.

In terms of procedure variables, the amount of initial exposure to a stimulus is known to effect length of retention. For example, 6-month-old infants will exhibit retention of an abstract pattern after a 48 h delay when initial study times are long (e.g., 2 min), but will not exhibit retention after even a few seconds when initial study times are brief (e.g., 5 s). Again, however, it is important to keep in mind that failure to find a novelty preference reflects a null finding, and that it may not be appropriate to attribute this failure to forgetting.

The Role of Attention in Habituation and Novelty Detection

Habituation and novelty tasks rely heavily on the visual attention system to inform the experimenter as to the presence or absence of memory. During the first year of life, the areas of the brain that mediate attention are rapidly developing. Attention facilitates habituation and novelty detection by increasing the speed and efficiency of information processing, resulting in faster habituation and better novelty detection at test.

Attention

William James described attention as the "... taking possession by the mind in a clear and vivid form one out of what seem several simultaneous objects or trains of thought ...". Contemporary researchers, however, recognize three different types of attention: arousal, selective attention, and executive attention. Arousal is a generalized state of vigilance or alertness that serves to facilitate information processing in a wide array of brain areas and functions. Selective attention, involves the selection of specific objects or features of the environment for increased or privileged processing. Selective attention can be controlled by either voluntary/endogenous processes (i.e., voluntary attention) or reflexive/exogenous biases (i.e., reflexive attention). Selection of information rarely depends on any one factor, however, but involves a dynamic interplay between voluntary and involuntary control that involves competition between reflexive biases and the goals and intention of the individual. The final type of attention, executive attention, involves voluntary control and regulation of the allocation of attention. Advancements in our understanding of the development of the arousal system, in particular, have provided useful information for understanding infant behavior in habituation and novelty tasks.

Effects of Arousal on Habituation

The brain systems involved in arousal involve connections between the mesencephalic reticular activating system (MRAS) and widespread areas of the cortex. Sensory input can activate the MRAS via inputs to the thalamus and the mesencephalic reticular formation (MRF), which is located in the brainstem. Activation of the arousal system enhances processing in a variety of cortical areas including sensory cortices, association cortices, and the limbic system (memory and emotion), resulting in increased processing efficiency, faster reaction times, better detection, and sustained performance over longer periods of time.

The development of the arousal system and its effect on habituation and novelty detection has been studied using indirect physiological measures such as heart rate (HR) and respiratory sinus arrhythmia (RSA the cycle of breathing that occurs due to sympathetic and parasympathetic nervous system activity). This is possible because the activation of neural and endocrine systems associated with increases in arousal causes a corresponding decrease in HR and increase in RSA. For instance, the activation of certain portions of the orbitofrontal cortex has an inhibitory effect on the peripheral nervous system (PNS), slowing HR when the arousal system is engaged. In effect, increases in arousal inhibit cardiac activity as well as other peripheral physiological processes, such as body movement. As a result, attention is facilitated and performance is improved on a variety of cognitive tasks.

John Richards has proposed that the activation of the arousal system may be divided into four distinct HR-defined phases: automatic interrupt, orienting response, sustained attention, and attention termination.

Automatic interrupt is defined as the time period before the arousal system is activated. The orienting response occurs as an object in the visual field captures the infant's attention, and at the same time, HR begins to decelerate. The sustained-attention phase is characterized physiologically by maintenance of a decelerated HR and behaviorally by maintenance of fixation on the object that initially captured attention, even in the presence of distracting stimuli. It is during the sustained attention phase that stimulus information is processed. After the stimulus information is processed, the attention termination phase begins. During attention termination, attention is disengaged and HR accelerates backup to baseline levels. Most research using HR to measure arousal has focused on the orienting and sustained attention phases and their relation to performance on habituation and preference tasks.

Although the arousal system is functional from birth, it undergoes significant development during the first 2 years of life. For instance, the level of HR deceleration during the HR-defined sustained attention phase increases between 3 and 6 months, suggesting an increase in infants' ability to focus and maintain their attention. This increase in a physiological correlate of sustained attention parallels behavioral developments in habituation. For instance, 6-month-olds habituate more quickly, suggesting that they encode stimuli faster, and are able to encode more complex stimuli than 3-month-olds. Furthermore, infants who spend more time in the sustained attention stage habituate more quickly, suggesting that increased arousal is related to increased processing speed.

Effects of Arousal on Novelty Detection

If sustained attention can facilitate processing speed in habituation tasks, how does sustained attention relate to novelty detection and memory? To manipulate arousal, experimenters often expose the infant to a highly salient stimulus, such as a movie clip. Images of the to-be-remembered object are then interspersed with the presentation of the movie clip, and HR is recorded. These types of studies have found that sustained attention during presentation of the to-be-remembered object is related to greater novelty preferences at test. In fact, exposure to a stimulus for just 5 or 6 s during sustained attention results in novelty preferences at test. Furthermore, infants are more likely to show a novelty preference at test when they are 'tested' during the sustained-attention phase; if in the attention in contrast termination phase, infants tend to look equally long at the novel and familiar stimulus. Combined, the results of these studies indicate that sustained attention, or increased arousal, facilitates the infant's ability to acquire information about a stimulus, resulting in faster habituation and enhanced novelty detection at test.

What Kind of Memory Do Novelty Preferences Reflect?

In general, longer looking to a novel stimulus (i.e., the novelty preference) has been interpreted to reflect recognition of the previously seen stimulus. Although there is a general consensus that novelty preferences reflect some form of memory, there is considerable debate regarding the type of memory novelty preferences might reflect. Some researchers argue that novelty preferences reflect a form of explicit or declarative memory. Other researchers argue that novelty preferences reflect a more primitive form of memory that requires only perceptual facilitation. Given the extensive use of habituation and novelty paradigms in developmental research, understanding the type of memory that supports infants' visual preferences has important implications for our understanding of cognitive development.

Distinctions between Different Types of Memory

According to most contemporary views of memory, memory is not a monolithic function. Numerous distinctions have been made between different forms of memory or memory systems (e.g., explicit and implicit, declarative and nondeclarative, episodic and semantic, taxon and locale, fast and slow). Hypotheses about the type of memory that supports infant novelty preferences have tended to focus on two distinctions in particular: the distinction between declarative and nondeclarative memory and the distinction between explicit and implicit memory.

Declarative memory is thought to support the conscious recollection of facts and events, and to be dependent on structures within the medial temporal lobe (MTL; i.e., the hippocampus and adjacent entorhinal, perirhinal, and parahippocampal cortices) and midline diencephalon. Nondeclarative memory, in contrast, is an umbrella term that is used to refer to a collection of separate memory systems that support different abilities such as skill and habit learning, classical conditioning, priming, etc. Different forms of nondeclarative memory are thought to depend on different neural subsystems, including for example the striatum for skill and habit memory, the cerebellum for classical conditioning, and the neocortex for priming. Nondeclarative memory systems share in common the observation that memory is typically expressed through performance rather than recollection and that learning can be outside of awareness.

Although the terms 'declarative' and 'explicit' have often been used interchangeably in the memory literature, the terms 'explicit' and 'implicit' were originally proposed as labels for different 'forms' of memory (and the tests used to measure them) and not memory systems. Explicit memory refers to the ability to deliberately retrieve, or consciously recollect, facts, events, and prior experiences, and is measured by 'direct' tasks that require intentional retrieval such as recall and recognition tests. Implicit memory refers to facilitation or changes in behavior resulting from involuntary retrieval of prior experience in the absence of 'conscious awareness', and is usually measured by indirect or incidental tests such as word-stem completion and repetition priming. Researchers who make a primary distinction between explicit and implicit memory emphasize that these two different forms of memory may simply describe different retrieval circumstances (i.e., intentional vs. unintentional retrieval), and do not necessarily imply different memory 'systems' in the brain.

What Type of Memory Do Novelty Preferences Reflect?

There has been considerable disagreement regarding the type of memory reflected in an infant's preferential fixation of novelty. In an early review of the infant memory literature, Daniel Schacter and Morris Moscovitch distinguished between two broad types of memory: an 'early' form and a 'late' form of memory. The early form of memory was described as unconscious or procedural memory of the kind that is largely preserved in patients with amnesia, and was argued to be available to the infant shortly after birth. This form of memory could be inferred from facilitation in performance on tasks that did not require explicit access to prior experience, such as is typically observed in implicit memory tasks. The 'late' form of memory was described as conscious or episodic memory (i.e., explicit memory) of the type that is typically observed in recall and recognition tasks, and was argued to not be available to the infant until the latter part of the first year of life. Based on a comparison of the kinds of variables that effect infants' preferential-looking behavior and what was known about explicit and implicit memory at the time, Schacter and Moscovitch argued that the kind of memory tapped by preferential-looking tasks was mediated by the 'early' memory system.

A decade later, Richard McKee and Larry Squire tested patients who had impairments in declarative memory resulting from damage to the MTL memory system and found that these patients were impaired relative to controls in the VPC. Based on this evidence, the authors argued that novelty preferences reflect an early capacity for declarative memory that is dependent on the MTL. Similarly, Charles Nelson reviewed studies examining the performance of human adults and nonhuman primates on the VPC task following damage to the MTL, and concluded that performance on the VPC was dependent on the hippocampus. Since the hippocampus is part of the MTL system that supports explicit memory, Nelson argued that novelty preferences reflect a form of explicit memory he termed 'pre-explicit'. According to Nelson, pre-explicit memory is available to the infant during the first 6 months of life, is

mediated by parts of the hippocampus that are early maturing, and supports performance on tasks involving novelty preferences over short delays. Novelty preferences over longer delays, however, were argued to reflect explicit memory and depend on later-developing areas within the hippocampus (e.g., the dentate).

The question of what kind of memory supports performance in the VPC task has important implications for our understanding of both memory development and brain development. For example, the proposal that novelty preferences reflect a form of explicit memory suggests that infants may have conscious, voluntary, or aware access to their memory from birth. In contrast, the proposal that novelty preferences reflect a form of implicit memory could be taken to imply that new learning cannot occur during the first few months of life unless a stimulus is repeated (as in a repetition-priming paradigm) or rewarded (as in a conditioning paradigm). Furthermore, since declarative and explicit memory are known to involve interactions between brain regions involved in memory storage and retrieval (e.g., the hippocampus and surrounding cortex), attention (e.g., the parietal lobe and cingulate cortex), and executive control (e.g., the prefrontal cortex) in adults, the proposal that novelty preferences reflect a form of explicit or declarative memory has implications for the development of functional interactions between these brain regions. Thus, the interpretation of infant novelty preferences raises important questions about infant learning, the development of conscious awareness, voluntary control over mental processes, and the development of functional interactions among wide-scale brain systems.

Neural Mechanisms Underlying Performance in the Visual-Paired Comparison

At the present time, the most popular view of novelty preferences is that they reflect a form of declarative or pre-explicit memory dependent on the MTL system, and the hippocampus in particular. A critical evaluation of the evidence for this view, however, and a review of the most recent evidence suggest that the MTL system is not necessary for novelty preferences. This evidence, in turn, raises the question anew of what neural systems may support novelty preferences and, critically, what 'kind' of memory novelty preferences might reflect.

Do Novelty Preferences Depend on the Hippocampus?

Encoding vs. retrieval in the Visual-Paired Comparison
Research investigating the neurobiology of novelty preferences has primarily used the VPC. It was noted earlier that the VPC consists of two phases: a familiarization

phase and a test phase. During the familiarization phase, infants must transform incoming sensory information into an internal (i.e., neural) representation of the familiar stimulus. During the test phase, infants must access this representation to show differences in looking behavior to the 'familiar' and the novel stimulus (e.g., novelty preferences). Thus, successful performance in the VPC requires at least two memory processes: memory encoding, whereby sensory information is initially stored into memory, and memory retrieval, whereby previously stored information is accessed for further processing.

There are two types of scientific methods that have been used to investigate the neurobiology of novelty preferences: the lesion method and neuroimaging. In studies using the lesion method, patients with pre-existing damage to a particular part of the brain (e.g., the hippocampus), or experimental animals with induced damage to a particular brain structure, are tested in a given task. Deficits in performing the task are subsequently attributed to the damaged brain structure. Thus, for example, if patients with damage to the hippocampus perform more poorly on the VPC than adults without hippocampal damage, researchers conclude that the hippocampus plays an important role in performance on the VPC. In studies using neuroimaging neural activity in different brain structures is examined as subjects perform a task.

An important limitation of lesions studies for investigating the neurobiology of novelty preferences is that it is not possible to determine whether the lesion impairs encoding or retrieval in the VPC. Since successful encoding is a prerequisite for successful retrieval, a lesion that impairs encoding would result in performance deficits in the VPC even if retrieval is not affected. This is an important point because the measure of successful performance in the VPC, novelty preferences, is measured at test and thus reflects retrieval. Neuroimaging methods, on the other hand, are able to distinguish between neural activity related to encoding and neural activity related to retrieval in the VPC.

The neural structures that support encoding versus retrieval in the VPC have important implications for the type of memory reflected in infant novelty preferences. Importantly, involvement of the MTL system during encoding does not mean that it is also involved during retrieval. For instance, words activated during an implicit memory task (e.g., word-stem completion) may have been initially encoded via the MTL system at some earlier point in time, yet successful retrieval during the implicit task can occur in the absence of conscious awareness and does not require the MTL. This is because implicit memory involves the reactivation of previously stored representations, regardless of how the representations were initially encoded. Similarly, it is possible for the MTL system to play a role in encoding during the familiarization phase of the VPC, yet not participate in the retrieval of information that produces differences in looking behavior at test.

Evidence from lesion studies

Nonhuman primates. Evidence from lesion studies in monkeys suggests that immediate and short-term memory in the VPC depends on perirhinal cortex and visual perceptual area TE, whereas long-term memory in the VPC may depend additionally on the hippocampus. Most recently, for example, Jocelyn Bachevalier and colleagues compared the effects of selective lesions to the hippocampus, parahippocampal gyrus, and perirhinal cortex, on the performance of adult monkeys in the VPC. They reported that hippocampal lesions impaired performance at 60 s delays, parahippocampal lesions impaired performance at 30 s delays, and perirhinal lesions impaired performance at 10 s delays. In contrast, adult monkeys with lesions of visual area TE were impaired in the VPC at all delays. These data suggest that lesions to different structures within the MTL system and visual perceptual areas impair VPC performance in adult monkeys in a delay-dependent manner. Importantly, hippocampal lesions do not appear to impair VPC performance in adult monkeys unless the delay between study and test is long (i.e., >60 s).

Patients with MTL amnesia. Only two studies have examined the effects of MTL damage in humans on performance in the VPC, and the results of these studies are inconsistent. In the first study, patients with amnesia and healthy adults were tested in the VPC at delays of 0.5 s, 2 min, 1 h, and 24 h. Since amnesic patients were impaired relative to controls, the authors of this study concluded that novelty preferences reflect a form of declarative memory that is dependent on the MTL memory system. It is important to note, however, that amnesic patients were impaired relative to controls only at delays of 2 min and 1 h. Both groups showed equivalent novelty preferences at the 0.5-s delay, and neither group showed novelty preferences at the 24 h delay. Furthermore, although amnesic patients were impaired relative to controls at the 2 min delay, amnesic patients did show significant novelty preferences at this delay. Thus, patients with damage to the MTL system showed significant novelty preferences at short delays, suggesting that novelty preferences *per se* may not depend on the MTL. More recently, Olivier Pascalis and colleagues reported that a patient with selective damage to the hippocampus (i.e., patient YR) did not show novelty preferences in the VPC at delays of 5 and 10 s, and concluded that novelty preferences depend on the hippocampus.

The performance of patient YR, however, is inconsistent with findings from the patient study discussed above and from lesion studies in nonhuman primates. As reviewed earlier, selective hippocampal lesions in nonhuman primates impair VPC performance at long delays (i.e., 60 s) but not at short delays, and amnesic patients show novelty preferences at delays as long as 2 min. One possible explanation for YR's deficits in the VPC is that she also developed damage to her parietal lobe, a part of the brain that is critical for the integration of stimulus representations with eye movement plans. Thus, YR's parietal damage could have affected her looking behavior in the VPC separately from her memory for the familiar stimulus. Indeed, when asked to report which stimulus she had seen before, YR was just as accurate as adults without hippocampal damage. The weight of the evidence across patient and animal studies, therefore, suggests that damage to the hippocampus impairs VPC performance at long but not short delays.

Summary. In summary, data from patients with MTL amnesia and monkeys with MTL lesions do suggest a role for the MTL, and the hippocampus in particular, in successful performance in the VPC. These data, however, do not tell us whether the MTL and hippocampus are important for successful encoding, successful retrieval, or both. Since successful encoding is necessary for successful retrieval, and damage to the MTL is known to impair encoding, lesion data may primarily provide evidence that the MTL and the hippocampus play a role in the long-term encoding of information about the object presented during the familiarization phase of the VPC. Subjects who have not encoded the object into long-term memory would necessarily not show novelty preferences at test (a measure of retrieval), even if the hippocampus were unnecessary for successful retrieval. Neuroimaging methods can be used to examine whether the MTL and hippocampus are important for retrieval in the task.

Evidence from neuroimaging studies

John Aggleton Malcolm Brown, and colleagues have examined neural activity in rodents during a task very similar to the test phase of the VPC. Using immediate early gene (IEG) imaging techniques, neural activity in different regions of the brain can be examined by measuring the relative amounts of a protein (Fos) that is synthesized by a gene (*c-fos*) expressed when a neuron is active. Aggleton and Brown have used this technique to examine which brain areas are active when an animal distinguishes between familiar and novel objects (i.e., item memory) vs. rearrangements of familiar objects (i.e., memory for spatial relations).

Using this technique, neural activity related to item memory has been observed in occipital visual processing areas, area TE, and perirhinal cortex, but not the hippocampus. Specifically, familiar compared to novel objects elicit a decrease in neural activity in perirhinal cortex and area TE. This finding is consistent with electrophysiological evidence in both humans and monkeys that neurons in perirhinal cortex and adjacent visual association cortex (area TE) respond less to visual stimuli that were previously encountered, a phenomenon known as 'repetition suppression'. In contrast, neural activity related to memory for spatial relations has been observed in the hippocampus, but not area TE and perirhinal cortex. Combined, these findings suggest that repetition suppression in perirhinal cortex and adjacent visual association areas provides a neural basis for discriminating between new and previously encountered stimuli (i.e., novelty preferences) during the test phase of the VPC. Importantly, hippocampal neurons do not respond differentially to novel versus familiar objects, suggesting that the hippocampus may not contribute to successful retrieval in the VPC.

More recently, researchers examined whether the MTL system was necessary for successful encoding or retrieval in the VPC. In this study, researchers injected benzodiazepine, a drug that temporarily inhibits neural activity in MTL structures, into the perirhinal cortex of rodents prior to either the encoding or retrieval phase of the VPC. Injections prior to encoding abolished novelty preferences at test, whereas injections prior to retrieval but after encoding had no effect on performance. These findings suggest that perirhinal cortex, like the hippocampus, might play a role in the long-term storage of object representations during the study phase of the VPC, but may not be necessary for successful retrieval at test. Taken together, data from lesion studies and neuroimaging studies suggest that the MTL system, and the hippocampus in particular, may be necessary for encoding information into long-term memory, yet does not participate in the retrieval of information that produces differences in looking behavior at test.

Summary

In summary, the available evidence does not fully support the view that novelty preferences reflect a form of declarative or pre-explicit memory dependent on the MTL system, and the hippocampus in particular. Patients with amnesia and nonhuman primates with hippocampal damage succeed in the VPC when the delay is short. This suggests that the hippocampus is not 'necessary' for novelty preferences. In addition, adult monkeys with lesions of visual area TE, but not the hippocampus or MTL, are impaired in the VPC, suggesting that the hippocampus is also not 'sufficient' for novelty preferences. Finally, recent imaging studies in rodents indicate that the MTL system is primarily involved in long-term storage of object representations during initial encoding, but is not necessary for successful retrieval during the test phase of the VPC. Taken together, these findings indicate that the MTL, and the hippocampus in particular, may play a role in encoding information into long-term memory, yet does not participate in the retrieval of information that produces differences in looking behavior at test (i.e., novelty preferences). Instead, novelty preferences may involve reactivation of previously stored representations in the absence of conscious awareness and voluntary control, similar to implicit memory.

The Interaction between Memory and Attention in the Visual-Paired Comparison

Understanding the neural basis of habituation and novelty preferences requires that we understand how visual attention is biased toward novel stimuli. After all, memory for a previously encountered stimulus could just as well take the form of a bias in looking longer at the 'familiar' stimulus.

Robert Desimone and John Duncan have proposed a model of selective visual attention (i.e., the 'biased competition model') that can account for the bias in visual attention toward novel stimuli. The biased competition model is predicated on the assumption that the nervous system has limited processing resources, and that objects in the visual environment must compete for these resources. Attention, then, is conceptualized as "...an emergent property of many neural mechanisms working to resolve competition for visual processing and control of behavior."

In the biased competition model, competition for visual-processing resources is biased by both bottom-up and top-down neural mechanisms. 'Bottom-up' biases are defined as automatic and not necessarily related to intentions or goals. Some bottom-up biases are best described as 'stimulus-driven', such as biases toward certain colors (e.g., red), high-contrast stimuli, movement, etc. The use of the term bottom-up, however, is not intended to imply only stimulus-driven biases, but also includes biases from information stored in memory that may influence early perceptual processing via feedback mechanisms. A classic example of this type of bias is the so-called 'cocktail party' effect: the automatic orienting to the sound of one's name spoken in a noisy room even when the focus of one's behavior is elsewhere. The bias toward novelty is another example of a bias from information stored in memory.

According to Desimone and Duncan, the visual system is biased toward processing new or not recently seen objects. The neural basis of this bias is a reduction in neural activity in the visual-processing pathway with stimulus repetition, a phenomenon known as 'repetition suppression'. Repetition suppression occurs when the population of neurons responding to a particular stimulus decreases as the stimulus is repeated, resulting in an overall reduction of neural activity elicited by the repeated stimulus. This decrease in the population of neurons activated by a repeated stimulus reflects a reduction in the responses of cells that were initially activated but were not highly selective for the features of the stimulus, and is therefore thought to reflect a form of learning. In theory, the reduction in activation to a repeated stimulus would result in a smaller neural signal for familiar (i.e., repeated) compared to novel stimuli, which would in turn bias the competition for visual processing resources, and hence visual attention, toward novel stimuli. This is supported by evidence that repetition suppression is sufficient to produce orienting to

a novel stimulus in monkeys. Thus, the bias in visual attention toward novel stimuli in the VPC may reflect competition for visual processing resources between the familiar and novel stimulus. Since the novel stimulus elicits a larger neural signal, visual processing resources are biased toward the novel stimulus and it has a stronger influence over behavior (i.e., eye movements and visual fixation). Thus, the biased competition model provides a mechanistic explanation for the bias toward novelty in the VPC.

This model of infant performance in the VPC suggests a plausible alternative to the hypothesis that novelty preferences depend on the hippocampus and reflect a form of explicit or declarative memory. It is consistent with the results of imaging studies in rodents indicating that repetition suppression in perirhinal cortex and adjacent visual association areas provides a neural basis for discriminating familiar and novel objects. Since repetition suppression is an intrinsic property of the visual processing pathway, and occurs independently of the hippocampus, this model also accounts for observations that patients with amnesia and nonhuman primates with lesions of the MTL succeed in the VPC when the delay between familiarization and test is short. Thus, novelty preferences may reflect the effects of repetition suppression on visual attention, independent of the hippocampus.

Electrophysiological Correlates of Infant Novelty Preferences

Understanding the neural mechanisms underlying infants' performance on preferential-looking tasks can help us to understand the type of memory that supports novelty preferences. It is very difficult to dissociate explicit and implicit memory in infants, however, since (1) measures that dissociate explicit and implicit forms of memory tend to rely disproportionately on verbal abilities not present in infants, and (2) brain imaging techniques with the requisite spatial resolution (e.g., functional magnetic resonance imaging) to assess the participation of neural structures which dissociate different forms of memory (e.g., the hippocampus vs. the striatum) are not feasible for use with infants participating in visual paradigms at this time. One brain imaging method that is appropriate for use with young infants, however, is event-related potentials (ERPs).

ERPs reflect the synchronous firing of neuronal populations in response to a discrete event (such as the presentation of a stimulus). They are recorded from electrodes placed on the scalp, are derived from the electroencephalogram, and provide excellent temporal resolution (on the order of milliseconds) of ongoing cognitive processes. There are numerous advantages to using ERPs to study cognitive development. They are noninvasive, do not require the subject to remain motionless for long periods of time, and do not require a behavioral response by the subject. Furthermore, the spatial and temporal information provided by ERPs permits the differentiation of cognitive processes that may not be directly reflected in behavior (**Figure 2**).

Two major components are typically observed in the infant ERP (see **Figure 3**): a mid-latency negative component (Nc) that peaks between 400 and 800 ms following stimulus onset and is observed over fronto-central scalp regions, and a long-latency slow-wave component (PSW) that begins around 1000 ms following stimulus onset and is maximal over temporal scalp regions. Since the Nc is thought to reflect aspects of attention and orienting, and the PSW is thought to reflect aspects of memory, ERPs are especially useful in investigating the neural basis of infants' performance on habituation and novelty tasks.

Work in our laboratory has used ERPs to investigate the neural mechanisms underlying infant habituation and novelty preferences. Our working hypothesis is that the decrease in infant attention to familiar (i.e., repeated) stimuli observed in habituation and novelty tasks reflects the effects of repetition suppression on visual attention. As a starting point, we examined the effects of stimulus

Figure 2 Six-month-old infant wearing an electrode cap for the recording of event-related potentials.

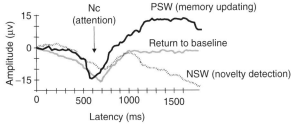

Figure 3 Illustration of the major event-related potentials (ERPs) components observed in previous ERP studies with infants. Adapted from de Haan M and Nelson CA (1997) Recognition of the mother's face by six-month-old infants: A neuro-behavioral study. *Development* 68(2): 187–210. No, negative component; NSW, PSW, long-latency show-wave component.

repetition on infant brain activity. In one study, we recorded 6-month-old infants' brain activity while they watched alternating pictures of two different faces on a computer screen. The faces consisted of a picture of the infant's mother (i.e., a familiar face) and a picture of a female stranger (i.e., a novel face). Each face was presented for 0.5 s, and repeated between 30 and 50 times. We then compared infants' brain activity in response to the first 15 presentations of each face (Block 1) and the second 15 presentations of each face (Block 2), and found that the amplitude of the PSW decreased across blocks (see **Figures 4** and **5**) for both the familiar and the novel face. The amplitude of a component is thought to reflect the amount of neural activity elicited by a stimulus. Thus, a decrease in the amplitude of the PSW across blocks indicates that the amount of neural activity elicited by the faces decreased as the faces were repeated across trials, consistent with the hypothesis that repeated stimuli elicit smaller neural signals than novel stimuli (i.e., repetition suppression).

The results described above help to establish evidence of repetition suppression in infants. Alone, however, they do not address questions about the mechanisms underlying habituation and novelty preferences since we did not measure looking behavior. Ongoing work in our laboratory, therefore, is investigating these mechanisms by examining the relation between infant brain activity and infant looking behavior. For instance, one study examined the brain activity of infants who showed a novelty preference in the VPC. In this study, 6-month-old infants were first tested in the VPC, and then watched pictures of the familiar object from the VPC and two novel objects while their brain activity was recorded. We found that the amplitude of the PSW was greater for the two novel objects compared to the familiar object. This finding suggests that the novel objects elicited more neural activity than the familiar object, consistent with the hypothesis that decreased looking to the familiar stimulus (i.e., novelty preferences) in the VPC reflects the effects of repetition suppression on visual attention.

The major findings that have emerged from this work are that (1) stimulus repetition results in a reduction of neural activity over temporal scalp regions (i.e., the PSW) in infants and (2) infant novelty preferences are associated with a reduction of neural activity over temporal scalp regions (i.e., the PSW) for familiar compared to novel stimuli. The pattern and topography of these effects are consistent with observations of repetition suppression in visual processing areas from electrophysiological recordings in nonhuman primates, imaging studies in rodents, and neuroimaging studies of human adults. This, in turn, suggests that infant novelty preferences may be mediated by repetition suppression and could reflect a form of implicit memory. Since repetition suppression is a general phenomenon observed across many structures in the

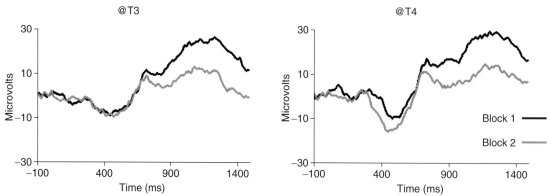

Figure 4 Grand mean event-related potential (ERP) waveforms illustrating the reduction in amplitude of the long-latency slow-wave component with stimulus repetition. Block 1 (black line) is the average of the first 15 presentations of the stimulus, and Block 2 (red line) is the average of the second 15 presentations of the stimulus. ERPs are shown for representative electrodes over left (T3) and right (T4) temporal regions of the scalp. Reprinted by permission of Oxford University Press, Inc. from Snyder KA (2007) Neural mechanisms of attention and memory in preferential looking tasks. In: Oakes LM and Bauer PJ (eds.) *Short- and Long-Term Memory in Infancy and Early Childhood: Taking the First Steps Toward Remembering*, pp. 179–209. New York: Oxford University Press.

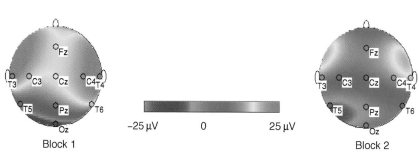

Figure 5 Topographic plots showing the scalp distribution of the long-latency slow-wave component (PSW) and changes in the amplitude of the PSW with stimulus repetition. The PSW is shown as patches of red over the left and right temporal regions. Block 1 is the average of the first 15 presentations of the stimulus, and Block 2 is the average of the second 15 presentations of the stimulus. Reprinted by permission of Oxford University Press, Inc. from Snyder KA (2007) Neural mechanisms of attention and memory in preferential looking tasks. In: Oakes LM and Bauer PJ (eds.) *Short- and Long-Term Memory in Infancy and Early Childhood: Taking the First Steps Toward Remembering*, pp. 179–209. New York: Oxford University Press.

visual processing pathway, and appears to encode different kinds of information in different parts of the pathway, more information is needed concerning the specific role of repetition suppression in preferential looking and its implications for the nature of the representation reflected in infants' visual fixations.

Summary and Conclusions

An important implication of the repetition–suppression model is that longer looking to a novel stimulus may be merely a consequence of reduced neural responses to previously encoded items; it may not require explicit awareness, voluntary or deliberate control, or even a 'comparison' between new and previously encoded items. Thus, memory for a familiar stimulus may influence visual attention in a very indirect sense in that the neural activity elicited by the familiar stimulus is reduced

and hence loses the competition for visual attentional resources. In this model, then, memory is an indirect, incidental influence on visual attentional preferences. Preferential looking effects may reflect attentional processes and implicit memory to a greater degree than explicit memory.

See also: Attention; Brain Development; Brain Function; Hippocampus; Memory; Neurological Development.

Suggested Readings

Aggleton JP and Brown M (2005) Contrasting hippocampal and perirhinal cortex function using immediate early gene imaging. *Quarterly Journal of Experimental Psychology* 58B: 218–223.
Desimone R and Duncan J (1995) Neural mechanisms of selective visual attention. *Annual Reviews in Neuroscience* 18: 193–222.

Diamond A (1995) Evidence of robust recognition memory early in life even when assessed by reaching behavior. *Journal of Experimental Child Psychology* 59: 419–456.

Fantz RL (1964) Visual experience in infants: Decreased attention to familiar patterns relative to novel ones. *Science* 146: 668–670.

McKee RD and Squire LR (1993) On the development of declarative demory. *Journal of Experimental Psychology: Learning, Memory, and Cognition* 19: 397–404.

Nelson CA (1995) The ontogeny of human memory: A cognitive neuroscience perspective. *Developmental Psychology* 31: 723–738.

Nemanic S, Alvarado MC, and Bachevalier J (2004) The hippocampal/ parahippocampal regions and recognition memory: Insights from visual paired comparison versus object-delayed nonmatching in monkeys. *The Journal of Neuroscience* 24: 2013–2026.

Pascalis O, Hunkin NM, Holdstock JS, Isaac CL, and Mayes AR (2004) Visual paired comparison performance is impaired in a patient with selective hippocampal lesions and relatively intact item recognition. *Neuropsychologia* 42: 1293–1300.

Pavlov IP (1927) *Conditioned Reflexes.* New York: Oxford University Press.

Schacter DL and Moscovitch M (1984) Infants, amnesics, and dissociable memory systems. In: Moscovitch M (ed.) *Infant Memory*, pp. 173–216. New York: Plenum.

Snyder KA (2007) Neural mechanisms of attention and memory in preferential looking tasks. In: Oakes LM and Bauer PJ (eds.) *Short-and Long-Term Memory in Infancy and Early Childhood: Taking the First Steps Toward Remembering*, pp. 179–209. New York: Oxford University Press.

Sokolov EN (1963) *Perception and the Conditioned Reflex.* (S.W. Waydenfeld, trans.). New York: Macmillan (Originally published, 1958).

Head Start

J W Hagen, University of Michigan, Ann Arbor, MI, USA
F G Lamb-Parker, Columbia University, New York, NY, USA

Glossary

Administration for Children, Youth and Families (ACYF) – This unit replaced the office of Child Development (OCD) when the Department of Health and Human Services (DHHS) was created.

Child Development Associate Program (CDA) – A program established in 1972 to provide this educational credential to teachers and home visitors.

Family and Child Experiences Survey (FACES) – A nationally representative information system used by Head Start since 1997 to collect data on programs, classrooms, teachers, parents, and children for examining the quality and effects of Head Start.

Head Start Bureau – The administrative home of Head Start, in the Administration for Children and Families (ACF), Department of Health and Human Services (DHHS).

Head Start Program Performance Standards (HSPPS) – Comprehensive criteria establishing areas to which all Head Start Programs must conform.

National Reporting System on Child Outcomes (NRS) – Launched in 1999–2000, assesses the school readiness of 4- and 5-years olds in Head Start, producing a national outcomes report on the congressionally mandated indicators.

Office of Child Development (OCD) – This office was established by President Richard Nixon in 1969 to centralize issues concerning children and became the administrative home for Head Start.

Office of Economic Opportunity (OEO) – The federal office established under President Lyndon Johnson's administration to address directly the problems of poverty in the US.

Introduction

Project Head Start was launched by the Office of Economic Opportunity (OEO) of the US Government in the summer of 1965. A panel of experts in child development, including Edward Zigler, was recruited by OEO's Director, Sargent Shriver, to develop guidelines for Head Start. It began as an 8-week summer program for low-income preschool children to help break the cycle of poverty of their families. Julius Richmond, an MD, pediatrician, and policy maker, was its first director.

The program, now in its 42nd year, was designed to be comprehensive with components that foster cognitive, language, social, and emotional development, as well as the physical health and nutrition of children. Families were an integral part of the program, being given decision-making authority over program content and management.

Head Start is distinguished by the fact that while it is federally funded, it is locally administered by community organizations and, more recently, public school systems. Researchers and policy-based research have played major roles in Head Start, especially in its early years and then again during the past decade. There have been many program variations, such as length of providing services to children and families and age levels served. Head Start continues to be the most important, federally mandated program for young children in the US, especially those who are at risk due to family income and other environmental factors.

The Beginnings of Head Start

In the Economic Opportunity Act (EOA) of 1964, the War on Poverty was launched by the Congress of the US. The focus initially was on youth and young adults. There were provisions for several important programs, including the Job Corp, the Community Action Program (CAP), and VISTA (the domestic Peace Corps). The OEO was given the mandate to establish and flesh out programs aimed at reversing the troubling trends in domestic poverty. Head Start emerged, in part, because of the lack of promise shown by the CAP.

The director of OEO was Sargent Shriver, brother-in-law of former President John F. Kennedy, and President Lyndon B. Johnson's staff person in charge of the War on Poverty. Anticipating a surplus in the budget for OEO during this first year, he directed his staff to recommend ways to use these funds effectively. When it was made evident that almost half of the 30 million poor in the US were children, it became a mandate to found a program aimed directly at this group. The initial idea was to launch a program designed to improve the intellect and school performance of these children, so that they would have the opportunity to rise out of the grips of poverty. Shriver's wife, Eunice Kennedy Shriver, had already worked on the President's Panel on Mental Retardation and had established the Joseph P. Kennedy Jr. Foundation (named for her brother who was killed while serving in the Navy in World War II).

Sargent Shriver recalled that a Kennedy Foundation project at George Peabody College in Nashville, Tennessee (now part of Vanderbilt University) had demonstrated that the inteligence quotient (IQ) scores of black preschool children could be improved with a program designed to increase cognition as well as motivation toward school. Susan Gray, professor of psychology at Peabody, was the director of the Early Training Project in Murfreesboro, Tennessee, and her work provided the impetus for the launching of Head Start on a national scale. Professor Gray went on to be one of the leading figures not only in Head Start but in the development of the preschool education movement. Harry Levin, a professor of child development at Cornell University, also provided the US Office of Education (OE) with an endorsement of the worth of preschool programs. While Head Start has never been administratively in Education,

Levin and other scholars with expertise in early child development played key roles in the initiating of and program development for Head Start.

Another relevant experience of Shriver's was his involvement with the School Board of the City of Chicago. He argued that schools, which were typically closed in the summer months, could provide the space for poor preschool children to be provided an opportunity to get a 'head start' on their education in first grade. Dr. Robert Cooke was the Shrivers' pediatrician and the science advisor to the Kennedy Foundation. He became a principal consultant with OEO to develop the model for Head Start. Since he was a pediatrician, the component of Head Start that still plays a prominent role today embracing children's health, can be attributed to Cooke. The EOA did authorize a preschool program but provided no specific direction, so Shriver and his advisors had a lot of latitude. In December, 1964, Dr. Cooke became the chair of a Head Start Planning Committee. It was a diverse group, with only two members coming from early childhood education. Edward Zigler, professor of psychology at Yale University and the first director of the Office of Child Development in Health and Human Services (HHS), became one of its members. He recalls that the committee was faced, among other things, with the dilemma of focusing on improving intelligence as a major goal of the proposed program.

Intelligence and Experience, written by a professor at the University of Illinois, James McVicker Hunt, had been published in 1961 and stirred a lot of interest but also controversy. Drawing from a wide literature, including animal research as well as human, it provided a forum for the view that proper environmental inputs could stimulate and hence improve the cognitive development of all young children. The notion of 'critical period' was also emphasized in Hunt's book, arguing that appropriate stimulation must be provided early enough if children were to benefit. The zeitgeist of the time led, in many people's view, by this pivotal book was embraced by the committee setting up the parameters for the newly launched Head Start program.

Another of the tenets of the committee was that parents should be involved in programs aimed at their children's development and well-being. Urie Bronbenbrenner, professor at Cornell University and founder of the 'ecology theory' of human development, was also appointed to the committee. According to Bronbenbrenner, "to have any lasting impact, the children's day-to-day environment – particularly their families, but also their neighborhoods and communities – must foster similar goals." His influence on the actions of the committee was apparent in the recommendations which included parents as community partners.

The notion that all children are capable of learning, given the appropriate opportunities, became a widely accepted position. The Elementary and Secondary

Education Act of 1965 included assistance of children age 5 years and older. This bill was introduced by Democrats, and the Republicans criticized it for ignoring early childhood education. It was amended to permit the inclusion of preschool programs and it passed both chambers in April 1965.

The executive branch was given flexibility in how to implement Head Start. In spite of professional advice discouraging its starting so soon, Shriver endorsed a plan to launch Head Start in the summer of 1965 as a summer only program. It was believed that a large-scale, short-term program would garner the most attention and support, especially from parents of children involved. In 1966, selected programs were offered on a full academic year basis, and by 1972, most programs were year round.

Meanwhile, Robert Cooke's Head Start planning committee issued its report, *Improving the Opportunities and Achievements of the Children of the Poor*. It strongly recommended that all programs include health, social, and educational services. Most members of the committee thought a small pilot program emphasizing quality was the way that Head Start should begin. However, the administration proceeded with its large-scale summer program, which became the nation's most ambitious attempt at staving off the problems of the youngest of the nation's poor.

The senior staff were selected by Shriver. Julius Richmond, MD, a pediatrician and dean of the Upstate Medical Center in New York, was appointed director of Head Start. Jule Sugarman was appointed as associate director, and they made a good team. Richmond started a program for disadvantaged children at Syracuse University and was committed to the value of early intervention. He insisted that meals be provided in all programs, and at least one of them was to be hot. Sugarman took leadership of day-to-day operations and brought with him considerable management experience at the federal level. He also knew how to make good use of volunteers. With this team in place, Head Start was launched as a summer program in 1965.

The launching of Head Start in the summer of 1965 had to proceed quickly, as there were only a few months to prepare. It was to be up and running in all 50 states by early summer. While many experts did not think an 8-week program would provide demonstrable effects for the children, they kept their opinions quiet. Further, the funding for individual programs was low since funds were being distributed across so many places. Many felt it was much too low. Thus, staff who were hired were mostly paraprofessional and not well trained. Later, when the program was shifted to a year-round program, the year preceding kindergarten for most children, the issue of cost per student became even more pressing.

A half million children were served by Head Start during its first summer, and the staff were sometimes parents of program participants. This had the advantage of providing employment in the local communities, but many believed it was not in the best interests of the children being served. There is little doubt that weak programs were funded during this initial phase of Head Start. It was striking, however, how quickly Head Start was hailed as being a success. In fact, its success was used to stave off the mounting criticisms of other activities of the OEO.

In the fall elections of 1966, Republican representation in Congress increased. While OEO was threatened, Head Start remained a favorite program. In fact, Republican legislators argued that it should receive more support within OEO. Shriver again fought attempts to have it moved to the Office of Education, and the educational components of Head Start were downplayed. Political battles ensued through 1968, and with the election of President Richard Nixon, Head Start was moved to the new Office of Child Development, headed by Edward Zigler, which was administratively located in Health, Education and Welfare (the predecessor of HHS). The emphasis was then placed more on demonstrating long-term effectiveness of Head Start.

The debate as to how Head Start should relate to the nation's public schools has continued through the years and will be addressed again later in this article. However, it is fair to say that since its inception, Head Start has weathered many storms, political and otherwise, and it is illuminating to try to identify the reasons for its bipartisan success and its expansions in so many ways over four decades.

The Early Years of Head Start

Intelligence and Early Intervention

Since the inception of Head Start, the debates surrounding intelligence, as measured by standard assessment instruments such as the 'IQ' or intelligence quotient tests, have flourished. Are there differences in intelligence related to characteristics of children, such as families' socioeconomic status or race or ethnicity? Can scores on tests of intelligence be raised by appropriate intervention programs? Should programs such as Head Start be evaluated on the success in improving measures of cognitive competence, which may include language, reading, mathematics, or others?

Intelligence testing has a long history in psychology and education, and the debates continue about its meaning and usefulness. Stephen J. Gould provides a fascinating account of these tests and how they have come to be used and changed over the years, and in his view, how they are misused. While originally designed to allow school systems to select children who would be candidates for special education, Alfred Binet, the inventor of the IQ test, deliberately chose a variety of diverse tasks to administer to children of different age levels. His goal was to be able to come up with a single score by combining each child's performance across tasks. In fact, Binet stated, "One might almost say, 'it matters very little what the tests are so long as they are numerous'." It did not take long for others to begin to reify the intelligence measure, and it became what many consider to be psychology's major contribution to society (whether that be a positive one or a liability).

While the tests themselves make no argument concerning from where 'intelligence' may come, it quickly became a topic of interest: is intelligence a born characteristic or is it subject to environmental inputs? Subsequent measures of intelligence include more than one score, but the debate continues whether these measures reflect actual intelligence, both now and predicting to the future for individuals. As evaluations of Head Start became formal, it was inevitable that the question of intelligence, and whether it would increase as a result of early intervention, would be addressed. Unfortunately, the early summer programs, lasting for only 6 weeks and often conducted by staff with little training in cognitive skill development or in matters of early education, became the target of mandated assessment.

A report, which came to be known as The Westinghouse Report, purported to show that the early Head Start programs did not boost intelligence for very long, and in fact reported a 'fade-out' effect. Many in the administration of Head Start, as well as scholars who were invested in the success of the program, became alarmed. Some called for earlier intervention, arguing that the summer before kindergarten was too late to provide the needed stimulation to produce longer-term effects. Issues of cultural bias and accusations of racial bias came from many quarters, and a major response has been that Head Start must be evaluated on its effectiveness in each of its areas, including health, nutrition, social development, and family factors. The importance of providing the children resources in these areas is considered later in this article.

However, those who specialized in early cognitive development argue for the importance of keeping 'intelligence' as a major area of concern in Head Start programs. Several reasons are cited that support the retention of the notion of improving intelligence in the children who participated in these programs. (1) Recent work based on highly controlled studies in the laboratory provide evidence that early experience and the rearing environment have powerful effects on both brain development and subsequent learning. (2) Studies of young humans demonstrate that specific experiences can lead to improvements in both specific skills and use of learning strategies. (3) There is increasing evidence of the range and nature of human competencies, and overall it supports the idea of early interests and skills and these lead to a wide range of abilities later in development. (4) Finally, there is now the work of the past 40 years that supports the value of early interventions, if they are high quality and appropriately educationally oriented.

Head Start began as a program to improve the chances of children succeeding in school and then later in life, and language and intellectual skills are clearly key in the pursuit of these goals.

Parent Involvement

From its inception, the belief that parents should play some sort of role in the programs comprising Head Start has been a key component. The CAP within OEO actually existed before Head Start. The concept that substantial parent involvement was necessary in Head Start was advocated strongly by Polly Greenberg, an early child educator and senior staff member of OEO in the early 1960s. Her notion was that parents were to be employees in the system and would become leaders and activists. They were skilled and committed and could make a critical difference. Greenberg left OEO just before Head Start was launched, but her legacy continued in that parents, as both employees and participants, became a mandated part of the program.

However, there was another, somewhat contradictory, view on the role of parents in Head Start, and it was implicit in the recommendations brought by many of the professionals and researchers: parents living in poverty were not necessarily good role models for their children. Thus, parents needed to be educated in the ways of parenting, often defined by the practices of the middle class. Both of these themes can be traced in the early years of Head Start, which was, after all, a program to help children and families escape the bondage of poverty.

There were advocates who felt that these two views of parents should be combined in creating the actual programs to operationalize Head Start in its first years. It is fair to say that Head Start in the early years was at best only modestly involved in community action as defined by CAP. As stated earlier, applicants for those first summer programs in 1965 included funds for paid staff, who were often paraprofessionals and sometimes parents of children in the programs as well. So parent involvement became a blend of the two 'views', that is, parents as an essential part of community involvement and parents who could benefit from involvement through training, either informal or formal.

Greenberg left Washington to launch the Child Development Group of Mississippi, which was founded by Tom Levin, MD, a psychoanalyst and social activist in New York, Art Thomas, Delta Ministry Executive Director, and Greenberg. They believed that African Americans in Mississippi needed to be incorporated into programs within their communities in order to gain political empowerment which could lead to social change. By providing parents with control in the Head Start Centers their children attended and by guaranteeing jobs for parents as well as others in the community, the stage would be set for lasting change. A core notion was that empowered parents would, in fact, serve as positive role models for their children. However, it proved to be difficult in the implementation.

By the early 1970s, research findings were interpreted to support the position that many parents in poor families lacked certain requisite skills and parenting styles to foster their children's development. Thus, training programs for parents were launched within Head Start as well as through other outlets. In a later section of this article, the descriptions of these programs and evidence concerning outcomes are discussed.

1978–89: New Issues Emerge

The first significant expansion of Head Start came with the election of Jimmy Carter in 1978 when Congress increased the budget by a third. Behind the scenes, the National Head Start Association (established in 1973) and the Children's Defense Fund had been lobbying heavily for the increase of appropriation of funds to Head Start. As a result of bipartisan support for the expansion, Head Start grew in size and scope, which continued through the presidencies of Reagan, Bush Sr., and Clinton.

One of the most significant issues that emerged after Carter's election was the proposed transfer of Head Start to the Department of Education (DOE). Renewed efforts by Republicans to move the program were revived, with the idea that after Head Start was moved to the DOE, it would then be transferred to the states. The Head Start community was shocked that the suggestion had come from a Democratic president, and mobilized a coalition of civil rights leaders, including Coretta Scott King and Jesse Jackson, to urge Carter to reject this notion. They argued that Head Start needed to be protected from take-over by segregationist/racist Southern school systems, and the rigid and bureaucratic demands of the public schools (i.e., teachers' unions, educational requirements), in general. The National Head Start Association marshaled the support of local Head Start staff and parents, along with Edward Zigler and other influential voices. Head Start was removed from the DOE bill and remained at the newly established HHS/Administration for Children, Youth, and Families (ACYF; new name for the Office of Child Development).

With Head Start's increased dollars and visibility came demands for more accountability. In 1980, at Carter's request, Edward Zigler chaired a commission to examine the state of Head Start programs and make recommendations for the program's future. The recommendations included decreasing class size, having Head Start comply with the Program Performance Standards, requiring teachers to work toward Child Development Associate (CDA) credentialing and increasing teachers' salaries.

By the time Ronald Reagan took office in 1982, inflation had affected program quality. According to Zigler, Reagan ignored the Commissions' recommendations and the situation was even more distressing: cutbacks in staff, hours, and services; increases in class size; decreases in per child expenditures; and cutbacks of more than 25% of the regional staff charged with monitoring the program.

Health

From its inception, Head Start planners viewed health as a critical component of child development. Services included physical and dental health, nutrition, and mental health. However, providing those services required agencies to partner with local community providers. By the late 1970s, local Head Starts each had a Health Services Advisory Committee (HSAC) that addressed community issues related to health. Although few comparative data were collected during that period, it was evident that the only place that low-income children were receiving health prevention services was in Head Start. Several studies that examined child health records and Head Start Program Information Report (PIR) data revealed that a much higher percentage of Head Start children had medical examinations, tuberculosis screens, and lead testing than non-Head Start children. Dental screening and examinations, and vision screenings were required by the Head Start Program Performance Standards (HSPPS). However, local programs often did not keep records, making it difficult to assess the true success of those components.

Information about mental health services was far less clear. Social and emotional development of young children was always a key component of Head Start. However, using the term 'mental health' to refer to family members was frequently viewed, by both parents and staff, as another way of categorizing people as 'crazy'. Euphemisms were used, such as 'emotional well-being', and 'emotional readiness', and problems were couched in terms, such as 'children with special needs', when actual parent workshop topics might be on substance abuse, child abuse, and developmental delays. Another issue that prevented clearer access to mental health data was that mental health coordinators (along with health and nutrition coordinators) often had multiple roles within a local agency, making documentation arbitrary and spotty. In addition, during this period, most of the mental health consultants were there to screen and assess 'identified' children. They only worked a few hours per week or even per month, and were seen as 'experts' who diagnosed and referred out to local mental health facilities. These often had long waiting lists, staff members who did not speak the language of their clients, and/or were unfamiliar with cultural mores of the local Head Start community.

Social Services

Head Start's comprehensive services model as outlined in the Head Start Program Performance Standards was designed to promote children's healthy development while making improvements in a cluster of family outcomes, including family functioning and adult growth and development. The premise underlying this approach was that there could be simultaneous support for child development and adult self-sufficiency. Changes would bolster parents' educational level, enhance career development, and reduce dependence on public assistance. Intertwined was the realization that it would be impossible to hire enough formally trained social workers to meet the needs of Head Start families. Head Start began experimenting in training paraprofessionals to deliver the services, using people from the local Head Start communities. By the late 1970s, many 'graduated' Head Start parents became Head Start staff, primarily in the areas of family support and referral.

What started as a need and an experiment soon became part of the fabric of Head Start. Staff members were usually of a similar culture to the parents, easily building rapport, and helping them through the myriad of problems endemic to poverty: housing and welfare issues, health problems, addictions, child abuse and neglect, public school liaisoning for older siblings, intergenerational family discord, etc.

As time went on, administrative staff at the local level became increasingly aware that paraprofessional staff members were not equipped to deal with the growing mental health and social services needs of families. Their own stress levels and increasing caseloads made it more and more difficult to be emotionally and professionally available to the families they served. Local social and mental health agencies also were experiencing a rise in number of people needing services, resulting in long waiting lists and increased staff frustration and turnover. Through advocacy efforts to change curricula in schools of social work, a bachelor's degree in social work became the entry level for those professionals, and was accredited by the Council of Social Work Education. This change increased the quality of social services offered to Head Start parents.

Both internal and external barriers to effective service delivery plagued Head Start during this period. Internal issues were related to record keeping, staff training and professional development, staff turnover, and hours of operation. External barriers included availability of community resources, turf conflict in partnering with community agencies, and federal and state funding issues that prevented integration of services within Head Start.

Parental Involvement

Since the EOA of 1964 mandated 'maximum feasible participation' of parents and the 1975 guidelines reaffirmed the role of parents as decision makers, parents have played a major role in the daily operations and planning for Head Start. Advocacy and decision making became a cornerstone of the program, not simply a mandated requirement. Roles included serving on management and policy committees as decision makers, volunteering, fundraising, and helping to design parenting education and self-help activities.

1989–96: A Critical Look at Head Start: Advisory Panels

During a 10-year period from 1989 to 1999, the ACYF and other professional groups assembled 'expert' panels to assess and make recommendations about future directions for Head Start. These included: *Head Start: The Nation's Pride, A Nation's Challenge* (National Head Start Association – 1989); *Head Start Research and Evaluation: A Blueprint for the Future* (ACYF – 1990); *Creating a 21st Century Head Start: Final Report of the Advisory Committee on Head Start Quality and Expansion* (Department of Health and Human Services – 1993); and *Beyond the Blueprint: Directions for Research on Head Start Families* (National Research Council (NRC)/National Academy of Sciences – 1996).

The first of these panels, conducted in 1989 by the National Head Start Association, made specific recommendations concerning future directions for improving Head Start quality, staff development and training, classroom practices and curricula, family support services and education, and federal research and evaluation efforts that encourage researchers to collaborate with community partners in early childhood and human services.

Following closely in time were the two advisory groups established by the ACYF that resulted in the *Blueprint* and *Creating a 21st Century Head Start*. The first focused on future research and evaluation and the second on quality and expansion issues. Research and evaluation recommendations included: the creation of a coordinated research strategy rather than conducting a single, large-scale study; use of diverse methodologies and multiple indicators to measure outcomes; identification of marker variables; a recognition of the importance of studying diverse children and families in diverse community settings using diverse outcome indices; the exploration of program variation in finding explanations of differential outcomes; and the enhancement of research and evaluation studies by building on existing strengths of Head Start staff and programs.

Recommendations for Head Start quality and expansion in the twenty-first century were to implement three broad principles: striving for excellence in serving children and families, expanding the number of children served and the scope of services provided that is more responsive to the needs of children and families, and forging partnerships with key community institutions and organizations in early childhood, family support education, health and mental health that are continually revitalized to fit the changing needs of families and communities, and reflect the changes in state and national social policies.

The NRC's Roundtable on Head Start research held its first meeting in November, 1994, to independently explore the parts of Head Start programming that had been understudied to that point. Subsequent meetings addressed ways of studying changes in families affected by poverty in order to help Head Start be aware of and deal with these new issues; develop innovative strategies to assess child and family outcomes; use secondary data analyses and archiving to enhance the benefits of funded research and evaluation studies; and create a forum for Head Start practitioners to discover their own research interests and needs. The resulting document, *Beyond the Blueprint*, paved the way for even more innovative ACYF research and evaluation initiatives.

1990–Present: Research/Evaluation Revived

New Funding Initiative from Administration on Children, Youth and Families /Head Start Bureau

With the appointment of Wade Horn as Commissioner of the ACYF in 1990 and the recommendations of the first advisory panels (i.e., conducted by ACYF and NHSA) came the revitalization of interest in research on Head Start. In a written communication, Horn summarized the available research on Head Start and stated that there were currently no available data on how positive Head Start effects are achieved or about how they might be enhanced or maintained over time. He felt that there was a need to address the question of "what Head Start practices work best, for whom, and under what circumstances"? He explained that this new research approach would examine how various models would impact subgroups of Head Start children, families, and communities. Since that time, a wide range of demonstration projects have been funded that included more rigorous evaluation components.

New Funding Initiative from Administration on Children, Youth and Families/Head Start Bureau

The first group of demonstration projects was formulated to address the issue of 'fade-out'. The reasoning was that there might be three causes for this purported phenomenon. One was that children needed more years of a comprehensive preschool experience. Another was that children and

their families needed more intense services. The third was that the child and family services needed to be extended through second grade. To address these three potential causes, three demonstration projects were funded: the 5-year Comprehensive Child Development Program (CCDP), the Head Start Family Service Centers Project, and the Head Start Transition Demonstration Projects, respectively.

The goals of the CCDP were to provide comprehensive services to children and their families from birth to age 5 years, directly providing childcare, early education, and healthcare, and indirectly by providing parents with education, job training, and family support services. The CCDP was implemented and evaluated in 21 sites across the nation. Results of the evaluation did not show that the program did improve child development outcomes. However, limitations of the evaluation included difficulty comparing intervention and control groups since controls also had referral services and inaccurate data resulting from collection prior to full implementation by local sites.

The Head Start Family Service Centers Project was aimed at providing more intense services to families. Sixty-seven sites were selected to be representative of Head Start programs nationally for the intervention. Of that group, 26 were designated as control sites. Intervention included reducing the ratio of families to social services staff, providing staff development and training, and hiring more skilled staff. Outcomes included evaluation of family drug and alcohol use, job training and employment status, and literacy level. Results did not show significant differences between the intervention and control groups on the outcomes. The lessons learned included the difficulties in assessing social service delivery and documentation of work done with families.

The Head Start-Public School Transition Projects were designed to help children and families move from Head Start to public school kindergarten through second grade. The program included a social service component with a reduced caseload to strengthen the link between families and the school; coordinated, comprehensive health and nutrition services; and joint planning for developmental continuity of curriculum, and intensive parent involvement and education. Thirty-one local public school sites with matched control sites participated in the evaluation. Results confirmed that fade-out did not occur. Former Head Start children showed early and large gains in reading and mathematics achievement, bringing them up to the national average. What was learned were the difficulties in sustaining community-based partnerships, the variability among families living in poverty, and the challenges of conducting a randomized study where the comparison (control) schools were also engaged in transition activities, parent education and involvement, and improving their programs.

The University-Head Start Partnerships were 3-year grants to support research conducted by university faculty in partnership with their local Head Start agencies. The goal was to improve Head Start services by applying new knowledge or testing theory-driven interventions or new instruments with a variety of populations and/or in various settings. These grants were given to four to eight universities (faculty) almost every year from 1990 to 2003.

A similar 2-year grant, entitled the Head Start Research Scholars Program, was offered to graduate students who were qualified doctoral candidates or those who had completed their master's degree and were enrolled in a doctoral program.

Early Head Start (EHS) began in 1994, following the recommendations of the Secretary's Advisory Committee on Services for Families with Infants and Toddlers. ACYF designed EHS and funded the first 143 programs (not necessarily within Head Start agencies) to implement the model. At the same time, ACYF selected 17 sites (including 3001 families) from the 143 for evaluation. The evaluation used a rigorous, large-scale random assignment design that provided for both process and outcome data collection, and mirrored the program approaches and family demographics of the larger population. During that same period the Head Start Program Performance Standards were revised to include pregnant women, infants, and toddlers, who were to be served by the new initiative. The results of the evaluation are ongoing, with results of consistent patterns of statistically significant, modest improvements across a range of outcomes for 2–3-year-olds, including cognitive and language development, and social–emotional development. Additionally, EHS had significant positive effects on parenting and parent support of children's language and preliteracy development. Intervention parents made more progress toward economic self-sufficiency and mothers were less likely to have subsequent births during their first 2 years of enrollment than control group parents. The positive impact on fathers and father–child interactions was also significant, compared with controls. Families with a higher number of demographic risk factors, African American families, and families who enrolled during pregnancy made greater gains than those families in other subgroups.

Beginning in 1995, the ACYF moved to enhance Head Start program quality and outcomes through a number of strategically designed initiatives. The first of these was the Head Start Quality Research Centers Consortium, a 5-year cooperative agreement with four universities. During this period, the Consortium built partnerships between researchers and programs explored what aspects of programs contributed to positive child and family outcomes, created and refined instruments and strategies to assess classroom quality and child outcomes. Consortium members served as technical advisors to the design, development, and implementation of the Head Start Family and Child Experiences Survey (FACES).

Head Start's System of Program Performance Measures, an outcome-oriented accountability method, was initiated in 1995, on the recommendations of the 1993 Advisory Committee on Head Start Quality and Expansion, and on the mandate of the Head Start Act of 1994. The Act delineates the methods and procedures that must be used by local Head Start agencies to annually assess the quality and effectiveness of their programs. In 1996–97, a conceptual framework was developed and the measures were finalized. The 'whole child' approach to school readiness was endorsed in keeping with Goal One of the National Education Goals Panel. Defined as a complex trajectory of developmental milestones, school readiness includes physical, social, emotional, and nutritional health; language, literacy, cognitive skills, and general knowledge; and positive approaches to learning.

FACES was launched in 1997 as an integral part of the accountability process. Annually, FACES collected data on a nationally representative sample of Head Start programs, classrooms, teachers, parents, and children to study its quality and impact. The field test in 1997 collected data on 2400 children and their families on 40 Head Start programs. The sample was increased to 3200 children and families each year, in 1998 and 1999. In 2000, a new national cohort of 2800 children was selected from 43 programs. Initial results showed that Head Start classrooms have higher quality than most center-based early childhood programs; most Head Start programs have smaller class sizes and a lower child/adult ratio for 3–5-year-olds than is required by the HSPPS and the NAEYC accreditation standards; and over 79% of Head Start teachers had a CDA certificate or other early child credential. Children benefit from Head Start, showing a significant growth in vocabulary and gains in social skills and cooperative behavior. However, children with emotional and behavior problems (a relatively small number) did not change over the course of the year. Families benefit from Head Start by learning the importance of reading to their children and practicing that skill, involving their children in activities at home, participating in many areas of the program, feeling supported by Head Start in raising their children, receiving help and services for their children with disabilities, and enhancing the role of fathers in raising their children.

The Head Start Act of 1998 (PL 105–285) reauthorized Head Start funding with two new major provisions addressing staff qualifications and child performance standards, and measuring and monitoring outcomes. At least one classroom teacher had to be trained and skilled at implementing the new educational performance standards that included developing and demonstrating an appreciation of books, developing phonemic, print and numeric awareness, identifying at least 10 letters of the alphabet, recognizing a word as a unit of print, and associating sounds with written words. The ACF has given guidance on these and other legislative changes regarding the child outcomes framework, performance measures, and monitoring (i.e., self-assessment and federal on-site systems monitoring).

In 1999, following the 1998 Head Start reauthorization bill, the Department of Health and Human Services established an Advisory Committee on Head Start Research and Evaluation. The resulting document, *Evaluating Head Start: A Recommended Framework for Studying the Impact of the Head Start Program*, made several recommendations concerning future directions and requirements for Head Start research and evaluation. These included: reviewing existing and ongoing research and evaluation studies that document the impact of Head Start; exploring alternative designs and methods for studying Head Start, develop a study or series of studies of the impact of Head Start services on children and families. The resulting initiatives reflect these recommendations.

In addition to establishing the Advisory Committee, the 1998 reauthorization congressionally mandated that a national, longitudinal study be conducted on the impact of Head Start. The National Head Start Impact Study involves approximately 5000 3- and 4-year-old children whose families applied to Head Start beginning in fall 2002, across 84 representative agencies. Participating children were randomly assigned to a treatment (receiving Head Start services) or control (receiving no Head Start services) group, but the study only takes place in those communities where there are more eligible children than can be served by the Head Start program. These children will be followed through the spring of their first-grade year (2006). The primary goals of the study are to determine how Head Start affects children's school readiness as compared with the school readiness of children who have not attended Head Start.

First-year findings were reported in 2005. Highlights include the following:

Cognitive domain – small-to-moderate statistically significant positive impacts on 3- and 4 year-old children on pre-reading, pre-writing, vocabulary, and parent's reports of children's literacy skills; no significant impacts were found for oral comprehension, phonological awareness, or early mathematics skills.

Social–emotional domain – small significant impact on children entering as 3-year-olds on one of the three social–emotional constructs, problem behaviors; no significant impacts on social skills and approaches to learning, and social competencies; no significant impacts in children entering the program as 4-year-olds.

Health domain – on children entering as 3-year-olds, small-to-moderately significant impacts on access to healthcare and better health status as reported by parents; for entering 4-year-olds, moderately significant impacts on access to healthcare, but no significant impacts for health status.

Parenting practices domain – for children entering as 3-year-olds, small significant impacts in two of the three parenting constructs: higher use of educational activities and lower use of physical discipline by parents; no significant impacts for safety practices; for children entering as 4-year-olds, small significant impacts on parents' use of educational activities. No significant impacts for discipline or safety practices as compared with children who did not receive Head Start services.

Future reports will examine additional areas of potential impact and explore variations in program (i.e., classroom quality, teacher education level) and community characteristics (i.e., unemployment level, homelessness).

The ACYF/Head Start Bureau and the ACF Office of Research and Evaluation created the Head Start Quality Research Center Consortium (2001) by awarding eight universities 5-year cooperative agreements with the goal of promoting school readiness by supporting ongoing quality improvement in Head Start. Their objectives were to develop, test, refine, and disseminate interventions to enhance child outcomes; staff development, training and mentoring; and parent involvement. The Consortium used common measures in intervention/control design evaluations. Consortium findings were compiled each year into an Interim Report where they also compared their results with those of FACES. This Consortium was expanded in 2006 to include additional universities, and is ongoing.

The ACYF has been field-testing a National Reporting System on Child Outcomes (NRS) since 1999/2000. When fully implemented, it will assess the progress of approximately 500 000 4- and 5-year-olds in Head Start. It will produce a national outcomes report of children's ability and progress on the congressionally mandated indicators.

The Role of the Head Start National Research Conferences

At about the same time that the Advisory Panels were making their recommendations, Horn and one of his senior research staff members, Esther Kresh, developed their ideas for a research conference that would interest the research community. A goal was to create an avenue for attracting university researchers to conduct studies of Head Start children and families and to create evidence-based programming in Head Start. The mission of the conferences was twofold: (1) to expose practitioners to research/evaluation as the foundation for sound program development, and (2) to help researchers understand how to apply their findings to real-life situations and explain their research in terms that would be understood by Head Start practitioners and the community served by Head Start.

The eight conferences have thus far successfully addressed the goal and mission established in 1990. These conferences have become a venue for cutting-edge research in the field, as well as a forum for all of the new research/evaluation and programmatic initiatives conducted by ACYF and other related government agencies. Additionally, they have served to stimulate partnerships and collaborations among researchers and practitioners across disciplines: child development, psychology, public health, pediatrics, neuroscience, social work, and economics, to name a few. The Society for Research in Child Development (SRCD) and Columbia University Mailman School of Public Health (CUMSPH) have been responsible for developing and conducting the conferences, with the assistance of multidisciplinary program committees made up of researchers, practitioners, and policy makers who are leaders in their field, as well as the logistics partners.

An analysis of the conferences across 15 years reveals three major themes that reflect not only the state of the field of early childhood development and education, but also the transformation of Head Start research and evaluation. The three themes are: (1) cutting-edge research in child and family development, child-care, and education; (2) culturally sensitive, relevant methods and measures with sound psychometrics; and (3) partnerships among researchers, practitioners, and policy makers.

There was a clear shift in the focus of research presented at the conferences when comparing the first three (1990–96) to the later ones (1998–2006). The studies that were presented at the conferences reflected the growing sophistication of the early child development and education research communities. The later years have reflected an emphasis on context and ecology, continuities and discontinuities across child and family development, a greater emphasis on the study of outcomes, and an emphasis on positive development.

In comparing Conferences III and VII, the shift in level of comfort with sound, culturally sensitive measures and methods is apparent. In 1996, words such as 'newness', 'innovation', and 'debate' were frequently found in the titles of presentations. Random assignment to intervention and control groups and statistical methods such as hierarchical linear modeling were looked upon with caution and suspicion. In 2006, for the most part, participants voiced feelings of comfort and understanding around these issues and were interested in learning how to apply them to more complex data.

The most obvious and positive change over the course of the eight conferences has been the depth and breadth of collaboration and partnerships between researchers and practitioners. The first several conferences reflected a level of distrust and animosity between the two groups, as reflected in titles of presentations such as *Research Partnerships Action: Dynamic Struggles*. The most recent conference (VIII) had little title reference to partnerships. However, most of the presentations reflected deep and ongoing partnerships between researchers and practitioners where the presentations were a melding of discussions about process, outcomes, and lessons learned from both perspectives.

According to Aletha Huston, then president-elect of SRCD, who spoke at the 7th Conference in June 2004, "the numbers of people in attendance and the vibrancy of the [conference] program attest to the continuing impact of these conferences. The lives of children, both those in Head Start and those who profit from the gains made from the success of Head Start, are the beneficiaries."

Summary

After 42 years, Head Start remains the largest federally funded program for children in the US and is viewed as largely positive by both political parties as well as advocates for children. During Funding Year 2005, over \$6.8 billion was allocated for Head Start programs in all 50 states as well as US territories. The enrollment was 906 993 children, and ranged from under 3 years (10%) to 3-year-olds (34%), 4-year-olds (52%), and 5 years or older (4%). In terms of race/ethnicity, 35% were white, 31% were black or African American, 32% were Hispanic/Latino, and 5% were American Indian/Native American. The total is more than 100% due to multiple categories for some children. There were 19 800 centers in 2005, and the average cost per child was \$7287. It is noteworthy that 91% of children had health insurance, a figure attributed to the emphasis on wellness and healthcare in Head Start programs.

During the four decades of Head Start, the program has faced many obstacles, has encountered pressures from virtually all levels, including the federal government (both the administrative and congressional branches), from communities and families, from public schools, and from the academic establishment. In this article we have provided evidence for these many pressures, the changes that have occurred, the attempts to evaluate and criticize, and, perhaps most importantly, for the buoyancy and resilience of Head Start. It continues to be a program that serves almost 1 million children a year and evidence continues to accumulate that when quality is maintained the children show both short- and long-term benefits.

See also: Family Support, International Trends; Preschool and Nursery School; School Readiness.

Suggested Readings

Vinovskis MA (2005) *The Birth of Head Start: Preschool Education Policies in the Kennedy and Johnson Administrations.* Chicago: University of Chicago Press.

Zigler E and Muenchow S (1992) *Head Start: The Inside Story of America's Most Successful Educational Experiment.* New York: Basic Books.

Zigler E and Styfco SJ (eds.) (2004) *The Head Start Debates.* Baltimore: Paul H. Brookes Publishing Company.

Zigler E and Valentine J (eds.) (1979) *Project Head Start: A Legacy of the War on Poverty.* New York: The Free Press.

Healthcare

S Russ, M Regalado, and N Halfon, University of California, Los Angeles, Los Angeles, CA, USA

Glossary

Developmental services – Services designed to monitor and promote the developmental health of young children. Services are categorized as assessment, education, intervention, and care coordination.

Healthcare – The provision, by medical, nursing, and allied health professionals of services, which promote health and well-being, prevent illness, treat identified conditions, and manage chronic illness.

Health promotion – The science and art of helping people change their lifestyle to move toward a state of optimal health. Lifestyle change can be facilitated by a combination of efforts to enhance awareness, change behavior, and create environments that support good health practices. Of these three, supportive environments will probably have the greatest impact in producing lasting change.

Medical home – The medical home is not a building, a house, or a hospital but rather is a team approach to healthcare that is accessible, continuous, comprehensive, family-centered, compassionate, and culturally effective. Care is delivered or directed by well-trained physicians who provide primary care and help to manage and facilitate essentially all aspects of pediatric care. The physician should be known to the child and family and should be able to develop a partnership of mutual responsibility and trust with them. Family and provider partner together to ensure that all aspects of the child's care are optimized.

Screening – It is performed to identify disease in an asymptomatic population. Screening tests must have acceptable sensitivity and specificity for the target condition, especially when screening for diseases with low prevalence.

State early childhood comprehensive services (SECCS) initiative – This initiative, launched by the US Federal Maternal and Child Health Bureau is designed to enable State Maternal and Child Health Directors to collaborate with partner agencies and stakeholders in developing comprehensive early childhood service systems. States receive grants to build leadership capacity for the development of cross-service systems integration. Systems must address the critical components of (1) access to comprehensive pediatric services and medical homes; (2) socioemotional development and mental health services for young children; (3) early care and education; (4) parenting education; and (5) family support.

Introduction

Over the past century the scope and delivery of healthcare has undergone tremendous change. When infectious diseases and unsafe living conditions posed the major threats to young children's health, and infant and child mortality rates were high, physicians focused almost exclusively on the management of acute illness. Improved sanitation and the introduction of immunizations and antibiotics led to significant decreases in the number and severity of cases of infectious diseases, and in the number of children presenting with potentially life-threatening acute conditions. Major advances in medical technology followed, leading to greater use of invasive high-technology interventions such as neonatal and pediatric intensive care. At the same time, growing understanding of the epidemiology of childhood illnesses led to increased emphasis on preventive healthcare, and on the management of chronic illness. Now, in what is often termed the 'third era of healthcare', health is defined as a positive capacity for life 'a state of complete physical, mental, and social well-being' and healthcare in early childhood is aimed at optimizing health across physical, emotional, cognitive, and social domains. The focus of healthcare services for young children has shifted from the hospital to the community, and child health providers are increasingly being called upon to address the 'new morbidities' – neurodevelopmental challenges, learning difficulties, psychosocial problems, and child maltreatment.

As a child's health is increasingly understood in the context of his or her family and community, healthcare services, if they are to be effective, must be integrated with a broader system of early childhood services including early intervention, family support, education, and welfare. Pediatric practices must develop new strategies to link with these other service sectors, moving toward a 'transactional' model of children's health development, that is, one responsive to the individual and environmental context. Structurally, a tiered care model is needed, where all children receive a universal package of basic healthcare services, while those children with identifiable risks, such as foster care placement, receive additional targeted services tailored to their health and developmental needs. As evidence continues to accumulate that events and experiences in the early years influence developing biological systems in ways that affect health not just in childhood, but throughout the life course, the importance of addressing both threats to health and opportunities to promote optimal health through a responsive early childhood healthcare system can no longer be ignored. In fact, a child healthcare system with appropriate emphasis on health promotion and illness prevention could pay big dividends for the health of the population throughout the life span.

Scope of Healthcare

In order to understand the scope of healthcare in early childhood it is first necessary to consider current definitions of child health, and the theoretical models that have influenced the historic development of healthcare services.

Definition of Children's Health

In 2000, the US Congress asked the Institute of Medicine and the National Research Council to convene an expert panel to consider how well children's health was being measured in the US. The subsequent report *Children's Health, The Nation's Wealth* proposed the following definition:

> Children's health is the extent to which individual children or groups of children are able or enabled to (a) develop and realize their potential, (b) satisfy their needs, and (c) develop the capacities that allow them to interact successfully with their biological, physical and social environments.

This concept of achieving 'positive' health, in addition to preventing and treating disease, has major implications for the goals of healthcare services, and for the way in which healthcare is conceptualized and delivered. In addition, this broader definition of health, which is no longer confined to the physical realm but includes cognitive, social, and emotional health has blurred the boundaries between 'child health' and 'child development' resulting in an interconnected conceptual framework. To be effective, service delivery models must move from existing uni- or even multidisciplinary approaches to ones which are more transdisciplinary in nature, with greater flexibility of professional roles in order to meet children's needs.

Theoretical Models of Child Health

Disease model
Traditionally, healthcare services were organized around a 'disease model', in which the principal goal was the prompt diagnosis and effective treatment of defined disease entities. This 'disease model' formed the basis of the 'medical model' on which the training of healthcare providers has been historically based. While the disease model works reasonably well for conditions with well-defined, preferably single etiologies and known effective treatments, it pays little attention to cultural and psychosocial issues, which influence the acquisition and progression of disease.

Although the medical model is widely regarded as outmoded because of these limitations, it still drives much of US healthcare policy and practice, and has a powerful influence on how healthcare is financed and reimbursed. Tests designed to diagnose specific disease entities, and technical procedures designed to cure or ameliorate established diseases are generally compensated at a much higher rate than services aimed at health promotion, risk reduction, and disease prevention.

It is within this setting that the practice of early childhood health is seeking to redefine itself. As child mortality falls, and as more infectious diseases are effectively prevented, less of the provider's time is spent on diagnostic and curative procedures, and more on the prevention, diagnosis, and management of conditions that have less well-defined etiologies such as developmental delays and behavioral difficulties – conditions where the medical model has limited applicability. Moreover, the medical or disease model is inherently a 'deficit' model, that is, one that focuses on identifying problems and fixing them. Thus, it is inadequate for guiding health promotion.

Maturational model
The maturational model strongly influenced the child development field at the beginning of the twentieth century. In this model, a child's developmental capacity is regarded as set at birth, unfolding over time in a predetermined sequence. Clinically observable developmental delays are conceptualized as resulting from genetic or prenatal influences affecting the child's ultimate potential. The model largely ignores the role of context and of environmental factors on the developmental trajectories of young children, so it places a low value on interventions for established delays, which are largely regarded as ineffective. Rather, the focus is on 'assessment' to identify children with established developmental deficits who might need alternative educational approaches. The model has had a definable influence on early childhood healthcare, promoting the use of office-based intermittent developmental assessments of the child's abilities, while placing less emphasis on evaluation of the child's family and social context, and on a range of community-based interventions to prevent or ameliorate developmental challenges or to promote optimal health over the life course. Growing realization of the crucial role that the social environment plays in children's health and development is leading to calls for

transformative change in the delivery of pediatric primary healthcare services founded on newer conceptual models, which take a more ecological view of health development and optimization.

Transactional model

Later models, most notably Engle's biopsychosocial model and the transactional model (Sameroff and Fiese) place a much stronger emphasis on the role of environmental factors in child health development. The transactional model regards neurological, psychological, and social development as dynamic processes resulting from complex interactions between the child and the caregiving environment. Developmental health is dependent on the child and the parent adapting to each other as developmental change progresses. The quality of the caregiver–child relationship is viewed as central to the child's well-being, so support for parents with child-rearing responsibilities is crucial for the child's positive health development. Although widely accepted in the child development field, the transactional model has not yet been fully integrated with the core tenets of the medical model to produce an integrated model that would guide delivery of child healthcare services. In fact, the current pediatric healthcare delivery system is largely based on an outmoded logic model focused almost exclusively on the child in isolation, rather than the child interactive with the environment. Consequently, although parenting advice, education, and support is gradually being incorporated into child health supervision guidelines, these activities remain largely under- or unreimbursed.

Life course models

Evidence is accumulating from longitudinal cohort studies that early childhood health indicators, such as birthweight, and family and social environments are strongly linked with later health and mental health outcomes. Starting with the pioneering work of David Barker on associations between birthweight and mid-life cardiovascular disease, the concept of developmental origins of adult disease (the so-called Barker hypothesis) has gained credence. There is now also growing evidence that events and experiences in early childhood can have a profound effect on later adult health. For example, exposure to abuse and family dysfunction in childhood has been associated with higher prevalence and severity of adult disease and mental illness. These findings underscore the need for healthcare in childhood to consider carefully family and environmental influences on a young child's development, and the importance of optimizing health across all its dimensions in the early years for future well-being and longevity.

Changing Patterns of Child Health Challenges

The physical and social environments in which young children are growing up have undergone considerable change. As the circumstances and contexts of young children's lives change, we see epidemiologic shifts in patterns of illness and threats to children's health – the 'new morbidities'. Child abuse, learning difficulties, and attention deficit hyperactivity disorder are increasingly prevalent in pediatric practice. Child health providers are being consulted about a broad spectrum of social difficulties, behavior problems, and developmental challenges affecting young children. There are widespread concerns about the effects of environmental factors such as media exposure, parental divorce, and quality of childcare on child well-being. Parent concerns about development are very common – almost half of parents have some concerns about their young child's speech, social development, or behavior – yet traditional healthcare systems offer a limited response to these newer threats to child health. Barriers to recognition and effective treatment include lack of provider training, lack of compensation for the time taken to identify and manage these disorders, and a lack of models for coordinating services across disciplines of pediatrics, mental health, and education.

While children's healthcare delivery systems struggle to cope with these new morbidities, other changes are affecting the healthcare system in different ways. For example, the HIV epidemic has produced a new generation of children with a congenital infectious disease who will require close lifelong management. Advances in newborn ventilation techniques have resulted in the survival of increasing numbers of very premature babies, some of whom have later developmental and sensory challenges such as hearing loss, retinopathy of prematurity, and cognitive and motor delays. Similarly, improvements in surgical techniques and postoperative care are resulting in more children with complex congenital heart diseases surviving to adulthood, and in children with end-organ failure surviving after transplantation. Many of these children then require lifelong medical care to ensure their continued well-being. Revolutionary advances in molecular biology, coupled with information emerging from the human genome project, and newer strategies for genetic engineering all hold promise for the future development of refined diagnostic techniques and targeted therapies for conditions that are currently incurable.

As technological advances continue, there are inevitable ethical issues that arise in individual cases where intensive treatment would result in survival but poor quality of life. In other cases, parents are called upon to make decisions early in a child's life, which may have lifelong health consequences, for example, determining whether a child with a profound hearing loss should receive cochlear implantation. The early childhood healthcare system must provide quality care across this wide range of morbidities if it is to address the health needs of the children of the twenty-first century effectively.

Implications for Healthcare Training and Practice

Child health providers of the future not only need advanced knowledge of molecular biology and applied genetics, but also the ability to recognize and manage milder developmental challenges as well as link families with effective services at the community level. These needs have created a tension within pediatric training programs that must strive to equip trainees with core technological skills coupled with competent interpersonal skills to be effective advocates for children's needs. As reported in Future of Pediatric Education II (FOPE II), new training guidelines have incorporated community-based clinical experiences for both residents and medical students. However, despite these efforts, significant numbers of pediatricians still feel that their training does not prepare them sufficiently well for the child health problems they are encountering in practice.

Providers are increasingly aware that the solutions to child health problems often lie outside the pediatric office, and require effective collaborations with other providers. For example, a physician who has treated multiple toddlers in the emergency room with near-drownings may decide to investigate local ordinances for pool safety, and may collaborate with other organizations and parent groups to advocate for legislation mandating pool fencing; a nurse-practitioner who has several preschool-age children in her practice with behavioral issues might collaborate with a local psychologist to run a joint parenting group; a family physician who is called upon to treat several cases of measles in children attending a local preschool might, on discovering that most pupils have not been immunized due to parental concerns about risks of autism, decide to give a presentation for parents and staff members on current evidence regarding the risks and benefits of vaccination.

The role of the child health provider is transitioning from one of predominantly stand-alone, office-based practice to that of a community-based provider who might deliver services in a variety of settings, as part of a team, closely connected with other services for children such as welfare and early education. To be effective in its mission of health promotion and optimization the pediatric office of the twenty-first century must be prepared to function as a central 'hub' tightly linked to a range of community-based resources (see **Figure 1**). While many professionals stand ready to embrace these changes, funding streams, insurers, and institutional policies have not yet adapted to these proposed models of integrated care.

Content of Healthcare

Treatment of Acute Illness

For many families the term 'healthcare' conjures up a picture of a physician in his office assessing, diagnosing, and treating a young child with an acute illness. Among the most common reasons for pediatric office visits are ear infections, fevers, and viral illnesses, the majority of which are treated as outpatients. Pediatric offices are now equipped to perform many diagnostic and therapeutic procedures, which previously were only available in a hospital setting, for example, simple blood tests, radiography, and nebulizer treatment for acute asthma. More serious acute illness is treated in emergency departments; however, even then, a period of more intense treatment or observation may be

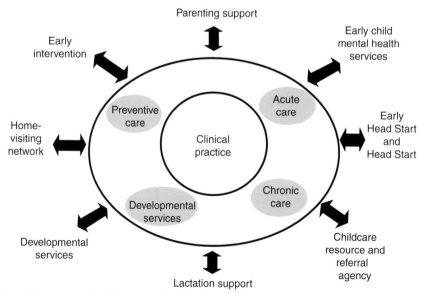

Figure 1   The pediatric office as a service delivery hub. The role of the clinical practice in the community. Reproduced from Halfon N, Regalado M, McLearn KT, and Wright K (2003) *Building a Bridge from Birth to School: Improving Developmental and Behavioral Health Services for Young Children.* New York: The Commonwealth Fund, with permission.

followed by close outpatient monitoring through telephone contact check-in, or next-day review rather than admission. Consequently, pediatric hospital admission rates for acute illnesses have fallen in recent years, with only the sickest children now generally warranting inpatient management.

Management of Chronic Illness and Children with Special Healthcare Needs

As more children survive perinatal health challenges such as premature birth and congenital abnormalities, and as more effective treatments are developed for previously fatal illnesses, for example, bone marrow transplantation for immune deficiencies, more children in the early childhood years have chronic conditions that require close healthcare supervision. For these children, optimal management involves close coordination and communication between the child's family, primary care provider, a range of subspecialist medical providers, ancillary healthcare professionals such as speech therapists and occupational therapists, and nonmedical professionals such as early interventionists and early childhood educators.

The US Maternal and Child Health Bureau has defined Children with Special Healthcare Needs (CSHN) as "those children who have or are at risk for chronic physical, developmental, behavioral or emotional conditions and who also require health and related services of a type or amount beyond that required by children generally." This definition includes a broad range of conditions such as cerebral palsy, asthma, cystic fibrosis, sickle cell anemia, developmental delay, and any child who has a significant medical problem that is expected to last at least 12 months. A recent national survey revealed that almost 13% children in the US have special healthcare needs. Some children simply require accurate diagnosis, initiation of appropriate treatment, and ongoing monitoring; however others, especially those with multiple health challenges, such as cerebral palsy, may be highly dependent on technology, require the input of multiple specialists and disciplines for adequate management, and need a range of care coordination, case management, and family support activities. There is general agreement, at least in the US, that these children face particular challenges in accessing all the services they need in a complex, fragmented healthcare system. Children with chronic illness now account for a much greater proportion of hospital admissions than they did in past decades – up to 80% of all child health nontraumatic spending is attributable to chronic illness.

Medical Home

The American Academy of Pediatrics has proposed the concept of the medical home, in which "the medical care of infants, children and adolescents should be accessible, continuous, comprehensive, family-centered, compassionate, and culturally effective. It should be delivered by well-trained physicians who provide primary care and help to manage and facilitate essentially all aspects of pediatric care. The physician should be known to the child and family and should be able to develop a partnership of mutual responsibility and trust with them." The medical home, therefore, is not a place, but a concept – regardless of the location of care (physician's office, hospital outpatient clinic, school-linked clinics), a designated physician must ensure that all necessary services are provided. Ideally, all children, not just those with special healthcare needs, would have a medical home.

Disease Prevention and Health Promotion: Bright Futures

Bright Futures is a set of expert guidelines, and a practical developmental approach for providing health supervision within the medical home for children of all ages. At the heart of Bright Futures is a commitment to health promotion – an active agenda to optimize the health of every child across physical, emotional, mental, and social domains. First published in 1994 under the leadership of the Maternal and Child Health Bureau, Health Resources and Services Administration, and the Medicaid Bureau, Health Care Financing Administration, the guidelines incorporate interview questions and anticipatory guidance for every child healthcare supervision visit. They aim to promote child development, strengthen the physician–family partnership, and help children develop healthy habits for life. The guidelines were revised in 2002, and further revisions are expected. Consistent with Healthy People 2010 national objectives, the guidelines are tools physicians can use to address the new morbidities of childhood.

Health supervision interview

Bright Futures provides an age-specific overview of development for infancy (birth to 11 months) and early childhood (1–5 years), with charts summarizing expected achievements and goals for each health supervision visit. To maximize use of time, the physician and family are advised to tailor issues addressed to individual needs, and to mail tools such as psychosocial and developmental screening instruments to the family for completion prior to the office visit. Families are also encouraged to bring reports from other providers to maximize communication and care coordination. A fundamental aspect of well-child care is the relationship between the primary care provider and the family, which should be open and friendly, incorporating play with younger children.

Developmental surveillance, screening, and assessment

The child's development over time is monitored through a longitudinal collaborative process between the professional and the family. This process, termed developmental surveillance, includes monitoring developmental milestones, use of developmental screening questionnaires, and referral for, or performance of, formal developmental assessments when there is either parental concern or a suggestion of delay or abnormality on surveillance. The health professional is encouraged to observe the parent–child interaction, monitoring for signs of parental depression or emotional difficulties in the child or adult, and forming an impression of the quality and reciprocity of the parent–child relationship. Ideally, continuous surveillance enables the clinician to guide the parent, child, and family through expected developmental challenges. Attachment theory provides a conceptual basis for this activity in suggesting that the quality and nature of the social and emotional relationship between mother and child has a strong influence on the child's developmental progression and ability to develop autonomy and acquire new skills. However attachment theory has not yet been fully accepted or incorporated into pediatric practice.

The late diagnosis of developmental delays in young children is recognized as a significant challenge, with reliance on informal developmental evaluations based on subjective professional opinion resulting in many delays and learning difficulties not being recognized until school entry or beyond. Physicians cite lack of time and reimbursement for more formal surveillance and screening activities, coupled with confusion over eligibility criteria for intervention services as contributors to this problem. Lack of knowledge of available support services, lack of staff to coordinate intervention strategies, and reluctance to label children on the part of both parents and professionals have also inhibited progress toward more effective developmental surveillance. In response to this challenge, newer instruments have been created for developmental surveillance and screening, including the Parents' Evaluation of Developmental Status (PEDS), which aims to elicit parent concerns, and the Ages and Stages Questionnaire (ASQ). The American Academy of Pediatrics has recently developed an algorithm to guide developmental surveillance and screening activities in primary care practice, which incorporates use of one or more of these tools. Testing of the algorithm and other strategies for provision of developmental services will be an important component of early childhood healthcare over the next decade.

Physical Examination

Physical examination is recommended at every visit with special emphasis on age-appropriate aspects, for example, hip stability in infancy, early dental caries development at age 1 year. Regular growth monitoring is emphasized, with measurements of height, weight, and head circumference plotted on growth charts throughout infancy. In the US, Center for Disease Control and Prevention (CDC) growth charts are recommended, and gender-specific charts are available for infants aged birth to 36 months, and for children and adolescents aged 2–20 years. In the UK, use of the UK90 reference charts is advised. Calculation and plotting of body mass index (BMI) should be performed from the 2-year visit onwards. Physical examinations may detect abnormalities, but are also valuable in reassuring families that their child's growth and development is within a normal range.

Additional Screening Procedures and Risk Assessment

As technological and genetic advances increase the number of conditions for which valid and reliable screening tests exist, the number of screening procedures incorporated into well-child health supervision is likely to increase. Screening may be universal, or may be targeted as groups of children known to be at increased risk of the condition. In this case, some form of risk assessment must precede the screening process. Conditions currently screened for include the following.

Metabolic screening. Newborn screening by bloodspot testing for phenylketonuria has been mandated in the US for all newborns for several decades, accompanied by screening for other conditions such as galactosemia, homocystinuria, and hypothyroidism. The advent of tandem mass spectrometry has enabled states to test newborns for multiple inborn errors of metabolism such as medium-chain acyl-CoA dehydrogenase deficiency more efficiently, and many states have responded by expanding newborn screening panels (see **Table 1**). Genetic screening for the most common mutations resulting in conditions such as cystic fibrosis is now also possible and has been introduced in several states.

Hearing screening. Screening shortly after birth, preferably before hospital discharge has been mandated in most states using either auditory brainstem response (ABR), or otoacoustic emissions (OAE). Infants who do not pass the screen must be referred promptly for audiologic assessment, so that losses are identified by 3 months of age and intervention commenced by 6 months of age. Ongoing surveillance and screening for hearing loss is recommended throughout early childhood, especially for those children with risk factors for loss such as family history of hereditary hearing loss, and head and neck abnormalities, even where newborn screening was passed. This may be achieved through use of OAEs in the office setting, or referral to an audiologist for visual reinforcement audiometry (VRA). Conditioned play audiometry is possible from about age 2 years on.

Vision screening. Office-based screening using simple tests such as Tumbling E or picture tests are usually possible from age 3 years onwards. For children who are 6 years of age or older, Snellen letters or numbers can be

Table 1   Disorders for which newborns can be screened (screening panel varies by state in the US)

1. Phenylketonuria	16. Medium-chain acyl-CoA dehydrogenase deficiency
2. Maple syrup urine disease	17. Very long-chain acyl-CoA dehydrogenase deficiency
3. Homocystinuria	18. Long-chain 3-OH acyl-CoA dehydrogenase deficiency
4. Citrullinemia	19. Trifunctional protein deficiency
5. Argininosuccinic acidemia	20. Carnitine uptake defect
6. Tyrosinemia type I	21. Sickle cell anemia
7. Isovaleric acidemia	22. HB S/Beta-thalassemia
8. Glutaric acidemia type I	23. HB S/C disease
9. Hydroxymethylglutaric aciduria or (HMG-CoA ase deficiency)	24. Congenital hypothyroidism
10. Multiple carboxylase deficiency	25. Biotinidase deficiency
11. Methylmalonic acidemia due to mutase deficiency	26. Congenital adrenal hyperplasia
12. Methylmalonic acidemia cblA and cblB forms	27. Classical galactosemia
13. 3-Methylcrotonyl-CoA carboxylase deficiency	28. Hearing loss
14. Propionic acidemia	29. Cystic fibrosis
15. Beta-ketothiolase deficiency	

Source: Johnson K, Lloydz-Puryear MA, Mann MY, Ramos LR, and Therell BL (2006) Financing state newborn screening programs: Sources and uses of funds. *Pediatrics* 117(5): S270–S279. Cited in An P (2007) Newborn screening: Current status. *Health Affairs* 26(2): 559–566.

used. Where there is concern about younger children, especially those with risk factors such as prematurity, referral to an ophthalmologist is advised.

Iron deficiency. Professional recommendations vary between screening all infants at 9–12 months and screening just those with risk factors such as premature or low-birthweight infants, those fed noniron-fortified infants formulas, and those with little iron in the diet. Rescreening is recommended at 15–18 months, with annual screening for children ages 2–5 years with poor diets or special healthcare needs.

Lead levels. CDC recommends that infants and children at risk, for example, those living in or visiting houses that might contain lead paint, be screened for elevated blood lead levels at 9–12 and 24 months. Universal screening is recommended in communities where risk of lead exposure is widespread.

Hyperlipidemia screening. Recommended at age 2 years for children with risk factors, for example, parent or grandparent with coronary atherosclerosis or myocardial infarction at 55 years of age or under, or parent with high cholesterol.

Immunizations

Immunizations are a cornerstone of pediatric preventive care, and status should be reviewed at every opportunity, including acute care visits. Much of the current periodicity schedule for well-child care (see **Table 2**) is built around the Recommended Childhood Immunization Schedule (see **Table 3**). Immunizations are currently administered in infancy and early childhood for hepatitis B, diphtheria, tetanus and pertussis, *Haemophilus influenzae* type B, polio, measles, mumps, rubella, varicella, Pneumococcus, hepatitis A, and influenza.

Anticipatory guidance

Anticipatory guidance prepares families for what to expect next in their child's development. As the list of topics that could be addressed at each visit grows, the pediatrician faces a dilemma in determining which topics to discuss. Guidance is most effective when personalized to individual circumstances, and delivered in the context of a relationship with a known and trusted physician. Topics include healthy habits, prevention of injury and illness, nutrition, social development, and family relationships. As time during office visits is limited, guidance can be supplemented with educational videos and written materials that can be studied at home, with parent educational classes, and with general health promotion messaging through the media.

Family-centered communication

Family-centered communication is a basic tenet of a successful healthcare encounter, and is facilitated by effective provider behaviors such as greeting family members by name, using easily understandable language, and providing a trained translator where needed. Providers need to acquire active listening skills, such as allowing parents to state concerns without interruption, and clarifying statements with follow-up questions. Nonverbal communication, such as sitting at the child's level and making good eye contact are equally important.

Electronic medical records

Electronic medical records can streamline the record-keeping process for the visit by ensuring that past history is available, and that new findings can be entered into preset screens. In the absence of an electronic record, a well-organized chart is used. Some countries have adopted a parent-held record, which the family brings to healthcare visits, but, apart from the immunization record, this has not been adopted in the US. Providers should identify and make referrals to resources that might help the family with any child health or development problems they are

Table 2   Periodicity schedule for well-child care in the US in infancy and early childhood: Anticipatory guidance sample content for visits 1 week to 5 years[a]

Age	Questions for parents	Developmental observation	Exam and screening	Health and safety habits	Parent–infant interaction	Family relationships/community interaction
First week	How is baby doing? Any concerns?	Startles to sound Fixes on human face and follows	Plot growth CDC charts Check screen results	Rear-facing car seat Back to sleep Breastfeeding	Hold, cuddle, play with baby	Encourage partner to help with care Accept support from family and friends
1 mo	Baby's personality? Feeding cues?	Lifts head momentarily when prone	Cradle cap Diaper dermatitis	Bath safety Delay solids until 4–6 mos.	Baby's temperament Crying peak at 6 weeks	Discuss childcare, return to work Family planning
2 mos	Parenting enjoyment/ difficulties?	Reciprocal coo/ vocalizing	Plot growth Torticollis, cardiac murmurs	Avoid soft bedding Never shake baby	Responsive? Maternal depression?	Take time for self Meet needs of other children
4 mos	Understand baby's need?	Raises body on hands Grasps rattle	Possible neglect Growth	Childproof home Start solids 4–6 mos	Talk, sing, read to baby Bedtime routine	Choose babysitters Consider parenting classes
6 mos	Feeding?	Babbles. Sits with support	Tone. Use of extremities	Water safety Avoid choking hazards	Separation anxiety?	Maintain family contact Folic acid if considering pregnancy.
9 mos	Sleeping? Family supports?	Understands words? Exploring?	Neurological exam Anemia screen	Poison center Number First aid/CPR	Encourage safe exploration Sibling reactions	Simple rules/limits
1 yr	Discipline?	Pulls to stand Social games says 1–3 words	Assess risk of hearing loss, TB, lead	Let child feed self, use cup No sleeping with bottle	Praise good behavior Set limits	Limit caregivers Discuss childcare
15 mos	Joint activities–books, games?	Says 3–10 words Points to body parts	Growth Gait/walking	Check window guards Eat meals as family	Praise accomplishments Discipline: time out	Help child express joy, anger, sadness, fear
18 mos	Playmates? Activities?	Says 15–20 words	Caries Anemia risk	Avoid television Brush teeth	Consistent, brief discipline	Simple, short family outings
2 yrs	Toilet training? Tantrums?	Two-word phrases Two-step commands?	Growth Eyes (strabismus) Risks for vision, hearing	Supervise play Playground safety Fluoride toothpaste	Toilet train when ready Read to child	Discuss playgroups, Mommy and Me, intervention
3 yrs	Understand speech? Preschool?	Knows name, age, copies circle	BMI Screen vision, blood pressure	Car booster seat when ≥40 lbs	Encourage talking, reading	Handle anger constructively Preschool/Head Start
4 yrs	Interest in other children?	Plays with other children	BMI for age Screen hearing, vision	Handwashing Pedestrian safety Promote physical activity	Talk about experiences, school	Create family time
5 yrs	School readiness?	Print name Know address/telephone number	BMI Risk, hearing vision screen	BMI Risk, hearing vision screen Limit television	Read interactively	Meet teachers Prepare child for school

[a]Note this table describes sample content for illustration. Some content, for example, plotting growth, examination for cardiac murmurs, etc., will take place at every visit.
BMI, body mass index; CDC, centers for Disease Control, CPR, cardiopolmonary resescitation mos, months; TB, tuberculosis; TV, television; yrs, years.
Adapted from Green M and Palfrey S (eds.) (2000) *Bright Futures: Guidelines for Health Supervision of Infants, Children, and Adolescents*, 2nd edn. Arlington, VA: National Center for Education in Maternal and Child Health, with permission.

encountering. At the conclusion of each visit, the principal points discussed should be summarized both verbally and in writing, key health messages reinforced, and understanding checked. Fully addressing a family's needs might involve further advocacy on the part of the provider – for example, writing a report for the local school district to advocate for special education services.

If the family has unresolved concerns, either a telephone follow-up or an additional office visit should be scheduled, or the family referred to another provider or community resource. The provider's role is changing from that of an expert advisor, to one of a partner who comes alongside the family and helps them to strategize solutions to problems. The family should be encouraged to voice concerns they have about the advice they are being given – for example, if they won't be able to carry out the provider's recommendations due to lack of resources, or to cultural considerations.

Measurement of Healthcare Quality

As healthcare providers struggle to deliver comprehensive services, there are increasing gaps between services that are recommended and those that are provided. As a first step toward quality improvement, measures are needed to capture information about the content and quality of children's healthcare. (Promoting Healthy Development Survey (PHDS))-PLUS is a parent report measure developed by the Child and Adolescent Health Measurement Initiative (CAHMI). The PHDS-PLUS has been implemented in nine states as a component of Medicaid quality improvement efforts. The survey asks parents questions about discussions and information exchanged with their child's pediatric clinicians, for example, whether their clinician asked them whether they had any concerns about their child's development and, if so, whether the concerns were fully addressed. To date the PHDS-PLUS has revealed significant healthcare disparities. Families from minority racial/ethnic groups are less likely to report receiving family-centered care and anticipatory guidance on desired topics, yet are more likely to report having been assessed for smoking or substance abuse. Children who are reported by their parents to be at-risk for developmental delays based on responses to the Pediatric Evaluation of Developmental Status (PEDS) questions are actually less likely to be receiving preventive and developmental services. The PHDS-PLUS measure holds promise as a means to assess and compare the performance of healthcare plans, compare regional variability in service provision, and compare quality of care received by subgroups of children.

As healthcare providers work toward quality improvements in the way both acute and chronic care is delivered to young children, there has been a growth in the learning collaborative approach to practice improvement, through organizations like National Initiative for Children's Healthcare Quality (NICHQ) and the Center for Children's Healthcare Improvement (CCHI). At the same time, growing emphasis on the need to base healthcare on the best available evidence is leading to a re-examination of the effectiveness of many longstanding pediatric practices in the light of systematic literature reviews.

Schedule for Healthcare

Although healthcare during pregnancy has traditionally been regarded as distinct from the healthcare for the child that begins at the time of birth, the time from conception through early childhood really represents a continuum of growth and development. Events and exposures at any time during these early years can have profound effects on later health and should be addressed through a continuum of healthcare services.

Preconception

Within the healthcare system, there is tremendous untapped potential for improving early childhood health through the provision of preconception guidance. An important set of guidelines for preconception care has recently been released by the CDC. Women of childbearing age can substantially reduce the risk of congenital abnormalities including spina bifida by consuming adequate amounts of folic acid before and during pregnancy. Successful preconception management of exposures to the fetus posed by drugs, alcohol, and smoking could result in significant reductions in the number of low-birthweight babies and in the eradication of fetal alcohol syndrome, the most common known cause of mental retardation in the US. Advice about healthy nutrition and exercise could also contribute to better pregnancy outcomes, as could greater awareness of the reproductive risks resulting from exposure to occupational hazards, vaccine-preventable diseases, and sexually transmitted diseases such as HIV. For women with chronic diseases such as diabetes, thyroid problems, and epilepsy, adjustments of medications and optimal disease management could improve later pregnancy outcomes. A scheduled preconception visit to an obstetrician offers one model for care, currently exercised by only a small minority of the population; however, 50% of pregnancies in the US are unplanned, indicating that this preconception advice might be better delivered as part of general well-woman care.

Prenatal

Prenatal care should begin as soon as the mother is aware that she is pregnant; however, in the US approximately one in seven women do not attend until the second

Table 3   Recommended immunization schedule for persons aged 0–6 years – US (2007)

Vaccine ▼ Age ►	Birth	1 month	2 months	4 months	6 months	12 months	15 months	18 months	19–23 months	2–3 years	4–6 years
Hepatitis B[a]	Hep B	HepB		Certain high-risk groups		HepB			HepB series		
Rotavirus[b]			Rota	Rota	Rota						
Diphtheria, tetanus, pertussis[c]			DTaP	DTaP	DTaP		DTaP				DTaP
Haemophilus influenzae type b[d]			Hib	Hib	Hib[4]	Hib			Hib		
Pneumococcal[e]			PCV	PCV	PCV	PCV				PCV	
Inactivated poliovirus[f]			IPV	IPV		IPV					IPV
Influenza[f]						Influenza (Yearly)					
Measles, mumps, rubella[g]						MMR					MMR
Varicella[g]						Varicella				Varicella	
Hepatitis A[h]							HepA (2 doses)			HepA Series	
Meningococcal[i]										MPSV4	

This schedule indicates the recommended ages for routine administration of currently licensed childhood vaccines, as of 1 December 2006, for children aged 0–6 years. Additional information is available at http://www.cdc.gov/nip/recs/child-schedule.htm. Any dose not administered at the recommended age should be administered at any subsequent visit, when indicated and feasible. Additional vaccines may be licensed and recommended during the year. Licensed combination vaccines may be used whenever any components of the combination are indicated and other components of the vaccine are not contraindicated and if approved by the Food and Drug Administration for that dose of the series. Providers should consult the respective Advisory Committee on Immunization Practices statement for detailed recommendations. Clinically significant adverse events that follow immunization should be reported to the Vaccine Adverse Event Reporting System (VAERS). Guidance about how to obtain and complete a VAERS form is available at http://www.vaers.hhs.gov or by telephone, 800-822-7967.

[a]Hepatitis B vaccine (HepB) (minimum age: birth)

At birth

• Administer monovalent HepB to all newborns before hospital discharge.
• If mother is hepatitis surface antigen (HBsAg)-positive, administer HepB and 0.5 ml of hepatitis B immune globulin (HBIG) within 12 h of birth.
• If mother's HBsAg status is unknown, administer HepB within 12 h of birth. Determine the HBsAg status as soon as possible and if HBsAg-positive, administer HBIG (no later than age 1 week).

After the birth dose

• If mother is HBsAg-negative, the birth dose can only be delayed with physician's order and mother's negative HBsAg laboratory report documented in the infant's medical record.
• The HepB series should be completed with either monovalent HepB or a combination vaccine containing HepB. The second dose should be administered at age 1–2 months. The final dose should be administered at age ≥24 weeks. Infants born to HBsAg-positive mothers should be tested for HBsAg and antibody to HBsAg after completion of ≥3 doses of a licensed

HepB series, at age 9–18 months (generally at the next well-child visit).

4-Month dose

- It is permissible to administer four doses of HepB when combination vaccines are administered after the birth dose. If monovalent HepB is used for doses after the birth dose, a dose at age 4 months is not needed.

[b]Rotavirus vaccine (Rota) (minimum age: 6 weeks)

- Administer the first dose at age 6–12 weeks. Do not start the series later than age 12 weeks.
- Administer the final dose in the series by age 32 weeks. Do not administer a dose later than age 32 weeks.
- Data on safety and efficacy outside of these age ranges are insufficient.

[c]Diphtheria and tetanus toxoids and acellular pertussis vaccine (DTaP) (minimum age: 6 weeks)

- The fourth dose of DTaP may be administered as early as age 12 months, provided 6 months have elapsed since the third dose.
- Administer the final dose in the series at age 4–6 years.

[d]*Haemophilus influenzae* type b conjugate vaccine (Hib) (minimum age: 6 weeks)

- If PRP-OMP (PedvaxHIB® or ComVax® [Merck]) is administered at ages 2 and 4 months, a dose at age 6 months is not required.
- TriHiBit® (DTaP/Hib) combination products should not be used for primary immunization but can be used as boosters following any Hib vaccine in children aged ≥12 months.

[e]Pneumococcal vaccine (minimum age: 6 weeks for pneumococcal conjugate vaccine (PCV); 2 years for pneumococcal polysaccharide vaccine (PPV))

- Administer PCV at ages 24–59 months in certain high-risk groups. Administer PPV to children aged ≥2 years in certain high-risk groups. See MMWR 2000;49(No. RR-9): 1–35.

[f]Influenza vaccine (minimum age: 6 months for trivalent inactivated influenza vaccine (TIV); 5 years for live, attenuated influenza vaccine (LAIV))

- All children aged 6–59 months and close contacts of all children aged 0–59 months are recommended to receive influenza vaccine.
- Influenza vaccine is recommended annually for children aged ≥59 months with certain risk factors, healthcare workers, and other persons (including household members) in close contact with persons in groups at high risk. See MMWR 2006; 55(No. RR-10): 1–41.
- For healthy persons aged 5–49 years, LAIV may be used as an alternative to TIV.
- Children receiving TIV should receive 0.25 ml if aged 6–35 months or 0.5 ml if aged ≥3 years.
- Children aged <9 years who are receiving influenza vaccine for the first time should receive two doses (separated by ≥4 weeks for TIV and ≥6 weeks for LAIV).

[g]Measles, mumps, and rubella vaccine (MMR) (Minimum age: 12 months)

- Administer the second dose of MMR at age 4–6 years. MMR may be administered before age 4–6 years, provided ≥4 weeks have elapsed since the first dose and both doses are administered at age ≥12 months.

[h]Varicella vaccine (minimum age: 12 months)

- Administer the second dose of varicella vaccine at age 4–6 years. Varicella vaccine may be administered before age 4–6 years, provided that ≥3 months have elapsed since the first dose and both doses are administered at age ≥12 months. If second dose was administered ≥28 days following the first dose, the second dose does not need to be repeated.

[i]Hepatitis A vaccine (HepA) (minimum age: 12 months)

- HepA is recommended for all children aged 1 year (i.e., aged 12–23 months). The two doses in the series should be administered at least 6 months apart.
- Children not fully vaccinated by age 2 years can be vaccinated at subsequent visits.
- HepA is recommended for certain other groups of children, including in areas where vaccination programs target older children. See MMWR 2006; 55 (No. RR-7): 1–23.

[j]Meningococcal polysaccharide vaccine (MPSV4) (minimum age: 2 years)

- Administer MPSV4 to children aged 2–10 years with terminal complement deficiencies or anatomic or functional asplenia and certain other high-risk groups. See MMWR 2005; 54(No. RR-7): 1–21.

trimester. Usually, 7–11 visits are scheduled per pregnancy, and incorporate estimation of the expected date of delivery; education and counseling to reduce risk behaviors and promote health; and assessment of fetal growth through measurement of fundal height and ultrasound monitoring.

Screening is undertaken for maternal anemia, and for serum markers of neural tube defects and some chromosome abnormalities, with option for amniocentesis or chorionic villous sampling for women at increased risk. Genetic counseling is offered where indicated. Vitamin supplementation is commenced or continued, together with education about breastfeeding, the process of delivery, and early newborn care. Like well-child care, many of the current recommendations about prenatal care are derived from expert opinion, with varied strength of the scientific evidence behind a number of common practices.

Interconception

Interconception care, defined as care delivered between pregnancies, is particularly important for women who have experienced an adverse outcome from a previous pregnancy, for example, infant death, birth defect, or premature birth. Although most women attend a postpartum check-up at 4–6 weeks after delivery, there is no further systematic follow-up or intervention for women with these critical risk factors. Family physicians and internists, the women, infants, and children (WIC) nutrition sites or home visiting programs could all provide interconception services aimed at reducing risks for future pregnancies, optimizing maternal health prior to next conception, and screening for common post-pregnancy conditions like maternal depression. Care at this time could also identify women who are at increased risk of weight retention following weight gain during pregnancy, a factor associated with higher BMIs later in adult life. However, at least in the US healthcare system, this type of care remains uncommon.

Infancy

The American Academy of Pediatrics recommends that the first visit to the pediatrician should be scheduled in the last trimester of pregnancy. This prenatal pediatric visit allows the physician to establish a relationship with the parents, to gather basic information on parent needs, concerns, on family history, and to provide information and advice regarding expected newborn behavior and routine care. The visit also provides a good opportunity to identify any high-risk situations such as adolescent or single mothers and to make appropriate counseling or other referrals. Parents can be encouraged to start to build their own parenting skills, and the periodicity schedule for well-child care and immunizations can be discussed. Some pediatricians offer group prenatal visits to extend the time available for information exchange and to encourage mutual support among pregnant women and spouses.

The next visit occurs in the newborn period, when the baby is given a full physical examination shortly after birth. Most babies are born healthy, and parents are reassured to hear that the examination is normal, and move on to the tasks of learning to feed and care for their newborn, establishing a routine, and preparing to take their newborn home. For parents whose babies are born premature or with a disability, however, this period is one of stress, when the health professional will need to pay particular attention to the care and well-being of the parents, with a compassionate yet honest explanation of the infant's condition, as well as the medical care of the newborn. Many parents benefit at the newborn visit from administration of the Brazelton Neonatal Behavioral Assessment Scale, which helps them to interpret and respond appropriately to their newborn's behavior.

Following the newborn visit, a further six visits are scheduled prior to the first birthday, many timed to coincide with the immunization schedule (see **Tables 2** and **3**). Visits are recommended within the first week of life, then at 1, 2, 4, 6, and 9 months, key content areas for each of these visits are highlighted in **Table 1**. Further visits then occur at 1 year, 15 months, 18 months, 2 years, 3 years, 4 years, and 5 years. The wisdom of tying visit timing to the immunization schedule has been challenged, with suggestions that some visits should focus on important developmental transitions, for example, 'starting preschool'. Similarly, there is increasing recognition that families' needs for health supervision differ, with some high-risk families needing more frequent visits than currently recommended. Consequently, change to a risk-tiered visit schedule has been suggested.

Access to Healthcare

In contrast to the UK, where healthcare for all is a basic tenet of the National Health Service, and to Australia, where government-funded healthcare is provided as a safety net for those who do not have private health insurance, significant numbers of women and children in the US lack health insurance, and hence access to even basic healthcare services.

Access to Preconception, Prenatal, and Interconception Care

Almost 40% low-income women rely on Medicaid, the US safety net for healthcare coverage. At this stage of life, many women access the healthcare system only for acute illness, or for family planning services, limiting opportunities for preconception care. Women who do not have children under the age of 18 years, or who lack documentation of legal status are not eligible for Medicaid; however, an increasing number of states exercise their federal waiver authority to expand family planning services to women who otherwise would not qualify. Once women become pregnant, they are eligible for Medicaid coverage for prenatal care if they have no other source of healthcare coverage. However many women are unaware of this option, and even for those who are, there is an inevitable time lag to enrolment, often resulting in delayed access to prenatal care, sometimes not until the second trimester or later. These women then lose their Medicaid eligibility after their postpartum visit at 4–6 weeks postdelivery. Expansion of coverage for 1 year postdelivery could significantly improve access to interconception care, especially for those women with adverse pregnancy outcomes.

Access to Healthcare in Infancy and Early Childhood

Children from minority racial/ethnic groups and those from low-income families are less likely to be insured, have a regular source of healthcare and be fully immunized. Although families with income levels below 100% Federal Poverty Level are eligible for Medicaid if they are legal residents, significant numbers of these families remain unenrolled due to lack of information about the enrolment process, language barriers, and misunderstandings about eligibility criteria. The State Child Health Insurance Program (S-CHIP) is designed to help families with incomes just above poverty level who do not qualify for Medicaid; however, state budget restrictions result in limited program size, and in practice, the complexity of the eligibility and application process results in significant proportions of eligible families remaining unenrolled. For many of the uninsured, access to healthcare is only possible through inappropriate use of emergency services. Consequently, families most in need lack access to many health prevention and health promotion services. 'Free clinics' may offer care to all families who are unable to pay, regardless of immigration or employment status, and provide a 'safety net' of care for uninsured children. However, with few exceptions, they are generally not able to offer a full range of anticipatory guidance and health promotion services, and access to specialists is particularly limited.

Healthcare Professionals

While almost all young children in the US have a usual setting for well-child care, less than half see a specific clinician at each visit. The proportion with a single clinician is highest among privately insured children, and lowest among the uninsured, while publicly insured children are less likely to be seeing a provider chosen by their family. Healthcare services are delivered not just by physicians but by a range of nurses, specialists, allied healthcare providers, mental health providers, and care coordinators.

Physicians

In the US, physicians undergo a 4-year graduate course in medicine. This is followed by a 3-year residency, which may be completed in family medicine, pediatrics, internal medicine, or a range of specialty and subspecialty areas. Physicians then become board-certified in a general or specialist field. The increasing specialization of medicine has also resulted in a need for primary care providers to assist patients to determine which types of provider can best address their problem. Involvement of multiple providers creates challenges with information flow, and a need for the primary care generalist to track an increasing amount of information related to each patient.

Pediatricians provide 80% of the primary care to children in the US. The remainder are served by family practice physicians and nurse practitioners, especially in rural areas where pediatric services might be limited. This situation is in contrast to the UK and Australia, where most primary care for young children is delivered by general or family practitioners with shorter periods of training in pediatrics (6–12 months), while pediatricians act as specialists providing secondary consultation. In both the UK and Australia, nurses also play a large role in the delivery of well-child care.

Young children with special healthcare needs usually see one or more specialists in addition to their primary care provider. Pediatric endocrinologists, neurologists, surgeons, otorhinolaryngologists, and cardiologists, may all contribute to care. Neonatologists deliver specialist care in the newborn period. Hospitalists care for general pediatric patients when they are admitted for inpatient investigations or treatment of acute illness. Hospital admission is now relatively rare for otherwise well children, having undergone a 45% decline between 1962 and 2000. Consequently, it is difficult for the child's regular provider to remain familiar with hospital procedures, resulting in an increased likelihood that a 'hospitalist' will direct care during an inpatient stay. However, this arrangement introduces another provider into an already complex system that can be confusing for parents and professionals alike. In the medical home model, the primary care physician usually directs and coordinates care. However, specialists may at times assume this role – for example a hematologist might direct many aspects of care while a child with leukemia receives chemotherapy.

Nurse Practitioners, Registered Nurses

In the US, nursing is transitioning to a postgraduate profession. This change promises to promote the perception of nursing as a professional discipline, and may help recruitment to address a nationwide shortage of nursing staff. Increasing numbers of nurses are training as independent nurse practitioners, working either in their own practices, or alongside physicians in a joint or group practice setting. Other nurses work in clinical outpatient settings, in inpatient wards, or in specialized care areas such as intensive care. Nurses contribute to the care, comfort, and well-being of both children and parents. They play a very significant role in parent education and often have expert knowledge of additional resources available in the community to assist patients.

Allied Health Services

A range of allied health professionals serve as practitioners in their own right, delivering predominantly intervention and therapy services in hospital, clinical, and educational settings and sometimes in the child's own home. These professionals have either masters or doctoral degrees, national licensure, and, sometimes, board certification in specialist pediatric services. Speech therapists provide assessments, formulate treatment plans, and deliver intervention programs to children with a range of speech and language challenges, frequently working as members of a team. They treat children who have difficulty making speech sounds, who have fluency problems such as stuttering, and, increasingly serve a range of infants and young children with feeding and swallowing disorders. Occupational therapists help patients to perform daily tasks of living, often working with children with permanent disabilities such as cerebral palsy. They may work in rehabilitation center's intervention programs, or in preschool and home settings. Physiotherapists (or physical therapists) use therapeutic exercise or other modalities to treat physical dysfunction or injury in a hospital setting, intervention center, school, or home.

Audiologists test, monitor, and diagnose disorders of the auditory and vestibular systems, evaluate children who have failed hearing screens, and monitor children with established hearing loss. Child psychologists specialize in the assessment and treatment of children with mental health disorders and learning disorders. A variety of family therapists (psychologists, social workers, and marriage-family counselors) provide counseling services to families who are experiencing relationship difficulties. Social workers provide social services and assistance to improve the well-being of children and their families. Medical social workers provide support to families facing a child's acute or chronic illness. Other social workers support children who have been abused or neglected or are in the foster care system. There is an increasing need throughout the healthcare system for specialist case managers and care coordinators who may themselves be nursing or social work professionals.

Organization and Delivery of Healthcare

In the US, 74% of young children access primary healthcare services through office-based practices, community health centers, or ambulatory care centers attached to hospitals. Subspecialty services are more likely to be hospital based or hospital linked. A small proportion of children, usually those who are uninsured, obtain their medical care through free clinics.

Although many acute illnesses are diagnosed and treated within the physician's office, more serious acute illness and injury is managed in emergency rooms. While children who live near large medical centers and specialty children's hospitals generally have access to specialized pediatric emergency care, few general emergency rooms carry all recommended pediatric resuscitation equipment, while less than 25% have access to a doctor who is board-certified in pediatric emergency medicine. There is similar variation in intensive care services, with some children in rural areas being treated alongside adults in intensive care settings. Newborns requiring specialized treatment are admitted to neonatal intensive care units – some are co-located with birthing facilities, while others are co-located with children's hospitals, requiring transport of the newborn for care.

Public health services for children consider the health of entire populations, implement and monitor screening programs such as newborn hearing and metabolic screening, monitor and track infectious diseases such as tuberculosis, and address newer threats to children's health such as terrorism. The pediatric public health infrastructure in the US is relatively underdeveloped, with little focus on population health in the early childhood years.

Although most healthcare for young children is still delivered face-to-face in traditional settings, newer trends are slowly being incorporated into the healthcare delivery system such as use of telemedicine where a specialist many miles from the patient can make a diagnosis and recommend treatment through a video-link. Telemedicine has also been used in urban childcare settings, resulting in less attendance days lost due to illness. Over time, wider use of the internet for email communication between professionals and patients, and of the media for health education is expected.

Early Childhood Systems of Care

There is growing recognition within the early childhood field that the problems and challenges faced by young children cannot be addressed adequately by any one sector – health, education, or social services acting alone, especially if the focus is on health optimization. The challenge now is to convert traditionally fragmented services to a comprehensive, integrated, coordinated system of care for young children and their families. The barriers to this effort are formidable – service sectors have completely separate funding streams with few resources devoted to service integration; some previously independent professionals have little experience of working as a member of a team, and some existing care-coordination efforts are themselves fragmented and of limited effectiveness. Lack of reimbursement for care-coordination services, and pressures on physician's time, mitigate against full implementation of a medical home model. The Bright Futures framework offers a very detailed template for delivery of comprehensive health promotion and illness-prevention services for young children. However, the reality of office visits, which last less than 10–15 min in a managed care environment, mean that few of the recommended topics can be addressed during the healthcare encounter. In an effort to maximize service effectiveness for children and their families the focus now must shift from services to systems of care.

While the concept of school readiness could serve as a unifying theme for all the early childhood disciplines, in practice a common conceptualization has not yet been realized. However, initiatives are underway in the US, UK, Australia, and Canada to align the goals of early childhood services to address children's needs to be healthy and ready to learn at school entry. The involvement of the healthcare sector in these initiatives has, to date, been varied, but they present an opportunity for development of new models of early childhood care. In the US, the State Early Childhood Comprehensive Service Systems (SECCS) initiative brings together state Maternal and Child Health (MCH) and Children with Special Healthcare Needs (CSHN) programs with partners from education, human services, juvenile justice, childcare, and other public and private agencies to create a plan for services coordination for children between the ages of birth and 5 years. Programs such as Reach Out and Read, which provide books and literacy counseling to families during well-child visits, are starting to bridge the gap between healthcare and early education. In the UK, Every Child Matters has set out a case for system-wide reform of children's services to address service fragmentation, lack of information sharing, and lack of clear accountability, and Directors of Children's Services have been appointed in all local authorities. The Sure Start initiative has delivered integrated support, and provided early learning and play opportunities for children under 4 years in some of the poorest areas of the UK. There are plans to create 4000 such centers across the UK. At the same time, the National Service Framework for child health and maternity services has set standards for healthcare at the local level and is regarded as the health contribution to Every Child Matters. However, closer links between Sure Start and the healthcare sector are still needed. Both internationally, and nationally there is a growing focus on the early childhood years, and the need for effective service integration.

Healthcare Financing and Early Childhood Programs

Healthcare services for young children in the US are financed through a combination of public and private sources. While most children are privately insured, almost one-third of children under 6 years of age are covered by Medicaid. Among poor children, however, almost three-quarters receive Medicaid coverage, often through a managed care organization with restricted choice of providers. Even for children with private insurance, usually obtained through parental employment, a change in parent's employment or a change of plan by the employer can result in changes of coverage and providers. Title V programs administered through the states authorize and pay for specialty healthcare services for eligible children with serious and/or chronic medical conditions such as some birth defects, cerebral palsy, cancer, etc.

Children under age 3 years who have, or are at increased risk for developmental disability or delay are eligible for intervention through Early Start. Children aged 3 years and above receive ongoing therapeutic services only if they have eligible conditions which are substantially disabling such as mental retardation and autism. Consequently, a significant number of children in the US who receive services until the age of 3 years are no longer eligible beyond their third birthday. Some of these children go on to experience difficulties in the school setting, and later enter special education. Children's mental health services are largely accessed through private and government insurance, though Departments of Mental Health provide some services to children with serious emotional disturbances, and certain children receiving special education services. Services are also provided for children who have or are at risk of being abused or neglected, and for children in foster care.

Funding for healthcare for young children in countries other than the US is generally much simpler and less fragmented. In the UK, apart from a small minority of children who receive some services through private insurance, all services are covered through the National Health Service. Children receive preventive healthcare services such as immunizations and growth monitoring through their local general practitioner, though, increasingly, services are provided by health visitors or other nursing staff who work alongside the physician. Pediatricians are specialists who are accessed as secondary providers for diagnosis and management. The general practice model has definite advantages for the provision of whole-family medicine and the treatment of children in the context of their family, as parents usually have the same primary provider; however, financial incentives result in practitioner focus on adult health, so the range of health promotion services offered to children in the UK system is limited.

Policy Issues

Despite widespread acknowledgment of the importance of the early years for future child health, the US still lacks a comprehensive, integrated, and clearly articulated national early childhood healthcare policy. The organization and administration of children's healthcare services in the US is largely determined at the state and local level, resulting in considerable regional variations in service provision. Apart from the SECCS initiative, to date funded only for planning activities on a small scale, the need for early childhood service integration across health, early care and education, and social services has not been addressed in the policy arena. In contrast, the UK, for example, has in the last decade made a significant commitment to a national early childhood policy agenda incorporating healthcare services for children through the new National Service Framework, and through Every Child Matters.

As the US considers the future of early childhood healthcare, questions of service integration and new strategies which might blend funding streams across traditionally separate sectors feature prominently in policy discussions. The potential for public–private partnerships, and opportunities for cross-disciplinary initiatives meeting the health, early care, and education needs of young families close to where they live will be high on the policy agenda.

Conclusions

Growing understanding of the importance of optimizing health in early childhood as a foundation for health in adult life is moving children's healthcare to the center of national policy agendas. Healthcare for children begins not at the moment of birth, but before conception, when interventions to improve reproductive health, educate future parents about the implications of lifestyle choices, and reduce environmental risks could have significant benefit for the future well-being of children. The conceptualization of children's health as a broad capacity for life has resulted in a closer integration of child health and developmental services. Child health is no longer viewed as an attribute of the child alone, but as a

product of factors in the child, the family and the wider community that combine to produce the clinical picture. Child health providers of the twenty-first century are challenged to address biological, social, and psychological influences on children's well-being. Recognition of greater need for care coordination and provision of family-centered, culturally proficient care has led to the concept of the medical home as a 'safe haven' for families as they struggle to interact with an increasingly complex healthcare system.

The new role of the child health provider – delivering care as part of an interdisciplinary team, advocating for patient needs in the wider community, and building expertise in all aspects of child development and behavior has major implications for the way healthcare providers are trained, and services are delivered. Universal access to healthcare for young children is a necessary, though not sufficient, step to ensuring that the health needs of the youngest members of the population are fully addressed. Healthcare services capable of providing optimal health promotion, prevention, and treatment services for young children will require major changes in financing and the creation of functioning early childhood systems of care. These systems will need to be flexible, and capable of adapting both to new treatments made possible by the molecular and genetic revolutions, and to environmental threats to children's health such as high levels of child poverty in the US and newer threats such as terrorism. In a rapidly changing world, the relationship between child health provider and family must redefine itself into a functional partnership focused on achieving the best possible health outcomes for the child both in the short and long term. An optimal early childhood healthcare system could yield great rewards for the future health of nations, as children enter adult life equipped to optimize their own health and to become good parents to the next generation.

See also: AIDS and HIV; Allergies; Asthma; Breastfeeding; Illnesses: Autoimmune Rheumatological Diseases; Prenatal Care; Screening, Newborn and Maternal Well-being.

Suggested Readings

An P (2007) New born screening: Current status. *Health Affairs* 26(2): 559–566.
Aufseeser D, Berry D, Michael Weitzman MD, *et al.* (2004) *Early Child Development in Social Context: A Chartbook.* New York: Child Trends and AAP Center for Child Health Research, The Commonwealth Fund.
Committee on Evaluation of Children's Health; Board on Children Youth, Families; Division of Behavioral and Social Sciences and Education, National Research Council and Institute of Medicine (2004). *Children's Health, the Nation's Wealth: Assessing and Improving Child Health.* Washington, DC: National Academies Press.

Green M and Palfrey JS (eds.) (2002) *Bright Futures: Guidelines for Health Supervision of Infants, Children and Adolescents*, 2nd edn., revision. Arlington, VA: National Center for Education in Maternal and Child Health.

Halfon N and Hochstein M (2002) Life course health development: An integrated framework for developing health and financing health intervention. *The Milbank Quarterly* 80: 433–479.

Halfon N, Regalado M, McLearn KT, and Wright K (2003) *Building a Bridge from Birth to School: Improving Developmental and Behavioral Health Services for Young Children.* New York: The Commonwealth Fund.

Halfon N, Russ S, and Regalado M (2005) Healthcare during early childhood: The life course health development model: A guide to children's health care policy and practice. *Zero to Three* 25(3): 4–12.

Hall DMB and Elliman D (eds.) (2002) *Health for All Children.* Oxford, England: Oxford University Press.

Johnson K, Lloyd-Puryear MA, Mann MY, Ramos LR, and Therell BL (2006) Financing state newborn screening programs: Sources and uses of funds. *Pediatrics* 117(5): S270–S279.

Johnson K, Posner SF, Biermann J, *et al.* (2006) Recommendations to improve preconception health and health care – United States. *A Report of the CDC/ATSDR Preconception Care Work Group and the Select Panel on Preconception Care. MMWR* 55 (RR06): 1–23.

Keating DP, Hertzman C, and Mustard JF (eds.) (1999) *Developmental Health and the Wealth of Nations: Social, Biological and Educational Dynamics.* New York: Guildford Publications.

Kirkham J, Harris S, and Grzybowski S (2005) Evidence-based prenatal care: Part 1. General prenatal care and counseling issues. *American Family Physician* 71: 1307–1316.

National Research Council and Institute of Medicine (2000) From neurons to neighborhoods: The science of early childhood development. In: Shonkoff JP and Phillips DA (eds.) *Board on Children, Youth, and Families. Commission on Behavioral and Social Sciences and Education*, ch. 13, pp. 337–380. Washington, DC: National Academies Press.

National Survey of Children with Special Healthcare Needs, 2001. http://www.cdc.gov/nchs/about/major/slaits/cshcn.htm (accessed on 16 July 2007).

National Survey of Early Childhood Health. http://www.cdc.gov/nchs/about/major/slaits/nsech.htm (accessed on 16 July 2007)

Sameroff AJ and Fiese BH (2000) Transactional regulation: The developmental ecology of early intervention. In: Shonkoff JP and Meisels SJ (eds.) *Handbook of Early Childhood Intervention*, 2nd edn., pp. 135–159. Cambridge, UK: Cambridge University Press.

Wise P (2004) The transformation of child health in the united states. *Health Affairs* 23(5): 9–25.

Relevent Websites

http://www.aap.org – American Academy of Pediatrics.
http://www.childtrends.org – Child Trends, Social Science Research.
http://www.healthychild.org – Healthy Child Healthy World.
http://www.cahmi.org – The Child and Adolescent Health Measurement Initiative, Oregon Health and Science University.
http://www.cmwf.org – The Commonwealth Fund.
http://www.kff.org – The Henry J. Kaiser Family Foundation.

Hippocampus

L Nadel and A Hupbach, University of Arizona, Tucson, AZ, USA

Glossary

Allocentric space – A form of spatial knowledge based on relations amongst the objects in a space, independent of the observer.

Cognitive map – A postulated mental representation of allocentric space.

Developmental amnesics – Individuals with hippocampal damage from early in life, who present with a loss of episodic memory capacity but relative sparing of semantic memory capacity.

Egocentric space – A form of spatial knowledge based on relations between the observer, and entities in the environment.

Episodic memory – Memory for an event in one's life that includes knowledge of where and when the event transpired.

Long-term depression – The weakening of synaptic transmission as the function of certain patterns of stimulation, different from those eliciting long-term potentiation. Presumed to contribute to synaptic plasticity.

Long-term potentiation – The facilitation of synaptic transmission as the function of certain patterns of stimulation, different from those eliciting long-term depression. Presumed to contribute to synaptic plasticity.

Semantic memory – Memory for general knowledge acquired through experience, separated from the contexts within which this knowledge was acquired.

Spatial context – The environment within which events transpire. Can be defined either by the configuration of stimuli in the environment, or by individual salient elements.

Synaptic plasticity – The ability of synapses to change in strength, presumed to underlie the storage of information.

Introduction

The hippocampus undergoes substantial postnatal maturation. This brain structure is central to episodic memory and spatial mapping, and infants lack these cognitive capacities until 18 months of age or older. The still-maturing hippocampus is subject to influences from environmental and genetic factors, helping us understand diverse developmental phenomena.

The Hippocampus in Infancy

The 'hippocampus', a structure in the medial temporal lobe (**Figure 1**), plays a critical role in spatial cognition and explicit memory. Though the relation between these two functions remains a matter of current debate, there is general agreement that it has a highly specific role in each case. In the domain of spatial function it plays a central role in allocentric spatial cognition, permitting the construction of neural cognitive maps, and the use of these internal representations to locate places and navigate between them. This function is built upon the existence of 'place cells' in the hippocampus, and inputs from a system of 'grid cells' in the entorhinal cortex and 'head-direction' cells in a number of structures, including the postrhinal cortex and anterodorsal nucleus of the thalamus. The combination of information about places, distances, and directions in the hippocampus is assumed to lie at its ability to construct spatial maps. In the domain of memory it plays a critical role in 'episodic memory' and a supporting role in 'semantic memory'. Although semantic memory function is relatively spared in children with hippocampal damage, acquiring semantic information proceeds more rapidly in children without such damage. The hippocampus seems unimportant in various forms of 'implicit memory'.

What makes the hippocampus of particular interest in the study of infant development is the fact that it appears to undergo extended postnatal maturation. This maturational trajectory is likely to be central to our understanding of how certain cognitive functions emerge in early life. In this article we discuss evidence, from a variety of species, about hippocampal developmental and its time course. We then consider implications of this delayed maturation for both normal and abnormal development.

The Development of the Hippocampus

Evidence about the development of the hippocampus comes from studies of both structure and function. At present the best evidence comes from studies with rodents, but we now know enough about primates and humans to state a general case. Across a wide range of species it appears that the hippocampus first becomes functional at about the natural time of weaning. Unfortunately, we do not know when this is for humans; hence, we must make guesses based on anatomical, physiological, and behavioral data to determine just when the hippocampus becomes functional in humans. Note that it is unlikely that this, or any other, brain structure suddenly 'becomes' functional, as if by the flipping of a switch. It is more likely that hippocampal function emerges piecemeal, taking a considerable time to reach the adult state.

Structural Development

The hippocampus proper is divided into several distinct regions (**Figure 2**), each with its own basic cell types and the connections among them, and a set of inputs and outputs. In the 'dentate gyrus' and *CA* fields there are both principal excitatory neurons, the 'granule' and 'pyramidal cells', respectively, and a wide range of inhibitory neurons. Since both classes of neurons are critical to its function, understanding the development of each is essential.

It has been known for several decades that the dentate gyrus of the rat is particularly subject to postnatal development. Large numbers of dentate granule cells are

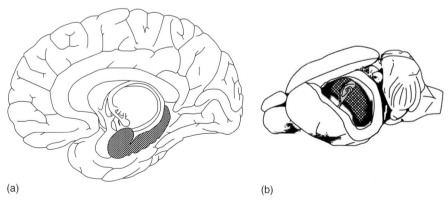

(a)   (b)

Figure 1 Location of the human (a) and rat (b) hippocampus within the brain (indicated by cross hatching).

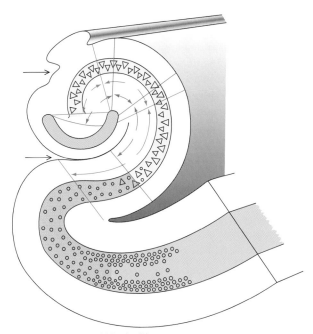

Figure 2 Areas within the hippocampus.

created after birth in the rat, in a special proliferative zone within the hippocampus itself. The discovery of this lifelong generation of new neurons disproved one of the central dogmas of central nervous system function – namely, that all of the neurons one will ever have are present at or shortly after, birth. We now understand that there is a steady creation of new dentate granule cells throughout life in the rat, at the rate of perhaps 10 000 per day, and that an animal's experiences help determine which, and how many, of these new cells survive. Exercise, for example, can increase the number of surviving cells. Recent work has suggested that exercise in a pregnant dam can increase the proliferation and survival, at least temporarily, of granule cells in that dam's pups. Going beyond this, the work of Meaney and colleagues, among others, shows that variations in how the mother rat treats her various pups – how much she licks each one, for example, translate into variations in hippocampal development. Although there is substantial evidence that new dentate neurons are incorporated into functional circuits, we do not currently understand how this happens, nor do we know if these newly formed neurons play some special role in memory.

Initially it was thought that rodents were unique, and that postnatal maturation of hippocampus was either absent or less prominent in primates and humans. This however turns out not to be the case. Even in these species the hippocampal system emerges into function well after birth.

Pyramidal cells, unlike granule cells, proliferate in the prenatal stage. But, two other critical components of any developed brain system, the integration of inhibitory neurons and the myelination of fibers, lag behind in

hippocampus. Much of the work supporting this claim was done by Laszlo Seress and colleagues, who conclude that while cells are generally born early, further steps critical to normal function are quite prolonged.

Specifics of Structural and Functional Development

A great deal is known about the physiological functions of the hippocampus, and its circuits. For example, we know that in the mature hippocampus one can observe not only place cells, but also characteristic patterns of collective neural activity demonstrating the coherent function of the structure as a whole. One such pattern is the 'theta rhythm', an oscillatory pattern seen across the entire extent of the hippocampus. This rhythm, typically 6–12 Hz in the rat (and perhaps 4–8 Hz, in primates and humans), plays a critical role in information processing by the hippocampus. Another feature of hippocampal physiology is the prominence of mechanisms of 'synaptic plasticity', such as 'long-term potentiation' and 'long-term depression', which are widely held to underlie its role in establishing spatial representations and episodic memories. If one asks when in a rat's development these signature features of physiological function are first observed, the answers are somewhat variable, but in most cases they suggest about 2–3 weeks of life.

The hippocampus, as a system, is subject to modulation from an extremely wide range of neurotransmitters and hormones. Cholinergic, dopaminergic, adrenergic, serotonergic, glutamatergic, and gamma-aminobutyric acid (GABA)ergic systems can all be observed, as well as other lesser-known transmitters that play a special role in inhibitory circuits (e.g., cholecystokinin or CCK and somatostatin). Given that the most recent count of inhibitory cell types within the hippocampus is greater than 20, one can imagine the wealth and diversity of such transmitters. In addition, the hippocampus is known to have particularly dense hormone receptor populations, among the densest in the brain. Both glucocorticoids such as corticosteroid (cortisol in primates and humans) and gonadal hormones such as estrogen play critical roles in hippocampal function. While the data on the emergence of these modulatory systems are not as rich, it is clear that many of them become functional only after several weeks of life in the rat.

In primates and humans we have less to go on. Granule cell proliferation is seen here as well, but we do not know a great deal about the maturation of adult-like physiology and pharmacology in these species. Anatomical studies, using postmortem material, show that at least inhibitory circuits in human hippocampus are still developing as late as 5 years of life. Structural neuroimaging studies also suggest an extended period of development, lasting at least 5 years, and perhaps longer. These data do not, of course, demonstrate the absence of hippocampal function during this entire period. Indeed, there is good evidence that function emerges earlier, rather than later, in this time frame. But adult levels of function might not be seen until early in childhood, well past infancy. Because the structural data from primates and humans are relatively sparse, much of our understanding of the developmental time course of hippocampus in these species comes from behavioral studies. Since we are not absolutely certain about the behavioral functions of this system, these data have to be interpreted cautiously. However, it is the functions of the system we are most concerned with ultimately; hence, findings in the behavioral domain are just as important, if not more important, than findings from structural studies. As we have already seen, structure emerges gradually over time, and translating structure directly into function is difficult if not currently impossible. Analysis of functional development may prove more revealing in the end. The major difficulty is making certain that the behavioral capacities we take as indices of hippocampal function actually depend critically on this structure. This turns out to be easier said than done.

Functional Studies of Hippocampal Development

It is known that in the rat the hippocampus is essential for a certain kind of spatial learning and memory, 'place learning'. The ability of a rat to locate itself or some goal such as a food source, or an escape hatch, clearly depends on the hippocampus, and can be readily measured in tasks such as the water maze, the radial maze, and the circular platform. In all these procedures rats (or mice) have to find a place using nonlocal cues, and it is generally assumed that they use distal information represented in 'allocentric' cognitive maps, to locate a place. These maps are also used to support learning about context, as a consequence of which the hippocampus plays a role in tasks such as contextual fear conditioning. In addition to this central role in place and context learning, the hippocampus also seems critical for spatial exploration, presumably because it is during such exploration that animals build up the cognitive maps they use to locate places and navigate.

In rodents, it seems, we could use the appearance of exploration and place learning as markers of the emergence of hippocampal function. Data from such studies in general support what was deduced from studies of structure – namely, that hippocampal function begins at about 3 weeks of life in the rat. There are several important caveats. First, there are marked individual differences – in any group of rats, exploration emerges in each rat more or less overnight, any day between

postnatal day 15 and 25. Exactly what generates this variation is poorly understood at present. Factors both genetic and epigenetic (e.g., the mother's licking and grooming of the pups) must exert influence here, but much more remains to be learned about the details. Second, the emergence of exploration is quite abrupt, literally overnight in any individual animal, but the emergence of place learning seems much more gradual. Place learning itself might reflect the interaction of multiple processes, making gradual maturation easier to understand. All this shows that there is no easy mapping from structural maturation to functional maturation, even in the rat.

But what about functional maturation of the hippocampal system in primates and humans? In contrast to the general agreement about the best tasks to assess the functions of the rat hippocampus, there is a history of disagreement about which kinds of tasks absolutely demand the presence of a functioning hippocampus in primates, and which do not.

Development of Hippocampal Function in Primates and Humans

As noted earlier, the two major cognitive functions that depend upon the hippocampus are episodic memory and memory for spatial location with reference to surrounding landmarks (allocentric spatial cognition). Episodic memory refers to memory for experiences, which includes information about both the content of the experience and the specific spatial and temporal context in which the experience occurred.

Episodic Memory

Since most studies of the development of episodic memory look at preschool and school-age children, little is known about the neuronal bases of these cognitive capacities in younger children. In general, little evidence of memory in standard recall and recognition tests is observed until the age of 3 or 4 years. It has been a methodological challenge to study episodic memory in infants, because infants are greatly limited in the responses they can provide, that is, they are not able to express themselves verbally and are also limited in their coordinated actions. However, several paradigms were developed in the past decade with an eye toward shedding light on the early maturation of episodic and spatial memory.

One task that some have assumed to reflect episodic memory is 'deferred imitation', a nonverbal analog to cued verbal recall in which infants observe an experimenter performing specific actions with novel objects. After a delay, the infant's ability to reproduce the actions is assessed. Memory is inferred when infants perform the observed actions more often than control actions that had not been demonstrated. It has been argued that deferred imitation taps episodic memory because imitation does not depend upon practice, and because a single demonstration of the target action is sufficient to show an imitation effect. The assumption here is that learning that requires only one trial necessarily involves the hippocampal system. In adults, remembered episodic memory experiences are often also encountered only once, in a specific spatiotemporal context. Additionally, deferred imitation was assumed to involve the hippocampus because patients with medial–temporal lobe amnesia have difficulties with age-adjusted versions of the task. The earliest evidence for deferred imitation is seen around 6 months of age. However, at this age, memory is neither reliable nor robust. Large age-related improvements are seen throughout infancy such that older infants encode more complex events, recall actions more often in the correct order, are able to retain information for longer periods, and are less susceptible to interference. Interestingly, these age-related improvements are apparently not due to differences in encoding; rather, they seem to reflect improvements in storage and consolidation processes. This conclusion is based on studies that relate delayed imitation performances to recognition of the presented sequences immediately after encoding (to assess how much was initially encoded) and again after a delay (to assess how much was stored). In one study, 9-month-olds watched the experimenter perform several sequences. Immediately after encoding and again 1 week later, recognition of the sequences was inferred from differential event-related potentials (ERPs) to pictures of previously presented and new sequences. ERPs measure the electrical activity of the brain in relation to the presentation of stimuli. One month after the last ERP measure, infants were invited to imitate the sequences. Interestingly, failure of ordered recall was linked to the delayed, but not to the immediate, ERP recognition indices. This result is suggesting that differences in recall were due to differences in storage and consolidation rather than encoding. One shortcoming of this approach is the presumed linkage to hippocampus itself. The amnesic patients who were impaired on this task had damage to the wider medial–temporal lobe region, and it remains unclear whether their problems with this task stemmed from hippocampal or extra-hippocampal damage in that brain region.

Two other memory tasks studied with infants and nonhuman primates that were presumed to reflect episodic memory are the visual-paired comparison (VPC) task, and the delayed nonmatching-to-sample (DNMS) task. In the VPC task, two identical visual stimuli are presented, as a pair, for a period of time. After a delay, one copy of the stimulus is presented again, but this time paired with a new stimulus. Looking time to each stimulus is measured. If the old stimulus is recognized, subjects should show a preference for the new stimulus, that is, they should look longer to the new, unfamiliar stimulus. This novelty preference is seen in infants shortly after birth and in nonhuman primates in the first weeks or month of life.

Because hippocampal lesions in adult humans and monkeys disrupted performance in the VPC task, it was assumed that the early emergence of competence on this task proved the early emergence of hippocampal function. However, visual preference is apparently not based on the same processes in infants and adults. Infants' ability to recognize the old stimulus, and preferentially attend to the novel stimulus, reflects familiarity alone, absent the recollective component of recognition memory observed in adults. In cases of developmental amnesia one observes an impairment of recollection-based memory with no impairment in familiarity-based memory.

It has been proposed that development of the context-rich memory capacity supporting recollection is associated with the progressive maturation of the dentate gyrus and hippocampus proper and their integration with media–temporal cortical areas in late infancy and childhood, and that the precursors of such memories, as seen in the early performance of the VPC task, are mediated by the perirhinal cortex. This assumption is supported by the finding that novelty preference in monkeys with selective neurotoxic lesions of the hippocampus does not differ from that in control monkeys at the ages of 1 and 6 months but starts to deteriorate around 18 months of age, especially at longer delays. Support also comes from case studies of children with developmental amnesia, referred to earlier, a condition that results from early hippocampal damage caused by hypoxic or ischemic episodes suffered early in life. These children show a severe global impairment of episodic memory including verbal, nonverbal, and spatial memory, but relative sparing of semantic memory. Most interestingly, the episodic memory deficit is not apparent early in life, but becomes evident in the middle childhood years. This has been interpreted as supporting the idea that the early precursors of episodic memories only gradually mature into context-rich hippocampally dependent functions later in middle childhood. Whether involvement of hippocampal regions develops 'gradually' remains controversial. As will be seen in the following section, rather abrupt qualitative changes can be observed around the age of 22 months, especially in the spatial domain.

In the DNMS task, a sample object is presented for a period of time. After a delay, the sample object is presented alongside a new object. Subjects are rewarded for choosing the new object over the old object. In comparison to the VPC task, children succeed in this task rather late, around 21 months of age. While early studies concluded that recognition memory and hence the medial temporal lobe mature late, subsequent studies have shown that it is not the memory requirement of the DNMS task that causes its late development but rather the ability to grasp the relation between the novel object and the reward. For instance, even 6-month-olds succeeded in the task when the objects themselves served as the reward. This does not, however, allow us to conclude that the hippocampus matures early. Much as turned out to be the case with the VPC task, more recent work has shown that performance on the DNMS task depends heavily on neocortical regions adjacent to the hippocampus, rather than on the hippocampus itself.

In sum, most of the data from the study of memory development presumed to address the functional emergence of the hippocampus comes from studies using tasks that are now known not to require this structure. This puts a premium on data from the study of spatial cognition, since the role of the hippocampus in this cognitive capacity is better understood, and tasks definitely requiring hippocampal participation are well known.

Spatial Cognition

Infants at quite a young age can learn about space as it relates to their body or its parts (eyes, hand, head). They can learn to crawl or walk to objects in space, and readily solve simple spatial tasks such as 'go right', or 'go to the door and turn left'. These kinds of spatial learning do not depend upon a functioning hippocampus.

Other spatial abilities rely upon the hippocampus. The most prominent of these abilities is 'place learning', the ability to locate places independent of one's own position based on the relations among surrounding distal landmarks. Remembering the location of more than one object, retaining an object's location for a prolonged period of time and remembering an object's location based on another object's position are other abilities that critically involve the hippocampus. Studies with infants and children report age-related improvements in all of these abilities between the first and second year of life.

In an early study, toddlers either 1 or 2 years of age were tested for their ability to relocate a hidden object. The experimental apparatus consisted of a quite large (c. 8 ft diameter) circular platform located in the middle of a room. Eight inverted pie plates were equally spaced around the perimeter of the platform. The toddler was encouraged to move onto the platform and to observe the experimenter hiding a toy under one of the plates. Then the toddler was led away from the apparatus, occupied for a short delay of 30–60 s, and then asked to go back to the platform to retrieve the object. Several conditions were employed to vary the kinds of strategies the toddler could use to solve this task. In one case, the platform was surrounded by a curtain, which cut off the toddler's view

of objects at a distance, and a large object was placed just near the 'target' pie plate. This object made it easy for the toddler to re-locate the toy. Comparable 'cue-based' tasks are readily solved by rats with damage to the hippocampus, and both the 1- and 2-year-old toddlers performed well. Much the same result was seen when the toy was hidden under a colored pie plate, making it easy to distinguish which pie plate to approach without reference to spatial location. However, when there were no local cues to help solve the task, and toddlers had to use the allocentric relations among the more distant room features to solve the task, the 1-year-old toddlers failed and the 2-year-olds succeeded. This kind of task is known to require hippocampal participation in rats and monkeys.

In a particularly important study carried out by Newcombe and colleagues, children aged 16–36 months observed an experimenter bury a toy in a rectangular sandbox. Then, children moved to the opposite side of the sandbox and were asked to retrieve the toy. In one condition, the sandbox was surrounded by several visible room landmarks. In another condition, a featureless curtain obscured the landmarks. Only children older than 22 months of age performed better when the landmarks were visible, that is, only they used the relationship between distal landmarks to remember the object's location.

The Special Case of Spatial Context

The hippocampus plays an important role in representing spatial contextual information, given its central role in spatial mapping. Considerable research shows that the ability of an adult rat to encode spatial context depends upon the hippocampus; hence, the emergence of this ability should tell us something about when the hippocampus becomes functional in development.

Rovee-Collier and colleagues, studying infants in an operant training procedure, manipulated context to address the emergence of hippocampal function. Their basic paradigm involves training infants to move an overhead mobile by kicking. During training a string links the infant's ankle and the mobile. Very young infants can learn that their leg-kicks make the mobile move, although this memory only lasts 1–2 days in 2-month-olds, increasing to 13 weeks in infants aged 18 months. The ability of infants to encode context was assessed by asking how specific the kicking habit is – would it persist when the context is changed? Using this paradigm, it appeared that quite young children, perhaps as young as 3–6 months, encoded features of the context, although they also appeared to forget them rapidly.

Unfortunately, these studies are difficult to interpret given that the hippocampus plays a critical role in mediating only certain kinds of contextual representations. The features of a place that define a situational context are represented in the brain both as part of a configuration and as isolated elements. The hippocampus is necessary for configurational context, but not for elemental context. The operant training studies manipulating context did not take into account this subtlety about the nature of spatial context. In the critical experiments what was taken as context was likely to have been learned in an elemental rather than configurational way. Hence the fact that contextual effects in these studies emerged early in life proves little about the development of the hippocampus. Only when configurational aspects of the context are manipulated are the functions of the hippocampus necessarily being assessed. In practice, this would require leaving all the elements in the situation but changing their configural relations.

Implications of Postnatal Maturation of the Hippocampus

There are several major implications of the postnatal maturation of the hippocampus. The first concerns behavior. We assume adult behavior reflects the presence of both hippocampal and nonhippocampal systems, what they do and how they interact. Prior to hippocampal emergence, however, behavior reflects functions/behaviors dependent on brain systems operational at birth. We discuss shortly what it means to grow up without a hippocampus.

The second major implication concerns development. A developing system is more susceptible to influence than an already developed one. This is presumably why environmental influences exert a particularly strong impact on the developing hippocampus. We will see below that susceptibility goes beyond the environment; certain genetic conditions also seem to affect hippocampus disproportionately.

Behavioral Implications – Growing Up with a Developing Hippocampus

Given the functions of the hippocampus, the absence of this brain system early in life should translate into an inability to form and retrieve episode memories and to form and use allocentric spatial maps. We have already discussed data concerning both of these assertions – it is precisely these studies that provide some of the strongest evidence that the hippocampus matures postnatally.

The absence of episode memories from the first 2 years of life resulting from the late maturation of the hippocampus can help us understand at least part of the syndrome of 'infantile amnesia'. It is a well-established fact that for most individuals few, if any, early episode memories survive into adulthood. It is only after 2–3 years of age that significant numbers of episode memories appear to be formed and retained. Over the years there has been considerable debate as to whether this syndrome, first discussed at length by Freud, reflects biological maturation, or some other factors, such as the mismatch between the

nonverbal coding of early memories and the verbal means used later in life to retrieve and report memories or the emergence of a sense of self at around 2–3 years of age. Arguments against the biological case depend on assertions that the hippocampus develops early in life, as noted above. These assertions, as we have seen, rested either on the use of inappropriate tasks or on incorrect interpretations of the nature of contextual coding and the hippocampal role in it. Now that a consensus has emerged to the effect that hippocampus is most likely to become functional between 18 and 24 months of age on children, we can conclude that a significant part of infantile amnesia reflects biological maturation.

Further support for this view comes from the study of the unique population of 'developmental amnesics', individuals with damage to the hippocampus caused, typically, by an early anoxic or ischemic event. These individuals, mentioned above, went unrecognized for quite a while because they did reasonably well in educational settings. Only careful testing brought out the fact that they suffered from quite severe losses in the domain of episodic and spatial memory. Developmental amnesics have general difficulties orienting in space and time, remembering events, finding their way through any but the most familiar environments, and remembering where they placed objects. However, they are usually not impaired in their social and language development and score low to average on standard tests of intelligence. They have a relative preservation of semantic memory and often show normal scores on immediate or short-term episodic memory tests, but they are unable to retain episodic information over longer periods of time. Studies using structural magnetic resonance imaging suggest that the described symptoms of developmental amnesia are caused by bilateral hippocampal volume reduction of at least 20–30%.

The increased susceptibility to influence following from postnatal development of the hippocampus manifests itself in two rather different ways. First, the hippocampus seems to be very sensitive to environmental perturbations. Careful studies of the neuropsychological impact of early exposure to lead, for example, suggest that impairment of hippocampal function contributes to the resulting cognitive deficit. Second, genetic conditions that influence development in a general way seem to have their greatest impact on late developing parts of the nervous system (and other organ systems as well). There is a kind of selection bias inherent here – genetic conditions that affect structures formed early in development might have such devastating effects that they are inevitably lethal. Influences on late developing structures might be prevalent simply because they are the only ones that can be survived.

Down syndrome presents such a case. This condition, resulting from an error in very early embryonic life, almost always reflects the existence of an extra copy of chromosome 21. As a consequence, extra gene product results, and this in turn leads to a variety of problems in a host of biological systems. In almost all cases these problems seem to impact the later developing parts of the relevant system. Thus, in the nervous system, the hippocampus, cerebellum, and prefrontal cortex, all of which mature late, are disproportionately affected. How these effects translate into the mental retardation observed in Down syndrome remains to be determined, and the creation of appropriate mouse models is moving toward that goal. Williams syndrome might present another such case, as it has recently been shown that children with this syndrome, caused by deletion of a subset of the genes on chromosome 7, have significant abnormalities in hippocampal structure and function.

Conclusions

Evidence from a variety of sources shows that the hippocampus matures late in infancy; in humans the best estimate is that few signs of behavioral functions attributable to the hippocampus can be observed prior to 16–18 months of age. As a result, infants prior to this age lack certain spatial and memorial capacities. Infant behavior, and learning, reflect instead the unfettered functions of other brain systems that emerge into function earlier in life. A great deal of learning does take place, but most of it fits into the category of implicit knowledge – how to do things and what things mean, but without any explicit sense of where this knowledge came from. What is more, this knowledge is unattached to its context of acquisition, a fact that can have important clinical implications when the learning in question concerns acquired fears for

example. It has been suggested that some phobias reflect early learning of this sort, the phobic person having little or no idea how, where and when their fear emerged. This state of affairs makes it all that much more difficult to treat the phobia itself.

Much more remains to be learned about the details of hippocampal development. We do not understand how gradual changes in the underlying neurobiological substrate translate into its various functions. We do not understand why some of the functions dependent on this structure emerge abruptly while others emerge gradually. Given that the late development of the hippocampus renders it susceptible to disruption from a number of sources, answers to these and other questions about this prolonged maturation promise to have substantial practical implications.

See also: Brain Development; Brain Function; Down Syndrome; Habituation and Novelty; Lead Poisoning; Memory.

Suggested Readings

Bachevalier J and Vargha-Khadem F (2005) The primate hippocampus: Ontogeny, early insult and memory. *Current Opinion in Neurobiology* 15: 168–174.

Frotscher M and Seress L (2007) Morphological development of the hippocampus. In: Andersen P, Morris R, Amaral D, Bliss T, and O'Keefe J (eds.) *The Hippocampus Book*, pp. 115–131. New York: Oxford University Press.

Johnson MH (ed.) (1993) *Brain Development and Cognition: A Reader.* Oxford, UK: Blackwell.

Nadel L and Willner J (1989) Some implications of postnatal maturation of the hippocampus. In: Chan-Palay V and Kohler C (eds.) *The Hippocampus: New Vistas*, pp. 17–31. New York: Alan R. Liss.

Humor

D Bergen, Miami University, Oxford, OH, USA

Glossary

Humor – A quality that emphasizes a sense of the ludicrous or incongruous; something designed to be comical or amusing and to provoke laughter.

Humor development – The process of changes in humor expression and appreciation during the life span, from infancy to adulthood.

Humor frame – A setting designated as open to expressions of the ludicrous, incongruous, comical, or amusing in which actions and responses are designed to elicit laughter.

Humor-related laughter – An expression of amusement that occurs within a humor frame.

Humorous hyperbole – Extravagant exaggeration used to provoke laughter.

Incongruity humor – Action or language that is incompatible with known information, which is designed to provoke a humor response.

Joking facade – Action or language that conveys socially unacceptable meaning within a false or superficial humorous frame.

Sense of humor – The mental faculty of discovering, expressing, or appreciating the ludicrous or absurdly incongruous; a pervasive style for approaching life events.

Social laughter – Reacting to action or language intended to be humorous within a social situation without understanding the meaning of the humor.

Introduction

The term 'humor' has been used to mean many different things over the course of history, including its original Latin meaning of 'fluid' (e.g., the humors of the body such as blood and bile). Perhaps because these fluids were also associated with health and temperament, humor generally became a word associated with personality; thus, having a disposition of cheerfulness was evidence of 'good humor'. At times the term humor has also been used to define unusual types of behavior, such as those exhibited by the 'jester', the 'comic', or the 'clown'. In general, however, humor has been considered a positive comprehensive term that signals ones' well-being. In fact, humor was considered one of the 'cardinal virtues' in the nineteenth century.

The concept of humor has at times also been differentiated from other similar concepts such as wit, irony, and satire, with the differentiation being on the basis of intentionality. Humor was often seen as an unintentional dispositional characteristic, while wit, satire, and other specific humor forms were seen as intentionally generated for an audience. Today there are still multiple uses of the term humor. Sometimes it is used as an 'umbrella-term' that encompasses other terms, and at other times it is considered just one element of the comic, which also includes wit, satire, sarcasm, ridicule, irony, and many other verbal or visual actions designed to elicit laughter. In discussions of the 'sense of humor', however, the term humor is usually considered as encompassing many facets of temperament, personality, cognition, and social–emotional life, and for the purposes of this review, this encompassing definition of humor is accepted.

In regard to the humor of adults, there have been many approaches to the study of the sense of humor, including empirical investigations of temperament qualities related to humor, cross-cultural comparisons of humor-eliciting material, the relation of humor characteristics to psychological and physical health, the uses of humor as a coping mechanism, the components defining humor as a personality trait, and the characteristics of humor used by professional comedians and clowns. Humor expression in fictional literary works has also been studied extensively, as have humor-related essays incorporating specific types of humor such as sarcasm, irony, and wit. The effects of humor use on performance in teaching, business, legal, and medical fields, and in other professions have also been of research interest, as have issues of gender differences in humor and its use in promoting or countering stereotypes of women, ethnic/racial minorities, or other groups. The role of humor in adult life thus has been examined by many scholars from both theoretical and research-based perspectives, but the question of how humor develops over the course of childhood has not been a subject of as great research or theoretical interest, nor has there been much interest in studying when and whether children can be said to have a sense of humor. One reason that humor researchers may not have viewed a sense of humor as being a facet of young children's personality was probably because they were focused on the more sophisticated forms of humor that require abstract thought, which is not evident in the humor of young children. However, the types of humor that children do exhibit are not lost at later ages; adults still laugh at physical humor (e.g., pratfalls), nonsense, jests, and social games.

The study of humor as a developmental phenomenon, in which its presence and changing manifestations over the years of early and later childhood are observed, has begun to be of theoretical and research interest in more recent times. Since this interest began, there has been progress in charting the course of humor development, explaining the purpose and course of that development from various theoretical perspectives, and providing information on how to promote humor development in children. Greater attention has been given to observing and facilitating young children's cognitive, social–emotional, language, academic, and even play development, however, than to issues of humor development. This is all the more surprising because one of the first indicators of social–emotional, language, and cognitive incongruity development is the child laughter that is elicited during infant and parent peek-a-boo and other early social games. Because humor development is embedded in many other developmental achievements, attention to this domain is certainly warranted. This article discusses what is known about humor development in early childhood, theoretical perspectives on the reasons for this development, how humor development may enhance young children's overall development, and the role of adults in fostering such development.

Humor Development

Ages Infant to 3 Years

Infant laughter may be observed even in the first few months of life as a response to tickling, but those laughter responses are not considered as evidence of humor.

Research indicates that these early laugh responses are probably related to emotional expression generated by the limbic system of the brain rather than to frontal lobe development. That is, they are more of an automatic response rather than a specific social response or observation of an incongruous action. Beginning at about 4–5 months, and definitely in the second half of the first year, as the frontal lobe of the infant brain begins to develop connections with the limbic system, children show the first evidences of true humor-related laughter. By 6 or 7 months, reciprocal social games such as peek-a-boo, which contain elements of behavioral expectations and routines of surprise on the part of both participants, are a primary source of humor. Observers of such interactive social games see progression from a situation in which the actions are initially controlled by the parent (parent actor/child responder) to one that is gradually taken over by the child (child actor/parent responder), with increasing expressions of child and adult laughter as the game becomes more intense and violations of expectations more elaborated by the child's actions. Humor results because the actions are 'misexpected' not 'unexpected'. The infant already knows what ordinary social interactions with the parent are like; these interactions are perceived as different because they are performed within a 'humor frame'. That is, even at this early age, young children can distinguish between 'serious' and 'humorous' behaviors in familiar adults. However, because their cognitive competence is still limited, they may have difficulty assimilating humor frame actions from unfamiliar persons and thus the incongruity behaviors of strangers may elicit fear responses rather than laughter.

There have been a number of recent studies of very young children's development of humor comprehension and expression. These studies show that infants and toddlers first use preverbal symbols, then deliberate finger and body movements, and finally symbolic play to initiate humor with parents. Toddler humor attempts include verbal humor such as mislabeling with incongruent labels, verbal puns, and nonsense word production. Two-year-old humor has been labeled 'iconoclastic' by researchers because it is often designed to gain control in social interaction situations. Toddlers self-generate much humor as well as being surprisingly sophisticated interpreters of humor events that are related to what they already know. That is, they demonstrate their increasingly sophisticated understanding of their world. Their ability to use 'practical deception' in a playful way indicates that they are beginning to have some sense that they are aware others think differently than they do. These behaviors are particularly observed in the pretend behaviors that are prominent in the second and third years of life. At this point, toddlers already seem to be aware of the 'audience' that is needed for humor to be effective. Because much toddler humor is self-generated and a response is expected from the adult, this is evidence that there is a humorous intent in the behavior.

Play and humor arise at similar times and are closely tied in infancy; however, when pretend play develops, humor begins to diverge from play to become a separate entity; that is, the 'play frame' and the 'humor frame' become differentiated. In 'serious' pretend play, the child tries to simulate the real world, using pretense to enact ordinary life events. Although often performed in the presence of others, this type of pretense can also be a solitary activity. In contrast, 'humorous' pretense requires an audience because the pretense is designed to deliberately distort reality in order to get a surprised or humorous response from other people. That is, humorous pretense is deliberately designed to get a reaction from another person and to trigger laughter. Toddlers' ability to use this type of playful deception is evidence that they are aware that the humor frame can be used to explore the ideas and expectations of other people.

In studies of parent reports of their young children's observed humor acts, a number of types of humor were described in the toddler years. Examples of toddler humor gained from parent reports include making 'funny' faces or exaggerated movements (clowning), repeating funny sounds or words (sound play), mislabeling objects or people (using incongruous language), using objects in unusual ways to elicit laughter (performing incongruous actions), provoking actions in another by calling names or grabbing possessions (teasing), and expressing joy in movement play and social games (social mastery). Another phenomenon often observed in toddlers is 'social laughter', joining into the laughter of others without understanding the meaning of the laughter. While this is not an indication of understanding humor, it is additional evidence that the child has learned the 'humor frame' and is able to interpret social occasions as either humorous or serious.

A recent study comparing the humor development of children with Down syndrome and those with autism (chronological age about 4 years but development age range of about 1–2 years) found that the children with Down syndrome who were of toddler developmental age exhibited teasing, clowning, and social laughter behaviors while the autistic children rarely did. Because autism often interferes with children's ability to interpret social interactions and connect socially with others, while Down syndrome does not interfere with children's interest in social interactions, these findings are not surprising. The children with Down syndrome were also much more likely to laugh socially without understanding the meaning of the humor event, than were the children with autism, who occasionally showed 'false' laughter when alone. Other observational studies done in early childhood programs for toddlers with special needs also have produced examples of laughter induced by social games, sound play, incongruous actions, and clowning, as well as evidence of the social laughter generated by being in a humor-related social setting. Often the teachers played a similar role to that of parents by being the initiators of these social games or other activities, but the humorous events were then continued and extended by the toddlers in the same manner that infants extend their early social games. Studies of gifted children's humor have also produced many examples of early humor development. Toddlers who are gifted often exhibit humor that is more typical of that shown in the preschool-age period. It may be that, because their knowledge base is usually more extensive, they see funniness in incongruous sounds, word use, or actions that other children do not yet notice. Often parents of gifted children indicate that one of the first reasons they suspected giftedness was because of their children's advanced appreciation and expression of humor.

Ages 4–6 Years

The age period from 4 to 6 years is a major time for humor development, and children's ability to enjoy and express humor grows exponentially. While children of this age continue to exhibit all of the forms of humor that toddlers express, they are particularly interested in incongruity humor, as their own knowledge of the world expands. Parental reports show examples of preschool children engaging in elaborations of familiar songs and stories (making simple parodies), substituting nonsense words or using word play in elaborated sequences (usually interactively with a peer), laughing at word play with multiple meanings (having snow in the bed will make ice cold pop), describing impossible events (exaggerated tall tales), and beginning to tell pre-riddles, riddles, and simple knock–knock jokes. They also enjoy these types of humor in books and on television or DVDs, and many book authors and script writers include the types of humor young children appreciate. For example, in the book *Butter Battle* of Dr. Seuss, one child said it is funny because they fight over whether "to eat butter upside down on their bread" and "keep getting bigger and bigger things to fight with."

Pretend play continues to be a vehicle for a wide variety of expressions of humor and the presence of the social group promotes this type of humor. In one study of humor occurring in preschool settings, the greatest number of humor events were observed in pretense situations with other children. For example, one child acted as the 'baby' using an exaggerated baby style of talking and acting, and another child was the 'mother' who used unconventional objects to care for the baby (e.g., combing the baby's hair with a wood rod) and an exaggerated 'mother' voice. The entire sequence was accompanied with giggles and laughter, until the teacher told them to stop their 'silliness'. Children may use many objects in ways not intended in order to garner laughter from other children (e.g., rolling up a placemat and 'eating' it as a fruit roll, or 'kissing' a piece of paper).

A recent study found that some children were adept at using hyperbole, which requires understanding of figurative instead of literal meanings. The children made outrageously false statements about their abilities (i.e., tall tales), which then caused other children to make such claims, resulting in increasing levels of laughter. The convention of social laughter that was observed with toddlers is also evident in preschool groups, particularly in the phenomenon of 'group glee', in which some incongruous event may start a few children laughing. The laughter may then be taken up by a larger group of children until it becomes 'out of bounds'. This group glee is often a social bonding event for children, although it may be problematic for teachers.

Through these early childhood years, children gain increasing sophistication in demonstrating the more conventional types of humor, such as telling riddles and jokes. By about age 4 years, children who have older siblings or joking parents may already begin to exhibit the social convention of 'joke telling', in which they tell pre-riddles that use the form of a riddle without understanding the humorous meaning. The children know that laughter should follow the telling of a riddle or joke, but the pre-riddle has the form of the riddle without the incongruity resolution. A real riddle has conceptual incongruity or word play that makes it funny; that is, there is a misexpectation that occurs when the answer is given because the listener had one meaning of the concept or word in mind while the riddle uses an alternate but still accurate answer. The humor of a riddle such as, "Why did the girl salute the refrigerator? Because it was General Electric" is derived from the conceptual incongruity of the term 'general'. If one does not have the knowledge base to understand why a general should be saluted and that the phrase is also the name of a refrigerator maker, the riddle is not funny. After her older sister told that riddle, a preschool-age child then told this riddle: "Why did the boy salute the refrigerator? Because he was hungry." The child had the form of the riddle but was missing the conceptual incongruity dimension. Of course, the adults who heard her pre-riddle followed the social convention of laughter at the pre-riddle. This learning of the humor form of riddle and joke telling is an important stage because it then leads to the ability to tell real riddles and jokes at a later age. One way to tell whether understanding is present is to observe the humor events that do initiate young children's laughter.

By age 5 years, most children are into a riddle-telling stage from which they derive great enjoyment. The telling of true riddles is often the major humor mode of kindergarten and early elementary children. They often tell the same riddle over and over to all who will listen, and because the audience reaction is a necessary part of the humor social circle, adults usually try to express laughter at hearing the same riddle over and over as well. In studies of riddle telling, when children are asked to tell a riddle or joke, the majority of children of kindergarten or first-grade age can do so with some skill. They usually tell a riddle with lexical ambiguity (double meaning of a word) or conceptual incongruity (double meaning of a concept). They are not adept at telling narrative jokes, however. This is a skill usually reserved for children of later elementary age.

Even when children of 5 or 6 years of age can tell a credible riddle, knock–knock joke, or narrative joke, they can rarely explain why it is funny. Children's ability to explain the incongruous reasons that made their riddle or joke funny rarely occurs before second-grade level. When asked why the riddle or joke is funny they either say they do not know or they give a 'social' answer, such as 'it makes people laugh'. For words and concepts that they are very sure of, they may be able to explain the double meaning. One child told the riddle, "What is a cat's favorite color? Purr-ple" and said, "See, the cat's purr says purple." Then he added, "I made it (the riddle) up myself."

Ages 6–8 Years

By the age of 8 years, the majority of children are quite adept at telling riddles and simple jokes. They are beginning to be able to explain why they are funny, but even if they know why they are funny, when they are asked that question, it is still sometimes hard to explain. Perhaps that is because most people who tell riddles and jokes expect the listener to understand without explanation. In other words, 'getting' the joke is really a test for the listener. In fact, the child who does not get the riddle or joke is at a disadvantage, and thus social laughter (laughing even when the joke is not understood) continues to be a part of the humor dialog. Because humor development that approaches adult abilities to understand it is not accomplished until middle childhood (when abstract concepts begin to be understood), there are many occasions in which younger children will not understand more sophisticated forms of humor. The disadvantage of not understanding ones' peers' riddles and jokes can be great for children with developmental delays in cognition because they will not be 'in' on the joke. Also, a characteristic of socially isolated children is their difficulty in using humor as a way to gain acceptance by peers. In a study of gifted children, however, when the younger group (average age 8 years) and the older group (average age 11 years) were compared, most of the younger gifted children already could 'get' the joke, demonstrating advanced abilities in understanding more sophisticated forms of humor. Because humor is a great social facilitator, the inability of children with cognitive or social deficits to understand the humor of peers can be problematic for their acceptance.

Researchers have been interested in elementary age children's ability to understand incongruity in humor. When young children hear examples of humor that

resolve the incongruity and examples that do not resolve it (did not really make sense), they said both were funny, while older children thought the one with incongruity resolution was funniest. Other studies of this issue have found mixed results and it is likely that the knowledge base of the particular children would make a difference in what humor they find funniest. Studies of spontaneous humor in school, on playgrounds, and in other nonhome settings have found that boys usually express more humor. Teachers usually rate the sense of humor of boys and girls similarly in early childhood grades but rate boys as having a greater sense of humor at later ages, although there is no difference between boys' and girls' ratings of their own sense of humor. Parents also rate their children's humor similarly regardless of gender, and parents of young children often report earlier humor expression in daughters, perhaps due to the earlier language development of many girls. The reason that 'public' expression of humor is more noticeable in boys may be due to the social expectations children learn as they get older. At later ages, girls often serve as the audience while boys are allowed more humor expression, but this appears to be a result of social convention rather than humor understanding.

Theoretical Explanations of Humor Development

Children's ability to express and comprehend humor has been considered a meaningful indicator of their development by theorists from a number of different perspectives, including anthropological/sociological, psychodynamic, and constructivist ones.

Anthropological/Sociological/Communication Theory

The anthropological/sociological theoretical perspective on humor has also been supported by communication theorists. In this view, the very early adult–child interactions, such as the peek-a-boo example given earlier, are vehicles for communicating shared cultural understandings and frames for appropriate behaviors. When adults interact with infants in a playful way, they give signals such as smiles, open mouths, exaggerated language, and expressive body movements that help children understand that these interactions are playful, not serious interactions. Thus, infants and toddlers learn early what behaviors can be exhibited in the 'not serious' (i.e., humorous or playful) interactive frame, which helps children differentiate the boundaries between these types of social interactions. The interactions also contain the metacommunication that within this humorous frame, the role one takes differs from the role taken in nonhumorous situations. According to these theorists, even at this very young age, children are learning to differentiate humorous and serious communication interaction signals. That is, they learn the cues for 'this is humor'. Such cues as exaggerated facial expressions, high-pitched and emphasized voice quality, intense play gazes, and smiles and laughter that are exhibited in social games such as peek-a-boo enable infants of 4 or 5 months of age to distinguish playful from serous modes. They show their understanding by their smiles, laughter, excitement, and other positive affect. An interesting test of this theoretical view can be observed if an unfamiliar adult attempts to play peek-a-boo with an infant or if a familiar adult increases the arousal level too quickly or intensely. Either of these actions may result in a fearful rather than a humorous response from the infant because the infant is less able to read the cues for humor in those situations. Thus, the early humor context must be both safe and playful. From this theoretical perspective, children's ability to develop a good sense of humor is based on these early adult–child social play experiences, which transmit to the child the metacommunication knowledge of humor as an appropriate communication frame. One implication of this perspective is that the human capacity for humor develops best if these types of social interactions begin in the first year of life. An interesting research question is whether high levels of adults' social skill in expressing and comprehending humor could be traced to their earliest humor-related social interaction experiences. It is the case that some children are less able to interpret communication interactions appropriately and distinguish when a humor frame is being used in a communication event. This also happens when an adult is in a new cultural environment (either a different country, family constellation, or professional group) because the signals for the humor frame may be unfamiliar. From this theoretical perspective, humor can be used to bond a social group and also to limit membership in the group by having humor communications that only those 'in the know' can understand.

Psychodynamic Theory

Another theoretical perspective on humor comes from psychodynamic theory, which began with Sigmund Freud's interest in the meaning of adult joking behavior. Freud was particularly interested in the joking behavior of adults because he thought that jokes revealed much about adults' unconscious emotions and motives by allowing them to express otherwise prohibited ideas (e.g., hostile and sexual) in a socially acceptable manner (it's only a joke!). He reserved the word 'humor' for its use as a method of coping with difficult situations in which fear, sadness, or anger might be the likely emotions generated. For example, people living in oppressive regimes often use humor to help them cope, as do those with severe illnesses or others in dire life circumstances. Although Freud's major focus was on adult joking, as part of his discussion of this topic he described three stages of joking development,

beginning in early childhood. He called the first 'play' (ages 2–3 years), which involves repeating sounds or practicing unusual actions with objects to 'rediscovering the familiar'. This stage has little cognitive purpose but it does indicate how children of toddler age juxtapose objects or actions in incongruous ways and find that funny because they know their actions with the objects are not correct. According to Freud, this stage is followed by a 'jesting' stage (ages 4–6 years), which Freud saw as the originating point for 'nonsense' humor. It is the first stage that requires an audience, but the child does not expect the adult to get particular meaning from the jest. By this age children know most adults expect reasonable behavior so jesting is an attempt to get their reaction to absurd behavior. Finally, true 'joking' behavior begins about age 6 or 7 years, and this mode gradually becomes more refined and extends through adulthood, resulting in expert use of the 'joke façade', which allows expression of tendacious feelings (i.e., hostility, sexual thought) to be expressed in public. An example of a child's humor play in the first stage is the 2-year-old who first pushes his toy car along the floor but then begins having it do 'tricks' such as flipping over, going in circles, or driving up the wall, all of which behaviors are accompanied by laughter. At the jesting stage, adults may enter in and allow themselves to be 'fooled' by the child's jest. For example, a child might call all the adults in the family 'mommy' and they might go along with the jest by responding as a mother would respond rather than telling the child he or she has made a mistake. Even at this early age, jesting may help children cope with anxieties about their abilities, especially in situations where they have just mastered some concept or experience but are still anxious about their knowledge or skill. For example, they may find it very funny to give their wrong name or say the wrong name of animals even though they know the correct names. The joking facade learned in the later age period starts out very crudely, perhaps with jokes about body functions, but as children grow older they become adept at using this form in various ways. For example, 'insult' jokes are very popular by middle childhood. This perspective on humor is useful in explaining how it can provide a vehicle for many types of emotional expression. Although not all adult humor has a hostile or sexual overtone, much of the humor used by professional comedians, in literature and other media, and in everyday social interactions, does have such connotations. The ability to laugh at such humor does not just depend on whether one understands the joke but on whether the meaning is derogatory of the group to which one belongs. Some interesting analyses of differences in humor understanding between males and females have been reported in a number of studies. These studies usually reported that men had a greater sense of humor (i.e., found cartoons funnier); however, the researchers often used humor-eliciting cartoons that were derogatory toward women. It is not surprising that the researchers reported women found the cartoons less funny than did men. Thus, the ability to understand the joke is not the only factor in humor appreciation; the nature of its message is also a factor.

Constructivist Theory

The constructivist theoretical perspective, described by Piaget, has also affected understanding of humor development. Much humor is derived from the recognition of cognitive incongruity, and is thus evidence of knowledge construction. Even for young children, humor has an incongruity recognition element that requires knowledge of what is correct or expected in actions, language, concepts, or meanings. When incongruous or unexpected (i.e., surprise) events occur, there is a humor response. Often humor is triggered by the realization that there is an incongruous visual, verbal, or conceptual event. Such an event may be spontaneous, such as a verbal mistake, or it may be planned, such as a riddle with word play. Incongruity-based humor is also the vehicle for many advanced types of humor, such as wit and hyperbole. In order for incongruity to be considered humorous, however, the individual must have knowledge of what would be the 'reasonable' or expected assumption. Then, if there is a juxtaposition of two unrelated ideas, a substitution of one idea for another, or a misexpected consequence that occurs, the event is seen as humorous.

From the Piagetian constructivist perspective, children's stages of humor development parallel their cognitive development, and thus at an early age they only perceive incongruous actions as funny. For example, an infant or toddler may laugh at seeing a picture of a dog wearing a hat, or at being swung up and down by a parent. The actions of the peek-a-boo game and of the car doing tricks on the wall are other examples in which there is an incongruous element that triggers laughter. By about age 2 years, when children begin to have a command of language, they will also begin to find humor in incongruous language and sound play. Language becomes a major means of expressing humor in rhymes with funny sounds, repetition of noises, and calling people or animals by the wrong name. These are funny because the child now knows what 'should' be said and is deliberately creating an incongruous element. The child of about age 4 years has a rather sophisticated knowledge regarding the basic concepts of the world and so conceptual incongruity, in which ordinary conceptual elements are put together in incongruous ways become funny to the child.

Television cartoons in which the characters do things that are conceptually incongruous are common elicitors of conceptual incongruity humor beginning about age 4 or 5 years. For example, trees that dance or flowers that talk may elicit laughter because the children know that trees and flowers do not act in those ways. They also delight in 'mistakes' made by people who do not know as much as they know. Depending on the child's facility with language, word play with multiple meanings becomes a major vehicle for humor by age 5–7. Children of these ages love to tell riddles with word play elements; that is, where a word has a double meaning and is used in the riddle. The riddle 'Why are Saturday and Sunday the strongest days?' with the answer being 'Because the rest of the days are week (weak) days' is an example of word play with multiple meanings. For young children, this humor has an incongruity recognition element that requires knowledge of what is correct or expected in actions, language, concepts, or meanings. When incongruous or unexpected (i.e., surprise) events occur, there is a humor response. In the early childhood years (kindergarten through third grade) riddles and 'knock–knock' jokes are prime examples of the use of these incongruity elements in humor. Humor gradually changes from being a product of concrete thinking to more abstract levels, paralleling cognitive development. As children begin to laugh at sophisticated humor in cartoons, books, or other media, they demonstrate their increasing knowledge base and ability to understand more subtle conceptual incongruity and linguistic multiple meanings. Thus, in the constructivist view, humor is both a vehicle for demonstrating cognitive development and a means for extending such development. The essential knowledge base for finding humor funny expands at later ages; however, it is still the case that if the realm of knowledge is not familiar (e.g., physics, geography, politics, music), adults will not find the humor attempts funny.

Other Theoretical Explanations

There have been other theoretical versions of explanations for the functions of humor, but these have not typically been related to children's humor development. However, in regard to adult and adolescent humor, one perspective suggests that the desire to show 'superiority' is a motive for much humor, and this explains a type of humor often called 'disparagement' humor. This type of humor is directed at some 'out' group in order to make the 'in' group laugh. Many comedians use a version of this, which is 'self-disparagement' in order to make the audience feel superior to them. Another perspective stresses the 'relief' function that humor can give to emotional or social stresses, and this view is closely tied to psychodynamic and to communication theory, because it suggests that the use of humor in stressful social situations opens lines of communication, relieves tension, and allows the group to bond. This then enables greater productivity to occur because underlying emotional and social strains may be dissipated. The incongruity perspective, which forms the basis of constructivist explanations of humor development, has also been discussed by others. For example, Immanuel Kant saw humor as a form of cognitive incongruity, because it transforms existing expectations by juxtaposing ideas and circumstances in a surprising or unexpected way. The ability of humor to change ones' train of thought may also lead to creative and unconventional ways of problem solving. That is, humor may 'shake up' thought and make it more productive. Although laughter often accompanies humor, laughter may also occur in nonhumorous situations. For example, laughter may signify pride, uncomfortableness in unfamiliar situations, or embarrassment.

Humor Development in Relation to Other Developmental Domains

Interest in children's humor has also been promoted by evidence that humor development appears to be related to other developmental domains.

Cognitive Development

Because there is a body of evidence that shows how children's understanding of humorous incongruity is closely tied to the sequence of cognitive development outlined by Piaget and other constructivist theorists, the tie between humor and cognition seems to be evident. Early indications of humorous responses to incongruous actions, language, or concepts seem to parallel young children's thinking because when young children recognize incongruous actions and language and respond with laughter, they are demonstrating what they already know about their world. Their engagement in the humor frame appears to include some sense of a separate self-identity, and when they later begin to initiate incongruous acts and utterances in order to get responses, they show that they have in mind some expectations of how others will react, which is related to 'theory of mind' development. Theory of mind is defined as the ability to understand that other people have minds that may be thinking different thoughts than oneself. When children try to 'fool' other persons through the children's actions or language, it seems that they must have some idea that the other persons will have different thoughts. That is, they must predict the 'difference in mind' of the other persons because that is what will allow them to be fooled (misexpectations). At later ages, when they laugh at increasingly sophisticated humor in cartoons, books, or other media, and when they begin to tell pre-riddles, riddles, and jokes, they are demonstrating their increasing knowledge of conceptual incongruity and linguistic multiple meanings. By observing what children think is funny at each age, one can chart quite easily how their knowledge is being constructed. When children can tell true riddles and simple jokes and can explain

the conceptual incongruity or multiple meanings that make the riddles and jokes funny, they are clearly demonstrating their knowledge. They also gain sophistication in understanding some specific types of humor. For example, children's comprehension of irony begins about age 5 or 6 years but is not fully developed until about age 10 years. In studies of the humor of children age 11–12 years, researchers have found that they have reached the stage of beginning to understand abstract concepts and to 'play' with these concepts in their humor. Of course more sophisticated cognition continues to show development in adolescent and adult humor expression, but the basic cognitive stage progress is evident in the jokes of middle childhood. Children reveal the knowledge they have gained and their understandings of the world, and thus, what they think is funny changes with their cognitive growth. One study found, for example, that when children had just mastered the concept of conservation, they found humor that needed that understanding most funny. Cognitive appraisal techniques also enable them to use humor as a coping mechanism. While 'nonsense' humor continues to be appreciated even into adulthood, adult humor is highly cognitive, requiring recognition of subtle incongruities in concepts and language, and a great deal of factual knowledge from many knowledge systems.

Language Development

Play with language almost always leads to laughter and many of children's earliest attempts at humor involve language or nonsense sound play. Infants gain pleasure from manipulating the sounds of language, and toddlers and preschoolers enjoy engaging in language chants and playful rhythmic exchanges with peers and siblings. Although these humor-related activities with language may seem to be nonserious, through their elaboration and repetition, children are also practicing the phonological, syntactic, semantic, and pragmatic aspects of language. Young children's sound and word play in chanting or rhyming is usually accompanied by increasing bouts of laughter, but it also serves as a way to practice the syntactic forms of language. They also play with the meanings of language and make up words to express their ideas, as well as using language as an accompaniment to their play. In pretend play, they narrate their actions, negotiate with peers, and to try out the language of various roles (e.g., using a 'Teacher' voice.) Their riddles and knock–knock jokes are often funny because of language misexpectations. They develop parodies of familiar songs such as substituting 'I hate you' for 'I love you' in the Barney theme song, and they adore books that have multiple meanings in the words (a favorite is 'Amelia Bedelia'). They enjoy 'Mad-Libs' which substitute similar syntactic but dissimilar meaning forms of language into stories. They tell 'tall' tales and sing favorite playground rhymes. Indeed, much of the language culture of early childhood is deliberately designed to cause laughter.

Social–Emotional Development

Humor, from infancy on, develops best within social interaction settings. Even toddler humor attempts require an 'audience' and humor often serves as a get-acquainted strategy, a bonding mechanism, and a reliever of social tension. Expression of humor requires an ability to interpret social cues (serious or humorous occasion), and a 'safe' environment in which children can take the risk of humor expression. Depending on their socialization in early childhood, as well as their own personalities (e.g., outgoing or shy), children show a wide range of social uses and extensiveness of humor expression. The humor exhibited in the social interactions of preschoolers at play, the kindergarten or first-grade child's riddle telling, and the 'jokes' that are told by 8-year-olds all require social skill. Recent studies of bullying in schools have differentiated behaviors that may elicit or escalate bullying. Although not true of such behaviors in general, at least a portion of the teasing behaviors that may escalate to bullying can be dealt with by humorous responses. Children can make use of humor an effective social strategy in dealing with at least some forms of such teasing by learning to interpret various forms of humor and responding appropriately to the ambiguous messages often conveyed in teasing behavior. When elementary-age children rated the responses to teasing interactions in videotape examples, the children judged hostile and ignoring responses as less effective than humorous responses. Most children learn to distinguish humor-related teasing from hostile teasing; however, teachers may not be aware of many types of the teasing behaviors present in school settings. Given that teasing and other humor-related behaviors, such as clowning, are often a social problem in schools and that certain groups of children are more likely to be teased, to clown, or to use humor in hurtful ways, and given that many variations of humor, including teasing, are pervasive in human society, it is important to help children learn how to interpret and use humor in ways that facilitate their social competence rather than in ways that harm others or make them open to being victims of bullying. In reports of older children who have performed antisocial actions in school, there is often information about their social isolation; it is at least possible that their ability to use humor as a way to bond with the social group was not well developed. Knowing when to interpret an action or a verbal comment as 'this is humor' is an important social skill. Most older children and adolescents will rate a peer who has a 'sense of humor' very positively; thus, a sense of humor fosters social acceptance and friendship.

Physical and Motor Development

One of the major ways humor is initially expressed is in social games that have physical elements. Although physical play, especially when it leads to exuberant laughter, is often frowned upon in school, is also an important vehicle for humor in early childhood. Toddler humor most often has a physical and motor element, and even in preschool, the types of humor that involve physical activity and motor skill are prominent. Laughter almost invariably accompanies interactive physical play; thus such play enhances not only physical development but also humor development. The 'rough-and-tumble' play of childhood can be distinguished from fighting behavior by the humor-related signals (reciprocity, open facial signals, laughter). Recent research showing that frontal lobe development may be enhanced by physical activity has not yet shown linkages to humor. However, because the limbic systems' involvement in emotional expression and the fact that laughter is a strong accompaniment to incongruous actions suggests that research on physical and motor development should also record the accompanying humor elicited by physical and motor actions in young children.

Individual Differences in Humor Expression

Having a 'sense of humor' may be affected by genetic and experiential differences. For example, children vary on the temperament dimension of 'playfulness', which includes ability to show manifest joy and appreciate humor. Also, adults have temperamental differences in the amount of optimism/pessimism or sadness/bad mood they self-report. Experiences related to humor expression in families may also affect children differentially. For example, some families encourage joking and teasing, while others do not. Safety factors in an environment are also relevant for humor expression; with more humor usually being expressed in settings where individuals feel comfortable. Humor may also be initiated as an attention-getting device for a certain group of individuals, as the 'class clown' demonstrates. Finally, people of groups that have been stereotyped by humor are not as likely to enjoy humor that reflects those stereotypes.

Methods for Fostering Humor Development

It is evident from both research and general observation that adults play a major role in encouraging children's humor development. By appreciating children's humor attempts, initiating humor that children can understand, and exposing children to many humor examples, adults can foster this development. However, there is wide individual variation in how much parents and teachers encourage humor development. Humor is often seen as a peripheral skill rather than an essential one. Part of the answer to the puzzle of why some children are adept at using humor and some are not may lie in the social interactions of parents and children in the children's earliest years. Similarly, the emotional tone of educational environments, which may encourage or discourage humor, may contribute to children's development of varied humor strategies. One study using teachers' self-report of their encouragement of humor in the classroom showed that elementary teachers were even less likely to encourage humor than were middle school teachers. Many parents and educators are unaware of the research on humor development and do not realize that humor is one of the many domains of development that progresses from infancy to late elementary years. Thus, they may not be cognizant of ways that they can help young children learn how to use humor as a facilitator of social competence. This discussion suggests ways that the use of humor can be a positive feature of home and educational environments.

The Role of Parents and Other Caregivers

Since the earliest development of humor occurs in the first year of life, the role of parents and other caregivers is very important in helping infants understand the difference between humorous and serious social interactions. Of course, the ability to discover the humor frame in many other social settings develops over many years, but its first manifestation is an important building block for later humor development. Caregiver physical and social play, using the signals of exaggerated voice and facial expression will enable infants to begin their understanding of humor. Other important adult humor facilitation techniques in the toddler years are sharing in children's laughter at incongruous actions and language, acting as the audience when toddlers make humor attempts, being a model of playfulness and humor, and continuing to respond when the humor act is repeated over and over.

When children begin jesting (i.e., teasing) behaviors, adults can be 'fooled' again and again and can give exaggerated humorous responses. They can also 'tease back' in kind ways so that children learn to note the ambiguity of the teasing act and interpret it correctly. Adults can also provide opportunities for peer humor interactions and allow the long sound, word, and action nonsense interactions among peers to escalate without cutting them off too soon. They can provide material and activities that encourage humor appreciation, such as CDs with silly songs and books with funny stories or pictures, and they can provide other media experiences for children that are appropriate for their humor development level. They can participate with their children in these activities and talk about the incongruity elements that occur that make them funny.

When children begin pre-riddle telling, adults can respond to the form of the riddle with laughter, and they can tell riddles that have simple meanings to enable their children to get the understanding of the conceptual and word play aspects of riddles. They can read riddle books to their children to enable them to have a source for riddle telling. They can ask about the reasons why a riddle or joke is funny so that their children can begin to articulate that understanding, and give their own explanations so that children's understanding will grow. They can be tolerant of socially inappropriate and crude joking attempts, knowing that these are just practice for the refinement of the joking facade. When true joke telling begins, adults need to have patience because the telling of the joke may take a while. It is often hard to get the narrative of a joke correctly told on the first try. Because the use of humor as a coping strategy is important to learn, adults can also model this skill by being lighthearted and creative in dealing with problems that occur. For example, an exaggerated, joking response to a child's minor complaint can help the child gain perspective. Most importantly, they can create a climate in the home that signals humor is welcome. If children learn about humor at home, they will be able to carry that knowledge to other settings and interpret humor attempts in those settings appropriately.

The Role of Teachers and Other Adults

All of the techniques discussed for home use can also be used in the school, playground, or other environments. However, in addition, there are some ways that humor development can be enhanced in educational settings, and these techniques may result in greater learning and motivation to learn. Obviously, the educator should never model humor that ridicules, insults, or demeans any groups in stereotypic ways. (Although children find teacher 'self'-disparagement humor funny.) Classroom humor can be very useful in developing social bonds with children in the class and stimulating positive rapport among teacher and students.

In relation to specific techniques for facilitating learning through humor, one way that humor can be used in learning environments is as an attention-getting strategy. If children are to learn particular concepts, they must be attending to the information. A humorous story or joke about a topic can often increase children's initial attention to the topic and attention can be maintained better if some incongruous changes or positive emotional events are built into the activity. Of course, the humor has to be appropriate to the age level of the children. Humor can also increase children's motivation for learning so having some projects that involve learning 'funny' facts or requiring incongruous actions or language can also be helpful.

When tension inducing situations are present, for example, at standardized testing times, having some humor-related activities to provide relief from tension can be very useful. Within the curriculum objectives, humor can sometimes be used to teach the concepts. For example, phonological knowledge can be learned as well by having children make up nonsense words that rhyme as by having them use a list of real words, and investigating cartoons that comment on a historical event can provide additional information on the social effects of that event.

While all of these ideas can lead to planning for humor in the classroom, educators also can promote humor development just by conveying an openness and acceptance of children's humor expression within the educational setting. Humor is sometimes used 'iconoclastically' to deride the values and conventions of an educational setting, as the 'class clown' knows, and of course, it can be used deliberately to hurt other students through teasing or bullying. These less desired forms of humor can be controlled best if all of the students in the class are socially skilled in humor expression and understanding, and comfortable within the 'humor frame'.

Summary

Humor is a term with many meanings, many uses, and many variations. While it has long been recognized as a feature of adult life, it is also a pervasive part of young children's lives, because it is a basic human quality. Much in now known about the course of young children's humor development, and there are some useful theoretical explanations for its development and purposes. There is also evidence that a sense of humor is highly related to children's competencies in cognitive, language, social–emotional, and physical-motor realms. The development of humor can be facilitated by the adults in children's lives, if they understand how humor develops, and know how to provide both home and educational environments that help young children to become skilled humor users.

See also: Cognitive Development; Cognitive Developmental Theories; Emotion Regulation; Language Development: Overview; Play; Smiling; Social and Emotional Development Theories; Temperament.

Suggested Readings

Bergen D (2000) *Enjoying Humor with Your Child (ACEI Speaks Series)*. Olney, MD: Association for Childhood Education International.

Bergen D (2006) Play as a context for humor development. In: Fromberg DP and Bergen D (eds.) *Play from Birth to Twelve : Contexts, Perspectives, and Meanings*, pp. 141–155. New York: Routledge.

Loomans D and Kolberg K (1993) *The Laughing Classroom: Everyone's Guide to Teaching with Humor and Play*. Tiburon, CA: H. J. Kramer.

McGhee P (2002) *Understanding and Promoting the Development of Children's Humor*. Dubuque, IA: Kendall-Hunt.

Ruch W (ed.) (1998) *The Sense of Humor: Explorations of a Personality Characteristic*, pp. 329–358. Berlin: Mouton deGruyter.

Sinclair A (1996) Young children's practical deceptions and their understanding of false belief. *New Ideas in Psychology* 14(2): 152–173.

Sobstad F (1990) *Preschool Children and Humor*. Trondheim: Skriftserie fra Pedagogisk institutt, Univeritetet i Trondheim. Rapport nr. 1.

Illnesses: Autoimmune Rheumatological Diseases

J B Soep and J R Hollister, University of Colorado at Denver and Health Sciences Center, Denver, CO, USA

Glossary

Aneurysm – Localized dilation or ballooning of a blood vessel.

Antibody – A protein used by the immune system to identify and neutralize foreign objects like bacteria and viruses. In autoimmune diseases, antibodies are directed against self tissues and/or organs.

Arthritis – Swelling of one or more joints with associated pain, warmth, limited range of motion, and/or tenderness.

Autoimmune – When the immune system attacks itself by mistake and causes harm to the involved cells or tissues. Autoimmune diseases can affect many parts of the body, including the skin, joints, muscles, nerves, brain, and kidney.

Inflammation – A response of body tissues to injury or irritation, characterized by pain, swelling, redness, and heat.

Intravenous immunoglobulin (IVIG) – Pooled antibodies extracted from the plasma of blood donors, used to suppress inflammation in several autoimmune diseases.

Pauciarticular – Arthritis involving four or fewer joints.

Polyarticular – Arthritis involving five or more joints.

Purpura – Reddish/purplish discoloration of the skin, caused by small bleeding vessels underneath the skin.

Rheumatoid factor – An antibody that can bind to other antibodies that is measurable in the blood and is positive in a subset of juvenile rheumatoid arthritis.

Rheumatology – The study of diseases of inflammation and autoimmunity with special interests in causes of rash, fever, arthritis, weakness, weight loss, fatigue, joint and muscle pain.

Synovitis – When the synovium becomes thickened, inflamed, and engorged with fluid, causing joint pain, swelling, and warmth.

Synovium – The soft tissue that lines the non-cartilaginous surfaces of joints.

Systemic – Spread throughout the body, affecting many organs or body systems.

Uveitis – Inflammation of the middle layer of the eye, termed the uvea, which includes the iris (the colored part of the eye), the ciliary body (behind the iris), and choroid (the lining under the retina).

Vasculitis – A group of diseases featuring inflammation of the wall of blood vessels.

Introduction

The immune system normally protects the body from infection. In autoimmune diseases, the immune system is directed against the host, attacking the body's own organs and tissues. Rheumatologic diseases develop when this autoimmune response causes inflammation involving the musculoskeletal system, skin, and blood vessels. Pediatric rheumatology is the medical subspeciality focused on caring for children with these conditions (**Table 1**).

Because rheumatologic conditions are often associated with chronic joint pain and impaired function, pediatric patients may experience gross-motor and fine-motor delays. Fortunately, with appropriate treatment, the majority of young children with rheumatic diseases can eventually have normal growth and development.

Arthritis

Nomenclature

There are three classification systems for chronic arthritis in childhood (**Table 2**); each has attempted to categorize this heterogeneous group of patients to improve communication among caregivers, standardize research, and improve patient care. While each classification takes a slightly different approach to dividing the patients with chronic arthritis, they all contain three common subtypes: systemic, polyarticular (five or more joints), and pauciarticular/oligoarticular (four or fewer joints).

Epidemiology

Juvenile idiopathic arthritis (JIA) is the most common rheumatic illness in pediatrics. Arthritis is defined as swelling of one or more joints with associated pain,

Table 1   Pediatric rheumatologic diseases

Juvenile idiopathic arthritis
  Systemic
  Polyarticular
  Oligoarticular
  Enthesitis-related arthritis
  Psoriatic arthritis
Systemic lupus erythematosus
Scleroderma
Dermatomyositis
Sarcoidosis
Vasculitis
  Polyarteritis nodosa
  Henoch-Schönlein purpura
  Wegener's granulomatosis
  Takayasu's arteritis
  Behcet's syndrome
  Kawasaki disease

warmth, limited range of motion, and/or tenderness. Symptoms must be present for at least 6–12 weeks. Diagnostic criteria also include disease onset before the age of 16 years and exclusion of other causes of arthritis. The systemic, polyarticular rheumatoidn factor-negative and oligoarticular subtypes may all present between the ages of 0 and 3 years. The peak age of onset for oligoarticular disease is 2 years. There is a bimodal age distribution for polyarticular arthritis with a peak in toddlers and then again in school-age and adolescent children. The systemic form of JIA has a more uniform age distribution, presenting anytime between infancy and adulthood. In general, girls are affected with chronic arthritis more frequently than boys.

Genetics

While the cause of JIA in childhood is currently unknown, there appears to be a genetic predisposition. Multiple genes related to inflammation and immunity seem to be involved. Children with arthritis often have family members with a history of other autoimmune diseases such as lupus and rheumatoid arthritis.

Pathophysiology

The synovium, or joint lining, is the target organ for inflammation in JIA. The inflammation results in proliferation of the synovial tissue and secretion of increased amounts of joint fluid. The net result is joint swelling, increased blood flow, and increased inflammatory cells within the joint. If the synovitis persists long enough in

Table 2   Classification of pediatric chronic arthritis

Juvenile rheumatoid arthritis (American College of Rheumatology[a])	Juvenile chronic arthritis (European League Against Rheumatism[b])	Juvenile idiopathic arthritis (International League of Associations for Rheumatology[c])
Systemic	Systemic	Systemic
Polyarticular	Polyarticular, rheumatoid factor negative	Polyarticular, rheumatoid factor negative
	Juvenile rheumatoid arthritis (Polyarticular, rheumatoid factor positive)	Polyarticular, rheumatoid factor positive
Pauciarticular	Pauciarticular	Oligoarthritis
		Persistent
		Extended
	Juvenile ankylosing spondylitis	Enthesitis-related arthritis
	Juvenile psoriatic arthritis	Psoriatic arthritis
		Undifferentiated arthritis
		Fits no other category
		Fits more than one category

[a]Brewer EJ, Jr., Bass J, Baum J, et al. (1977). Current proposed revision of JRA criteria. *Arthritis and Rheumatism* 20(supplement): 195–199.
[b]European League Against Rheumatism (EULAR) Bulletin No. 4 (1977) Nomenclature and classification of arthritis in children. Basel. National Zeitung AG.
[c]Petty RE, Southwood TR, Baum J, et al. (1998) Revision of the proposed classification criteria for juvenile idiopathic arthritis: Durban 1997. *Journal of Rheumatology* 25: 1991–1994.
Reproduced from Cassidy JT and Petty RE (2001) *Textbook of Pediatric Rheumatology*, 4th edn., p. 215. Philadelphia, PA: Elsevier Saunders, with permission from Elsevier.

a particular joint, permanent destruction of the cartilage, underlying bone, and other surrounding joint structures such as ligaments and tendons may occur.

Clinical Characteristics

Pauciarticular

Oligoarticular or pauciarticular arthritis is the most common form of chronic arthritis in childhood, representing approximately 50% of patients. This form of arthritis involves four or fewer joints and typically affects the large joints in an asymmetric pattern. Extra-articular disease is unusual except for uveitis, chronic inflammation in the anterior chamber of the eye. Uveitis is asymptomatic and affects approximately 10–20% of children with pauciarticular arthritis. Risk factors for uveitis include female gender, disease onset under 7 years, and a positive antinuclear antibody (ANA). Uveitis may cause blindness if untreated. The activity of the eye disease does not correlate with the activity of the arthritis and the risk remains elevated for at least 4 years after the initial diagnosis of arthritis. Therefore, routine ophthalmology examinations, including a slit lamp examination, are required to evaluate for uveitis and if present, necessitates treatment with anti-inflammatory eye drops or systemic medications. Patients with pauciarthritis are generally otherwise well and frequently remain very active. Based on the frequent asymmetric distribution, patients who develop arthritis before the age of 3 years may develop muscle atrophy and a leg length discrepancy with the affected leg overgrowing because of increased growth factors in areas of increased blood flow.

Polyarticular

Polyarticular disease is defined as arthritis involving five or more joints within 6 months of diagnosis. The arthritis often involves both large and small joints in a symmetric pattern. Polyarthritis comprises approximately 35% of all patients with JIA. There are two subgroups within this category: rheumatoid factor-negative disease (25%) and rheumatoid factor-positive disease (10%). The rheumatoid factor is an antibody associated with more chronic, severe arthritis. Rheumatoid factor-positive disease is typically not seen until late school-age or adolescence. Systemic features of polyarthritis may include fatigue, anemia, and growth failure.

Systemic

Systemic arthritis, also known as Still's disease after George Still who made some of the early observations about juvenile arthritis, makes up approximately 15% of children with JIA. The arthritis is generally polyarticular, affecting both large and small joints. The hallmark is a high spiking fever, often as high as 39 to 40 °C with rapid return to baseline or subnormal temperatures. The fever typically occurs 1–2 times per day, frequently in the late afternoon or evening. There is also a characteristic rash that consists of salmon-pink flat lesions of different sizes. The rash moves all over the body, not lasting in one location for more than minutes to hours. It is most often seen over pressure areas and when the fever is present. The rash is occasionally itchy. Patients frequently have other systemic features including enlarged liver and spleen, swollen glands, inflammation of the lining of the heart and/or lungs, tendonitis, and hepatitis.

Impact on Growth and Development

JIA is often associated with abnormalities of growth and development. Due to the chronic joint symptoms, including pain, swelling, and stiffness, patients may have delayed motor skills. Patients may present with delays in fine and gross motor development. Young children may have difficulty pulling to a stand and cruising or parents may note an abnormal gait once the child learns to walk. Toddlers may have trouble with coordination and may have difficulty keeping up with their peers. Occasionally children are diagnosed with cerebral palsy due to the asymmetric abnormalities in range of motion and function. Alternatively, patients may be noted to lose developmental milestones, coinciding with the onset of their joint symptoms. Proper treatment of the disease should allow the patient to 'catch-up' and again meet their normal milestones. The disease has no significant impact on cognitive development.

Chronic systemic inflammation is frequently associated with retardation in linear growth. In addition, treatment with steroids, at doses of greater than 3 mg per day, are growth suppressing. During remission, patients usually return to their baseline growth velocity. If patients continue to be significantly below the fifth percentile in height, even when their disease is adequately controlled and after they have tapered down on their steroids, they can be treated successfully with growth hormone. There may also be localized growth abnormalities. Increased blood flow and growth factors can lead to accelerated linear growth surrounding an involved joint with a resultant leg length discrepancy or may lead to localized bony overgrowth. Alternatively, patients may have premature closure of the growth plates or destruction of a growth center leading to shortening of a limb or digit. Micrognathia, shortening of the jaw, may be seen when there is long-standing inflammation of the temporo-mandibular joint and can lead to significant pain, facial deformity, difficulty opening the mouth, and chewing.

Laboratory Tests

There are no specific or diagnostic laboratory tests for JIA. Markers of systemic inflammation, such as sedimentation rate and c-reactive protein, are typically quite elevated with active systemic illness and may be mildly elevated with polyarticular involvement. Most commonly all of the laboratory tests are normal in the case of oligoarticular disease. Synovial fluid analysis, if performed, typically demonstrates a white blood cell count between 5000 and 60 000 cells μl^{-1} with a normal to slightly decreased glucose.

Radiologic Studies

Standard radiographs are not diagnostic of early juvenile arthritis. Early nonspecific findings include osteoporosis and soft-tissue swelling. The primary purpose of X-rays in early disease is to exclude other conditions that may be associated with bony changes. Late changes of chronic arthritis include joint space narrowing due to thinning of the cartilage and erosions of the underlying bone. Magnetic resonance imaging may demonstrate joint damage earlier than standard X-rays and, if performed with contrast, can help identify areas of active synovitis.

Differential Diagnosis

Because there are no diagnostic tests for JIA and because it is a diagnosis of exclusion, it is important to rule out other causes of the clinical findings prior to making the diagnosis. Often the differential diagnosis is quite broad, including orthopedic abnormalities, infectious etiologies, and malignancy (**Table 3**). There are a few key features that can help distinguish these different entities. Characterizing the timing of the pain can be very helpful. In inflammatory conditions such as arthritis, patients frequently have increased symptoms in the morning with associated morning stiffness and gelling–stiffness after periods of inactivity. In contrast, patients with a mechanical problem typically have the least pain in the morning and have worsening symptoms throughout the day and with activity. Orthopedic problems may also be associated with popping, locking, and giving out of the joint. The classic features of growing pains are poorly localized pain occurring at night, waking the child from sleep with no objective signs of inflammation, and absence of symptoms during the day. Patients with growing pains usually like to have the affected area massaged, while this is typically not seen in arthritis.

When considering infectious causes, we need to observe for the presence of focal symptoms, usually in association with significant pain, swelling, warmth, and possibly redness of the involved area. Patients often have a persistent fever. Bacterial infections may involve the joint, as in septic arthritis, or the bone, as in osteomyelitis, or both. If infection is being considered it is important to obtain appropriate

Table 3   Common causes of joint pain in children aged 0–3 years

Mechanical/orthopedic
   Trauma
   Hypermobility
   Growing pains
Infectious diseases
   Bacterial
   Osteomyelitis
   Septic arthritis
   Viral
   Parvovirus
   Epstein Barr Virus
   Reactive arthritis
   Other
   Lyme disease
Malignancy
   Leukemia
   Lymphoma
   Neuroblastoma
   Osteoid osteoma
Rheumatic diseases
   Dermatomyositis
   Vasculitis
   Sarcoidosis

cultures. In cases of postinfectious or reactive arthritis, a preceding illness is identified in approximately 50% of cases. Typically the onset of arthritis is acute and severe and may affect one or multiple joints and may have a migratory pattern. A very important distinction between reactive arthritis and chronic arthritis is the duration of symptoms. In order to meet criteria for chronic arthritis, symptoms must be present for at least 6–12 weeks. In contrast, the symptoms associated with reactive arthritis typically resolve completely within 4–6 weeks with a low rate of recurrence.

Features that may suggest an underlying malignancy include pain out of proportion to physical findings, pain and swelling around the joint instead of the joint itself, enlarged liver or spleen, swollen glands, and an elevated lactate dehydrogenase (LDH) or uric acid. X-rays may demonstrate direct bone infiltration or nonspecific findings including increased or decreased density lines in the broad portion of the bone called metaphyseal bands.

Treatment

Goals of treatment are to control pain; preserve range of motion, strength and function; manage systemic complications; and facilitate normal nutrition, growth, and physical and psychological development. The traditional approach is to begin with the safest, simplest, and most conservative measures and then intensify treatment as needed to manage the signs and symptoms of the disease. Nonsteroidal anti-inflammatory medications (NSAIDs), such as ibuprofen and naproxen, are the mainstay of therapy. Steroids are reserved for the severely affected child, primarily patients with systemic disease. Monoarticular or oligoarticular disease can be treated with local steroid joint injections. Other disease-modifying, anti-rheumatic medications include methotrexate, leflunomide, and cyclosporine. Newer biologic medications, such as etanercept, infliximab, adalimumab, and anakinra, inhibit specific cytokines – proteins that are known to play a significant role in the inflammation and chronic bone and cartilage changes seen in chronic arthritis.

Rehabilitation services, such as physical and occupational therapy, are very important to minimize pain, maintain and restore function, and prevent deformity and disability. Splinting and special exercises to prevent deformity and contractures may be needed. Treatments include heat and cold, water therapy, ultrasound, range of motion and strengthening exercises, gait training, joint protection, serial casting, and shoe lifts.

Prognosis

The course and prognosis for JIA is variable. With oligoarticular disease, many patients eventually go into remission within a few years without any long-term sequelae. Patients rarely have permanent cartilage or bone damage. However, patients may have fixed flexion contractures or leg length discrepancies that can impact their normal gait and function. In addition, these patients may be at higher risk for osteoarthritis in the future. There is a subgroup of patients, those with extended oligoarticular disease, who have a progressive increase in the number of involved joints so that they ultimately have a polyarticular course and may have more chronic or severe disease.

The prognosis for chronic anterior uveitis has been improving with the current options for treatment. However, visual loss may still occur. Other complications include glaucoma and cataracts that may lead to increased visual impairment.

The rheumatoid factor-negative polyarticular disease seen in young patients generally goes into remission within several years without permanent joint damage. Patients in this age group with the worst prognosis include those who have been referred late in their course and those with early involvement of the small joints of the hands and feet.

The systemic features associated with systemic arthritis, including the fever and rash, tend to remit within months to years. However, these symptoms may recur with subsequent exacerbations of the arthritis. The ultimate prognosis in this form of chronic arthritis is determined by the extent of their arthritis. Those patients with a more polyarticular course of arthritis have a worse functional outcome.

Lupus

Pediatric systemic lupus erythematosus is very rare under the age of 5 years, more typically presenting in school-age children and adolescents. However, neonatal lupus erythematosus is a form of lupus that occurs in infancy. This condition is associated with specific maternal antibodies that cross the placenta and attack fetal and neonatal tissues. It most commonly affects the heart, skin, blood, and liver.

Pathophysiology

Specific maternal antibodies, anti-Ro and anti-La, are required for the development of neonatal lupus. Mothers may have an underlying autoimmune condition such as systemic lupus erythematosus or Sjogren's syndrome or may be asymptomatic.

These antibodies cross the placenta and react with fetal and neonatal tissues, causing an inflammatory reaction. Findings become apparent at birth or in the early postnatal period. Aside from the congenital heart block (CHB), the other clinical features are transient, coinciding with the presence of the antibodies and usually resolving by 6–12 months as the antibodies are broken down.

Clinical Manifestations

Cardiac

The most significant manifestation of neonatal lupus is CHB in which the electrical impulses fail to conduct normally through the heart. This may become apparent either *in utero* or soon after birth. To date, third-degree atrioventricular block, when the atria and ventricles beat independently, is irreversible. CHB is associated with significant complications and risk of mortality. A majority of patients require pacemakers during their entire lives. Other less common cardiac manifestations include structural abnormalities and inflammatory processes such as myocarditis (inflammation of the heart muscle), or pericarditis (inflammation of the lining of the heart).

Skin

The rash associated with neonatal lupus consists of oval, red lesions on the face, scalp, trunk, and extremities. The rash is typically found in sun-exposed areas and is strongly photosensitive. The lesions may be present at birth or develop postnatally. Patients often present after being exposed to the fluorescent lights in the newborn nursery or after beginning phototherapy for high bilirubin. Generally the rash resolves without a scar.

Blood

Neonatal lupus can be associated with immune-mediated low platelet, white blood cell, and red blood cell counts. Occasionally, these effects on the blood lines are severe enough to require transfusions.

Liver

Infants with neonatal lupus may present with liver dysfunction. Typically patients have an enlarged liver, with or without an enlarged spleen, bile stasis, and increased liver function tests. The liver function abnormalities usually resolve without any permanent dysfunction.

Treatment

The majority of the manifestations of neonatal lupus resolve without any specific treatment once the maternal antibodies are broken down, typically within 6–12 months. Severe systemic manifestations occasionally require treatment with steroids or intravenous immunoglobulin (IVIG).

Prognosis

The blood, liver, and skin manifestations typically resolve without any long-term sequelae. Babies with associated heart block have a more guarded prognosis as they are at risk for congestive heart failure and generally require long-term pacemakers.

Vasculitis

Nomenclature

Vasculitides, autoimmune conditions associated with inflammation of blood vessels, are often classified based on involved vessel size (**Table 4**).

Table 4   Classification of vasculitides

Large vessel
Takayasu's arteritis
Giant cell arteritis
Medium vessel
Kawasaki disease
Wegener's granulomatosis
Polyarteritis nodosa
Churg-Strauss syndrome
Small vessel
Henoch-Schönlein purpura
Microscopic polyarteritis

Henoch-Schönlein purpura
Epidemiology

Henoch–Schönlein purpura (HSP) is one of the most common forms of systemic vasculitis in children. Onset of HSP is most common in the winter. Often there is a preceding, viral, upper respiratory infection or streptococcal disease.

Clinical manifestations

The common clinical characteristics include purpura, arthritis, abdominal pain with or without gastrointestinal bleeding, blood and protein in the urine, and inflammation of the testicles. The typical rash consists of palpable, purple, nonblanching lesions, most commonly on the lower extremities. They often begin as red, flat spots or hive-like lesions that become purpuric in nature, turning purple, then brown, and then slowly resolving. Young children with HSP frequently have significant swelling of the scalp, extremities, scrotum, and around the eyes. Patients may also have vasculitis and swelling of the lining of the intestine, leading to crampy abdominal pain, with or without hemorrhage. Small intestine intussusception, when the intestine telescopes on itself, is one of the most common gastrointestinal complications, presenting with colicky pain, a distended abdomen, and vomiting. Kidney disease, manifested as blood and protein in the urine and high blood pressure and less commonly renal failure, occurs in approximately one-third of patients. The kidney findings generally develop within 3 months of the onset of symptoms. Joint pain and/or frank arthritis occur in most patients. Less common manifestations include central nervous system vasculitis and hemorrhage into the lungs.

Acute hemorrhagic edema, a variant of HSP in children less than 2 years of age, is manifested as fever, purpura, and significant swelling of the face and extremities. Kidney and gastrointestinal involvement in this form is uncommon.

Laboratory tests

There are no diagnostic laboratory tests for HSP. General markers of inflammation, including sedimentation rate and c-reactive protein, are typically elevated. The antinuclear antibody and rheumatoid factor are usually negative. Antibodies associated with vasculitis, antineutrophil cytoplasmic antibodies (ANCA), may be present. Serum immunoglobulin A levels may be elevated.

Treatment

Treatment of HSP is supportive, focusing on maintaining hydration and managing pain. Generally, management with acetaminophen or NSAIDs such as ibuprofen is sufficient to control the pain. Systemic steroids are indicated to manage severe abdominal pain and/or hemorrhage. If steroids are discontinued abruptly, patients often experience a rapid return of symptoms. Therefore, once steroids have been started, it is recommended to taper them over several weeks to avoid this rebound of symptoms. Severe renal disease may also be managed with high-dose steroids with or without chemotherapeutic agents such as cyclophosphamide.

Prognosis

Generally, the signs and symptoms of HSP are self-limiting, with complete resolution within 1 month. However, it is not unusual to have at least one recurrence, often within the first couple of months after the first occurrence. Typically, subsequent episodes are briefer and less severe. When children have multiple episodes of HSP, it is important to screen for streptococcal disease; if this is identified as a trigger, preventive antibiotics may be helpful in preventing subsequent episodes.

The renal disease associated with HSP has a more variable outcome. Patients who present with isolated mild blood and/or protein in the urine generally do well, with no long-term sequelae. Patients with more severe kidney inflammation, manifested as high blood pressure and decreased kidney function, have a higher rate of chronic renal disease with a small percentage of children developing end-stage renal failure.

Polyarteritis
Clinical manifestations

There are two main types of polyarteritis. Polyarteritis nodosa (PAN) typically presents with fatigue, weight loss, fever, rash, abdominal pain, and arthritis. Patients may also have muscle pain; testicular pain; kidney involvement such as high blood pressure and blood in the urine; and neurologic symptoms such as seizures, focal deficits, and visual loss. The skin lesions include lumps under the skin called nodules, purpura, or ulcerated areas. Laboratory testing typically reveals anemia, increased white blood cell counts, platelet counts, and other markers of inflammation. In classic PAN, the ANCA is generally negative. Angiograms, special imaging studies that evaluate blood vessels, may demonstrate areas of dilated or narrowed vessels, particularly involving the kidney and intestine. Biopsies of involved areas confirm the presence of segmental vasculitis of small and medium arteries.

There is a cutaneous form of PAN that is limited to fever, rash, and joint symptoms. The most characteristic finding is purpura, most commonly of the lower extremities and sometimes on the soles of the feet. The lesions are often quite tender and can interfere with walking. Outbreaks can be triggered by streptococcal infections and in these cases, may be prevented by using prophylactic antibiotics.

Microscopic polyangiitis, in contrast, generally presents with pulmonary hemorrhage and rapidly progressive kidney inflammation. Patients may also have muscle pain, arthritis, abdominal pain, and purpura. Laboratory tests demonstrate increased inflammatory markers and frequently reveal blood and protein in the urine with abnormal kidney function tests. A positive P-ANCA is seen in a majority of patients. Angiograms are typically negative because these imaging studies usually cannot detect small vessel disease. A biopsy of involved tissue demonstrates vasculitis of small vessels.

Treatment

Treatment of both forms of polyarteritis includes systemic steroids to manage the acute manifestations. Additional immunosuppressive agents such as cyclophosphamide, azathioprine, or methotrexate may be indicated for more severe disease or for those patients who need a steroid-sparing agent.

Prognosis

The prognosis of polyarteritis is variable. Patients with cutaneous PAN generally have a good outcome; however, they may have relapses over a period of several years. In general, patients with classic PAN and microscopic polyangiitis require long-term treatment with immunosuppressive medications. With these treatments, patients may have significant complications, such as kidney failure, high blood pressure, and seizures, but appear to have relatively low mortality.

Kawasaki disease
Epidemiology

Kawasaki disease (KD) is another common form of vasculitis in young children, with a peak incidence between 6 and 11 months. Infants may not present with typical characteristics and therefore may have a delay in diagnosis and treatment and ultimately a worse outcome. The cause of this multisystem, inflammatory condition is unknown. Many features of this disease suggest an infectious etiology; however, no single agent has been identified. There are reports of seasonal peaks and clusters in different geographical areas.

Clinical manifestations

The fever is typically 39–40 °C, for 5 or more days. The fever is unresponsive to antibiotics and usually poorly responsive to acetaminophen and ibuprofen. Patients often have bilateral conjunctivitis without eye drainage and sparing the area closest to the iris. The swollen glands, also known as lymphadenopathy, seen with KD, are typically located on one side of the neck and are greater than 1.5 cm in diameter. The rash is variable and may consist of red, flat, or raised areas, may be purpuric, or can resemble the rash of scarlet fever. The rash may involve the trunk, face, extremities, and diaper area. As the rash resolves, there is often peeling of the affected areas. While the fever is present, children frequently have red, dry, cracked, swollen lips and/or a 'strawberry' tongue. The typical extremity changes include swelling of the hands and feet in the early phases of the disease and later peeling of the tips of the fingers and toes.

The most serious manifestation of KD is heart disease. There is a predilection for involvement of the coronary arteries, the arteries feeding the heart. The vasculitis may lead to aneurysms of involved vessels. Severe sequelae may include impaired heart function, heart attack and abnormal heart rhythm. Patients may also have dilation of other vessels such as arteries in the arm and leg. Other manifestations include sterile meningitis with headache and extreme irritability, uveitis, joint pain, arthritis, muscle inflammation, inflammation of the gallbladder, and white blood cells in the urine with negative urine cultures.

Laboratory and imaging studies

During the acute phase of KD, patients typically have significant elevation of inflammatory markers including sedimentation rate, c-reactive protein, and white blood cells. The platelet count often rises 2–4 weeks into the illness. As with other forms of vasculitis, patients may have a positive ANCA. Patients may also have mild elevation in the liver function tests, anemia, white blood cells in the urine and spinal fluid with negative bacterial and viral cultures. Echocardiograms are necessary to diagnose and monitor coronary artery abnormalities. Biopsies of involved tissue demonstrate vasculitis of medium-sized arteries.

Treatment

Standard treatment for KD includes IVIG $2 \, g \, kg^{-1}$ as a single dose. Administration of IVIG within the first 10–12 days of illness is usually associated with improvement in all clinical manifestations and reduction in the frequency and severity of coronary artery abnormalities. Occasionally, patients will have a recurrence of symptoms such as fever, rash, and the lip and tongue changes, and in these cases, they often benefit from a second dose of IVIG. Patients should also be treated with aspirin, at anti-inflammatory doses during the acute phase of the disease and then at lower doses to achieve antiplatelet effects to decrease the risk of blood clots in the abnormal vessels. The role of steroids in the treatment of KD is controversial and usually reserved for patients with severe or resistant disease. In addition, stronger immunosuppressive medications such as cyclophosphamide and infliximab have been used for recalcitrant cases.

Generally, patients should have an echocardiogram at the time of diagnosis and then have a repeat study within 2–6 weeks. No additional studies are needed for patients who have no evidence of coronary involvement on the repeat scan. Patients who have evidence of coronary abnormalities, however, require regular follow-up studies to monitor for evolution of their disease and to screen for premature cardiovascular disease that may be a late sequelae of KD.

Prognosis

In general, the clinical manifestations of KD resolve with appropriate treatment without any long-term sequelae. The major exception is in those with coronary involvement who may have significant complications and some risk of early and late mortality.

Dermatomyositis

Epidemiology

Dermatomyositis is the most common inflammatory muscle disease of childhood. This condition may present at any age, with a peak age of onset around 7 years of age and a second peak in adulthood. The cause of dermatomyositis is unknown and likely multifactorial, involving a genetic predisposition, environmental factors such as sun exposure, and possibly, in at least some cases, a viral trigger.

Pathophysiology

The clinical features of dermatomyositis are caused by abnormalities of small blood vessels, ultimately leading to decreased blood flow and damage to the end organs, including striated muscle, skin, and gastrointestinal tract.

Clinical Manifestations

Constitutional

Poor appetite, weight loss, fatigue, fever, and malaise may be present.

Musculoskeletal

Patients have symmetrical weakness, primarily affecting the muscles of the neck, abdomen, shoulders, and hips. Children frequently have difficulty climbing stairs, getting up from a chair, and combing their hair. The muscles in the larynx, pharynx, and palate can be involved, causing nasal speech, weakness of the voice, and regurgitation of liquids through the nose and increasing the risk of aspiration of fluids into the lungs. Patients frequently have a positive Gower's sign; when asked to get up from sitting on the floor, they use their hands to walk up the anterior aspects of their thighs to compensate for their pelvic muscle weakness. Neck flexor weakness is a particularly sensitive indicator of muscle impairment. Patients may also have muscle pain, as well as swelling and tightness over the muscles. After long-standing disease, patients may eventually develop muscle atrophy. The position of comfort is flexion of the limbs, promoting the development of flexion contractures. Patients may have arthritis, usually symmetric, involving both large and small joints.

Skin

The typical rashes may precede or follow the onset of muscle weakness and may occur in the absence of elevated muscle enzymes. Swelling around the eyes and dilated, tortuous, superficial vessels over the eyelid are often seen. One of the classic findings in dermatomyositis is the heliotrope rash, manifested as a purple discoloration of the eyelids. The rash is frequently photosensitive. Sun exposure may exacerbate the rash alone, or may activate the muscle inflammation as well. Another pathognomonic rash is Gottron's papules, thickened, pale, or red raised plaques over the knuckles, elbows, and knees. Patients may also develop a red rash on the cheeks and nasal bridge, on the chest ('V' rash), or upper back ('shawl rash'). Diffuse vasculitis, manifested as abnormal blood vessels along the cuticle edge and ulcers of the skin around the mouth or on the finger tips, may be associated with more severe disease. Calcinosis, calcium deposits under the skin, occurs in up to 70% of patients. Calcinosis frequently develops months to years after the onset of disease and is often located at sites exposed to trauma. While the cause of calcinosis is unknown, it appears to be related to disease severity and duration. Patients treated early and aggressively have a decreased risk of developing soft tissue calcifications.

Gastrointestinal

Patients may have esophageal hypomotility that can contribute to the swallowing dysfunction. Vasculitis can affect any part of the gastrointestinal tract and may impair absorption, cause weight loss, and progress to ulceration with perforation of the intestine.

Cardiopulmonary

Patients may have electrocardiogram abnormalities, most commonly asymptomatic changes in the electrical conduction within the heart. Decrease in ventilatory capacity in the absence of respiratory symptoms may occur due to muscular weakness. Pulmonary inflammation and scarring may also occur.

Diagnostic Criteria

There are five diagnostic criteria for dermatomyositis, including characteristic rash, symmetrical proximal muscle weakness, elevated muscle enzymes, typical muscle pathology on biopsy, and inflammatory changes in the muscle by electromyography (EMG), a technique to study the physiologic properties of muscles. In order to make a definitive diagnosis of dermatomyositis, patients need rash and 3 or 4 other criteria. Patients have probable disease if they have rash with two criteria and possible dermatomyositis with rash and one criterion. Usually, the diagnosis is made based on the physical and laboratory findings. An EMG and/or biopsy are usually not necessary unless the features are atypical.

Laboratory and Radiologic Data

Muscle-derived enzymes (creatine kinase, LDH, aspartate transaminase (AST), alanine aminotransferase (ALT), aldolase) may all be elevated, or a single value may be abnormal. Usual indications of inflammation, such as sedimentation rate and white blood cell count, are often normal, despite widespread inflammation. A magnetic resonance imaging study of the involved muscles may be helpful in confirming the presence of muscle inflammation, monitoring disease activity, or assisting in locating an appropriate location for biopsy.

Pathology

Biopsy of involved areas includes vasculitis and noninflammatory blood vessel abnormalities affecting arterioles, capillaries, and venules. Muscle biopsy findings reveal atrophy of the muscle fibers surrounding the involved blood vessels, vascular inflammation with muscle fiber degeneration, cell death, and regeneration.

Treatment

There are several emergent issues that need to be assessed when the patient presents. Children should be evaluated for any evidence of respiratory compromise, keeping in mind that patients may not exhibit all of the typical signs of respiratory distress because of their significant weakness. Patients also need to be assessed for intestinal vasculitis if they have any abdominal pain or diarrhea since this complication is associated with significant complications and mortality. Evaluations to consider include checking the stool for blood and an abdominal computed tomography scan. In addition, any patient who has voice changes and/or reports of swallowing difficulty should not be allowed to take anything by mouth until appropriate swallowing evaluations can be performed to assess for risk of aspiration.

Steroids are the therapy of choice. Because patients may have some degree of intestinal inflammation, intravenous dosing may be indicated for moderate-to-severe disease to improve absorption. Steroids are gradually tapered to a low maintenance dose while monitoring the physical examination and muscle enzymes. Children usually require treatment with these small doses of steroids for at least 2 years since stopping this medication sooner is associated with an increased risk of an exacerbation in their disease. It is important to monitor for long-term side effects of steroids, including osteoporosis, glaucoma, cataracts, growth retardation, and steroid myopathy that can contribute to muscle weakness and atrophy. In patients with more resistant disease or with significant steroid side effects, additional medications may be added, such as methotrexate and cyclosporine. IVIG and hydroxychloroquine are particularly good for managing rash. Sun protection, using sunscreen with greater than or equal to sun protection factor (SPF) 30, is very important. Physical and occupational therapy should be used to prevent loss of range of motion and development of contractures by implementing passive range of motion exercises in the early phases of disease and more intensive, graded exercises at later stages focused on stretching and strengthening.

Prognosis

At least 80% of patients have a unicyclic course. Therefore, only a small percentage of children have resistant disease with more continuous or recurrent courses. It is difficult to predict the outcome at the onset of illness. Factors that have been associated with a poor prognosis include persistent, severe disease activity, extensive vasculitis, calcinosis, difficulty swallowing, and voice changes. There are certain muscle-specific antibodies that are associated with more severe disease. Also, delay in treatment or inadequate treatment, is associated with a worse prognosis.

Sarcoidosis

Clinical Manifestations

Sarcoidosis is a multisystem autoimmune condition. There are two patterns of presentation, including a group of patients who present before the age of 4 years. These patients with early-onset sarcoid typically have skin, joint, and eye disease. The rash may be flat, raised, or nodular. The arthritis associated with sarcoidosis is typically quite proliferative with significant thickening of the synovium and large collections of fluid in the joints. The physical findings are often out of proportion to the joint symptoms with minimal pain, decreased range of motion, and stiffness. Patients may develop uveitis, involving the anterior and/or posterior areas. The collections of white blood cells seen in the eye can produce a 'snowbank' appearance when examined by an ophthalmologist. Other manifestations, such as swollen glands, enlarged liver and spleen, and lung involvement, seen in older-onset sarcoidosis are rare in young children.

Genetics

There have been familial cases of patients with early-onset disease. Some of these cases have a specific gene mutation and have been classified as having Blau syndrome. The relationship between sarcoidosis and Blau syndrome is not entirely clear but they appear to be along a similar spectrum of disease.

Laboratory and Pathologic Findings

Laboratory abnormalities include increased markers of inflammation, increased immunoglobulins, and elevated calcium in the blood and urine. Pathologic specimens demonstrate granulomas – nodular collections of inflammatory cells. Angiotensin-converting enzyme (ACE) is produced by cells within the granulomas; therefore, serum levels are often elevated, although this is less common in young children. It is important to recognize that serum ACE levels are higher in children and therefore it is necessary to use appropriate normal values to interpret the results of this test.

Treatment

Treatment generally involves systemic steroids and additional immunosuppressive agents, such as methotrexate, azathioprine, and infliximab may be used to achieve better disease control and to minimize the side effects of prednisone.

Prognosis

Children with sarcoidosis tend to have chronic symptoms and may suffer from long-term complications of this disease. Specifically, the joint disease can lead to severe growth delay as well as destruction of cartilage and bone. Patients with uveitis may develop significant visual impairment.

Conclusions/Future Directions

Pediatric rheumatic diseases are rare autoimmune conditions that may have significant impacts on development and quality of life and can be associated with long-term sequelae. Clinical and basic science research is now focused on standardizing diagnostic criteria and outcome measures, validation of quality of life instruments, further investigations of possible genetic and environmental triggers, and novel therapies that will hopefully improve the overall outcomes of affected children.

See also: Allergies; Asthma; Colic; Crying; Failure to Thrive; Feeding Development and Disorders; Immune System and Immunodeficiency; Physical Growth; Prenatal Development; Screening, Newborn and Maternal Well-being; Screening, Prenatal; Vision Disorders and Visual Impairment.

Suggested Readings

Cassidy JT and Petty RE (2001) Textbook of Pediatric Rheumatology, 4th edn, p. 215. Philadelphia, PA: Elsevier Saunders.
Cassidy JT, Petty RE, Laxer RM, and Lindsley CB (2005) *Textbook of Pediatric Rheumatology,* 5th edn. Philadelphia, PA: Elsevier Saunders.

Compeyrot-Lacassagne S and Feldman BM (2005) Inflammatory myopathies in children. *Pediatric Clinics of North America* 52: 493–520.

Dedeoglu F and Sundel RP (2005) Vasculitis in children. *Pediatric Clinics of North America* 52: 547–575.

European League Against Rheumatism (EULAR) Bulletin No. 4 (1997) Nomenclature and classification of arthritis in children Basel: National Zeitung AG.

Klippel JH (1997) *Primer on the Rheumatic Diseases,* 11th edn. Atlanta: Arthritis Foundation.

Ravelli A and Martini A (2007) Juvenile idiopathic arthritis. *Lancet* 369: 767–778.

Tse SML and Laxer RM (2006) Approach to acute limb pair in childhood. *Pediatric in Review* 27: 170–180.

Weiss JE and Ilowite NT (2005) Juvenile idiopathic arthritis. *Pediatric Clinics of North America* 52: 413–442.

Relevant Websites

http://www.aap.org – American Academy of Pediatrics.
http://www.rheumatology.org – American College of Rheumatology.
http://www.arthritis.org – Arthritis Foundation.
http://www.niams.nih.gov – NIAMS, National Institute of Arthritis and Musculoskeletal and Skin diseases.
http://www.myositis.org – The Myositis Association, Juvenile Dermatomyositis.

Imagination and Fantasy

J D Woolley and A Tullos, The University of Texas, Austin, TX, USA

Glossary

Fantasy – A subset of imagination in which the imagined entity, object, or scenario is more extravagant or less constrained by reality.

Imagination – The formation of mental imagines of entities or events that are not present to the senses.

Individual differences – Characteristics of children's biological, social, environmental, or genetic makeup that make them different from other children the same age. Without individual differences, all children of the same age would develop similarly.

Object substitution – Involves using one object to stand for another. For example, children might pretend that a cardboard box is a castle.

Pretend play – An activity in which children's behavior involves some form of nonreality. It often involves some or all of the following six behaviors: (1) self-pretense, (2) object substitution, (3) animation of objects, (4) pretending about imaginary objects, (5) pretending to be another person or entity, and (6) pretending to have imaginary companions.

Pretense – Involves mental, verbal, or physical engagement in nonreality.

Role play – Involves imagining and acting out the role of another person or creature. It can involve acting like another person, behaving toward a toy as if it is really what it represents, or interacting with a pretend being, such as an imaginary companion.

Introduction

Walk into any preschool classroom, and evidence of young children's imagination abounds. In one corner of the room you might observe children playing dress-up, in another the products of a finger-painting project, and in another a child building a castle out of colorful blocks. Many consider the preschool years to represent the peak of imaginative and fantastical thinking. In this article we explore the origins and development of imagination and fantasy from its earliest observable manifestations in older infants and toddlers through its peak in the later preschool years.

We must begin by considering what we mean by imagination and fantasy. The word 'imagination' is certainly used in a multitude of ways to mean many things: "use your imagination," "she or he's got a good imagination," "I can't imagine what it would be like," are some common examples. In its most basic sense, imagination is the formation of a mental image of something that is not present to the senses; it is the act of conceiving of an alternative to reality. Imagination is the ability to think of things as otherwise than we see them or as different from how they exist in the world. Imagination can include thinking about the immediate future (e.g., imagining how good a cookie would taste) and the distant future (e.g., imagining being a grown-up), as well as the more prototypical uses found in the quotes above. Fantasy is most often taken to be a subset of imagination, or imagination that is somehow farther removed or less restricted by reality. For example, a fantasy may involve slaying dragons or time travel, things that are impossible, but would not include improbable imaginations like winning the lottery or traveling to the moon.

The ability to engage in imagination and fantasy underlies many activities in which adults engage, including art, music, fiction, appreciation of movies and plays, and other more mundane activities as well, such as planning one's future. Imagination allows one to experience different realities without actually living them. Teenagers, for example, can imagine what it would be like to be a doctor or an architect, what it would be like to have children or to live in another country. The capacity to imagine provides an alternative universe to envision different futures. Thus, imagination is believed to be critical for children to grow into their future selves. In the next section, two important questions will be addressed: (1) What are the origins of imagination and fantasy? (2) When do children come to share this important ability with adults?

One problem that is faced in seeking answers to these questions is that external manifestations are required to discern the presence of imagination. That is, without some kind of behavior, it is difficult to know when someone is imagining, especially in infants. The traditional developmental perspective is that infants do not imagine or participate in fantasy, and that this ability develops with age. This perspective is not based on evidence that infants do not imagine; rather, it is based primarily on a lack of evidence that they do. Psychologists have not yet developed a method to assess the presence of imagination in infants. Part of the reluctance to attribute imaginal abilities to infants stems from Piaget's proposal that mental representation is not possible until toddlerhood. However, given that recent research in cognitive development is uncovering earlier evidence of object permanence, imitation, and other representational abilities previously thought to be absent in infancy, it seems reasonable to consider that imagination may be present earlier too. We can consider this possibility from a theoretical perspective, but from an empirical perspective researchers are still limited to external signs of imagination, most notably, pretense. Thus we begin with this question: When do children begin to pretend?

Imagining, Pretending, and Fantasizing: The Developmental Course

Imagination and Pretending

As with imagination and fantasy, we must first consider what we mean by pretending or pretense. Pretending or pretense are mental activities involving imagination, in which alternative identities are projected onto reality. Pretend play is the behavioral manifestation of pretense. While pretense can be a solely mental activity (such as daydreaming), pretend play involves physical activity and

thus can be observed and documented. A wide range of behaviors can be classified as pretend play. **Table 1** shows five criteria that have been proposed for symbolic or pretend play. These include: (1) familiar activities may be performed in the absence of necessary material or a social context (e.g., pretending to stir soup in an empty pot), (2) activities may not be carried out to their logical outcome (e.g., when pretending to go out to dinner, children do not actually leave the house and drive to a restaurant), (3) a child may treat an inanimate object as animate (e.g., offer food to a teddy bear), (4) one object or gesture may be substituted for another (e.g., a block becomes a pot), and (5) a child may carry out an activity usually performed by someone else (e.g., pretending to be a doctor).

As shown in **Table 2**, children engage in the following six forms of pretense: (1) self-pretense (e.g., a child pretends to be asleep), (2) object substitution (e.g., a child uses a stick as a spoon), (3) animation of objects (e.g., a child feeds a stuffed bear), (4) pretending about imaginary objects (e.g., pretending to drive an invisible car), (5) pretending to be (or act) like someone else, and (6) pretending to have imaginary companions. Many of these forms of pretense are readily observable in any preschool classroom across the US. However, pretend play is clearly not limited to classrooms.

Table 1   Five criteria for pretend play

Criterion	Example
1. Familiar activities performed in the absence of necessary material	Pretend to stir soup in an empty pot
2. Activities not carried out to logical outcome	Children pretending to go out to dinner do not actually drive to or from the restaurant
3. Treat inanimate object as animate	Offer food to a teddy bear
4. Object or gesture substituted for another	A block is used as a pot
5. Child may carry out activity usually performed by someone else	Pretend to be a doctor

Table 2   Six forms of pretense

Pretense form	Example
1. Self-pretense	Pretending to be asleep
2. Object substitution	Using a stick as a spoon
3. Animation of objects	Feeding a stuffed bear
4. Pretending about imaginary objects	Pretending to drive an invisible car
5. Pretending to be someone else	Impersonating Spiderman
6. Pretending about imaginary other	Having an imaginary friend

Researchers have observed pretend play in a wide range of cultures; thus, it is believed to be universal in its occurrence. Not only does pretend play seem to be prevalent across cultures, there are also certain specific aspects of pretend play that appear to be universal. One of these is children's use of objects in their pretend play. Most of children's pretend play occurs in relation to toy objects such as blocks and baby dolls. When toys are not readily available, children often use objects from nature. A second universal characteristic of pretend play is its interactive context. Although solo pretend play does occur, caregivers, siblings, and peers are most often an essential component of children's pretend play. Since cross-culturally children engage in pretend play, the question often arises as to how this ability develops.

Symbolic pretense was proposed by Piaget to derive initially from imitation of oneself, which extends to others as children get older. The primary trajectory is from solitary play toward play with others, or sociodramatic play. The earliest observed indications of pretending are at around 12–13 months, and children's pretending abilities develop significantly between the ages of 15 and 24 months. In addition, the incidence of pretend play increases significantly between the ages of 1 and 4 years. Based on Piaget's work, children are believed to progress through three basic levels in this pathway. Children first reproduce regular actions. Here, the child's own body can be a prop (e.g., pretend sleeping). Next they show similar actions but with one part missing (e.g., cup with no liquid), and begin to incorporate objects as props into their play. For example, if they are pretending to scramble an egg, they may use a stick to represent the whisk and their cupped hand to represent the bowl. With age, the ability to pretend with substitute objects continues to improve, and children also become more able to imagine scenarios in a purely cognitive realm without the aid of objects or body parts. For example, a child may be able to pretend to make scrambled eggs without using any props. Finally, children start performing pretend actions on others, acting out others' actions, and coordinating joint pretense. This is the developmental trajectory of pretend play in general. In addition, there are subsets of pretend play that also provide a glimpse of how pretense develops.

Role play is a type of pretend play that involves children's ability to imagine and act out the role of a person or creature. There are three different ways children can participate in role play: (1) by acting like another person (e.g., pretending to be a mother), (2) by treating a toy as if it is what it represents (e.g., by acting as if a baby doll is sleeping), and (3) by structuring interactions around a pretend being (e.g., having a conversation with an imaginary companion). Role play is quite common in typically developing humans but limited in nonhumans (although there is some evidence in great apes and bottlenose dolphins). The most frequent context for role play is with other children, most often siblings or peers. This type of pretend play, in which children enact roles with one another, is often referred to as sociodramatic play. Factors that influence this sort of play include the age of the partner, the child's relationship to the partner, and the child's culture.

The social relationship between mother and child facilitates the development of children's pretense. The mother's participation in play increases the duration, complexity, and diversity of children's pretend play. Mothers often begin introducing pretense to their 12-month-olds through nonliteral comments such as "I bet your doll is really hungry – she hasn't eaten since breakfast." By 18 months, mothers begin to add requests to their nonliteral comments. For example, mothers of younger children might scaffold the pretend play by making a request such as "Why don't you scramble an egg for your doll?" At this age, children will often go along with their mother's request and engage in the pretense, but they are less likely to initiate the pretense or create the plot on their own. There is considerable development between the ages of 1 and 3 years in the extent to which young children initiate play themes. Younger than 2 years, mothers initiate most play; they suggest ideas, and pull children from solo to joint play. After age 2 years, children become increasingly more likely to initiate themes of pretend play on their own. Even so, mothers continue to play an important role in maintaining and enhancing children's initiatives. While research is just beginning to investigate the role of fathers in caretaking, studies have shown that fathers scaffold their toddlers' pretend play similarly to mothers. However, there are sex differences in the play themes that fathers initiate with their children. Fathers tend to use explicit guidance in initiating traditional, male play themes with their sons, such as playing with cars or tools. In contrast, with their daughters, fathers are more implicit in their guidance and suggest domestic themes, such as cooking. This research demonstrates the utility of the parental role in initiating pretend play, providing more support for the suggestion that parents use pretend play as a vehicle for teaching social/gender roles, and in general for preparing the toddler to socialize with family and peers.

Sibling relationships also play a unique role in children's pretending. Children's ability to engage in joint pretend play can be enhanced by their participation in a warm and affectionate sibling relationship. Younger children's pretend play can be scaffolded by the involvement of an older sibling. The sibling most often sets up and directs the pretense, with the younger sibling occasionally making unique contributions. Siblings give each other more control and input into the pretend play situation than do mothers, and also require a higher level of cooperation from each other. Thus, siblings and parents appear to play unique but complimentary roles in the development of joint pretend play.

Cultural differences in beliefs about the value of pretend play can affect the frequency of others' involvement in children's pretend play and the orientation of the play. Some research has shown that mothers from different cultures have different goals about the role of pretend play, and that these goals influence the themes they initiate with their children. For example, Chinese caregivers have been shown to use play to teach morals and social routines, whereas Irish-American parents often use play to involve children in fantasy. These goals are often reflected in the children's play themes. For example, in a study comparing children from these cultures, the Irish-American children's play centered around themes such as superheroes, and Chinese children's play more often focused on social behaviors, such as cooking dinner. Most of these sorts of play scenarios involve role play with peers or family members, which is often considered the most sophisticated form of pretense. We will now turn our attention to a less common and more highly debated form of role play in which children interact with imagined others.

Imaginary Companions

The creation of imaginary companions is arguably one of the most imaginative types of pretend activity in which children engage. The incidence of imaginary companions in preschool children ranges from 13% to 75%, depending on the definition used by the researcher and the method of study. Whereas some researchers only include children with invisible companions, others include children who animate their stuffed animals. Some researchers require parental validation of children's reported imaginary companions whereas others do not. According to Marjorie Taylor, who has studied children with imaginary companions extensively, imaginary companions represent a high level of pretend play not found in any other species besides humans. Unlike everyday pretend play, the creation of an imaginary companion represents a pretense activity that is often sustained for a long period of time; a child may have the same imaginary companion for weeks or even months. Although earlier research had indicated that imaginary companions rarely last beyond the preschool years, recent research reveals that having an imaginary companion is as common in the early elementary years as it is in the preschool years. However, there is not much stability in this type of role play; often a child's imaginary companion in preschool will not be the same one that the child has in the early elementary years. In identifying children with imaginary companions, researchers consider three types of activity: (1) creating an invisible companion, (2) impersonating a known character, like a superhero, and (3) endowing a stuffed animal with animate characteristics and/or personality.

The clinical portrait of children who create imaginary companions has been somewhat negative, suggesting that these children are lonely, shy, or friendless. However, Taylor's extensive research indicates that children who create imaginary companions differ very little from other children in most respects. They do seem to display advantages in areas such as sociability, creativity, and positive affect in play with other children (we discuss these patterns more fully in the section on individual differences). Children create imaginary companions for a variety of reasons; their companions provide them with fun and companionship, a vehicle for dealing with anger or fear, and help in coping with problems. In most cases, children begin to create imaginary companions during the preschool years and eventually give them up for a variety of reasons, including lack of interest, creation of a new imaginary companion, and parental intervention through engagement in more social activities.

Parents often wonder whether it is normal or acceptable for their children to have imaginary companions. Should a parent intervene and stop a child from talking to an imaginary companion? As previously mentioned, people have historically wondered if children with imaginary companions were mentally ill. However, recently parents in Western culture have come to accept that pretend play is a valuable component of children's development and that having imaginary companions can be an important part of that development. Whereas not all parents are aware of their children's foray into the world of imagination, a majority of parents are knowledgeable and respectful of their child's interest in imagination. Some parents even facilitate their child's relationship with the imaginary companion; in one reported case, parents set an extra place at the dinner table each night. However, in some religious groups, such as the Mennonites, imaginative play and imaginary companions are discouraged by adults. Researchers have found that this discouragement does not successfully squelch the child's engagement in pretense. Rather, the intervention often forces the children to be more secretive in their pretend play and creation of imaginary companions. Thus, research has found that children with imaginary companions are engaging in a fairly common and potentially beneficial form of play that in many cases seems to be an integral part of their development.

Fantastical Beings

Children in many cultures exhibit strong beliefs in fantastical beings. As we have discussed, family or peers initially supply the themes for very young children's pretense, but later in the preschool years, children begin to initiate and create the play themes on their own. Individual children and adults are similarly involved in the creation of imaginary beings. When children create the fantastical beings themselves we call them imaginary companions, but cultures also create fantastical beings and introduce them to children. In Western culture, these culturally supported fantastical beings include specific event-related beings such as Santa Claus and the Tooth Fairy and also generic beings such as fairies and monsters. What is the developmental course of children's participation in fantasy worlds around these beings?

Children in Western culture participate in numerous rituals around culturally supported fantastical beings. These rituals include leaving cookies for Santa Claus on Christmas Eve, hunting for Easter eggs, and checking for monsters under the bed. Participating in rituals involving fantastical beings serves important roles for both parents and children. The Tooth Fairy ritual, for example, provides a vehicle for parents to maintain what many perceive as the innocence and magic of childhood. This ritual can also aid children in a period of loss, and provide them with empowerment in the form of money, a symbolic form of adult society. Santa Claus inspires more complex rituals, and arguably also serves as a vehicle for parents to prolong in their children what they see as a period of innocence and magic. Santa Claus rituals can also provide a means of behavioral control for parents (e.g., parents' threat of Santa putting coal in the Christmas stocking rather than toys). Some have proposed that children's experiences with these fantastical beings play an important role in the development of faith and spirituality. Specifically, children learn to believe in something that they cannot see or experience directly, and this ability is thought to facilitate later belief in God and other religious entities.

What Do Children Understand about Imagination and Fantasy?

The first part of this article has focused on what children do – when and how they start imagining and pretending, and when they tend to have imaginary companions and engage in rituals around them and other fantasy figures. The remainder of the article will be devoted to addressing what children understand about imagination and fantasy. At the heart of this issue is children's understanding of the distinction between reality and nonreality. In other words, do children realize that when they are pretending to eat a cookie, that they are not really eating a cookie; do they perceive a difference in the reality status of Santa Claus and that of their parents?

When do children differentiate the real from the unreal? It is difficult to assess the presence of this distinction in infants. It has been shown that by 9 months of age, infants behave differently toward objects and photographs of those objects, reaching more often for the objects themselves when the two are presented simultaneously. Thus, infants do distinguish between real objects and physical representations of those objects. Although it is clear that these young infants treat objects and pictures differently, it is unlikely that a concept of reality or nonreality

underlies this behavior. However, by 19 months of age, children do appear to have a concept of a picture as something that is not real. Children's understanding of the properties of real objects vs. the properties of not-real objects continues to develop through the preschool years.

The most convincing evidence that children make this distinction comes from observations of their early language. Thus, we again focus our attention on toddlers and preschool-age children. Recording of children's conversations shows that, by 2.5 years of age, children use the words 'real' and 'really' to make a number of contrasts between the real world and various alternatives. Children use the word 'real' to contrast reality with a wide range of alternatives, the most common being toys, pictures, and pretense. For example, a child might point to a stuffed animal and say: "That's not a real dog; it's just pretend." Thus at a fairly young age children are beginning to carve the world into things that are real and things that are not real.

Understanding of Pretending and Imagination

When do children begin to understand that pretense, in particular, is distinct from real life? For a child to be truly pretending he or she must understand that what he or she is doing is different from reality. If a child who appears to be pretending to play with a toy cookie begins to take a (real) bite of the cookie, then it is more appropriate to say that this child thought he or she had a real cookie rather than that he or she was pretending. Research shows that, by 3 years of age, children are able to identify both a real object (e.g., a block) and the pretend identity someone has assigned to it (e.g., an airplane). One way to test children's understanding that pretend objects and actions are distinct from real ones is to interfere with children's pretending and observe their reactions. Interference may involve another person entering the room or one of the play participants leaving, or it may be subtler, such as one participant changing the plot of the pretence (e.g., "Now let's pretend this table is a cave instead of a tower"). Young elementary-age children can handle an interruption to their pretend play quite well and can incorporate the source of the interruption into their pretense. Preschool-age children do not handle interruptions well and often will terminate the pretense game if interrupted. These findings suggest that older children have a better grasp on the boundary between fantasy and reality than do younger children. However, more extreme violations of the pretend-real boundary seem to bother both younger and older children. For example, in one study, a researcher actually bit into a pretend cookie. If children confused the pretend cookie with a real one, this sort of action should not have bothered them. However, it did. Even preschoolers were clearly shocked by this action, indicating that they were able to maintain the pretend-real boundary while playing.

To engage in pretend play with others, children must also learn to tell when other people are pretending and to interpret their actions accordingly. Imagine a child who has not shown any evidence of pretending, and then imagine what that child thinks when her mother pretends to pour tea into an empty cup and hands it to her. Research shows that, when pretending with their children, mothers act differently than when they are really performing an action. For example, they look at their child longer when pretending than when they really perform the same action in real life, they smile more when pretending, and they make more exaggerated movements. By the age of 2 years, children are able to pick up on these cues and to become engaged appropriately in pretense. Children of this age also learn to understand that an object has taken on a pretend identity. Between the age of 2 and 3 years, children develop the ability to identify the pretend outcome of another's action. For example, if a child sees someone pretend to give a doll a bath, he or she will appropriately pretend to dry the doll off. The ability to imagine a pretense scenario and actively engage another person to join in the pretense develops around this same age.

Children of 3–5 years of age also understand that objects of imagination differ from real physical objects in important ways. In one study, children were told stories about characters who were thinking of something (e.g., thinking about a cookie), characters who were 'pretending' something (e.g., pretending to have a cookie), and characters who really were in possession of an object (e.g., had a cookie). Then children were asked to make judgments concerning three criteria – behavioral-sensory properties, publicness, and consistency. For example, children were asked, for each character, whether he could see and touch the cookie (behavioral-sensory evidence), whether someone else could do these things (publicness), and whether he could eat the cookie at some point in the future (consistency). Children claimed that, unlike real physical objects, imagined objects could not be seen, touched, or acted upon by themselves or others. Children as young as 3 years are also able to comment on and manipulate their mental images. For example, children claim that, just by thinking about it, they can make an imagined balloon stretch or imaginary scissors cut.

Children's explanations of their responses to these sorts of questions reflect their rich knowledge of imagination. For example, when asked to explain why a child could not eat a cookie that she was just thinking about, 3-year-olds offered explanations like "Pretend ones aren't real ones," and "he or she wants to eat it and he or she can because it's not imaginary." Other children replied, "Cause it's invisible; cause you just imagine it" (4-year-old), and "Because if you're blind or not you can still see things in your imagination" (5-year-old). The frequency with which children spontaneously used the word 'imagination' in these studies, along with the richness of their comments, strongly suggests that preschool-age children know quite a lot about the mental nature of imagination, and about the not-real status of imagined entities.

Other research shows that in addition to understanding these important properties of imagination, children also understand how imagination is different from other mental states. For example, by the age of 3 years, children understand that knowledge reflects reality more than does imagination. That is, if one person claims to know something about the world, and another states that he or she is just imagining, children will expect the world to reflect the contents of the former person's mind. In addition, children understand that if a person thinks that something is the case, he or she will be more likely to act upon that mental state than if he or she is only imagining a particular outcome. For example, if a child thinks that a box really contains a toy, he or she will be more likely to eagerly rip the box open than if he or she is just fancifully imagining that the box contains a toy.

The research we have discussed shows that children understand some basic differences between imagination and reality. In addition to understanding these differences, it is important that children also understand the causal relations between imagination and reality. Most adults in Western culture believe that one cannot cause physical events with one's imagination. Research with children shows that, by the age of 3 years, children understand that objects of their imaginations do not come to life. This is especially clear with respect to everyday objects – children know that even though they imagine a pencil in an empty box, the box will remain empty. However, emotion can sometimes disrupt this understanding, or at least its expression. That is, even though a child knows that monsters are not real, the thought of a monster under a bed might be enough to make a child refuse to go into his room at night. Indeed, research shows that children have a more difficult time displaying their understanding of the causal relations between imagination and reality when they are asked to pretend or imagine scary things, like monsters. In one study, preschool children were shown an empty box and were asked to imagine a monster inside. All children agreed that the box was empty. However, when they were left alone with the box, they exhibited fear and avoidance of it. Although this behavior might suggest that children confuse fantasy and reality, one must consider that adults may engage in similar behaviors. For example, an adult might cover his or her eyes when watching a scary movie, or might cry while reading the tragic conclusion to a love story. These sorts of reactions suggest separate emotional and cognitive systems, and have led researchers to propose that emotional reactions to imaginary objects may develop independently of a child's understanding of the reality status of the entity.

Imaginary companions are a classic area in which children have been thought to be confused about the nature of imagination. Children often exhibit complex behavioral routines around their imaginary companions (e.g., insisting that a place be set for them at the dinner table). Because of this, children are traditionally thought to believe that their imaginary companions are real. However, children with imaginary companions are, for the most part, quite clear about the fantasy status of their imaginary companions. They understand that they are not real, and often, if engaged in a discussion about their imaginary companion with a researcher, feel compelled to clarify to the researcher that, "She's just pretend, you know."

One interesting question is whether children with imaginary companions differ from children without imaginary companions in their general understanding of the mental nature of imagination. As mentioned earlier, historically children with imaginary companions were thought to be exhibiting early signs of mental illness and therefore to have difficulty understanding that imagination is a mental activity different from reality. However, research has shown that, when given standard tasks to assess their understanding of imagination, children with imaginary companions do not perform differently from children without imaginary companions. However, children with imaginary companions do show a higher level of engagement in fantasy play than children without imaginary companions. Thus, although children with imaginary companions may be more highly disposed to engage in fantasy than children without imaginary companions, their understanding of the mental nature of imagination is comparable to their peers.

What Do Children Understand about Fantastical Beings and Events?

The traditional view of young children is that they are credulous, forming firm beliefs in everything their parents tell them about the world. Some have even proposed that such credulity is an adaptive mechanism in childhood, helping children to stay safe in a dangerous world. Others have argued that, because of the way beliefs are formed, young children lack the cognitive resources necessary to doubt claims they hear others make about fantastical sorts of entities and events. These general arguments suggest that children would indiscriminately hold strong beliefs in fantastical beings and events.

Fantastical events. Do children understand that certain kinds of events are not possible in the real world? By the age of 4 years, children are quite good at differentiating events that are possible in reality from those that are impossible. For example, children understand that events like turning applesauce into apples or walking through a wall are impossible. Older preschool-age children can even make this distinction when they see pictures of fantastical events. In one study, researchers showed 3–5-year-old children a set of pictures taken from children's storybooks, some

realistic (e.g., a mother bird feeding its young), and some fantastical (e.g., a rabbit sweeping the floor while another rabbit bakes a cake). Children were asked to indicate whether the depicted events could really happen. Results indicated that 3-year-olds had considerable difficulty with the task, but by the age of 5 years children were able to identify the pictures correctly. As with causal relations between imagination and reality, emotional content appears to affect such differentiation. When depicted real situations invoke fear, children are more likely to incorrectly claim that they are not real, even when they are able to successfully differentiate real from pretend nonemotional scenarios.

Young children seem to differ from adults regarding their beliefs about the reality of magic. In one study, 4–6-year-old children were told a story about a box that supposedly transformed pictures into the real objects they represented. Almost all children understood that this sort of box could not exist in reality. However, later on, the researchers presented a box to the children and suggested that it was the same sort of box as in the story. When left alone with the box, the majority of the children tried in some way to use the box to create real objects. When it did not work, they expressed disappointment. Thus, even though they seemed to understand that this sort of box was not possible, they still tried to work magic on it. This research shows that, although children seem to have some skepticism about magic, they are not entirely sure that it does not exist in the real world.

When children do not understand how an unusual event might have happened, they tend to attribute it to magic. However, there are age differences in what children mean when they attribute an event to magic. Younger (preschool-age) children seem to believe that magic is a real force in the world, one that can make seemingly impossible events possible. Older children are more likely to conceive of the event as a trick, or as someone's attempt to deceive them. However, even though younger children are more likely to believe in certain magical events, they are able to tell the difference between a magical and an ordinary event. For example, preschool-age children know that putting a marble in a box with one's hand is an ordinary event, whereas moving a marble with one's mind is magical.

Fantastical beings. Fantastical beings often generate extreme emotions in children, ranging from acute terror over the monster under the bed to gleeful adoration of Santa Claus. The extreme behavioral reactions of children to fantastical beings contribute to the common belief that children are confused about fantasy and reality. Researchers have assessed children's understanding of the reality status of a variety of fantastical entities. In one study, children were presented with pictures of generic supernatural creatures like witches and dragons, specific fantasy figures from popular culture such as Big Bird and Smoky the Bear, and real entities like birds and frogs. Children received both free sorting tasks, in which they were asked which pictures went together, and a task in which they were asked to categorize each item as being 'real' or 'pretend'. On the categorization tasks, even kindergartners were able to properly place these entities into pile of 'real' and 'pretend', with this ability continuing to develop through the grade-school years. However, until grade 6, children rarely spontaneously used fantasy status as a dimension with which to categorize entities. Thus, it appears that, in young children, the fantasy–reality distinction is in place, but the ability and motivation to use it in the same way that adults do continues to develop throughout childhood.

It is important to distinguish between two types of fantastical beings: generic beings, such as monsters, and specific event-related beings, such as Santa Claus. With regard to generic fantastical beings, recent studies show that, with a few exceptions, preschool-age children understand that they are not real. Young children can put pictures of monsters, ghosts, and witches into a 'make believe' box and pictures of everyday entities like dogs into a 'real' box. In contrast, many young children in Western culture appear to hold strong beliefs in specific event-related fantasy figures, most notably, Santa Claus, the Easter Bunny, and the Tooth Fairy. Results of research investigating these beliefs confirm that the majority of preschool-age children raised in families that celebrate Christmas believe that Santa Claus is real. Age is a significant determinant of the degree of children's beliefs in these figures. By the age of 8 years, belief in Santa Claus has declined significantly, with less than 25% of 8-year-olds still believing. Parents also report that their young children believe that event-related figures such as the Tooth Fairy and the Easter Bunny are real (e.g., exist in the real world), but report a lesser degree of belief in nonevent-related figures such as dragons, witches, ghosts, monsters, and fairies.

Event-related fantasy figures are often strongly tied to religious beliefs, and as such, it is possible that non-Christian children lack many of the associated experiences. In a sample of American Jewish children aged 3–10 years, level of belief in Santa Claus was found to be significantly lower than belief levels in Christian children. However, surprisingly, belief in the Tooth Fairy was significantly lower as well. One possible explanation is that a child's first experience with fantasy figures may color attitudes toward subsequent ones. Children typically learn about Santa Claus first, and to Jewish children he is presented as unreal. When they later hear about the Tooth Fairy, they may also assume that she is unreal.

Researchers have attempted to address what sorts of factors influence initial acceptance of the existence of fantastical beings. In one study, researchers introduced preschool- and elementary school-age children to a novel fantastical being, the Candy Witch. The Candy Witch was presented as a nice witch who visits children on Halloween, and trades a new toy for unwanted candy. They found that among older preschoolers, children who participated in the Candy Witch ritual in their home exhibited stronger beliefs in the Candy Witch than did those who did not. Among children who participated in the ritual, older children had stronger beliefs than did younger children. Belief in the Candy Witch remained high 1 year later. Children who believed in more fantastical beings when they were introduced to the Candy Witch also had stronger beliefs than children who believed in fewer fantastical beings. Thus, parental support, age, and the number of fantastical beings in which a child already believes, all influence the extent to which a child will form a belief in a fantastical being. Overall, despite having a clear understanding of certain important aspects of the fantasy–reality distinction, beliefs in the real existence of certain culturally supported fantastical beings persist into the early elementary-school years.

Fantasy in the media. Storybooks and television often transport children to imaginary worlds and introduce them to fantastical beings and processes. Thus, an important question concerns children's understanding of the reality status of the material they encounter in interactions with these media. Do children believe that Big Bird is real? What about all the people and creatures they encounter for the first time in books?

Young children do exhibit some confusion about the reality status of objects, people, and events on television. One might expect that children mistakenly believe that everything they see on television is either inside the television or is really happening somewhere else. However, by the age of 4 years, and possibly somewhat earlier, children understand that the things that they see on television are not real, physical objects; they understand that they are pictures. With regard to televised events, rather than being credulous and believing that events on television are real, 5-year-old children have a bias to claim that all events on television are fictional. By age 7 years children learn to recognize cues indicating that certain television shows or events are real, whereas others are not. Specifically, children learn to distinguish between realistic shows such as the news and documentaries and fictional shows like sitcoms.

Most early research on storybooks showed that young children's interpretations of stories are that they are events that happened in the past – they are historical rather than fictional. From this research it was concluded that children begin to doubt the reality of stories at around age 5 or 6 years of age, and that not until age 7 years did they let go of literal beliefs in fiction. More recent research indicates that reality/fantasy differentiation regarding storybook events develops toward the end of the preschool years. By age 4 years, children know what sorts of events are possible in fairy tales versus in reality. For example, when questioned about the possibility of a child passing through a wall, 4–6-year-old children understand that this sort of event cannot happen in the real world but could happen in fairy tales.

Research involving reading children entire storybooks (vs. presenting them with isolated events) reveals even earlier understanding. This research shows that, by the age of 3 years, children begin to differentiate realistic, fantastical, and religious stories in terms of the reality status of the characters and events. Three-year-olds are more likely to judge story characters as real than are 4- and 5-year-olds, but most preschool children judge storybook characters as not real with all story types. This is important, as it indicates that young children may, in fact, be skeptical about storybook content, rather than credulous, as many have believed. Children of all ages understand that events in realistic stories can happen in real life more so than events in fantastical stories. Interestingly, 5-year-olds are more likely than younger children to claim that events in religious stories can happen in real life. Religious background plays a role in these judgments, with children from more highly religious backgrounds being more likely to claim that religious events really happened. Now that we have reviewed when children understand the difference between reality and nonreality, we can address what factors might make some children develop this distinction earlier than others, or might simply make some children think differently about it.

Individual Differences in Imagination, Pretense, and Fantasy

Most of the research discussed in this article has addressed age norms in the development of imagination and fantasy. However, as many have observed, some children simply seem more attracted to or more engaged in imagination and fantasy than others. Some researchers have proposed that this reflects a general personality disposition, which has been referred to as fantasy proneness or fantasy predisposition. Those with a greater fantasy predisposition are thought to be better able to create alternative environments of the sort employed in pretend play. Others have suggested that children who pretend more are those that are more socially skilled. Others have suggested that creativity is an important factor. Although it is not certain what is at the root of these differences, they have been observed at many levels.

Researchers have uncovered individual differences even in those aspects of pretense that seem simplest and most basic. For example, regarding object pretense, children of the same age vary in their willingness to use imaginary objects – some children need objects to represent pretend identities whereas others can more easily conjure an imagined representation. There also appears to be significant variation in role play pretense, both in terms of factors that are considered to contribute to individual differences and factors believed to be a result of these differences (in most cases it is impossible to infer

the direction of causation). One increasingly common finding is that children who engage in more role play are more socially skilled than other children. They have a better understanding that different people may have different ideas, different desires, and different emotions, and tailor their interactions with people accordingly.

Familial factors also appear to affect role play. Having an older sibling is associated with more role play, perhaps because siblings provide increased opportunities for role play. Some studies have shown that living in poverty can affect fantasy play. These studies show that, although children living in poverty are capable of engaging in high-quality fantasy play, they engage in it less often than do other children, and they show less diversity in the themes of their pretend play. However this may be due more to motivational factors than to cognitive or social limitations, as the simple presence of fantasy-promoting toys can increase the frequency of high-level play in these children. The fact that there are no social class differences in the onset of pretend play or in its development during the first year or so supports this interpretation.

There are sex differences in the types of role play in which children participate. With regard to the objects used in their pretend play, patterns follow traditional gender stereotypes. For example, girls often involve dolls in their pretense and boys often involve trucks. Girls and boys also differ in the themes that are the focus of their pretend play. Boys most often play adventures, fantasy characters, superheroes, and television-related roles, whereas girls most often pretend-play family roles, house, and dress-up. The characters that children pretend to be also differ by sex, with boys' impersonated characters more likely to be fictional and girls' more likely to be real.

As in role play, there are sex differences regarding imaginary companions. Girls are often reported as being more likely to have imaginary companions than are boys. However, some studies report no gender differences in the frequency of imaginary companions. Boys and girls differ more obviously in the kinds of companions they create. Girls are more likely to create true imaginary companions who serve as playmates. Boys, however, more often impersonate superheroes and other characters. Although this is different from actually having a companion, the level and type of imagination involved is quite similar. Paralleling this, girls' imaginary companions are more often invisible beings, whereas boys' are more often based on toys. Some research also shows that boys may begin to create imaginary companions later in their development than girls.

There are also other individual differences with regard to the creation of imaginary companions. First-born and only-children are somewhat more likely to have imaginary companions. This may be partially due to a need for companionship. However, as mentioned previously, children who create imaginary companions differ very little from other children in most respects. With regard to personality, there are very few significant differences between children with and without imaginary companions in the incidence of behavior problems. Children with imaginary companions do show some slight behavioral advantages over those without, in areas such as cooperation and aggression. Although the common stereotype of these children suggests that they are more shy and withdrawn than children without imaginary companions, research does not confirm this difference. Research comparing children with and without imaginary companions also reveals no differences in intelligence between the two groups, and very slight differences in creativity, favoring children with imaginary companions. Children with imaginary companions also appear to be better able to take another person's perspective, that is, to understand that someone else may have different thoughts, beliefs, or desires. This is thought to be a critical component of social interaction.

With regard to belief in fantastical beings, one might expect that children who pretend more often or who have imaginary companions would be more likely to believe in Santa Claus and other fantasy figures. However, there does not appear to be a relation between these factors; children who are highly involved in fantasy in their daily lives are not more likely to believe in fantastical beings. As discussed earlier, children who already believe in multiple fantastical beings are more likely to believe in a new fantasy figure. It is not clear whether this reflects a personality factor, a cognitive facilitation, or some aspect of those children's culture. Parental promotion of belief, however, does distinguish children who believe strongly in fantastical beings from those who do not. Children whose parents encourage belief through participation in activities centered on particular fantastical beings are more likely to believe in fantastical beings than are children whose parents do not promote these activities. Thus, parental encouragement can create individual differences in children's beliefs in fantastical beings.

Summary and Conclusion

The first section of this article presented a developmental portrait of children's imagination and fantasy. While little is known about the possibility of infant imagination, by the first birthday, parents begin to engage their children in pretense through statements about nonreality. Later, parents scaffold children's pretense by initiating themes during pretend play. By 2–3 years of age, children frequently engage in pretend play on their own and with peers, and begin to offer their own comments about reality and nonreality. Parents encourage pretend play for socialization purposes and to develop children's ability to form mental representations. By

preschool age, children begin to engage in role play, they develop beliefs in fantastical beings such as Santa Claus, and they may invent their own imaginary companions. Between the ages of 3 and 5 years, children hone their skills in distinguishing reality from nonreality, but their practiced differentiation can be thwarted when the topic is highly emotional.

The second section of the article reviewed children's understanding of imagination and fantasy. When children pretend or imagine, do they understand that the contents of their thoughts are not real? Again, it is difficult to know if preverbal infants understand this distinction. However, around the age of 2.5 years, children begin to differentiate reality from nonreality in their everyday language, making comments such as "Bo-Bo is not really a bear." Preschool children demonstrate their understanding between mental verbs such as 'thinking' and 'pretending' and physical verbs such as 'holding'. For example, preschoolers understand that a child who is thinking about a cookie or pretending to have a cookie cannot really eat the cookie, unlike a child who is holding the cookie. By the early elementary school years, children are adept at separating the physical world from the mental world, and are able to switch between the two easily. For example, when mothers interrupt children's pretend play, children are able to disengage from the pretense, interact with their mothers, and then return to the pretend play scenario where they left off. Thus, children demonstrate a keen understanding of the difference between their mental and physical worlds. While this ability is useful for compartmentalizing play themes in childhood, adults also use it when they mentally rehearse scenarios before actively engaging in real life situations. In the late preschool and early elementary school years, children also demonstrate an understanding that imaginary companions, fantastical beings, and events exist primarily in their minds and in storybooks and are not real.

The third section explained how individual differences play a role in children's development and participation in imagination and fantasy. Children who are more interested in fantasy participate more in pretend play, which has been shown to be related to the development of social skills. Children who engage more in pretend play demonstrate better socialization with family, peers, and others. Familial encouragement has shown to be important in the development of pretense and fantasy. Parents and older siblings can encourage pretend play by providing themes for the play. Children whose families and culture encourage belief in fantastical beings show a higher level of belief than children who receive little encouragement. Lastly, birth order and gender have been shown to affect the creation of imaginary companions. Children who are firstborns or only children are more likely to invent imaginary companions than are children with older siblings. With regard to sex differences, boys tend to conjure superheroes for imaginary companions, whereas girls are more likely to fabricate completely invisible, imaginary companions.

In conclusion, imagination and fantasy are an integral part of children's social and cognitive development. Pretense emerges early in development and appears to be present in all cultures. From a cognitive perspective, the ability to differentiate reality from a variety of alternatives – imagination, fantasy, books, and television – is critical to children's ability to learn about the world. From a social perspective, pretending and imagining can help children overcome emotional difficulties and can facilitate social interactions. More research is needed to understand the origins and early development of imagination and fantasy, as well as the various factors that affect children's ability to make the fantasy-reality distinction throughout the preschool and early elementary years.

See also: Birth Order; Cognitive Development; Exploration and Curiosity; Future Orientation; Gender: Awareness, Identity, and Stereotyping; Humor; Play; Socialization in Infancy and Childhood; Social Interaction; Television: Uses and Effects.

Suggested Readings

Clark CD (1995) *Flights of Fancy, Leaps of Faith: Children's Myths in Contemporary America.* Chicago, IL: University of Chicago Press.
Harris PL (2000) *The Work of the Imagination.* Malden, MA: Blackwell Publishers Inc.
Mitchell RW (ed.) (2002) *Pretending in Animals and Children.* Cambridge, UK: Cambridge University Press.
Taylor M (1999) *Imaginary Companions and the Children Who Create Them.* New York, NY: Oxford University Press.

Imitation and Modeling

A N Meltzoff and R A Williamson, University of Washington, Seattle, WA, USA

Glossary

Binding problem – Binding refers to the mechanism by which a particular motor response is 'glued to' perceptual input – usually a visual or auditory stimulus.

Intermodal – A connection that spans across perceptual modalities, for example, touch to vision or audition to vision. Watching someone else speak provides intermodal input because they are seen as well as heard.

Invisible or opaque imitation – A term used to refer to a particular kind of imitation in which the behavior of the model and imitative response cannot be perceived within the same modality. Facial imitation qualifies: Although the actor can see the model's face, she cannot see her own face. It remains invisible.

Proprioception – The perceptual process by which we monitor our own body position in space and the relation between our moving body parts. If you close your eyes and move your fingers, hands, or feet you can 'sense' the form your body takes through proprioception. You monitor your own facial expressions through proprioception.

Social cognition – Perception and cognition about other people (as opposed to space, objects, numbers). Social cognition typically involves processing other people's internal states including their wants, thoughts, and emotions; but more elementary levels may involve processing how other people act and other basic social information.

Introduction

Human infants are avid learners, and as Aristotle noted, young humans excel in learning by watching and imitating. Imitative learning is a means by which human infants profit from information that has been learned by previous generations. It provides a mechanism for the transmission of acquired characteristics from one generation to the next. Imitation is faster than independent discovery (the type of learning emphasized by Piaget) and safer than trial-and-error learning (the type of learning emphasized by Skinner).

The imitative skills of human infants go hand in hand with the motivation of adults to teach their young. Adult pedagogy, in the form of purposely showing a child what to do, is so common that it is often taken for granted. Adult modeling and infant imitation are important pillars of human culture and early apprenticeship learning.

Humans as the Imitative Animal

Imitation provides an efficient channel through which the young incorporate behaviors, skills, customs, and traditions. Bona fide instances of imitative learning in animals are rare enough to be noteworthy. Animal behavior texts devote discussion to the unusual case of a troop of Japanese macaques that began washing their sweet potatoes in the sea after watching a few juveniles who invented this technique. In contrast, even casual observation of human behavior reveals myriad instances of imitation in young children – the imitation of parental postures, facial expressions, and tool use. It is commonly observed that a little girl will reach into her mother's purse to pull out the treasured lipstick and apply it to her lips or studiously poke at the keys of the parental computer. Parents often discourage the particular behaviors, but they persist in part because children see these actions everyday and copy them.

In the 1930s, Margaret Mead highlighted the role of childhood imitative learning in non-Western societies. She published photographs from her research of the Balinese people in Indonesia. Mead's plates provide snapshots of behavior that would be unusual in Western infants and may be partly attributable to imitation of experts in that culture. One photo shows an infant just under 1 year of age who is wielding a machete-like knife. Another shows an older infant playing a 'tjoengklink', a bamboo musical instrument, using the distinctive manual techniques employed by adult experts.

A bold experiment in comparative psychology from the 1930s also underscores the special imitative prowess of *Homo sapiens*. Ironically, the goal of this study was to downplay the genetic bases of differences between humans and apes. The authors sought to attribute behavioral differences to differential rearing conditions. The Kelloggs raised an infant chimpanzee alongside their infant son, providing them with environments as identical as possible. Both were diapered, talked to while playing on the Kelloggs' laps, hugged, and so on. Much to the researchers' disappointment, the infant chimpanzee never grew to be very human-like. But the report reveals that the human infant may well have learned from watching the chimpanzee. The boy was reported to scrape paint off walls with his teeth, to engage in certain mauling play tactics, and most dramatically, to imitate the food barks and grunts of the chimp when he saw the chimp's favorite food. It seems likely that these behaviors were performed by the human child in imitation of the ape – a direction of transmission that had not been anticipated by the Kelloggs.

Distinguishing Imitation from Other Forms of Social Learning

So far the concept of imitation has been used in a commonsense way to mean that the observer duplicates the act that the model performs. Researchers have sought an operational definition of imitation that can be used in designing experiments on infants and nonhuman primates. Imitation seems to require that three conditions are met: (1) the perception of an act causes the observer's response; (2) the observer produces behavior similar to that of the model; and (3) the equivalence between the acts of self and other plays a role in generating the response. In imitating, the goal of the observer is to match the target behavior. Equivalence need not be registered at a conscious level, but if it is not used at any level in the system (neurally, cognitively, computationally), then lower-order nonimitative processes may be more parsimonious.

Several decades of careful analysis and experiments have taught us that it is useful to distinguish imitation from other closely related behaviors. These fine-grained distinctions are useful because (1) the underlying mechanisms may be different and (2) research has shown that true imitation is more prominent in humans than in other species. There is wide consensus that distinctions need to be drawn among imitation, social facilitation, contagion, and stimulus enhancement.

Social facilitation is an increase in the production of a target behavior due to the mere presence of a conspecific. Suppose an adult waves bye-bye to a young baby. In response the baby may flap her arms, duplicating the motor pattern that was demonstrated. This could be an imitative response, but if the arm flapping is due to the child being excited at seeing an adult, it would be more sensibly classified as social facilitation.

Contagion is a term that emerges from the animal literature. It covers an increase in an instinctual behavior pattern upon observing a similar pattern by a conspecific. For example, some animals increase their eating behavior upon seeing their conspecifics eat. In this case the observer is neither learning a new behavior nor sculpting a behavior in its repertoire to match what it sees. Seeing another animal eat triggers feeding behavior in the observer and the shared biology assures that the stimulus and response take the same form.

Stimulus enhancement and local enhancement refer to the fact that the model draws the observer's attention to a stimulus object or location in performing a target act. Jane Goodall noted that the juvenile chimpanzees in the Gombe Stream Reserve were often attracted to the place where the adults fished for termites and played with the same sticks the adults used. If the young chimps later use the sticks to obtain termites, this could be because they discovered the use of the stick through their increased chance manipulations rather than through a strict duplication of the adult's actions.

In addition to these classical distinctions, comparative researchers such as Michael Tomasello and Andrew Whiten have attempted to differentiate imitation from what they call emulation. In both there is an attempt to match. In the former it is the bodily act that is copied; in the latter it is the end-state or outcome. For example, if the adult puts one block on top of another with a flourish, the child might copy: (1) the distinctive motor pattern used by the model, which is imitation or (2) the end result of one block on top of the other using any means available (called emulation). A current debate is whether these should be considered different processes or whether they are two exemplars of the more general category of imitation, one oriented toward the bodily act and the other toward the end-state.

Origins of Imitation in Humans

The Binding Problem

There is no question that children are avid imitators, but there is debate about when imitation begins. Questions about development and mechanism are intertwined. At issue is how infants come to 'glue' together an observed stimulus with a matching response of their own. What links the observed behaviors of others to one's own body parts and movements, underwriting the imitative response? We will call this the binding problem. Others have referred to this conundrum as the mechanism question or the correspondence problem. The use of the term 'binding' has an advantage of remaining neutral with respect to the psychological processes and neural underpinnings involved. Whatever one's theory of imitation, the stimulus and response are linked, bound, or connected in some way.

There are three classical theories of how infants first come to match the acts of others and solve the binding problem: operant conditioning, associative learning, and Piagetian theory.

Learning to Imitate by Operant Conditioning

In the 1950s, Skinner developed the idea that imitation is simply a special case of operant conditioning where the stimulus and response happen to match. He noted that pigeons can be conditioned to peck a key when they see other pigeons peck. If a pigeon (P-1) pecks at a key and an observer pigeon (P-2) is reinforced with food for pecking upon seeing this event, P-2 will eventually be shaped to peck when seeing P-1 pecking. Note that P-2 did not produce this act because it was motivated to match the other animal's behavior. All that has happened is that the behavior of P-1 became a discriminative cue for eliciting a conditioned response in P-2. The observer pigeon could be conditioned to perform a nonimitative act just as easily. The similarity of the stimulus and response plays no role.

Strong operant conditioning theorists hold that there can be no infant imitation without a prior period of

shaping which binds the discriminative cue to the response. For example, when a young infant sees a mother perform a simple act such as shaking a rattle, the infant at first does not know what movements to recruit to copy this act. Rather, the parent needs to shape the child's response through operant conditioning. Mom shakes the rattle, and the infant responds with random motor acts. Mom selectively reinforces those acts that are similar to her own shaking movements. Over time, the mother's motions come to serve as a discriminative cue (a light would do as well) that elicits the reinforced act (the baby's rattle shaking).

Infants and young children may learn certain acts in the ways described, but there are two drawbacks to this theory as a complete account of imitation. First, it cannot easily account for the imitation of novel acts – acts that the caretakers have not explicitly shaped up. Second, most ethnographic reports of parent–child interaction do not report the type of extensive shaping procedures needed to account for the range of acts infants and young children can imitate.

Learning to Imitate by Associative Learning

A second theory of the origins of imitation, and a possible solution to the binding problem, is based on associative learning. In this view, the infant's act and the adult's act are bound together by temporal contiguity. The prototypical learning case arises because parents tend to imitate their children. When the baby waves her hand, the parent enthusiastically waves back; when baby bangs an object, the parent bangs one in order to play a reciprocal game. According to the theory, infants come to associate their own acts with the similar ones of the parents. Thus, when they see the parent's act in the future, they produce the matching act that has been associated with it through regular temporal contiguity. In a sense, infants come to imitate adults to the extent that the adults have previously imitated their infants.

There have been many reports of parents enthusiastically copying their infants. These exchanges are so well timed that social theorists in the 1980s, such as Berry Brazelton and Hanus Papousek, described them as a gestural dance. There is ample opportunity for infants to bind together the acts of self and other in these reciprocal imitation games. However, the associative learning view would have a difficult time explaining the imitation of novel acts that have not served as familiar games in the past. Moreover, many observers of parent–child interaction remark that parents embellish and vary their infant's behavior, rather than simply mirroring it. This would predict associations between nonidentical behaviors and consequently imitative errors of a type that have rarely been observed. (A variant of this view holds that infants learn to imitate others through associating an action such as shaking a rattle with the outcome; and then when the adult later produces the outcome the infant generates the associated motor actions. Again the challenge is provided by the imitation of novel acts that are not familiar games for the infant.)

Piaget's Theory of Imitative Development

It is clear that human beings, at some age at least, are capable of spontaneously imitating novel adult displays for which there is no previous training history, no physical molding of the body, and no coaxing in any way other than the brief presentation of the model. Jean Piaget devoted his book *Play, Dreams and Imitation in Childhood* to the ontogenesis of this capacity. He was not concerned with specially trained matching responses (or pseudoimitation as Piaget calls it). In his view imitation is intertwined with cognitive development and unfolds in a series of invariantly ordered stages.

Piaget postulated six stages in infants' imitation, and for ease of summary they will be collapsed into three major levels. In level-1 (0–8 months of age; sensorimotor stage 1–3) infants are restricted to the imitation of simple hand movements and vocalizations. For example, the Piagetian 6-month-old would be expected to imitate a simple hand-opening gesture or an /a/-vocalization even if the infant had never been specifically trained to do so. Piaget's notion is that both of these types of imitation are similar in that they can be accomplished on the basis of an intramodal matching process. In principle, the infant could directly compare the adult's hand movements with those of his own visible hand, and thereby use vision as a guide in the matching process. Similarly, the infant could use audition to monitor both his own and the model's vocalizations and to guide his own vocalizations until they sounded like the model's. From Piaget's cognitive-developmental perspective, visually guided manual imitations are analogous to auditorially-guided vocal imitations.

In level-2 (8–18 months of age; sensorimotor stages 4–5) infants first become capable of imitating facial behaviors and novel acts. The fundamental claim made by Piaget is that the difficulties involved in manual and vocal imitation pale in comparison to those involved in facial imitation. Because infants cannot see their own faces, they cannot directly compare their own acts with the ones they see. According to Piaget, facial imitation (or invisible imitation as it is sometimes called) is a landmark cognitive achievement that is first passed during stage 4 of the sensory-motor period.

Finally, level-3 (18–24 months; sensorimotor stage 6) is characterized by the emergence of deferred imitation – the ability to perceive a behavior at one point in time and then, without having responded in the presence of the demonstration, to delay the duplication for a significant period. Deferred imitation directly implicates mnemonic and representational capacities, and Piaget predicted that it emerged synchronously with other complex cognitive abilities such as high-level object permanence (the search for invisibly displaced objects), symbolic play, and insightful problem-solving prior to action. All these synchronous developments constituted what Piaget termed stage 6, the last purely sensory–motor stage of infancy before the emergence of language.

In summary, Piaget's cognitive-developmental hypothesis is that infants gradually become able to imitate events that are farther and farther removed from the immediate sensory field. First they imitate those involving intramodal comparisons (manual and vocal acts), next those involving cross-modal comparisons (facial acts), and finally those implicating a stored representation of the modeled act (deferred imitation). Piagetian theory makes at least three strong predictions that have sparked considerable empirical work in over the past 30 years: (1) facial imitation is impossible before about 8 months of age (stage 4), (2) deferred imitation is impossible until about 18 months of age (stage 6), and (3) infants will progress through the stages in an invariant order, it being impossible to reach higher stages without having achieved the milestones of the preceding stage. As we will see below, these predictions have not received support in empirical tests, which has in turn generated new theorizing about the roots and development of imitation.

Imitation of Facial Acts

In many circumstances it is difficult to determine whether the stimulus-response matching is rooted in operant conditioning, associative learning, Piagetian development, or another process altogether. The problem, in most cases, is that one does not have full knowledge of the child's (or animal's) reinforcement and learning history.

Using a novel act as the target is one way to address this issue. A different approach is to test infants before they have had a chance to learn to link the stimulus and response through conditioning or association. Such demonstrations of imitation prior to the required learning would weigh against the operant conditioning and associative learning views. The Piagetian account can explain early manual and vocal imitation, because infants can compare their own acts with the ones they see. Infants cannot, however, see their own faces. If they are young enough they will never have seen their own faces in a mirror. Piaget predicts that facial imitation is beyond the cognitive abilities of the infant younger than about 8–12 months of age. Because it provides such a powerful test of extant theories of imitation, developmental psychologists have actively investigated the first appearance of facial imitation in human infants.

In 1977, Meltzoff and Moore reported the surprising results that 12- to 21-day-olds imitated four different gestures, including facial and manual movements. The infants confused neither actions nor body parts. They responded differentially to tongue protrusion with tongue protrusion and not lip protrusion, suggesting that they can identify the specific body part. They also responded differentially to lip protrusion versus lip opening, showing that different action patterns can be imitated with the same body part. This was later confirmed and extended by research showing that infants differentially imitate two different kinds of movements with the tongue. Published studies document a range of acts that can be imitated, including mouth opening, lip protrusion, tongue protrusion, selected emotional expressions, head movements, and simple hand and finger movements. In all, there are more than 30 published studies of early imitation from more than 13 independent laboratories. Attention has shifted beyond tests of the raw existence of early behavioral matching to investigations of the basis and functional significance of this behavior.

These findings argue against the classical solutions to the binding problem. Current approaches to this question investigate both the neural and psychological processes used for linking the observation and execution of isomorphic acts. Two discoveries are key. First, early imitation is not restricted to immediate duplication. In one facial imitation experiment, the infants had a pacifier in their mouths so that they couldn't imitate during the demonstration. The pacifier was then withdrawn, and the results showed that the infants initiated their imitation in the subsequent 2.5 min response period while looking at a passive face. Second, infants correct their imitative response. They converge on the match without feedback from the experimenter. An infant's first response to seeing a facial gesture is the activation of the corresponding body part with a gradual homing in on the action demonstrated.

The Active Intermodal Mapping Hypothesis

Meltzoff and Moore proposed that facial imitation is based on active intermodal mapping (the Active Intermodal mapping (AIM) hypothesis). The key claim is that early imitation is a matching-to-target process. The active nature of the matching process is captured by a proprioceptive feedback loop. The loop allows infants' motor performance to be evaluated against the seen target and serves as a basis for correction. AIM proposes that such comparison is possible because the observation and execution of human acts are coded within a shared framework. It is termed a supramodal act space because it is not restricted to modality-specific information (visual, tactile, motor, etc.). In this view, although infants cannot see their own facial expressions, they still have perceptual access to their facial movements through proprioception. AIM does not rule out the existence of certain basic acts that can be

imitated on first try without the need for feedback, but it allows proprioceptive monitoring and the correction of responses for novel acts.

This hypothesis of a supramodal framework that emerged from developmental science fits well with proposals from cognitive science about action coding (the common coding thesis of Wolfgang Prinz) and discoveries in human social neuroscience using functional magnetic resonance imaging by Jean Decety, Marco Iacobani, and others concerning shared neural circuits for the perception and production of action. Nonetheless, newborn humans are different from monkeys, who are in turn different from human adults. More analytic work is needed to determine whether the current convergences are merely surface similarities or more substantive (see the section on mirror neurons). Moreover, young infants do not imitate the full range of gestures copied by adults; thus, mechanisms of developmental change will need to be articulated.

Using Imitation to Learn about Objects

Imitation of Novel Acts from Memory

Moving beyond the binding problem and granting children the ability to copy the behaviors of others, another important question to consider is how children make use of this ability. For imitation to serve as a powerful learning mechanism in infancy and early childhood, infants will need to imitate not only facial gestures and other simple body acts, but also tool-use and other object-related behaviors. Moreover, they will need to imitate novel acts after significant memory delays. Human parents engage in purposeful pedagogy, often demonstrating a new skill at a time and place far removed from when the infant has an opportunity to imitate. If the human young could not imitate after a lengthy memory delay, this would necessarily constrain theories about the role of imitation in the transmission of culture. Thus if we want to draw inferences about cultural transmission, we need to know about imitative generalization across time and space.

In the 1980s, Meltzoff conducted a series of relevant studies. One study with 14-month-olds had three features: (1) imitation was tested after a 1 week delay, (2) infants were required to remember not just one demonstration but to keep in mind multiple different demonstrations, (3) novel acts were used. One of the acts was to bend forward from the waist and touch a panel with one's forehead which made it illuminate. This unusual act was not observed in more than 100 infants in free play, and certainly qualified as a novel display (baseline measures were also taken in the experiment).

Infants in the imitation group were shown six different acts on different objects on the first day of testing. They were not allowed to touch or handle the objects. They were confined purely to watching the displays. Infants were then sent home for the 1 week delay. Upon returning to the laboratory, the infants in the imitation group were presented with the objects. In a baseline control group, the adult meets the infants in session 1, but he did not manipulate the test objects; he simply talked pleasantly to the mother and child. The second session assessed the spontaneous likelihood of the infants producing the target acts in the presence of the adult, and this controlled for social facilitation. Contagion and stimulus and local enhancement were ruled out through a third group called the adult-manipulation control. For this group, the adult played with the same objects during session 1; but he did so using different movement patterns. For many stimuli, such as the head-touch gesture, even emulation was ruled out, because in the adult-manipulation control group the end-state (the panel light turning on) occurred but was activated through a different means than the novel head-touch act. The results showed significantly more target acts in the experimental group than in each of the controls, providing clear evidence for deferred imitation from memory after the delay (**Figure 1**).

Rachel Barr, Harlene Hayne, and colleagues have reported that infants as young as 6 months old can perform deferred imitation, which is especially significant given Piaget's prediction that deferred imitation first emerged at about 18 months. Patricia Bauer and Leslie Carver have shown that infants imitate novel sequences of behaviors from memory. Taken as a whole the studies on deferred imitation of object-related acts all suggest that infants imitate multiple targets, including novel ones, after lengthy delays, which suggests that imitation is capable of playing a significant role in human development prior to linguistic instruction.

Imitation of Peers Outside the Dyad

The ecology of child rearing is changing in the US. With the increase of women in the work force, infants are spending increasingly more time with peers in daycare settings. In most of the previous experiments adults were used as models. However, other children can also be important sources of information for how things work and the appropriate ways to act in different social situations. Do infants take advantage of this source by learning from and imitating their peers in daycare centers and other sites?

In one study, by Elizabeth Hanna, 14-month-old naïve infants observed tutor infants. These tutors had been previously trained to play with the toys in novel ways. After observing the peer play with five objects, the naïve infants left the test room. When they later returned and were presented with the test objects in the absence of the peer, they imitated. Further research extended to a daycare setting in which the demonstration was not one-to-one. Instead the tutor infant played with objects as a large group of naïve infants in a daycare center simply observed. The naïve infants were not allowed to approach or touch the toys. After a 2 day delay, a new experimenter (not the one who had accompanied the tutor) brought a bag of objects to the infants' homes and laid them out on a convenient table or floor. Neither the parent nor this new experimenter had been present in the day-care center 2 days earlier. The results showed significant imitation, providing evidence for deferred imitation across a change in context (a shift from daycare to home site). The fact that infants can transfer their imitative learning to a different environment from the one in which they observed the model, can do so after a

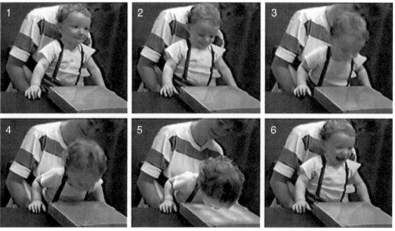

Figure 1   Fourteen-month-old infants can imitate novel acts such as touching their head to a panel. After successful imitation, infants often smile at the adult as shown in plate #6. This article was published in *Journal of Communication Disorders*, Vol. 32, Meltzoff, AN, *Origins of theory of mind, cognition, and communication* 251–269, Copyright Elsevier 1999.

long delay, and will imitate peers as well as adults, again supports the idea that imitation may play a role beyond the laboratory.

Using Imitation to Learn about People

Imitation and Social Communication

Children use imitation to learn about the physical world, to learn causally efficacious ways of manipulating objects and tools. However, typical children also use imitation for social purposes, such as communicating, sharing, and affiliating with others. What should be imitated to engage another person socially differs in a number of interesting respects from what should be imitated in an instrumental task such as using a tool. Behaviors used in the context of solving physical causality problem involve causally relevant manipulations of the inanimate world. Those used for social purposes can be more arbitrary and unconventional as long as there is a shared history. The imitation of unusual social acts is often incorporated into identification routines (a private 'handshake' or cultural practice) and used in communication to establish and maintain common ground. Important cultural conventions often revolve around arbitrary acts; the in-group knows the routine, which fosters group membership and cohesion. Thus, the criteria used for choosing what to imitate may be very different for achieving physically causal ends versus social-communicative goals.

Moreover the motivation to be like the social other is an important component of human imitation. The research suggests that infants and young children actively strive to match the form of their acts to those they see. Human infants do not need to be motivated by food in order to imitate; imitation is its own reward, a goal in itself. The motivation to 'be like' the other may be less compelling to nonhuman primates and children with autism (see section titled 'Autism'). It suggests a drive for social connection and communication in typically developing children.

Roots of Social Cognition

Scholars concerned with social understanding have often commented on the wide gulf between knowing the self and the other – dubbed the 'problem of other minds'. We experience our own thoughts and feelings but do not see ourselves from the outside as others see us. We perceive visual and auditory signals emanating from others but do not directly experience their mental states. There is a gulf that divides us. Analogously and for similar reasons, developmental scientists are struck by the binding problem in behavioral imitation. Infants experience their own bodies and movements from the inside, but watch the movements of others from a completely different point of view. There seems to be a gap between the behaviors they see and their own behaviors. The solution to this binding problem is the Holy Grail of imitation research. There are preliminary attempts to explain how infants bridge this gap, ranging from mirror neurons to the AIM hypothesis, but more work is needed to provide detailed models at both the psychological and neuroscience levels.

The fact that typical children have the capacity for behavioral imitation provides them an important foothold in social development. Human parents often engage in reciprocal imitation games. The same neurocognitive machinery that enables infants to imitate may make them sensitive to being imitated by others. In this case infants would be recognizing a match between themselves and others instead of producing one. In 2007, Meltzoff articulated a model of early social cognition called the 'Like-Me Framework' which proposed that parental imitation of children's behavior holds special significance not only because of the temporal contingencies involved, but because infants can recognize the structural congruence between the adult's acts and their own. The detection that something out there in the world is 'like me' and can do what I do could have cascading developmental effects. Children may use analogical reasoning to make crucial inference – entities who externally act like me may also share my internal emotions, intentions, and desires. According to this view, imitation is not only an aspect of early social cognition but an engine in its development.

The Regulation of Imitation

Adults are not blind imitators. They choose when, what, and whom to imitate. Developmentalists are beginning to investigate the regulation of imitation by children. The results are intriguing because they show that children do not automatically imitate what they are shown. Instead, there is a high degree of flexibility in childhood imitation.

Regulation of Imitation by Goals and Intentions

Children do not always imitate what you do, but often what you mean to do. If an adult makes a mistake or is unsuccessful in his attempt to complete a task, children will copy the intended goal instead of the outcome they observed. For example, Malinda Carpenter and Michael Tomasello showed 14–18-month-olds two actions that produced an interesting effect on an object. One of these acts was done in an accidental way and verbally marked by saying, "Woops!" The other act was done cleanly and the adult looked satisfied saying, "There!" The children skipped over the accidental acts and imitated those that appeared purposeful.

Actions do not have to be linguistically marked for children to understand the goal of the adult's act. Children will also use patterns of behaviors to infer the model's goal, even if he does not successfully achieve it. For example, Meltzoff showed 18-month-olds an adult who repeatedly pulled at the ends of a barbell-shaped object, as if striving to pull it apart. When given a chance to manipulate the object, the children firmly wrapped their hands around the ends and yanked the object apart. Even though they had never seen the completed act, the children inferred the goal of the act from his try-and-try again behavior. The children did not slavishly imitate the unsuccessful motion by letting their fingers slip from the object, but instead completed the intended goal. This and other related work strongly suggests that infants can interpret what the adult is trying to do and re-enact the goal of the act, not what was literally done.

Regulation of Imitation by Emotions

A recent study by Betty Repacholi investigated whether 18-month-old infants will regulate their imitation based on another person's emotional reaction to the target act. For example, a model performed a series of novel acts on objects and a bystander either became angry (indicating these were forbidden acts) or remained pleasantly interested in what the model was doing. After this emotional reaction, the bystander adopted a neutral face. The toddler watched this interaction between the two adults, and the question was whether they regulated their subsequent imitation based on the bystander's reaction to the model's action. A second factor that was manipulated was whether the bystander was looking at the toddler when she was given a chance to imitate. The experimental conditions included: (1) the bystander left the room, (2) the bystander was present but had her back turned, and (3) the bystander was looking at the toddler. Each of these three conditions was crossed with whether the bystander had exhibited anger or interest in the action when it was shown.

The results showed that if the adult had not exhibited anger at the action, the toddlers imitated at high levels regardless of whether or not the adult could see them. But if the adult had exhibited anger at the action, then the toddlers were significantly less likely to imitate the acts only when the adult was monitoring their behavior. If the previously angry adult left the room or had her back turned, the toddlers' imitation was not reduced.

It was not just the fact that the bystander expressed anger that accounted for the results. These effects cannot be explained by emotional contagion, because the infant had the chance to 'catch' the adult's emotion equally well in all groups. Instead the toddlers' were regulating their imitation based on the conjunction of two factors:

(1) whether the bystander had a negative reaction to the act and (2) whether the bystander was watching what the toddler did. Evidently, toddlers regulate their imitative response based on the emotional reactions that others have to the target act and whether the emoter can monitor their imitative reactions or not. Toddlers seem to realize that they can be a target of other people's perception and will not imitate an action when the emoter is watching them produce those actions. Imitation is thus not automatic and inflexible, at least by 18 months of age. Instead, toddlers choose when to imitate.

Regulation of Imitation by Prior Experience and Success of the Model

Rebecca Williamson and colleagues further investigated whether children are blind imitators or if they flexibly employ imitation depending on the circumstances. In one series of studies 3-year-old children were tested to see if they were more open to imitating another person's technique if the child had a prior experience of difficulty with a task. Children were randomly assigned to two independent groups. One group had an easy experience and the other a difficult experience in achieving an outcome, such as opening a drawer to retrieve an object. For the difficult group the drawer was surreptitiously held shut by a resistance device. Then the model demonstrated a distinctive technique for opening the drawer. The same distinctive technique was demonstrated to both the easy and difficult groups. The results showed that children were significantly more likely to imitate after a prior difficult experience with the task. These results fit together well with work in school-age education emphasizing the value of hands-on prior experience in structuring a student's understanding. The gist of the educational research is that some prior experience confronting difficulties with a problem can help the student be more ready to learn from an expert, as was also shown here.

In a related study, children watched a model who demonstrated a particular technique, but for half the children the technique led to success and for the rest it led to the model's failure. The results showed that children took the model's efficacy into account and preferentially imitated the actions when they led to success. Moreover, studies by Stephen Want and Paul Harris show that preschool children learn from seeing not only a successful model, but the learning steps that led up to that performance. Children who saw the model make mistakes and correct the behavior were more likely to imitate the successful act than those who did not see the errors. Mark Nielsen adapted this procedure for 12-month-olds. If the infants first saw an adult try but fail to open a box with his hand, they were more likely to imitate his subsequent demonstration of how to use a certain tool to succeed. Taken together, this research suggests that infants and young children are not blind imitators, their imitative responses are altered depending on a larger envelope of the model's behavior.

Infant Imitation as an Emerging Interdisciplinary Field

Mirror Neurons

There has been an explosion of interest in imitation in the neuroscience community. This owes to the fact that in the late 1990s Giacomo Rizzolatti, Vittorio Gallese, and a team of other neuroscientists in Parma, Italy discovered neurons in the premotor cortex of the monkey's brain (area F5) with peculiar properties. These were dubbed mirror neurons because they fire both when the monkey performs certain goal-directed acts, such as grasping food, and also when they observe another perform the same act. These neurons code the act regardless of whether it is performed by the self or the other. Mirror neurons bring together the observation and execution of motor acts.

Following the initial discovery of mirror neurons in monkeys, Marco Iacobani, Jean Decety, and others reported that there are neural circuits in adult humans that have similar mirror properties. These shared circuits become activated whether the adult performs a certain act, for example, raising and lowering his index finger, or merely observes another person doing so.

Some have theorized that mirror neurons provide the neural substrate for imitation – that they solve the binding problem. However, the existence of mirror neurons may not solve the psychological puzzle involved in imitation. First, even though their brains house mirror neurons, monkeys are notoriously poor at imitating (once stimulus enhancement and contagion are controlled). This shows that imitation requires more than this neural tissue. Second, neuroscientists have yet to map the ontogenesis of mirror neurons. Adult monkeys have repeatedly watched themselves grasp objects. Mirror neurons could code visuomotor associations forged from such learning experiences. Such gradual learning, if it occurs, would suggest that mirror neurons are the product of observation–execution associative pairings and may not underlie them in the first instance. Mirror neurons may develop.

There are two ways of testing whether mirror neurons develop through experience. One is to test newborn monkeys who have not had a chance to watch themselves reach. A second approach is selective rearing in which the experimenter arranges a situation that prevents monkeys from visually monitoring their own grasps, for example, by wearing a collar that blocks the view of their hands. The critical question is whether mirror neurons can be found in the brains of such animals. If they have functioning mirror neurons, it would suggest that mirror neurons do not emerge from learned associations of repeatedly seeing oneself grasp an object. This experiment has yet to be done.

Moreover, canonical mirror neurons cannot be the whole story of human imitation. Mirror neurons are best suited to explaining immediate resonance phenomena. John Braugh and colleagues have reported motor resonances in adults, such as when a therapist and patient unconsciously adopt the same posture (he calls these chameleon effects). But such immediate motor resonances, while they exist in adults and children, do not exhaust the imitative capacities of adults or even of infants and young children. They do not easily explain the following empirical demonstrations: (1) imitation of novel acts, (2) the correction of the imitative act so that it more closely resembles the target, (3) deferred imitation 1 week or several months after the stimulus has been withdrawn, and (4) the regulation of imitation – infants and toddlers do not imitate under certain circumstances and there is flexibility in their choosing what and whom to imitate. Current research is dedicated to investigating the nature, scope, and limits of the mirror neuron system in monkeys and adults in order to discover what additional factors are needed to generate and control imitation.

Autism

Children with autism have a core deficit in the ability to communicate with others and in understanding others' thoughts, feelings, and actions. It has long been known that children with autism have deficits in a cluster of skills such as language, symbolic play, and social reciprocity. More recently, there has been great excitement surrounding the empirical studies establishing that children with autism also show atypical performance on a variety of imitation tasks. This has been demonstrated in both high- and low-functioning children with autism, even after careful matching against mental-age controls.

In 2001, Justin Williams and colleagues suggested that children with autism might have a mirror neuron deficit. Regardless of the debate surrounding this claim, research by Peter Hobson and colleagues reveals that children with autism have more difficulties with certain aspects of imitation than with others, and this will need to be taken into account. Hobson presented tasks in which children were shown how to perform a novel act using a certain style or manner of doing so. His results showed that the children with autism often achieve the same outcome as the adult; however, they do not use the same style. Using the terms introduced earlier, the children could emulate the adult and recreate (aspects of) the end-state; but they did not imitate the distinctive way the adult moved. Further research is needed to characterize the precise nature of the imitative deficit in children with autism, and to distinguish when different aspects of behavior (means, ends, goals, intentions) are imitated. It is also possible that children with autism lack the fundamental motivation to imitate social others, to 'be like' their social partners.

Robotics

In computer science, researchers are becoming increasingly interested in robotic imitation. One motivation is that roboticists want to build robots that interact more naturally with humans. They have noted that imitative responses are part and parcel of natural social exchanges and may help make robots more user-friendly. Another motivation is that it is burdensome or impossible to write code that anticipates all of the complex, novel acts that a user may want the robot to perform. An imitative robot would allow you to teach it to act in much the same way you teach a pre-verbal child – by showing them what to do. If you want your robot to pour a cup of tea, demonstrate how to pour your particular tea pot in front of the robot's sensors and a processor would translate the observed actions into commands to the robot's effectors.

It has quickly become apparent that solving the binding problem is not an easy task – in this case the issue is how to connect an observed action performed by a human to the corresponding action performed by the robotic device. In 2007, Chrystopher Nehaniv and Kertin Dautenhahn published a collection of the recent advances in robotic imitation in one volume that also includes work from developmental and evolutionary psychology. The hope is that biological models of imitation can be used in the design of robots that can learn by imitation; and conversely that work in robotics will help sharpen developmentalists' ideas about underlying mechanism.

Summary and Future Directions

Imitation provides a mechanism, prior to language, through which the human young learn by watching others. Researchers have adopted a definition of imitation that distinguishes imitation from other related concepts (e.g., social facilitation, contagion, and stimulus enhancement). This has allowed them to address three crucial issues: existence, mechanism, and function of imitation. At the psychological level, the AIM mechanism holds that the perception and production of human acts are mediated by a common code, a 'supramodal' framework. Neuroscientists debate whether mirror neurons underlie infant imitation, or whether additional neural machinery is needed to explain the full range of imitative phenomena evident in human children. Regardless of this debate,

the capacity for flexible deferred imitation of peers and adults suggests that imitation is a powerful learning mechanism and plays a role in the transmission of human culture.

Future work on imitation will rely on techniques in developmental cognitive neuroscience to more fully explicate the mechanisms binding together perception and production. Other future work will focus on robotics. Computer scientists seek to design robots that can learn by observing and imitating others; and they are increasingly turning to developmental science for a 'biologically plausible' model of imitative learning. Finally, the bridge to autism is promising, because children with autism have core deficits in social understanding, including dysfunctions in imitation. Cutting-edge interventions aimed at promoting imitation skills in young children with autism may have more general effects of improving their understanding of people.

Acknowledgments

Support was provided by grants from the National Institute of Child Health and Human Development (HD-22514), the National Science Foundation (SBE-0354453), and the Tamaki Foundation.

See also: Autism Spectrum Disorders; Cognitive Developmental Theories; Intermodal Perception; Learning; Piaget's Cognitive-Developmental Theory; Symbolic Thought.

Suggested Readings

Heyes CM and Galef BG, Jr (1996) *Social Learning in Animals: The Roots of Culture.* San Diego: Academic Press.
Hurley S and Chater N (eds.) (2005) *Perspectives on Imitation: From Neuroscience to Social Science,* vols. 1 and 2. Cambridge, MA: MIT Press.
Meltzoff AN (1999) Origins of theory of mind, cognition, and communication. *Journal of Communication Disorders* 32: 251–269.
Meltzoff AN (2007) 'Like me': A foundation for social cognition. *Developmental Science* 10: 126–134.
Meltzoff AN (2007) The 'Like Me' framework for recognizing and becoming an intentional agent. *Acta Psychologica* 124: 26–43.
Meltzoff AN and Prinz W (eds.) (2002) *The Imitative Mind: Development, Evolution and Brain Bases.* Cambridge: Cambridge University Press.
Nadel J and Butterworth G (eds.) (1999) *Imitation in Infancy.* Cambridge: Cambridge University Press.
Nehaniv CL and Dautenhahn K (eds.) (2007) *Imitation and Social Learning in Robots, Humans, and Animals: Behavioural, Social and Communicative Dimensions.* Cambridge: Cambridge University Press.
Piaget J (1962) *Play, Dreams and Imitation in Childhood.* (Attengno C and Hodgson FM (Trans.)) New York: Norton.
Rogers SJ and Williams JHG (2006) *Imitation and the Social Mind: Autism and Typical Development.* New York: Guilford.

Immune System and Immunodeficiency

A Ahuja, National Jewish Hospital, Denver, CO, USA

Glossary

Adaptive immune system – Comprised of specialized T cells, B cells, and plasma cells that protect the host from infection in a highly specific manner; the immune response adapts antibody formation and cell-mediated immunity (CMI) to the specific antigen it encounters, and with subsequent attacks from the same antigen it is able to eliminate it more quickly and efficiently.

Anaphylaxis – A severe immediate allergic reaction to an antigen resulting in a constellation of symptoms including shortness of breath, wheezing, vomiting, diarrhea, urticaria, swelling, hypotension, and even death.

Antibody – A molecule produced by B lymphocytes and plasma cells in response to an antigen.

Antigen – Any substance that elicits an immune response.

Apoptosis – Also known as programmed cell death; a series of enzyme reactions that leads to cell death without disruption of the cell.

Cytokines – Proteins released by cells of the immune and hematopoietic systems that act as intercellular mediators of the immune response and inflammation.

Degranulation – Release of the contents of cytoplasmic granules.

Hematopoiesis – The generation and development of blood cells.

Hypoplasia – Incomplete or underdevelopment of an organ or tissue.

Immunoglobulins (Ig) – The classes (isotypes) of proteins secreted by plasma cells that contain antibodies; the five immunoglobulin isotypes are Igs G, A, M, D, and E.

Innate immune system – Comprised of cells and mechanisms that protect the host from infection in a nonspecific manner and without conferring specific immunologic memory.

Interleukins – A subgroup of approximately 30 cytokines, abbreviated IL.

Isotype – One of five types of immunoglobulins (Igs G, A, M, D, and E) that differ in structure and function.

Isotype switching – The process by which the cell switches from secreting one isotype of immunoglobulin to another.

Lymphadenitis – Infection of a lymph node.

Mannose – A sugar residue expressed on the surface of many microbes.

Microbes – Another term for microorganisms – bacteria, viruses, protozoa, mycoplasma, and chlamydia.

Opsonin – An antibody or complement component that coats an antigen and makes it more susceptible to phagocytosis.

Osteomyelitis – Infection of the bone.

Otitis media – Infection of the middle ear.

Passive immunity – Transfer of humoral immunity in the form of antibodies from one individual to another.

Pathogen – A microorganism that causes disease.

Phagocytosis – The act of engulfment of a microorganism by a phagocyte (neutrophil, monocyte, or macrophage), which normally results in microbial killing.

Phagosome – A membrane-bound vesicle in a phagocyte containing a microbe engulfed during phagocytosis.

Introduction

The immune system is the body's primary defense against infectious agents. The term immunity refers to protection from adverse events, such as infections and malignancies. This system includes numerous cells, enzymes, and proteins that together function to maintain the integrity of the human body. However, if essential parts of the immune system become dysfunctional, increased susceptibility to infections and malignancies can result. Additionally, dysregulation of the immune system can lead to various autoimmune disorders such as systemic lupus erythematosus and rheumatoid arthritis, which will not be discussed in this article. The human immune system can be divided into two parts, the innate immune response and the adaptive immune response. The innate response is the first component of the immune system to respond to foreign pathogens. The second arm of human immunity is the adaptive immune response, which consists of humoral and cell-mediated immunity (CMI). These components work integrally in a sophisticated manner to optimize the host's defense against invasion of infectious agents such as bacteria, viruses, and fungi.

Development

The development of the human immune system begins during fetal gestation. Hematopoiesis (the generation and development of blood cells) appears in the yolk sac at 3 weeks, and by 6-weeks, gestation, these hematopoietic stem cells are detected in the fetal liver. During gestation weeks 8–12, the stem cells migrate to primary lymphoid organs, the bone marrow, and thymus. Secondary lymphoid organs (spleen, lymph nodes, tonsils, gastrointestinal lymphoid tissue) develop soon thereafter and serve as sites for further cell maturation and differentiation. Lymphoid stem cells differentiate into T, B, or natural killer (NK) cells. From the bone marrow, T cells migrate to the thymus where they undergo further maturation and gain characteristic cell markers. Once T cells mature, they can travel to secondary lymphoid organs, where they may perform their effector functions. B lymphocytes undergo their maturation and differentiation in the bone marrow. Once mature, B cells can differentiate into plasma cells, which secrete antibodies for use in the humoral immune response. NK cells develop from bone marrow precursors, just as B and T lymphocytes do, and can be found in the thymus, spleen, and lymph nodes.

Innate Immunity

The innate immune system is the first defense mechanism the body has against pathogens. This component of the immune system recognizes patterns and structures common to microbes but unlike those on host cells. Different types of microbes can share similar structures and constituents that are common to microbes and foreign to the host. Structures or components such as RNA or DNA sequences that are inherent to many pathogens can elicit an immune response. Cells of the innate system have receptors that recognize lipopolysaccharide (LPS), which is a component of the cell walls of Gram-negative bacteria (bacteria that do not retain crystal violet dye with standard Gram staining technique). The innate immune system relies on pattern recognition of pathogens through a limited repertoire of receptors. Because of this it has limited diversity and lacks specificity for microbial killing,

unlike the adaptive immune system. However due to effective recognition of microbial specific patterns, the innate immune system is quite efficient at discriminating self (host) from foreign (microbial) molecules.

Components of the innate immune system include host physical barriers, effector cells, and certain proteins, particularly those of the complement system, which will be described (**Table 1**). Physical barriers include epithelial layers such as the skin, respiratory mucosal surfaces, and intestinal mucosal surfaces. These are the first line of defense against environmental pathogen entry. The epithelia also produce peptides, including defensins that have natural antibiotic function.

The effector cells of innate immunity function to combat pathogens that actually make it through the physical epithelial barriers. These cells are phagocytes (neutrophils, monocytes, and macrophages) and NK cells. All of these arise from hematopoietic stem cells in the bone marrow during fetal development. When a microbe evades the host's physical barriers and enters the body, it is recognized as being foreign and elicits an immune response. Monocytes, which mature into tissue macrophages, and neutrophils (together with lymphocytes, termed 'leukocytes') represent the initial influx of inflammatory cells. Their primary functions are to identify, phagocytose, and kill microbes.

Neutrophils and macrophages have receptors for particular structures that are expressed only by microbes. These structures as well as substances released by microbes elicit an immune response. This includes a release of inflammatory proteins, known as cytokines at sites of infection. The cytokines attract phagocytes to sites of microbial invasion by increasing their adherence to the endothelium. Through a sophisticated mechanism, neutrophils roll along the endothelium encountering proteins that enhance adhesion and eventual migration to the site of infection. Once on site, neutrophils and macrophages are able to phagocytose the microbes that have been coated with opsonins (antibody and complement). During phagocytosis, the cells release numerous enzymes and reactive oxygen and nitrogen radicals that kill the ingested microbe.

Neutrophils are the first cells to respond to a microbe. They migrate to the site of an infection within a few hours and can remain viable for up to 12 h. Monocytes are immature forms of macrophages derived from a different

Table 1   Major components of the immune system

Components	Innate immunity	Adaptive immunity
Physical and chemical barriers	Skin, mucosa antimicrobial chemicals	Epithelial lymphocytes and antibodies
Blood proteins	Complement	Immunoglobulins (IgG, IgA, IgM, IgE, IgD) complement
Cells	Phagocytes (neutrophils, monocytes, macrophages), NK cells	T lymphocytes (helper and cytolytic), B lymphocytes

lineage of stem cells in the bone marrow than neutrophils. These cells respond to infection almost as quickly as neutrophils, but are able to survive longer.

Macrophages have numerous functions other than phagocytosis and are an integral part of both the innate and adaptive immune systems. They release numerous cytokines that promote inflammation and activate other inflammatory cells to sites of infection in both types of immune responses. Macrophages have a distinct ability to facilitate tissue repair by removing debris and enhancing wound healing. Macrophages also assist in antibody formation and CMI, which will be discussed later in this article.

NK cells are a subset of lymphocytes found mostly in the blood and spleen. Their primary function is to kill host cells infected with viruses and intracellular bacteria. NK cells are normally in an inhibited state but can be activated and recruited to sites of infection by various cytokines released by other inflammatory cells such as activated macrophages and T and B lymphocytes. NK cells kill infected cells by degranulating and thereby releasing their enzyme products. These enzymes enter the infected cells and induce apoptosis. Another significant function of NK cells is to promote further macrophage activation. When macrophages become activated due to a microbial infection, they secrete the cytokine interleukin-12 (IL-12), which promotes activation of NK cells. Activated NK cells kill cells infected with viruses and intracellular bacteria and also secrete a cytokine known as interferon-gamma (IFN-γ), which further promotes macrophage killing of microbes.

Adaptive Immunity

The adaptive immune system is the second arm of the human immune response. Similar to the innate system, adaptive immunity is able to recognize the difference between foreign substances and host cells and so has the ability to not react against itself. However, some pathogens are able to evade killing mechanisms of the innate immune response and thus challenge the killing tactics of the adaptive system. Recall that the innate immune response lacks specificity and kills microbes based on pattern and structural recognition. The adaptive system is highly sophisticated in that its immune response is specific to individual antigens that characterize specific microbes. Because of this specificity, adaptive immunity is able to respond to a much larger variety of microbes and other molecules. This specific immunity can distinguish even very closely related pathogens. Also it has memory, thereby facilitating a heightened and more effective immune response when an antigen is encountered for a second time.

The two types of adaptive immune responses are humoral and CMI. Lymphocytes are the key cellular components and immunoglobulins (Igs) are the key humoral proteins of these systems. T and B lymphocytes are derived from lymphoid stem cells in the bone marrow. B lymphocytes undergo maturation and differentiation in the bone marrow and T lymphocytes mature in the thymus and migrate to peripheral organs. Both humoral and CMI mechanisms use these cells in an integrated fashion to fight infection. Cells and cytokines of the innate immune system are also used along with cells and proteins of the adaptive system for microbial killing.

Humoral Immunity

Humoral immunity is the main adaptive defense mechanism against extracellular microbes and toxins. The principal mediators of this function are the antibodies secreted by plasma cells. Once extracellular microbes or toxins are encountered by the host, B lymphocytes are stimulated to mature into plasma cells, which secrete antibodies that bind these antigens to neutralize or eliminate them.

B Lymphocytes

As noted earlier lymphocytes originate from stem cells in the bone marrow. B lymphocytes continue to mature in the bone marrow, whereas T lymphocytes migrate to the thymus for further maturation. As lymphocytes mature, they acquire specific cell-identifying markers. These cell-surface markers, known as cluster of differentiation (CD) markers, denote a particular cell lineage and/or particular stage of lymphocyte maturation. By using CD markers, a T or B lymphocyte can be identified and its stage of development can be elucidated. B lymphocytes begin as pre-B cells and progress through stages of immature, mature, and activated B lymphocytes, and finally antibody-secreting plasma cells. Most mature B cells express CD19 and CD20 cell markers. B cells will lack these markers if full B-cell maturation does not occur, which can be detected with laboratory testing.

Immunoglobulins

Plasma cells are able to secrete the Ig isotypes that contain antibody function. There are five isotypes IgG, IgA, IgM, IgE, and IgD. The basic structure of these molecules is similar; however, each can be stimulated to respond to distinct types of antigens. They can all function to kill microbes in conjunction with complement proteins and phagocytes, and to neutralize microbial toxins. They also have the ability to present antigens to T lymphocytes in order to facilitate microbial killing through other mechanisms that will be discussed later in this article.

The core structure of an antibody is made up of two heavy chains and two light chains of amino acids bonded together. Each Ig is made of a constant region and two variable regions (see **Figure 1**). The variable regions are on one end of the molecule and are comprised of heavy and light chains, and the constant region consists of two heavy chains on the other end of the molecule. The variable regions can bind a wide variety of antigens with tremendous specificity. The high specificity and variability of antigens that can be bound is partially due to sophisticated recombination of the amino acids of the variable regions. The different classes of antibodies are determined by the structural difference of their constant regions. The constant region (Fc) of the various Ig is recognized by a variety of circulating cells and proteins, for example, complement components.

IgG is the most abundant antibody in human serum followed by IgA, IgM, IgE, and IgD. It is the only Ig transferred from the mother to the baby via the placenta during fetal development. IgM and IgD are present on B cells during their later stages of maturation. The function of IgD is not well defined. IgM is the largest Ig and is the first to respond to foreign antigens during an immune response, followed by IgG. IgA is mostly present in mucosal surfaces such as those of the gastrointestinal and lung. It helps to eliminate pathogens from these sites. Also IgA is the only maternal antibody that can be passively transferred to the baby via breast milk. Secretion of IgE increases in response to antigens such as parasites and helminths. IgE is also the predominant antibody involved in the inflammatory process of severe allergic reactions such as anaphylaxis and to airways inflammation in asthma.

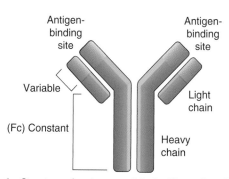

Figure 1   Structure of an immunoglobulin. The antigen-binding site is the site where the antigen binds to the molecule and is located on the variable region. There are two variable regions, each made up of a light chain and a heavy chain. The constant region (Fc portion) is made up of two heavy chains. The isotype and function of the immunoglobulin is determined by the constant region.

Plasma cells can produce different forms of antibodies based on the particular immune response. Antibodies can be made in membrane-bound and secreted forms. They also have the capability of isotype switching in response to antigen. The variable regions do not change, but to facilitate elimination of invading organisms, the constant regions switch to the appropriate isotype for the particular antigen encountered. For instance, the IgM isotype switches to the IgG isotype, which is more efficient and lives longer in the circulation. Also, the constant region of an IgG molecule may switch to that of an IgE antibody in response to a parasitic antigen.

Passive Immunity

Lymphocytes begin formation and maturation during fetal development, as discussed previously. Antibodies are not secreted into fetal circulation until the second trimester. The newborn immune system relies on maternal IgG antibodies passively transferred via the placenta and maternal IgA antibodies transferred via breast milk during the first few months of life. This constitutes passive immunity. Breastfeeding is commonly encouraged for this reason.

Memory

One of the hallmark features of the adaptive immune response is the ability to maintain memory. When a foreign antigen is encountered by the host, the appropriate antibody response occurs and works to eliminate the infection. This is the primary immune response, in which there is proliferation of B lymphocytes and antibodies specific for that antigen. After the infection subsides, a reservoir of memory antibody-producing cells migrates from peripheral lymphoid organs to the bone marrow, where they remain for months to years. When that same antigen or infection is encountered again, the long-lived memory cells are recruited from the bone marrow into the circulation and lymphoid organs where they secrete antibodies to eliminate the antigen quickly and effectively. This phenomenon of more rapid antibody response is known as the secondary immune response. This principle is behind the protective humoral immunity provided by vaccinations.

Complement System

The complement system is made up of several proteins that interact in a series of sequential steps leading to the killing of microbes. It plays a role in both innate and adaptive immune responses. The complement system consists of the classical, alternative, and lectin pathways. The central event in complement activation is the cleavage of the complement protein C3 which yields C3b, the active protein that binds the microbe or antibody. Each of these pathways is triggered by different stimuli; however, they all lead to a common killing mechanism, referred to as the membrane attack complex (MAC).

Microbes can activate the alternative pathway directly. The complement fragment C3b has the capability to bind to microbial surfaces, thereby initiating activation of this cascade. Through a series of steps, as shown in **Figure 2**, the C3 cleaving enzyme is generated, which splits C3 into two fragments. The major fragment, C3b, makes up part of the C5 cleaving enzyme, which cleaves C5 and initiates the next steps leading to the formation of the MAC. C3b is an important protein fragment because not only does it help form the MAC for microbial killing, but it binds microbes and serves as an opsonin and also initiates the alternative complement cascade, as schematized in **Figure 2**.

The classical pathway requires an antibody that is bound to a microbial antigen for activation. IgM and IgG can activate C1q (a component of the complement protein C1), and thereby the rest of the complement system after binding microbial antigen. Antibody and C3b then opsonize the microorganism. Opsonization prepares the microbe for phagocytosis, leading to microbial killing. This is another

way in which the innate and adaptive immune systems work together to eliminate foreign antigens from the host. Different complement proteins are needed for the classical pathway and the alternative pathway to generate the C3 and C5 cleaving enzymes, but the end result, formation of the MAC, is the same.

As described earlier, a common feature in the innate immune system is recognizing common molecular patterns on microbes to target for killing. This pattern recognition is used in the lectin pathway. Serving as the initiating step, a circulating plasma lectin, mannose-binding lectin (MBL), binds mannose residues on microbial cell walls. MBL acts as C1 does in the classical pathway, but the remaining steps are identical to those in the classical pathway and lead to formation of the MAC.

The MAC complement proteins form a circular complex that kills the microbe by forming pores in the microbial cell membrane, thereby allowing water and salt ions into the cell. The water and salt ions cause cellular swelling and eventual rupture of erythrocytes and death by apoptosis in nucleated cells.

There are several regulatory proteins that help to control complement system activation. Regulation is needed to ensure that the system is active for the killing of microbes and not for normal host cells. If the complement system is not tightly regulated, it can become overly activated, which can cause unwarranted harm to host cells.

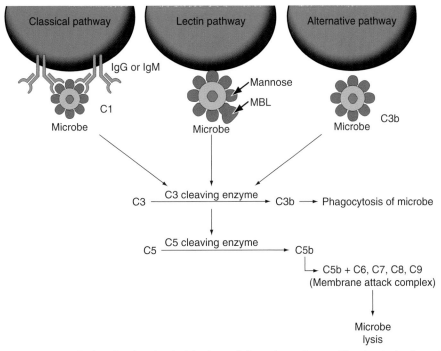

Figure 2 The complement cascade denoting the classical, lectin, and alternative pathways. The classical pathway is activated by a microbe bound to IgG or IgM, plus the complement protein C1. The alternative pathway is activated by a microbe coated with the C3b complement protein. Mannose-binding lectin (MBL) binds to a mannose residue on the microbe for initiation of the lectin pathway. After the initial activation of each pathway, they all commonly cleave C3 to generate C3b which promotes phagocytosis and killing of the microbe. C5 is also cleaved to generate C5b, which in conjunction with C6–9 forms the membrane attack complex (MAC) for microbial lysis.

Cellular Immunity

The second branch of the adaptive immune system is CMI. This is the host's principal defense mechanism against intracellular microbes and viruses. T lymphocytes are the primary mediators of CMI. In CMI, T lymphocytes must contact specialized cells known as antigen-presenting cells (APCs), which present antigens to T cells for recognition and subsequent elimination (see **Figure 3**).

CMI can enhance the microbial killing mediated by innate and humoral immune responses in numerous ways. Recall that B cells undergo isotype switching from IgM to the more versatile IgG; however, T cells must release specific cytokines that mediate this switch. Isotype switching of humoral immunity would be impaired without the presence of T CMI. Some microbes may escape the innate killing mechanisms of phagocytes and survive in phagosomes. When this occurs T cells can release cytokines such as IFN-γ to enhance intraphagocytic killing and elimination of these intracellular microbes. Macrophages mediate many of the effector functions of CMI, and thus they serve as a continuous link between adaptive and innate immune responses.

Professional APCs are mainly macrophages, dendritic cells, and B lymphocytes. These cells first recognize and bind foreign antigens for presentation to T cells. Antigens on the APCs must also be bound to the major histocompatibility complex (MHC) in order for T cells to become fully activated (**Figure 3**). The MHC is a group of proteins encoded together on a gene locus that varies from individual to individual. The task of displaying the APC-associated antigen to T cells is the function of the MHC. MHC proteins can be divided into two groups, MHC class I molecules and MHC class II molecules.

T lymphocytes, like B lymphocytes, have cell surface (CD) markers that distinguish various T-cell subsets functionally. Mature T cells are CD3+ cells. Also, like B cells,

T cells have the capability of memory. Memory T cells have different cell-surface protein markers that distinguish them from naive or unstimulated T lymphocytes. T lymphocytes that are not antigen stimulated are known as naïve T cells and are CD45RA+ cells. Memory T cells that develop after antigen stimulation are CD45RO+ cells. These memory cells, like B lymphocyte-derived memory cells, survive for up to years without the need for antigen exposure. Once T cells are activated after antigen recognition, they differentiate into either helper T cells or cytolytic T cells. Helper T cells are CD3+CD4+ and cytolytic T cells are CD3+CD8+. There is a 2:1 ratio of helper T cells to cytolytic T cells in circulation under normal circumstances. APCs that display antigens bound to MHC class I molecules preferentially bind to CD4+ T helper cells. MHC class II molecules preferentially bind CD8+ cytolytic T cells.

CD4+ T helper cells have different effector functions from cytolytic CD8+ cells. Through the release of various cytokines, helper T cells can have numerous effector functions such as to activate macrophages; enhance T and B lymphocyte proliferation; stimulate cytolytic T-cell differentiation; and upregulate release of inflammatory mediators, such as ILs. CD4+ T helper cells can be divided into the two subsets Th1 and Th2. Each of these releases different cytokines that mediate functions specific for that subset. The cytokines from one subset can inhibit functional responses from the other subset.

Whether the immune response gravitates toward the Th1 response vs. the Th2 response depends on the type of stimuli or antigen encountered. Bacteria and viruses that involve innate immune components such as macrophages and NK cells cause stimulation of the Th1 pathway of inflammation and microbial killing. Antigens, such as parasites, that do not significantly challenge innate immunity or macrophages stimulate the Th2 pathway. This is the inflammatory pathway that predominates in allergic disorders. Cytokines released from the Th2 pathway upregulate production of IgE and numbers of circulating eosinophils, which can contribute to IgE-mediated disorders such as asthma, atopic dermatitis, food allergy, allergic rhinitis, and anaphylaxis.

Cytolytic T cells become activated after recognition and binding of intracellular microbes or viruses. Cytolytic killing can occur through release of enzymes and other proteins that enter and kill the infected cell. A second mode of killing is through induction of apoptosis of the infected cells.

Immunodeficiency Diseases

The human immune system consists of several sophisticated and complex mechanisms to fight infection. Dysfunction or deficiency of any of various proteins or cells

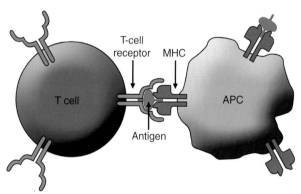

Figure 3 Interaction of a T cell with the antigen-presenting cell (APC)-antigen-major histocompatiblity complex (MHC) complex. An antigen must be bound to the MHC in order for an APC to present it to the T lymphocyte. The T-cell receptor then is able to bind the antigen that is presented by the APC.

among these defense mechanisms can lead to an increased susceptibility to recurrent or severe infections. It is estimated that approximately 1 in 500 individuals in the US have some type of defect in their immune system. There are numerous immunodeficiency syndromes that have been described as a result of these defects. When there is a genetic abnormality of the immune system leading to disease, the condition is termed a 'primary or genetic immunodeficiency'. When an immunodeficiency develops as a consequence of an underlying condition such as cancer, drugs, or infection, the immunodeficiency is said to be 'secondary or acquired'. The immune system can also lose the ability to distinguish self from nonself so that immune cells attack the host, leading to autoimmune diseases such as thyroiditis, lupus, or juvenile diabetes. Individuals with an immunodeficiency have a greater tendency to develop autoimmune diseases as well as frequent infections.

Cells or proteins of the innate immune system or those of the adaptive immune system may be adversely affected and lead to an immune disorder in which the individual becomes more susceptible to recurrent infections. Infections may be very invasive leading to severe symptoms, and at times death. Depending on the nature of the defect, the types of infections and the organisms causing them can be predicted.

In innate immunity, interruption of physical barriers or phagocyte dysfunction can lead to recurrent bacterial infections. A deficiency of a type of phagocyte or a defect in the steps required to perform phagocytosis and microbial killing can lead to recurrent infections with bacteria such as *Staphylococcus* species, enteric bacteria such as *Escherichia coli*, and other pyogenic organisms, which refers to bacteria that make pus or form abscesses. These infections commonly occur in the respiratory tract or on the skin.

Essential complement protein deficiencies are rare. Since the complement system acts as a cascade of reactions, one reaction leading to the next, one protein or enzyme deficiency can affect the development of others downstream in the cascade. Proteins such as C3 are needed for opsonization and phagocytosis; and a deficiency of this component can result in serious infections with pyogenic bacteria. Deficiencies of components of the MAC can result in recurrent infections with *Neisseria* bacteria, such as meningitis due to *Neisseria meningitides* or infection with *N. gonorrheae* at multiple body sites.

In humoral immunity deficiencies there can be B lymphocyte abnormalities or defects in the antibodies they generate. This can result in recurrent bacterial infections of varying severity. Also since IgG or IgM are needed for activation of the classical complement cascade, oposonization and phagocytosis can also be impaired due to Ig defects.

Those that suffer from T-cell, or CMI, dysfunction will often have an increased susceptibility to viral, intracellular microbial, and fungal infections. T-cell function plays a vital and integral role in humoral and innate immunity. For instance, recall that macrophages are activated by proteins (cytokines) released by T cells, which increases macrophage phagocytic killing and antigen presentation. Also isotype switching of Igs require T-cell function. Those unfortunate individuals who have combined humoral and cell-mediated immunodeficiencies are prone to suffering from all types of infections including invasive bacterial, viral, and fungal infections.

The following section will discuss examples of primary immunodeficiencies that should be recognized by healthcare providers despite their rare occurrence. Additionally, HIV-AIDS, the most common acquired immunodeficiency, will be briefly discussed.

Immunodeficiencies of the Innate Immune System

Chronic granulomatous disease (CGD) is an immunodeficiency syndrome resulting from a defect in the phagocyte oxidase enzyme system necessary for killing of ingested bacteria and fungi by neutrophils and macrophages. Without this enzyme phagocytes do not generate the reactive oxygen intermediates that kill microbes. This rare disorder has an incidence of 1 per 200 000 individuals. Clinical presentation can occur as early as the newborn period and as late as young adulthood. Patients suffering from this disease are plagued with recurrent bacterial and fungal infections. The most common infections are pneumonia, skin abscesses, lymphadenitis, and osteomyelitis. Bacteria that do not produce hydrogen peroxide such as *Staphylococcus aureus*, intestinal bacteria and fungi are the most common pathogens. Defective phagocyte production of microbicidal oxidants can be detected through laboratory testing. These patients are best treated aggressively with antibiotic and antifungal therapies aimed at cultured organisms and with surgical drainage of abscesses. Patients are placed on antibiotics prophylactically to help prevent bacterial infections. An immunomodulating agent, IFN-γ, is a more recent treatment option shown to enhance other phagocytic enzymes and therefore microbial killing. The only cure for CGD to date is bone marrow transplantation.

Leukocyte adhesion defect (LAD) is characterized by an inability of neutrophils and monocytes to adhere normally to blood vessels around the site of an infection. Defective cells do not express certain outer membrane proteins termed integrins that allow leukocytes to adhere to endothelial cells. Since the leukocytes are not able to adhere to the vessel wall, they cannot penetrate the endothelial lining to enter the underlying area of infection. This defect also inhibits phagocytosis of complement-opsonized organisms.

The incidence of the major form of LAD is approximately 1 in 1 000 000. Patients suffer recurrent bacterial and fungal infections, as well as impaired wound healing. The defect varies in severity. Children with severe defects present early in life with recurrent bacterial infections, including skin infections, skin ulcers, and gingivitis. Infants can present with delayed separation of the umbilical cord (beyond 3 weeks after birth). Infections are present without signs of pus since pus formation requires leukocyte adhesion and migration to sites of inflammation. Clinical laboratories can test for the presence of the integrin proteins. Bone marrow transplantation is the best treatment option for severe LAD. Other treatment modalities include prophylactic antibiotics and supportive care such as aggressive treatment of infections with appropriate antibiotic therapy.

Immunodeficiency of the Humoral Immune System

Hypogammaglobulinemia is a condition in which one or more of the different Ig isotypes is very low or absent. The most common of these Ig deficiencies is 'selective' IgA deficiency, with an incidence of approximately 1 in 700 Caucasian individuals. Patients with this condition may actually be asymptomatic, but others will have an increased incidence of bacterial infections such as otitis media, chronic bronchitis, and sinusitis. Laboratory values will show absent or very low IgA levels in the serum. There is no treatment for IgA deficiency other than prevention and aggressive treatment of the bacterial infections.

Bruton's agammaglobulinemia, or X-linked agammaglobulinemia (XLA) is a disorder characterized by very low or no Igs of all isotypes. This condition affects males with an incidence of 1 in 100 000–200 000 individuals. The defective protein, Bruton's tyrosine kinase (Btk), is essential for mediating early B-cell maturation. Individuals have low or no B cells in their circulation or lymphoid organs and are antibody deficient, so that they have an increased susceptibility to severe bacterial infections, such as abscesses, pneumonia, and meningitis. Most patients with XLA present during their first year of life with invasive bacterial infections. However, some may have milder symptoms and may not be diagnosed until later in childhood. Genetic testing for the *Btk* gene is available for diagnosis. Ig levels as well as the B-cell markers CD19+ and/or CD20+ will be low or absent. There is no cure for this disease, but treatment with monthly intravenous infusions of gamma globulin (IVIG) minimizes symptoms and allows patients to live a near normal life. Some patients may also need maintenance prophylactic antibiotics.

All infants are relatively hypogammaglobulinemic and rely during their first 6 months of life on IgG antibodies transferred from the mother during pregnancy. However, in transient hypogammaglobulinemia of infancy, patients have low levels of Igs that extend beyond 6 months of age.

These patients may have an increased susceptibility to bacterial infections while their antibody levels are low. Their antibody response to vaccines will be normal, although their circulating Ig levels will be low. Patients suspected to have transient hypogammaglobulinemia of infancy should be monitored closely and have regular testing of Ig levels. This developmental delay in Ig synthesis is transient and usually resolves by 2 years of age. Intravenous gamma globulin is sometimes needed for these patients.

Hyper-IgM syndrome is a rare disorder which can be caused by several genetic defects. Males are most commonly affected, but females can be affected as well. Both IgM and IgD are expressed on the cell surface of B cells during maturation. The IgM isotype must undergo isotype switching to other Ig classes. When there is a defect in the genes involved in isotype switching or if T CMI is impaired, isotype switching may not occur normally, and super-normal synthesis of IgM can develop. Individuals with this condition suffer from recurrent bacterial infections and invasive, opportunistic infections such as *Pneumocystis carinii* pneumonia. Patients will often present during childhood. Upon testing, IgM levels will be high, but IgG and IgA levels will be low. There is no cure for this disease, but treatment is similar to that for hypogammaglobulinemia, and monthly IVIG infusions are protective.

Common variable immunodeficiency (CVID) refers to a group of immunodeficiency disorders with common features but with variable presentations and severity. Patients may present during infancy, although presentation is usually later in life in the form of recurrent infections. These individuals also have an increased susceptibility to autoimmune disorders and malignancies. Patients often suffer more from symptoms resulting from these autoimmune disorders and malignancies than from the CVID. Ig levels are low and there is decreased antibody responsiveness to vaccines or infection. B cells and CMI may be normal or decreased. Treatment for these patients involves monthly IVIG as well as aggressive treatment of secondary disorders that may be present.

Disorders of Cell-Medicated Immunity

A malformation in fetal life leading to defective development of the thymus can adversely affect T-cell maturation. Thymic hypoplasia is a hallmark feature of DiGeorge syndrome, along with other anatomical abnormalities, including cardiac anomalies and unusual facies. Parathyroid glands are usually also hypoplastic, and patients may present with symptoms related to decreased circulating calcium levels. Most patients present early during infancy. DiGeorge syndrome is the result of a deletion of the genes on the 22q11 chromosome. Because T cells are not able to mature in the thymus, they lack cell-mediated defense mechanisms. Also some humoral and innate responses that rely on T lymphocyte help are impaired. Patients are susceptible to intracellular microbial and opportunistic infections. Genetic testing for the chromosomal deletion is available. Total T lymphocytes and CD4+ and CD8+ T-cell subsets may be low, and T-cell function may be impaired. Many patients with DiGeorge syndrome have small amounts of thymic tissue which may be enough to maintain at least partial T-cell maturation and activation. These patients may have normal T-cell function in laboratory tests and no significant immunodeficiency. However, they should undergo regular testing of T-cell numbers and function and review of infection history during the first few years of life to be certain that they are not predisposed to serious infections.

Combined Immunodeficiencies

Severe combined immunodeficiency (SCID) refers to disorders of humoral and CMI responses because of underlying T-cell and B-cell abnormalities. SCID can be caused by a variety of gene defects. The resulting clinical disorder, however, is relatively the same, with an increased incidence of recurrent bacterial, viral, and fungal infections. Because of the severe immunodeficiencies that are typical in SCID patients, they present early in life, usually with recurrent invasive infections. T- and B-cell function and levels are usually low. Diagnostic genetic testing for particular mutations is available. Treatment includes monthly infusions of IVIG. Depending on the etiology, enzyme replacement therapy may be warranted as well. Bone marrow transplantation can be curative, with the best prognosis being transplantation with a related matched donor.

AIDS

As opposed to the immunodeficiencies that result from a primary defect in the immune system, AIDS is the most common of all immunodeficiencies. AIDS is caused by infection of HIV. This epidemic has infected millions of people across the world and has caused millions of deaths of adults and children. The disease may be contracted through infected bodily secretions such as semen or vaginal fluid or via intravenous routes such as with transfusions or infected drug needles. Helper CD4+ T cells are the main cells targeted by HIV. Numerous other cells such as macrophages and dendritic cells are affected as well.

When the HIV viral load increases and the CD4+ T cells decrease, AIDS develops. Patients with AIDS suffer from invasive opportunistic infections, severe immunosuppression, malignancies, and central nervous system degeneration. Research in this field has made remarkable strides in treatment for this deadly disease. While there is no cure for the disease currently, patients with HIV can now live over 20 years without the development of AIDS because of antiviral therapy.

HIV-AIDS is a devastating disease for the patients and their families. All racial and socioeconomic groups are affected worldwide. Although HIV was once considered to infect mainly homosexual males, the incidence of HIV is highest in the heterosexual population. Unprotected sexual intercourse with someone who has the virus is the leading means of transmission. In the US, one of the fastest rising prevalence of HIV is among heterosexual African-American females. Children born to mothers with HIV require early identification and intervention. Transmission of HIV to the fetus can be prevented by early detection and treatment of HIV infection in the pregnant woman.

Conclusion

Certain immunodeficiencies are X-linked and occur only in males, but most immunodeficiencies can affect all races and both genders in all socioeconomic groups. These diseases are not only physically strenuous, but also emotionally and mentally challenging for the patients and their families. Treatment should be focused on these aspects as well. In addition to physicians and nurses taking care of the recurrent infections, particular attention should be addressed to other facets of the illness and its impact on the patients and their families.

Commonly, a multispecialty approach is beneficial to the well-being of these individuals and the family unit. Nutritionists can concentrate on helping the patient avoid malnutrition. Psychologists, psychiatrists, counselors, and social workers can play vital roles in treating depression, anxiety, and daily stress on quality of life. Social workers can identify available resources to address various economic and financial stressors. Child life specialists can be particularly a great source of support for children with these diseases. Finally, because of the genetic basis of the immunodeficiencies, genetic counseling can be important for family planning.

See also: AIDS and HIV; Allergies; Asthma; Illnesses: Autoimmune Rheumatological Diseases; Prenatal Development.

Suggested Readings

Abbas AK and Lichtman AH (2005) *Cellular and Molecular Immunology,* 5th edn. Philadelphia: Elsevier Saunders.
Behrman R, Kliegman R, and Jenson H (2000) *Nelson Textbook of Pediatrics,* 16th edn. Philadelphia: W.B. Saunders Company.

Leung D, Sampson HA, Geha RS, and Szefler SJ (2003) *Pediatric Allergy Principles and Practice.* St. Louis: Mosby.

Rich R, Fleisher TA, Shearer WT, Kotzin BL, and Schroder HW (2001) *Clinical Immunology Principles and Practice,* 2nd edn. Philadelphia: Mosby.

Stiehm R, Ochs H, and Winkelstein J (2004) *Immunologic Disorders in Infants and Children,* 5th edn. Philadelphia: Elsevier Saunders.

Relevant Website

http://www.primaryimmune.org – Immune Deficiency Foundation. The National Organization dedicated to research, education and advocacy for the primary immune deficiency diseases.

Independence/Dependence

S C Mangelsdorf and M S Wong, University of Illinois at Urbana–Champaign, Champaign, IL, USA

Glossary

Attachment – A close emotional bond between two people. The first attachment that an infant forms is usually with a parent. These relationships endure over time, are based on a history of social interactions, and are classified along a continuum of experienced security to insecurity.

Emotion regulation – The processes in which emotion reactions are monitored, evaluated, and modified to accomplish goals. Young infants often rely on their parents to co-regulate their emotions.

Goodness of fit – The degree of match or mismatch between a child's temperamental predisposition and the demands of the environment, including demands that come from parenting.

Social-learning theory – Emphasizes the learning of social behaviors, including dependence and independence. Mother provides contingent care for her infant's physical needs so that the infant will come to associate the mother with relief from discomfort and hunger.

Object relations – The internalization of a self-structure based on the early relationship between mother and infant that is used to establish and maintain future relationships and has implications for the self and personality development.

Introduction

During the 1950s, researchers worked to conceptualize and measure independence and dependence. In this article we outline various definitional issues regarding independence and dependence. We then review various theoretical perspectives on the development of independence and dependence in children, including psychoanalytic, social learning, and attachment theories, and examine how these theoretical accounts have held up to empirical study. We also discuss the current state of the constructs of independence and dependence and how the goodness-of-fit framework may explain these constructs.

Conceptualizing and Measuring Independence and Dependence

Much work was done during the 1950s in conceptualizing and measuring independence and dependence. Researchers such as Glen Heathers proposed that young children are entirely dependent on others for satisfying all of their needs during early childhood. During that time, dependency was operationalized as young children's behaviors in eliciting nurturance and reinforcement from others. Thus, early on young children must learn effective ways to get others to care for them. However, children must also gradually work to become independent where they can successfully transfer some of their needs for dependence from adults (e.g., parents and teachers) to themselves or friends. Researchers argued about the definition of these constructs and disagreed on whether or not different components within dependence and independence reflected a single construct. In other words, are components within dependency multidimensional or unidimensional? There were mixed findings, supporting both views. When researchers considered the association between independence and dependence, however, most of them agreed that they were related but separate constructs.

There are many ways for children to manifest their dependence to parents. Emanuel K. Beller studied components of dependency in preschoolers and identified five different components. These components included: (1) seeking help, (2) seeking physical contact, (3) seeking proximity, (4) seeking attention, and (5) seeking recognition. He tested these components using teachers' ratings and found that some of these components were moderately correlated with others. Hence, Beller argued that these five components reflected one single dependency drive in the children who he studied.

In addition to dependence, Beller also studied independence, which he operationalized it in terms of self-reliance and achievement striving: (1) taking initiative, (2) overcoming obstacles, (3) having persistence, (4) finding satisfaction from work, and (5) wanting to do things by oneself. Those children who take initiative are active in manipulating the environment to achieve their goal. Over time children may encounter many obstacles in achieving a goal, but it is important for them to keep working, that is having persistence, until the goal is met. Children also need to have satisfaction from work so that they can have enough motivation to do things independently. Lastly, children need to try working on their own so that they are not relying too much on parents' or teachers' help. When examining the correlations among these components, Beller found that they were quite strongly correlated with one another. As such, children who try hard to overcome obstacles are also likely to persist, find satisfaction from work, and enjoy working independently. Based on these findings, he argued that independence was similar to dependence such that it referred to a general acquired drive.

Some other researchers were skeptical that independence and dependence each reflected a single dimension. According to Glen Heathers, there are four different types of dependence/independence. The first one is instrumental dependence, when a person seeks help to achieve goals. For example, infants cry to signal hunger and rely on their mother to satisfy their physical needs. Second, emotional dependence refers to a person seeking affection, reassurances, and approval from others. In this case, infants who scrape their knee approach and reach the mother so that they can be held for comfort and reassurance. Third, when a person conducts activities and copes with problems without seeking help, this person is demonstrating instrumental independence. For example, young children may be able to solve a puzzle on their own without getting help from parents. Finally, emotional independence is also known as emotional self-reliance, referring to the situation where a person does not look for reassurance, affection, or approval from others. For instance, young children who have recently learned how to tie shoelaces on their own may not rely on praises and approvals from parents, but rather they are satisfied with their mastery of the task. Together, these four types of dependence/independence represent different ways that children can demonstrate dependence and independence, suggesting that these constructs are at least two-dimensional. In a way, it seems plausible that instrumental dependence is the exact opposite of instrumental independence, whereas emotional dependence is the opposite of emotional independence. Interestingly,

Heathers actually found that some of these components within the dependence and independence constructs were significantly related to one another (e.g., self-assertion was negatively related to affection seeking), while others were not. In sum, these findings suggested that independence and dependence might be separate constructs, rather than the exact opposite of one another.

It is often assumed in the literature that independence is associated with positive outcomes such as autonomy, whereas dependence is associated with negative outcomes such as regression. Consider a child who runs to mother for physical contact. Some researchers, such as Lois Murphy, considered such actions as dependent because the child had not fully developed better coping skills. Such behavior, however, has to be interpreted in light of the child's developmental stage, including cognitive ability, learning and mastery of coping skills, and the ability to choose and manipulate the environment. Children who insist on doing something on their own may seem to have achieved independence, yet they may also miss out opportunities where parents can offer them help especially with tasks that are too difficult to manage alone. As such, whether instrumental independence is adaptive or not really depends on the contexts. Similarly, instrumental dependence (i.e., help-seeking behavior) can be considered as competent behavior when the situation permits.

Some researchers found only weak associations between the independence and dependence constructs, hence suggesting that the underlying components within these constructs might be multidimensional. For example, different infants may manifest different behaviors to achieve their goal (e.g., getting attention from their mother.) One infant may vocalize and approach the mother with a smile. Another infant may sit passively and burst into tears, waiting for the mother's return. A third infant may seek contact actively by reaching the mother and wanting to be picked up. As such, these infants are all dependent on their mother, but each of them manifests their dependence in slightly different ways. This idea was supported by Jacob Gewirtz, when he examined preschool children's strategies of gaining adults' attention and found that different children indeed used different strategies to elicit attention. More specifically, Gewirtz analyzed nine observational measures and came up with factors that were pointing into fairly distinct dimensions of behavior. The first factor involved direct attempts to gain attention from adults, for example, "Look at me". The second factor involved more passive and nonverbal attempts to gain adult attention. Thus Gewirtz concluded that even attention-seeking, which is only one type of dependent behavior in young children, was at least two dimensional, and therefore the dependence construct was also likely to be multidimensional. Similarly, N. Mann also provided converging evidence. He conducted research on preschooler children and coded frequencies of various types of dependent behaviors such as seeking physical contact, seeking to be near, seeking reassurance, seeking positive attention by socially appropriate behavior, seeking help, and seeking negative attention by socially disapproved behavior. He found that these behaviors were not significantly correlated and therefore concluded that dependence was multidimensional, not unidimensional.

Although researchers presented mixed evidence regarding whether the components within independence and dependence were unidimensional or multidimensional, most of them agreed that independence and dependence were related, but separate constructs. Emanuel K. Beller, for example, found a modest negative association between independence and dependence ($r = -0.53$), and speculated that there was an overlap between independence and dependence such that they were not entirely separate constructs. If they were indeed truly orthogonal (i.e., unrelated to one another) the correlation would have been zero ($r = 0$). Moreover, he also believed that independence should be conceptualized as something more than the lack of dependence, such that these two constructs are not the exact opposite of one another. For example, it is possible that parents' behavior may facilitate both independence and dependence in young children. Therefore he concluded that it was not appropriate to assume that independence and dependence represented either ends of a continuum on a bipolar scale, but instead they were separate but also related constructs.

How exactly should we make sense of these seemingly contradictory findings? Willard W. Hartup provided some great insights on this issue in his literature review. According to Hartup, the way in which researchers operationalized independence and dependence affected their view of the constructs as unidimensional or multidimensional. In the past, researchers had used methods such as direct observations, teachers' reports, self-reports, projective tests, and behavioral tasks to measure independence and dependence. According to Hartup, it is possible that these different methodologies are in fact measuring different aspects of dependency and independence. For example, dependency motivation is best captured by projective tests, and direct observations best measure dependency response strength. Depending on the methodologies used, researchers may or may not find associations among the components within the independence and dependence constructs. As such, it will be a good idea to employ multiple methodologies from different informants to understand independence and dependence in children better.

Theoretical Accounts of Dependency

Up to this point, we have reviewed significant work from researchers who greatly contributed to conceptualizing

and operationalizing independence and dependence. One way to understand these constructs better is to see them through different theoretical perspectives, including psychoanalytic, social-learning, and attachment theories. Each of these perspectives has its own unique way of explaining the origins and implications for independence and dependence. It is noteworthy that many of these earlier writings referred to mothers because they were generally the main caregivers, and it is still true today that more research has been conducted on mothers than fathers. However, when reading the following paragraphs, the word mothers can be used interchangeably with other child caregivers.

Freud's Psychoanalytic Theory

According to Sigmund Freud, the initial bond that infants form with their mother has special importance for the infant's psychological development. Freud believed that there were two different instincts in children: ego instincts (which refer to hunger and thirst) and sexual instincts. Mother, who is usually in charge of caring, feeding, and protecting the infants, become infants' earliest sexual objects. Early psychoanalysts believed that infants during early stages cannot differentiate between themselves and their mother. Toward the age of 8 months, infants begin to develop a sense of separateness from their mother. These theorists also believed that infants go through different psychosexual stages, including oral, anal, and genital stage in young childhood. They argued that if the fundamental needs were not met in these stages the child would become fixated and throughout life would have psychological issues that would relate to these fixations. An example often used is that if a child's needs for oral gratification are not met in infancy then they will have an oral issue that would result in substitute oral activities in later life, excessive eating, smoking, nail biting, gum chewing, etc. It has been suggested by some psychoanalytic theorists that fixation at the second stage, referred to by Freud as the 'anal stage', and by Erikson as 'autonomy' vs. 'shame' and 'doubt', could lead to excessive dependency if their needs for autonomy with a supportive environment are not provided for. As such, these theorists argued that mother's behavior was especially important because by either allowing too much autonomy (without warm and support) or too little autonomy could lead to a fixation that would affect the child's capacity for independent behavior in later life.

It is clear that caregivers play an important role in satisfying infants' various needs. For example, when infants suck on their mother's breasts for feeding, their primary drive will be reduced. Since birth, infants depend on their mother to meet various physical needs such as hunger, thirst, shelter, and warmth. As time goes by, infants will associate their mother as a source of gratification. In other words, the mere presence of the mother will bring joy and comfort to the infant. According to 'object relations theory' the early relationship infants form with their mothers has important implications for infants' personality development, and shapes how infants perceive themselves and the world around them. According to Freud, dependency is thus rooted from the satisfaction of basic primary drives, and infants form attachments to their mothers because their physical and psychological needs are gratified.

Other Psychoanalytic Theorists

Following Freud, psychoanalysts such as Donald W. Winnicott, Margaret S. Mahler, and Harry S. Sullivan all agreed that infants and young children depended on their mother to satisfy their needs, both physically and emotionally. In addition, these theorists also recognized the developmental goal for infants to grow from relative dependence toward independence, though they believed that this process developed much slower in the socioemotional than physical domain. Winnicott and Mahler emphasized the importance of holding infants so that they would feel loved and cared for. Likewise, Sullivan proposed that infants experienced anxiety and only through the fulfillment of their needs by their mother can their anxiety be lowered. Finally, Mahler suggested that mothers should be sensitive and responsive to their infants' needs so that their infants could strive toward the optimal development of independence. We will discuss each of these theoretical accounts in more detail below.

Donald W. Winnicott. According to Winnicott, infants are born into the world with absolute dependence. With experience, infants slowly build up their confidence in the world, such that they begin to learn that their needs will be satisfied by their mother. In other words, Winnicott emphasized the role of mother, such that she has to be sensitive in meeting their infants' physical and emotional needs. For example, it is not sufficient for a mother just to provide food and clothing for her infant. Instead, she also needs to hold and love and comfort her baby in order to fulfill the baby's emotional needs. As such, it is important for mothers to recognize infants' dependence and be able to satisfy their needs. According to Winnicott, infants whose physical and emotional needs are met responsively will fare better socially and emotionally than those whose needs are not met. More specifically, these infants will develop confidence in their mother, which will eventually extend to other people. As a result, they will be able to trust others and become mature, reliable, and adaptive individuals.

Margaret S. Mahler. Similar to Winnicott, Mahler also believed the importance of holding infants. She believed that babies could reduce their tension and would feel safe and secure when they were held by their mother.

According to Mahler, mother should be sensitive in picking up infants' signals, so that the timing for holding will be optimal – not too long (i.e., infants will be able to develop independence) and not too short (i.e., infants will feel safe and secure in their mother's arms).

Mahler proposed four phases of the 'separation–individuation process' that all young children go through in individuating from their mother. For each of these four different phases, Mahler's suggestions for mother have great implications for infants' development of independence. In the 'differentiation and body image' phase (peaking at 4–5 months), infants start to develop a sense of self that is separate from their mother. Infants take their first steps in breaking a little bit away from their mother to explore the environment. Occasionally, infants will look at their mother (known as social referencing) for more cues about the environment. In this phase, mothers should encourage their infants' needs and curiosity to explore the environment and try not to attract the infants' attention, which would satisfy her own needs more than the infants'.

In the 'practicing phase' (7–15 months), infants have improved a great deal in their motor skills so that they can increase physical distance from their mother and thereby focus on the exploration of environment. This phase is comprised of two parts. First is the 'early practicing phase' which overlaps with the previous differentiation phase, when infants begin to crawl, climb, and hold themselves in an upright position. Hence, mother should fulfill the infants' need for physical contact and at the same time encourage the exploration of environment. The second part is the 'practicing period proper', where infants are able to walk freely. In this phase, mother should recognize the development of independence and allow their infant to explore the environment freely. It is important that mother should foster optimal development: not being too overprotective or too pushy toward independence. The development of independence comes with a greater sense of self-esteem and autonomy.

In the 'rapprochement phase' (16–35 months), infants have mastered walking and are more aware of their individuation from their mother. On the one hand, they are learning many new skills and becoming very excited about sharing their discoveries with mother. On the other hand, they also become more concerned about their mother's presence and are active in approaching them when they feel threatened. By giving her infant praise, the mother is encouraging her infants' greater sense of autonomy and independence. Thus, infants can be emotionally close to their mother and at the same time feel safe to be independent in exploring the world.

By the fourth phase, 'object constancy' (36 months and beyond), children have internalized the image of their mother and do not need her presence to explore the world. In other words, children of this age have formed an internal representation of their mother. Greater independence will be achieved when young children can tolerate longer separation by understanding that mother will return after an absence. It is noteworthy that Mahler believed that it was possible for a child to regress to previous phases. For example, a child who gets angry at the mother and manifests separation anxiety would result in substantial regression in the development of independence. Hence, it is important to examine carefully different factors that may foster independence and autonomy in children.

Harry S. Sullivan. Sullivan proposed a 'theory of interpersonal psychiatry', which focused on the understanding of tension and anxiety in infants. According to Sullivan, anxiety is the main factor in social relationships and has great implications for well-being. Everyone experiences anxiety starting from infancy and such anxiety originates from our dependency toward mother, where we rely on her to satisfy our physical and biological needs during infancy. Hence, mother plays an important role in reducing infants' anxiety and fostering emotional security. In addition, Sullivan also believed infants might experience anxiety through other channels. For example, a mother who is experiencing anxiety may induce anxiety in her infant. Providing food in this case, cannot reduce the infant's anxiety. As such, Sullivan argued that mother needs to understand the causes of an infant's anxiety in order to provide the most appropriate care. Through the interaction with mother, infants will develop their own unique way of dealing with their anxiety and eventually form a model of how they could relate to the world. As such, infants move from dependence toward independence in regulating their anxiety.

Social-Learning Theory

Similar to the notions of primary and secondary drives proposed by psychoanalytic theorists, social-learning theorists, such as Sears, Gewirtz, Bandura, and Walters, contributed to the conceptualization of dependency by examining the role of drives, while viewing dependence and independence as learned behaviors. According to these theorists independence and dependence were learned behaviors, like other social behavior. Innate drives, such as hunger and thirst, are present in infants at birth. The state of equilibrium is disturbed when infants are hungry so that they will cry and try other behaviors (e.g., sucking fingers) that may temporarily reduce the tension. After being fed the tension is reduced and equilibrium returns. Even very young infants are capable of learning; thus, quickly infants come to associate factors that are contingent with feeding, with the satisfaction of feeding itself. As such, young infants will soon associate being picked up with being fed. Some social-learning theorists believed that this happened as early as 4 weeks of life. With time, young infants come to associates the mother with relief from the discomfort of hunger and thirst.

Researchers such as Celia Burns Stendler suggested that over the course of the first year of life infants develop an increasing awareness of the value of their mother's presence. In fact they develop a dependency drive, so that by the end of the first year whenever they encounter events that create tension or frustration (hunger, cold, thirst, presence of a stranger, a toy out of reach), they will turn to the mother to solve the problem. In other words, infants' behaviors (clinging and clutching mother, turning toward mother, and smiling at mother) are reinforced by the gratification given by mother. Eventually, mother's sole presence will be soothing to the infants because of conditioning. Similarly, stimuli associated with the presence of mother will also become secondary reinforcers.

Social-learning theorists believed that there are a number of conditions that underlie the presence of dependent behaviors in children: one is that their mother is the reinforcer and supplies gratification for the infants; that is, mother's nurturing and feeding of the infants becomes the source of gratification, which fosters dependency in infants. On the other hand, mothers can also be punitive toward an infants' display of dependency. For example, mother's punitive behavior can threaten young children's dependency toward her. Her lack of response may also weaken the dependency relationship. Finally, children's dependency can also be learned because the presence of mother reduces children's anxiety since mother has become a secondary reinforcer. Together, children's dependency becomes contingent upon mother's behavior. The flip side of this of course is how parenting influences independence. According to social-learning theorists if parents reward children's independent behaviors they will increase in frequency. So, for example, the child who gets dressed by himself for the first time and is given praise, "You did it all by yourself!" will be more likely to pursue further independent behaviors in the future than the child who is criticized, "You have that shirt on backwards."

Bowlby's Attachment Theory

Part of what we have introduced about dependence thus far has to do with infants' and young children's physical and emotional needs that have to be satisfied by their parents. John Bowlby's theory differs from the psychoanalytic and social-learning theories discussed earlier, in that Bowlby believed that infants are born with the predisposition to form attachment relationships to the people who care for them. Even when infants' needs are not met adequately, their attachment will still develop and be directed toward attachment figures. Winnicott, Mahler, and Sullivan had highlighted the importance of being sensitive and responsive to infants' signals. Similarly, Bowlby's theory of the development of attachment relationships during the late 1960s also emphasized the same ideas. According to Bowlby, mothers differ in the degree to which they can provide sensitive and responsive care to their infants, which affects infants' individual differences in the security of attachment relationships. Mary S. D. Ainsworth and colleagues developed the 'strange situation procedure' to systematically study the individual differences in attachment security.

The strange situation procedure involves a series of separations and reunions between the caregiver and the infant, and the infant's interactions with a stranger. Attachment researchers are most interested in the episodes where the baby reunites with the mother after brief separations. The goal of this procedure is to activate the attachment system through separations and examine the underlying organization of the attachment behaviors. Based on infants' behaviors, researchers have distinguished four types of attachment categories: secure, avoidant, ambivalent, and disorganized attachment.

Bowlby believed that how parents behave would have an effect on the quality of the infants' attachment relationships. This is supported by research, such that parents of secure infants are generally sensitive and responsive in meeting the needs of their infants. Parents of avoidant infants are often hostile and rejecting, and those of ambivalent infants provide inconsistent care. Finally, some disorganized infants' parents are abusive or disturbed. Of course, research on attachment today has brought in other factors besides parenting into the picture, such as child temperament, parent personality, life stresses, marital quality, etc., that can (1) interact with each other and (2) have a direct or indirect impact on the security of attachment relationships.

One important concept of Bowlby's theory is the notion of the development of 'internal working models,' based on infants' past and ongoing daily interactions and experiences with caregivers. In other words, infants form mental models and representations of the relationships with their caregivers, which will then guide their view of self and others. This idea is consistent with the 'trust' vs. 'mistrust stage' in Erik Erikson's psychosocial theory of development, such that infants develop a trust in their caregivers when their physical and emotional needs are met in a consistent and caring way. If these needs are not met, infants may become fearful and less trusting of others. Secure attachment relationships foster independence in infants because the infants will use their caregivers as a secure base and safe haven, so that they are free to explore the environment while being able to return to the caregivers for protection when they encounter threats.

Attachment and Dependency: Are They Related?

Although young children fleeing to their parent for comfort when distressed may seem like a dependent behavior,

attachment theorists believe that secure attachments ultimately lead to independence. When attachment needs are met responsively and sensitively, children will become more confident, self-reliant, and independent over time. Ainsworth carefully articulated the similarities and differences between dependency and attachment.

According to Ainsworth there are a number of different factors that researchers need to consider when comparing attachment with dependency. These include variables such as (1) specificity, (2) duration, (3) level of maturity, (4) affect implications, and (5) proximity seeking and contact maintaining. 'Specificity' refers to the fact that children direct attachment behaviors toward specific caregivers, but dependency is a generalized concept which may or may not involve the caregiver. 'Duration' taps into the observation that attachment is enduring, but dependency may or may not be enduring. For example, a child is still attached to the mother when she is out of sight, but he/she cannot depend on the mother when she is not physically present. 'Level of maturity' refers to the fact that although dependence implies immaturity, and thus declines over childhood, attachments occur across the lifespan. 'Affective implications' refers to the strong emotional component involved in attachment relationships, whereas dependence may or may not involve strong emotions. For example, an injured child may depend on the aid of the school nurse, but the child may not express any strong affect toward the nurse. 'Proximity seeking and contact-maintaining' behaviors are targeted toward the attachment figure, but there is no implication of that in dependency. A child is often dependent on people who are not attachment figures, as well as being dependent on those who are.

Alan Sroufe and colleagues in 1983 furthered the discussion about the differences between attachment and dependence by making the point that attachment has to do with the organization of behaviors, not behaviors *per se*. That also has to do with the stability of attachment relationships and the resulting continuity of organization of behaviors. In other words, infants may not exhibit exactly the same behavior, but the underlying organization of behavior presumably remains the same. Sroufe and colleagues also believed that we should employ a similar organizational approach to dependency. In the following sections, we introduce how attachment security can predict dependency, and how dependency is related to emotion regulation and crying.

Predicting Dependency from Attachment

Attachment researchers such as Sroufe believe that securely attached children will actually come to be less dependent than children who have insecure attachment relationships. For example, Sroufe and colleagues found that children who had been securely attached to their mothers were rated by their teachers as lower in dependency. Children who had avoidant or anxious-ambivalent attachment relationships with their mothers during infancy were rated by their teachers as overdependent. Consistent with psychoanalytic theory, such dependence is maladaptive in a number of ways. For example, being highly dependent on teachers' approval and attention may interfere with the opportunities where children can develop friendships with peers. In contrast, children who have secure relationships are effective in seeking contact so that they can quickly return to their peers and resume playing. The contact with teachers thus supports peer relationships. These children are also more involved in peer groups and are better liked by their peers and teachers. As such, the key point here is that secure children are more effective in expressing dependency behavior.

The implication of the attachment theory for the development of independence and autonomy goes beyond infancy. According to attachment theory infants who are securely attached have developed a confident expectation toward their mothers, which will eventually be generalized to the view of other people; that is, they develop an 'internal working model' of themselves and the world around them. As such, these babies will become more independent compared to other babies who do not have such confident expectations.

Dependency and Emotion Regulation

In his book on emotion regulation and attachment, Sroufe framed dependency in terms of emotion regulation. Following Ross A. Thompson, emotion regulation refers to the processes in which emotion reactions are monitored, evaluated, and modified to accomplish goals. According to Sroufe, young infants are entirely dependent on their caregivers, not just for being fed and clothed, but also for help with regulating emotions. Unlike older infants, young infants are incapable of regulating their own emotions. Their signals need to be detected by their parents so that their parents can help regulate their arousal state. Indeed, parents who are sensitive and responsive to infants' signals help infants to develop better skills in emotion regulation. These parents provide an equilibrium range of stimulation so that the infants will not be over- or understimulated. Through the interactions with parents, infants will eventually learn how effectively they can elicit responses from their parents. Thompson emphasizes the active role of parents in regulating their infants' emotions. As infants develop, their ability to signal also changes. According to Sroufe, beginning from birth to 2 months, infants signal alertness, discomfort, and other needs to anyone and do not discriminate among their caregivers. From 3 to 6 months infants are able to share positive affect with their parents and engage in reciprocal exchange.

Infants' use of goal-directed behavior begins at 6 months, where their behaviors (e.g., reaching up for the parent) are motivated by the achievement of specific goals (e.g. wanting to be picked up). These milestones highlight infants' developing organization of behaviors so that their behaviors are adaptive to how responsive their parents have been during earlier infancy. In other words, infants' inability to regulate their own emotions requires parents to respond to their signals and co-regulate their arousal state, and over time infants will eventually learn how effective they are in eliciting responses from parents.

Dependency and Crying

It is generally believed that parents who are sensitive and responsive to infants' signals help infants to develop better skills in emotion regulation and foster secure attachment relationships to parents. Among different signals, infant crying is definitely the one that is the most salient to parents. Research has found mixed results in how maternal responsiveness is associated with infant crying in later months. In their Baltimore study, Silvia M. Bell and Mary D. S. Ainsworth in the 1970s found that mothers who promptly responded to their infants' crying bouts during the first year had infants who cried less in subsequent months. These researchers argued against the social-learning theory premise that maternal responsiveness did not reinforce infants' crying. In fact, they suggested that responding promptly to infants' crying would foster independence and optimal development. In another study, Ainsworth and colleagues found that mothers who were responsive to infants' crying had infants who felt less distress during mothers' temporary absence. Similarly, in another study, Susan B. Crockenberg and Perrin Smith found that maternal unresponsiveness was related to more fussing and crying in infants. Taken together, these researchers argued that by being responsive, mothers could effectively soothe infants and terminate their crying. Further, these mothers might also create a caregiving environment that would elicit less crying from infants in the future.

Contrary to the aforementioned studies, Marinus H. Van IJzendoorn and Frans O. A. Hubbard in 2000 failed to replicate the Baltimore study with a bigger sample size ($N = 50$). Interestingly, they found that infants would cry less when their mothers had ignored their crying bouts during the previous 9 weeks. Moreover, although Ainsworth and colleagues predicted that mothers of secure infants would be more responsive to infants' crying, Van IJzendoorn and Hubbard found mothers of avoidant infants actually provided the most contingent responses to infants' crying. In another study in 1998, Ian St James-Roberts and colleagues found that mothers whose infants cried more also showed more sensitivity and affection toward their infants, and the amount of crying actually decreased as infants grew up, regardless of maternal responsiveness. Attempting to interpret these seemingly contradictory findings, Van IJzendoorn and Hubbard first noted the small sample used in the Baltimore study ($N = 26$). Second, they emphasized their equally extensive observations on families, and use of technologically advanced equipment allowed them to get a confident measure of infants' crying and maternal responsiveness. Third, extraneous variables including earlier crying and synchronous responsiveness were not controlled for in the Baltimore study, but were held constant in their study. In sum, Van IJzendoorn and Hubbard argued that the best way to reconcile these findings was to examine closely 'differential responsiveness' and the context of crying.

According to Van IJzendoorn and Hubbard, it is impossible for mothers to respond to every crying bout that infants make. What really matters is parents' ability to discriminate among different crying signals and to be responsive to those that signify greatest distress, that is, differential responsiveness. This ability also comes with experience, as noted in research with mothers of several children, and can be influenced negatively by parent and familial risk factors such as depression and marital conflict. Hence, it is important to consider infants' crying within its context and meaning. For example, Van IJzendoorn and Hubbard found that mothers whose infants were avoidant were surprisingly the most prompt in responding to infants' crying. It is possible that these mothers might interpret the situation as oversimulating for their crying infants and thus were more likely to control and minimize their infants' negative emotions. Similarly in a more recent study published in 2003, Lisa J. Berlin and Jude Cassidy found that mothers of avoidant infants (measured by the strange situation procedure at 15–18 months) reported greater control of their children's negative emotions. These children also grew up to be less expressive and willing to share their feelings 3 years later. As such, although these infants are acting more independent and showing less negative emotions in stressful situations like the strange situation procedure, they are in fact experiencing more physiological distress (e.g., increased heart rate) than secure infants. Unfortunately, their organization of behaviors does not allow them to regulate their emotions flexibly through seeking help from parents. In contrast, secure infants are able to regulate their emotions flexibly by expressing rather than hiding negative emotions. As a result, the open communication between secure infants and their parents allows these infants to signal distress and seek proximity to parents, thus regulating their emotions optimally so that they can return to the exploration of the environment. The secure infants will strive toward independence.

Goodness of Fit: The Interaction of Child and Parent Characteristics

In exploring parental responsiveness, the development of secure attachments and their impact on children's independence, it is important to acknowledge that different child, parent, and contextual factors may influence parental sensitivity and responsiveness to their infants. Past research has explored the direct and moderating effects of these factors. For example, Crockenberg reported in her 1981 study that irritable temperament during the newborn period was predictive of insecure attachment only in conjunction with low maternal social support; that is, neither infant temperament nor maternal support exerted a main effect on attachment. Instead, the interaction between these two variables predicted insecure attachment. Similarly, Sarah C. Mangelsdorf and colleagues reported in their 1990 study that security of attachment, as assessed at 13 months in the strange situation procedures, could be predicted by an interaction between infants' proneness-to-distress temperament and maternal personality. Mothers who scored high on the 'constraint scale' (rigidity, traditionalism, and low risk taking) of Auke Tellegen's 'multidimensional personality questionnaire' developed in 1982 and who had infants who scored high on proneness-to-distress measures at 9 months were also likely to have insecurely attached infants at 13 months. As in the Crockenberg study, temperament or maternal personality had no significant main effects, but the interaction between the two variables predicted insecure attachment. One can easily imagine how the combination of a fearful and rigid mother (i.e., the profile of high scorers on the constraint dimension) coupled with an easily distressed infant could result in a less-than-optimal relationship. Although infant temperament measures did not predict later insecure attachment, the interaction of maternal physical contact and infant intensity/activity significantly predicted insecure–avoidant attachment. In other words, highly intense and active infants who received little physical contact from their mothers appeared to be at-risk for developing avoidant relationships. Thus, the findings from these studies have provided empirical support for a goodness-of-fit or transactional model proposed by researchers such as Crockenberg, Arnold Sameroff, and Barbara Fiese. It appears that some infant characteristics, such as irritability or proneness-to-distress seem more likely to contribute to insecure attachment than others. Similarly, specific parental characteristics may be particularly important to attachment relationships, and certain forms of social support, particularly marital support, may be especially important for predicting sensitive parenting. In fact, an extensive body of literature documents the association between the quality of the marital relationship and multiple aspects of parenting behavior, including sensitivity, negativity, and intrusiveness.

All these factors may have direct or indirect effects in influencing children's development of independence.

Finally, infants' characteristics such as temperament not only affect parents' sensitivity and responsiveness, they also affect infants' outcomes. Based on previous research, Yair Ziv and Jude Cassidy have hypothesized that parents are more susceptible to poor parenting when they rear more-irritable infants than less-irritable infants. It is speculated that irritable infants may have more trouble with emotional and behavioral regulation, and thus are more dependent on adults for assistance in self-regulation. As such, the best approach to understanding infants' independence is to consider relevant child and parent characteristics as well as contextual factors.

Conclusions

In sum, over the last 50 years psychologists have theorized and researched dependency and independence from a variety of theoretical perspectives. The account that seems most relevant today is the one provided by the attachment theory. The Attachment theory proposes that the young children are born dependent in almost every way, but through the aid of loving and responsive adults they develop secure attachment relationships with parents. Gradually, over the course of development, these secure relationships allow infants to become more active in exploring the world and less dependent on their parents in regulating their emotions. Thus, the very behaviors that appear dependent in infancy, crying and seeking comfort when distressed, are associated with more independent and self-reliant behavior in later childhood. Trust in their caregivers becomes trust in themselves. Hence, the outcome of effective self-regulation is similar to self-reliance or independence.

See also: Attachment; Discipline and Compliance; Emotion Regulation; Fear and Wariness; Parenting Styles and their Effects; Self-Regulatory Processes; Separation and Stranger Anxiety; Social and Emotional Development Theories; Social Interaction; Temperament.

Suggested Readings

Ainsworth MDS (1972) Attachment and dependency: A comparison. In: Gewirtz JL (ed.) *Attachment and Dependency*, pp. 97–137. Washington, DC: V. H. Winston & Sons.

Beller EK (1955) Dependency and independence in young children. *Journal of Genetic Psychology* 87: 25–35.

Bowlby J (1969–1982) *Attachment and Loss: Vol. 1: Attachment.* New York: Basic Books.

Hartup WW (1963) Dependence and independence. In: Stevenson HW (ed.) *Child Psychology: The Sixty-Second Yearbook of the National Society of the Study of Education.* Chicago: University of Chicago Press.

Maccoby EE and Masters JC (1970) Attachment and dependency. In: Mussen PH (ed.) *Manual of Child Psychology,* 3rd edn., pp. 73–157. New York: Wiley.

Sroufe LA (1997) *Emotional Development: The Organization of Emotional Life in the Early Years.* New York: Cambridge University Press.

Sroufe LA, Fox NE, and Pancake VR (1983) Attachment and dependency in developmental perspective. *Child Development* 54: 1615–1627.

Sullivan HS (1953) *The Interpersonal Theory of Psychiatry.* New York: Norton & Company.

Thompson RA (1994) Emotion regulation: A theme in search of definition. *Monographs of the Society for Research in Child Development* 59: 25–52.

Winnicott DW (2002) *Winnicott on the Child.* Cambridge, MA: Perseus Publishing Books.

Relevant Website

http://www.psychology.sunysb.edu – Psychology department, Stony Brook University.

Intellectual Disabilities

D J Fidler and J S Jameson, Coloradoes State University, Fort Collins, CO, USA

Glossary

Adaptive behavior – The ability of an individual to perform behaviors that evidence age-appropriate and culturally appropriate levels of personal independence and social responsibility.

Behavioral phenotype – The observable expression of behavioral traits; in this case a profile of behaviors associated with a specific genetic disorder.

Diagnostic overshadowing – The tendency of a clinician to attribute co-morbid psychiatric symptoms to the presence of mental retardation/intellectual disability or a syndrome associated with mental retardation/intellectual disability.

Dual diagnosis – The diagnosis of comorbid psychiatric disorders in addition to intellectual disability.

Early intervention – A comprehensive set of services that are provided to children from birth to age three and their families to enhance a child's developmental potential.

Familial mental retardation – According to Zigler, mental retardation that results from the interaction between inherited and environmental factors, leading to a designation.

Indirect effects – The impact that behavioral characteristics associated with specific genetic disorders impact family members, educators, and other members of the community.

Individualized education plan – A plan that describes the educational program that has been designed to meet the unique needs of a child receiving US special education services (ages 3–18 years); it outlines the needs, goals, strategies, and methods of assessment that will guide instruction and intervention strategies.

Individualized family service plan – In the US, contains information about the services necessary to facilitate a child's development (ages 0–3 years) and enhance the family's capacity to facilitate the child's development; family members and service providers work as a team to plan, implement, and evaluate services tailored to the family's unique concerns, priorities, and resources.

Mental retardation/intellectual disability – According to the 2002 definition from the American Association of Mental Retardation, "a disability characterized by significant limitations both in intellectual functioning and in adaptive behavior as expressed in conceptual, social, and practical adaptive skills" that originates before the age of 18 years.

Organic mental retardation – According to Zigler, mental retardation that results from a biological insult on the genetic, neurodevelopmental, or pre/perinatal level.

Special education – Specially designed educational instruction, including supplementary aids and related services that allow a child with a disability to benefit meaningfully from his or her educational program.

Undifferentiated mental retardation – According to Zigler, mental retardation that cannot be reliably attributed to either organic or familial causes.

Introduction

According to the most current definition put forth in 2002 by the American Association on Mental Retardation (AAMR), the term mental retardation refers to "a disability characterized by significant limitations both in intellectual functioning and in adaptive behavior as expressed in conceptual, social, and practical adaptive skills." To highlight the developmental nature of mental retardation, this definition specified that cognitive limitations and adaptive behavior deficits must originate before the age of 18 years. The AAMR also stipulated that there are additional assumptions that should be made when applying the current definition of intellectual disability/mental retardation. First, functioning difficulties must be understood within the context of the community and environments that are appropriate for an individual's chronological age and cultural background. Second, appropriate assessment techniques that lead to a diagnosis of mental retardation must take both cultural/linguistic background and issues related to motor, sensory, and communicative functioning into account. The third assumption relates to the recognition that challenges in functioning often occur simultaneously with areas of strength in functioning. Fourth, one of the main purposes of identifying an individual's challenges relates to developing a profile of supports to address the individual's needs. And the final assumption of the AAMR definition relates to the idea that well-planned support systems implemented over time should lead to improvement in the functioning of the individual with intellectual disability/mental retardation.

While this definition of the construct 'mental retardation' is widely used in clinical and educational settings, it is the product of many decades of change. The most recent changes relate to the use of the term 'mental retardation' itself, which has increasingly fallen out of favor in both the advocacy and practice communities. In 2006, the majority of members of the AAMR voted to change the name of their organization to the American Association on Intellectual and Developmental Disabilities. This is the culmination of a larger movement worldwide to discontinue the use of the term mental retardation, in favor of terms such as intellectual disability, cognitive disabilities, and the more global term developmental disabilities. Thus, while the term mental retardation is still currently used in clinical and some educational settings, the term is becoming increasingly obsolete as organizations formally adopt other, more socially acceptable, terms. For the purposes of this article, the term mental retardation will be used to discuss any historic issues involving the definition of the phenomenon, but the term intellectual disability will be used for all current issues and topics. In addition, to illustrate the complex nature of this construct, in the following sections we will focus on the history of mental retardation/intellectual disability in the US, though additional cross-national information will be included in the discussion of service delivery.

Definition and Categorization

Definition History

In addition to changes in terminology, throughout much of the twentieth century, the behavioral sciences have struggled to operationalize a definition of mental retardation that defines accurately and humanely the specific characteristics that are common among individuals in this category. The many changes in terminology and the definition of mental retardation/intellectual disability reflect a century-long history of challenge regarding the science and study of individuals with impaired or delayed cognitive development. These struggles have led to many definitions, technical terms, and clinical criteria that often changed in accordance with broader political and societal movements. Regardless of the variations, the definition of mental retardation has had importance beyond the scientific community as throughout much of its recent history, the definition has had a direct impact on eligibility for services from government agencies.

The earliest definitions of mental retardation focused mainly on intellectual functioning exclusively, with the use of IQ tests serving as the main diagnostic criterion. In the 1920s, the AAMR introduced a classification scheme that categorized individuals according to the severity of their impairments, dividing the IQ ranges by 25 point ranges, with the cut-off IQ score for mental retardation designated at 75. With the introduction of the first edition of the Diagnostic and Statistical Manual in the 1950s, the term mental deficiency was introduced by the American Psychiatric Association (APA), with severity of impairment denoted by the terms mild deficiency (IQ range 70–85), moderate deficiency (IQ range 50–69), and severe deficiency (IQ of 49 and below). In one of the many controversial turns in the definition's history, this competing definition put forth by the APA designated the cut-off for mental deficiency at 10 IQ points higher than the earlier AAMR definition. This is the first of several differences between the APA and AAMR definitions to come in the latter part of the twentieth century. While these early definitions focused exclusively on intellectual functioning and IQ scores, during the first half of the twentieth century various opinions were expressed that IQ-only definitions were insufficient to characterize the true nature of mental retardation. By the 1930s and 1940s, the discussion of the definition of mental retardation widened to include competence in one's own environment. This led to an updated AAMR definition in the 1960s, that

included impairments in a construct titled 'adaptive behavior', in addition to subaverage intellectual functioning that originates in the developmental period. This 1960s definition also raised the IQ score cut-off to 85, in line with the APA definition at the time, and established five categories of severity of impairment: borderline, mild, moderate, severe, and profound mental retardation.

Those who have analyzed the history of the definition of mental retardation often note that this change mirrored the 1960s movement to be more inclusive in providing services to individuals in need. However, it is also noted that changes in the IQ cut-off raised the number of individuals who met at least the borderline definition of mental retardation to 16% of the general population, with concerns raised that there was an over-representation of minorities included in this range.

In addition, the introduction of the adaptive-behavior aspect of the definition proved controversial, with difficulties relating to reliability of assessments of this dimension, and the practicality of its use in actual diagnostic situations. The 1970s definition of mental retardation put forth by the AAMR made some minor changes in wording, specifying that subaverage general intellectual functioning must be 'significant', and that it must 'exist concurrently' with adaptive-behavior deficits. But one change had a strong impact, as the IQ cut-off was lowered to 70, lowering the percentage of individuals meeting the criteria to roughly 2% of the general population. Minor wording changes were also made to the AAMR definition in the 1980s, with specifications that the onset of mental retardation should occur before the age of 18, rather than the more general wording regarding manifestation during the developmental period as mentioned earlier. Perhaps the most controversial changes to the AAMR definition of mental retardation were introduced in the 1990s. Substantial changes were made to the AAMR definition of mental retardation, with specification that an individual must show impairment in two of 10 specific adaptive behavior skill areas. In addition, another major change related to the categorization scheme, that shifted from an IQ-based 'severity of impairment' approach to categorization of 'intensities of needed supports' (intermittent, limited, extensive, and pervasive), though the use of this system was challenged by the lack of readily available instruments for measuring these levels of need. Finally, this definition imprecisely identified the IQ cut-off as '70 to 75 or below', leaving the range of individuals meeting the criteria ranging from 2% to 5% of the general population. These changes proved to be so controversial that many organizations and agencies rejected the categorization scheme, and some voiced the need to develop their own definition for mental retardation. Others, like the APA, opted to adopt the new categorization scheme, but maintained clarity regarding an IQ cut-off with their prior designation of 70 (rather than 70–75). The 2002 definition of mental retardation, however, has reverted back to a severity of impairment categorization scheme and more general notions of adaptive behavior.

Adaptive Behavior

The term adaptive behavior refers to the ability of an individual to perform behaviors that evidence age-appropriate and culturally appropriate levels of personal independence and social responsibility. The inclusion of the adaptive behavior construct in the formal definition of mental retardation in the latter half of the twentieth century reflected awareness that intellectual functioning was not the sole predictor of one's ability to function in society. In addition, the inclusion of this construct was meant to encourage clinicians and educators to focus on remediation of disabilities, rather than simply categorizing children according to specific groups.

Adaptive behavior assessment became an important means of identifying behaviors that facilitated deinstitutionalization in the 1960s and brought about an increased awareness of the need for rehabilitation for individuals with disabilities in their communities. With the shift in focus from treatment and service delivery in the 1960s to normalization and legal rights in the 1970s, legislation was passed in some states that designated adaptive behavior assessment as a crucial measure of functioning. This reflected a concern that without adaptive behavior assessment and consideration of performance outside of academic contexts, there would be an over-representation of minorities in special education settings. By the 1980s, adaptive behavior assessment was seen as foundational for developing instructional approaches that would prepare individuals for living in their communities. The 1980s also brought about increased research attention into the construct of adaptive behavior in individuals with intellectual disability, leading to some specific criticism of the construct from researchers' perspectives. Some researchers argued that problematic aspects of the adaptive behavior construct – including lack of cohesive factor structure, lack of consensus regarding the best method for assessment, differing opinions regarding the relationship between intelligence and adaptive functioning – limited its utility.

Over the last few decades, the notion of adaptive behavior shifted from a broad concept to a more specific delineation of competence in specific areas. In the 1992 definition of mental retardation, adaptive behavior was redefined as adaptive skills comprising the following areas: communication, self-care, home living, social skills, community use, self-direction, health and safety, functional academics, leisure, and work. While these skill areas were thought to be related to the need for supports, and thus improved the characterization of individuals with mental retardation, these changes did not silent the debate regarding the utility of the adaptive behavior construct. Among

the main criticisms of the construct was the argument that, practically speaking, most clinicians did not use the construct when making a diagnosis. The 2002 definition of mental retardation has reverted back to the term adaptive behavior (instead delineating adaptive skill areas), with a renewed focus on adaptation in conceptual, social, and practical areas; however, the debate over the use of the construct in clinical and educational settings continues.

Two-Group Approach

Amidst these definitional issues, an additional view for categorizing individuals with mental retardation became prominent in the latter half of the twentieth century. This new categorization approach arose when researchers began to note that there are more cases of children with IQ scores lower than 50 than would be expected, based on a normal statistical distribution. Various theorists began to speculate that there were various pathways leading to mental retardation, culminating in Edward Zigler's argument that there are two distinct groups of individuals with mental retardation. The first pathway is through the interaction between inherited and environmental factors, leading to a designation of familial or cultural mental retardation. The second pathway is through a biological insult that could happen on the genetic, neurodevelopmental, or pre/perinatal level, leading to a designation of organic mental retardation. Zigler argued that the distinction between familial and organic mental retardation is so important that it should be included alongside intellectual functioning for the classification of individuals with mental retardation. Included in this scheme was also a group of individuals with 'undifferentiated' mental retardation, for whom a reliable assignment to a group was not possible. This undifferentiated group has historically received very little research attention, and thus, Zigler's approach has been called the 'two-group' approach for its primary distinction between mental retardation due to organic versus nonorganic causes.

Within this two-group approach to categorization, additional designations were made by Zigler and his colleagues. Within the familial group, they included children who had at least one parent with mental retardation; isolated cases of children who had parents of normal intelligence and from appropriate home environment, but inherited low intelligence; and children who experienced sociocultural deprivation. Within the organic group, Zigler included children with chromosomal disorders, metabolic disorders, neurological impairments, congenital birth defects, and perinatal complications. He theorized that children in the familial mental retardation group would show 'similar sequences' of development, and thus would pass through the stages of typical development in the same sequence as typically developing children, albeit at a slower pace. He also argued that children in the familial mental retardation group would show 'similar structures' of development, thus showing the same organization of developmental constructs as typically developing children. It is important to note that Zigler did not argue that the similar sequence and similar structure hypotheses would apply to children in the organic mental retardation group. Subsequent researchers argued for a more 'liberal' application of Zigler's developmental theories, suggesting that children with organic etiologies of mental retardation, such as Down syndrome, may conform to the similar sequence and similar structure hypotheses as well.

Etiology-Specific Approach

As an extension of Zigler's two-group approach to classifying individuals with mental retardation, Robert Hodapp, Jake Burack, and other researchers in the developmental approach argued that greater differentiation was needed within the organic mental retardation group. Specifically, they argued that it would advance both science and practice in mental retardation to distinguish among children with different organic syndromes, particularly among children with different genetic disorders. There are currently over 1000 known genetic disorders associated with intellectual disability that have been identified to date. Research on a small subset of these disorders suggests that there are identifiable patterns of outcome associated with these disorders, which may inform both the basic science of gene–brain–behavior pathways, as well as the delivery of educational and intervention services for individuals with intellectual disability.

In the past few decades, many research endeavors have been aimed at characterizing behavioral phenotypes, or the various patterns of behavioral outcomes associated with specific genetic disorders. Though there have been debates over what constitutes a behavioral phenotype, especially with respect to the issues of specificity and pervasiveness of specific symptoms, there is some emerging consensus regarding a middle ground. Elisabeth Dykens' definition of a behavioral phenotype includes the probabilistic notion that children with a given genetic disorder may have a heightened probability of showing a specific outcome or set of outcomes relative to children without the syndrome. Implicit in her definition is the notion that not every child with a specific genetic disorder will show the phenotypic outcomes associated with the disorder, and that an outcome need not be totally unique to a specific group.

In further discussion on the uniqueness of the effects of genetic disorders, Robert Hodapp has noted that some outcomes are partially specific, or shared characteristics among a handful of disorders, and some characteristics are totally specific, or unique to a specific syndrome. Amidst these debates, research on behavioral phenotypes has become increasingly advanced in recent years, involving

the use of more sophisticated developmental protocols, brain-imaging techniques, and genetic sequencing. These studies have made it possible to characterize the impact of genetic disorders such as Down syndrome, fragile X syndrome, Williams syndrome, Prader–Willi syndrome, Smith–Magenis syndrome, and 5p-syndrome on development in the areas of cognition, language, social and emotional functioning, motoric functioning, and outcomes related to psychopathology.

Dual Diagnosis

While the term 'intellectual disability' has referred to individuals with cognitive impairments and difficulties with day-to-day adaptation, individuals with intellectual disability are often at risk for showing other behavior problems beyond those captured in this definition. As a result, many individuals have been dually diagnosed with both intellectual disability and other co-morbid conditions, such as psychiatric disorders. The reported prevalence of individuals with dual diagnoses varies from study to study, with some reports as high as 40–50% of children with intellectual disability in middle childhood showing some degree of psychiatric symptomatology.

In addition, children with specific causes of their intellectual disabilities may be vulnerable to some psychiatric conditions, but not others. For example, individuals with Prader–Willi syndrome show increased rates of obsessive-compulsive behavior, including hoarding behavior, as well as well-documented obsessive food ideation symptoms. Children with Williams syndrome are at increased risk of showing difficulties in the area of anxiety and heightened fear responses. While children with Down syndrome tend to show lower levels of psychopathology than other children with intellectual disability, there is evidence to suggest that these individuals are at increased risk for autism and autism spectrum disorders, relative to the prevalence rates observed in the typically developing population.

Diagnosis of a comorbid psychiatric condition along with intellectual disability may pose many challenges to clinicians and therapists. Researchers in this area have noted that many clinicians are prone to attribute the behavior problems associated with psychiatric conditions to the diagnosis that a child already has, leading to the phenomenon called diagnostic overshadowing. In other words, the diagnosis that a child already has – for example, Down syndrome – becomes the explanation for poor communication and impairments in social interaction, rather than exploring the alternative possibility that the child might meet criteria for autism as well. This is notable in that impairments in social interaction are unusual in most children with Down syndrome, who tend to show competence in achieving early intersubjective milestones in infancy and toddlerhood. Thus, understanding the relative contributions of the intellectual disability and a possible comorbid disorder may make it possible to improve the precision with which decisions are made regarding appropriate services and intervention strategies.

Yet, making dual diagnoses of this nature can be challenging for a number of reasons. First, the manifestation of a psychiatric disorder may be modified in an individual with intellectual disability. For example, an anxiety disorder may manifest itself differently in a child who has pronounced expressive language delays versus a child who has an age-appropriate ability to express his/herself. In addition, when a child has pronounced intellectual disability that are in the severe or profound IQ score range, additional difficulties present themselves with regard to accurate dual diagnosis. If a low-functioning child with Down syndrome shows many of the behavioral hallmarks of autism, including poor joint attentions skills, poor initiation, language delays, or a lack of pretend play, it is possible that the child simply has not yet reached an overall developmental level wherein a clinician would expect to observe those behaviors. As a result, an autism diagnosis may not be appropriate in this situation, especially if these deficits are observed in the context of some other, more basic behaviors that evidence impairment in social interaction (e.g., sharing enjoyment or interest).

Identification, Intervention, and Education

Identifying Young Children with Intellectual Disability

Evaluation of young children during the first 2 years of life involves identifying children who already show pronounced developmental delays, as well as identifying children who are at high risk of showing later developmental delays. Newborn assessment begins in the earliest moments of life with Apgar scoring. Lower Apgar scores indicate an increased risk of neurological impairment, and newborns with low scores generally require close observation during the first weeks of life. Additional screening during the first few months of life includes assessment of reflexes and screening for genetic abnormalities via blood testing, if needed.

The pathways into the referral process vary internationally. For example, in Spain and many other countries, children are monitored by pediatricians or pediatric nurses, who use protocols that detect warning signs for developmental delays during regular visits. The Israeli early intervention system stresses both the importance of parent-initiated referrals, as well as referrals through the public well-baby care centers that are found throughout the country. In addition, infants determined to be at greater risk because of low birth weight or other factors, are referred to a child development center for closer

monitoring. In Sweden, referrals can come from parents or Child Health Services, but often children who do not have established disabilities are referred by preschool professionals because of the general system of preschool services provided to all children in that country.

Though systems for identifying children with or at risk for intellectual disability vary greatly internationally, there are some features that are commonly found. In general, the first line in detecting developmental delays involves those professionals who have the greatest interaction with infants, including pediatricians and other healthcare workers. If delays are suspected, additional professionals are recruited into the clinical team, including developmental specialists, social workers, and other interventionists. Subsequent to the newborn-screening process, additional evaluation of development can take place throughout infancy, with measures such as the Bayley Scales of Infant Development and the Mullen Scales of Early Learning.

Specific assessment of the development of areas such as language, social–emotional functioning, and adaptive behavior can also be conducted with standardized measures that have become the norm for typically developing infants and other infants with delays. Because of their psychometric properties, in the US, commonly used measures in infancy include the Preschool Language Scales IV, the Reynell Developmental Language Scales, the Battelle Developmental Inventory, the Brazelton's Neonatal Behavioral Assessment Scale, and the MacArthur Communication Development Inventories (Infant and Toddler form). For preschool-aged children, assessment of various aspects of development continues. To assess cognitive development, commonly used measures include the Wechsler Preschool and Primary Scale of Intelligence – Revised and the Stanford Binet. Language assessment is often assessed using the *Peabody Picture Vocabulary Test* (3rd edn.) and the *Preschool Language Scales* (4th edn.). Social and adaptive behavior development is often measured using the Vineland Adaptive Behavior Scales and the AAMR Adaptive Behavior Scales.

In general, children with lower IQ scores tend to be identified earlier in development than children with more mild impairments. Thus, the prevalence of children with IQ scores below 50 or so remains somewhat steady throughout development. In contrast, children with milder intellectual disability tend to be identified later in development, often upon beginning formal schooling. As a result, the prevalence of children with mental retardation tends to increase for children once they reach school years.

Early Intervention

Beyond identification of intellectual disability in young children, a primary goal of early assessment is to enable children with identified intellectual disability to receive appropriate early intervention services. Early intervention is a comprehensive set of services that are provided to children from birth through the early childhood years (generally lasting through to ages 3–6 years, depending on the country) and their families to enhance a child's developmental potential. The family-focused approach to early intervention is found in many different countries, including the US, Austria, Canada, the UK, Israel, Spain, and Sweden, among others. The structure and implementation of early intervention services internationally varies greatly. In this section, we explore the model implemented in the US, though references for additional information are given ahead about early intervention in other countries.

In the US, federal law Individuals with Disabilities Education Act (IDEA), with the 1997 Amendment (Public Law 105–17), specifies that children under the age of three years are eligible for early-intervention services should they show delays in one or more areas of development or if they have a diagnosis of a condition that is generally associated with developmental delays. Named 'Part C', early-intervention services include a few over-riding principles: families are at the center of the early-intervention process; and services should be provided to young children within natural contexts (typically the child's home). A service coordinator is assigned to each child to act as the family's main point of contact for the provision of these services. In many cases, early intervention involves a teacher (or an early-intervention specialist), various therapists, the family, and the child, working together to minimize the effects of the child's disability on his or her development. Specialists in the area of family training, counseling, respite care, home visits, physical therapy, occupational therapy, speech-language therapy, audiological services, and many other areas may be included in this team according to each individual child's and family's needs.

In the US early intervention involves the development of an individual family service plan (IFSP), which is created by a team in order to identify both short- and long-term goals and strategies for early intervention. The IFSP contains information about the services necessary to facilitate a child's development and enhance the family's capacity to facilitate the child's development. Through the IFSP process, family members and service providers work as a team to plan, implement, and evaluate services tailored to the family's unique concerns, priorities, and resources. According to IDEA, included in the IFSP are the following elements: (1) Current level of functioning – this section includes a detailed description of the child's present levels of development in all areas (cognitive, communication, social or emotional, and adaptive development). (2) Resources – this area outlines the family's resources and concerns relating to enhancing the development of their child. (3) Desired goals and outcomes – this section lists the major outcomes to be achieved for the child and the family. It includes the criteria, procedures,

and timelines used to determine progress; and whether modifications or revisions of the outcomes or services are necessary. (4) Access to early intervention services – specific early-intervention services are identified that are necessary to meet the unique needs of the child and the family. This section also indicates the frequency, intensity, and the method of delivery for recommended services. (5) Integration into environments with typically developing peers – this section describes the natural environments in which services will be provided, including reasoning as to the extent, if any, to which the services will not be provided in a natural environment. (6) Timeline – the timeline documents the projected starting and ending dates for delivery of services. (7) Identification of service provider – this section, unique to the IFSP, identifies the specific service provider who will be responsible for implementing the plan and coordinating with other agencies and persons. (8) Plans for transition into the formal educational environment – this final section identifies the steps to support the child's transition to preschool or other appropriate services upon reaching the age of three.

Special Education

Special education services refer to specially designed educational instruction, including supplementary aids and related services, that allow a child with a disability to benefit meaningfully from his or her educational program. These strategies include both instructional accommodations and developmentally designed learning environments inside the classroom and outside intervention programs with specialists. The changes in attitudes toward educating children with intellectual disability are reflected in the twentieth century history of disability law in the US. Prior to the passage of IDEA, in the US, the standards for educating children with disabilities varied tremendously among states. When it was first enacted in 1975, IDEA introduced the notion of guaranteed 'free, appropriate public education' to children with disabilities and mandated that, to the 'maximum extent appropriate', they be educated with their non-disabled peers in the 'least restrictive environment'. In addition to creating standards for the education of children with intellectual disability and other conditions, IDEA brought into the public schools slightly more than 1 million children with disabilities who had previously received only limited educational services.

Beyond guaranteeing children an education that was free and appropriate, an important shift in education for children with intellectual disability in the US came in the stipulation that children should be educated in the 'least restrictive environment'. Prior to this landmark legislation, children with disabilities who were permitted into public schooling environments were often assigned to self-contained classrooms. The implementation of IDEA in educational settings was not without controversy. Teachers and administrators cited issues related to a lack of preparation and training to accommodate the needs of children with developmental delays, and parents of typically developing children expressed concerns over the issues of equity and access to quality. In particular, some parents were concerned that the quality of the education that their child would receive might be in some way compromised by the presence of a child with intellectual disability in the classroom.

The concept of full inclusion calls for teaching students with disabilities in regular classrooms, rather than in special classes or pull-out sessions, and is now adopted in many countries, including the UK and Australia. In the US, federal special education law states that, to the 'maximum extent appropriate', children with disabilities should be educated with nondisabled peers in the 'least restrictive environment possible'. While inclusion has grown more common, most severely disabled students are still typically included in regular education classes for only a few subjects a day, such as art or physical education. The inclusion of children with disabilities in the general education classroom and access to a developmentally appropriate curriculum has improved in recent years with increased training for teachers in all classrooms and a better understanding of intervention strategies and assessments.

Individualized Education Plan

Education planning for older children with intellectual disability

From age 3 to 21 years, children with intellectual disability in the US may qualify for special education services through the public educational system. Criteria state that the child must have a disability that interferes with their ability to benefit from a regular educational program. Within an educational environment, specialists, educators, and parents work together to identify common goals and strategies to assist the child with developmental disabilities in achieving critical developmental milestones. Once a child reaches the age of 3, they no longer receive an IFSP through Part C services. Rather, children over the age of three are given an individualized education plan (IEP) to guide their development and learning both in and out of the classroom. Each child's IEP describes, among other things, the educational program that has been designed to meet that child's unique needs. It is created in collaboration and reviewed at least once per year, possibly more often, if requested by a parent or teacher.

The IEP includes pertinent information outlining the needs, goals, strategies, and methods of assessment that will guide instruction and intervention strategies. Included in the IEP are the following elements: (1) Current performance – the IEP must describe the child's current performance (known as present levels of educational performance). The statement about current performance includes how the child's disability affects his or her involvement and progress in the general curriculum. (2) Annual goals – these are goals that the child can reasonably accomplish in 1 year. Goals are broken down into short-term objectives or benchmarks. Goals may be academic, address social or behavioral needs, relate to physical needs, or address other educational needs. The goals must be measurable; it must be possible to quantify whether or not the student has achieved the goals. (3) Special education and related services – this section outlines the particular intervention strategies and how they will be implemented during the child's time at school. (4) Participation with nondisabled children – addresses the amount of time spent in a classroom with typically developing peers and the amount of time in pull-out intervention programs. (5) Dates and places – the IEP must state when services will begin, how often they will be provided, where they will be provided, and how long they will last. (6) Measuring progress – the IEP must state how the child's progress will be measured and how parents will be informed of that progress.

The IEP differs from the IFSP in several ways. First, the IFSP revolves around the family, as opposed to the educational environment where older children spend the majority of their day. The IFSP includes outcomes targeted for the family, while the IEP focuses primarily on the eligible child. The IFSP includes the notion of natural environments that encompass home or community settings such as parks, childcare, and gym classes. This community-oriented focus allows for learning interventions in everyday routines and activities, rather than limiting the implementation to formal educational settings. Finally, it names a service coordinator who will assist the family during the development, implementation, and evaluation of the plan.

Etiology and Education Planning

With a new wealth of knowledge regarding the impact of specific genetic syndromes on behavioral outcomes, there is a growing awareness that this information might be used to inform intervention and educational planning for children with intellectual disability. Given that children with different genetic disorders can be predisposed to very different profiles of strength and weakness in areas such as cognition, language, social–emotional functioning, and other important areas of development, it may be possible to incorporate these profiles into the educational planning process for children with different disorders. This approach can be incorporated into educational programming for children in primary and elementary education settings, as well as early intervention programs for infants, toddlers, and preschool-aged children.

In terms of instruction in educational settings, it has been recommended that aspects of a child's syndrome-specific predispositions be used to modify the presentation of materials and to inform the selection of instructional techniques. For example, children with Williams syndrome are predisposed to deficits in various aspects of visuospatial processing, but they show relative strengths in the area of verbal processing. Children with Down syndrome show the opposite profile, evidencing pronounced deficits in verbal processing and strengths in visual processing. Thus, in coordinating instructional techniques for a child with Down syndrome and a child with Williams syndrome – even if they show similar overall severity of impairment – it would be advantageous to take into account these diverging profiles with subtle modifications. A simple example might be to support verbal instruction with visual scaffolds for a child with Down syndrome, and to support visually based instruction with verbal scaffolds for a child with Williams syndrome. A teacher who is informed regarding these information-processing profiles might make such decisions seamlessly, without needing to disrupt his/her instruction in a larger class setting, with great impact. Other etiology-linked aspects of learning may be taken into account in this type of instructional modification, including executive function, simultaneous/sequential processing, and motivation.

In terms of early-intervention planning, it may be possible to use information regarding etiology-specific predispositions to identify potential areas of vulnerability during the earliest stages of development. Interventionists may take into account, for example, that the majority of middle childhood-aged children with Down syndrome show strengths in receptive language and pronounced delays in expressive language. When treating a toddler with Down syndrome, rather than waiting for a distinct split between receptive and expressive language to emerge in order to begin to address the issue with intervention, an interventionist could use knowledge about this predisposition to target a potential split from very early stages of development. They may choose to monitor early precursors of expressive language to identify an evidence of a disrupted pathway, and make effective intervention-planning decisions from the beginning. Thus, using an etiology-specific approach it may be possible to monitor areas of later strength and weakness from the earliest stages of development in order to detect and target subtle manifestations of a later, more pronounced, profile.

Critics argue that such an approach might not be cost-effective in that not all children with a given syndrome show a given outcome. In addition, there are concerns regarding defining groups too narrowly in the educational system such that it becomes both costly and cumbersome to address the needs of each identified group. These issues will doubtlessly be explored in debates regarding special education policy in upcoming years. Yet, as scientific research in the area of behavioral phenotypes continues to become more sophisticated, it may be inevitable that families and educators work together to connect phenotypic learning profiles in various syndromes with educational pedagogy.

Families of Children with Intellectual Disability

Though a great deal of attention was placed on the definition of mental retardation during the first half of the twentieth century, little attention was placed on families of individuals with mental retardation. In the 1960s, however, families became a focus of research attention as a greater emphasis was placed on improving child outcomes. It was theorized that families can have a direct influence on a child's achievement and their adaptation to their environment, and targeting home environments might be an important way to improve outcomes for children with mental retardation.

The main focus of initial research on families of children with mental retardation was on negative outcomes in the family, with an emphasis on issues such as social isolation, divorce, sibling identity, and parental depression. Case reports focused largely on parental experiences of mourning and the responses of parents to the loss of the 'ideal' typically developing child they had expected. More current research continues to focus on negative outcomes to some degree, though the focus of such work has been updated to include issues such as work–family balance and quality of the spousal relationship. In addition, more recent work has focused on the notion of stress in families of children with intellectual disability, where such a child is viewed as one stressor in the larger family environment. The notion of stress in this line of research refers to a perceived disparity between the situational demands and one's ability to respond to them. Thus, in families of children with intellectual disability, stress may result from a mismatch between the demands of caring for a child with cognitive impairments and the resources available to the family to address those needs.

Recent research on outcomes in families of children with intellectual disability has also begun to focus on positive aspects of the parenting experience, such as feelings of satisfaction and enjoyment. Parents in these studies have reported feelings of reward in watching their child make small achievements, enjoying the various aspects of everyday life, enjoying when demands were decreased, or the child's prognosis was good. Other positive outcomes in research on families of children with intellectual disability are parents reporting that their child with intellectual disability may provide challenges but also makes them feel needed, and even provides a sense of purpose in life. Research on families of children with intellectual disability has also focused on coping style and family supports. Factors impacting parental coping involve demographic factors such as Socioeconomic status, and also cognitive factors such as being problem-focused versus emotion-focused. Social support networks can influence outcomes like maternal stress and family adjustment, though some characteristics of support networks, such as increased density (many members of the support network are known to one another), may be less helpful than others.

Specific child characteristics may also have an impact on family outcomes as well. Some studies show that the child's age is positively correlated with family stress. These findings may support a 'wear-and-tear hypothesis', where the stress associated with parenting a child with a disability builds up over time. Other studies do not show this positive association between child age and stress, and some suggest that there is a lack of linearity in the relationship between the two. A nonlinear model of stress in families of children with intellectual disability suggests that specific periods in the child's development may increase a family's vulnerability to stress, while other periods of time may place families at lower risk for stress. For example, certain age milestones throughout development may lead parents to make normative comparisons to typically developing children, leading to 'wistful' thoughts about what their child may have been experiencing if they did not have intellectual disability.

Another child characteristic that has been shown to impact family outcomes is maladaptive behavior. Problem-behavior, associated with outcomes such as parental depression, pessimism, time demands, dependency and management, lifespan care, and maladaptive behavior, is a stronger predictor of parenting stress than some other possible factors, such as severity of cognitive impairment. Family outcomes may also be influenced by the specific etiology of the child's intellectual disability. It has been hypothesized that genetic disorders predispose children to specific outcomes, and that these outcomes may indirectly affect family stress, coping, and other outcomes. Robert Hodapp termed this phenomenon the indirect effects of genetic syndromes associated with intellectual disability, and has shown that different genetic disorders indirectly affect families in various ways. For example, families of children with Down syndrome report lower levels of overall family stress than families of children with other genetic disorders, such as Williams syndrome, and Smith–Magenis syndrome. These findings have been replicated in several studies, and possible reasons for the disparity may be related to child-personality characteristics, lower levels of maladaptive behavior, perceived immaturity, and parent-demographic characteristics.

Summary

In the past century, important advances have been made in both science and practice in intellectual disability. The needs of children with intellectual disability and their families have moved to the center of education service delivery in many countries, and early-intervention practices have become standard in many countries for children who are at risk or identified as having intellectual and developmental disabilities. However, the historical struggle to define and treat intellectual disability in the most humane and appropriate ways will likely continue into the next century. As attitudes continue to shift, it is likely that the political, economic, and social environments will continue to intersect and influence the ways in which children with intellectual disability are identified and educated.

See also: Autism Spectrum Disorders; Bayley Scales of Infant Development; Down Syndrome; Genetic Disorders: Sex Linked; Genetic Disorders: Single Gene; Genetics and Inheritance; Learning Disabilities; Mental Health, Infant; Special Education.

Suggested Readings

Borthwick-Duffy SA, Palmer DS, and Lane KL (1996) One size doesn't fit all: Full inclusion and individual differences. *Journal of Behavioral Education* 6: 311–329.

Dykens EM (1995) Measuring behavioral phenotypes: Provocations from the 'new genetics'. *American Journal on Mental Retardation* 99(5): 522–532.

Guralnick MJ (1997) Second-generation research in the field of early intervention. In: Guralnick MJ (ed.) *The Effectiveness of Early Intervention*, pp. 3–20. Baltimore, MD: Paul H. Brookes Publishing.

Guralnick MJ (2005) *The Developmental Systems Approach to Early Intervention*. Baltimore, MD: Paul H. Brookes Publishing.

Hodapp RM (1997) Direct and indirect behavioral effects of different genetic disorders of mental retardation. *American Journal on Mental Retardation* 102: 67–79.

Hodapp RM (2004) Behavioral phenotypes: Beyond the two group approach. *International Review of Research in Mental Retardation and Developmental Disabilities* 29: 1–30.

Hodapp RM and Fidler DJ (1999) Special education and genetics: Connections for the 21st century. *Journal of Special Education* 33: 130–137.

Lipsky DK and Gartner A (1998) Factors for successful inclusion: Learning from the past, looking toward the future. In: Vitello SJ and Mithaug DE (eds.) *Inclusive Schooling: National and International Perspectives*, pp. 98–112. Mahurah, NJ: Lawrence Erlbaum Associates.

MacMillan DL and Reschly DJ (1997) Issues of definition and classification. In: MacLean WE, Jr. (ed.) *Ellis' Handbook of Mental Deficiency, Psychological Theory and Research,* 3rd edn., pp. 47–74. Mahwah, NJ: Lawrence Erlbaum Associates.

Relevant Websites

http://www.aamr.org – AAIDD, The American Association on Intellectual and Developmental Disabilities.

http://www.assid.org.au – Australasian Society for the Study of Intellectual Disability.

http://www.dh.gov.uk – British Department of Health, Providing Health and Social Care Policy, Guidance and Publications.

http://www.iassid.org – International Association for the Scientific Study of Intellectual Disabilities.

http://www.mencap.org.uk – MENCAP, Understanding Learning Disability.

http://www.psych.org – The American Psychiatric Association.

http://www.thearc.org – The Arc.

http://www.cec.sped.org – The Council for Exceptional Children, The Voice and Vision of Special Education.

http://idea.ed.gov – U.S. Department of Education, Promoting Educational Excellence for all Americans.

Intermodal Perception

L E Bahrick, Florida International University, Miami, FL, USA

G Hollich, Purdue University, West Lafayette, IN, USA

Glossary

Amodal – Information that is not specific to a particular sense modality, but is perceivable and completely redundant across two or more senses. For example, rhythm and tempo are redundant across vision and audition.

Bimodal – Occurring in two sense modalities.

Increasing specificity – Progressive differentiation of finer levels of stimulation as a result of perceptual experience.

Intersensory – Across the senses; intermodal.

Intersensory redundancy – The co-occurrence of amodal information (e.g., rhythm, intensity changes) across two or more sense modalities; this information is highly salient to infants.

Invariant – A property or relation that remains constant across transformation.

Localization – Using auditory, visual, or tactile information to determine the location in space of a speaker or object.

Modality-specific – Information, such as color or timbre, that can be perceived through only one sense modality.

Multimodal – Information that can be experienced through multiple-sense modalities.

Perceptual narrowing – Progressive improvements in perceptual discrimination as a function of experience in a given domain and progressive decline in perceptual discrimination in related domains to which we are not exposed.

Proprioception – Information about self-movement based on feedback from the muscles, joints, and vestibular system.

Speech segmentation – Extracting words or other important units from the fluent stream of speech.

Temporal synchrony – Changes in events (e.g., from different senses) that occur at the same moment in time. For example, there is temporal synchrony between the movements of the lips and sounds of speech in natural audiovisual speech.

Introduction

Intermodal perception, the perception of unitary objects and events from concurrent stimulation to multiple senses, is fundamental to early development. Early sensitivity to temporal, spatial, and intensity patterns of events ('amodal' information) that are redundant across stimulation to different senses, guides infants' perceptual, cognitive, and social development. Intermodal perception develops rapidly across infancy. Even very young infants are sensitive to amodal information, allowing them to perceive unitary multimodal events by linking sights and sounds of speech, emotional expressions, and objects, as well as information across visual and tactile, olfactory, and proprioceptive stimulation. Perceptual development proceeds along a path of differentiation of increasingly more specific levels of stimulation and perceptual narrowing with experience.

Historical Conceptions of Intermodal Perception

The world provides a richly structured, continuously changing array of stimulation to all the senses. Our senses provide overlapping and redundant information for objects and events in the environment. Despite the fact that information about the world arrives through distinct sensory channels, we perceive a stable world of unitary objects and events rather than separate sights, sounds, and tactile impressions. How do we accomplish this?

Dating as far back as the time of Aristotle, philosophers and scientists have been intrigued and puzzled by the specificity of the different senses and the overlap among them. How do we experience objects and events as unitary when they stimulate different receptors and give rise to such different sensations? Aristotle postulated the *'sensus communis'* that allowed us to perceive the qualities of stimulation that were common across different senses ('common sensibles') such as rest, magnitude, number, form, and unity. These properties are remarkably similar to those that scientists today view as common across the senses ('amodal'), serving as the basis for perceiving unitary objects and events.

Centuries later, philosophers such as Locke and Berkeley promoted a different view of intermodal perception. They argued that we must learn to integrate and interpret sensations across separate sensory channels before meaningful perception of objects and events was possible. This 'constructivist' view provided the foundation for many modern theories of perception. According to this view, sensations from different receptors must be integrated and organized in the brain. This view, in turn, posed a 'binding' problem for perception in that mechanisms must be discovered that translate information from different sensory codes into a common language. The constructivist view dominated thinking about the development of perception through most of the twentieth century, including the views of Piaget, a pioneer in theories of cognitive development. According to Piaget, infants must learn to integrate and coordinate information across the senses through a gradual process of association across development. Integration was thought to occur through interacting with objects and experiencing concurrent stimulation from different senses and associating, assimilating, or calibrating the different senses to one another. From this perspective, not until after the first half year of life did infants begin to integrate touch and vision. Prior to this activity-based achievement, infants perceived a world of unrelated tactile impressions and visual images that would shrink and expand, appear and disappear capriciously. Infants were thought to experience a world described by William James in 1890 as a 'blooming, buzzing, confusion'.

Not until 1966 when J. J. Gibson published his seminal work on the 'ecological' view of perception, was the constructivist view seriously questioned. In a clear departure from traditional views, Gibson proposed that the existence of different forms of sensory stimulation was not a problem for perception. Rather, it provided an important basis for our ability to perceive coherent multimodal objects and events. He asserted that the sensory systems work in concert, as a unified perceptual system, to detect 'invariant' aspects of stimulation. A critical type of invariant for intermodal perception is 'amodal' information. Amodal information is information that is common across more than one sense, similar to the concept of the *sensus communis* formulated by Aristotle. Temporal and spatial aspects of stimulation are typically conveyed by multiple senses and are fundamental dimensions of amodal information. For example, the sights and sounds of hands clapping are temporally synchronous, share a common rate and rhythm, and occur across a common spatial location.

We now know from a large body of research on the development of intermodal perception generated since the 1970s that young infants detect a wide array of amodal properties of events across visual, acoustic, tactile, and proprioceptive stimulation. Inspired in large part by Gibson's ecological approach to perception, we have discovered that the ability to detect amodal information is a foundation for perceiving meaningful multimodal events in the first months of life. This ability provides a radical and efficient solution to the binding problem created by the constructivist views. That is, if infants detect amodal information in early development, then there is no need to integrate and coordinate separate sources of sensory information. Rather, by detecting information that is common to multiple senses, a naïve perceiver can explore unitary events in a coordinated manner, without binding.

In the next sections, we outline some terms and definitions relating to intermodal perception as well as discuss some key principles of intermodal development. We then describe what is known about the development of infants' sensitivity to audiovisual, visual-tactile, visual-motor stimulation, and other sensory combinations as well as how each of these types of information provides the basis for infants to learn about different aspects of the environment. We then discuss fetal and neural development and their relation to key principles of intermodal perception.

Key Terms and Definitions

What Is Intermodal Perception?

Intermodal perception (also called intersensory or multimodal perception) is the perception of unitary objects or events that make information simultaneously available to more than one sense. For example, a bouncing ball can be seen, heard, and touched. This information is typically spatially collocated and temporally coordinated. The sights, sounds, and tactile impressions come from the same location and share the same temporal pattern. Since most objects and events are experienced through multiple senses, most everyday perception is intermodal.

Amodal vs. Modality Specific Information

Objects and events make two different types of information available, amodal and modality-specific. Amodal information is information that is not specific to a particular sense modality, but can be conveyed through more than one sense. It is information that is completely redundant across different senses. For example, the rhythm and tempo of a bouncing ball can be detected visually or acoustically. Amodal information can be characterized along three primary dimensions: time, space, and intensity. Since all events occur over time and space and have a characteristic intensity pattern, all events provide amodal information.

Sensitivity to amodal information is fundamental for the development of event perception. In early infancy, amodal information unites stimulation across the senses. For example, perceiving temporal synchrony, common rhythm, tempo, or intensity patterns between the sights and sounds of the bouncing ball allows the infant to experience a unified, multimodal event without intermodal knowledge to guide this process.

Where does our sensitivity to amodal information such as synchrony come from? It is an outcome of neural development and the responsiveness of the nervous system to co-occurring patterns of stimulation. 'Coincidence detection' is a basic property of the nervous system. Stimulation that occurs together elicits heightened neural responsiveness and attention. This, in turn, creates stronger neural pathways between co-occurring patterns of stimulation. (For further details, see section titled 'Neural bases of intermodal perception'.) Thus, sensitivity to amodal stimulation such as synchrony is a developmental outcome of neural plasticity in a multimodal world rich with stimulation that co-occurs across two or more senses. This plasticity is particularly evident in prenatal development but also persists to some extent throughout the lifespan.

In contrast to amodal information, all events also provide modality-specific information. Modality-specific information is information that can be perceived only through a particular sense modality. For example, color and pattern can be perceived only visually, timbre only acoustically, and temperature only through touch. Perception of modality-specific information allows us to differentiate between a blue and a red ball or between the faces or voices of two different individuals.

Intersensory Redundancy

When the same amodal information (such as rhythm, tempo, or intensity patterns) is simultaneously available through different senses, this is called 'intersensory redundancy'. In audiovisual stimulation, intersensory redundancy entails synchronous, collocated sights and sounds, as in the natural stimulation from a bouncing ball or clapping hands. Intersensory redundancy is highly salient to infants, both human and animal. This redundancy can capture and direct attentional selectivity at the expense of other information. For example, in exploring an event, a young infant might notice the redundant aspects such as its rhythm and tempo, but not the appearance of the object or the specific nature of its sounds. This redundancy is so salient that young infants

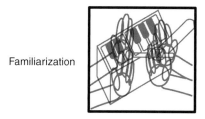

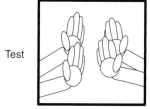

Figure 1   Superimposed movies presented to 4-month-old infants. During familiarization, when the soundtrack to one event was turned on, creating intersensory redundancy, infants were able to selectively follow one event and ignore the other. During the test trials, infants then watched the 'novel' unattended event. From Bahrick LE, Walker AS, and Neisser U (1981) Selective looking by infants. *Cognitive Psychology* 13: 377–390.

can use it to select one of two superimposed movies while ignoring the other. When the soundtrack to one event, such as a hand-clapping game, is turned on, young infants can selectively follow the flow of action, even when it is superimposed with another similar silent event such as a hand striking the keys of a xylophone (see **Figure 1**).

Thus, in early development we perceive both amodal and modality-specific information. Amodal information is typically more salient, particularly when it is detected redundantly across two or more senses, and plays an important role in guiding perceptual development. The nature of its role in perceptual development is described in more detail in the section ahead.

Key Principles of Intermodal Development

Sensitivity to Amodal, Redundant Information Guides Perceptual Development

Our senses provide us with a constantly changing flow of multimodal stimulation. How do we learn to select and attend to relevant stimulation and ignore the vast amount of stimulation that is irrelevant to our needs, goals, and actions? Moreover, how do infants, with no knowledge of the world, determine which sights, sounds, and tactile impressions belong together and constitute coherent events, and which are unrelated and should be ignored? With a limited attentional capacity we can selectively attend to only a small portion of the stimulation available, while the vast majority of concurrent stimulation remains in the background. How this process is guided and develops into economical patterns of attention and perception that are increasingly more in line with that of adult perceivers has puzzled scientists and philosophers for decades.

Perception of redundant, amodal information across the senses provides one answer to these questions. That our senses provide redundant information about objects and events is no excess of nature. Instead, this highly salient intersensory redundancy is fundamental for guiding the development of perception and cognition in infancy. It provides a reliable basis for focusing early selective attention on patterns of stimulation that belong together and constitute unitary events and for ignoring stimulation from unrelated events. For example, if infants focus on the redundancy between faces and voices during speech such as the synchrony, rhythm, tempo, and intensity changes common to the voice and movements of the face/lips, this ensures that infants attend to stimulation from unified events (a person speaking) and not to concurrent sounds or the movements of an unrelated person or object nearby. A large body of infant research (reviewed briefly in the section titled 'The development of audiovisual perception') has accrued since the 1970s and reveals that early perception is quite organized and there is no evidence that infants experience the blooming, buzzing confusion postulated by William James more than 100 years ago. Sensitivity to redundancy across the senses thus promotes attention to unified events in the presence of competing sounds and motions. Once unitary events are differentiated from the flux of multimodal stimulation, the process of perception and learning can proceed in a meaningful way.

Increasing Specificity Characterizes Perceptual Development

Eleanor Gibson formulated the developmental account of James Gibson's ecological theory of perception in the 1960s. She argued that perceptual development is characterized by a process of progressive differentiation of finer and finer levels of stimulation. That is, across development, infants detect global, abstract levels of stimulation and progress to increasingly more specific information about objects and events. Thus, our early perception of events, such as a person walking, might begin with the general perception of a person walking, and progress to more detail regarding perhaps the gender and age of the person, how they walked, how they talked, and finally to their identity and specific appearance. This pattern, Gibson proposed, is a general characteristic of perceptual learning. Thus, it also characterizes child and adult learning in new domains, such as mastering a new language or developing expertise in new areas such as bird-identification or wine-tasting. This principle goes hand in hand with the early salience of amodal, redundant

information. Amodal information is considered abstract, and global, in the sense that it is not specific to one sense modality, but is common to several. It is therefore detected early in the process of perceptual differentiation, and thus can serve as a general framework for later perception of specific details, as illustrated in the research described in the section titled 'The development of audiovisual perception'.

Perceptual Narrowing with Experience

Perceptual narrowing is a process that occurs with the development of expertise in a domain. It consists of progressive improvements in perceptual discrimination in the domain to which we are exposed and progressive decline in perceptual discrimination in related domains to which we are not exposed. Perceptual narrowing has been known to characterize auditory perception of speech sounds since the later quarter of the twentieth century, but it was only in the first few years of 2000s that it was demonstrated for perception of visual and multimodal information.

In speech perception, it was found that infants younger than 6 months of age were able to discriminate phonemes (speech sounds) that occurred in a variety of languages, but by 10–12 months, they were no longer able to discriminate some phonemes that did not occur in their native language. Perception of native phonemes improved as a result of experience, but perception of nonnative phonemes declined as a result of lack of experience. Similarly, in the area of face perception, infants of 6 months were able to discriminate among a variety of different human faces and monkey faces; however, by 9 months, discrimination was limited to human faces. Intermodal perception of face–voice relations may also undergo perceptual narrowing. Infants of 4, 6, 8, and 10 months were shown pairs of monkey faces producing two different vocalizations, a coo and a grunt, along with a soundtrack synchronized with both but matching only one of them. Only the two youngest groups showed intersensory perception and looked at the face that matched the soundtrack. This suggests that intersensory tuning to face–voice relations is initially broad across the first year and it may narrow as infants acquire more experience with human faces than monkey faces.

Thus, it appears that perceptual narrowing, like increasing specificity, is a general process that characterizes the development of expertise across a variety of domains. Perceptual narrowing is economical because it allows perceivers to focus resources on aspects of stimulation that are relevant to their particular environment and ignore those that are irrelevant. It is similar to the notion of increasing specificity in that there are improvements in perceptual discrimination with experience consistent with differentiation of more specific detail. However, it is different in that we observe a compensatory decline in discrimination of related material to which the perceiver is not exposed. This process is consistent with recent advances in our understanding of neural development, discussed in more detail further. Research on perceptual narrowing provides some of the only examples of perceptual abilities possessed by infants that are superior to those of children and adults!

The Development of Audiovisual Perception

Connecting sight with sound is fundamental to a host of activities: from lip-reading and learning words to matching a face to a voice or locating the person who is calling your name in a crowded room. Discovering the connections between what one sees and what one hears is essential to making sense of our environment and vital to our survival.

Even in the first weeks of life, infants have developed a primitive coordination of audiovisual space. They turn their eyes toward the locus of a sound. This coordination is important, because there is typically visual information about an audible event in the direction of the sound. This ability ensures that infants will focus their eyes and ears in the same general location, ready to pick up intersensory redundancy, should any be available. Localization is imprecise at first but improves with age. Experience helps infants calibrate or align their auditory–visual spatial maps.

Infants appear to be quite skilled at detecting amodal, redundant information uniting visual and acoustic stimulation. For example, they can detect the temporal synchrony between sights and sounds of an object's impact, between faces and voices during speech, and between showing and naming an object. They are sensitive to more fine-grained amodal information in faces and voices for emotion and for the gender and age of a person. Infants perceive auditory and visual information for the changing position of an object moving through space, and the substance and composition of an object striking a surface. These remarkable capabilities and what we know about their development are discussed in more detail in the sections that follow.

In contrast to the large research focus on infants' detection of amodal information and its importance in linking information across the senses, fewer studies have focused on infants' detection of arbitrary relations across the senses and their ability to perceive modality-specific properties of stimulation. However, perception of objects and events relies on the development of both amodal and arbitrary audiovisual relations. In particular, the development of language and social perception rely to a greater extent on mastering knowledge of arbitrary relations. In order to relate objects with speech sounds, one must learn the arbitrary relation between the speech sound and the particular object to which it refers. Social perception, for example, requires that we learn to differentiate among individuals by discriminating among hundreds of different faces, and learn to relate the appearance of specific faces with specific voices.

Development of Object and Event Perception

Increasing specificity in event perception

Research has shown that infants' detection of amodal redundant information, such as temporal synchrony, typically precedes and provides a basis for learning arbitrary relations such as those between speech sounds and objects, between specific faces and voices, or objects and their particular impact sounds. Thus, research focusing on the development of object and event perception illustrates the principle of increasing specificity.

Temporal synchrony is thought to be the most global type of amodal information, serving as the glue that binds information across auditory and visual stimulation. Research shows that for events such as a bouncing ball, the temporal synchrony window for infants is approximately 350 ms and decreases with age, to approximately 80 ms for adults. This window may be larger for detecting synchrony between faces and voices. A more fine-grained level of temporal information called 'temporal microstructure' serves as the basis for perceiving the relation between the type of sound and the type of movement an object makes. For example, object substance (e.g., hard vs. soft) and composition (e.g., single vs. multiple components) are perceived by detecting temporal microstructure when the object contacts a surface. Research indicates that very young infants (3 weeks of age or younger) perceive the temporal synchrony (global information) between the movement of an object and the natural impact sounds it produces, and a few weeks later (by 6 weeks of age), they perceive the substance and composition (microstructure) of the same object. A few months later infants detect arbitrary, modality-specific relations such as the relation between the pitch of the impact sound and the color and shape of the object. This illustrates the principle of increasing specificity where detection of global amodal relations (synchrony) promotes detection of more specific, nested, amodal relations (temporal microstructure) and finally, further exploration promotes detection of arbitrary, modality-specific relations (pitch-color/shape).

In this manner, detection of amodal information can guide and constrain perceptual learning about increasingly more specific aspects of multimodal stimulation. Amodal relations such as temporal synchrony, common rhythm, and tempo provide a basis for selecting unitary sights and sounds. This promotes continued processing of the unified event and, in turn, differentiation of temporal microstructure and modality-specific properties such as color, pattern, pitch, and timbre. Detection of amodal information thus provides a natural avenue for connecting the correct sights and sounds and a buffer against connecting the wrong connections.

A training and transfer study with young infants illustrated this principle. Following training with films and soundtracks of objects striking a surface, 3-month-old infants were able to learn the correct sight-sound connections but unable to learn the incorrect sight-sound ones. Infants received training with films depicting a single, large marble and a cluster of small marbles striking a surface along with the natural soundtracks to each (see **Figure 2**). Training occurred under one of four conditions; the films were paired with the correct vs. the incorrect (mismatched) soundtracks and the films were presented either in synchrony or out of synchrony with the soundtracks. Results indicated that only infants who were trained with synchronized and correctly paired films and soundtracks learned to match the film with the soundtrack they had received during training.

Learning of sight-sound relations occurred only when both temporal synchrony and temporal microstructure specifying object composition were correct (e.g., single objects make single impact sounds and compound objects make compound impact sounds). Infants did not learn to relate objects with inappropriate impact sounds, even when their movements were synchronized with the sounds, at least following a single training session. This illustrates that detection of redundant, amodal information can serve as a gatekeeper, promoting processing of sights and sounds that belong together and buffering against processing of unrelated ones.

Intersensory redundancy promotes perceptual development

Recent research suggests that this remarkable early sensitivity to unitary events may be based on selective attention to redundancy across the senses. The 'intersensory redundancy hypothesis', a theory of selective attention, asserts that information that is redundant across the senses is highly salient, particularly to young organisms, and attracts attention to amodal, redundantly specified properties of stimulation. In other words, redundancy across the senses causes amodal information to become 'foreground' and other aspects of stimulation to become 'background'. In contrast, when stimulation is unimodal (visual or auditory only), attention is promoted to modality-specific aspects of stimulation such as color, pattern, pitch, or timbre. **Figure 3** illustrates the predictions of the intersensory redundancy hypothesis.

Research with young infants supports these predictions. Infants were shown a toy hammer tapping in a rhythmic pattern. Infants were able to detect a change in the rhythm and a change in the tempo of the hammer if they experienced the event bimodally (they could both see and hear the hammer tapping). However, they were unable to detect the change in rhythm or tempo if they experienced the event unimodally (they could either hear or see the hammer) or asynchronously (the movements of the hammer were out of synchrony with the sounds). It was not until a few months later, when attention became more flexible, that infants were able to perceive the change in rhythm and tempo in unimodal auditory or visual stimulation alone. A similar developmental pattern was found in a study of infant sensitivity to serial order information. When three distinctive objects, each with a distinctive sound, appeared in sequence, young infants

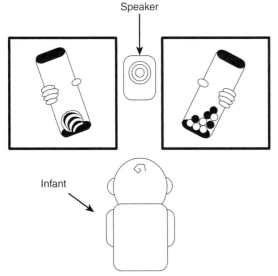

Figure 2 Illustration of the experimental set-up of videotaped events used. From Bahrick LE (1988) Intermodal learning in infancy: Learning on the basis of two kinds of invariant relations in audible and visible events. *Child Development* 59: 197–209.

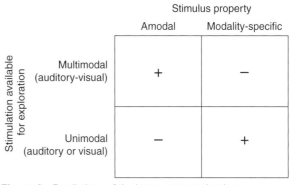

Figure 3 Predictions of the intersensory redundancy hypothesis: stimulus properties (amodal vs. modality-specific) and the type of stimulation available for exploration (multimodal vs. unimodal) together determine whether attention and perceptual processing of a stimulus property are facilitated (+) or inhibited (−). From Bahrick LE and Lickliter R (2002) Intersensory redundancy guides early perceptual and cognitive development. In: Kail R (ed.) *Advances in Child Development and Behavior*, vol. 30, p. 166. New York: Academic Press.

detected the order of their occurrence when they were seen and heard together, but not when they were seen or heard alone. Only older infants detected serial order information in unimodal visual or unimodal auditory stimulation. Thus, perception of amodal information such as rhythm, tempo, and serial order information initially develops in the context of multimodal stimulation, and later in development, perception is extended to unimodal stimulation. In contrast, perception of nonredundant information that is specific to a single sense modality (such as the pitch of a voice, the configuration of a face, the color or orientation of an object) develops first in unimodal stimulation and is later extended to multimodal stimulation. For example, 5-month-old infants who were shown a toy hammer tapping downward vs. upward were able to detect a change in the orientation of the hammer's motions only if they viewed the hammer tapping silently (unimodal) but not if they viewed it and could hear its synchronous sounds (bimodal). Later in development, by 8 months of age, infants were able to detect the change in orientation in both unimodal and bimodal stimulation. These findings suggest that domains that provide a great deal of multimodal, redundant stimulation such as social interaction, speech, live music, dance, or stimulation from the self, can highlight and promote earlier learning about salient amodal aspects of stimulation. In contrast, domains that involve exploration through only a single sense modality, such as viewing a silent object or event, listening to music or speech with no visual accompaniment, are more likely to promote learning about nonredundant, modality-specific aspects of stimulation. Further, these principles may also extend beyond infancy and apply to the learning of novel content for children and adults as well.

Even nonhuman animals show a remarkable advantage for the perception of amodal information when it is redundantly presented than when it is available in unimodal stimulation alone. Bobwhite quail embryos learned the temporal characteristics of a maternal call four times better and remembered it four times longer when the call was presented in synchrony with a flashing light as compared with no visual stimulation.

Social Development

The world of social interaction provides a great deal of multimodal information, making intermodal perception critically important for learning and functioning in this domain. Understanding emotion and communicative intent, relating the faces and voices of individuals, identifying who is speaking in a crowd, and sharing experience with another, all rely on connecting information across the senses.

At birth, infants look longer at faces accompanied by voices. Around 4–6 months (but not at 2 months) infants

learn to relate the specific face and voice of a novel individual on the basis of a few minutes of familiarization. At this same age, infants can also match unfamiliar faces and voices on the basis of age and gender of the speaker. They appear to know that males and adults have larger faces and features and deeper voices than females and children. By 3 months of age, infants can match facial and vocal expressions of emotion, such as happy, sad, and angry, in their mothers, and by 5–7 months, they can do so with unfamiliar adults too. Research has shown that perception of emotion, like perception of the rhythm and tempo of events, also emerges first in multimodal stimulation and is later extended to unimodal auditory and then to unimodal visual stimulation. One study showed that at 4 months of age, infants discriminated between happy, sad, and angry expressions in unfamiliar adults when they were seen and heard together; by 5 months they discriminated these expressions in vocal stimulation alone, and by 7 months they were able to distinguish the facial expressions alone.

Infants not only recognize the emotional expressions of others, but they use others' expressions as information about external events. This skill, called social referencing, involves discriminating an adult's emotional expression and connecting it to an ambiguous object or event, such as a novel toy or situation, and allowing the emotional expression of the adult to influence exploratory behavior toward the novel event. Social referencing also likely emerges first in a multimodal context, where the caregiver provides coordinated auditory and visual emotional information, and then is later extended to unimodal contexts. For example, a fearful facial and vocal expression might inhibit exploration at first, and later a visual expression alone might suffice.

Infants not only detect amodal information across the senses, but they participate in temporally coordinated, interactions with adults. In close face-to-face interaction, infants coordinate their movements and sounds with those of the adult in a burst-pause, turn-taking pattern. This 'protoconversation' involving sensitivity to the emotional dynamics and temporal characteristics of social interaction promotes emotional attunement and a sense of shared experience between the infant and caretaker. It provides an important foundation for social development and communication.

In contrast to perception of emotion, perception of individual faces and voices is promoted in unimodal visual and unimodal auditory stimulation, respectively. Recall that amodal, redundant information is more salient than modality-specific information, at least for unfamiliar events. Faces are discriminated primarily based on modality-specific information such as the appearance of individual features and their configuration and voices are primarily discriminated on the basis of pitch and timbre. Consistent with principles of the intersensory redundancy hypothesis, detection of this modality-specific information is selectively promoted in unimodal stimulation in early development (see **Figure 3**). Research has supported this view and shows that discrimination among faces of unfamiliar women emerges by the age of 2 months in unimodal visual stimulation following a single training session, but is not present in multimodal, audiovisual stimulation until somewhat later in development. Similarly, discrimination among voices of unfamiliar women emerges first in unimodal auditory stimulation and is later extended to bimodal, audiovisual speech.

Thus, young infants are already quite skilled at perceiving multimodal stimulation in social events. Detection of amodal properties of stimulation appears to develop first in redundant, multimodal stimulation, whereas detection of modality-specific properties such as that underlying recognition of specific faces and voices develops first in unimodal, nonredundant stimulation. It is not yet known to what extent these principles characterize adult perception, particularly when tasks are difficult or adults are learning new information.

Intermodal Development of Speech Perception and Language

Another important domain of audiovisual perception is language. Language, by its very nature relies on uniting visual with auditory stimulation: From localizing a particular speaker, to lip-reading and learning that sounds stand for particular objects, combining sights and sounds is fundamental to typical language acquisition. Language development can also be seen as a special case of social development; however, because of the large and varied research on this topic, and because of the important role of arbitrary relations between speech sounds and their referents, we include it as a separate topic.

Localizing speakers through audiovisual synchrony

We are often exposed to multiple sources of sound and motion when observing someone speaking. For example, a television may be heard in the background at the same time as the caregiver is speaking to the infant. Despite the potential perceptual processing difficulty for an infant, detecting audiovisual synchrony can assist in localizing the speaker. Infants' abilities to localize sound are poor when they have only auditory information. For example, 6-month-olds can only locate objects within about 19 degrees using auditory information alone. Although adults are more accurate, they also make extensive use of visual information in localizing talkers. This is illustrated by the 'ventriloquist effect'. By moving the dummy's mouth in synchrony with the ventriloquist's own speech sounds, a ventriloquist is able to fool observers into thinking the dummy is speaking. Infants especially rely on this visual information to localize a speaker and are

sensitive to the temporal synchrony between movements of the mouth and speech sounds. Thus, 10–16-week-old infants prefer to look at faces that are synchronized with speech sounds as opposed to faces that are out of synchrony with speech sounds.

Face–voice connection

Infants not only can find the person who is talking using audiovisual correspondence, but they also rapidly develop the ability to perceive faces and match faces to appropriate voices. Not only can they link faces and voices on the basis of gender, age, and identity, but infants also remember and predict the kinds of speech sounds that people are likely to make. They link the shape of a persons' mouth with the sounds that they produce. For example, 2-month-olds can determine which of two women is producing an /i/ sound and which is producing an /a/ sound by simply looking at their mouth movements.

Perceptual illusions also highlight the powerful interactions of auditory and visual speech perception. The McGurk Effect is an auditory-visual illusion that illustrates how perceivers merge information for speech sounds across the senses. For example, when we hear the sound 'da' while seeing the face of a person articulate 'ga', many adults perceive the sound 'ba', a third sound which is a blend of the two. Similarly, infants also show evidence of this effect in the first half-year of life.

In addition, adults typically speak to infants using exaggerated intonation, called 'motherese' or infant-directed speech. Natural infant-directed speech contains a great deal of amodal, redundant information such as exaggerated rhythm and tempo changes, longer pauses, more repetition, wider pitch excursions, and shorter utterances that can be experienced in the sounds of speech, facial movements, and gestures together. Research indicates that infant-directed speech and the accompanying facial expressions are highly salient and preferred over adult-directed speech by infants, regardless of culture or language spoken, in part because of the high degree of multimodal information and intersensory redundancy. However, even in unimodal auditory speech, the preference for infant-directed speech is already apparent in the first months of life. Given that infants have prenatal exposure to the sounds of speech (see section titled 'Fetal development'), learning about the sounds of speech in one's native language is particularly rapid.

Hearing better through sight

Another way in which intermodal perception is useful for language is in helping us to separate a speech stream from a background of noise. It appears that infants can actually use what they see to hear better and to selectively attend to a particular speech stream. When it is noisy, adults can use the information in the speaker's face to help them figure out what is being said. This is one reason why it is often more difficult to understand a person on the telephone than in person. Infants, as well, appear to gain an advantage by seeing the face of a speaker. When a face is synchronized with the voice, infants are better at picking out individual words (speech segmentation) in the context of greater background noise than for auditory speech alone. Interestingly, infants also are able to segment words from speech better if, instead of a face, an oscilloscope pattern (a wiggly line) is synchronized with the voice, demonstrating the importance of audiovisual redundancy for speech segmentation. So infants likely can use any synchronous movement to help them hear better – even gestures, or head movements.

Word learning

Perhaps the most dramatic evidence of relating what infants hear with what they see comes in the form of early 'word learning'. Part of the earliest language acquisition involves learning associations between the sound patterns of words and meaning as, for example, when one learns to connect the visual image of a rose to the sound combination /roz/. Recent investigations have shown that by 6 months of age, infants are already starting to learn the meanings of some very common words such as 'mommy' and 'daddy'. Using the intermodal preferential-looking paradigm (see **Figure 4**), 6-month-olds were presented with two videos, one of their mother and the other of their father, playing side-by-side simultaneously. Alternating recordings of a voice, saying "mommy" or "daddy," were presented. Infants looked more often at the correct video in response to hearing the names. Of course, it is not known whether 6-month-olds truly understand that the speech sounds "mommy" and "daddy" actually refer to their own mother and father or if they simply have noticed that those speech sounds and sights are associated (e.g., "mommy" is heard when mother is present). In either

case, it is clear that infants have made some connection between the acoustic words /mami/ "mahmee" and / dædi/ "dadee" and their visual referents.

In keeping with an increasing specificity view of perceptual development, this learning may be driven, in part, by amodal synchrony. For example, 7-month-olds can learn the links between two speech sounds and two objects if the speech sounds occur in synchrony with the motions of the object, but show no learning if they are out of synchrony. In one study, infants saw a hand move one of two unfamiliar objects (a toy crab and a porcupine, or a lamb chop and a star), in synchrony with the vowel sound /a/ "ahhh" (e.g., for the crab) and /i/ "eee" (e.g., for the porcupine). Each time the object was moved, the sound was uttered, simulating showing and naming an object. In the unsynchronized condition the same movements were made; however, the vowels were uttered between the object movements. We are not suggesting that this is all it takes to learn a word. Word-learning is a complicated task involving multiple cues, and including numerous social-pragmatic factors. However, when infants begin to learn words, audiovisual synchrony is one way they can jumpstart the process.

In fact, parents appear to have an implicit understanding of this principle. When mothers were asked to teach their infants novel names for objects, they used a great deal of temporal synchrony between movements of the object and the verbal label, particularly for younger infants. This helps young infants learn that objects have names. For older infants who understand this idea, mothers adapted their style to include more naming and pointing, and somewhat less synchrony.

The Development of Visual-Tactile Perception

Amodal information also unites perception across vision and touch. Information for shape, texture, substance, and size are invariant across visual and tactile stimulation. When we feel a ball in our hands, we perceive the same shape, size, texture, and substance that we see. Typically, we see and feel an object concurrently and during visual-tactile exploration, we detect redundant information for these properties through touch and sight. Research using the 'cross-modal transfer' method has been conducted to investigate perception of visual-tactile correspondence in infants and adults. In this method, an object is presented to one sense modality alone and a preference test is then given in another sense modality to determine whether the information transfers across modalities. Using this method, research has shown that even 1-month-old infants can perceive the correspondence between an object they experienced tactually, through oral exploration of the object on the back of a pacifier, and a three-dimensional

Figure 4 The intermodal preferential-looking procedure. Infants are expected to look longer at the screen that matches the auditory information. In this case, they would be looking longer at the picture of their mommy.

version of the object available visually. Infants looked more to the object of the shape and texture they had previously experienced orally than to a novel object of a different shape. Infants are also able to transfer information about the substance of an object (rigid vs. deforming) across touch and sight.

Evidence also shows that infants can transfer information obtained through manual exploration to vision, and this develops across the first year. One factor determining the extent to which manual information is perceived is whether exploration is active or passive. Tactile exploration develops over the first year. Young infants tend to grasp objects, whereas older infants become more adept at obtaining tactile feedback by moving their hand relative to the object's surface. By 4 months, infants can perceive whether two parts of an object are connected or separate by the type of motion they produce during haptic exploration. By 6 months, infants can recognize the shape of an object visually that they have manually explored, as long as exploration is active. One study found that even newborns could transfer information about the shape of an object from touch to vision for two shapes that could be easily discriminated by grasping (objects with straight vs. round contours). Following tactile exploration of a cylinder or a cube, newborns showed a visual preference for the object they had touched.

The Development of Visual-Motor Correspondence and the Self

Amodal information also serves as the basis for infants' ability to perceive the self. Research has shown that young infants, including newborns, can imitate facial expressions. After viewing an adult model a tongue protrusion or a mouth opening, young infants show an increase in their production of the gesture they have just seen. In order to do this, they must relate their own production of the facial expression with the visual appearance of the adult's facial expression. This is likely guided by proprioceptive information. Proprioception is information about self-motion provided by feedback from the muscles, joints, and vestibular system. Facial imitation reveals evidence of an early intermodal coordination between motor behavior and visual information, and this coordination continues to develop across the first year.

Another procedure which reveals evidence that infants are able to perceive their own body motion by detecting amodal information is one where they receive live video feedback from their own limb movements (see **Figure 5**). In this method, infants view two video images side-by-side: one, a live visual display of their own motion, and the other a prerecorded image or an image of another infant's motion. Research reveals that by 3–5 months of age, infants can distinguish between a live video of their

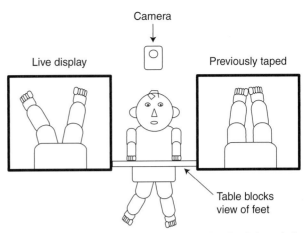

Figure 5 Infants can distinguish live video feedback from their own limbs from that of a prerecorded display of their limb motion. From Bahrick LE and Watson JS (1985) Detection of intermodal proprioceptive-visual contingency as a potential basis of self-perception in infancy. *Developmental Psychology* 21: 963–973.

own legs kicking and a video of another infant's legs kicking, a spatially incongruent video of the legs, or a prerecorded video of their own legs. Further, infants consistently look more to the prerecorded image or the image of the peer, indicating a preference for social stimulation over stimulation from the self by the age of 5 months. Infants apparently use redundant, amodal information including temporal synchrony and spatial congruence between the proprioceptive experience of their own limb motions and the visual image of the motion in the video display to make this discrimination between self and other.

Coordination between vision and motor development is also evident by the rapid development of 'visually guided reaching' during the first year. Visually guided reaching entails continuous adjustments in the reaching and manual behavior of infants as a function of visual input about the size, shape, and position of objects. Infants show evidence of this coordination in the first months of life. They are even able to contact a moving object by aiming their reach ahead of it and taking into account the speed and direction of their own arm motion in relation to that of the object. Later, infants show an ability to adapt their crawling and exploratory behavior as a function of visual information about the slant and solidity of the surface. These examples illustrate a close relationship between vision and motor behavior and an understanding of self in relation to objects.

Posture-control is a critical factor in the infant's development, allowing the child to maintain a stable relation to the environment and is a prerequisite for exploratory behavior such as reaching, grasping, and locomoting. Posture-control is considered an example of intermodal perception because vision plays a critical role in the maintenance and control of posture. We rely on a visual frame of reference for orienting in space and maintaining

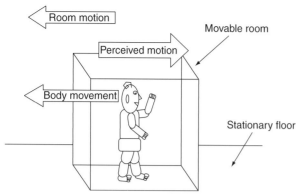

Figure 6 The moving-room paradigm. Infants experience perceptual motion as a result of the optic flow created when the room walls move toward them. They then attempt to compensate for the perceptual motion and show backward body sway.

an upright posture. Studies using a moving-room paradigm, where a conflict between visual and proprioceptive information is created, have demonstrated that vision can override proprioceptive information, particularly in inexperienced walkers. In this method, the observer is placed in a room with a stable floor and walls that can either move or display visual information characteristic of motion (see **Figure 6**). When visual information (optic flow) specifies that we are moving forward, we compensate by moving backward, and this compensatory body sway can be observed and measured. Infants as young as 5 months show postural sway while sitting. Postural sway increases up to 9–13 months of age and then levels off or decreases. Infants show greater sway in response to optic flow in the early stages of learning a posture (sitting up or standing) and with experience they are better able to resolve the conflict between vision and proprioception. Even adults show some degree of body sway in the moving-room paradigm.

Other Sensory Combinations

Young infants show recognition of their mother on the basis of her odor in the first weeks of life. Breastfed infants orient preferentially to the odor of their mother over that of another lactating female. This illustrates their sensitivity to natural object–odor combinations. Research suggests that this learning may originate in fetal development. The chemical make-up of the mother's amniotic fluid is similar to that of her scent. A few months later, infants can also detect arbitrary object–odor relations. In one study, infants were presented with two objects side-by-side for a baseline visual preference test. Then one of the objects was paired with a distinctive cherry odor. During the test trials that followed, the two objects were presented side-by-side, with the cherry odor (experimental trial), and without the cherry odor (control

trial). Four-month-old females showed greater looking to the object paired with the odor during the experimental than the control trial, demonstrating that they learned the arbitrary relation between the visual appearance of the object and the cherry odor. In another study, 6-month-olds demonstrated the ability to relate the color of a food with its temperature.

Similarly, the link between taste and vision is amply illustrated by the toddler who turns her head away long before the broccoli comes in contact with her mouth, and who struggles to reach for the box of cookies. Research indicates that children have a 'sweet tooth' from birth and by the time they are fed solid foods learn to quickly recognize which colors and foods are tasty and which are not, much to the dismay of parents.

Fetal Development

Currently, little is known about the development of intermodal perception during fetal development. However, it is known that the senses develop in an invariant sequence (common across birds and mammals) during fetal development, with tactile/vestibular development, followed by the chemical senses (taste and olfaction), followed by audition, and finally visual functioning. Auditory stimulation from external sounds and the mother's voice is detected by the fetus during the third trimester. Research, using a nonnutritive sucking procedure, has demonstrated that newborns prefer their mother's voice over that of a female stranger. Research has also found that neonates, aged 1–3 days, show a visual preference for the face of their mother over that of a female stranger. A recent study demonstrated that this preference disappeared if neonates were prevented from hearing their mother's voice from birth until the time of testing. Preference for the mother's face was shown only by neonates who had postnatal experience with the mother's face–voice combination. This suggests that the early preference for the mother's face is the result of intermodal perception: neonates are attracted to their mother's face shortly after birth because it occurs in synchrony and concurrent with her voice, a familiar stimulus with which they have had several months experience. In fact, it is possible that the preference for the mother's voice is not only a result of familiarity, but also a result of intermodal perception during prenatal development. In the fetal environment, the mother's voice is likely accompanied by synchronous movements of her body, vibrations of the spinal column, and movements of the diaphragm. This would create a great deal of amodal, redundant information that may make the mother's voice and its prosody particularly salient to infants when they encounter it later, providing a basis for early maternal preferences after birth. Research has yet to directly test these hypotheses.

Neural Bases of Intermodal Perception

Current neuroscience research is consistent with and provides a biological basis for the behavioral findings of intermodal perception reviewed earlier. Virtually every major area of the brain, including early sensory cortex, receives and sends input from different sensory modalities. Recent work has identified especially high concentrations of these multimodal neurons, neurons that respond to input from multiple modalities, in the superior colliculus (a nerve bundle early in sensory processing that is linked to attention and orienting). These neurons respond in a manner that is often described as super-additive. That is, while they may respond to input from one modality alone (e.g., visual), they respond most strongly when inputs from two or more modalities are combined (e.g., visual plus auditory). In addition, there are other neurons that are tuned to particular locations in space. Although they respond primarily to stimulation in one modality, prior experience with multimodal events allows the brain to relate auditory and visual input from the same spatial location, for example.

Research in the neurosciences is also consistent with the principles of perceptual narrowing and increasing specificity that characterize intermodal perception at the behavioral level. The developing brain can be understood as a mass of interconnected neurons, whose connections are strengthened (through a process called long-term potentiation) or gradually weakened (through a process called long-term depression) in accord with experience. For example, if input to the visual modality is somehow modified (by wearing glasses with prisms that distort one's vision), the receptive field of cells in the superior colliculus can compensate and realign with those of the other modality to maintain a coherent spatial mapping, by adjusting the strength of neural connections. This constant process of reorganization and tuning allows the brain to be extremely plastic not only to new experiences but to injury as well. Following amputation, areas of the brain once devoted to the missing limb become responsive to sensations from other areas of the body. Unfortunately, the brain occasionally interprets this information as having come from the missing limb, leading to phantom limb sensations.

In early development, unused and weakened synapses atrophy or are pruned altogether. Pruning is a process by which the neural connections that are not used disappear. Early in development, the brain massively overproduces neurons and their connections rapidly increase reaching a peak near the end of the first year of life. Connectivity is continuously pruned back as a function of experiences such as reaching, looking, and listening, particularly across the first years of life. In other words, the structure of the brain is a 'history of its use'. Coordinated visual, auditory, and motor behavior may thus lead to more intermodal neural connectivity, in turn supporting more intermodal coordination. Although this plasticity is most apparent in early development, the brain continues to exhibit some plasticity throughout the lifespan. The early plasticity of the brain, its sensitivity to multimodal inputs based on coincidence detection, and its reliance on experience in the multimodal world to guide neuronal development provides a neural basis for the behavioral findings on the early development of intermodal perception.

Conclusions

From combining sight with sound, touch, or motor movements, intermodal perception is fundamental to early development and perception of most objects and events in the environment. Early sensitivity to amodal information, the temporal, spatial, and intensity patterns of events that are redundant across stimulation to different senses, guides infants' perceptual, cognitive, and social development. The senses work together as a coordinated perceptual system and intermodal perception develops rapidly across infancy. Even very young infants are sensitive to amodal information, allowing them to perceive unitary multimodal events by linking sights and sounds of speech, emotional expressions, and objects, as well as information across visual and tactile, olfactory, and proprioceptive stimulation. Perceptual development proceeds along a path of differentiation of increasingly more specific levels of stimulation, from amodal to arbitrary relations, and exhibits perceptual narrowing with experience. The early plasticity of the brain, its multimodal nature, and its reliance on experience to guide neural development provide a neural basis for this developmental process.

Acknowledgments

This article was supported by grants from the National Science Foundation (SBE 0350201) and the National Institutes of Mental Health (RO1 HD25669) to the first author.

See also: Auditory Perception; Imitation and Modeling; Language Development: Overview; Motor and Physical Development: Locomotion; Motor and Physical Development: Manual; Object Concept; Perception and Action; Perceptual Development; Self Knowledge; Taste and Smell; Visual Perception.

Suggested Readings

Bahrick LE (1988) Intermodal learning in infancy: Learning on the basis of two kinds of invariant relations in audible and visible events. *Child Development* 59: 197–209.

Bahrick LE and Lickliter R (2002) Intersensory redundancy guides early perceptual and cognitive development. In: Kail R (ed.) *Advances in Child Development and Behavior,* vol. 30, pp. 153–187. New York: Academic Press.

Bahrick LE and Watson JS (1985) Detection of intermodal proprioceptive visual contingency as a potential basis of self-perception in infancy. *Developmental Psychology* 21: 963–973.

Bahrick LE, Walker AS, and Neisser U (1981) Selective looking by infants. *Cognitive Psychology* 13: 377–390.

Gibson EJ and Pick AD (2000) *An Ecological Approach to Perceptual Learning and Development.* New York: Oxford University Press.

Gogate L, Walker-Andrews A, and Bahrick LE (2001) Intersensory origins of word comprehension: An ecological-dynamic systems view. *Developmental Science* 4: 1–37.

Lewkowicz DJ (2000) The development of intersensory temporal perception: An epigenetic systems/limitations view. *Psychological Bulletin* 126: 281–308.

Lewkowicz DJ and Lickliter R (1994) *The Development of Intersensory Perception: Comparative Perspectives.* Hillsdale, NJ: Lawrence Erlbaum Associates.

Rochat P (1995) *The Self in Infancy: Theory and Research.* New York: Elsevier.

Rosenblum LD (2005) Primacy of multimodal speech perception. In: Pisoni D and Remez R (eds.) *Handbook of Speech Perception*, pp. 51–78. Malden, MA: Blackwell.

Stein BE and Meredith MA (1993) *The Merging of the Senses.* Cambridge, MA: MIT Press.

Walker-Andrews A (1997) Infants' perception of expressive behaviors: Differentiation of multimodal information. *Psychological Bulletin* 121: 437–456.

Relevant Websites

http://www.faculty.ucr.edu – Audiovisual speech web-lab of Dr. Lawrence D. Rosenblum, University of California, Riverside, CA.

http://infantlab.fiu.edu – Infant Development Lab, Dr. Lorraine E. Bahrick, Florida International University, Miami, FL.

http://infantcenter.fiu.edu – Infant Development Research Center; Director Lorraine Bahrick, Co-director, Robert Lickliter, Florida International University, Miami, FL.

http://hincapie.psych.purdue.edu – Infant Lab, Dr. George Hollich, Purdue University, West Lafayette, IN.

http://infantstudies.psych.ubc.ca – Infant Studies Center, Dr. Janet F. Werker, Department of Psychology, University of British Columbia, Vancouver, BC.

http://www.psy.fau.edu – Perceptual Development Lab, Dr. David Lewkowicz, Florida Atlantic University.

http://www.media.mit.edu – Robot word learning; Dr. Deb Roy, MIT, Cambridge MA.

http://kidshealth.org – The Senses and Your Newborn: Nemours Foundation.

L

Language Acquisition Theories

S Goldin-Meadow, University of Chicago, Chicago, IL, USA

Glossary

Canalization – Canalization in genetics is a measure of the ability of a genotype to produce the same phenotype regardless of variability in the environment. More broadly, canalization refers to the developmental path of least resistance, the path typically followed by a species.

Corpus – A large collection of spontaneously produced utterances.

Ergative languages – An ergative language is one in which the subject of an intransitive verb (e.g., 'Elmo' in "Elmo runs home") is treated in grammatical terms (word order, morphological marking) similarly to the patient of a transitive verb (e.g., 'Bert' in 'Elmo hits Bert') and differently from the agent of a transitive verb (e.g., 'Elmo' in 'Elmo hits Bert'). Ergative languages contrast with nominative languages such as English; in English, both the subject of the intransitive verb ('*Elmo* runs home') and the agent of a transitive verb ('*Elmo* hits Bert') are placed before the verb, whereas the patient of a transitive verb is placed after the verb ('Elmo hits *Bert*').

Morpheme – A meaning-bearing linguistic form that cannot be divided into smaller meaning-bearing forms, for example, 'unbearable' is composed of three morphemes, *un*, *bear*, and *able*.

Morphology – The study of how morphemes are combined into stems and words.

Motherese/parentese – The kind of speech that mothers (and others) produce when talking to infants and young children. It is characterized by higher pitches, a wider range of pitches, longer pauses, and shorter phrases than speech addressed to adults (also referred to as child-directed speech or infant-directed speech).

Null-subject languages – Some languages allow pronouns to be omitted from a sentence when the referents of those pronouns can be inferred from context (e.g., Japanese); other languages do not allow pronouns to be dropped (e.g., English). Languages that only allow omission of the subject pronoun are called 'null-subject languages' (e.g., Spanish, Italian).

Predicate – The portion of a clause that expresses something about the subject.

Segmentation – The breaking down of a unit into smaller parts; for example, the word 'dislike' can be broken down into two smaller parts (in this case, morphemes), 'dis' and 'like'.

Specific language impairment – A delay in language development in the absence of any clear sensory or cognitive disorder (as labeled in the *Diagnostic and Statistical Manual of Mental Disorders*, 4th edn.).

Subject – The element in a clause that refers to the most prominent participant in the action of the verb; often (but not always) this participant is the one that does or initiates the action named by the verb.

Syntax – The study of how words combine to form phrases, clauses, and sentences.

Transitional probabilities – A conditionalized statistic which tracks the consistency with which elements occur together and in a particular order, baselined against individual element frequency; for example, if B follows A every time A occurs, the transitional probability for this A–B grouping is 1.00.

Introduction

The simplest technique to study the process of language learning is to do nothing more than watch and listen as children talk. In the earliest studies, researcher parents made diaries of their own child's utterances (e.g., Stern and Stern in the 1900s, and Leopold in the 1940s). The diarist's goal was to write down all of the new utterances that the child produced. Diary studies were later replaced by audio and video samples of talk from a number of children, usually over a period of years. The most famous of these modern studies is Roger Brown's longitudinal recordings of Adam, Eve, and Sarah.

Because transcribing and analyzing child talk is so labor intensive, each individual language acquisition study typically focuses on a small number of children, often interacting with their primary caregiver at home. However, advances in computer technology have made it possible for researchers to share their transcripts of child talk via the computerized Child Language Data Exchange System (CHILDES). A single researcher can now call upon data collected from spontaneous interactions in naturally occurring situations across a wide range of languages, and thus test the robustness of descriptions based on a small sample. In addition, naturalistic observations of children's talk can always be, and often are, supplemented with experimental probes that are used with larger number of subjects.

Thus, it is possible, although time-consuming, to describe what children do when they acquire language. The harder task is to figure out how they do it.

Many theories have been offered to explain how children go about the process of language learning. This article begins by reviewing the major accounts. We will find that, although there is disagreement among the theories in the details, all modern-day accounts accept the fact that children come to the language-learning situation prepared to learn. The disagreement lies in what each theory takes the child to be prepared with: A general outline of what language is? A set of processes that will lead to the acquisition of language (and language alone)? A set of processes that will lead to the acquisition of any skill, including language? The article then goes on to describe theoretical and experimental approaches that have been applied to the problem of determining the constraints that children bring to language learning. We end with an analysis of what it might mean to say that language is innate.

Theoretical Accounts of Language Learning

Behaviorist Accounts

Consistent with the psychological theories of that era, prior to the late 1950s language was considered just another behavior, one that can be acquired by the general laws of behavior. Take, for example, associative learning, a general learning process in which a new response becomes associated with a particular stimulus. Association seems like a natural way to explain how children learn the words of their language, but it is not so simple. Quine's

famous theoretical puzzle highlights the problem: Imagine that you are a stranger in a foreign country with no knowledge of the local language. A native says 'gavagai' while pointing at a rabbit running in the distance. You try to associate the new response 'gavagai' with a particular stimulus, but which stimulus should you choose? The entire rabbit? Its tail? Its ears? The running event? The possibilities are limitless and associative learning solves only a small piece of the problem.

In addition to association, imitation, and reinforcement were also proposed as mechanisms by which children could learn the grammatical 'habits' that comprise language. However, even the most cursory look at how children learn language reveals that neither of these mechanisms is sufficient to bring about language learning.

Children learn the language to which they are exposed and, in this broad sense, learn language by imitation. But do children model the sentences they produce after the sentences they hear? Some do, but many children are not imitators. Moreover, the children who are imitators do not learn language any more quickly than the nonimitators. Even the children who routinely imitate do not copy everything they hear – they are selective, imitating only the parts of the sentences that they are able to process at that moment. Thus, imitation is guided as much by the child as by the sentences the child hears.

What about the responses of others to children's sentences? Parents might positively reinforce sentences their children produce that are grammatically correct and negatively reinforce sentences that are grammatically incorrect. In this way, the child might be encouraged to produce correct sentences and discouraged from producing incorrect ones. There are two problems with this account. The first is that parents do not typically respond to their children's sentences as a function of the grammatical correctness of those sentences. Parents tend to respond to the content rather than the form of their children's sentences. Second, even if children's grammatically correct sentences were treated differently from their grammatically incorrect sentences, it is still up to the child to determine what makes the correct sentences correct. For example, if the child says the grammatically correct sentence, "I colored the wall blue," and mother responds with positive reinforcement (thus ignoring the sentence's troubling content and focusing on its form), the child still has to figure out how to generalize from the sentence; she needs to understand the patterns that generate the sentence in order to recognize that one analogous sentence (e.g., "I saw the wall blue") is not grammatically correct while another (e.g., "I pounded the clay flat") is. In other words, there would still be a great deal of inductive work to be done even if children were provided with a set of correct sentences from which to generalize.

The behaviorist account of language was dealt a devastating blow with the publication in 1959 of Noam

Chomsky's review of BF Skinner's *Verbal Behavior.* Chomsky argued that adult language use cannot be adequately described in terms of sequences of behaviors or responses. A system of abstract rules underlies each individual's knowledge and use of language, and it is these rules that children acquire when they learn language. When viewed in this way, the language acquisition problem requires an entirely different sort of solution.

Nativist Accounts

The premise of the Chomskian perspective is that children are learning a linguistic system governed by subtle and abstract principles without explicit instruction and, indeed, without enough information from the input to support induction of these particular principles (as opposed to other principles) – Plato's problem or the poverty of the stimulus argument. Chomsky went on to claim that if there is not enough information in the input to explain how children learn language, the process must be supported by innate syntactic knowledge and language-specific learning procedures. The theory of Universal Grammar (UG) formulates this *a priori* knowledge in terms of principles and parameters that determine the set of possible human languages. UG is assumed to be part of the innately endowed knowledge of humans. The principles of UG provide a framework for properties of language, often leaving several (constrained) options open to be decided by the data the child comes in contact with. For example, word order freedom is a parameter of variation. Some languages (English) mandate strict word orders; others (Russian, Japanese) list a small set of admissible orders; still others (Warlpiri, an Australian aboriginal language) allow almost total scrambling of word order within a clause. Input from a given language is needed for learners to set the parameters of that language.

One important aspect of this theory is that setting a single parameter can cause a cluster of superficially unrelated grammatical properties to appear in the language. For example, the null-subject parameter involves a number of properties: whether overt subjects are required in all declarative sentences (yes in English, no in Italian), whether expletive elements such as 'it' in 'it seems' or 'there' in 'there is' are exhibited (yes in English, no in Italian), whether free inversion of subjects is allowed in simple sentences (no in English, yes in Italian), etc. The prediction is that the input necessary to set the null-subject parameter results in the simultaneous alignment of all of these aspects within a child's grammar. There is, at present, controversy over whether predictions of this sort are supported by the child language data.

Innate knowledge of the principles underlying language is, however, not sufficient to account for how children acquire language. How are children to know what a noun or a subject is in the specific language they

are learning? Children obviously need to identify subjects and verbs in their language before they can determine whether the two are strictly ordered in that language, and before they can engage whatever innate knowledge they might have about how language is structured. Thus, in addition to innate syntactic knowledge, children also need learning procedures, which may themselves be language-specific.

One example is a set of rules linking semantic and syntactic categories. Under this hypothesis, children are assumed to know innately that agents are likely to be subjects, objects affected by action are likely to be direct objects, etc. All they need do is identify (using context) the agent in a scene; the linking rules allow them to infer that the term used to refer to that agent is the subject of the sentence. Their innate knowledge about how these elements are allowed to be structured can then take over. Again, controversies exist over whether child language data support these assumptions (e.g., ergative languages do not straightforwardly link agents with subjects and yet are easily acquired by young children).

Social/Cognitive Accounts

The nativist position entails essentially two claims: (1) at least some of the principles of organization underlying language are language specific and not shared with other cognitive systems, and (2) the procedures that guide the implementation of these principles are themselves innate, that is, centered in the child and not the child's environment. Note that, while these two claims often go hand-in-hand, they need not. One can imagine that the principles underlying linguistic knowledge might be specific to language and, at the same time, implemented through general, all-purpose learning mechanisms (although such mechanisms must be more complex than the mechanisms behaviorist accounts have offered). This position has come to be known as a social or cognitive account of language learning.

For example, by observing others' actions – where they look, how they stand, how they move their hands and faces – we can often guess their intentions. Young children could use this information to help them narrow down their hypotheses about what a word means. In fact, if a speaker looks at an object while uttering a novel word, a child will assume that the speaker's word refers to that object, even if the child herself is not looking at the object. In other words, children can use general cues to speaker intent to guide their guesses about language.

Children do not sound like adults when they begin to speak – clearly, there is developmental work that needs to be done. The question is what type of work is required? One possibility, favored by some nativists, is that children have in place all of the grammatical categories and syntactic principles they need; they just lack the operating systems that will allow those principles to run. The developmental work to be done does not, under this view, involve a changing grammatical system.

Another view suggests that the child's language changes dramatically during development, transforming from a system based on semantic categories to one based on syntactic categories. This transformation could be determined maturationally or guided by innate linking rules. However, the transformation could also result from an inductive leap children make on the basis of the linguistic data available to them, in conjunction with the cognitive and/or social skills they bring to the task – this inductive leap is at the heart of all social or cognitive accounts of language acquisition.

Cognitive underpinnings are obviously necessary but they may not be sufficient for the onset of linguistic skills. For example, the onset of gesture plus speech combinations that convey two elements of a proposition ('open' plus point at box) precedes the onset of two-word combinations ('open box') by several months, suggesting that the cognitive ability to express two semantic elements is not the final stumbling block to two-word combinations. More than likely, it is the inability to extract linguistic patterns from the input that presents the largest problem.

Social and cognitive accounts claim that there is, in the end, enough information in the linguistic input children hear, particularly in the context of the supportive social environments in which they live, to induce a grammatical system. Ample research indicates that adults alter the speech they direct to their children. Speech to children (often called 'motherese') is slower, shorter, higher-pitched, more exaggerated in intonation, more grammatically well-formed, and more directed in content to the present situation than speech addressed to adults. And children pay particular attention to this fine-tuned input, interpreting it in terms of their own biases or operating principles (e.g., paying attention to the ends of words).

However, one problem that arises with postulating motherese as an engine of child language learning is that child-directed speech may not be universal. In many cultures, children participate in communicative interactions as overhearers (rather than as addressees) and the speech they hear is not likely to be simplified in the same ways. Nevertheless, children in these cultures become competent users of their grammatical systems in roughly comparable timeframes. These observations suggest that there may be many developmental routes to the same end – a reasonable conjecture given the robustness of language.

One very interesting possibility that skirts the problem that children do not universally receive simplified input is that the children may do the simplifying themselves. For example, young children's memory limitations may make them less able to recall entire strings of words or morphemes. They would, as a result, be doing the analytic work required to abstract linguistic regularities on a smaller, filtered database (the 'less is more' hypothesis). This filtering may be just what children require to arrive at their linguistic systems. Moreover, it is a general process that children around the globe presumably bring, in equal measure, to the language-learning situation.

Connectionist Accounts

Connectionism is a movement in cognitive science whose goal is to explain human intellectual abilities using artificial neural networks (also known as neural nets). Neural networks are simplified models of the brain composed of large numbers of units (the analogs of neurons) and weights that measure the strength of the connections between those units. In a connectionist account, behavior is shaped by selective reinforcement of the network of interconnected units. Under this view, language development is a process of continuously adjusting the relative strengths of the connections in the network until linguistic output resembles linguistic input.

In a sense, connectionism is more of a technique for exploring language learning than an explanatory account. But connectionism does come with some theoretical baggage. For example, most connectionist models are based on the assumption that language (like all other cognitive skills) can be explained without recourse to rules.

Connectionism offers a tool for examining the tradeoff between the three components central to all theories of language learning – environment (input to the system), structures the child brings to the learning situation (architectures of the artificial system), and learning mechanisms (learning algorithms). For example, a great deal of linguistic structure is assumed to be innate on the nativist account. Connectionism can provide a way to explore how much structure needs to be built in to achieve learning, given a particular set of inputs to the system and a particular set of learning mechanisms. As another example, networks have been shown to arrive at appropriate generalizations from strings of sentences only if the memory span of the network for previously processed words begins small and gradually increases (reminiscent of the 'less is more' hypothesis described earlier). In principle, connectionism is agnostic on the question of whether the architecture of the system (the child) or the input to the system (the environment) determines the relative strengths of each connection. However, in practice, most connectionists emphasize the importance of input. And, of course, the unanswered question is what determines the units that are to be connected in the first place.

Constrained Learning

All theoretical accounts agree that human children are prepared to learn language. But what are they prepared with? Do children come to the learning situation with specific hypotheses about how language ought to be structured? Or do they come with general biases to process information in a particular way? This second view suggests that the strong inclination that children have to structure communication in language-like patterns falls out of their general processing biases coming into contact with natural language input.

The language that children learn must, at some level, be inferable from the data that are out there. After all, if linguists manage to use language data to figure out the grammar of a language, why can't children? But linguists can be selective in ways that children are not able to be. Linguists do not have to weigh all pieces of data equally, they can ask informants what an utterance means and whether it is said correctly, and they have at their disposal a great deal of data at one time. The question is – what kinds of learning mechanisms can we realistically impute to children that will allow them to make sense of the data they receive as input?

One learning mechanism that has been proposed is known as statistical learning. The assumption underlying this mechanism is that children are sensitive to the patterns in their input, and can perform rapid and complex computations of the co-occurrences among neighboring elements in that input. By performing statistical computations over a corpus, children can pick out the recurring patterns in the data and thus are less likely to be misled by individual counter-examples.

However, children must also face the problem that a corpus can be analyzed in many different ways. How do they know which computations to perform on a given corpus? Perhaps children are only able to perform a limited set of computations. If so, this limitation would effectively narrow down the range of possible patterns that could be extracted from a database. Thus, one way that children may be prepared to learn language is that they come to language learning ready to perform certain types of computations and not others.

To discover which computations young language learning children are able to perform, we can provide them with a corpus of data constructed to exhibit a pattern that can be discovered using a particular computation. If the children then extract the pattern from the data, we know that they are able to perform this type of computation on a corpus. As an example, 8-month-old infants were exposed to a corpus of nonsense words playing continuously on an audiotape for 2 min. The corpus was arranged so that the transitional probabilities between sounds were 1.0 inside words, but 0.33 across words. The only way the infant could figure out what the words in the corpus were was to (1) pay attention to these transitional probabilities and (2) assume that sequences with high probabilities are likely to be inside words and that sequences with low probabilities are likely to be the accidental juxtapositions of sounds at word boundaries. The infants not only

listened differentially to words vs. nonwords, but they were able to discriminate between words and part-words (part-words contained the final syllable of one word and the first two syllables of another word; they were thus part of the corpus the infants heard but had different transitional probabilities from the words). The 8-month-olds were not merely noting whether a syllable sequence occurred – they were inducing a pattern from the sounds they had heard, and using a mechanism that calculates statistical frequencies from input to do so.

Infants are thus sensitive to the transitional probabilities between sounds and can use them to segment speech into word-like units. Can this simple mechanism be used as an entry point into higher levels of linguistic structure? If, for example, children can use transitional probabilities between words (or word classes) to segment sentences into phrases, they could then use this phrasal information as a wedge into the syntax of their language. In other words, children may be able to go a long way toward inducing the structure of the language they are learning by applying a simple procedure (tabulating statistical frequencies) to the data that they receive. A related domain-general approach that has been taken to the problem is the Bayesian inference framework, a tool for combining prior knowledge (probabilistic versions of constraints) and observational data (statistical information in the input) in a rational inference process. The theoretical assumption underlying all of these approaches is that children come to language learning equipped with processing strategies that allow them to induce patterns from the data to which they are exposed.

The open question at the moment is – how sophisticated do the data-processing strategies have to be in order for children to induce the patterns of their language from the input that they actually receive? Can children get by with the ability to calculate transitional probabilities, building up larger and larger units over developmental time? Or are there units over which children are more, or less, likely to calculate transitional probabilities? For example, children may (or may not) be able to calculate statistical probabilities over units that are not immediately adjacent (i.e., dependencies between units that are at a distance from one another, for instance, in the sentence, 'the cats on the couch are beautiful,' the verb 'are' is plural because it depends on 'cats', the subject of the sentence, which occurs several words earlier). Some of the constraints that children exhibit during language learning may come from the processing mechanisms they bring to the situation.

Two questions are frequently asked about language processing mechanisms. (1) The task-specificity question – are the mechanisms that children apply to language learning unique to language, or are they used in other domains as well? (2) The species-specificity question – are the mechanisms children apply to language learning unique to humans, or are they used by other species as well?

The task-specificity question can be addressed with respect to statistical learning by providing children with nonlanguage input that is patterned (e.g., musical patterns, visual patterns) and observing whether young infants can discover those patterns. They do, suggesting that calculating transitional probabilities is a general purpose data-processing mechanism that children apply to their worlds. The species-specificity question can be addressed with respect to statistical learning by exposing nonhumans to the same type of language input that the human infants heard, and observing whether they can discover the patterns. It turns out that cotton-top tamarin monkeys can extract word-like units from a stream of speech sounds just as human infants do. But, of course, tamarin monkeys do not acquire human language. The interesting question, then, is where do the monkeys fall off? What types of computations are impossible for them to perform? This theoretically motivated paradigm thus allows us to determine how the mechanisms children bring to language constrain what they learn, and whether those constraints are specific to language and specific to humans.

Constrained Invention

When children apply their data-processing mechanisms to linguistic input, the product of their learning is language. But what if a child was not exposed to linguistic input? Would such a child be able to invent a communication system and, if so, would that communication system resemble language? If children are able to invent a communication system that is structured in language-like ways, we must then ask whether the constraints that guide language learning are the same as the constraints that guide language invention.

Language was clearly invented at some point in the past and was then transmitted from generation to generation. Was it a one-time invention, requiring just the right assembly of factors, or is language so central to being human that it can be invented anew by each generation? This is a question that seems impossible to answer – today's children do not typically have the opportunity to invent a language, as they are all exposed from birth (and perhaps even before birth since babies can perceive some sounds *in utero*) to the language of their community. The only way to address the question is to find children who have not been exposed to a human language.

In fact, there are children who are unable to take advantage of the language to which they are exposed. These children are congenitally deaf with hearing losses so severe that they cannot acquire the spoken language that surrounds them, even with intensive instruction. Moreover, they are born to hearing parents who do not know a sign language and have not placed their children in a situation where they would be exposed to one. These

children lack an accessible model for human language. Do they invent one?

The short answer is yes. The children are able to communicate with the hearing individuals in their worlds, and use gesture to do so. This is hardly surprising since all hearing speakers gesture when they talk. The surprising result is that the deaf children's gestures do not look like the gestures that their hearing parents produce. The children's gestures have language-like structure; the parents' gestures do not.

The children combine gestures, which are themselves composed of parts (akin to morphemes in conventional sign languages), into sentence-like strings that are structured with grammatical rules for deletion and order. For example, to ask an adult to share a snack, one child pointed at the snack, gestured eat (a quick jab of an O-shaped hand at his mouth), and then pointed at the adult. He typically placed gestures for the object of an action before gestures for the action, and gestures for the agent of an action after. Importantly, the children's gesture systems are generative – the children concatenate gestures conveying several propositions within the bounds of a single-gesture sentence. For example, one child produced several propositions about snow shovels within a single sentence: that they are used to dig, that they are used when boots are worn, that they are used outside, and kept downstairs. The gesture systems have parts of speech (nouns, verbs, adjectives), are used to make generic statements (as in the snow shovel example), and are used to tell stories about the past, present, future, and the hypothetical. The children even use their gestures to talk to themselves and to talk about their own gestures.

In contrast, the children's hearing parents use their gestures as all speakers do. Their sloppily formed gestures are synchronized with speech and are rarely combined with one another. The gestures speakers produce are meaningful, but they convey their meanings holistically, with no componential parts and no hierarchical structure.

The theoretically interesting finding is not that the deaf children communicate with their gestures, but that their gestures are structured in language-like ways. Indeed, the children's gestures are sufficiently language-like that they have been called home signs. It is important to note that the deaf children could have used mime to communicate – for example, miming eating a snack to invite the adult to join the activity. But they do not. Instead, they produce discrete, well-formed gestures that look more like beads on a string than a continuous unsegmentable movement.

Segmentation and combination are at the heart of human language, and they form the foundation of the deaf children's gesture systems. But segmentation and combination are not found in the gestural input children receive from their hearing parents. Thus, the deaf children could not easily have taken data-processing strategies of the sort that have been hypothesized and applied them to the gestural input they receive in order to arrive at their home-sign systems. Although it is clear that children must be applying data-processing strategies to the particular language they hear in order to acquire that language, it is equally clear that children can arrive at a language-like system through other routes. A communication system structured in language-like ways seems to be overdetermined in humans.

The deaf children invented the rudiments of language without a model to guide them. But they did not invent a full-blown linguistic system – perhaps for good reason. Their parents wanted them to learn to talk and thus did not share the children's gesture systems with them. As a result, the children's systems were one-sided; they produced language-like gestures to their parents, but received nonlinguistic co-speech gestures in return.

What would happen if such a deaf child were given a partner with whom to develop language? Just such a situation arose in the 1980s in Nicaragua when deaf children were brought together in a group for the very first time. The deaf children had been born to hearing parents and, like the deaf children described above, presumably had invented gesture systems in their individual homes. When they were brought together, they needed to develop a common sign language, which has come to be called Nicaraguan Sign Language (NSL). The distance between the home signs invented by individual children without a partner and the sign system created by this first cohort of NSL can tell us which linguistic properties require a shared community in order to be introduced into human language.

But NSL has not stopped growing. Every year, new deaf children enter the group and learn to sign among their peers. This second cohort of signers has as its input the sign system developed by the first cohort. Interestingly, second-cohort signers continue to adapt the system so that the product becomes even more language-like. The properties of language that crop up in this second and subsequent cohorts are properties that depend on passing the system through fresh minds – linguistic properties that must be transmitted from one generation to the next in order to be introduced into human language.

NSL is not unique among sign languages; it is likely that all sign languages came about through a similar process. As another recent example, a community was founded 200 years ago by the Al-Sayyid Bedouins. Two of the founders' five sons were deaf and, within the last three generations, 150 deaf individuals have been born into the community. Al-Sayyid Bedouin Sign Language (ABSL) was thus born. ABSL differs from NSL in that it is developing in a socially stable community with children learning the system from their parents. Because ABSL is changing over time, the signers from each of the three generations are likely to differ, and to differ systematically, in the system of signs they use. By observing signers

from each generation, we can therefore make good guesses as to when a particular linguistic property first entered the language. Moreover, because the individual families in the community are tightly knit, with strong bonds within families but not across them, we can chart changes in the language in relation to the social network of the community. We can determine when properties remained within a single family and when they did not, and thus follow the trajectory that particular linguistic properties took as they spread (or failed to spread) throughout the community. This small and self-contained community consequently offers a unique perspective on some classic questions in historical linguistics.

Because sign languages are processed by eye and hand rather than ear and mouth, we might have expected them to be structured differently from spoken languages. But they are not. Sign languages all over the world are characterized by the same hierarchy of linguistic structures (syntax, morphology, phonology) and thus draw on the same human abilities as spoken languages. Moreover, children exposed to sign language from birth acquire that language as naturally as hearing children acquire the spoken language to which they are exposed, achieving major milestones at approximately the same ages.

However, the manual modality makes sign languages unique in at least one respect. It is easy to use the manual modality to invent representational forms that can be immediately understood by naive observers (e.g., indexical pointing gestures, iconic gestures). Thus, sign languages can be created anew by individuals and groups, and are particularly useful in allowing us to determine whether language-creation is constrained in the same ways that language learning is.

Computational and robotic experiments offer another approach to the problem of language invention. These studies explore whether communication systems with properties akin to those found in natural human language can emerge in populations of initially language-less agents. There are two traditions in this work. The first functional approach assumes that linguistic structure arises as a solution to the problem of communication, for example, as a way of limiting search through possible interpretations. The second structural approach does not rely on communication pressure to motivate change but rather examines the emergence of structure as the system is passed from one user (or one generation of users) to the next. Studies in this second tradition have found that a compositional system with recursion, grammatical categories, and word order inevitably results from passing an initially unstructured communication system through generations of learners. These are just the properties found in the deaf children's home-sign gesture systems, but the home-sign systems are not passed through a series of learners and are instead invented by individual children who are the sole users of their systems. Once again, we find that there is more than one way to arrive at language-like structure. In general, modeling studies, combined with observations of actual cases of language learning and language invention, can help us appreciate the range of circumstances under which language-like structure can arise and the mechanisms responsible for that structure.

Is Language Innate?

Children are likely to come to language learning constrained to process the language data they receive in certain ways and not in others. The constraints could be specifically linguistic, but they need not be. Constraints are assumed to be internal to the child at the moment when a particular skill is acquired. But are they innate?

Innateness Defined as Genetic Encoding

The problem of innateness has been addressed repeatedly and elegantly in other disciplines, especially ethology, and many definitions of innateness have been proposed. One of the most common, albeit not the earliest, definitions of an innate behavior is that it have a genetic base. Some have claimed evidence for grammar genes – not for a single gene responsible for all the circuitry underlying grammar but for a set of genes whose effects are relevant to the development of the circuits underlying parts of grammar. The dispute is whether the genes are specific to the grammatical aspects of language.

What might it mean to claim that language has a genetic base? At one level, the claim is obviously true – equipped with the human genetic potential, humans develop language. But what does this claim buy us if our interest is in understanding how children learn language? We could study twins, both fraternal and identical, to explore the phenomenon of language learning. However, in this regard, it is important to note that, in twin studies conducted to explore the genetic basis of intelligence (i.e., IQ), the focus is on differences among individuals relative to a normative scale. In contrast, claims about the innateness of language are claims about the commonalities among people, not the genetic differences between people. In arguing that language is genetically based, there is no obvious claim that two individuals who are genetically related have linguistic systems that are more alike than two individuals who are not genetically related. All humans who are genetically intact have, at base, comparable linguistic systems – comparable in the same way that all human bodies have two arms and two legs. The details of the arms of any two unrelated individuals (their length, width, definition, etc.) are likely to differ (and those differences may or may not be grounded at the genetic level) but the basic twoness and structure of the arm is constant across all genetically intact humans – so too for language.

So why then (assuming we are not geneticists) should we care about the genetic base of language learning? Perhaps we should not. Of all of the very large number of definitions and criteria that have, over the years and over the disciplines, been applied to the term innate, one could argue that the definition that is least central to the notion's core is having a genetic base. A useful definition of innate need not be anchored in genetic mechanisms.

Innateness Defined as Developmental Resilience

An alternative definition of an innate behavior is that it is developmentally resilient. A behavior is developmentally resilient if its development, if not inevitable, is overdetermined in the species; that is, it is a behavior likely to be developed by each member of the species even under widely varying circumstances. The way we traditionally explore the boundaries for the development of a behavior is to manipulate the conditions under which that behavior is typically developed, extending the range until the behavior no longer appears. For obvious ethical reasons, we cannot tamper with the circumstances under which children learn language. But we can take advantage of variations in language-learning conditions that occur naturally, and thus explore the boundary conditions under which language development is possible.

Resilience in the face of external variation

Language learning is not infinitely resilient. When human children are raised by animals, they do not develop language. And when children are raised by inhumane parents who mistreat them physically and emotionally, including depriving them of a model for language, they do not develop language. But given a reasonable social world, children seem to be able to develop language under a wide range of circumstances.

Consider first the effects of variability in the way adults speak to children within a culture. Adults in each culture tend to use a distinct register of speech with their children. There is, however, variability across adults in how much they talk to their children and in the frequency with which certain constructions are used. Variability in the amount of talk a child hears has been shown to affect that child's rate of vocabulary growth, and variability in how often a particular construction is used in speech to a child has been shown to affect how quickly the child develops that construction. However, despite the effects of input on the pacing of language learning, there is no evidence that the particular way in which an adult speaks to a child affects whether or not language is ultimately learned by that child.

Indeed, the amount of input a child receives can be quite minimal and still the child will learn language. For example, hearing children born to deaf parents often get very minimal exposure to speech. But it turns out that they do not need much; 5–10 h a week of exposure to hearing speakers is typically sufficient to allow language learning to proceed normally. As another example, twins share their language-learning situation with one another, making the typical adult-twin situation triadic rather than dyadic. Nonetheless, language learning proceeds along a normal trajectory, although often with mild delays. A child may develop language more or less quickly, but almost all intact children in almost all linguistic environments eventually develop language.

The resilience of language learning in the face of across-culture variability is even more impressive. Cultures hold different beliefs about the role that parents need to play to ensure the child's acquisition of language. Not surprisingly, then, children around the globe differ in how much, when, and what types of language they receive – not to mention the fact that, in each culture, the child is exposed to a model of a different language. Indeed, many children are exposed to input from two different languages and must learn both at the same time. Despite the broad range of inputs, children in all corners of the earth learn language and at approximately the same pace.

Resilience in the face of internal variation

Language learning is also resilient in the face of many organic variations from the norm, variations that alter the way children process whatever input they receive. For example, intermittent conductive hearing losses from repeated middle ear infections can cause a child's intake of linguistic input to vary over time in amount and pattern. Despite this variability, spoken language development for the most part proceeds normally in children with this type of hearing loss. As a second example, blind children live in a nonvisual world that is obviously different from the sighted child's world, and that offers a different spectrum of contextual cues to meaning. However, this difference has little impact on language learning in the blind child.

Organic variation can be much more severe and still result in relatively intact language learning. For example, grammar learning in the earliest stages can proceed in a relatively normal manner and at a normal rate even in the face of unilateral ischemic brain injury. As a second example, children with Down syndrome have numerous intrinsic deficiencies that complicate the process of language acquisition. Nevertheless, most Down syndrome children acquire some basic language reflecting the fundamental grammatical organization of the language they are exposed to (the amount of language that is acquired is in general proportion to their cognitive capabilities). Finally, and strikingly, given the social impairments that are at the core of the syndrome, autistic children who are able to learn language are not impaired in their grammatical development, either in syntax or in morphology, although they do often have deficits in the communicative, pragmatic, and functional aspects of their language.

Interestingly, even when children do have trouble learning language, some properties of language (the resilient ones) are spared. For example, a basic understanding of the organization that underlies predicates appears to be intact in children with specific language impairment (children who have neither hearing impairment, cognitive deficit, nor neurological damage yet fail to develop language normally). However, these children have difficulty with morphological constructions. As another example, children who are not exposed to a usable language until adolescence have no trouble mastering word order when learning language late in life, but do have difficulty with morphology. Some properties of language appear to be robust, and some fragile, across a variety of circumstances and internal states.

There may be no greater testament to the resilience of language than the fact that children can invent language in the absence of a model for language. A combination of internal factors (the fact that the children are profoundly deaf and cannot acquire a spoken language) and external factors (the fact that the children have not been exposed to a conventional sign language) together create the unusual language-learning circumstances in which the deaf children described earlier find themselves. Despite their lack of a model for language, these children still communicate in language-like ways.

In sum, language development can proceed in humans over a wide range of environments and a wide range of organic states, suggesting that the process of language development may be buffered against a large number of both environmental and organic variations. No one factor seems to be ultimately responsible for the course and outcome of language development in humans, a not-so-surprising result given the complexity and importance of human language.

Mechanisms that Could Lead to Resilience

Another way of describing the language-learning process is that the range of possible outcomes in the process is narrowed. This narrowing or canalization is often attributed to genetic causes. However, canalization can also be caused by the environment. Consider an example from another species. Exposing a bird to a particular stimulus at one point early in its development can narrow the bird's learning later on; the bird becomes particularly susceptible to responding to that stimulus, and buffered against responding to other stimuli. Note that, in order for acquisition to be universal when the environment is playing a canalizing role, the relevant aspect of the environment must be reliably present in the world of each member of the species. In a sense, the environment must be considered as much a part of the species as its genes.

For language, it looks as though there is a basic, resilient form that human communication naturally gravitates toward, and a variety of developmental paths that can be taken to arrive at that form. In this sense, language development in humans can be said to be characterized by equifinality, an embryological term coined to describe a process by which a system reaches the same outcome despite widely differing input conditions. No matter where you start, all roads lead to Rome.

Are there any implications for the mechanisms of development that we can draw once having identified language as a trait characterized by equifinality? Two types of systems seem possible:

1. A system characterized by equifinality can rely on a single developmental mechanism that not only can make effective use of a wide range of inputs (both external and internal) but will not veer off track in response to that variability, that is, a mechanism that is not sensitive to large differences in input. The gross image that comes to mind here is a sausage machine that takes inputs of all sorts and, regardless of the type and quality of that input, creates the same product.
2. A system characterized by equifinality can rely on multiple developmental mechanisms, each activated by different conditions but constrained in some way to lead to the same end product. The analogy here is to several distinct machines, each one designed to operate only when activated by a particular type of input (e.g., a chicken, pig, cow, or turkey). Despite the different processes that characterize the dismembering operations of each machine, the machines result in the same sausage product. At first glance, it may seem improbable that a variety of developmental mechanisms would be constrained to arrive at precisely the same outcome. However, it is relatively easy to imagine that the function served by the mechanisms – a function that all of the developmental trajectories would share – might have been sufficient to, over time, constrain each of the mechanisms to produce the same product. Communicating via symbols with other humans might be a sufficiently constraining function to result in several mechanisms, each producing language-like structure.

Which of these scenarios characterizes what actually happens when children learn language is an open question. But what is clear is that language-like structure is overdetermined in human children. Many paths lead to the same outcome, and whatever developmental mechanism we propose to explain language learning (or language invention) is going to have to be able to account for this equifinality.

Language is Not a Unitary Phenomenon

Until now we have been discussing language as though it were a unitary phenomenon, as though it were obvious what the appropriate unit of analysis for language is. However, it is clear that language is not a unitary whole, particularly when it comes to issues of resilience and innateness.

Children who are not exposed to a conventional language model create communication systems that contain some, but not all, of the properties found in natural human languages. Thus, the absence of a conventional language model appears to affect some properties of language more than others. Even when linguistic input is present, it is more likely to affect rate of acquisition for certain properties of language than for others. Further, when language is acquired off-time (i.e., in late childhood or adolescence) certain properties of language are likely to be acquired and others are not. Thus, some properties of language are relatively resilient, while others are relatively fragile. Moreover, there is some evidence that the same properties of language (e.g., using the order of words to convey who does what to whom) are resilient across many different circumstances of acquisition – acquisition without a conventional language model, with varying input from a language model, and late in development after puberty. Thus, language as a whole need not be said to be innate.

The definition of innate that best fits the language-learning data is developmental resilience. This notion operationalizes innateness by specifying the range of organisms and environments in which language learning can take place. There clearly are limits on the process of language development; children raised without human interaction do not develop language. But the process of language development can proceed in children with a range of limitations and in children raised in environments that vary radically from the typical. What we see in exploring this resilience is that certain aspects of language are central to humans – so central that their development is virtually guaranteed, not necessarily by a particular gene but by a variety of combinations of genetic and environmental factors. In this sense, language is innate.

See also: Bilingualism; Grammar; Imitation and Modeling; Language Development: Overview; Learning; Literacy; Pragmatic Development; Preverbal Development and Speech Perception; Semantic Development; Speech Perception.

Suggested Readings

Bishop D and and Mogford K (eds.) (1988) *Language Development in Exceptional Circumstances.* New York: Churchill Livingtone.
Bloom P (ed.) (1993) *Language Acquisition: Core Readings.* New York: Harvester Wheatsheaf.
Brown R (1973) *A First Language.* Cambridge, MA: Harvard University Press.
Fletcher P and and Mac Whinney B (eds.) (1995) *The Handbook of Child Language.* Oxford: Blackwell Publishers.

Gleitman LR and Newport EL (1995) The invention of language by children: Environmental and biological influences on the acquisition of language. In: Gleitman LR and Liberman M (eds.) *Language Vol. 1, Invitation to Cognitive Science Series*, pp. 1–24. Cambridge, MA: MIT Press.

Goldin-Meadow S (2003) *The Resilience of Language: What Gesture Creation in Deaf Children Can Tell Us About How All Children Learn Language.* New York: Psychology Press.

Lust BC and and Foley C (eds.) (2004) *First Language Acquisition: The Essential Readings.* Oxford: Blackwell.

Mac Whinney B (ed.) (1987) *Mechanisms of Language Acquisition.* Hillsdale, NJ: Erlbaum.

Pinker S (1994) *The Language Instinct: How the Mind Creates Language.* New York: Morrow.

Slobin DI (ed.) (1985–1997) *A Cross-Linguistic Study of Language Acquisition,* vols 1–5. Hillsdale, NJ: Erlbaum Associates.

Tager-Flusberg H (ed.) (1994) *Constraints on Language Acquisition: Studies of Atypical Children.* Hillsdale, NJ: Erlbaum Associates.

Wanner E and and Gleitman LR (eds.) (1982) *Language Acquisition: The State of the Art.* New York: Cambridge University Press.

Language Development: Overview

E Lieven, Max Planck Institute for Evolutionary Anthropology, Leipzig, Germany

This article is reproduced from the *Encyclopedia of Language and Linguistics,* 2nd edition, volume 6, pp. 376–391, © 2006; Elsevier Ltd.

Glossary

Grammar – The study of classes of words, their inflections, and their functions and relations in a sentence.
Morphology – The system of word-forming elements and processes in a language.
Phonology – The study of speech sounds.
Semartics – The study of the meaning of words.
Syntax – The way in which words are put together to form phrases, clauses, or sentences.

Introduction

All over the world, children learn to talk on a roughly equivalent timetable. They do so by learning the language or languages of their environment. There is considerable debate over what cognitive, social, or specifically linguistic, innate capacities they bring to language leaning. This article begins with a brief timetable of development and then focuses in turn on the major aspects of language learning in terms of infancy, learning words, learning morphology, early grammar, later grammar, and the learning of pragmatic and metalinguistic skills. It concludes with some brief reflections on atypical development. The relevant theoretical issues are covered as they arise in each section and are considered again in the last section on learnability and constituency.

During infancy, children develop a wide range of cognitive and social skills together with a developing ability to segment the speechstream into meaningful units. They usually produce their first recognizable words somewhere between 10–18 months of age and their first multiword utterances between 14–24 months. By age 3 years, children are often able to produce quite long utterances and are beginning to be able to combine more than one clause into coordinate and subordinate constructions (e.g., relative clauses, cleft sentences). Between the ages of 4 to 7 years, there are major advances in children's ability to take the perspective of the listener into account and to produce coherent discourse and narrative sequences. These abilities, as well as the ability to reflect on language as an object of knowledge, develop throughout the school years and are much influenced by the extent of literacy or other complex language (for instance, ritual language) to which children are exposed.

Throughout this developmental timetable, there are major individual differences in the ages at which children reach these points and, in addition, in the balance of skills that a particular child may manifest at a particular point in time. There are also individual differences in how children tackle any of these tasks. This is an important point to remember when considering theories that rely for their confirmation on a particular order of development or on a particular relationship among different skills. It is also important to remember that many children (perhaps most) grow up hearing and, to some extent at least, learning more than one language. The evidence to date is that doing so does not have a significant impact on the developmental timetable for language learning in the early years.

Overview of Development

Infancy

Children are born with the ability to discriminate their mother's voice from that of other women and to discriminate speech from nonspeech, presumably because of their experience in the uterus. In the earliest months of life, they seem able to discriminate sounds produced in the languages of the world, but this ability diminishes until, by 8 to 10 months, their ability to discriminate between sounds is confined to the sounds of their native language(s).

Experiments with children between 6 to 10 months of age indicate a developing sensitivity to the prosodic indicators of major phrasal units in the speechstream. Thus, 9-month-old infants prefer to listen to speech that is segmented using pauses at major clause boundaries, rather than within clauses, whereas there is no difference in listening preferences for 6-month-olds. Around 7.5 months infants also become able to identify words in the speechstream. Experiments with English-, Japanese-, and French-learning children have shown that children can discriminate words that they have heard before from those that they have not, even when the words were embedded in speech. They can also discriminate highly frequent words in their language from low-frequency words, and words that are typically learned early by children from words that are not typically learned early.

Experiments with children about 10 months of age have indicated that they are sensitive to the ordering of words in their language, thus being able to discriminate normal English sentences from ones in which determiners and nouns were reversed (e.g., *kitten the*) or ones in which some grammatical morphemes were replaced by nonsense syllables. Older children (at 18 months but not at 15 months) can discriminate sentences in which the combination of auxiliary and verb was correct (*is running*) from those in which it was not (*can running*). Finally, using simple artificial languages, it has been claimed that infants between 7.5 to 17 months are able to recognize strings with the same ordering rules, but with different 'vocabulary' after a short exposure. However, it seems that this discrimination is possible only when there are patterns of repetition in the 'vocabulary items'.

These experiments show a clear path of development during the first 12 to 18 months of life. As children's experience with language develops, so do their segmentation, word recognition, and pattern recognition skills. These skills are obviously central to the child's ability to parse the input and to start to connect it to meaning. It is important to note that all these experiments depend on the infant's ability to discriminate one stimulus from another. They do not have to understand or use the stimuli in communication nor connect them to any meaning in the environment.

However, infants do make huge developmental strides in their cognitive and social development during the first 12 months of life. Cognitively, infants (probably from birth) have clear expectations about the ways in which objects will behave, and these expectations develop in sophistication over the first year of life. Before their first birthday, they are able to form categories of objects based both on form and, to some extent, on function.

During the first 6–8 months of life, children develop the ability to interact with others, to make demands, and to resist them. At around 8 to 9 months, there is a major 'step change' as the infant starts to understand that others have intentions that may be different from their own and to incorporate this understanding of other minds into their behavior; for instance, imitating the perceived intentions of others and showing objects that they know their interactant has not seen. Infants aged 12–18 months are clearly starting to associate attention sharing, demanding, and assisting others with specific gestures that they use and, also perhaps, with systematic vocalizations. This development is highly correlated with word learning, as it seems to be the beginning of the attempt to match form to meaning.

Thus, by about age 10–12 months, infants are ready to put the patterns that they have extracted together with their communicative and meaning-inference skills. It is this combination that is the true start of human language learning.

How many of these developing abilities are unique to humans, and how many are shared with the other great apes or primates? This is obviously a contentious issue, and researchers of different theoretical persuasions have made very different claims. Much more research remains to be done to tease apart the exact nature of the skills and their precise developmental sequence. However, a number of experiments have indicated that many of the pattern recognition skills shown by human infants may be shared by other primates. In contrast, the intention-reading and communicative skills shown by infants in the last trimester of their first year do seem uniquely human, though nonhuman primates show some precursors of these abilities, especially those few who have been reared in a 'human' environment.

Early Comprehension and Production

The time when children first start to show signs of comprehension and to start producing words varies. However, because much depends on how comprehension and production are defined, it is difficult to give an exact range of variation. Comprehension of individual words such as *No* starts very early, and children can use contextual cues to interpret the utterances of those around them without parsing much of what they hear. Although most well-controlled studies of early word learning have found that comprehension is achieved in advance of production and starts early, production is more variable, with some children producing their first words (as reported by parents) at around 10 months, whereas others might not produce more than a few recognizable words before 16 to 18 months. For most children, progress in comprehension and in production is highly correlated, but there are reports of some children whose comprehension outstrips their production by much more than the normal extent.

Studies have shown that, even when infants know a word, it will take 15-month-olds much longer to process it and to look to a matching picture than it will older infants. Thus, 15-month-olds need to hear the whole word before looking to the matching picture, whereas 18- and 24-month-olds process it 150 and 300 ms faster, respectively. These two older groups shift their gaze before the word has ended, using the ongoing phonological information to discriminate the matching picture from a distractor. This development of automatization is clearly one of the major processes taking place between the earliest word-meaning mappings and the point where vocabulary learning develops rapidly.

The production of utterances also goes through a long process of automatization and refinement. Initially, infants' utterances can match the adult form quite closely. However, they go through a subsequent stage in which each child produces a wider range of words, most of which are reduced to a phonological 'template.' The nature of this template varies from child to child, though it always bears a phonological and segmental relationship to the particular language being learned. Children vary greatly in how accurately they can produce the phonology of their language and in how long it takes for this accuracy to develop. They may also differ early on in the extent to which they pick up on the major tunes of the language, as some children tend to produce shorter and more well-articulated utterances.

Some early words are highly context dependent – for example, Piaget's classic example of his daughter, Jacqueline who used *voua-ou* (wow-wow) to refer to everything that could be seen from the balcony – but it seems to be the case that children also produce relatively context-independent words from early on (e.g., *more* to request a number of items, not just food). Context dependence is similar to 'underextension' in which the child uses the word to refer to a limited set of referents. This contrasts with overextension where the word is used to refer to a wider group of referents than in the adult language (an example is the use of *Daddy* to refer to all men whom the child encounters). Much early word comprehension and production shows both characteristics and initially is not stable.

One of the most striking aspects of very early speech is its phonological inaccuracy. Analysis makes it clear that the phonological errors that children produce are systematic. Individual children drop syllables or substitute a particular sound of their own for sounds in their language (for instance, *Puggle* for *Puddle*) while still being able to hear the difference between their own production repeated to them and the 'real' word. Children will not, in fact, accept a repetition of their version of a word as being the 'real' word. This phenomenon raises interesting issues for the relationship between comprehension and production. There is major theoretical debate, however, concerning how it should be analyzed. The debate is

between a 'templatic approach,' which characterizes the process as the child assimilating words to a production template or an optimality theoretical approach that sees the child as seeking to resolve a set of constraints on production, such as 'faithfulness' (i.e., getting as close to the model as possible) and 'markedness'.

A second issue is the extent to which children's communicative behavior in these early stages is already 'linguistic' in the sense of being conventionalized, context free, and combinatorial. Thus, researchers have suggested that children's early communicative acts (e.g., showing as a precursor of declaratives and demanding as a precursor of imperatives) develop into 'protolinguistic' symbols; that is, each child uses a specific set of sounds and gestures to convey different meanings.

Learning a Vocabulary and Developing Meaning

After an often slow start, children's vocabulary grows exponentially, with new words being added at a rate of 9 to 10 words per day between the ages of 2 and 6 years. In industrialized and urbanized societies, children add about 3000 words per year for each year in school. Vocabulary size is related closely to the amount of Child-Directed Speech (CDS) in the early years and to various measures of family talk and schooling in the later years.

For children learning many languages, including English, nouns form the largest single category of words, but children also learn a wide range of words from other categories (e.g., *want, me, no, what*). The extent to which nouns predominate early on varies among children learning the same language and among children learning different languages. Young children, under certain pragmatic conditions, require only a minimal number of exposures to a novel noun and its referent to learn its meaning.

One issue concerns when children form categories of the words that they are learning. The answer to this depends, in part, on how a category is defined, but evidence suggests that a category of nouns develops relatively early in many languages; that English-speaking children can substitute the determiner *a* for *the* early (while taking many years to learn the full range of determiners and their scope); and that fully fledged categories of verb and adjective take more time to develop.

When children learn a new word, what meaning do they give it? It could be the meaning the word has in the language that they are learning or a meaning based on their cognitive categorizations of the world. For instance, children the world over might already have developed nonverbal categories of 'in-ness' and 'on-ness' during infancy, and when they learn words that express the relation between objects, they might initially match these words to these pre-existent categories. There has been considerable research on this issue, and it seems that this is not what happens. Instead, children seem to learn the word and its referent together. Thus, English-learning children use the prepositions *in* to refer to one object contained within another and *on* to refer to one object supported by another, irrespective of how tight the fit is between the objects. However, Korean-learning children use the verb *kkita* to refer to one object inside another only if the fit is tight (e.g., a cassette in a box) and for other tight fit relations between objects (e.g., one object stuck to another with Velcro). The verb *nehta* is used to refer to a loose fit, regardless of whether one object is inside another or on top of it. Children do under- and over-generalize, but they seem to do so along the lines of categorization indicated by their language.

How does a child know what someone is referring to when that person uses a word? In principle, the speaker could be referring to any part of the scene. This problem of reference was elucidated most clearly by the philosopher, Quine. The general answer is to suggest that children come to word learning with some already pre-given interpretative skills. One group of researchers has suggested that these skills are in the nature of innate constraints; for instance, the child initially assumes that a word applies to the whole object and that a novel word will not apply to an object for which the child already has a word. Another group suggests that these skills derive from the pragmatics of the situation that the child already knows about. A series of experiments indicating that children pre-verbally know what is relevant to a situation and to the perspective of another and that, simply through using context, they can find the referent for a word they have never previously seen paired with the referent, suggest that the latter explanation is more likely to be correct.

Another major debate in the literature is over the status of nouns as the first category to be learned. In 1982, D. Gentner claimed that nouns are universally easier to learn and that they initiate the process of category learning. She argued that this occurs not only because the use of nouns tends to be very frequent in CDS but also because their reference is more transparent – to concrete, imageable objects – and children already have developed a considerable knowledge of objects and their behavior pre-verbally. In opposition to this theory, researchers have argued that children learn a range of words, not just nouns, from the beginning and that there are languages, such as Korean, in which the proportion of nouns in the lexicon does not exceed the proportion of verbs (more or less broadly defined). This issue has not been resolved: on the one hand, it *is* easier in many languages to learn many object words; on the other hand, children are also building up other categories of their language from the beginning. Developing categories helps the child segment the other words they hear, and the relative growth of these categories depends on the characteristics of the language being learned and the way it is used in CDS.

Learning Grammar

Learning Morphology

Inflections change the grammatical meaning of words. Languages differ greatly in the amount and kind of inflectional morphology that they show. English has very little inflectional morphology (plural – *s* and past tense *–ed* are two examples). Free morphemes also mark grammatical meanings in languages. For instance, in English, *he* indicates the nominative masculine pronoun (subject argument), whereas *him* marks the accusative masculine pronoun (direct or indirect object argument). The English pronoun system shows irregularity: each pronoun in the English paradigm changes somewhat differently between nominative, accusative, and genitive (e.g., *he, him, his, we, us, our*). In addition, multiple meanings are encoded in one morpheme: number, case, and gender. Other languages encode meaning much more extensively and systematically with both inflectional and free morphemes. Inflections can mark either a local meaning (e.g., plural on a noun in English) or a relational meaning (e.g., plural on a verb to agree with the subject or object; a case marker on a noun as a function of its syntactic role). In either case, productive inflectional marking involves constituency: the ability to understand how plurality is marked on the whole noun phrase within the language being learned and how the noun phrase is coordinated with marking on the verb phrase. Thus, in some languages, determiners, adjectives, and nouns are all marked for plurality and/or case and/or gender, in others not; in some languages there is both subject and object marking on the verb and/or its auxiliaries and in others not.

Children may start by rote learning some frequent words together with their inflections while omitting non-salient inflections (omission errors). Later, children may over-generalize and use incorrect forms (errors of commission). For instance, in English, children leave out tense markers (*It go there* for *It goes there*), over-regularize past tense marking (*goed* for *went*), and use incorrect forms (*I think her was crying for me*). In languages in which all words in a class carry an inflection, the child may initially use only one inflection and over-generalize it to all members of that class.

A central question is when children become productive with morphology. Researchers from different theoretical persuasions tend to interpret the data in predictably different ways. Those arguing for early, abstract knowledge point to the fact that children learning highly inflected languages produce words with inflectional marking from the beginning, usually accurately. Those who emphasize that the abstract representations underlying inflectional morphology are learned point to the potentially rote-learned nature of early inflectional marking and the limited range of items with which particular inflections are used.

There have been many different ways of defining productivity in naturalistic corpora: for instance, percentage provision in obligatory contexts, use of the same inflection on a number of members of the class, or use of different inflections on the same word. Inevitably, these measures yield different results, depending on how stringent the criteria are and how good the sampling is. Methods are being developed that control for the range of forms in the child's lexicon and then compare the degree of productivity between the child's system at different developmental points and between the child's system and the adult's. For two children learning Spanish, a language with rich inflectional morphology on verbs, this method has shown that productivity develops even after the child can provide all the forms and that the children's range of inflectional provision on the same verbs as their parents, even when the range of inflections is controlled for, is still significantly different at age 2.6 years.

How quickly children learn the morphology of their language seems to depend on the following factors and the interaction among them: type frequency (how many different lexemes are inflected in the same way) and token frequency (the relative frequency of different surface forms) in the input; salience (can they be heard?); transparency of meaning (is the semantics accessible?); formal complexity (is one meaning or more encoded?); and the regularity and distributional consistency of the inflectional paradigm. In such languages as Turkish, in which suffixes are added in a consistent order and with consistent form to indicate local meaning (e.g., plural, location, possessive), children seem to be at least partially productive relatively early. Other languages present more difficulty – those in which the morphemes are: (1) portmanteau (more than one meaning is combined in one form; e.g., the nominative for 'water' in Russian is *vodá*; the dative plural form is *vodám*); (2) distributed (e.g., marked with a free form and an inflection, Serbo-Croatian locative markers); and/or (3) in complex and partial paradigms (e.g., Polish case endings).

One sure way to know that children have a productive system is to test for their ability to mark words that they have never heard before ('nonce' words). Otherwise, one can never know whether each word and its accompanying inflection have been learned from the input on a one-by-one basis. In Berko's classic 'wug test,' children are first introduced to a novel creature called *a wug*, and then another of these creatures is produced. The child is then asked, *Now we have two – ?* We know that children have productive plural morphology if they answer *wugs*.

This method can be extended to other word classes. For instance, experiments with novel verbs in English suggest that productive past tense morphology for verbs develops somewhat later than does plural morphology for nouns. Note that this is also a way of determining what type of category is represented in the child's system and its level of abstraction (for instance, action verbs only or all verbs or concrete nouns only or all nouns). Nonce experiments have not been conducted in many languages other than English, but their wider use would certainly help clarify some very complex issues in the learning of inflectional morphology. However, they are not easy to conduct with children younger than age 2, and children learning some languages may be partially productive before this age.

Because inflectional morphology can be extremely complex and children seem to demonstrate early sensitivity and productivity, it is often used as a testing ground for debates about whether children have very early abstract linguistic representations. An example is the extensive debate on past tense marking in English. Children start by producing a small number of forms (many of them irregular) and subsequently start to over-generalize the regular *–ed* marker to irregular verbs (e.g., '*runned*' rather than '*ran*'). Children concurrently use the correct form and may continue to over-regularize some forms for many years. Proponents of early abstract representations argue that, once children have learned the past tense rule, they seek to apply it to all new forms that they learn and stop doing so only when they learn the new irregular form that 'blocks' the application of the rule. This model is called the 'dual route model': one route for regulars and one for irregulars. The claim is that this learning occurs even in languages, unlike English, for which the rule is not the most frequent form (i.e., is a 'minority default' rule). Challenges to this position come from 'single-route models' that claim: (1) the developmental pattern of marking can be closely modeled in connectionist networks that have only one (not two) mechanisms; (2) these networks can also model the development of marking in languages in which the 'default' marking is not the most frequent; (3) detailed studies of children's marking in languages either with a 'default' or with no default show a long process of development during which children over-generalize a variety of markers, depending on such factors as frequency and phonological similarity, before arriving at the adult system; and (4) the fact that over-generalizations continue for a long time after the child has learned the correct form does not suggest that there are two entirely separate processes involved.

As well as being a potential window on the nature of children's underlying syntactic abstractions, inflectional morphology can also provide a window on the development of children's underlying semantic representations. An example of this is the 'aspect before tense' debate. Here, the issue is whether children are initially sensitive only to the aspectual features of situations and their marking on verbs (e.g., punctual or durative events: *hit* vs. *singing*) or also to the temporal features (past vs. present events: *sit* vs. *sat*). Because languages differ greatly in how these features are coded on verbs, crosslinguistic comparison of children's development has been essential in this debate. Methodological problems and the complexity and inter-relatedness of the tense and aspect systems in different languages mean that we do not yet have a final answer to this issue.

Early Syntactic Development

Children's first utterances containing more than one word appear between 18 to 24 months of age. Almost all researchers agree that, in the early stages, some utterances are rote learned as a whole (e.g., *what's that?*), and others may be slot-and-frame patterns (e.g., *where's X gone?* or *more X*, where X denotes a range of referents). However, there is disagreement as to the extent of these low-scope patterns: what part they play, if any, in children's developing linguistic representations; and how utterances that are considered not to derive from them should be represented. For instance, when it is suggested that the child is using rules for the combination of underlying categories, the hypothesized categories can be very varied. One suggestion would be semantic categories; for instance 'agent' and 'action verb' to generate an utterance like *Lion swim.* However, a different researcher might analyze the same utterance in terms of syntactic relations, such as 'subject' and 'intransitive verb.' In the case of any particular utterance, these alternatives cannot be distinguished: A corpus of utterances (the larger, the more reliable) must be analyzed together with clear definitions of productivity before it is possible to suggest whether the utterance is likely to have been generated productively and on the basis of what linguistic representations. As noted for morphology, naturalistic data never allow one to be completely certain that an utterance is productive.

Many of children's early utterances are missing features that are provided in adult speech: subjects are frequently omitted, as are function words (e.g., auxiliaries, complementizers, prepositions). Utterances often lack finiteness marking (e.g., no third person *−s* on main verbs in English; nonfinite for finite verbs in Dutch and German).

Children's utterances also reflect features of the input very closely. Thus, English-speaking children's early verbs are those that occur most frequently in the input, children mark verbs in accordance with the most frequent marking on those same verbs in the input, and they use verbs in the argument structures that their mothers use most frequently. In fact, whatever system one looks at, there are strong correlations with frequency in the input. This is not, however, the only factor affecting the child's use: as with phonology and semantics, complexity and salience also play a role, together with, most importantly, what the child wants to talk about.

None of these facts are in serious dispute in the literature; however, their interpretation certainly is. The major divide is between those who interpret them as indicating that the child has early abstract and, specifically, linguistic knowledge (for some researchers, innate) and those who argue that abstraction develops throughout the process of learning language. Clearly, even though children's utterances show a great deal of lexical specificity and partial marking, they could still reflect underlying abstract linguistic knowledge, limited by these four factors:

1. lexical learning of the forms of the language
2. learning the syntactic features particular to the language
3. processing constraints on production (e.g., a limit on the length of what the child can produce)
4. late biological maturation of some part of the system that underlies the abstraction.

Each of these factors is briefly considered below.

In addition, all theories need to account for the patterns of errors that children show. Those maintaining the existence of innate linguistic knowledge must answer this question: If children have innate grammar, why do they make errors that seem to reflect the lack of knowledge of fundamental linguistic systems, such as tense, agreement, and the provision of arguments? Those maintaining that abstractions are constructed must determine how the interaction between the child's current system and the input explains the pattern of errors.

In the case of (1) above, it is obvious that, whatever the underlying system, children have to learn the specific forms of their native language. The clear implication is that claims to underlying structure or the lack of it should not be made until it is established that the child is able to fully comprehend or produce the forms reflecting the hypothesized abstraction.

Within nativist linguistic approaches, one solution to the issue of how children use the hypothesized Universal Grammar (UG) to work out the syntactic particularities of their input language (point 2 above) is to suggest that they have to set a range of parameters as the result of hearing (a small number of) utterances. Within this literature, there are major debates on the number of parameters, whether or not they are initially set, and how many settings there can be (one, two, or more). An example is to hypothesize a 'head direction parameter' that determines how children identify the input language as being 'left' or 'right branching.' In principle, children then know how to order words across a range of phrasal structures (e.g., noun phrases, prepositional phrases, and verb phrases). Alternative constructivist accounts would suggest that children do this on the basis of the particular strings that they learn from the input, from which word-order patterns are subsequently abstracted in conjunction with the learning of word classes. This hypothesis would make it easier to account for the many instances of inconsistency of head direction in languages. The success of the Principles and Parameters approach in its own terms depends on the number of parameters being relatively small and on agreement among researchers as to how the specified settings can account for the range of relevant phenomena in language development. At the present time, it is not clear that either of these conditions can be met.

In the case of processing constraints (3 above), there clearly are length constraints on what the child produces. Probably, the single most obvious aspect to the lay observer of children's developing language is that children's utterances get longer as they grow older. However, is this an output limitation imposed on a much fuller underlying abstract representation, or does it reflect what the child has actually learned up to this point? For instance, if children are processing the input by using already identified strings as the basis for building new strings, doing so would also yield increasingly long utterances over time. In addition, the way in which patterns were added would mean that the distribution of marking would also change over time. Research incorporating this type of learning mechanism has been successful at modeling children's patterns of finiteness marking not only in English but also in Dutch and Spanish.

An alternative linguistic nativist approach is to hypothesize that, although UG is innate, some parts of the system are on a later maturational timetable, which can account for some of the early error patterns shown by children (point 4 above). Two well-known accounts that use this approach are Borer and Wexler's attempt to explain the late use of full eventive passives by English-speaking children and Wexler's Agreement-Tense Omission Model (ATOM). In the first, the authors suggest that children are late with eventive passives because 'argument-linking chains' are a late biological maturation. This theory cannot account for the fact that full passives emerge early in some languages.

The ATOM model (of which the Optional Infinitive hypothesis for typically developing children and the Extended Optional Infinitive hypothesis for children with SLI are earlier versions) predicts that, because prematuration children are subject to 'the unique checking constraint,' they will only be able to check either for tense or for agreement. This constraint is intended to account for patterns of incorrect finiteness marking found in young children's speech across a range of languages. One aspect of this model concerns agreement marking. Because, in the model, children can only check for either tense or agreement, a pattern of errors is predicted that, in English, sometimes results in non-nominative pronouns appearing in subject position (e.g., *me* for *I* errors or *her* for *she* errors). The only error predicted *not* to occur at levels greater than noise is the use of a non-nominative pronoun (e.g., *me, him, her, them*) with a finite verb that agrees with the subject (e.g., *Me am going, Her wants that*), because this would result from both tense and agreement having been checked. However, researchers have shown that if

agreement rates are broken down by the specific pronoun, errors with *her* in subject position and an agreeing verb occur too often to be disregarded as noise. One implication of this analysis is that it is important to analyze errors in terms of the particular form, rather than to sum across a category defined by the adult system, because the child's system may not be operating at this level of abstraction.

The other main theoretical approach to children's syntactic development argues that grammatical abstraction emerges from interaction between the input and innate learning mechanisms and that these are *not* restricted to the domain of syntax. Constructivist approaches maintain that children start by learning low-scope constructions based around specific words or morphemes. These constructions become more complex, and abstractions (for instance, of tense, agreement, subject, and transitive) build up. Initially, a child may have no understanding of the internal structure of a construction (e.g., *what's that?*), but uses it as a whole with a specific meaning. As development proceeds, functional distributional analysis based on the relation between a form and (child-identified) functions leads to representations of constructions developing internal structure. Patterns of relationships build up between constructions and their parts, in a process of increasing complexity and schematization (**Table 1**).

One critical aspect of this theory is that, once a slot develops in a construction, it will be paired with a meaning: thus, a 'noun phrase' slot always denotes a referent. In time, the child will learn to refer in increasingly complex ways; for instance, in English with a range of determiners and adjectives. Constituency thus develops hand in hand with the function of the constituent in the construction and becomes increasingly schematic.

M. Tomasello (2003) provided the most comprehensive statement of this position to date. He suggested that, rather than having to postulate innate syntactic categories or linking rules, it is possible to account for the development of abstract categories and constructions on the basis of general communicative and cognitive processes, such as intention reading, analogy making, and distributional

Table 1 Examples of different types of constructions and their meanings

Form	Meaning	Level of abstraction
What's that?	Requesting a name	Rote-learned
It's a <Noun>[1]	Naming <referent>	Slot-and-frame
Double object construction: <Noun> <Verb> <Noun> <Noun>	Agent-Verb of transfer-Recipient-Transferred Object	Schematic
Mary gave John the ball		

[1]< > denotes an open slot.

analysis. The critical aspect of this approach is that utterances have meanings as a whole and that, for children to be able to work out what role a word or inflection is playing in an utterance, they have to know, first, what the whole utterance means and then, in a process that Tomasello calls 'blame assignment,' identify the part of the meaning for which the particular form is responsible. In this approach, abstract constructions develop through analogies based on semantic similarity between the meanings of different item-based constructions; for instance, *A hits B, X loves Y, C pushes D* may give rise to the transitive construction and its syntactic roles.

Tomasello's 'verb island hypothesis' was an early example of such an approach. He claimed that children initially build up constructions around individual verbs, rather than having more general and abstract categories, such as subject, direct object, and transitive verb, from the beginning. Thus, a child who knows the verb *hit* may have a slot before the verb for the 'hitter' and one after for the 'hittee' without having the abstract representation of a transitive construction. A wide range of production experiments that test English-speaking children's ability to use novel verbs in transitive constructions supports this claim. Although most children aged just over 2 years old are already using verbs they know in some two-argument constructions, the ability to demonstrate this knowledge with a verb they have never heard before develops between the ages of 2 and 3 years and can be affected strongly by the experimental method employed.

The verb island hypothesis has been challenged by studies using the preferential looking paradigm. They suggest that children can discriminate between a transitive utterance that matches a scene they are looking at and one in which the argument roles are reversed at younger ages than those shown for success in production experiments. Some researchers have suggested that this indicates that children are innately equipped either with a notion of subject or with rules that link the notion of agent to subject. However, it seems difficult to argue for an innate notion of subject, because subject is not a universally identical category across languages.

Other researchers, less contentiously, suggest that children are already sensitive to the number of arguments in an utterance and their relationship to a causative scene with two actors and that this allows them to make the preferential-looking discrimination. Because children are sensitive pre-verbally to causation and many already know how to name people and objects by the time they take part in preferential-looking studies, this finding seems plausible – particularly because there seems to be a correlation between the child's vocabulary level and success in these tasks.

Children's avoidance of using ungrammatical transitives and intransitives in production experiments also suggests earlier sensitivity to some aspects of verb argument structure. In addition, experiments show that English-speaking children manage to use the transitive construction with a novel verb somewhat earlier when case-marked pronouns, rather than nouns, are used as arguments. It may be that languages, such as German, with relatively clear case-marking of argument roles, also assist children in schematizing these roles somewhat earlier. Pine *et al.* have argued for patterns building up not only around verbs but also around other high-frequency markers, such as *I + Verb* or *Verb + it*. Thus, the child, as well as building up a 'transitive verb' category, would, at the same time, be learning that *I* and other frequent referents in first position can be in a range of semantic roles in relation to the verb. Childers and Tomasello found supporting evidence for this suggestion. Thus, more recent constructivist accounts suggest that the abstract transitive construction builds up from a number of different sources: pre-verbal knowledge of causality, the ability to match arguments in an utterance to referents in the environment, the development of other lexically specific constructions around pronouns, and high-frequency items. The combination of these factors may result in the child being able to perform correctly in some tasks using less fully specified representations than would be required for others (e.g., using a novel verb that has never been heard before in a transitive construction).

From a constructivist perspective, there is initially no necessary relation in the child's system between one construction and another; for instance, between a declarative and a *wh*-question that would be related in the adult system as would be maintained in any analysis based on one or other generativist theory of island constraints (e.g., movement, gaps or checking). However, such relationships do develop. This can be seen from children's increasing conversational flexibility as they question previously mentioned constituents, manipulate topic and focus, and, in English, expand contracted auxiliaries, insert DO-support when rephrasing a previous utterance, and so on. Many experimental studies also show that children become increasingly able to hear a nonce form in one construction (for instance, an active) and to transform it into another (a passive). For linguistic nativists, this should be a relatively automatic outcome of children's abstract linguistic representations.

However, within constructivist approaches, these relations are seen as being learned. This learning occurs in part through the identification of the same meaning-based categories in different constructions and in part through relating the overall meanings of constructions to each other. For instance, the simple active statement, *I want a banana*, communicates something different from the cleft: *It's a banana I want*. Children's over-generalizations of constructions are explained relatively easily within this framework: For instance, when a child says *Don't giggle me* (meaning *Don't make me giggle*), she has analogized *giggle* as having causative meaning and therefore placed it into a causative transitive construction. There are, however, considerable problems both for linguistic nativists and construction-based accounts in explaining how children cut back from such over-generalizations.

Later Syntactic Development

As children's language develops, major changes occur at both clausal and sentential levels. Noun phrases and verb phrases increase in complexity: for instance, although English-speaking children use *a* and *the* early on, it may take many years before they can operate with more complex determiners and their scope (*some*, *every*, and *each*). Likewise, children may be able to use some auxiliaries (e.g., *I'm X-ing, Can I Y?*) and verb complement structures (e.g., *I want to play out*) from early on, but the full development of complex verb phrases takes considerable time. At the sentential level, although English-speaking children produce many questions between the ages of 2 and 3 years, initially most of these are with contracted copulas (*What's that?*, *Where's X?*) or contracted auxiliaries (*What's Mummy X-ing?*, *Where's Y gone?*). Some questions with subject-auxiliary inversion (*Can I X?*, *Are you Y-ing?*) also start appearing during this period, but it is not until approaching age 3 and older that children start to show considerable flexibility in the range of subjects, auxiliaries, and *wh*-words that they can use in inverted *yes/no-* and *wh*-questions. Clause coordination and subordination (e.g., complement structures, causatives, relative clauses) also develop over a considerable time period – both when these structures start to appear and when they increase in internal complexity.

In principle, it is rather difficult for linguistic nativist theories to explain this slow and somewhat patchy development of complex syntax and the accompanying errors that children make. Once the lexical forms are learned, why should children make uninversion errors (*Where she is going?*) or find some embedded relatives easier than others? Linguistic nativist explanations of children's later syntactic development all start from the claim that children could not learn the abstract basis of these constructions because the constituents involved could not be abstracted from a surface analysis of the input. Errors are accounted for in two ways: (1) they arise from the particularities of the language being learned and not from the absence of the abstract representations of Universal Grammar; or (2) children have full competence and errors arise from faulty methodologies. In constructivist accounts, complex constructions, such as *wh*-questions or relative clauses, begin as item-based or with simpler structures that then build toward greater complexity and schematicity.

Uninversion errors in English-speaking children's *wh*-questions have given rise to several different linguistic nativist accounts. For example, it has been proposed that questioning arguments is easier than questioning adjuncts.

An alternative account, related to the particularities of English, suggested that the errors in children's inversion are explained by the fact that only main verb BE can invert (unlike in German where all main verbs can invert in questions) and DO-support is also unique. Recent constructivist accounts have explained inversion errors in terms of the relative frequency of *wh* + auxiliary combinations in the input. Thus, it has been suggested that children are learning correct inversion from high-frequency combinations of a *wh*-word plus a specific form of the auxiliary and that uninversion errors occur when they have not yet learned the correct combination and produce a 'groping pattern' by putting together a known *wh*-word and a known declarative.

However, the overriding argument, from the linguistic nativist position, against the possibility of learning syntax is that children can deal with complex constructions that could not have been learned from the input. An example is extraction from embedded clauses in *wh*-questions: *Who do you think John likes?* In UG accounts, children operate with abstract formalisms that relate the object of the embedded clause first to the object of *you think* and from there to the position at the front of the sentence. These formalisms could not, it is argued, be learned from the sequential probabilities of strings on the surface of the input; in addition, the structures are rare to nonexistent in the input and therefore could not be learned as a whole. Whether this latter point is the case awaits much denser sampling of the input, but it should be noted that this type of extraction is not possible in German and that a much wider range of extraction occurs in Italian. This considerable cross-linguistic variation therefore requires, in UG terms, a complex parametric account and, from the point of view of the language learner, close attention to the particularities of the language.

From a constructivist point of view, children solve these tasks by building up their knowledge of constituency and using already established form-meaning mappings to identify potential constituents in novel constructions. Thus, although children may not have had previous experience with the type of sentence noted above, they will already know constructions that identify the matrix *wh*-clause as a constituent asking for an act of reference, thus allowing them to attempt to identify the referent of the embedded relative. For instance, English-speaking children's early relative clauses tend not to be restricted (i.e., adding more information about a referent: *The cow that the dog bit ran away*), but presentational (i.e., introducing a topic: *That's the cow that goes there*). Presentational relatives do not involve embedding one clause within another; the main clause is usually a copula (one of the earliest constructions that English-speaking children learn), and the relative clause is not presupposed information but contains the new information to be conveyed. It has been suggested that all these factors make these constructions easier to produce and also make them the basis for the development of more complex relative clause structures. The idea that already existing constituents can be used to work out the meaning of a novel construction is supported by a modeling study in which a connectionist network was shown to generalize correctly to previously unlearned constructions on the basis of having learned a variety of simpler constructions.

Developing Pragmatic and Metalinguistic Skills

Children are immersed in communicative interaction with others from infancy, but there are many aspects that take years to develop. Coordinating reference across speaker and listener roles involves manipulating and understanding given and new information, deictic and anaphoric pronouns, temporal information, and so on. In most of the cultures studied, these skills develop initially in conversations with others, and children's attempts to narrate sequences of events start to develop slightly later. Both conversation and narrative require the ability to ground utterances and to refer to referents in ways that require complex cognitive, communicative, and linguistic skills. Children also have to learn to adjust their speech to the genre of the task (conversation, personal narrative, reporting, arguing) and to fit the social context in which they are communicating (for instance, levels of politeness and formality).

Conversation

Early conversations with young children typically show a great deal of scaffolding. Thus, background and setting and the identification of referents are provided by the child's interlocutor. Around the age of 2 years, children are more fluent participants when the conversation is highly 'scripted' around routine activities and when they can join in a multiparty conversation at moments that they choose. Between the ages of 2.6 to 3.0 years, the first, more subtle, discourse particles start to be used (for instance, in English, *now* and *just*), but their range and presence continue developing up to and beyond the school years. Topic continuity in terms of responding to questions and maintaining the topic over a number of turns also improves radically between the ages of 2 and 4 years. Clarification requests by children and children's responses to them show clear development as well: Children respond to clarification requests with more nuanced answers as they get older, and they also make more of them, though even at the age of 7 years, children in a referential communication task do not make clarification requests either as much or in as focused a way as is required by the task. Children's rhetorical skills develop throughout the school years, with the ability to bring arguments to bear, to return to a conversational topic, and to introduce new topics in an appropriate way, all taking many years to perfect.

Narrative

Children's early narratives tend to be a set of short utterances with no attempt at cohesion among them. For a child to be able to narrate an event to another who was not present requires taking into account the hearer's lack of knowledge of the timing of the event, its sequence, and the participants. This is a complex task in itself, and children also have to learn to coordinate sequences of utterances to keep track of referents and events such that, for instance, already referred-to participants are referred to in one way, and novel ones in another.

Once children start being able to produce some coordination between utterances in a narrative, they often use very repetitive devices: for instance, maintaining reference to the same referent as thematic subject throughout the story (e.g., using *He* at the beginning of every utterance) or using *and then* at the beginning of every utterance to coordinate the action. Clearly, the development of narrative abilities is based on the development of a range of skills: Children must be able to take into account the perspective of the listener in terms of what the listener does and does not know. They must also know the linguistic devices of the language that coordinate clauses within utterances (e.g., temporal sequencing, subordination) and across utterances (e.g., the use of pronouns for anaphoric reference), and they must know how their language encodes perspectives; for instance, in English, manner of motion tends to be encoded in the verb, whereas in Spanish it tends to be encoded in adverbials.

Metalinguistic Skills

Children gradually become able to consciously reflect on language, to correct their own and others' utterances, and to notice features of language at all levels: Rhyming relationships, the explanation of metaphors and idioms, and grammaticality judgments. A. Karmiloff-Smith has incorporated language development and metalinguistic awareness into her general theory of the development of cognitive skills. In this approach, the early period of language learning is concerned with skill automatization: children have to learn the forms of the language and to use them relatively effortlessly. Once language becomes relatively fluent and automatic, it can become an object of reflection.

Karmiloff-Smith also discussed children's increasing awareness of the plurifunctionality of forms. She sees metacognition as going through several stages in which initially awareness is implicit and only later, as a result of 'representational redescription,' does it become available to conscious reflection.

For many children, the process of moving to conscious awareness of the forms of language and how they fit together is almost certainly aided by learning to read and write. It has been argued that many of the structures that linguists are concerned with can only be found in written texts and thus that children only learn them during the school years. Competence is, therefore, still developing, rather than being either innate or language development being 'all over by 3.0.' How rapidly these skills develop and how far children get with them is related to the complexity of the language that they hear at home and at school and to levels of literacy.

Clearly, literacy cannot be the only way in which speakers become aware of language as an object of reflection. Preliterate children already show some metacognitive awareness of aspects of language as indicated by Karmiloff-Smith; for instance, they can sometimes correct ungrammatical utterances in naturalistic and experimental situations. There must be many aspects of oral interactions that also afford this ability; for instance, argumentation, speech making, traditions of oral narrative, and the learning of complex ritual language are all likely to be media through which speakers and listeners come to be able to reflect on linguistic structure and its meaning. The important point is that these genres may contain much more complex language than children are likely to learn early on. Thus, language competence, often in the structures in which linguists are most interested, continues to develop over many years.

Atypical Development

Some children grow up in situations that are radically different from those in which typically developing children learn an oral language. The study of these children's atypical development often throws light on the processes involved in language learning and their inter-relationships, though caution should be exercised because one has to see the child and his or her situation as a whole. It is therefore impossible to treat these cases as controlled experiments in which only one variable is changed.

First, from the study of children who grow up from birth in a home where the language used is one of the sign languages of the world, it is clear that these children go through the normal stages of language development on the same timetable as children learning oral languages. Sign languages differ from oral languages not only in the obvious dimension of the medium but also, as a result, in the degree of simultaneity of signs and in the ways in which the face and hands are used grammatically and suprasegmentally. Thus, comparisons between the ways in which children learn the morphology, syntax, and pragmatics of oral and sign language can be extremely illuminating.

There are two groups of children whose nontypical development has been of particular interest to the study of language development: children whose language seems relatively poor by comparison with their nonverbal cognitive levels (children with SLI) and children with Williams's syndrome, whose language seems relatively advanced compared to their very low level of nonverbal cognitive development. Researchers coming from a more linguistic nativist background have claimed that these two syndromes are evidence for an innate basis to grammatical development (compromised in SLI, preserved in Williams's syndrome) that is separate from more general cognitive development. In the case of SLI, the issue is the nature of the biological compromise. Most children with SLI have a range of problems with language, some of which may be more typical earlier and some later. Articulatory and phonological problems, together with delayed inflectional marking, are typical early problems that often resolve, leaving apparent grammar-only problems later on. There is certainly no agreement in the field that the pattern of impairment in SLI children indicates the presence of an innate module for syntax, though some have made claims to this effect.

In the case of Williams's syndrome, it is clear that these children also suffer from a wide range of problems with language and that none of them ever reach the language levels of age-matched, typically developing controls. Karmiloff-Smith *et al.* emphasized a developmental model for these children that suggests that, although language development is atypical from the outset, the problems that children demonstrate change with development and depend on the strategies for producing language that they have developed at earlier stages in the absence of the processes available to typically developing children. Here, too, then, there seems no clear evidence for a specific innate module for syntax.

Learnability and Constituency

The field of language acquisition has been dominated until recently by the so-called learnability issue; namely, that children cannot learn correct syntax from only positive evidence (the so-called poverty of the stimulus argument). Chomsky's various versions of a postulated innate Universal Grammar were attempts to provide these constraints, and the various nativist proposals outlined above aimed to show how these constraints explain different aspects of language development.

Several solutions have been proposed, all of which involve changing the premises of the learnability problem in one way or the other, usually to make the generation of sentences in the language probabilistic, rather than all or nothing. Although the leap from the higher reaches of statistical theory to the details of children's language development is rather large, this solution actually accords quite well both with constructivist approaches to language learning that emphasize the larning of the distributional probabilities in the input and to various attempts to model computationally how distributional probabilities might lead to phrasal learning. Despite not incorporating any model of semantics, these attempts have been quite successful at detecting distributional regularities in the target language that could form one basis for the establishment of categories and of syntagmatic learning.

However, language learning must go beyond the mere learning of immediately sequential probabilities between words. Simply calculating the transitional probability between one word and the next will ignore constituency and produce ungrammatical sentences. This was the basis for Chomsky's 1957 attack on the behaviorist theory of language development. Sentences involve constituents; the subject noun phrase, however long it is, agrees with the main verb, regardless of how many subordinate clauses occur in between; the relationship between an inverted question and its declarative version involves the relationship between the *wh*-word and the whole questioned constituent, independent of the length of the constituent or what occurs between it and the main verb. Thus in *The boy wearing a green hat who I saw yesterday in the park is very nice*, the subject NP (*The boy*) must agree with the main verb (*is*). The relationship between *Is the boy who is wearing a green hat nice?* and *The boy who is wearing a green hat is nice* is that the first *Is* in the question parallels the second *is* in the declarative; otherwise, we would have *Is the boy who wearing a green hat is nice?*

From a constructivist point of view, the crucial extra ingredient is that children are intention readers and meaning makers and that they learn about constituency by building up increasingly complex paradigmatic slots that connect form to meaning. Thus, a child who has heard and used literally hundreds of thousands of copula sentences of the form – *The boy's nice*; *The bus is red*; *They're the ones I want*; *They are really really good*; *The ones over there are the ones I want*; *The boy wearing a green hat is nice* – will know that *the boy wearing a green hat* refers to a particular object or person. This learned structural knowledge of constituency is then used to parse and produce the more complex embedded structures.

Conclusion

Humans have developed language and it has a biological basis. Yet, precisely what this basis is (or, more likely, bases are) still needs a great deal of precise specification. For instance, localization of language in the brains of adults is much more determined than it is in children: Children who have early damage to the areas of the brain that subsume language in adults can learn language to normal levels and will have language represented in other parts of the brain as adults. Thus, it seems that language modularity, and the relative independence of syntax and semantics that characterizes the results of some experiments with adults, may be an outcome of development, rather than being pre-given. Chomsky's insistence on a separation between syntax and meaning, as well as the claim that syntax is essentially unlearnable and therefore that there must be an innate

module for grammar, has ultimately had a negative impact on the scientific study of how children learn to talk. However, many of the issues raised by researchers working within this tradition, especially with regard to the development of more complex syntax, present challenges that have not yet been met fully by those who suggest that, whatever else is innate, syntax is learned through the application of general cognitive skills to the communicative tasks set for children by those around them.

Both positions face a number of challenges. In both, there is a need for greater specification of the processes involved so that proposals can be tested empirically. The challenge to linguistic nativists is to specify in advance the postulated performance limitations and late maturing processes precisely enough so that, rather than invoking them on an *ad hoc* basis to deal with counter-evidence, they can be used to make falsifiable predictions. In addition, these accounts often lack any notion of development: how does what a child is doing at one stage affect what happens next? Finally, because there are input effects at all levels of language acquisition, such theories tend to under-theorize the role of the input, not just in the quantity required by the child but also in the ways in which its precise characteristics are reflected in the child's system and how this interacts with any hypothesized innate knowledge.

The challenge to constructivists is to specify more precisely the ways in which the cognitive and communicative development of the child and the distributional information in the input interact to generate the patterns of learning and of errors and to test this with a wider range of languages and a wider range of input densities and conditions. There is a long way to go, even in the study of English language learning, to say nothing of other languages, in specifying the precise ways in which children expand their inventory of constructions and how they become increasingly schematic.

Children are creative communicators from the start. The question is the basis of this creativity, its scope, and how it develops.

See also: Auditory Perception; Bilingualism; Grammar; Imitation and Modeling; Language Acquisition Theories; Literacy; Pragmatic Development; Preverbal Development and Speech Perception; Semantic Development; Speech Perception.

Suggested Readings

Aguado-Orea J (2004) *The acquisition of morpho-syntax in Spanish: implications for current theories of development*. Ph.D diss., University of Nottingham.

Bates E (1976) *Language and context: the acquisition of pragmatics*. New York: Academic Press.

Bates E, Bretherton I, and Snyder L (1988) *From first words to grammar: individual differences and dissociable mechanisms*. Cambridge: Cambridge University Press.

Berman R and Slobin D (1994) *Relating events in narrative: a crosslinguistic developmental study.* Hillsdale, NJ: Erlbaum.

Bernhardt B and Stemberger JS (1998) *Handbook of phonological development.* San Diego: Academic Press.

Bowerman M (1988) 'The "no negative evidence" problem: how do children avoid constructing an over-general grammar?' In: Hawkins JA (ed.) *Explaining language universals.* Oxford: Blackwell.

Bowerman M and Choi S (2001) 'Shaping meanings for language: universal and language-specific in the acquisition of spatial semantic categories' In: Bowerman M and Levinson S (eds.) *Language acquisition and conceptual development*, pp. 475–511. New York: Cambridge University Press.

Carey S and Bartlett E (1978) 'Acquiring a single new word' *Paper and Reports on Child Language Development* 15: 17–29.

Carpenter M, Nagell K, and Tomasello M (1998) 'Social cognition, joint attention and communicative competence from 9–15 months of age' *Monographs of the Society for Research in Child Development* 255.

Chang F (2002) 'Symbolically speaking: a connectionist model of sentence production' *Cognitive Science* 26(5): 609–651.

Clark E (2003) *First language acquisition.* Cambridge: Cambridge University Press.

Crain S and Thornton R (1998) *Investigations in Universal Grammar: a guide to experiments on the acquisition of syntax.* Cambridge, MA: MIT Press.

Croft W (2001) *Radical construction grammar: syntactic theory in typological perspective.* Oxford: Oxford University Press.

Dabrowska E (2004) *Language, mind and brain.* Washington, DC: Georgetown University Press.

Demuth K (1992) 'The acquisition of Sesotho' In: Slobin DI (ed.) *The crosslinguistic study of language acquisition,* vol. 3, pp. 557–638. Hillsdale, NJ: Lawrence Erlbaum.

Diessel H (2003) *The acquisition of complex sentences in English.* Cambridge: Cambridge University Press.

Drozd K (2004) 'Learnability and linguistic performance (plus commentaries)' *Journal of Child Language* 31: 431–457.

Elman J, Bates E, Johnson M, Karmiloff-Smith A, Parisi D, and Plunkett K (1997) *Rethinking innateness: a connectionist perspective on development.* Cambridge, MA: MIT Press.

Fenson L, Dale P, Reznick JS, Bates E, Thal D, and Pethick S (1994) 'Variability in early communicative development' *Monographs of the Society for Research in Child Development* 242(59): 5.

Fernald A, Pinto J, Swingley D, Weinberg A, and McRoberts G (1998) 'Rapid gains in speed of verbal processing by infants in the second year' *Psychological Science* 9: 28–31.

Fodor J (2001) 'Setting syntactic parameters' In: Baltin M and Collins C (eds.) *The handbook of contemporary syntactic theory*, pp. 730–767. Oxford: Blackwell.

Gentner D (1982) 'Why nouns are learned before verbs: Linguistic relativity versus natural partitioning' In: Kuczaj S (ed.) *Language Development,* vol. 2, pp. 301–333. Hillsdale, NJ: Erlbaum.

Gobet F, Freudenthal D, and Pine JM (2004) 'Modelling syntactic development in a cross-linguistic context' In: Sakas WG (ed.) *Proceedings of the First COLING Workshop on Psycho-computational Models of Human Language Acquisition*, pp. 53–60.

Gomez RL, Gerken L, and Schvaneveldt RW (2000) 'The basis of transfer in artificial grammar learning' *Memory & Cognition* 28(2): 253–263.

Hart B and Risley T (1995) *Meaningful differences in the everyday experience of young American children.* Baltimore, MD: H. Paul Brookes.

Hickmann M (2003) *Children's discourse: person, space and time across languages.* Cambridge: Cambridge University Press.

Huttenlocher J, Vasilyeva M, Cymerman E, and Levine S (2002) 'Language input and child syntax' *Cognitive Psychology* 45(3): 337–374.

Jusczyk P (1997) *The discovery of spoken language.* Cambridge, MA: MIT Press.

Karmiloff-Smith A (1994) 'Precis of beyond modularity: a developmental perspective on cognitive science (with peer commentary)' *Behavioral and Brain Sciences* 17(4): 693–706.

Karmiloff-Smith A, Brown JH, Grice S, and Paterson S (2003) 'Dethroning the myth: cognitive dissociations and innate modularity in Williams's syndrome'. *Developmental Neuropsychology* 23(1&2): 229–244.

Köpcke K (1998) 'The acquisition of plural marking in English and German revisited: schemata versus rules' *Journal of Child Language* 25: 293–319.

Leonard L (1998) *Children with specific language impairment.* Cambridge, MA: MIT Press.

Lewis JD and Elman J (2001) 'A connectionist investigation of linguistic arguments from poverty of the stimulus: learning the unlearnable' In: Moore JD and Stenning K (eds.) *Proceedings of the Twenty-Third Annual Conference of the Cognitive Science Society.* Mahwah, NJ: Erlbaum.

Lieven E (1997) 'Variation in a crosslinguistic context' In: Slobin DI (ed.) *The crosslinguistic study of language acquisition,* vol. 5, pp. 199–263. Hillsdale, NJ: Lawrence Erlbaum.

Lieven E, Behrens H, Speares J, and Tomasello M (2003) 'Early syntactic creativity: a usage-based approach' *Journal of Child Language* 30: 333–370.

MacWhinney B (2004) 'A multiple process solution to the logical problem of language acquisition (plus commentaries)' *Journal of Child Language* 31: 883–914.

Mandler J (2000) 'Perceptual and conceptual processes in infancy' *Journal of Cognition and Development* 1: 3–36.

Maratsos M (2000) 'More overgeneralisations after all' *Journal of Child Language* 28: 35–54.

Markman E, Wasow J, and Hansen M (2003) 'Use of the mutual exclusivity assumption by young word learners' *Cognitive Psychology* 47(2): 241–275.

Miller J and Weinert R (1998) *Spontaneous spoken language: syntax and discourse.* Oxford: Clarendon.

Morris W, Cottrell G, and Elman J (2000) 'A connectionist simulation of the empirical acquisition of grammatical relations' In: Wermter S and Sun R (eds.) *Hybrid neural symbolic integration.* Berlin: Springer Verlag.

O'Grady W (1997) *Syntactic development.* Chicago: University of Chicago Press.

Peters A (1997) 'Language typology, prosody and the acquisition of grammatical morphemes' In: Slobin DI (ed.) *The crosslinguistic study of language acquisition,* vol. 5, pp. 135–197. Hillsdale, NJ: Lawrence Erlbaum.

Pine J, Lieven E, and Rowland C (1998) 'Comparing different models of the development of the verb category' *Linguistics* 36: 4–40.

Pine J, Rowland C, Lieven E, and Theakston A (2005) 'Testing the Agreement/Tense Omission Model: why the data on children's use of non-nominative 3psg subjects count against the ATOM'. *Journal of Child Language* 32: 2.

Plunkett K and Juola P (1999) 'A connectionist model of English past tense and plural morphology' *Cognitive Science* 23(4): 463–490.

Ravid D and Tolchinsky L (2002) 'Developing linguistic literacy: a comprehensive model (plus commentaries)' *Journal of Child Language* 29: 417–447.

Rice M and Wexler K (1996) 'Towards tense as a clinical marker of specific language impairment in English-speaking children' *Journal of Speech and Hearing Research* 41: 1412–1431.

Rowland C and Pine J (2000) 'Subject-auxiliary inversion errors and *wh*-question acquisition' *Journal of Child Language* 27(1): 157–181.

Santelmann L, Berk S, Austin J, Somashekar S, and Lust B (2002) 'Continuity and development in the acquisition of yes/no question: dissociating movement and inflection' *Journal of Child Language* 29: 813–842.

Slobin DI (1985) 'Crosslinguistic evidence for the language-making capacity' In: Slobin DI (ed.) *The cross-linguistic study of language acquisition,* vol. 2, pp. 1157–1256. Hillsdale, NJ: Lawrence Erlbaum.

Slobin DI, Gerhardt J, Kyrattzis A, and Guo J (1996) *Social interaction, social context and language: essays in honor of Susan Ervin-Tripp.* Mahwah, NJ: LEA.

Tomasello M (1992) *First verbs: a case study of early grammatical development.* New York: Cambridge University Press.

Tomasello M (2000) 'Do young children have adult syntactic competence?' *Cognition* 74: 209–253.

Tomasello M (2003) *Constructing a language.* Cambridge, MA: Harvard University Press.

Tomasello M and Stahl D (2004) 'Sampling children's spontaneous speech: How much is enough?'. *Journal of Child Language* 31: 101–121.

Valian V (1991) 'Syntactic subjects in the early speech of American and Italian children' *Cognition* 40: 21–81.

Vihman M (1996) *Phonological development.* Oxford: Blackwell.

Weist R, Pawlak A, and Carapella J (2004) 'Syntactic-semantic interface in the acquisition of verb morphology' *Journal of Child Language* 31(1): 31–60.

Wexler K (1998) 'Very early parameter setting and the unique checking constraint: a new explanation of the optional infinitive stage' *Lingua* 106: 23–79.

Wexler K (2002) 'Lenneberg's dream: learning, normal language development and specific language impairment'. In: Schaffer J and Levy Y (eds.) *Language competence across populations: towards a definition of specific language impairment.* Mahwah, NJ: Lawrence Erlbaum.

Lead Poisoning

R L Canfield, Cornell University, Ithaca, NY, USA
T A Jusko, University of Washington, Seattle, WA, USA

Glossary

Anthropogenic – Arising from human activity.

Biokinetics – The ways substances behave after they enter the body, how are they distributed to various organs, and how long they persist in the body.

Brain death – A total and irreversible cessation of brain function as manifested by the absence of consciousness and absence of all brainstem functions, including spontaneous movement and respiration.

Cellular proliferation – An increase in the number of cells through cell division and in the size of cells through growth.

Computed tomography (CT) scan – A diagnostic imaging procedure that uses a combination of X-rays and computer technology to produce detailed cross-sectional images of the body.

DMSA (dimercaptosuccinic acid) – Also known as succimer (Chemet) is an orally active chelating agent often used to treat lead poisoning in children with blood lead concentrations $>45\,g\,dl^{-1}$.

Encephalopathy – A general term describing degeneration or dysfunction of the brain, which can be defined more specifically by reference to a set of symptoms.

Erythrocyte – A red blood cell, containing hemoglobin, which is responsible for transporting oxygen throughout the body.

Executive functions – Cognitive operations that control and manage lower-level cognitive processes, such as those involved in planning, the selection of relevant and filtering of irrelevant sensory information, attentional flexibility, abstract thinking, rule acquisition, and inhibiting inappropriate actions.

Glial cell – Any of the cells making up the network of branched cells and fibers that support and nourish the tissue of the central nervous system.

Half-life – The time required for a biological system to eliminate by natural processes half the amount of a substance, such as toxin, that has entered it.

Hippocampus – A brain structure involved in forming, storing, and processing memory.

K-XRF (bone scan) – X-ray fluorescence method used to estimate lead-exposure in bone.

Meta-analytic study – A collection of statistical methods for analyzing the results of multiple independent studies for the purpose of integrating the findings.

Migration – The movement of nerve cells from where they were originally generated in the neural crest to their eventual location in the mature brain.

Myelination – The process of forming a fatty sheath (myelin) around axons and dendrites, thus enabling neural impulses to travel faster.

Neural plasticity – The malleability of brain structure and function as a result of experience.

Osteoporotic – A condition that affects especially older women, characterized by a decrease in bone mass with decreased bone density and enlargement of bone spaces producing porosity and brittleness.

Protein kinase C – An enzyme found throughout the body's tissues and organs that is capable of modulating many cellular functions, including neuronal growth, ion channel function, and gene expression.

Socioeconomic status (SES) – A measure of an individual or family's relative economic and social ranking.
Synaptogenesis – The formation of nerve synapses.

Introduction

A simple axiom of human development is that growth and change result from a confluence of genetic and environmental forces that shape individual life trajectories. Environmental toxins can be among the most influential forces for permanently altering the course of development. Although recognized as a serious health threat for more than two millennia, more children are known to be adversely affected by lead (Pb^{2+}) than by any other environmental pollutant. In the US today, as many as 1 in 10 children will be exposed to a potentially dangerous amount of lead at some time during infancy or early childhood. Largely as a result of human activity, this confirmed neurotoxin has been distributed throughout the environment in a manner that makes infants and young children likely targets of exposure, making it especially regrettable that infants and children are also the most vulnerable to lead's potentially devastating effects. It has long been known that at very high levels of lead exposure children suffer encephalopathy (acute brain swelling), resulting in extensive permanent brain damage and even death. Only since the 1970s has it become widely appreciated that children with low-level lead exposure and who show no clinically observable symptoms nevertheless have impaired iron, calcium, and vitamin D metabolism, and also lasting cognitive and behavioral deficits – the primary focus of this article.

Childhood lead poisoning is a problem as multifaceted as the study of child development itself. To understand this toxin's personal and societal impact requires the collective efforts of researchers in the physical and biological sciences, the social and behavioral sciences, medicine, public health, and policy studies. These efforts focus on addressing several questions, including (1) what are the sources of lead in the environment and how do children become exposed; (2) what happens to lead after it enters the body and what are the mechanisms of toxicity; (3) what are the harmful effects of lead and how do they relate to the amount of exposure, the age of exposure, and other characteristics of the individual; and (4) are the adverse effects of lead permanent, or can they be reversed or reduced in severity by removing lead from children's bodies? Answers to these questions are used to guide the medical treatment of lead-exposed children, to inform regulatory agencies about appropriate standards of environmental management of lead contaminated homes and industrial sites, and for setting permissible lead content in consumer products. The knowledge also provides guidance to parents whose children might be at risk, and motivates the broader society to ensure that no child's developmental potential is limited by exposure to lead. This article will review these four questions in detail, providing information on exposure to lead, its mechanisms and effects, and whether and how those effects can be mitigated.

Human Exposure to Lead

Lead is a naturally occurring element that has been part of human culture for millennia. Its malleability and durability make it useful for creating products that meet a broad range of practical and esthetic human needs. Examples of these include decorative lead beads discovered in Turkey, dating to about 6500 BC, and a small lead statue discovered in Upper Egypt dating to approximately 3800 BC. Use of lead bowls and jugs for oil and wine is evident from 3000 to 2500 BC, and lead's use as a pigment for pottery glazes, paints, and cosmetics are similarly ancient.

The more extreme symptoms of acute lead poisoning, such as severe abdominal pain and paralysis of the extremities, were described by Nikander (185–135 BC), a Greek physician writing about poisons and their antidotes. We now know the progression of symptoms to include colic, muscular weakness and clumsiness, disorientation and confusion, encephalopathy, paralysis, and death. The Romans used lead to build an elaborate system of pipes to convey freshwater into their city, and some attributed the poor health among pipe fitters to lead exposure. A modern English word for pipe fitter, plumber, is derived from the Latin word for lead, plumbum, which gives us a term for lead poisoning, plumbism. Medical concern with lead poisoning lagged behind concerns about many other poisons that are more obviously linked to their consequences. Symptoms of arsenic poisoning occur about 30 min after it is ingested, whereas lead poisoning generally progresses more slowly, obscuring the temporal relation between cause and effect. Also, lead poisoning has always tended to be a malady of the poor, such as slaves who worked in lead mines, potters, and laborers. Even today, lead disproportionately affects those of lower socioeconomic status (SES).

In modern times, exposure to lead extends well beyond those who mine, smelt, or otherwise work directly with the metal. Lead's value as a pigment in paint, as an additive to increase octane in gasoline, and in many industrial processes has resulted in its widespread distribution throughout the environment. Consequently, many children in the industrialized world, and increasingly in some developing countries, are exposed to 20–100 times as much lead as was common during prehistoric or preindustrial times.

Although historically high, the average exposure of children in the US today is less than one-seventh of what it was only 30 years ago.

Especially when exposures are low, the symptoms of lead poisoning can be very subtle. Also, the delay between the exposure and the adverse outcome can be very long, which directly affects the sense of urgency needed to adequately address the problem. The need to establish a cause–effect link between lead exposure and children's health, and the need to know the minimum exposure required to produce a meaningful adverse effect are the overarching motivations for the study of childhood lead poisoning.

Sources of Environmental Lead, Exposure Mechanisms, and Biokinetics

Although a naturally occurring element, the primary sources of environmental lead are anthropogenic. Prior to the banning of leaded gasoline in the US, Europe, and many other countries, most of the lead released into the environment was from automobile emissions. The gradual removal of leaded gasoline was one of the most important environmental health successes of the twentieth century, and children's blood lead levels (BLLs) declined in concert with the gradual removal of lead from gasoline. Although the lead content of gasoline was greatly reduced beginning in 1986, it was not completely banned until 1996. **Figure 1** shows two time series, spanning the years 1970–2000, illustrating the relation between the total

amount of lead used for transportation in the US and the average BLL in children. During this 30-year span of time the average BLLs of young children declined from about 15 to about $2\,\mu g\,dl^{-1}$. The similar rate of decline in the two time series suggests that leaded gasoline was the primary source of children's exposure. In countries where gasoline still contains lead, children's BLLs are similar to those in the US prior to its ban.

The major sources of environmental lead, the pathways of exposure, and biological fate of lead after it enters the body are illustrated in **Figure 2**. Currently, industrial activity is the largest contributor of lead released into the environment, which includes lead released from smelters, from the manufacture of lead-acid batteries for automobiles and computer backup systems, and from chemical production. The current source of greatest exposure to children living in the US is from lead-based paint. In 1990, the US Food and Drug Administration estimated that 75% of the total lead exposure for a typical 2-year-old child originates from household dust contaminated with small particles of lead, with only 16% coming from food, 7% from water, and 2% from soil and other sources.

In part because paint is the primary source of exposure, the age and quality of housing is an important predictor of the amount of lead found in a child's body. Children living in houses built prior to 1940 (when lead content in paint was highest) are more than twice as likely as other children to have elevated blood lead. The correlation between lead-based paint and housing quality means that lead exposure is not equally distributed

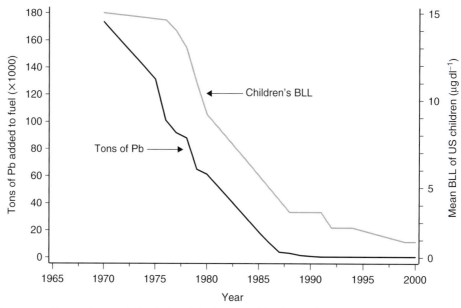

Figure 1 Declining use of lead in transportation fuel and declines in children's blood lead levels (BLLs) in the US: 1970–2000. The black line corresponds to the left axis, showing the yearly use of lead (in thousands of tons) for all transportation purposes in the US. The gray line corresponds to the right axis, showing the change over time in the mean BLL of children during the same historical period. The similar rates of decline of the two time series suggests the importance of leaded gasoline as source of children's exposure. Lead was completely banned as an additive for commercial gasoline in 1996.

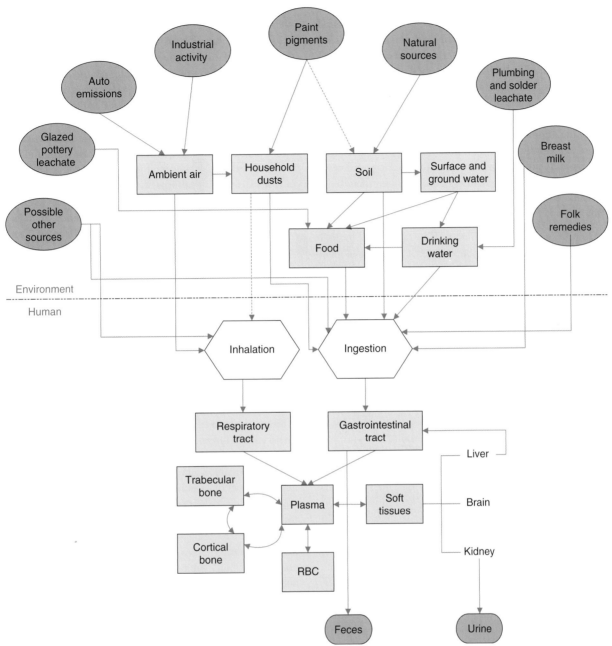

Figure 2 Sources of environmental lead, routes of exposure, and biologic fate. The figure shows the flow of lead from the environmental sources through the human body. The most common source of exposure in children is lead-based paint, although some children are poisoned by more idiosyncratic sources, such as inexpensive metallic jewellery items and toy soldiers; plastic lunch boxes; Tamarindo jellied fruit candy from Mexico; calcium supplements; canned foods; imported vinyl miniblinds and some plastics; crystal decanters and glasses; cosmetics; hair dyes; tobacco; Lozeena, an orange powdered food coloring from Iraq; metal urns and kettles, and curtain weights. RBC, red blood cells.

across groups defined by income and ethnicity. Children from low-income families, who are more likely to live in older buildings that are in poor condition, have been found to be eight times more likely than are children from high-income families to have dangerously elevated BLLs. For similar reasons, non-Hispanic black children are nearly 2.5 times more likely to have dangerous levels

of lead in their blood than are non-Hispanic white children (see **Figure 3**).

Other aspects of a child's environment can also influence their exposure to lead. For example, soil lead levels can be high in some urban areas near roadways that were heavily traveled when leaded gasoline was in use. Children living near smelters or other past or present

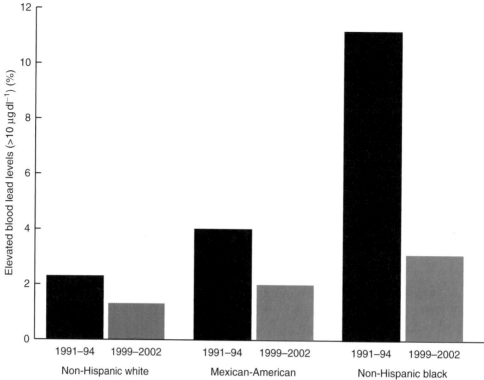

Figure 3   Racial and ethnic group differences in the percentage of children the US with blood lead levels greater than $10\,\mu g\,dl^{-1}$ in 1991–94 and 1999–2002.

industrial sites are also at greater risk of harmful exposure. Less frequently, children are exposed to dangerous amounts of lead from toy jewelry and other metal trinkets, from lead-pigmented plastic consumer products (e.g., lunch boxes, window blinds), and from imported foods (e.g., candy stored in lead-glazed pottery).

Lead Exposure in Early Childhood

Lead enters the body mostly through inhalation or ingestion (see **Figure 2**). As noted above, the primary route of exposure for infants and children, at least in the US, is ingestion of contaminated household dust. Leaded paint applied to friction areas such as door frames and double-hung window frames gradually wears away, releasing lead particles that collect on the floor, sills, and other flat surfaces. Cracking and peeling paint on ceilings and walls can also release lead particles. Contaminated soil can be tracked into the house, and lead from the parent's workplace or lead used in hobbies can increase their children's exposure. Very dangerous amounts of lead can be released when lead-based paint is disturbed during home remodeling.

Infants explore the world and learn about the properties of objects and about their own bodies by sucking on their fingers and mouthing toys, blankets, and other objects. In a house contaminated by lead, these objects, especially when

wet with saliva, will accumulate lead particles that can be readily ingested. When infants begin crawling and walking, they cover much more territory and are at risk of greater exposure than pre-locomotor infants; consequently, it is during toddlerhood, from about age 18–36 months, that children's BLLs tend to reach their maximum. Declining hand-to-mouth behavior and improving personal hygiene usually result in less exposure and declining BLLs throughout childhood and adolescence.

In addition to ingesting more lead during infancy than later in life, infants absorb lead more efficiently than adults. Up to 70% of the lead ingested by children and pregnant women can be absorbed into the body, compared to 20% for adults. Also, whereas adults excrete approximately 99% of the lead they absorb, children excrete only about two-thirds of absorbed lead.

In the body, lead is distributed and redistributed among three compartments: blood, soft tissues, bones, and teeth (see **Figure 2**). Lead is initially taken up into blood plasma and then distributed to erythrocytes (where 99% of blood lead is found), soft tissues, and bone. Soft-tissue lead is found mostly in the liver, kidney, lungs, and brain, and eventually 90% or more of an adult's total body lead burden is stored in the bones and teeth.

The half-life of lead in adult bone can be several years to several decades. However, during skeletal growth, pregnancy and lactation, osteoporotic bone loss and other periods of bone remodeling and calcium stress, lead is released from the bones to circulate in the blood and accumulate in tissue and other body compartments. Recirculating pre-pregnancy bone lead can account for one-third or more of lead in the blood of pregnant women and, because the placenta does not protect the fetus from lead in maternal blood, maternal pre-pregnancy lead exposure can enter fetal tissue. Maternal body lead can also be transmitted to the infant through breast milk.

Lead Neurotoxicity

Measuring Exposure

Identifying lead poisoning and linking it to a health outcome depends on knowing how much lead has been absorbed into the body. Although lead damages the brain, it is not possible in humans to measure brain lead levels. Thus, methods have been developed for measuring lead concentration in the other body compartments – blood, bones, and teeth. The concentration of lead in whole blood is the most common measure of exposure. Blood lead reflects primarily current and recent exposure and is the most widely used measure in both clinical and research settings.

Possible Biological Mechanisms of Lead Neurotoxicity

The overt symptoms and potentially lethal sequelae of acute lead poisoning in children were clearly described in the medical literature more than a century ago, and are briefly reviewed below. However, only since the 1970s has it become widely accepted that lead poisoning can cause subtle deficits in the cognitive and behavioral performance of children who show no overt symptoms of poisoning – children for whom their exposure would go unnoticed without a biological indicator such as BLL. The specific biological mechanisms responsible for these subtle neurobehavioral deficits are not well understood, but it is established that lead affects fundamental inter- and intracellular biochemical processes. Using animals and *in vitro* preparations it has been possible to manipulate directly the amount of lead exposure and then examine the damaged tissues and cells thought to be the basis of functional behavioral deficits in the whole organism. This research has shown that lead does not act through a single biochemical mechanism. As a divalent cation (Pb^{2+}), lead shares properties with calcium (Ca^{2+}), iron (Fe^{2+}), and zinc (Zn^{2+}), all essential micronutrients. And although it has no nutritional value, lead can mimic the actions of these other minerals, allowing it to participate in and potentially disrupt a wide range of critically important cellular processes.

Lead's similarity to calcium may be responsible for many of its adverse effects at low exposure levels. For example, lead has been implicated as a cause of abnormal programmed cell death (apoptosis) by activating a cascade of intracellular processes normally regulated by calcium. Even very low concentrations of lead can alter calcium homeostasis in ways that produce an abnormal buildup of intracellular calcium. This excess calcium can trigger a sequence of events that will induce otherwise healthy cells to activate the enzymes involved in normal apoptosis.

Other calcium-related processes are also highly sensitive to lead. For example calmodulin, a binding protein involved in intracellular calcium homeostasis, is activated by lead at nanomolar concentrations. Protein kinase C (PKC), normally a calcium-activated enzyme, can be activated by lead in picomolar concentrations, much lower than it can be activated by calcium. PKC is involved in a broad range of cellular functions including neuronal growth and differentiation, and in specific biochemical processes fundamental to learning and memory, including long-term potentiation (LTP) in the hippocampus.

Altered calcium homeostasis can also affect neural function by disrupting both the spontaneous and the evoked release of neurotransmitters such as dopamine (DA) and alter dopamine D1 and D2 receptor protein expression in nucleus accumbens, hippocampus, and frontal cortex. Some studies indicate that the mesocorticolimbic DA system is especially sensitive to lead exposure. Other mechanisms of lead toxicity include the inhibition of *N*-methyl-D-aspartate (NMDA) receptors, delayed differentiation of glial cell progenitors, and reduced growth and abnormal branching of dendrites.

Frank Lead Poisoning

Individuals differ greatly in their sensitivity to lead. Some infants begin to exhibit overt symptoms of lead poisoning at blood concentrations as low as $40–50 \, \mu g \, dl^{-1}$, and at about $60 \, \mu g \, dl^{-1}$ in young children. These levels are sometimes seen in children who have ingested household dust contaminated with particles of high lead-content paint, or in children who frequently eat food stored in lead-glazed pottery. At these BLLs, highly sensitive children show abdominal cramping and become irritable. This can progress to increased intracranial pressure, edema, and other forms of encephalopathy. Children who experience encephalopathy nearly always suffer permanent deficits in cognitive and behavioral functioning.

Extremely high BLLs can result from ingesting paint chips or other objects with high lead content. In two recently described cases, BLLs greater than $100 \, \mu g \, dl^{-1}$ were observed in children who swallowed pieces of low-cost jewellery. In one case, a 4-year-old boy swallowed a charm from a metal bracelet that had been provided as a free gift for purchasing a pair of athletic shoes. Approximately 2 days after seeing a physician for unexplained abdominal complaints, the child was admitted to the hospital with severe gastric pain, persistent vomiting, and listlessness. Ten hours after admission the boy became agitated and aggressive and shortly thereafter suffered seizure and respiratory arrest. After being resuscitated, a computed tomography (CT) scan revealed cerebral edema. Subsequent studies on the following day revealed that the boy had suffered brain death; his BLL was $180\,\mu g\,dl^{-1}$. Upon autopsy, the metal charm was found in the boy's stomach. Chemical analysis showed the charm to contain 99.1% lead.

A very different outcome was seen in another 4-year-old boy who swallowed a medallion from a toy necklace purchased at a vending machine. After 3–4 weeks the medallion was discovered and the boy was diagnosed with lead poisoning; at that time his BLL was $123\,\mu g\,dl^{-1}$. The child was immediately treated with several courses of chelation therapy using succimer (dimercaptosuccinic acid; DMSA). Chelation therapy is a means of removing circulating lead ions; the chelator tightly binds to lead and forms a water-soluble compound that is excreted through urine. After chelation, the child's BLL had declined to approximately $25\,\mu g\,dl^{-1}$. Surprisingly, extensive psychometric, neuropsychological, and electrophysiological evaluation revealed no obvious cognitive impairment. Repeated cognitive testing over a period of more than 1 year revealed no immediate evidence of adverse effects in this child.

These two cases illustrate that children vary greatly in their sensitivity to lead. Indeed, cases of fatal poisonings have been reported in children with BLLs of only $80\,\mu g\,dl^{-1}$, but there also are reports of children who are asymptomatic with lead levels as high as $300\,\mu g\,dl^{-1}$. The reasons for these individual differences are unclear, but it is possible that children who appear especially sensitive have had one or more previous poisonings that went unreported. Genetic differences, nutritional status, and previous or concurrent exposure to other toxins might be involved also.

Neurobehavioral Correlates of Low Blood Lead Levels

Medical experience with lead-exposed children established that BLLs as low as $60\,\mu g\,dl^{-1}$ – exposure sufficient to cause gastric symptoms in most infants and young children – were strongly associated with subsequent cognitive and behavioral deficits and were, therefore, recognized to be unsafe as early as the 1930s. However, after it was discovered that BLLs as low as $40\,\mu g\,dl^{-1}$ interfered with heme biosynthesis in otherwise asymptomatic children, the notion of insidious lead poisoning was proposed. Insidious poisoning refers to the idea that when severe damage is caused by acute high-level exposure to a toxin, lower-level chronic exposure will produce more subtle adverse effects. The possibility of insidious lead poisoning was identified as a top research priority in a 1972 National Academy of Sciences report

to the US Environmental Protection Agency (EPA). As a result, the primary focus of research during the past 35 years has been to establish what amount of exposure, if any, can be considered safe for the health and long-term development of infants and young children.

Methods for detecting insidious lead poisoning

Case reports and descriptions of the long-term developmental outcomes of lead-poisoned infants and children were an inadequate basis for detecting possible subtle neurobehavioral effects of BLLs less than about $40\,\mu g\,dl^{-1}$. Thus, researchers began formal studies that involved large numbers of children and more sophisticated research designs. These studies also used sensitive measures of cognitive and behavioral functioning that allow for making fine distinctions between levels of performance. The primary outcome measure used in these early studies, and in nearly all subsequent studies of pediatric lead exposure, was some form of a standardized psychometric intelligence test. These tests yield a global index score to represent the quality of general intellectual functioning. Although the terminology for the global index scores differs, for ease of presentation we use the term 'intelligence quotient' (IQ) to refer to the omnibus score from any such test.

In addition to examining the possible effects of lead on IQ scores, several studies have assessed the relationship between lead exposure and more specific areas of cognitive function. These studies employ neuropsychological tests originally developed for the diagnosis and evaluation of patients with psychiatric problems or probable brain damage. Also, several studies have investigated the possible effects of lead exposure on children's social, emotional, and psychological function – focusing primarily on a link between early exposure and later externalizing behaviors (e.g., conduct problems, aggressiveness, and delinquency).

Lead exposure and intelligence test performance

Early formal studies of what, at that time, was considered low-level lead exposure employed cross-sectional research designs for which the exposure measure (typically BLL) and the outcome (typically IQ) were measured at a single time point. Importantly, these studies were designed with the recognition that exposure to lead is only one of many factors that can influence a child's performance on an IQ test. As a result, information was obtained about possible prenatal and birth complications, postnatal health, family structure, SES, and parental education, among other possible influences. This information was then used in statistical analyses to estimate the independent contribution of lead exposure on IQ. Although the findings of individual studies were not fully consistent, when the results of 24 cross-sectional studies were systematically analyzed, a broad consensus emerged among most researchers studying lead exposure: that BLLs as low as $25\,\mu g\,dl^{-1}$, and possibly as low as $10\,\mu g\,dl^{-1}$, adversely affect children's intellectual functioning. Taking a precautionary approach, in 1991 the Center for Disease Control and Prevention (CDC) lowered the definition of an elevated BLL from 25 to $10\,\mu g\,dl^{-1}$.

Although the cross-sectional studies were highly influential in shaping public policies, research using that methodology cannot rule out critically important alternative explanations. For example, suppose that brain damage was caused by an undetected prenatal event not related to lead exposure. It is possible that neurologically compromised infants engage in more hand-to-mouth behavior, which causes them to ingest more lead. In this case, one would observe an inverse association of BLL and IQ but the conclusion that lead causes lower IQ scores would be unwarranted.

Criticisms of the early studies also revolved around the issue of confounding. Confounding occurs when a variable (measured or unmeasured) is associated with the exposure and the outcome of interest. Maternal IQ would be a potential confounder because it reflects the mother's genetic contribution to her child's IQ, but also because it can contribute to economic disadvantage and poor housing quality, and therefore to the child's exposure to lead. In this way, maternal IQ is associated with children's BLLs (exposure) and also with children's IQ (outcome). If confounding is present and not adequately addressed, the estimated association between blood lead and IQ could be either spuriously strong or weak. Although the cross-sectional studies did attempt to identify possible confounders and adjust for them, they often lacked measurement of key confounding variables such as maternal IQ and the quality of stimulation in the home environment. Based on these and other challenges to the validity of these early studies, the scientific basis for the CDC action was vigorously questioned by some.

Prospective, or longitudinal, cohort studies address many of the limitations of the cross-sectional design, and in the late 1970s and 1980s prospective studies were initiated in Boston and Cincinnati, in the US, Kosovo in the former Yugoslavia, Mexico City, and Port Pirie and Sydney in Australia. Although originally designed to examine the effects of prenatal substance abuse, a prospective study conducted in Cleveland also examined childhood lead exposure in relation to intellectual development. These studies followed children, typically from birth, to ascertain BLLs and measure neurobehavioral performance on multiple occasions during infancy and childhood. Again, the primary outcome was the child's score on an IQ test, but other outcomes were examined in one or more individual studies.

These longitudinal studies also focused more intensely than earlier studies on the problem of possible confounding by parental IQ, SES, and the quality of the childrearing environment (e.g., maternal warmth and responsivity, encouragement of learning, and provision of competence-building toys). Pregnancy and birth complications and many other indicators of child health were also considered.

The Boston study was unique in that the average BLL of the children who participated was consistently below $10\,\mu g\,dl^{-1}$, which contrasted with the higher lead levels found in Cincinnati, Cleveland, Sydney, and Port Pirie. In the Yugoslavia study, approximately one-half of the subjects resided near a lead smelter, refinery, and battery plant, whereas a comparison town had much less environmental exposure and thus BLLs ranged considerably, from 1 to $70\,\mu g\,dl^{-1}$, in that study cohort. Five of the seven prospective studies (Boston, Cincinnati, Cleveland, Mexico, Port Pirie, Sydney, Yugoslavia) reported that higher BLL, measured either as cumulative exposure or exposure at a particular age during infancy or early childhood, was associated with lower IQ scores – after statistical control for many possible confounders. Moreover, for each study that reported adverse effects, the lead–IQ association was replicated at two or more ages. Reports from the Cleveland and Sydney studies indicated no association between BLL and IQ. No studies have reported significant positive associations between BLL and children's intelligence test performance. When the results from all the prospective cohort studies were subjected to meta-analysis, the effect of an increase in BLL from 10 to $20\,\mu g\,dl^{-1}$ was estimated to be a 1–4-point decrease in children's IQ scores.

Specific cognitive and neuropsychological functions

Intelligence test scores reflect a sort of average of a person's performance on multiple individual subtests, each assessing competence in a general domain of cognitive functioning. Although IQ scores are reliably associated with children's BLLs, they reveal little about the specific types of cognitive functions that are affected. If, as is found with many toxins, lead selectively affects some biochemical or neurophysiological processes but spares others, then the cognitive functions most dependent on those more vulnerable processes would be disproportionately damaged. Consequently, a better understanding of the types of cognitive processes affected by lead could uncover more sensitive measures for indicating the presence of adverse effects of lead, and it might also open avenues to possible behavioral or neuropharmacological interventions for lead-exposed children.

Researchers have used two main methods to identify what some have called a behavioral signature of lead toxicity. One method has been to examine patterns of performance across the individual subtests used to derive an overall IQ score. A potentially stronger methodology has been to use clinical neuropsychological tests initially developed to characterize the pattern of behavioral deficits associated with localized brain damage. Studies using these methods are suggestive of several broad areas of cognitive function that are especially vulnerable to lead exposure – visual–motor integration, attention, and executive functions.

Visual–motor integration involves the ability to coordinate fine motor skills with visual–spatial perception in order to draw and copy geometric forms, assemble puzzles, and arrange blocks to create a specified configuration. Reviewing patterns of subtest performance across studies suggests that lead-related deficits in the overall IQ score are influenced by a particularly strong inverse association between BLL and performance on block-design tasks. The block-design subtest is also the most consistent among all subtests in showing a statistically significant association with BLL. Studies using neuropsychological tasks designed specifically to assess visual–spatial abilities and visual–motor integration and have produced a consistent set of findings; namely, that BLL is inversely related to fine motor skills, eye–hand coordination, and standardized testing of the ability to copy geometric forms. Although these results are mostly consistent, in one longitudinal study visual–spatial abilities were most impaired at age 5 years, whereas extensive neuropsychological testing conducted at age 10 years revealed no clear deficit in visual–spatial skills.

Attention, a second area of possible special vulnerability, involves cognitive functions for sustaining performance over time, and for selecting particular stimuli for intensive cognitive processing. Some studies have used index scores based on combinations of IQ subtests and neuropsychological tests thought to reflect sustained and focused attention. Although sustained attention is generally unrelated to lead exposure, more highly exposed subjects in these studies showed poorer performance on tasks requiring focused attention.

Executive functions enable planning and goal-oriented cognition based largely on the ability to coordinate the activities of more specialized cognitive functions, such as memory, attention, and visual–spatial processing, and to flexibly apply these cognitive functions to meet changing task demands. Importantly, the line between certain aspects of attention and executive functioning is not clearly drawn. For example, focused attention involves the controlled use of attention and therefore is sometimes included as a component of executive functioning. Attentional flexibility is more generally considered to reflect executive functioning and involves the ability to shift the focus of attention between different sources of information or to consider alternative problem-solving strategies.

Two prospective studies have examined children's performance on classical measures of executive functioning, arriving at similar but not identical conclusions. In one study of 10-year-old children, BLL during childhood was associated with an increase in several measures of perseverative behavior. For example, although childhood BLL was unrelated to how quickly children learned a simple rule, children with higher BLLs appeared to be less cognitively flexible – after the rule changed they were more likely to continue making the previous, but now incorrect, response. Cognitive rigidity was also seen in a study in which 5-year-old children completed a computerized test battery. Lead exposure was unrelated to the ability to sustain attention on a simple task, but children with higher BLLs made more errors when they were required to shift to a new rule. These children also showed planning deficits when solving multistep problems. Children with higher BLLs made impulsive choices on the first step of the problem, which made subsequent steps more difficult, thereby causing them to make more errors. Finally, a study of young adults given a large battery of neuropsychological tests showed that tooth lead levels were inversely related to performance on groups of tasks that assessed focused attention and attentional flexibility (although not sustained attention).

Externalizing behaviors and juvenile delinquency

A curious symptom during a period of acute lead poisoning is a high level of aggressiveness and combativeness, even in young children. Lasting effects of lead on behavior problems were described in an early case study of the long-term outcomes of boys treated for acute lead poisoning. As adolescents, many years after being treated, these boys were found to have extremely high rates of delinquency. This report was one motivation for studies investigating whether lead exposure at subacute levels is associated with problems of behavioral and emotional self-regulation. Based on parent and teacher ratings on child behavior checklists, children with higher lead exposure early in life were found to have more conduct problems and were more defiant, withdrawn, and destructive than children with lower lead levels. Studies of behavior problems in older children focus on antisocial, delinquent, and pre-delinquent behaviors. For example, in one study of 300 boys, the frequency of their antisocial and delinquent behaviors at ages 7 and 11 years was rated by their parents and teachers using the Child Behavior Checklist (CBCL). One major scale of the CBCL assesses behaviors such as disobedience at home and school, destructiveness, cruelty, and truthfulness. The boys rated their own behaviors using the Self-Reported Antisocial Behavior (SRAB) and Self-Reported Delinquency (SRD) scales. SRAB measures nonviolent and violent antisocial behavior in terms of frequency, whereas SRD defines delinquent behavior operationally as activities that violate legal statues and often involve some risk of arrest. Childhood cumulative lead exposure was measured using K-XRF at age 12 years. Evidence for lead-related influences on delinquency was inconsistent. When the boys were rated at age 11 years, CBCL ratings of problem behaviors were positively associated with bone lead. However, there was no association between bone lead and self-reported behaviors, or between bone lead and parent and teacher ratings at age 7 years. Because many children might under report their socially undesirable activities, and because eventual levels of delinquency and problem behaviors might not have developed by age 7 years, these findings provide some, albeit limited, support for the hypothesis that exposure to lead increases the risk of problem behaviors among boys during late childhood.

A subsequent study addressed the age issue by selecting adolescents, and the reporting bias issue by selecting children who already had been arrested and adjudicated. In this case-control study design, cases were those adjudicated as delinquent and controls were nondelinquent age-mates selected from high schools in the same county as the cases. Results from this study indicated that, compared to nondelinquent controls, adjudicated delinquent adolescents were four times more likely to have a bone lead concentration greater than 25 parts per million (ppm).

Whereas the previously described studies lacked detailed information about subjects' history of lead exposure during childhood, one study measured blood lead more than 20 times between birth and 6.5 years. When they were 19–20 years old, the young men and women reported on their delinquent and predelinquent behaviors and their parents provided independent reports. After controlling for a range of other factors that might predict both lead exposure and delinquent behavior, this study revealed that children with higher BLLs as neonates engaged in more problem behaviors later in life; average childhood lead concentrations were also positively associated with self-reports and parent reports of delinquency.

The consistency of findings from studies using different measures of problem behaviors and different measures of lead exposure (bone, blood, and dentin) suggests the possibility of a causal relation between early lead exposure and later delinquency. Although the BLLs among the children in the studies just described were substantially greater than what is common in the US today, these findings cannot be dismissed as irrelevant. Still today, thousands of children living in substandard housing in many inner cities of the East and Midwest are likely to experience similar amounts of lead exposure as the children in these studies. Also, the relation of lead and delinquency has been little explored in samples of children with very low exposure and so it remains unknown whether behavior problems are significantly increased in such children, or whether there is a threshold exposure below which lead and delinquency are unrelated.

Susceptibility

Is There a Safe Level of Exposure?

In 1991, the CDC issued its fourth statement on preventing lead poisoning in young children. The main outcome of

this report was a change in the definition of an elevated blood lead from $25 \mu g \, dl^{-1}$ to its present level of $10 \mu g \, dl^{-1}$. In this report it was explicitly acknowledged that some studies indicated harmful effects at levels at least as low as $10 \mu g \, dl^{-1}$, and that no threshold had been identified. Partly in consideration of the inadequate base of evidence, $10 \mu g \, dl^{-1}$ was described as a level of concern. The CDC also established recommended courses of action for treating lead-exposed children. For example, for a 1-year-old infant with a BLL of $10 \mu g \, dl^{-1}$ or less, it is recommended that the lead test be repeated at age 2 years. If the result is again of $10 \mu g \, dl^{-1}$ or less, then no additional testing is recommended. Implicit in this approach is that BLLs of $10 \mu g \, dl^{-1}$ are safe. However, because no safety threshold had been indicated by research carried out prior to the 1991 statement, some researchers and policymakers were concerned that using $10 \mu g \, dl^{-1}$ as a cutoff lacked a strong scientific justification. Of particular concern was that nearly all the research findings available in 1991 were based on populations of children with BLLs greater than $10 \mu g \, dl^{-1}$.

Concerns about using $10 \mu g \, dl^{-1}$ as an implicit safety threshold were heightened by findings from a prospective study initiated in the late 1990s to track the development of children in Rochester, New York. Reflecting secular trends in lead exposure (see **Figure 1**), the children who participated in this study had very low BLLs throughout infancy and early childhood. Indeed, most children had BLLs less than $10 \mu g \, dl^{-1}$ at every assessment (i.e., at 6, 12, 18, 24, 36, 48, and 60 months). The results of intelligence tests administered when the children were 3 and 5 years of age showed an inverse association between IQ scores and average BLL during infancy and childhood. More specifically, after controlling for nine pre-specified covariates, it was estimated that as lifetime average BLLs increased from 1 to $10 \mu g \, dl^{-1}$, children's intelligence test scores declined by an estimated 7.4 points. These results suggested that subtle adverse effects on children's cognitive functioning occurred at BLLs well below $10 \mu g \, dl^{-1}$. Statistical modeling revealed the dose–response curve shown in **Figure 4**. The shape of this curve did not indicate a safety threshold at around $10 \mu g \, dl^{-1}$. Indeed, rather than there being no change in IQ as BLL increased from 0 to $10 \mu g \, dl^{-1}$, the results indicated a substantial decline in IQ across that range of exposures. Indeed, the shape of the nonlinear function suggests that at lower levels of exposure a one unit increment in blood lead is associated with more than a one unit decrement in performance. However, at higher exposure levels (approximately $10–15 \mu g \, dl^{-1}$), the function appears approximately linear (see **Figure 4**). The linear slope in this region of the curve is consistent with previous research based on children with BLLs greater than $10 \mu g \, dl^{-1}$.

Using the Rochester data it was possible to address a more focused question of central importance to public

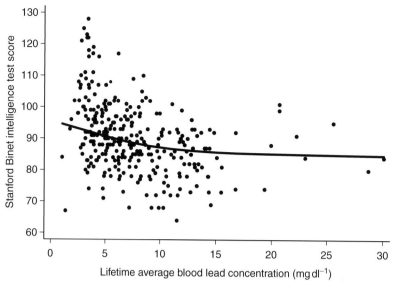

Figure 4 The relation between lifetime average blood lead levels (BLL) and children's Stanford Binet intelligence test score when tested at both 3 and 5 years of age. The points represent the IQ–BLL values for individual children and the smoothed curve is the empirically derived dose–response function estimated by a nonlinear regression model. The function shows that the rate of decline in IQ scores is greater at BLLs below 10 μg dl^{-1} than above 10 μg dl^{-1}. As estimated by the function, as children's blood lead concentration increases from 0 to 10 μg dl^{-1}, IQ decreases by 7.4 points. By contrast, the estimated decline in IQ across the range from 10 to 30 μg dl^{-1} is only 2.5 points. The biological interpretation of a faster-than-linear decline in IQ at very low BLLs remains unclear. Adapted from Canfield, RL, Henderson, CR, Cory-Slechta, DA, *et al.* (2003) Intellectual impairment in children with blood lead concentration below 10 μg per deciliter. *The New England Journal of Medicine* 348: 1517–1526.

health; namely, for children who, throughout infancy and early childhood, have BLLs consistently below the CDC definition of an elevated BLL, do they nevertheless show detectable adverse effects of lead? The answer to this question pertained in particular to the performance of the more than 100 children in the Rochester study whose BLLs were less than 10 μg dl^{-1} at each of the seven blood draws. This group would be comparable to many children in the general population whose blood lead tests are considered normal throughout early childhood. Results of this analysis indicated that even in this group of children, higher lead exposure was associated with significantly lower IQ scores.

These surprising and potentially troubling results motivated two reanalyses of previous studies to test the generality of the findings. The first reanalysis involved data from the 48 children in the Boston cohort that had BLLs less than 10 μg dl^{-1} through age 10 years, and the results were consistent with findings from the Rochester study. Remarkably, the two studies generated nearly identical statistical estimates for the size of the lead effect on IQ.

The close correspondence of results from the Rochester and Boston studies is especially notable because the subject samples differed in many ways. Children from Rochester were 70% non-white and largely from low-income families in which 70% of the mothers had 12 or fewer years of education. In the Boston cohort children were 80% white, and approximately 50% of the parents had some postcollege education. In addition, the average child IQ in the Rochester study was approximately 90, whereas the average child IQ was approximately 115 in the Boston study. Obtaining such similar results from samples at opposite ends of the SES is inconsistent with a leading alternative explanation of the magnitude of the low-level lead effects estimated from the Rochester study, that is, that children suffering from multiple risk factors in addition to lead exposure will be more severely affected by lead. Instead, the effects appear consistent across samples with very different risk profiles.

Because both studies were limited by a small sample size, a second reanalysis was carried out using the combined data from nearly all the previous longitudinal cohort studies of pediatric lead exposure. The study included 1333 children, 244 of whom had peak BLLs less than 10 μg dl^{-1}. Consistent with the Boston and Rochester studies, the dose–response function indicated that an increase in BLL from 2.4 to 10 μg dl^{-1} was associated with a decline in IQ of almost 4 points.

The effects of very low BLLs estimated by these studies suggest that the IQs of children with BLLs of 10 μg dl^{-1}, the current CDC definition of an elevated BLL, will be approximately 5 points lower than for children with BLLs of only 1–2 μg dl^{-1}. These results have been used to support arguments favoring primary prevention of lead exposure in children, as opposed to waiting to find that a child has an elevated BLL (currently defined as 10 μg dl^{-1}) and only taking action after the test results are confirmed.

Timing of exposure

As noted above, the developmental timing of exposure to a toxin is likely to affect the nature and severity of its effects on the developing organism. Environmental influences typically are most influential when neural plasticity is greatest, during the period of gestation and, especially in humans, during infancy and childhood. During this time the brain is rapidly developing the basic structural organization, connectivity, and functional capacities that are the foundation for learning, cognition, and behavioral self-regulation. Timing of exposure to lead is indisputably an important factor in determining the magnitude of the adverse outcomes. The time of greatest vulnerability, in both humans and non-human animals, is during gestation, infancy, and early childhood. However, it is unclear whether there are specific times during this period of vulnerability when exposure is most damaging. It is also poorly understood which neurodevelopmental processes, for example, cellular proliferation, migration, synaptogenesis, myelination, or apoptosis, are most disrupted by lead.

The biokinetics of lead, the chronic nature of childhood exposure, and the lack of infant tests that are good predictors of later neurobehavioral functioning all limit our ability to identify critical periods of vulnerability. Unlike some toxins, absorbed lead remains in the body for weeks, months, or years so that even a single exposure event can cause elevated lead for a prolonged period. Studying age-specific effects in children is further complicated because in most cases exposure is chronic for a period of years. As a result, BLLs in children are highly correlated from one age to the next, making it conceptually and statistically problematic to determine whether exposure at any specific age is the most important cause of later deficits.

Although not fully surmounting the methodological difficulties, several of the prospective longitudinal studies described above have examined the relative predictive capacity of prenatal vs. postnatal lead exposure, with varying results. Across studies, prenatal maternal BLL is inconsistently associated with cognitive and behavioral outcomes in the child. However, few data are available for exploring the possible special importance of exposure during a particular stage of prenatal development. Studies of postnatal exposure are somewhat more consistent, typically finding that BLLs measured during the first year of life are poor predictors of concurrent or later behaviors. Instead, BLL during the second and third years of life, the period when BLLs are generally highest, tend to be most strongly related to neurobehavioral outcomes. However, some studies report that IQ scores at ages 5–7 years are most highly correlated with BLL when the two are measured concurrently. Together with studies suggesting that prenatal and postnatal lead exposure have independent effects on cognitive outcomes, these findings are difficult to reconcile with the view that

vulnerability to lead is when the brain is developing most rapidly or when particular structures and functions are emerging. These varied results likely reflect the complex interactions between lead and brain development, which are further veiled by differences among studies in terms of the amount and timing of exposure, characteristics of the study sample, age when lead exposure is assessed, age when outcomes are assessed, types of outcomes measured, covariates considered, and approaches to statistical analysis. At this time, however, the combined evidence does not justify the singling out of any particular age or developmental stage as a window of special vulnerability.

Are the effects of early lead exposure transient or permanent?

Evidence from long-term follow-up testing of children who participated in the prospective cohort studies suggests that early deficits endure into the later teenage years. Follow-up testing has been completed through age 10 years in the Boston and Mexico cohorts, age 11 years in the Yugoslavia cohort, age 13 years in the Port Pirie cohort, and age 16 years in the Cincinnati cohort. In every case, even though children's lead levels had declined greatly, prenatal or early postnatal BLLs were inversely associated with the cognitive outcomes. These results suggest that lead effects are enduring.

If exposure to lead during infancy and early childhood results in lasting cognitive deficits, then it was hoped that by reducing BLLs in highly exposed infants and children that lead's detrimental effects on cognition could be reduced or avoided altogether. To test this hypothesis, the treatment of lead-exposed children (TLC) study enrolled children with elevated BLLs and randomized them to placebo or succimer. The TLC study was carried out simultaneously at several research sites, enrolling 780 children between 1 and 3 years of age who had a confirmed BLL between 20 and 44 $\mu g\,dl^{-1}$. A main objective of this study was to determine whether neurobehavioral deficits can be prevented or lessened by administering succimer – presumably by reducing lead concentrations in blood and tissue, including brain.

At baseline, children in the TLC trial were given tests of intelligence, behavior, and neuropsychological function, and then randomly assigned to treatment or placebo. Treatment consisted of up to three 26-day courses of succimer, administered orally. After 3 years of follow-up, children's cognitive function was reassessed. Although BLLs were, at least initially significantly lower in the treated group, scores on cognitive, behavioral, and neuropsychological tests did not differ between the groups. A second round of assessments was conducted when children were 7 years old, but again no benefits of succimer therapy were observed.

The implications of the TLC trial are clear: according to this protocol, chelation therapy with succimer has no affect on subsequent cognitive function for young children with

BLLs in the range studied. One interpretation of these results is that the children were permanently damaged by their lead exposure prior to the age when they began chelation. Another possible reason for the lack of a beneficial effect of chelation is suggested by the findings from research with children having very low BLLs; namely, that the benefits of chelation might be evident only after children's BLLs are reduced to much less than $10\,\mu g\,dl^{-1}$. Whether a more aggressive regimen would be deemed safe and whether it would produce measurable long-term benefits to children's cognitive functioning remain open questions. In agreement with other evidence, the results from the TLC trial emphasize the importance of taking effective environmental action to prevent children from being exposed to lead.

A Perspective on Lead Exposure during Infancy and Early Childhood: The Importance of Small Effects

Research into pediatric lead exposure reveals a consistent pattern of findings showing that early lead exposure, at levels that produce no overt symptoms, is associated with decrements in later IQ scores, and that these deficits persist into later adolescence. Emerging evidence also suggests that early exposure might cause an increase in antisocial and delinquent behaviors. It must be emphasized, however, that all of these effects are small relative to other factors that shape a child's life. For example, nearly all studies of low-level lead exposure find that parental education, and the quality of the childrearing environment are more important than low-level lead exposure for shaping children's intellectual development and social adjustment. Specifically, whereas lead generally

accounts for less than 5% of the variability in intelligence test scores, measures of the childrearing environment typically account for between 10% and 20% of the variance – independent of what is explained by lead. Nevertheless, small effects can have important ramifications for the affected individuals and for society as a whole.

Over the past several decades IQ test scores have been viewed with an increasingly skeptical eye. Concerns are commonly expressed about cultural bias, about the narrow range of abilities tested, and about the value of these tests for predicting success in both academic and nonacademic settings. Nevertheless, scores on IQ-like tests can have profound practical significance for an individual person. Most affected would be individuals with an ability test score that is, merely by chance, near one of the mostly arbitrary cutoff values routinely used to inform decisions about school placement, aptitude for college work, or opportunities for training and advancement in the workplace. For example, inevitably each year some proportion of high school students is denied access to college because of poor admission test scores. In some of those cases, an increase of only a few points on an IQ-like aptitude test would have allowed an otherwise qualified student the opportunity to obtain higher education. It is sobering to realize that early lead exposure, even at blood lead concentrations below the current level of concern, could be very costly to such a person.

The importance of a small adverse effect of lead also can be gauged by taking a societal or population perspective. **Figure 5** depicts the normal distributions of IQ scores for two groups of children. One distribution represents children drawn from a population not exposed to lead. The mean IQ of this unexposed group is 100. The second distribution represents the predicted IQ scores for a population of children who experienced average BLLs

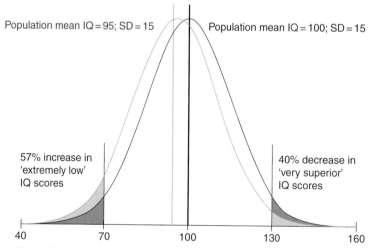

Population mean IQ = 95; SD = 15   Population mean IQ = 100; SD = 15

57% increase in 'extremely low' IQ scores

40% decrease in 'very superior' IQ scores

40   70   100   130   160

Figure 5 Population-level effects of lead exposure. Hypothetical distributions of IQ scores in two populations of children. The distribution shown by the black line represents children who are unaffected by lead exposure, and the distribution shown by the gray line represents children with a 5-point lead-induced decrease in IQ test scores. Note that a 5% difference in the population mean IQ is associated with a disproportionate difference at the tails of the distributions.

of about $10\,\mu g\,dl^{-1}$ during infancy and early childhood. The estimated mean IQ for that group, based on the combined evidence from the longitudinal cohort studies, is approximately 95. As illustrated in **Figure 5**, one consequence of this 5-point (5%) downward shift in IQ for the exposed group is a disproportionate (57%) increase in the number of children with IQ scores in the extremely low range (<70). An IQ test score less than 70 is consistent with the need to place a child in a special education program – an unfortunate necessity for the child and an approximate doubling of the cost for his or her education. Similarly, this 5% downward shift in the average IQ of a population would cause a disproportionate 40% reduction in the number of children who score in the very superior range (IQ > 130). An IQ score of 130 is often a requirement for access to accelerated courses in high school. Thus, a small effect of lead can be very costly for individuals and for society as a whole.

Summary

Despite the long and cheerless history of lead's detrimental effects on human health, the efforts of public health advocates over the past half-century have resulted in an impressive reduction in childhood exposure throughout most of the industrialized world. However, although lead exposure is almost entirely preventable, millions of children throughout the world continue to suffer the adverse effects of excessive exposure to this potent neurotoxin. The neurobehavioral effects of lead are subtle, but they can be detected in children with blood concentrations below the CDC definition of an elevated BLL, and they appear to be lasting. Moreover, efforts to restore cognitive function in lead-exposed children through medical treatment suggest little reason for optimism. The shared perspective of developmental psychologists and medical and public health specialists is that only through primary prevention of lead exposure during gestation, infancy, and childhood is it possible to protect children from this ancient threat to human health.

See also: Anger and Aggression; Attention; Brain Development; Brain Function; Cognitive Development; Developmental Disabilities: Cognitive; Emotion Regulation; Neurological Development; Social-Emotional Development Assessment; Safety and Childproofing.

Suggested Readings

Agency for Toxic Substances and Disease Registry: ATSDR Toxicological Profile on Lead. http://www.atsdr.cdc.gov – (accessed on 14 July 2007).
Canfield RL, Henderson CR, Cory-Slechta DA, *et al.* (2003) Intellectual impairment in children with blood lead concentrations below 10 μg per deciliter. *The New England Journal of Medicine* 348: 1517–1526.
Centers for Disease Control and Prevention: Prevention of Lead Poisoning in Young Children. http://www.cdc.gov – (accessed on 14 July 2007).
Dietrich KN, Ware JH, Salganik M, *et al.* (2004) Treatment of Lead-Exposed Children Clinical Trial Group. Effect of chelation therapy on the neuropsychological and behavioral development of lead-exposed children after school entry. *Pediatrics* 114(1): 19–26.
Koller K, Brown T, Spurgeon A, and Levy L (2004) Recent developments in low-level lead exposure and intellectual impairment in children. *Environmental Health Perspectives* 112(9): 987–994.
Markowitz G and Rosner D (2000) Cater to the children: The role of the lead industry in a public health tragedy, 1900–1955. *American Journal of Public Health* 90: 36–46.

Relevant Websites

http://www.asmalldoseof.org – A Small Dose of Toxicology by Steven Gilbert, A Small Dose of Lead.
http://www.atsdr.cdc.gov – Agency for Toxic Substances and Disease Registry: ToxFAQs for Lead.
http://www.cdc.gov – US Center for Disease Control and Prevention (CDC). CDC Childhood Lead Poisoning Prevention Program.
http://www.hud.gov – US Department of Housing and Urban Development (HUD), Office of Healthy Homes and Lead Hazard Control.
http://sis.nlm.nih.gov – US National Library of Medicine Enviro-Health Links: Lead and Environmental Health.

Learning

R L Gómez, The University of Arizona, Tucson, AZ, USA

Glossary

Classical conditioning – A process of behavior modification by which a learner comes to respond to a previously neutral stimulus. When the neutral stimulus is repeatedly paired with an unconditioned stimulus, it begins to elicit the desired response even in the absence of the unconditioned stimulus.
Discrimination – After familiarization with novel information, infants are tested for learning in terms of their ability to differentiate a stimulus consistent with their learning experience versus a stimulus

that is not consistent, measured in terms of the time they orient to the two stimulus types. Discrimination, and hence learning, is said to occur if attention to the two stimulus types differs across a group of infants.

Frequency – The number of times a unit occurs.

Generalization – A process involving abstraction away from specific stimulus materials that leads to perception of higher-order regularities or rules. Generalization enables learners to recognize new examples that are similar, but not identical, to previously encountered examples.

High-amplitude operant sucking procedure – Infants in this procedure are tested in a reclining seat, facing forward toward a colorful display. The infant sucks on a blind nipple (one without a hole) connected by a rubber hose to a pressure transducer that produces a signal on a polygraph machine. High-amplitude sucks (the top 33% of responses) are reinforced to a particular stimulus. After time, the infant's sucks will diminish as the infant becomes familiar with the stimulus. At that point a new stimulus is introduced. An increase in the quantity of high-amplitude sucks is interpreted as the infant having noticed a difference in the old and new stimulus.

Joint probability – The probability of two units occurring together.

Observational learning – A process by which learners acquire behaviors by observing others then imitating what they have observed.

Operant conditioning – A process of behavior modification in which the probability of a specific behavior is increased by applying positive reinforcement after the occurrence of the behavior. The occurrence of a behavior can be decreased through negative reinforcement.

Statistical learning – The discovery of structure in perceptual information in terms of the statistical properties of perceptual units. In language the perceptual units can be phonetic segments, syllables, or words. Taking English as an example, certain phonetic segments (e.g., the -ng sound in any word ending in '-ing') are statistically probable at the ends of words, but are nonexistent at the beginnings of words, whereas this segment can occur with high statistical probability at the beginnings of words in some languages.

Transitional probability – The probability of the occurrence of one unit given another (the probability of event B given event A is the joint probability of event A and event B divided by the probability of event A).

Introduction

Learning is a relatively stable change in behavior that results from exposure to a novel stimulus. Developmentalists have long been interested in learning because of its potentially important role in cognitive development. Learning is a fundamental process that operates in concert with other perceptual and cognitive processes, but the extent of its contribution to early cognition (in contrast to the contribution of biological constraints) is largely unknown. One goal of current research is to identify core infant learning mechanisms in an effort to better characterize the infant's initial state. Before detailing the research to date, the author briefly reviews the history of learning as it has pertained to issues in child development.

The impetus behind human development, whether caused by nature or nurture, has been debated for centuries. John Locke (1632–1704) espoused the view that children were born with a *tabula rasa* (blank slate) and must therefore acquire all knowledge through experience. In contrast, Jean-Jacques Rousseau (1712–78) emphasized the role of innate knowledge in development. An emphasis on learning re-emerged in the last century with Pavlov (1849–1936) who showed with classical conditioning that an unconditioned response (a reflex such as salivation) could be trained to respond to a conditioned stimulus (CS; the sound of a bell) if the CS was paired with an unconditioned stimulus (US) such as food. Eventually, the food could be taken away to show that the CS was sufficient for producing the response. Based on these principles, John B. Watson (1878–1958) advocated a psychology of learning called behaviorism. This movement dominated theories of human development in the early half of the twentieth century. In particular, B. F. Skinner (1904–90) developed a theory of learning based on principles of operant conditioning, emphasizing the role of reinforcement and punishment in shaping specific behaviors. His work culminated in the book *Verbal Behavior*, which attempted to explain how a complex skill (such as language) could be acquired by principles of operant learning, where learners receive reinforcement for particular linguistic behaviors. However, in 1957, Noam Chomsky argued that Skinners' theory was inadequate for explaining the complex rules that underlie human language, rules that enable children to understand sentences they have never heard and generate novel sentences. Chomsky also rejected the notion that the processes advocated by Skinner could explain how human children can acquire language so rapidly. Chomsky rejected the simple processes proposed by Skinner in favor of the notion that children are biologically prepared to acquire language such that fundamental principles of language are hard-wired into the circuitry of the brain.

Although Chomsky's arguments were directly relevant to language acquisition, they reflected a paradigm shift spreading across the field of psychology at that time. The notion that human behavior could be explained in terms of associative learning principles was widely abandoned in favor of theories emphasizing underlying cognitive processes. Other scientists also argued that simple associative learning principles were inadequate for explaining human behavior. For instance, Lashley (1890–1958) pointed out that many human endeavors, such as language, involve hierarchically organized behaviors as opposed to chains of stimulus response associations. Additionally, in 1961, Albert Bandura showed that children could learn through vicarious observation (observational learning) without need for direct reinforcement. In the area of language acquisition, learning theories were replaced by theories emphasizing inborn principles and parameters (where principles are rules common to all languages and parameters are rules capturing the possible differences between languages).

In recent years the tide has turned back toward an emphasis on learning. This has been driven by the success of computer models demonstrating that simple associative systems can accomplish fairly complex learning, as well as broad acceptance of the fact that the perceptual input to learners is rich in statistical information. Finally, experimental work with infants has led to exciting discoveries regarding early learning abilities suggesting that human learning is more powerful than originally conceived in behaviorist theory. This experimental work, and precursors to it, is the focus of this article.

The remaining sections summarize some of the early work on learning before detailing recent experimental work on infants' ability to detect statistical structure. The article ends by posing open questions and challenges for learning research.

Early Work on Learning

Much of the earliest research on infant learning was methodological in nature. Driving questions were whether human infants were even capable of learning and if so, what types of learning they would exhibit. Researchers were also interested in determining when learning might begin to take place in development. Before these questions could be answered, fundamental methodological details had to be worked out. For instance, it was important to rule out the possibility that a change in behavior reflected acclimatization to a stimulus or a response to a particularly appealing reward, behaviors that mimic but do not reflect learning. Additionally, a number of early studies failed because researchers did not know how much or how little exposure to a stimulus would promote learning or which types of rewards were needed.

The earliest studies investigated whether infants could be classically conditioned to associate a conditioned stimulus with an unconditioned response by pairing a CS with an UCS. In 1920, John B Watson and Rosalie Raynor exposed an 11-month-old child named Albert to an UCS (a loud sound) each time he touched a CS (a white rat). The loud sound caused Albert to cry and withdraw his hand, so that subsequently, merely seeing the rat led to the same behavior, demonstrating memory of a learned stimulus–response pairing.

Infants just a few hours old can be classically conditioned also. In 1984, E M Blass and colleagues followed a stroke on the forehead (the CS) by immediate oral delivery of sucrose to infants through a glass pipette (the UCS). A control group was exposed to the same number of CS–UCS pairings, but the time interval between the pairings varied across trials. Another control group received only the UCS in order to rule out the possibility that repeated deliveries of sucrose itself would result in a change in behavior. During an extinction phase where infants received the CS but not the sucrose delivery, the experimental group cried when the sucrose was not delivered whereas infants in the two control groups did not. All three groups experienced withdrawal of sucrose, so this in itself could not explain the experimental group's behavior. Their behavior could only be explained in terms of their having learned the predictive CS–UCS relationship. This study, and others in this general vein, established that infants could be classically conditioned from birth.

Researchers were also interested in determining whether infants were capable of learning using operant principles. Operant conditioning involves reinforcing a naturally occurring response to increase or decrease the rate of that response. For instance, positively reinforcing a response leads to an increased rate of that behavior. This is in contrast to classical conditioning, which involves a learned association between a CS and UCS. The first study to obtain evidence for operant conditioning in newborns was conducted in 1966 by Siqueland and Lipsett. They paired differential auditory stimuli with an unconditioned tactile stimulus (stroking the infant's cheek). The stroking produces an unconditioned rooting reflex to that side and by necessity a head turn. In their study, when the pairing of the positive auditory stimulus (a buzzer) and the tactile stimulus produced a head turn, this was always followed by a positive reinforcer (administration of sugar water). However, a head-turn in response to the pairing of the tactile stimulus and the negative auditory stimulus (a tone) was never reinforced. Responding to the presence of the positive auditory stimulus increased over time whereas responding to the negative auditory stimulus decreased suggesting that infants were discriminating between the two types of auditory stimuli based on operant conditioning.

An operant paradigm that has been used extensively to study learning and memory in infants since then, is the mobile conjugate reinforcement procedure developed by Carolyn Rovee-Collier in 1969. In this procedure, an infant is placed on his back in a crib beneath a mobile.

A ribbon runs from a suspension hook on the mobile to the infant's ankle (in the reinforcing condition) or from a hook that will not move the mobile (the nonreinforcing condition). First, a measure of baseline kicking is obtained by observing the number of kicks in the nonreinforcing condition (a pretest). After obtaining a baseline measure, the ribbon is tied to the suspension hook so that when the infant kicks he moves the mobile, resulting in a high rate of kicking and attention to the mobile. Memory of the learned experience can then be assessed after various delays by positioning the infant beneath the mobile, attaching his ankle to the nonreinforcing hook (to prevent additional learning), and measuring the number of kicks he produces. Learning is evidenced by a greater rate of kicking relative to baseline when infants are tested with the same mobile as compared to a different one. This procedure was used to show that 2-month-old infants could remember a learning experience occurring 24 h earlier.

Infants and young children do not necessarily need reinforcement to learn. In a seminal study of observational learning reported in 1961, Bandura showed that 4-year-olds who simply observed an adult beating up a Bobo doll were more likely to direct similar behaviors toward the doll in subsequent play than were children in a control condition who did not see an adult exhibiting such behavior. This type of learning is referred to as observational because learners imitate an observed behavior with no stimulus–response pairing or any kind of reinforcement. Observational learning does not appear to have a lower age limit. In deferred imitation, another type of observational learning, an experimenter models a sequence of actions and the infant is later tested on the ability to reproduce the behavior. In 1992, Patricia Bauer and Jean Mandler showed that infants as young as 11.5 months of age can learn and later imitate novel actions in an event sequence like making a rattle. Events were simple, consisting of two or three actions, but infants readily reproduced the actions in their correct order. Interestingly, the type of sequence matters, such that arbitrary sequences involving a series of events that are not causally related (like banging, turning, and stacking a ring on a dowel) are much more difficult to learn than causally related actions that require actions to be performed in a certain order (such as making a rattle by putting a ball in a paper cup, joining the mouth of the cup with the mouth of another paper cup, and shaking). In a different experimental paradigm demonstrating observational learning, Rachel Barr and colleagues in 1996 showed that infants as young as 6 months of age can remember and imitate portions of a sequence they have observed being modeled. The sequence, consisting of removing a mitten from a puppet's hand, shaking the mitten (causing a bell inside the mitten to sound), and placing the mitten back on the puppet, was imitated by the infants after a 24 h delay. In most cases,

exposure was very brief. The event sequences were modeled just twice with 11.5-month-olds and six times with the 6-month-olds. Additionally, infants as young as 2 months of age can engage in learning without feedback as shown by Naomi Wentworth and Marshall Haith in a study reported in 1992. Infants were exposed to an alternating left–right pattern of visually presented pictures. On one side (left or right) the picture was always the same and on the other side the picture varied. Infants showed learning of the visual content of the picture as evidenced by their tendency to anticipate the location of the stable picture and to respond to it more quickly as compared to the location of the unstable picture.

Given these findings it becomes important to ask just how early learning occurs in human development. Given the results detailed above, it is reasonable to think that learning may occur as soon as infants are able to process sensory information, indeed that they might even begin learning *in utero*.

One of the earliest indications of fetal learning was the finding that newborns prefer their mother's voice to that of another female speaker. They also prefer sentences from their native language to sentences from another language. Passages read in French produced higher sucking rates in French newborns than passages read in Russian. Other studies have shown that these preferences are not specific to French. Therefore such preferences must be shaped by prenatal experience with maternal speech. What might infants be learning? We know from intrauterine recordings that low-frequency components of maternal speech, including its rhythmic qualities are audible *in utero* and infants born prematurely at 24 weeks are able to react to sounds, raising the possibility that learning may begin this early.

In 1986, Anthony DeCasper and Melanie Spence showed that newborns, whose mothers read a passage aloud each day during the last 6 weeks of pregnancy, were able to discriminate the passage from an unfamiliar one at birth. Two-day-olds were tested, using a high-amplitude operant sucking procedure, to see whether the familiar passage would be more reinforcing than an unfamiliar one, even when read in another woman's voice. It was, suggesting that infants had learned features from their training passage involving its prosodic (or rhythmic) qualities over and above features specific to their mother's voice. The passages were not read aloud before the newborns were tested, and thus learning must have occurred *in utero*. A later study, by DeCasper and colleagues, used heart rate as a dependent measure to test learning in 37-week-old fetuses. Mothers recited one of two rhymes out loud, once a day, over 4 weeks. At 37 weeks' gestational age the fetuses were stimulated with recordings of the familiar and unfamiliar rhymes. The familiar rhyme elicited a decrease in fetal heart rate, whereas the unfamiliar one did not, suggesting discrimination of the two passages, and hence learning.

Statistical Learning

Despite the success of these early studies, learning was not studied in its own right for many years. In the past 10 years, however, researchers have begun to document learning of statistical regularities in perceptual input. Statistical learning, the ability to track probabilistic patterns, is an important mechanism because probabilistic structure abounds in the information available to our senses.

Statistical structure can take many forms including the frequency of individual units, joint probability, or the transitional probability of one unit given another. Joint probability is defined as the probability of two units occurring together. Transitional probability is the probability of the occurrence of one unit given another (the probability of event B given event A is the joint probability of event A and event B divided by the probability of event A). There are other forms of statistical structure but common to all forms is the requirement that units occur with some regularity that lends itself to mathematical description (and presumably also to computation).

As an example of statistical learning, a problem infants must solve in speech perception is identifying words in running speech. This is a daunting task because words are rarely demarcated by pauses. One popular proposal is that infants might learn a few words spoken in isolation and use the boundaries of these known words to discover the boundaries of words that co-occur. However, useful information is conveyed in the higher transitional probabilities occurring between syllables in words as compared to the lower probabilities of syllables spanning words. In a landmark study reported in 1996, Jenny Saffran, Richard Aslin, and Elissa Newport showed that very young infants are able to capitalize on this kind of information. For instance, in the phrase 'pretty baby', the syllables 'ba' and 'by' occur within a word, whereas 'ty' and 'ba' span words. As such 'by' is more highly predicted by 'ba' than 'ba' is by 'ty'. Saffran and colleagues implemented this idea experimentally by exposing 8-month-old infants to continuously running syllables such as tupirotiladogolabudabikutupirodabikugolabu.... where tupiro, dabiku, tilado, and golabu were words that were presented in random order. For instance, in the first four syllables in this particular example 'tu pi' and 'pi ro' are syllables within words, whereas 'ro' and 'ti' are syllables spanning words.

Although statistical learning occurs in multiple modalities, much of the research has been conducted in the context of language acquisition. In these studies infants are exposed to artificial language materials they have never heard before. In natural language cues are correlated making it difficult to pinpoint the locus of learning, but artificial languages are devised with particular learning cues in mind, enabling more precise control over the input to learners. Artificial languages also control for prior exposure and therefore provide insights into learning capabilities at a given point in time instead of tapping a developing sensitivity midstream.

A typical study involves a familiarization phase followed by a test. Length of familiarization in infant studies varies from 2 to 3 min. Most studies counterbalance stimulus materials so that half of the infants are exposed to one version of the language and half to another version. At test, infants are exposed to strings from both versions so that what is grammatical for one group is ungrammatical for the other (e.g., version A strings violate the constraints of version B and vice versa). This ensures that the structure of the language, instead of something idiosyncratic about the sound tokens, is responsible for learning. Infants are tested using procedures for recording the amount of time they attend to different stimulus types. If learning has occurred, a group of infants should listen differentially to strings conforming to their training language versus strings that do not conform.

Statistical learning appears to play a role in the formation of speech categories, in the identification of word-like units in running speech, in the ability to track adjacent and nonadjacent word dependencies, and in generalizations involving the acquisition of categories and their relationships in speech. Learning research has also investigated whether infants can learn in the presence of noisy input and whether they can use prior experience to bootstrap learning of more difficult patterns from simpler ones. That research, as well as research conducted in the visual modality, will be summarized with the goal of describing a range of statistical learning studies including research conducted in the author's laboratory.

The Role of Frequency in the Formation of Speech Categories

Infants are sensitive to a wide range of speech contrasts very early in development. An example is the contrast between the consonants /b/ and /p/. Very young infants even discriminate contrasts that do not occur in their native language but by 8–10 months of age, discrimination only occurs for those contrasts in their native language. This finding is widely recognized as experience dependent, but until recently we did not have a very good candidate for the process underlying this change. One possibility, found in the literature on statistical learning, is that infants use statistical information to home in on phoneme categories. Although phonemes may vary acoustically along a dimension, such variation is not random. It patterns bi-modally such that the most frequent tokens of one category occur at one end of a dimension and tokens from another category occur at the other end. This is in contrast to a unimodal distribution in which the most frequent tokens occur between two ends of a continuum. Will distributions with these different characteristics influence infants' ability to distinguish speech contrasts such that exposure to bi-modal distributions results in discrimination of a speech contrast, whereas exposure to a unimodal distribution prevents discrimination?

In the earliest infant experiment exploring this hypothesis in 2002, Jessica Maye, Janet Werker, and LouAnn Gerken familiarized 6- and 8-month-olds with one of two distributions of eight speech sounds on a /da/– /ta/ continuum (the voiced unaspirated /d/ in day and the voiceless unaspirated /t/ in stay) (**Figure 1**). Infants this age can make this discrimination, but if perception of speech sounds is malleable then exposure to a unimodal distribution should interfere with discrimination whereas exposure to a bi-modal distribution should preserve it. This pattern of findings would support the proposal that sensitivity to the frequency distributions of speech sounds is instrumental in learning. Infants in both unimodal and bi-modal conditions heard the same eight speech sounds along the continuum, but those in the bi-modal distribution condition heard speech sounds near the end (2 and 7) most frequently whereas infants in the unimodal distribution condition heard the middle speech sounds (4 and 5) most often. After familiarization, infants were tested on their ability to discriminate alternating speech sounds (the endpoints 1 and 8) from nonalternating ones (repeats of speech sounds 3 or 6). Only infants in the bi-modal condition discriminated alternating from nonalternating speech sounds, supporting the idea that exposure to the bimodal distribution led to preservation of two categories of speech sounds whereas exposure to the unimodal distribution resulted in the formation of one. In subsequent studies Jessica Maye and colleagues have shown that exposure to a bi-modal frequency distribution can also

enable detection of an initially undetectable speech sound contrast. Thus, the ability to learn the frequency characteristics of speech sounds can blur distinctions between previously known categories or they can enable the formation of new ones.

The Role of Joint Probability and Transitional Probabilities in Visual Statistical Learning

Infants are also able to keep track of joint probabilities in learning the most frequent associations between objects in visual sequences. Natasha Kirkham, Jonathan Slemmer, and Scott Johnson in a study reported in 2002 familiarized infants, ages 2, 5, and 8 months, to a continuous series of objects, presented one at a time in sequence. The stimuli were six shapes (e.g., turquoise square, blue cross, yellow circle, pink diamond, green triangle, red octagon, where the square was always followed by the cross, the circle by the diamond, and so on). The infants were then tested to see if they would discriminate legal pairs of objects from illegal ones (e.g., turquoise square followed by the pink diamond) by manifesting longer looking times to the illegal combinations. All three age groups showed discrimination, demonstrating early sensitivity to joint probability in visually presented stimuli (**Figure 2**).

In a study reported the same year, Josef Fiser and Richard Aslin showed that infants can track transitional probabilities in objects co-occurring in visual scenes by 9 months of age, but because these studies have not yet

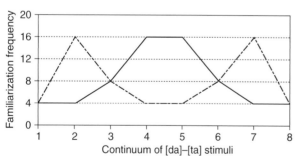

Figure 1 Bimodal versus unimodal distributions of [da]–[ta] stimuli during familiarization in a study of speech-category formation. The continuum of speech sounds is shown on the abscissa with Token 1 corresponding to [da] and Token 8 corresponding to [ta]. The ordinate axis plots the number of times each stimulus occurred during the familiarization phase. The presentation frequency for infants exposed to a bimodal presentation is depicted by the dotted line, and for the unimodal presentation by the solid line. Reproduced from Maye J, Werker J, and Gerken LA (2002) Infant sensitivity to distributional information can affect phonetic discrimination. *Cognition* 82: B101–B111, with permission from Elsevier.

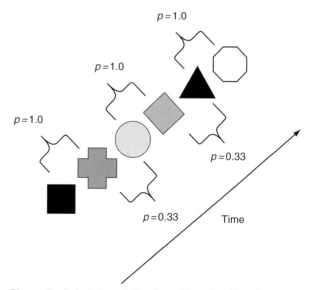

Figure 2 A depiction of stimuli used in a visual learning study to assess learning of joint probability. Reproduced from Kirkham NZ, Slemmer JA, and Johnson SP (2002) Visual statistical learning in infancy: Evidence for a domain general learning mechanism. *Cognition* 83: B35–B42, with permission from Elsevier.

been conducted with younger infants it is not known whether there is a lower limit on the ability to track transtitional probabilities.

The Role of Transitional Probabilities in Segmenting Words in Continuous Speech

As described briefly earlier, infants can also keep track of more complex statistics, such as transitional probabilities in sequences of syllables, and they can use this information to discover word boundaries. Such learning has been tested in 7- and 8-month-olds by exposing them to continuous streams of four randomly ordered three-syllable words (e.g., tupiro, dabiku, tilado, golabu in a string such as tupirotiladogolabudabikutupirodabikugolabu....). Although syllable pairs within words occurred with identical joint frequency to those occurring between words, higher transitional probabilities for syllables within words versus those spanning words, can provide cues to word boundaries. Take a phrase like 'naughty puppy'. The syllable transition in 'naugh-ty' has a higher transitional probability than the transition 'ty-pu' because 'naugh' in the word 'naughty', is more likely to predict 'ty' than 'ty' is to predict 'pu'. Jenny Saffran has shown in a series of studies that infants are able to use the differences in transitional probabilities within-words versus between-words to identify word boundaries in running speech such that they show longer listening times to part-words (words that span word boundaries, e.g., bikuti) than to words (e.g., tupiro). This pattern of listening makes sense if we assume that once infants have learned the words, they will find them less interesting, and hence will listen to them for a shorter time than they will listen to novel part-words. Infants can also track transitional probabilities in tone sequences, showing that such learning is not confined to linguistic stimuli.

Even though such learning is not specific to a particular context if it is relevant for language, one might predict that when infants segment syllable sequences (as opposed to tone sequences) they should treat these as candidates for words. This would be evidenced by a greater likelihood of discriminating words and part-words in the context of English sentence frames. If the segmented syllable strings have a word-like status, then we might expect infants to listen longer when words (as opposed to part-words) are embedded in English frames ("I like my tupiro" vs. "I like my bikuti"). This is because if syllable strings are 'candidate words' they should sound more natural in the context of familiar natural language frames than part-words, and infants should listen longer. However, it could be that infants are doing nothing more then discriminating legal from illegal patterns of syllables (tupiro vs. bikuti). Thus, an important control is one where the words and part-words are embedded in nonsense frames (such as "Zy fike ny tupiro"). If infants are treating words and part-words alike, then performance should be the same in English and nonsense frame types: as in English frames they should listen longer to nonsense strings with embedded 'words' as compared to part-words. Jenny Saffran found that 8-month-olds only discriminated words and part-words in English sentence frames suggesting that they treat the words they segment as more language-like than the part-words. Another clue that infants treat segmented nonsense words as candidates for real words is the fact that older 17-month-olds more readily map newly segmented words onto word meanings than part-words onto word meanings. Katharine Graf Estes, Julia Evan, Martha Alibali, and Jenny Saffran first exposed infants to a continuous stream of nonsense words, with transitional probabilities as the only cue to word boundaries. For half of the infants, two of the nonsense words were paired with visually presented objects. For the remaining infants the word forms used to label the objects were part-words. If the segmented units are treated as candidates for real words, infants should be more likely to map the word labels to objects than the part-word labels, and they were.

How Infants Might Tune in to Long Distance Dependencies

The research summarized early on shows that infants are adept at tracking sequential dependencies between adjacent elements. Indeed, this tendency occurs across species (for human, nonhuman primates, and rats), across development (in infants and adults), and even under incidental learning conditions, suggesting that it may be a default. However, many dependencies occur across longer distances, especially in language. Some examples are dependencies between auxiliaries and inflectional morphemes (e.g., *is* quickly runn*ing*), and between nouns and verbs in number and tense agreement (The boy*s* in the tree *are* laughing). If the tendency to track adjacent structure is pervasive, how might learners begin to track more remote dependencies in sequential structure?

Rebecca Gómez investigated this question in 2002 by familiarizing infants with one of two artificial languages. Language 1 sentences followed the patterns aXb or cXd (e.g., pel-wadim-jic, vot-kicey-rud). In Language 2 the relationship between the first and third elements was reversed to aXd or cXb such that pel sentences ended with rud, and vot sentences ended with jic (pel-wadim-rud, vot-kicey-jic). The a, b, c, d, and X elements were restricted to the same positions in the two languages and adjacent dependencies were identical (aX occurred in both languages as did Xd) so that strings could only be distinguished by learning the relationships between the nonadjacent first and third words. The size of the pool from which the middle element was drawn was also manipulated (set-size = 3, 12, or 24) while holding frequency of exposure to particular nonadjacent dependencies constant (see **Figure 3**). The purpose of this manipulation was to determine whether high variability in the middle element would lead to better perception of nonadjacent dependencies even though these were equally frequent in all three set-size conditions. The motivation for the variability manipulation was the observation that long-distance dependencies in natural language between frequently occurring words such as 'is' and '-ing' occur with a large number of verbs as opposed to a small number (e.g., 'is running', 'is playing', 'is sleeping'). Perhaps the variability of verbs contributes to detection of the long-distance dependencies. Infants as young as 15 months of age acquired the nonadjacent dependency when the intervening element came from a set of 24 possible words, but not when intervening set size was smaller (3 or 12). One might have expected the added noise to impede learning; however, high variability appeared to increase the perceptual salience of the nonadjacent words compared to the middle word, resulting in learning.

Generalization in Learning

Rebecca Gómez and LouAnn Gerken in a study published in 1999 familiarized 12-month-olds with strings from an artificial grammar in one vocabulary and tested them on strings in entirely new vocabulary (e.g., infants heard FIM-SOG-FIM-FIM-TUP and were tested on VOT-PEL-PEL-JIC). Although the constraints on word-ordering remained the same between training and test, vocabulary did not. Infants could not distinguish the two grammars based on transitional probabilities between remembered word pairs because of the change in vocabulary. The infants made the discrimination suggesting that they had abstracted something about grammatical structure above and beyond pairs of specific words. In the same year Gary Marcus and his colleagues reported similar findings for younger

7-month-olds. Infants in their studies were familiarized with ABA versus ABB (wi-di-wi vs. wi-di-di) patterns. Infants discriminated strings with the training pattern from those with a different pattern despite a change in vocabulary (e.g., ba-po-ba vs. ba-po-po).

These are important findings but it is crucial to ask to what degree such learning extends to real-world problems such as those faced by children learning language? The infant abstraction abilities documented in these studies are dependent on learning patterns of repeating and alternating elements (e.g., ABB, ABA, ABBC), a form of generalization that is fairly limited in language. Whereas recognizing ba-po-ba and ko-ga-ko as instances of the pattern ABA entails noting that the first and last syllables in sequence are physically identical, most linguistic generalizations involve operations over variables that are not perceptually bound. If we compare the pattern-based representation ABA to the category-based representation Noun Verb Noun, abstracting ABA from ba-po-ba involves noting that the first and third elements in a sequence are physically identical, and thus recognition is perceptually bound. In contrast, the Noun Verb Noun relation holds over abstract categories that do not rely on perceptual identity. "Muffy drinks milk" and "John loves books" share the same category-based Noun Verb Noun structure, despite the obvious physical dissimilarities between category members such as milk and books. Given this observation, researchers have begun to examine learning involving abstract variables.

The ability to perceive category relationships among words in strings is essential to linguistic productivity. For instance, an English speaker must be able to generalize from a novel string like "The pleg mooped" to "Is the pleg mooping?" Generalization is extremely powerful – once a novel word is categorized children can automatically apply all of the syntactic constraints associated with other words in its category. How do children achieve such generalization? Although semantic information most

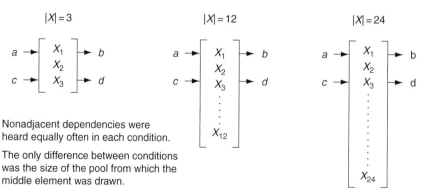

Figure 3   An abstract depiction of an artificial language from Gómez (2002) demonstrating the variability manipulation that showed that adjacent dependencies that are sufficiently low, as they are in the set-size 24 condition, will result in nonadjacent dependency learning.

certainly factors into such learning, infants must parse syntactic categories in the speech they hear in order to link them with semantic referents. This involves learning phonological regularities within words of a category (e.g., noun or verb), and co-occurrence relations between categories (e.g., determiner and noun). An infant who is able to parse the relevant categories in speech has a leg up on the ultimate task of mapping meaning to syntactic phrases.

One way to investigate this kind of learning with artificial languages is to give categories arbitrary labels such as a, X, b, and Y. Words from these categories are then combined to form legal phrases. For instance, aX and bY might be legal in a language whereas aY and bX are not. To give an example, imagine that a-elements correspond to 'a' and 'the' and b-elements to 'will' and 'can' (see **Table 1**). Infants will only be successful at discriminating a new legal phrase (e.g., 'a cat') from an illegal one ('a eat') if they have learned that a-elements go with nouns (the Xs), but not with verbs (the Ys). As in natural language, where the set of determiners has very few members and the set of nouns is large, a- and b-categories have fewer members than Xs and Ys. Also, in natural language nouns and verbs tend to have distinguishing phonological features. For instance, in English nouns tend to have more syllables than verbs. Therefore, it is important to incorporate such phonological features into the aX bY language.

Rebecca Gómez and Laura Lakusta in 2004 reported research asking whether 12-month-olds could learn the relationship between specific a- and b-words and features defining X- and Y-categories. During training infants heard one of two training languages. One language consisted of aX and bY pairings, the other of aY and bX pairs. Xs were two-syllable words and Ys were one syllable so that infants could use syllable number as a feature for distinguishing X- and Y-categories. At test, for example, infants trained on aX and bY pairings had to discriminate these from aY and bX pairs. However, in order to assess generalization, all X- and Y-words were novel. The infants successfully

discriminated the legal from illegal pairs, suggesting that they had learned the relationships between the a- and b-elements and the abstract feature characterizing X- and Y-words (syllable number). Similar learning may occur in natural language, where children exposed to English may pick up on distributional regularities distinguishing nouns and verbs and link these to specific function words.

Although this study was important for determining whether 12-month-olds could learn to associate a- and b-words with different category features, the next step is to determine whether infants can form categories of a- and b-words by themselves. This is an important ability in natural language. For instance, once children form the category of determiner, if they hear a novel word predicted by 'the' they will know to use 'a' with that word also. At a more general level, this kind of learning feeds into the ability to use the occurrence of words of one category to label the syntactic category of a following word (e.g., using the presence of a determiner in the phrase 'a dax' to label the novel word 'dax' as a member of the noun category).

How might this kind of learning be realized in our artificial language paradigm? After learners have associated a- and b-words with X/Y-cues, they might then go on to categorize individual a- or b-elements based on their joint association with particular X- and Y-cues (for instance, in natural language, children would form a category containing 'a' and 'the' based on features that tend to occur with nouns and not verbs; see **Table 2**). Once function-word categories are formed, children can rely on memory for a phrase they have heard (e.g., 'the dax') and the fact that 'the' and 'a' are in the same category to make an inference about a phrase they have not heard (e.g., 'a dax'), regardless of whether the novel word has a defining feature.

LouAnn Gerken and colleagues in 2005 investigated such learning with 17-month-old American infants by exposing them to Russian words in which feminine word stems appeared with the case endings −oj and −u and masculine word stems appeared with the case endings -ya

Table 1 A paradigm for investigating category abstraction

Natural language example	X_1	X_2	X_3	X_4	X_5	X_6
a_1 = the	boy	girl	ball	dog	cat	car
a_2 = a	boy	girl	ball	dog	cat	car
	Y_1	Y_2	Y_3	Y_4	Y_5	Y_6
b_1 = will	jump	run	play	sleep	eat	wait
b_2 = can	jump	run	play	sleep	eat	wait
Artificial language example	X_1	X_2	X_3	X_4	X_5	X_6
a_1 = alt	coomo	fengle	kicey	loga	paylig	wazil
a_2 = ush	coomo	fengle	kicey	loga	paylig	wazil
	Y_1	Y_2	Y_3	Y_4	Y_5	Y_6
a_1 = ong	deech	ghope	jic	skige	vabe	tam
a_2 = erd	deech	ghope	jic	skige	vabe	tam

The top half of the table demonstrates the paradigm with natural stimuli with phrases like 'the boy' and 'will jump'. The bottom half of the table demonstrates the paradigm with artificial language stimuli. Infants are familiarized with phrases like 'alt fengle' and 'erd ghope' then are tested to see if they will generalize correctly to strings with new X and Y words (an example of a new aX string is 'alt roosa' and a new bY string is 'erd pel').

Table 2   Steps in syntactic category-based abstraction

1. Learners associate *a*-words with *X*-features and *b*-words with *Y*-features.
2. They can then form a functor-like word category of '*a*-elements' based on the joint association of individual *a*-words with particular *X*-features. For instance, in English 'the' and 'a' belong to the category of determiners.
3. Once function-word categories are formed, children can rely on memory for a phrase they have heard (e.g., 'the dax') and the fact that 'a' is in the same category as 'the' to make an inference about a phrase they have not heard (e.g., 'a dax'), regardless of whether the novel word has a defining feature.

and –em. Case endings in these experiments were equivalent to *a*- and *b*-elements. Additionally, cues distinguishing *X*s and *Y*s (feminine and masculine words) were present for a subset of the items. For instance, three of six of the feminine *X*-words contained the derivational suffix -k (e.g., *polkoj, polku*) whereas three of the masculine *Y*-words contained the suffix -tel (e.g., *zhitelya, zhitelyem*). Infants were familiarized with a subset of stimuli and were tested to see if they would attend differentially to novel *aX* and *bY* stimuli versus ungrammatical *aY* and *bX* ones even when the distinguishing suffix was absent (e.g., generalizing to *vannoj* and *pisarem* after hearing *vannu* and *pisarya*). The infants were able to do this, showing that they had categorized *a*- and *b*-words (using the feminine and masculine case endings). Having heard *vannu* (for which the distinguishing suffix was absent) they were able to treat *vannoj* equivalently. This finding is important for showing that by 17 months of age, infants can form categories and dependencies between them from distributional cues in speech.

Current Issues

The results of the studies in the growing literature on infant statistical learning reveal precocious learning abilities in young infants. The findings are intriguing and raise more general questions. For instance, can infants learn any kind of predictable structure or are there limits on their ability to detect statistical structure? Are the changes lasting or are we only measuring short-term discrimination? If learners are changed by their experiences, do prior learning experiences shape subsequent ones? And finally, does statistical learning observed in the lab have any connection to learning in the real world?

The first question has to do with the robustness of infant learning, especially when the information in perceptual input is noisy. In language all children are exposed to inconsistencies of one type or another during acquisition, in adults' informal speech, in children's own ungrammatical utterances, and in the ungrammatical utterances of other learners (such as playmates and siblings). Inconsistencies also occur naturally in language, for instance, in English the degree to which verbs take the regular -ed ending for the past tense, or in Spanish the extent to which feminine nouns end in -a. Other instances of noise in linguistic input are less widespread, such as

when children are exposed to nonnative language input (a deaf child who is exposed to American Sign Language through a hearing parent who has not achieved proficiency in this language). In all of these instances, children must distinguish grammatical from ungrammatical instances, and they must generalize beyond the data to which they are exposed, making it important to ask how well infants learn on exposure to probabilistic structure.

Rebecca Gómez and Laura Lakusta investigated this question by familiarizing 12-month-olds with artificial languages with three levels of probabilistic structure. In the 100/0-condition all of the training strings were from the infants' 'predominant' training language. In the 83/17-condition, approximately 83% of the training strings were from the predominant language (the remaining 17% of the strings were from the other language and thus constituted noise). In the 67/33-condition, the split between the predominant and nonpredominant training languages was 67% and 33%. Infants in the 100/0 and 83/17 conditions learned equally well, whereas learning was diminished in the 67/33-condition. The findings suggested that infants are able to track regularities in probabilistic input even when the regularities do not occur with perfect probability (as was the case with the 83/17 ratio) and so infant-learning is robust to some noise. However, learning does need to be based on some minimum degree of regularity, as demonstrated by the fact that infants in the 67/33-condition failed to learn.

Another question has to do with determining whether the learning observed reflects a permanent change. Otherwise, statistical learning studies may simply be registering acclimation to a particular stimulus. Familiarization in statistical learning studies is typically brief (3 min or less) and testing is immediate. Given that very young infants show forgetting of short-term memory after a 15 s delay it is important to determine whether discrimination extends past this window. Very little work has explored long-term memory of a brief learning experience, but recent studies by Rebecca Gómez, Richard Bootzin, Almut Hupbach, and Lynn Nadel show retention of an artificial language after delays of 4 and 24 h. These findings are important for ruling out the possibility that statistical learning studies only measure short-term effects; however, more information is needed regarding how memories for statistical patterns persist and how they affect later learning experiences over the long term. Should parents worry that exposing their children to artificial languages might affect their natural language learning? They should not. Exposure in the lab is brief in comparison to the overwhelming experience children have with their natural language, and although infants may remember their learning experiences, their learning of natural language will take precedence over information they have acquired in the laboratory.

A third question has to do with whether and how learning at one point in time impacts learning at another point. Jill Lany and Rebecca Gómez recently investigated this question in the context of learning of categories in sequential structure. They familiarized 12-month-olds with aX and bY strings where X- and Y-elements were distinguished by different morphological endings (e.g., -ee or -oo). Infants had to learn that a-elements went with Xs and not Ys (and vice versa for b-elements). After familiarization with the aX/bY structure the infants were able to detect the a-X and b-Y relationships in a more complex language involving long-distance dependencies (e.g., in acX and bcY sentences). This language was particularly challenging because the intervening c-element required the infants to track nonadjacent dependencies between a- and X- and b- and Y-elements. Infants with prior experience with consistent aX and bY pairings were able to generalize to the nonadjacent acX/bcY structure over infants in a control group. This finding is important for showing how infants might scaffold learning of complex structure from learning of more simple forms and is particularly significant because of previous work showing that infants this age are unable to track nonadjacent dependencies.

A fourth question has to do with whether the learning observed in the laboratory scales up to real-life learning. One way to determine this is to ask whether the output of learning can be used as input to real-life learning processes. As discussed previously, Jenny Saffran and her colleagues have addressed this issue in the context of language acquisition in several studies by showing that infants prefer to listen to newly segmented artificial words in the context of natural language sentences frames (as opposed to nonsense frames), and also more readily learn a mapping between these newly segmented words and novel objects (as opposed to a mapping of a nonword and an object). Another approach is to determine whether statistical learning and real-life learning show similar developmental trajectories. Although learning occurring in the real world is far more complex than that observed in the lab, similar developmental trajectories would be partial support for a shared process. Initial evidence for this comes from work by Rebecca Gómez and Jessica Maye showing that the ability to detect long-distance dependencies in an artificial language comes online at 15–18 months, roughly the same time infants begin to detect long-distance dependencies in natural language.

Finally, certain kinds of statistical learning (frequency, joint probability, and transitional probability learning)

occur across a broad range of organisms and across different modalities. This suggests that statistical learning may be a very general process and raises questions about how it interacts with other processes and mechanisms known to be involved in memory change. One such mechanism is sleep. New studies with adults show that sleep is instrumental in memory consolidation such that it enhances memory, improves generalization, and also leads to qualitative change. A recent study reported by Rebecca Gómez, Richard Bootzin, and Lynn Nadel tested the effects of sleep on infant learning. Infants who napped in a 4-h interval between familiarization and test were able to generalize a rule in an artificial language. In contrast, infants who did not nap had excellent memory for the strings of the artificial language but they did not generalize. Generalization is a critical form learning that results in greater flexibility. Such learning plays an essential role in cognitive development by sustaining sensitivity to previously encountered information, while enabling learners to generalize to novel cases.

Another important mechanism involved in memory change is memory reconsolidation. According to the literature on this phenomenon, memory is much more dynamic than previously thought. Previous research suggested that memories become crystallized as the result of a consolidation process, varying only in their access. But recent evidence shows that consolidated memories are open to change because when they are accessed, they go into a labile state. Once in this state, memories can be enhanced, altered, or overridden depending on new information encountered. Studies with rats and humans have found that a consolidated memory can be overwritten by new information when exposure to it follows memory reactivation. When the memory is not reactivated, exposure to the new information has no effect. Such a process has important implications for understanding how children recover from erroneous generalizations (if children's memories can be overwritten by new learning after reactivation of erroneous information) and could also explain how new learning becomes integrated with existing knowledge if it can be shown that new information is merged with old information as part of the reconsolidation process. Almut Hupbach, Rebecca Gómez, Oliver Hardt, and Lynn Nadel have recently shown that such merging does indeed happen, suggesting that reconsolidation can be a constructive process in learning.

Summary

In sum, infants show remarkable learning abilities ranging from the ability to detect statistical patterns of varying complexity to the ability to generalize from these patterns. Learning is rapid, and appears to occur early in development. Infants show learning for a range of different types of statistical structure including frequency, joint probability, and transitional probability. These particular forms of statistical learning occur across species, across development, and with no explicit intent to learn suggesting that they may be fundamental in learning. Infants also show learning over different types of units including phonetic segments, syllables, words, and visual objects, and they learn at different levels, for instance, at the level of specific syllables or words or at the level of generalization. Although many questions remain with respect to bridging statistical learning and learning in the world in terms of (1) understanding how learning in the lab scales up to real-life learning, and (2) delimiting the robustness of learning in terms of infants' ability to find signal in noise, their ability to retain their learning experiences, and their ability to build on what they have learned, such learning is sure to play a central role in development.

To go full circle in terms of the history of learning, it is important to note that while the field of learning in the 1960s and 1970s focused primarily on reinforcement issues and paradigms, it has since moved to a greater appreciation of how much infants seem to learn from simple observation of regularities in their environment, both in the language and in other domains. Even so, there are still critics of learning points of view. One classic argument against learning is that simple learning mechanisms are not sufficiently powerful to explain learning of complex information found in the world (such as in language). However, in contrast to the simple learning mechanisms documented by the behaviorists, statistical learning appears to be quite powerful, with mechanisms capable of tracking vast amounts of information as well as engaging in generalization. Such sophistication raises the possibility that infant-learning may contribute substantially to the acquisition of complex skill. Yet, no matter how powerful infant-learning turns out to be, it must certainly be constrained by the biological dispositions learners bring into the world. Just how much is contributed independently by learning, how much by the child's biological preparedness, and how much arises in the interaction of the two, has yet to be determined. Ongoing and future studies will be important for specifying the kinds of learning mechanisms children are born with and how they develop.

See also: Auditory Perception; Categorization Skills and Concepts; Cognitive Development; Imitation and Modeling; Language Acquisition Theories; Learning Disabilities; Memory; Perceptual Development; Preverbal Development and Speech Perception; Semantic Development; Speech Perception.

Suggested Readings

Aslin R, Saffran J, and Newport E (1998) Computation of conditional probability statistics by 8-month-old infants. *Psychological Science* 9: 321–324.

Gerken LA, Wilson R, and Lewis W (2005) 17-month-olds can use distributional cues to form syntactic categories. *Journal of Child Language* 32: 249–268.

Gómez RL (2002) Variability and detection of invariant structure. *Psychological Science* 13: 431–436.

Gómez R and Gerken LA (2000) Infant artificial language learning and language acquisition. *Trends in Cognitive Sciences* 4: 178–186.

Gómez RL and Lakusta L (2004) A first step in form-based category abstraction by 12-month-old infants. *Developmental Science* 7: 567–580.

Gómez RL, Bootzin R, and Nadel L (2006) Naps promote abstraction in language learning infants. *Psychological Science* 17: 670–674.

Kirkham NZ, Slemmer JA, and Johnson SP (2002) Visual statistical learning in infancy: Evidence for a domain general learning mechanism. *Cognition* 83: B3–B42.

Maye J, Werker J, and Gerken LA (2002) Infant sensitivity to distributional information can affect phonetic discrimination. *Cognition* 82: B101–B111.

Saffran J (2003) Statistical language learning: Mechanisms and constraints. *Current Directions in Psychological Science* 12: 110–114.

Saffran J, Aslin R, and Newport E (1996) Statistical learning by eight-month-old infants. *Science* 274: 1926–1928.

Learning Disabilities

H Liang and E Simonoff, King's College London, London, UK

Glossary

Autosomal dominant – A form of genetic (Mendelian) inheritance in which a single copy of a mutant gene will cause the disorder. Autosomal dominant disorders affect both sexes equally and are passed from parent to child, on average in 50% of cases.

Autosomal recessive – A form of genetic (Mendelian) inheritance in which two copes of a mutant gene, one from each parent, are required to cause the disorder. Autosomal recessive disorders affect both sexes equally. Parents are usually unaffected carriers and each child has, on average, a 25% chance of developing the disorder.

Global learning disabilities – Learning disabilities that affect all domains of thinking or intellectual functioning. Sometimes referred to as mental retardation or intellectual disability.

Macrocephaly – An abnormally large head, compared to body size. This may indicate an underlying disorder that can be associated with learning disability.

Microcephaly – An abnormally small head compared to body size. This may indicate an underlying disorder that can be associated with learning disability.

Non-disjunction – A failure of the two chromosomes in a pair to split during cell division. This can lead to an abnormal complement of chromosomes in the offspring, causing disorders such as Trisomy 21, where there are three copies rather than the normal two of chromosome 21, causing Down syndrome.

Specific learning disabilities – Learning disabilities where overall intellectual functioning is within the normal range but where specific abilities, most commonly reading, spelling, and mathematics are operating at a level well below that predicted by overall ability.

Trisomy – Having three rather than the normal two chromosomes, one from each parent. The most common is Trisomy 21 or Down syndrome.

Twin concordance – The percentage of cases where, if one twin is affected with a disorder, the other twin is also affected. Differences in twin concordance rates between identical (monozygotic)) and non-identical (dizygotic) twins provide an index of how important genetic factors are in causing the disorder (heritability).

Variable expression – Some single gene (Mendelian) disorders show a range of expression among individuals with the same mutation, from few and mild signs to a very severe presentation. Mild cases may not be identified until another family member presents with a more severe condition.

X-inactivation – The X chromosome is present in two copies in females and only one in males (who also have a much smaller Y chromosome). During fetal development, one of the two X chromosomes becomes inactivated in females, ensuring that they have the same dose of gene products as males. This process occurs in each cell separately and is a random phenomenon.

X-linked – A form of genetic (Mendelian) inheritance in which the X chromosome carries the mutant gene. Because males have one X chromosome and females two, the disorder is usually apparent only in males while females are generally carriers passing on the mutant copy to their offspring.

Introduction

The field of learning disabilities is confused by a range of terminology, used in various ways. In this article, we are referring to 'global learning disabilities', which are also called 'mental retardation' or 'intellectual disability' and affect all domains of thinking or intellectual functioning. Global learning disability needs to be distinguished from 'specific learning disabilities', also referred to as (specific) 'learning difficulties', where overall intellectual functioning is within the normal range but where specific abilities, most commonly reading, spelling, and mathematics, are operating at a level well below that predicted by overall ability. In this article, we shall use the terms mental retardation and learning disability interchangeably. There are three major classification systems for mental retardation: the American Association of Mental Retardation (-AAMR), the Diagnostic and Statistical Manual (DSM), and the International Classification of Diseases (ICD) (**Table 1**). All three systems require the presence of not only globally reduced intellectual functioning but also significant impairment in adaptive functioning, that is, the ability to function in an age-appropriate way in areas of everyday life including learning, working, enjoying relationships, caring for oneself, and living independently.

Intellectual functioning is usually assessed by tests of cognitive functioning that produce a measure called the intelligence quotient (IQ). The IQ is measured by tests that examine thinking and knowledge in a range of areas. These areas usually include both verbal skills such as vocabulary knowledge, the ability to understand conceptual similarities between words and short-term (working) memory for verbal material, and nonverbal skills, such as completing puzzles, identifying missing parts of pictures and completing pictorial sequences. Because ability to complete such tasks changes with age, IQ tests are standardized across a range of ages. The IQ is the mental age divided by chronological age multiplied by 100, where mental age refers to the average score achieved by children of a certain chronological age. Therefore, an IQ of 100 is average. The scores on IQ tests are usually standardized to produce normally distributed scores with not only a mean of 100 but also a standard deviation of 15. People with mental retardation are expected to have IQs at the extreme low end of the normal distribution of IQ.

Table 1 Classification of mental retardation

Classification of mental retardation International Classification of Diseases (World Health Organization, 1992)			Diagnostic and Statistical Manual-IV			American Academy of Mental Retardation (2002)	
General: Arrested or incomplete development of the mind, characterized by impairment of skills which contribute to the overall level of intelligence			*General:* Subaverage intellectual functioning that is accompanied by significant limitations in adaptive functioning in several (at least two) skill areas			*General*: Mental retardation is a disability characterized by significant limitations both in intellectual functioning and adaptive behavior, originating before age 18 years	
Term		*Definition*	*Term*		*Definition*	*Statement*	*Component*
Mild	F70	IQ 50–69	Mild	317.0	IQ 50/55–69		Mental retardation is a disability
Moderate	F71	IQ 35–49	Moderate	318.0	IQ 35/40–50/55	First requirement	Significant limitations in intellectual functioning
Severe	F72	IQ 20–34	Severe	318.1	IQ 20/25–35/40	Second requirement	Significant limitations in adaptive behavior as expressed in conceptual, social and practical adaptive skills
Profound	F73	IQ <20	Profound	318.2	IQ <20/25		
Other	F78		Unspecified	319.0			
Unspecified	F79						

Subheadings relating to behavioral impairment
.0 No or minimal behavioral impairment
.1 Significant behavioral impairment requiring attention or treatment
.8 Other behavioral impairment
.9 Without mention of behavioral impairment

IQ, intelligence quotient.

Degree or severity of mental retardation is largely classified by the IQ or an equivalent measure of intellectual ability. Mild mental retardation is defined in the ICD-10 and DSM-IV as IQ 50–69, moderate retardation as IQ 35–49, severe retardation as IQ 20–34, and profound retardation an IQ less than 20 (**Table 1**). IQ estimates are approximate and particularly difficult to measure precisely in more severely affected individuals. While the classification systems state that a criterion of impairment should also be met, none specify how this should be determined. Much of the epidemiological and biological research on mental retardation has collapsed the categories of moderate, severe, and profound retardation and referred to this group as having severe mental retardation.

Epidemiology

Using an IQ of less than 70 (2 standard deviations below the mean) as the criterion for learning disability or mental retardation should result in prevalence rates of 2.3% based on the properties of the normal distribution. Studies of mild mental retardation have produced widely varying prevalence estimates, however, from less than 0.5% to over 8%. There are at least several reasons for this variation. First, identification, or ascertainment, of the 'at risk' population affects the rate, with studies that survey the entire population producing higher rates than those relying on cases formally identified because of health or educational problems, as many people with IQs between 50 and 70 may not be formally registered. Second, the test administered may affect the rates identified. Because performance on IQ tests has improved over the years (a phenomenon called the Flynn effect), the use of older and 'easier' tests may produce a lower rate of learning disability. There may also be real differences in the rate of mental retardation across different populations, with more advantaged populations having lower rates of learning disability. Some of this population difference may be due to bias in test content, so that children from developed countries who attend school from an early age may be more familiar with the type of items on conventional IQ tests. However, use of the supposedly culture-fair test does not eliminate the differences in rates of learning disabilities.

For severe mental retardation, however, the reported prevalence rates have been more consistent and average around 0.4–0.5%, which is about 10 times greater than expected where the normal distribution maintained. This extra 'hump' at the bottom of the normal IQ distribution is likely to represent the children whose learning disabilities have a clear 'organic' origin whether caused prenatally, perinatally, or postnatally.

These findings have led to a suggestion of a 'two-group' approach to learning disability. The first group represents the lower end of a normally distributed population, for which no organic cause can be ascertained and encompasses the majority of children with mild learning disability. Environmental deprivation has classically been cited as the cause of cognitive delay in this group, although this is now criticized for being too simplistic. The second group consists of those children with defined organic or biological cause for their cognitive impairment, which may be more severe. Again, this is likely to be an oversimplification of the heterogeneity of learning disability, and as advances are made in molecular genetics, increasing numbers of children with mild learning disability are likely to be found to have genetic disorders. However, the division of learning disability into these two broad etiological groups has been a useful starting point for researchers in this field.

There is also criticism of the use of IQ as sole discriminator of learning disability for both epidemiological studies and administrative purposes. In terms of judging prevalence rates based on IQ, problems arise due to the fact that IQ may not remain stable throughout development and IQ scores in infancy typically have only low correlations with scores in later childhood. Further, researchers found that although once formal schooling begins IQ scores tend to be more robust, individual cases can still show major gains or losses in cognitive ability. Up to now, however, there has been no agreement on the way in which adaptive behavior should be measured and impairment defined to meet this additional criterion for diagnosis.

The term 'administrative prevalence' has been used to mean the numbers for whom services would be required in a community which made provision for all who needed them. Here again, using IQ alone as discriminator is inadequate as IQ scores do not correlate with social adaptation in all instances. Indeed, researchers found that although 2.5% of children in the study could be classified as having learning disability based on their IQ scores, only half of these children were sufficiently impaired in their daily lives to require the additional provision of services. Functional impairment is dependent not only on the child's developmental level, but on wider social issues of available family and community resources. Thus, it is unsurprising that administrative prevalence is somewhat higher in lower socioeconomic groups.

Gender differences are also apparent in the rates of learning disability with a male to female ratio of 1.5:1, which may reflect the male preponderance in certain genetically mediated disorders affecting cognitive ability. These differences are more clear-cut for those with severe learning disability.

Etiology

As suggested in the two-group approach, learning disability is heterogeneous and it is likely that multiple factors and their interaction contribute to its etiology. These factors can largely be divided into environmental and genetic factors.

Environmental Factors

Social factors

Learning disability is associated with adverse social conditions: low socioeconomic status, poverty, poor housing, and an unstable family environment. To establish whether this is a cause or consequence of learning disability, researchers endeavored to manipulate the outcomes for at risk children. A group of deprived children in residential care were given a special education provision and these children were found to have higher IQ scores compared to a control group 20 years later. Indeed, positive social environmental influences may increase IQ scores by as much as 20 points. However, other studies indicate that environmental enrichment may not 'normalize' IQ, so that deprived children receiving enrichment do better on IQ tests and measures of educational attainment than deprived children without enrichment but less well than advantaged children. Large-scale projects aimed at early environmental enrichment, such as Head start, have suggested that the improvements in IQ may be short term only, although there may be wider benefits of such programs for overall development.

Obstetric factors

Pregnancy and birth factors have traditionally been thought of as important causes of learning disability. Indeed fetal alcohol syndrome, associated with maternal alcohol consumption in pregnancy, can cause up to 10% of mild learning disability. Intrauterine infections (including rubella, toxoplasmosis, cytomegalovirus, and herpes) are recognized causes of learning disability in the offspring. Maternal malnutrition and irradiation during pregnancy may increase the risk of learning disability, particularly during vulnerable periods of fetal brain development. Prematurity and low birth weight have been associated with learning disability, but earlier studies estimating that clinically recognizable birth injuries accounted for about 10% of learning disability have fallen out of favor. The relationship to severe prematurity, for example, 32 weeks' gestation or less, birth weight less than 2500 g, and significant anoxia during delivery remains clear, and is often associated with abnormalities observed on brain scans. However, the relationship to more subtle obstetric adversity is less certain. Studies finding a link between milder obstetric adversity and later developmental delay have not adequately addressed whether there is a direct link or whether minor obstetric adversity is indexing other factors that are responsible for the association. Babies born with genetic disorders associated with learning disability, such as Down syndrome and

Prader–Willi syndrome, have increased rates of mild obstetric adversity, presumably due to fetal abnormalities. Thus, it cannot be differentiated whether the adversity resulted in learning disability, or that existing fetal brain abnormalities led to complications at birth. Current thinking supports the latter explanation. Furthermore, some of the milder obstetric adversity is more common in mothers from socially disadvantaged backgrounds, who may themselves have lower cognitive ability, raising the possibility that obstetric adversity is a confounder.

Other environmental factors

Postnatally, important environmental factors include lead poisoning, meningitis, malnutrition, and hypothyroidism (e.g., due to iodine deficiency). Severe or prolonged seizures, head injury, brain tumors and their treatment, and brain irradiation are all causes of acquired learning disability. While these factors are less significant causes of learning disability in developed countries compared to genetic, social, and perinatal factors, these environmental factors are the main causes of learning disability in developing countries and malnutrition in the first 2 years of life is probably the most common cause of learning disability worldwide.

Genetic Factors

Genetic factors can cause or contribute to learning disability in different ways. Some specific genes are recognized to cause particular syndromes which present with cognitive impairment. More complex genetic influences involving the operation of multiple genes or the interaction of genetic vulnerability with the environment may also play a part.

As advances in medical genetics have been made, over 100 genetic disorders that present with learning disability as a symptom have been identified. Most of these are extremely rare, but some such as Down syndrome and fragile X syndrome are relatively common. They also provide good examples of chromosomal and single-gene abnormalities that can lead to learning disability.

Chromosomal abnormalities

Chromosomal abnormalities can cause learning disability. Down syndrome is the most common single cause of severe learning disability, accounting for up to a third of all cases and occurring in 1 in 600 live births. A trisomy (having three rather than two copies) of chromosome 21 due to nondisjunction is the cause of 95% of Down syndrome, with the remaining 5% due to translocations and mosiaicism. Nondysjunction is associated with increasing maternal age, and hence, the incidence of Down syndrome in older mothers is increased. Children with Down syndrome have distinct physical features (e.g., short stature, small head, round face, and epicanthic folds)

in association with cognitive impairment and frequently cardiac and gut abnormalities.

Having too many sex chromosomes (XXY males, XYY males, and XXX females), or too few (XO females) may also cause learning disability to varying extents. More subtle deletions and rearrangements of chromosomal material, invisible under the microscope but identifiable with DNA probes, called microdeletions, have been demonstrated in several conditions, including William's syndrome, Smith–Magenis syndrome, and velo-cardio-facial syndrome. These can now be diagnosed reliably using a laboratory technique called fluorescent *in situ* hybridization (FISH). In addition to being implicated in causing distinct syndromes, researchers found that subtle chromosomal abnormalities were present in 7% of children with moderate to severe learning disability compared to 0.5% of children with only mild mental impairment. These as yet unidentified abnormalities may be an important cause of learning disability.

Single gene effects

After Down syndrome, fragile X syndrome is probably the next most common cause of learning disability and occurs in 1 in 2000 males and 1 in 4000 females, and is the most common to be inherited (because Down syndrome is usually not inherited). Fragile X syndrome is caused by an expanded triplet repeat of DNA sequence (CGG) on the X-chromosome (Xq27.3). X-inactivation of one of the two X syndrome chromosomes in girls explains the reduced prevalence in females. It is thought that the expanded triplet repeat interferes with the transcription of the gene *FMR1*, whose protein product familial mental retardation protein (FMRP) is thought to be important in regulating proteins important in brain signaling pathways. Fragile X syndrome largely causes moderate learning disability, but can present with mild learning disability or normal intelligence. Its associated physical features in males include large protruding ears, long face, prominent jaw, and enlarged testicles. Because the expansion of the triplet repeat DNA sequence occurs over the course of generations (but only in female germ cells), it is common for the phenotype, or outward characteristics, to appear *de novo*.

Rett syndrome is another X-linked disorder that only occurs in females because the presence of the Rett mutation in the *MECP2* gene is lethal in males. However, other mutations have been identified in the *MECP2* gene causing a range of syndromes associated with mild to moderate learning disability and frequently also spasticity. It is uncertain how prevalent these mutations are but it has been suggested that they may be as common as fragile X in causing learning disability. There are a large number of other X-linked mutations associated with learning disability and, as single gene causes of learning disability, they appear to be disproportionately represented.

Autosomal recessive disorders causing learning disability include phenylketonuria and a range of other metabolic disorders. Many of the autosomal dominant disorders show either high rates of spontaneous new mutations, such as in tuberose sclerosis, or variable expression, as in neurofibromatosis, consistent with the reduced reproduction rates in people with significant learning disability.

Imprinting effects

Some genetic abnormalities vary in the features depending upon whether the mutation is maternally or paternally derived. Prader–Willi and Angelman syndromes are two genetic disorders with distinct characteristics. Prader–Willi syndrome is associated with mild learning disability (and nonverbal ability may be in the normal range), early hypotonia, small hands, and feet. Characteristic features include compulsive overeating, skin-picking, and emotional lability. Angelman syndrome, on the other hand, is associated with severe to profound learning disability, epilepsy, an abnormal gait, and jerky movements. Both disorders are caused by abnormalities in the same region of chromosome 15, and may occur where this area is deleted in one of the chromosomes. However, Prader–Willi syndrome occurs where the deletion is from the chromosome of paternal origin and Angelman syndrome where it is of maternal origin.

Multiple gene effects

Many family, twin, and adoption studies have consistently shown that polygenic inheritance (such as that involved in other attributes such as height) is important in determining IQ within the normal range. In comparison, surprisingly few studies have investigated polygenic inheritance in learning disability. Available evidence, however, points toward a moderate role for genetic factors.

One study of siblings of learning disability children found that siblings of mildly impaired children also tended to have lower than average IQ scores. The familial component of mild learning disability is further supported by a study of the families of people with mild learning disability. This showed that if one parent has mild learning disability, the risk of a similar diagnosis in their offspring was 20%. If both parents were affected, almost half their children would also suffer from mild learning disability. These findings show that mild learning disability runs in families and suggests genetic factors may have a role.

In the first major twin study of mild learning disability, including a sample of 3886 twins, twin concordances were 74% for monozygotic (identical) twins, 45% for same-sex disygotic twins, and 36% for opposite-sex dizygotic (fraternal) twins, indicating substantial genetic influence. Group heritability (the amount of variance in the phenotype, learning disability that is explained by genetic factors) was about 50%. These results suggest that mild learning disability is genetically influenced and is therefore a good target for research on global brain function and dysfunction.

In contrast to findings for mild learning disability, in the same sibling study mentioned above, siblings of moderately and severely impaired children were found to have average intelligence. New gene mutations and chromosomal abnormalities or environmental insults (such as those described above) could explain the nonfamilial nature of moderate and severe learning disability. This lends support to the two-group approach suggesting that mild learning disability is familial, possibly representing the lower tail of intelligence which is determined by polygenic inheritance, while moderate and severe learning disability is nonfamilial and could represent the 'hump' of learning disability caused by biological factors.

Gene–Environment Interplay

Interplay between genes and environment in learning difficulties is likely to be very common but it is difficult to detect until individual susceptibility genes are identified. However, the role of family stress on behavioral problems in boys with fragile X syndrome has been documented, highlighting that even disorders caused by a single gene are influenced by environmental factors.

Clinical Features of Learning Disability

Typically, learning disability affects all aspects of cognitive ability (learning, memory, problem-solving, language) uniformly; however, it is not uncommon for some children to have a more varied profile of ability. Identifying particular weaknesses can help predict areas where the child may struggle and require extra assistance in order to prevent frustration and the consequent behavioral problems which may result.

Of children with learning disability, the vast majority (85%) will have mild disorder. Moderate learning difficulty children account for 10%, with severely and profoundly affected children accounting for 3–4% and 1–2%, respectively. Children with mild learning disability are often unremarkable in appearance and with only slight motor or sensory deficits if any. Their language and social behavior develop close to normally and they are able to manage activities of daily living independently. They are often undiagnosed and attend mainstream schools without extra educational provision, albeit many may feel that they have to struggle to keep up at school. Of the moderately learning disabled, receptive language skills are often superior to expressive language, which is often easier for carers to understand than strangers. Use of simplified signing systems, such as Makaton or picture exchange, may be useful in this group to allay the frustrations of being misunderstood. Activities of daily living can usually be mastered with rehearsal and time in these children. In contrast, children with severe and profound learning disability will usually require close supervision at all times. Severely learning disabled children may be able to learn simple activities of daily living with supervision and may be able to communicate basic needs. In the profound group, support and supervision are generally required for all activities of daily living, and function in all domains is equivalent to that of a 1-year-old child.

Behavioral Phenotypes

On studying children with particular syndromes associated with learning disability, certain nonadaptive behaviors have been commonly identified in affected children. Such behaviors include hand-wringing in Rett syndrome, voracious eating in Prader–Willi syndrome, bouts of inappropriate laughter in Angelman syndrome, self-injury in Lesch–Nyhan and Cornelia de Lange syndrome, self-hugging in Smith–Magenis syndrome and a shrill cat-like cry in Cri-du-chat syndrome. For these and other syndromes, there appears to be a strong correlation between the behavior and the syndrome. As the genetic basis of these syndromes is known, research is now focused on identifying the links between the genetic basis and the phenotypic behavior shown. Not only will elucidation of the pathway from gene to abnormal behavior gain greater understanding of the syndrome and brain function in general, but offer potential avenues for treatment.

Further study has shown that other behaviors appear to span a variety of syndromes. Inattention and hyperactivity are frequent in fragile X syndrome, William's syndrome; sequential processing deficits are common in fragile X and Prader–Willi syndromes. Individuals with velo-cardio-facial syndrome have a markedly increased rate of psychosis. Thus, a number of syndromes have distinctive but not necessarily unique behavioral features. Dykens suggests that such behavioral phenotypes involve an increased probability or likelihood that people with a given syndrome will show certain behavioral features relative to those without the syndrome. Researchers are now also beginning to study such 'between-syndrome' behavioral phenotypes: examining genetic, environmental, and psychosocial correlates which may predispose to the observed behaviors. The identification of behavioral phenotypes and its study is a move forward from the broad two-group approach and has allowed finer dissection and closer examination of the etiology of learning disability in particular syndromes.

Common Comorbities

Associated problems, or comorbid conditions, are common in learning disability. The cause of the learning disability may have a range of effects on the brain and other organ systems. Other central nervous system disorders are frequent. Cerebral palsy is frequently associated with learning disability. Epilepsy is much increased occurring in some 20–30% of children with learning disability compared to 1% of the general population. The seizures often begin in the first few years of life in those with learning disability as opposed to a later onset in other people.

Children with learning disability are more likely to have motor, hearing, and vision problems. Some of these may be immediately apparent, such as severe cerebral palsy, blindness, and deafness. Although individuals with some syndromes and/or more severe learning disability are particularly likely to have such impairments (so that about 50% of those with Down syndrome have hearing problems), the rates of such problems are also increased in those with mild learning disability (with hearing problems occurring in about 20% and visual impairment in about 4%). However, many deficits are more subtle and are unlikely to be detected unless routine screening is undertaken. Children with learning disabilities are also more likely to have chronic physical health problems requiring increased medical treatment, and are more likely to miss school because of such problems. This may add to poor educational attainments.

Almost all child psychiatric problems are substantially increased in children with learning disabilities but Emerson showed that autism and attention deficit hyperactivity disorder (ADHD) are those most strongly associated with lower IQ. Between 50% and 75% of people with autism also have an IQ less than 70 and the mean IQ among children with ADHD is about 7–12 points below the general population. Other emotional problems, such as anxiety, depression and obsessive-compulsive disorder, and conduct problems, such as oppositional defiant disorder, are more frequently seen in children with learning disability. While delinquent problems and conduct disorder are more common in those with borderline low and mild learning disabilities, those with moderate and severe learning disabilities are relatively protected from such problems at least in part become they are more socially isolated. However, less organized aggression is common in children with moderate to severe learning disability. In addition, as learning disability becomes more severe, it is increasingly difficult to identify psychiatric disorders as they are expressed in typically developing children. This is partly because children with significant learning disability may lack the communication skills to describe their emotional state. Behavior may seem odd or unpredictable because parents and carers are unaware of the child's experiences and internal mental state. In addition, there are also some behavioral problems that are almost exclusive to the learning disability population; these include certain forms of self-injury (biting, chewing skin-picking, eye-poking) and pica (eating nonfood material).

Children with global learning disabilities are not exempted from having specific learning disabilities such as reading and spelling problems (dyslexia) but such problems are often less likely to be identified. A diagnosis of a specific learning disability requires that the problems in that area exceed what is expected based on overall intellectual functioning. Children are not generally expected to have achieved many reading milestones before the age of 7 years, so that children with a mental age of less than this age will not be recognized as having dyslexia. However, with children and young adults functioning at a higher mental age, the possibility of specific learning disabilities exists, especially if they are struggling with basic numeracy and literacy despite an appropriate educational placement.

Assessment

Assessment starts from the point of referral. From here it is important to establish why the referral has been made and who has raised concern. Parents and teachers are usually good judges of a child's ability level and can often give a good estimate as to the child's developmental level. Even so, sometimes a child's ability can be misjudged; in particular, where the cognitive profile is varied, strengths in one area may allow the child to hide weaknesses in others. Teacher and parental expectations may differ and, again, lead to differences in their judgments of developmental level. It is also useful to consider the timing of the referral. Children with mild learning disability often only present when they are older and are referred for emotional or behavioral problems (somewhat

often consequent to their learning disability) rather than for developmental delay. Any pre-existing family beliefs and expectations should also be evaluated.

Assessment of learning disability is largely directed at three areas: (1) establishing etiology of the learning disability; (2) establishing level of cognitive function, adaptive behavior and social skills; and (3) assessing for the presence of any comorbid psychiatric and physical difficulties (**Table 2**).

Assessment of Etiology

Establishing any underlying etiology for learning disability is dependent on a thorough history and physical examination. The history should pay particular attention to any family history of inherited disorders and abnormalities in the pregnancy or birth of the child, including maternal alcohol consumption. A full developmental history including milestones should be taken as well as documentation of any associated medical conditions such as congenital defects, epilepsy, and cerebral palsy. The physical examination should include observation for dysmorphic features and neurocutaneous skin signs. Relevant dysmorphic features include the round face and up-slanting eyes of Down syndrome and the long face and prominent ears of fragile X syndrome. Relevant skin signs include the neurofibromata of neurofibromatosis, adenoma sebaceum of tuberose sclerosis and port-wine stain of Sturge-Weber. Examination under Wood's lamp for typical ash-leaf like skin patterns may be required if tuberose sclerosis is suspected. Head circumference, height, and weight should be documented against standardized gender-specific norms, certain conditions being associated

Table 2 Features of the assessment of learning disability that aid identification of etiology, developmental level, and associated comorbidity

	History	Examination and investigations
Etiology	• Family history of inherited disorders • Pregnancy and birth abnormalities • Developmental history including milestones • Medical history	• Examination of dysmorphic features and neurocutaneous skin signs • Measurement of head circumference, height, and weight • Neurological examination • Neuroimaging, electroencephalogram, and genetic testing may be indicated
Developmental level	• School reports and previous psychological reports should be sought • Parental estimate of developmental level is often an accurate predictor	• General standardized psychometric testing (e.g., Wechsler Intelligence Scales for Children, Mullen Scales, Vineland Adaptive Behavior Scales) • Additional specific tests may be indicated (e.g., Autism Diagnostic Interview)
Associated comorbidity	• Systematic review of symptoms (e.g. inattention, over-activity, impulsivity, eating, sleeping, emotional and behavioral difficulties) • Structured instruments (e.g., Strengths and Difficulties Questionnaire, Conners' Rating Scales) may be helpful • Good behavioral examples should be sought	• Behavioral observation in clinic setting • Behavioral observation in school setting

with macrocephaly (autism), microcephely (cri-du-chat, fetal alcohol syndrome), short stature (Down syndrome), and tall stature (Soto syndrome). A neurological examination is also important, and should include assessment of vision, hearing, coordination, and gait. Asymmetry in motor skill, tone, reflexes, or limb size may suggest hemisphere dysfunction or other pathology. Specialist assessment of hearing and vision should be undertaken if there is any suspicion that these are abnormal.

Investigations may need to be undertaken to supplement history and examination findings. This may include neuroimaging, electroencephalogram, and genetic testing for chromosomal abnormalities, fragile X syndrome or metabolic diseases. The likelihood of finding a medical condition is greatest in children with severe and profound learning disabilities.

Assessment of Developmental Level

Cognitive assessment by an educational or clinical psychologist using standardized psychometric tests is invaluable in assessing learning disability. Ingenuity and patience are required to allow a child to maintain interest and perform at their best. Tests should be selected to suit the expected developmental level of the child and start with tasks well within the child's capabilities to avoid early frustration. A variety of psychometric tests have been developed, among the most popular being the Wechsler Intelligence Scales for Children and the Stanford-Binet. Whenever possible both nonverbal and verbal aspects of ability should be assessed as these may vary and building on a child's strengths can promote their development. In some cases, a test that has not been standardized for the child's developmental age is the most appropriate; this will produce age equivalents, which can be used to give a ratio IQ [(age equivalent ÷ chronological age) × 100]. Although the latter may be less accurate, it nevertheless gives a broad estimate of the child's level of functioning. On occasion, it is not possible to gain a child's cooperation in testing; in such instances an assessment based on parent/carer report of skills, such as the Vineland Adaptive Behavior Scales, will give an estimate of a child's functional level. The results of such testing should always be evaluated in the light of all other available information. Further standardized tests are also available for specific developmental problems and neuropsychological deficits, such as reading, language, problem solving, or social development.

Assessment of Comorbidity

A systematic approach should be taken to the assessment of possible comorbid problems, including physical disorders, psychiatric problems, and additional cognitive impairments. Close liaison with pediatricians caring for the child

is essential as many physical problems may present in unusual ways, including as an exacerbation of or new behavioral difficulties. Children with learning disability are at increased risk of a range of psychiatric disorders as well as emotional and behavioral difficulties. It is more difficult to identify comorbid conditions in children with learning disabilities as they may not be able to express difficulties as well as other children. Further, comorbid psychiatric diagnoses are often underdiagnosed in this group of children as it is often assumed that their difficulties are due to the underlying learning disability. A systematic review of symptoms in the history, including symptoms such as inattention, overactivity, impulsivity, and eating, sleeping, emotional, and behavioral difficulties should be conducted. Structured instruments such as the Children's Behavior Checklist (CBC-L), the Strengths and Difficulties Questionnaire, and the Conners' Rating Scales may be administered to parents as an aid to identifying and assessing difficulties. Scales particularly designed for children with learning disability include the Developmental Behavior Checklist and the Aberrant Behavior Checklist. Behavioral observation is an important tool and parents should be asked for specific behavioral examples in the history. Careful observational assessment of the child in clinic or school setting may also be beneficial.

Treatment

Treatment should focus on two areas: learning disability and comorbid conditions. As treatment options for learning disability are limited, identification of comorbid disorders, which play a key role in overall morbidity, becomes a priority.

Treatment of Learning Disability

Prevention is one of the most important aspects of learning disability and treatment. In relation to prenatal care, healthy pregnancy and delivery can significantly reduce the rate of mental retardation due to obstetric factors and is likely to be one reason why there are lower rates of mental retardation in developed countries with national health systems. The identification of potential genetic disorders either prior to conception or during early pregnancy allows prospective parents greater choice in their family choices. However, many genetic disorders are impractical to identify prenatally. Where prenatal testing is possible, it is unclear that additional active population-based screening, for example for fragile X syndrome, would lead to a significant reduction in the number of cases. However, genetic testing for high risk groups, such as Ashkenazi Jews at risk of Tay-Sachs disease, or cascade screening of at-risk relatives of affected people, as in fragile X syndrome, can reduce genetic disorders causing mental retardation in targeted groups. Population-based postnatal screening is practical where the test is automated and straightforward to interpret, and most importantly where early detection has treatment implications. Hence, population screening for phenyl-ketonuria and hypothyroidism has been implemented in many countries. Malnutrition is rare in developed countries and most likely to occur in the context of other medical problems but routine infant healthcare is important in its identification.

The underpinnings of any treatment for learning disability include clear identification of the overall level of functioning, along with areas of strength and weakness, as these will aid in appropriate educational placement and psychoeducation for the family and other carers. Policies regarding education in mainstream vs. special schools/units have varied across time and countries. There is almost certainly a place for both alternatives. In either instance, the objective is to provide an individual educational plan that builds on the student's areas of strength. Education should also ensures the student achieves his potential both scholastically and in life skills. Very often those with milder degrees of learning disabilities will benefit from at least some attendance in mainstream classes to allow participation in less academic subjects and to mix with peers, to extend their social skills. However those with severe learning disability, particularly at secondary levels of education, may require a differentiated curriculum and may also have different social needs, so that mainstream education is unlikely to meet their needs. Educational goals and placement should be reviewed regularly.

Providing parents and other carers with as much information as possible will help them to set realistic goals. Many parents have difficulty in coming to terms with their child's mental retardation and may need considerable support in understanding and accepting the situation. As the child gets older, the gap in comparison to typically developing children widens (a 4-year-old child with an IQ of 50 roughly behaves like a child of 2 years of age while a 16-year-old child with an IQ of 50 behaves like a child of 8 years of age), so the developmental abnormalities often become more apparent with age. In addition, parents frequently require additional support at certain points in development. Children with learning disability (and especially those with autism) have difficulty coping with their emerging sexual feelings during puberty. At a time when increased privacy and independence is the norm for typically developing children, those with learning disability may not have attained sufficient awareness for parents to allow this.

Parents often find it helpful to know the cause of mental retardation, where it has been identified. Often societies exist for particular disorders to provide information and support to families and are usually perceived as extremely helpful. Where a cause has not been identified or no such group exists, the voluntary organizations focusing on families affected by mental retardation and disability can offer a similar role. There is also an important role for social services in providing family assistance, including respite care. The family should be supported in engaging in the full range of family activities, including time alone for the adults and also with their other children. While siblings may benefit from taking a caring role in relation to a child with learning disability, they are also likely to get less attention and nurturing from their parents.

Treatment of Associated Problems

As mental problems are increased in children with learning disability, professionals should be alert for early signs. The evidence for prevention, for example, by behavioral advice and support to parents, is limited. Although it is unlikely to be harmful, it is uncertain whether prevention and early intervention services are effective or efficient. However, in certain instances, alerting parents to common problems and how to prevent them may reduce their incidence. For example, in disorders such as Cornelia de Lange syndrome where self-injury is common, informing parents about the early signs and describing appropriate management strategies may help to avoid serious problems.

When they present, emotional and behavioral problems should always be systematically assessed, looking for comorbidities as well as identifying the main problem. In most instances, there is limited evidence for treatment efficacy specifically for children with learning disability and treatment choices will be similar to those without learning disability. Where behavioral treatments are to be used, appropriate modification should be made for the child's cognitive level, including simple explanations to the child, use of visual as well as verbal prompts, and immediate and frequent reinforcement of behavior. Generalization of treatment is often more difficult for children with learning disability so consistency across home, school and other situations is especially important. Cognitive-behavioral approaches can sometimes be successfully simplified to work directly with children, but parallel intervention with parents so they can reinforce the treatment between sessions is usually necessary. Pharmacotherapy has a place but the increased sensitivity of the brains of children with learning disability to both beneficial and adverse effects should be borne in mind. Initial low doses, cautious increases and frequent monitoring for adverse effects should be the rule.

As physical health problems are more common in children with mental retardation, regular reviews should be undertaken by a pediatrician with expertise in their examination and treatment. Dental care also requires personnel with expertise and patience in achieving compliance. A frequent cause of new or exacerbations in behavior problems, where no environmental precipitant can be identified, is a physical problem causing pain.

Prognosis

Parents frequently want information about their child's longer-term prospects, particularly about the ability to live independently, work, and have intimate relationships in adult life. Prediction about adult outcome can be difficult in early childhood as developmental trajectories may vary. Some conditions, such as Down syndrome and fragile X syndrome, may show a plateau in development in late adolescence or early adult life. In part, this may reflect that the type of new cognitive abilities acquired by typically developing adolescents involve a higher level of abstraction that is not achievable with certain forms of learning disability. About one-third of people with Down syndrome will develop early onset Alzheimer's disease, usually in their 40s. In other instances, people may continue to develop new skills and cognitive abilities well into adult life. Often by late childhood or early adolescence it is possible to make more specific predictions about the degree of adult independent living anticipated and this is very helpful for families in longer-term planning.

Physical health remains poorer amongst those with learning disability. In part, this is due to the physical problems associated with the underlying causes of mental retardation but also aspects of the life style of people with learning disability increase their risk of poor health; opportunities for exercise are reduced and obesity is common. However, tobacco, alcohol and substance use/misuse are less common, especially amongst those with severe retardation. The health needs of those with learning disability are more likely to go untreated and in many countries transfer from pediatric to adult healthcare is associated with the cessation of regular health reviews and screening.

Research Directions

Research into the molecular basis of learning and cognition is likely to make significant advances in the next decade. Alongside animal models of genetic defects that affect cognition, these should have important implications for human learning disability. However, previous experience with nonbrain-based disorders has shown that applications of such knowledge, for example, through gene and stem cell therapy, present a new and different set of challenges. While it is likely that such interventions will have a role in treatment and prevention, of learning disability the extent of their applicability is uncertain. For this reason, research should continue to focus on prevention, both through pre-pregnancy and prenatal

identification of single gene mutations and also the reduction in environmental factors causing learning disability. The latter involves higher-quality universal healthcare in both Western and developing countries and also better public education in relation to the effects on the fetus and child of maternal alcohol and substance use and the importance of regular prenatal care. In developing countries, adequate nutrition and protection from infectious disease can play an important role in prevention.

For those with learning disability, future research needs to focus on better prevention and treatment of associated physical and mental health problems. Such research needs to include both basic science components aimed at exploring the underlying causes of associated disorders and also applications that focus on effective treatment strategies. The latter approaches should consider the challenges of improving identification of comorbid conditions. Finally, there is a strong need for research involving people affected with learning disability to discover their priorities for health, education and social services. Frequently the extra effort required to communicate effectively with people with learning disability interferes with the process of discovering their own service priorities and identifying the factors that impair their quality of life. While each of these research areas presents many challenges, the rewards of meeting these to reduce the burden of learning disability are great.

See also: ADHD: Genetic Influences; Autism Spectrum Disorders; Cerebral Palsy; Developmental Disabilities: Cognitive; Down Syndrome; Fetal Alcohol Spectrum Disorders; Fragile X Syndrome; Genetic Disorders: Sex Linked; Genetic Disorders: Single Gene; Genetics and Inheritance; Intellectual Disabilities; Mental Health, Infant; Special Education; Teratology.

Suggested Readings

Dykens EM (2000) Psychopathology in children with intellectual disability. *Journal of Child Psychology and Psychiatry* 41: 407–418.

Knight SJ, Regan R, Nicod A, Horsley SW, Kearney L, and Homfray T (1999) Subtle chromosomal rearrangements in children with unexplained mental retardation. *Lancet* 354(9191): 1676–1681.

O'Connor TG (2003) Early experiences and psychological development: Conceptual questions, empirical illustrations, and implications for intervention. *Development & Psychopathology* 15(3): 671–690.

Rutter M, Graham P, and Yule W (1970) *A Neuropsychiatric Study in Childhood.* London: Spastics International Medical Publications.

Simonoff E, Bolton P, and Rutter M (1996) Mental retardation: genetic findings, clinical implications and research agenda. *Journal of Child Psychology and Psychiatry* 37: 259–280.

Sternberg RJ (2004) Culture and intelligence. *American Psychologist* 59 (5): 325–338.

Tizard JP (1975) Etiology of mental retardation. *Proceedings of the Royal Society of Medicine* 68(9): 561.

Zigler E, Balla D, and Hodapp R (1984) On the definition and classification of mental retardation. *American Journal of Mental Deficiency* 89: 215–230.

Literacy

C M Connor and S Al'Otaiba, Florida State University, Tallahassee, FL, USA

Glossary

Alphabetic principle – The concept that letters and letter combinations represent individual sounds, or phonemes, in written words.

Comprehension – Understanding the meaning of what one is reading, the ultimate goal of all reading activity.

Decoding – The ability to determine the pronunciation of a word employing knowledge of sound symbol correspondences; the act of deciphering a new word by sounding it out.

Emergent literacy – An early stage of early reading development that occurs prior to formal schooling and includes skills, knowledge, and attitudes that are developmental precursors to conventional forms of reading and writing.

Expressive language – Language that is spoken.

Fluency – Ability to read text quickly, accurately, and with proper expression, that allows the reader to focus on meaning.

Lexical access – The process of mapping a printed word onto a specific meaning in the reader's memory.

Lexical semantics – The study of meanings of words and their relationships.

Lexicon – The mental dictionary or body of word knowledge that includes memory of the meanings and pronunciations of words; also referred to as vocabulary.

Literacy – Broadly, the skills involving processing written language including listening, speaking, reading, and writing.

Metalinguistic – An awareness of language structure and function that allows one to reflect on consciously manipulating the language; for example, understanding that the sounds in 'dog' are /d/ /o/ /g/ and not 'bow-wow', or the sound a dog makes.

Morpheme – The smallest meaningful unit of language. For example, 'preview' has two morphemes: 'pre-' and 'view'.

Morphemic or structural analysis – An analysis of words formed by adding prefixes, suffixes, or other units of meaning to a base or root word.

Morphology – The study of word structure including inflection, derivation, and the formation of compounds; refers to how words are formed and relate to each other.

Morphosyntactic awareness – An awareness of the connection between grammar and word forms.

Onset – Most syllables contain an onset, or an initial consonant or consonant cluster before the vowel; (e.g., in the word 'lap', the onset is 'l'. In the word 'star', the onset is 'st').

Phonemic awareness – The ability to notice, think about, or manipulate the individual phonemes (sounds) in words and to understand that sounds in spoken language work together to make words; the highest level of phonological awareness (awareness of individual phonemes in words).

Phonics – The relationship between letters and the sounds they represent – also, reading instruction that teaches the correspondence between sounds and symbols.

Phonogram – A series of letters that represents the same phonological unit in different words, such as 'igh' in 'light', 'sight', and 'sigh'.

Phonological awareness – A sensitivity to, or explicit awareness of, the sound structure of words in a language, including awareness of phonemes in individual words, sentences, syllables, and onset-rime segments.

Receptive language – Language that is heard.

Rime – The part of a syllable following the initial consonant or consonant cluster that includes the vowel and any letters that follow it; different from rhyming. (For example in the word 'lap', the rime is 'ap'. In the word 'star', the rime is 'ar')

Semantics – The study of the meanings of words and phrases; the ways in which language conveys meaning.

Vocabulary – All of the storage of information about word meanings and pronunciations necessary for communication. Readers need to know many word meanings to comprehend text.

Introduction

In the enactment of the No Child Left Behind Act our society has recognized literacy as a right and not a privilege. Yet teaching all children how to read and write proficiently has proved to be difficult. Indeed, the most recent results of the National Assessment of Educational Progress (NAEP), which has been called the nation's report card, reveals that we fail to teach more than one-third of our students to read proficiently by fourth grade. Yet at the same time, our understanding about how children learn to read and become literate members of society has increased greatly since the mid-1980s. In this article, we focus on what we have learned about how children learn to read and the essential skills that comprise proficient reading. We will start with a brief history of literacy instruction and will then discuss the salient but complex links between children's oral language skills and their literacy abilities, the emerging insights offered by neurological research, and how links between language and literacy have important implications for designing effective instruction from pre-school through third grade. As we will show, unlike talking, reading and writing must be taught and so we will discuss literacy development in the context of instruction – in both home and school environments. Moreover, accumulating research reveals that the impact of any particular instructional strategy depends on the language and literacy skills children bring to the learning environment. Additionally, we will discuss reading disabilities in the context of 'response-to-instruction', and how definitions of reading disabilities are changing.

We use the terms 'literacy' and 'reading' throughout this article. Generally, when we refer to reading, we mean a specific set of skills. However, our use of the term literacy carries broader implications and includes the knowledge and skills that facilitate learning. The hallmarks of proficient literacy are the ability to comprehend, or understand what is read, to learn from what is read, and to express ideas in written form. We will also briefly touch on emergent literacy in the context of children's developing skills.

The History of Literacy Instruction

The history of literacy instruction has been characterized by contention and division and reflects a debate in the field of education that finds its early roots in romanticism and the traditional versus progressive movements. Fruits of this debate can be traced across the content areas, such as math and science, but have been most public in the recent Reading Wars, which, as we will discuss, pitted whole-language against code-based instruction.

Until the early 1800s, *Webster Spellers*, introduced in 1782, provided the most popular method of reading instruction in the US. The *McGuffey Readers*, which slowly replaced the *Webster Spellers*, incorporated both alphabetic and phonics methods while promoting the virtues of honesty, thrift, and kindness. Then, in 1832, stating that learning should not be 'tiresome drudgery' (as exemplified by the McGuffey reader), John Miller Keagy introduced the whole-word

method. Proponents of the method, also advocates of romanticism, stated that learning to read should be 'as natural as learning to talk', predating the claims of contemporary whole-language approaches. In the 1930s through the 1950s, the Dick and Jane series, using the whole-word method, gained widespread popularity. In 1955, Flesch wrote *Why Johnny Can't Read*. This book reached the national bestseller list and further charged the bitter debate about phonics versus whole-word. Coupled with rising criticism of public education, the general press proposed phonics as the solution to reading problems, while this stance was rejected by educators and educational researchers as opinion rather than science.

In 1967, Chall's *Learning to Read: The Great Debate*, which had been commissioned by the Carnegie Corporation of New York, was supposed to settle the debate. However, as Chall soon discovered, comparing reading methods' efficacy was complex. Moreover, no one method of instruction fully insured reading success for all children. Teachers frequently used a combination of old and new methods. For example, Chall observed that phonics instruction survived in the 1930s because some teachers "got out their old phonics charts, *closed the doors*, and hoped the supervisor or principal would not enter unannounced" (p. 7). One clear message from the research was that an early emphasis on decoding and phonics (i.e., code-focused) instruction appeared to be critical for children's reading success.

Throughout the 1970s, the notion that learning to read was like learning to talk or that it was a 'psycholinguistic guessing game' was emerging. These ideas formed the foundation of the 'whole-language' approach. Its proponents suggested that learning to read was a natural process (in line with romanticists' principles and social constructivism); children needed only to be exposed to 'authentic' text and coached by their teacher to enable them to succeed and to construct their own knowledge. While highly similar in many ways to the largely discredited whole-word look-say approach, educators were enthusiastic. The response to whole language was, in part, a reaction to the overemphasis on script, drill, and workbooks that was typical of the 1970s and early 1980s. Whole-language approaches de-emphasized explicit and systematic teaching of phonics, tended to empower teachers, and promoted using interesting books and instilling a joy for reading over a focus on basic skills and phonics. Nevertheless, researchers in the 1990s rediscovered what Chall had found in the 1960s – many children required systematic and explicit instruction in phonics, phonological awareness, and fluency (i.e., code-focused instruction) and explicit instruction in comprehension strategies if they were to become successful readers. Although the debate continues, the most current research has shown that elements of both whole-language and code-focused instruction are important for developing readers.

Learning to Read versus Learning to Talk

Speaking a language is a common human characteristic found within every human society – and reading is not. Although linguists may get contentious on the topic, there are no public debates regarding how to teach children how to talk. Yet schools' failures make headlines and every year the National Assessment of Educational Progress (NAEP) shows that one-third of children are not reading proficiently whereas we assume that virtually all the children are talking proficiently. Indeed, when provided even a marginally acceptable linguistic environment, adequate hearing, and cognitive wherewithal, epidemiological studies show that approximately 93% of children learn to talk without any specific instruction or intervention. There appears to be a 'language instinct'. That is not to say that the child's home and learning environments do not matter. If they did not, all of us would speak the same language and all children would have very similar language abilities. Children do show widely different language abilities within a normal range and a large part of this variability can be traced to the home linguistic environment. Nevertheless, following highly predictable timetables, babies babble, toddlers talk, and 3-year-olds carry on conversations.

The same highly predictable and resilient development is not evident for literacy. Although some children learn to read almost regardless of instruction, and many children who receive good instruction overcome initial difficulties and successfully learn to read, too many children (by some estimates 30–60%) fail to reach functional levels of literacy. Some of these children who struggle with learning to read have learning disabilities; fewer have specific language impairments or other communication challenges, such as deafness. However, the reason that most of these children fail to learn how to read and write proficiently is because they do not receive the amount, intensity, and types of instruction that they need.

Accumulating evidence reveals that the effect of any particular type of instructional strategy depends on students' reading and language skills. Connor and Morrison recently showed that what is effective for a student who reads competently, may not be effective for a student still struggling with basic decoding skills. These child-by-instruction interactions have been found across school communities, across the country, and across grades from preschool through third grade. Moreover, the results of their recent random field trial reveal that, at least in first grade, these child-by-instruction interactions are causally implicated in students' letter-word reading and reading comprehension skill growth.

As we will discuss in more detail, this emerging theory of literacy teaching and learning relies on conceptualizing literacy as a phenomenon or construct composed of multiple dimensions that cross the boundaries between oral and written language, that affect each other reciprocally, and

that are greatly influenced by the learning opportunities provided. Increasingly, researchers are showing that proficient literacy requires children to have a strong foundation in oral language – including lexical and semantic knowledge (e.g., vocabulary), metalinguistic awareness including phonological awareness, and strong overall receptive and expressive language skills coupled with explicit and systematic instruction in decoding, comprehending, and writing text. Any part of the system that breaks down (e.g., phonological awareness) impacts the entire system.

Brain imaging techniques, known as hemodynamic studies (e.g., functional magnetic resonance imaging (or fMRI), evoked-response potential (or ERP), and neuromagnetic (or MEG) are improving, which allow researchers to examine the brain activity of children and adults while they complete tasks like reading words. A number of interrelated neural systems are activated during reading. However, there is now an accumulation of evidence that brains of individuals with reading disabilities show different, and less-efficient patterns of processing (including under- and overactivation of specific neural circuits or differences in onset latencies within certain regions). These most-researched areas include the temporo-occipital region, the temporoparietal region, and the left inferior frontal regions, which are related to phonetic decoding. Recent work has also focused on networks within the posterior temporal and temporo-occipital cortex that appear to support sight word reading. For example, good readers employ their left temporo-parietal region to process letter–sound correspondences. A less-effective pattern (including underactivation of the posterior temporal and temporoparietal cortices and overactivation in the inferior frontal and right posterior temporal cortices) is found when imaging brains of individuals with reading disabilities.

Interestingly, researchers have also begun to use imaging before and after intensive explicit decoding and other code-focused interventions and have demonstrated changes in brain activation in individuals with reading disabilities. Pre- to postintervention changes in brain activity indicate a more normalized pattern within the specific brain areas that, research has shown, support word-reading accuracy. Moreover, these changes also account for significant variance in pre- to post-treatment growth in children's oral-reading accuracy scores. Such research is important because it confirms that the brain is malleable and fluidly organized. Although early intervention to prevent reading difficulties appears easier than remediation later in life, even adult brains respond to training and become more efficient at reading. Furthermore, it appears this positive reorganization endures.

For these reasons, any successful conceptualization of literacy development will integrate characteristics of both students and instruction into the model. Nevertheless, understanding the components that comprise proficient literacy skills is critical. Thus, we will first discuss the language skills that appear to contribute directly to proficient literacy as well as skills that are specific to the skill of reading, keeping in mind that they are all part of a complex system that supports literacy.

Language

Our ability to use language to communicate feelings, ideas, emotions, and plans is a unique human ability that affects every aspect of our lives. It is the medium by which we learn and teach. By 3 years of age, most children are using language for relatively sophisticated purposes, as any parent knows. Toddlers negotiate nap time, they express joy, anger, and frustration, they even begin to deceive and manipulate. By 4.5 years, children are masters at communicating, ready to maneuver through the complexities of home, community, and school interactions. When children learn to talk, they increasingly become part of their family and social community. Moreover, children develop proficient language skills unless they encounter neurological, physical, or environmental barriers, and even then they may learn to compensate.

Generally, linguists describe language as comprised of various components although these are only theoretically discrete, and interact and support one another. These include the individual sounds of language (phonemes), vocabulary, semantics (the meaning of what is said), morphemes (the smallest units of language that carry meaning, like '-ed', which marks past tense, or '-s', which marks plurals), syntax (the ways in which we order words, use pronouns and verbs, and structure sentences), and pragmatics (the ways in which we use language, such as how we take turns talking, decide who gets to talk, and use language that is appropriate for the setting). In contrast to these linguistic skills, which are largely unconscious, metalinguistic awareness is the conscious use and manipulation of language (e.g., an appreciation of nursery rhymes, the deft skill of punsters, the ability to say 'ink' when asked to say 'link' without the /l/); it is integral to the process of learning to read and provides an important link between language and reading. Moreover, as the medium of teaching and learning, oral language is the essential foundation of literacy instruction.

There are also important social and pragmatic aspects to language that have implications for children's learning. For example, children who do not learn the rules about how to talk in the classroom (e.g., tell stories with a beginning, middle, and end or to answer questions in order to show what they have learned) may encounter difficulty within the school environment both on the playground and in the classroom. Due to problems interacting with peers and teachers, these students may be at a disadvantage during class discussions and during peer-learning opportunities.

Links between Language and Literacy

In general, children who achieve at the highest academic levels use oral language with flexibility, fluency, and skill. Children who start kindergarten with stronger oral language skills become the most proficient readers and writers by high school. At the same time, children with specific language impairments are much more likely to experience reading disabilities than are their peers with typical language skills. Accumulating research reveals three language skills most frequently identified as components of reading – vocabulary, metalinguistic awareness (including phonological awareness), and listening comprehension (i.e., receptive oral language skills).

Children's vocabulary is highly predictive of their literacy. Moreover, there is accumulating evidence that vocabulary influences the types of instruction that will be more effective for particular children. The National Reading Panel identified it as one of the key component skills of reading. Children with stronger vocabulary skills are, on average, better readers and better able to take advantage of a wider range of literacy instruction activities. While there is some evidence that it is very difficult to change the rate of vocabulary development, other evidence indicates that explicit vocabulary instruction can improve students' reading skills.

Phonological awareness, a type of metalinguistic awareness, is the ability to consciously manipulate the individual sounds (i.e., phonemes) within words and, as we will discuss below, is considered a critical skill for proficient reading. Children who could, for example, respond 'horse' when asked what word is left in 'racehorse' without 'race' or who could blend onsets (first sound 't') and rimes (the rest of the word 'oy'; answer 'toy') were consistently better readers than were children who could not do these tasks. However, there is also evidence that learning to read contributes to phonological awareness. Identified by the National Reading Panel as a key skill of proficient readings, we will discuss phonological awareness, in the context of instruction, more fully later in this article.

Emerging research indicates that other aspects of metalinguistic awareness are also intricately linked with children's developing literacy. Children's morphosyntactic awareness, which is the ability to manipulate the grammar and structure of language (e.g., that 'public' and 'publicity' share the same root and that adding – er to the end of 'farm' changes the meaning of the word to the person who farms, the 'farmer') is related to reading comprehension.

Listening comprehension or receptive oral language is a key part of the Simple View of Reading, one of the most consistently supported theories of reading. Originally proposed by Hoover, Gough, and colleagues, the Simple View of Reading states that proficient reading is the product of decoding and listening comprehension. Because proficiency is the product and not the sum, a breakdown in either component leads to less proficiency. For example, children with specific language impairments are much more likely to have reading difficulties than are children with similar cognitive abilities but who do not have language impairments.

The links between language and literacy are proving to be more intricate than the simple relation between letters and sounds and the Simple View of Reading suggest, however. This is largely because language develops. For example, Scarborough reported that the strongest predictors of whether children might develop reading disabilities were how accurately they pronounced words and the complexity of their sentences when they were 20 months of age. However, by the time they were 42 months, vocabulary predicted more strongly than did pronunciation. By 5 years of age, only phonological awareness differentiated between children with reading difficulties and those without.

Literacy Skills

Development of Literacy Skills and Phases of Learning

While it is increasingly apparent that, for many children, proficient literacy will not develop in the absence of explicit instruction, there are phases that most children who receive appropriate instruction will experience as they follow the path toward proficient literacy. Ehri describes these phases as: 'pre-reading', 'learning to read', and 'reading to learn', which, not surprisingly, overlap and support one another.

Pre-reading phase
During the pre-reading phase, very young children begin to develop the fundamental language skills that are necessary for learning to read and, as they hear books being read to them, they learn the foundation of code-focused skills: print awareness and phonological awareness. Their growing receptive language skills enhance their understanding of what they hear, build their vocabulary and listening comprehension skills, and enable verbal thinking skills that are essential for reading comprehension. As their expressive language develops, they learn to communicate their thoughts. The onset of the code-focused aspect of this phase depends on exposure to print, that is when they hear books being read, and it extends through preschool and kindergarten. During this period, young children can learn that print represents spoken words, and they may be interested in letters and reciting or singing the alphabet song.

Parents and educators capitalize on young children's budding interest by providing learning opportunities so children may also begin to acquire some initial awareness of the phonological structure of words (i.e., that words can be divided into parts (or phonemes) or that they can have the same beginning or ending sounds). With support, children may also start to recognize some very familiar words by sight including their own names, names of playmates, family members, and favorite characters. Further, children in this pre-reading phase begin to use visual memorization and context cues to recognize familiar signs and words such as '7-Up', 'milk', or 'Cheerios'. Although they may at times correctly identify the first letter in a word like 'milk', children are not yet able to independently use the correspondence between letters and sounds to read. Children frequently engage in pretend reading and, with guidance, begin to develop basic concepts about print (holding the book upright, pointing to words as they tell the story, left to right orientation).

The learning-to-read phase
While students continue to develop the language, listening, and critical thinking skills, they began to acquire during the pre-reading phase, a sign that students are entering the learning-to-read phase is that they shift from using distinctive visual features to recognize words (i.e., the M in the McDonalds arches), to using the relations between letters and sounds in words (i.e., grapheme phoneme correspondence) as their main clue to a word's identity. Thus, during this stage, effective instruction supports students' mastery of the alphabetic principle so that they can reliably use the correspondences between letters and sounds in words to identify words they have never seen before in print.

For most students, this stage begins in kindergarten when they begin to 'sound out' at least a few letters in a word. At the very beginning, because they are still trying to guess the word, they are not very accurate. But throughout kindergarten and into first grade, if students are explicitly taught how to use letter–sound correspondences to phonetically decode new words, they can reliably sound out more of the phonemes in words (particularly the vowels), and they become more accurate readers. The accuracy of their reading is also enhanced when they realize that another important clue to the identity (and mistaken identity) of new words comes from the meaning of what they are reading. So, as students master this learning-to-read phase, they learn to integrate information about letter–sound relations with their background knowledge and their sense of the meaning of the passage, to find a word that matches the sounds they have decoded and that also 'makes sense'. In addition, with enough practice, they begin to accurately identify more words by sight and they build more reliable representations for words in their memory. When students have been taught to map the sounds in words to spellings, these representations may be created quickly and efficiently. However, students who do not yet understand these letter–sound mappings will have more difficulty learning to recognize words at a single glance and will have more difficulty entering the next phase of reading, 'reading to learn'.

The reading-to-learn phase

In this phase, students continue to develop and integrate language, listening, and critical thinking skills as they start to gain new information from a broader array of reading materials and genres. Additionally, students will encounter increasingly more unique words and multisyllabic words. Thus, learning explicit strategies to decode complex words and implicit strategies to integrate new vocabulary with what they already know will support their improving skills. Guided practice to use both types of strategies as students analyze text and read critically and to generalize these strategies to different text structures and genres also supports developing literacy. In essence, the reading-to-learn stage never ends because the students' vocabulary and other language skills, background knowledge, and strategies become increasingly sophisticated.

Components of Reading and Effective Instructional Practices

The report of the National Reading Panel, published in 2000, emphasized five key components of reading. These components are phonological awareness (as discussed, one of the most salient links between language and literacy skills), phonics (knowing the rules that relate letters and clusters of letters to sounds and morphemes), fluency (the ability to read facilely with appropriate intonation and prosody), vocabulary (as discussed previously, includes both size of lexicon and semantic flexibility), and comprehension (including foundational language and specific text-related strategies). We discussed phonological awareness briefly and vocabulary more extensively in the previous section on language. In this section, we focus further on phonological awareness, phonics, fluency and reading comprehension while keeping in mind that each dimension is highly related to the others and together – along with other skills – comprise a system of proficient literacy.

Phonological awareness

Phonological awareness, a metalinguistic skill, is among the most important links between children's oral language and literacy skills. Instruction in phonological awareness trains children to recognize and manipulate individual sounds, or phonemes, as well as clusters of phonemes (e.g., rimes) in spoken words. It is this ability that allows students to map or link the sounds in words with the letters that represent these sounds in written words. Converging research has shown that students who do not develop this ability at the discrete level of the individual

phoneme (phonemic awareness), struggle with learning to read and spell, and are at risk for reading disabilities. Fortunately there is a robust research base demonstrating that students can be taught to develop their phonemic awareness skills through systematic, explicit instruction. Additionally, combining phonological awareness instruction in the presence of text and linking this instruction to letter–sound instruction appears to be more effective and to contribute to stronger reading skill development for students.

Ideally, most children receive such instruction and develop phonological awareness during the 'pre-reading' phase. Initially, they are taught and thus learn to identify words that rhyme or words that start with the same sound, then they can blend and segment short words at the onset and rime level (e.g., /c/ /at/ is 'cat'). Eventually, with instruction, they are able to blend and segment at the level of the individual sound (i.e., the sounds in 'man' are /m/ /a/ /n/), to count the sounds in words, and to manipulate and delete sounds (e.g., say 'mat', then say it again without the 'm'). However, many children, particularly those at risk for reading difficulties, continue to struggle with these later, more difficult phonological awareness skills well into the learning-to-read phase.

Phonics

Phonics instruction teaches children about the regular relations between spoken sounds and letters in words and morphemes (the smallest unit of meaning in language). It is important that they learn about the alphabetic system so they can use phonics to decode and to write new words. After reviewing recent research on reading from a number of disciplinary perspectives, Raynor and colleagues concluded that 'mastering the alphabetic principle' was essential to becoming a good reader. Students who do not master phonics during the learning-to-read phase will lack efficient strategies to sound out words they have not seen before. Thus, phonics instruction, just like phonological awareness instruction, should be systematic and explicit. Many individuals who have reading difficulties are not able to use phonics knowledge when they encounter novel words, particularly multisyllabic words, and continue to need explicit instruction well into the learning-to-read phase.

Fluency

Fluency instruction and practice helps students develop skills to read text accurately, quickly, and with appropriate intonation and prosody. Research indicates that fluent readers not only recognize individual words quickly and automatically, but they are able to simultaneously comprehend the meaning of what they are reading. Not surprisingly, fluency and reading comprehension operate to support each other in a reciprocal fashion, especially for young readers. To begin to develop readers' fluency, it is helpful to provide a fluent adult model of reading, or to allow children to practice through partner reading. Then, once students have acquired the skills to read accurately, fluency develops most directly through extended reading practice. Fluency development is a goal of the instruction during the learning-to-read phase. Thus, the real key to helping students move beyond the learning-to-read phase is for teachers to systematically teach phonological decoding skills while at the same time building a large vocabulary of words that children can recognize by sight and for which they can develop mental representations. In fact, it is the latter accomplishment that appears to be a prerequisite for fluent reading. As students learn to recognize more words at a single glance, they become more fluent readers, which, in turn, supports their ability to self-monitor and self-correct when a word does not make sense. However, if students are not taught to read accurately and fluently above a second grade developmental level, they will make too many mistakes. In turn, they will not be able to build the phonological representations for words in their memory, which is the foundation for getting information and building new vocabulary from what is read.

However, fluency with increasingly difficult or unfamiliar material continues to develop long after entering the reading-to-learn phase and is a life-long challenge for most individuals with reading difficulties. Improving students' reading fluency may compensate for weaker vocabulary skills. For example, first graders with lower vocabulary but higher oral reading fluency scores achieved reading comprehension scores, on average, that were highly similar to their peers with stronger vocabulary scores.

Reading comprehension

Reading comprehension requires the reader's active extraction and construction of meaning from text. Many factors can influence the reader's comprehension of text, including the other components of proficient reading and the instruction they receive. Children's spoken language skills provide a foundation for proficient reading comprehension but, in the absence of effective instruction, are not sufficient for developing proficient literacy. Vocabulary, for example, is one of the stronger predictors of reading comprehension. Children may have the decoding skills required to read an unfamiliar word, but if the word is not part of their lexicon, they may not be able to attach meaning to the decoded text. On the other hand, if they cannot decode the word to begin with, their vocabulary skills will not help them understand what they are reading.

As the RAND report reveals, there is compelling evidence that 'accurate and fluent (automatic) word recognition is a prerequisite for adequate reading comprehension'. Children's background knowledge and exposure to the world around them may affect how well they

understand what they read, as may children's home literacy environment. Children enter the process of understanding what they read with very different skills and backgrounds, which appears to influence the types of home and classroom reading experiences that will most effectively support their learning of comprehension of text.

Explicit instruction contributes significantly to children's reading comprehension growth, especially in the early grades. For example, explicitly teaching children comprehension strategies leads to stronger reading comprehension specifically, and reading proficiency generally. The National Reading Panel meta-analysis identified a number of different strategies that, when taught, positively affected children's reading comprehension skills and, in some cases, generalized to improved overall reading proficiency. The most effective instruction included multiple combinations of strategies (e.g., reciprocal teaching). A list and descriptions of comprehension strategies are provided in **Table 1**.

Literacy Learning Environments

For many children, the process of becoming fully literate begins at home and in preschool. However, traditionally, the teaching of reading and writing begins when children start formal schooling in kindergarten. First grade is most clearly identified as the time during which children are expected to master the basics of reading. However, children begin school with highly notable individual differences in both their language and emergent literacy skills. These individual differences appear to be the result of home, parenting, preschool, and social/cultural influences children experience, as well as children's cognitive abilities, social skills, and temperament. Moreover, the impact of this instruction depends, in large part, on the language and literacy skills children bring to the classroom. In this article we focus on two important learning environments, the home and the classroom, fully recognizing that preschool, community, and other important learning environments exist.

Home

Learning to read is a long-term process that begins with emergent literacy, the period of time between birth and when children begin to read and write conventionally. The interplay between language and literacy is highlighted in the practice of parents (and teachers) and children reading together. Shared book reading is one of the most successful methods that parents and teachers can employ to enhance children's language and emergent reading skills. Over 30 years of converging research findings support the importance of reading aloud to children to develop vocabulary, improve reasoning skills, introduce story grammar, and build

Table 1   Description of comprehension strategies

Comprehension instruction is intended to increase students' comprehension of written or oral text. This includes instruction and practice in using comprehension strategies and demonstration of comprehension abilities. Comprehension activities generally follow or are incorporated into reading or listening of connected text (e.g., silent sustained reading followed by a comprehension worksheet, comprehension strategy instruction using a particular example of connected text, an interactive teacher read aloud during which the teacher models various comprehension strategies). Research suggests that using strategies in combination is generally more effective that focusing solely on one strategy.

Strategy	Description
Previewing	Previewing includes activities that involve thinking about what might occur in a story based on the illustrations (including taking a 'picture walk' through a book), cover, title, etc. Previewing activities always precede reading and involve predictions about the general content of a text, which helps to distinguish it from Comprehension>Predicting. Previewing often leads into activating prior knowledge related to the story.
Schema building	Schema building includes activities that involve clarifying a concept and building background knowledge. For example, the teacher tells the students about the middle ages while reading a fairy tale.
Question response and generation	Questioning includes activities that involve generating or answering questions regarding factual or contextual knowledge from the text (e.g., What did Ira miss when he went to the sleepover? What was the name of _____?). Other comprehension activities incorporate questioning including 'activating prior knowledge' (e.g., when the teacher uses a question to scaffold children in activating personal knowledge related to the text: "When you go to an amusement park, what do you expect to see?"), comprehension monitoring (e.g., when the teacher uses a question aimed at stimulating students' metacognitive assessment of whether they comprehended the text: "Did I understand what happened there?"), or 'predicting' (e.g., when the teacher asks students to predict what will happen next: "What do you think the lost boy will do now?").
Activating prior knowledge	Activating prior knowledge includes activities that involve activating students' personal knowledge as it relates to the content of text in order to facilitate comprehension. An example would be asking "Have you ever slept over a friend's house?" when reading Ira sleeps over. This relates to the student's personal knowledge.
Comprehension monitoring	Comprehension monitoring includes activities that involve stimulating students' metacognitive awareness regarding their comprehension of text or sharing strategies to provoke students to think about whether they are fully understanding. Generally, these activities involve thinking about one's own understanding of a particular text and whether the text is making sense (e.g., the teacher pauses and says "Did that make sense to you? If not, how can we fix it?" or "Wait, did I understand that?" or "That didn't make sense to me. Let's go back and reread"). These may include identifying areas of difficulty while reading, using think-aloud procedures to pinpoint difficulties, looking back in the text, restating or rephrasing text, or looking forward to solve a problem.
Predicting and inferencing	Predicting and inferencing include activities that involve predicting future events or information not yet presented based on information already conveyed by the text (e.g., making predictions from foreshadowing). Predicting occurs while reading a story and involves specific details or events.
Highlighting/identifying	Highlighting/identifying includes activities that involve picking out the important details conveyed through a text. Examples include verbally listing, underlining, highlighting, or otherwise noting major points. Highlighting differs from 'summarizing' because it explicitly involves identifying the important details within text.
Summarizing	Summarizing includes activities that involve generating an overall statement or identifying the main ideas of the content of the text. This activity condenses the text to the main points. This might include generating a sentence that tells the story or drawing a picture in response to the text just read.
Retelling	In retelling activities, students are asked to retell a story using their own words. This differs from summarizing because a retell ideally mimics the text structure and includes as many details of a text as possible.
Context cues	Context cues include activities in which students are using pictures, the title, or previous parts of the text to understand a new event or new information presented in the text. For example, a teacher might advise a child to look at picture to identify the setting of a story. It should be noted that this strategy is generally considered a weak substitute for fluent phonological decoding.
Graphic/semantic organizers	Graphic/semantic organizers include activities in which students are using graphic or semantic organizers (e.g., Venn diagrams, story webs) in order to aid their comprehension. Graphic/semantic organizers are frequently used to help students organize their writing efforts.
Comparing/contrasting	Comparing/contrasting includes activities that involve making comparisons across or within texts. For example, asking "how are lions and tigers the same and how are they different?"

knowledge about the alphabetic principle. A particular focus of this work has been to contrast the frequency of book reading in middle- versus low-socioeconomic status (SES) homes. The gap in book reading experiences is startling.

At the start of school, Adams estimated that children from low-SES families have experienced only 25 h of book reading, whereas children from middle-SES families have experienced between 1000 and 1700 h.

Moreover, there is a well-documented predictive relation between the frequency of early parent–child book reading and later reading skills. Bus and colleagues conducted a meta-analysis of 33 studies, which demonstrated that the frequency of children's preschool reading experiences accounted for at least 8% of the unique variance in children's reading scores in elementary school. Furthermore, findings from longitudinal studies have shown that the frequency of children's preschool reading experiences predicted their reading, spelling, and intelligence quotient (IQ) scores into seventh grade. Children's development of early reading habits is associated with their later familiarity with popular books and stronger comprehension skills in high school. The more book titles elementary school children recognize (an indicator of their 'print exposure'), the greater their growth in vocabulary, spelling, and reading comprehension skills. These findings appear to support what Stanovich termed 'the Matthew effect' in which most children who experience rich early literacy experiences grow to be good readers and it is difficult for children with impoverished early literacy experiences to ever catch up.

Classroom Instruction

So far, we have focused on the components of language and literacy that comprise proficient reading skills and noted that, in the absence of effective instruction, children may not learn how to read. The classroom learning environment is highly complex and relies on both the teacher and the students as they interact around literacy learning and incorporates both the content of the instruction (phonics, comprehension, etc.), how this instruction is implemented, and the knowledge and skills both the students and the teacher bring to the learning environment. Starting with teacher characteristics that, research shows, do and do not contribute to student learning, we will then present multiple dimensions of instruction and, finally will discuss how the impact of this instruction appears to depend on the language and literacy skills children bring to the classroom (i.e., child-by-instruction interactions). Of note, as we discuss effective instruction, we are defining it as the combination of practices, methods, and strategies that lead to stronger student literacy outcomes.

Characteristics of effective teachers

Surprisingly, teachers' years of education, holding a credential, and their years of experience do not consistently predict student outcomes, especially early literacy outcomes. While we would expect that more experienced teachers and those with masters or other advanced degrees and credentials would be more effective teaching children how to read, accumulating research shows that the link is weak and indirect. Other sources of influence, such as the characteristics of children in the classroom, are much better predictors of students' outcomes. More direct assessments of teachers' knowledge about language and literacy have been shown to predict students' reading outcomes more directly. The implementation of research-based (also called evidence-based) instructional practice supported by rigorous teacher knowledge in the area of language, literacy, and teaching is associated with stronger student outcomes. Teachers who know more about the components of language and literacy and how to implement instruction effectively (e.g., use assessment results to determine learning goals for individual students) and who actually enact this knowledge and skill in the classroom tend to be more effective than teachers who know less about language and literacy instruction.

Accumulating research clearly documents that teachers' greater warmth and responsiveness to their students (in contrast to detachment) during teacher–student interactions is associated with stronger student outcomes. There is also evidence that teachers who coach their students and are more interactive are more effective than are teachers who tell their students information and offer fewer opportunities for teacher–student interactions. Also well supported by research is that teachers who can clearly impart classroom rules and routines, organize and manage their classrooms well, plan ahead, explain instructional concepts and how to do the activities supporting these concepts clearly are more effective than are unorganized teachers who do not plan or who are unclear in their instruction.

Multiple dimensions of instruction

One reason the reading wars raged is because, traditionally, classroom instruction has been viewed as one-dimensional – whole-language or phonics – or as too complex to reduce to simple pieces (e.g., social constructivism or critical theory). Certainly, teaching and learning are highly complex processes and attempts to measure them necessarily fail to capture some of their complexity. Fruitful emerging conceptualizations present teaching and learning as multidimensional with the model becoming more complex as additional dimensions are considered. As we have discussed, literacy itself is multidimensional so using a parallel argument, if literacy has multiple dimensions, then examining sources of classroom influence on literacy multidimensionally will be more informative than examining their impact globally at the curriculum level. As research on classroom instruction continues, more dimensions will be identified. Here we present four of the more salient dimensions, teacher- versus child-managed, code-versus meaning-focused, student- versus classroom-level, and change over time. These dimensions operate simultaneously and may be conceptualized as two tables with teacher- versus child-managed as columns and code- versus meaning-focused as rows with a table for classroom and another table for student-level instruction.

The dimension teacher- versus child-managed instruction is a continuum that ranges from the teacher lecturing while students listen (teacher-managed) to more interactive teaching (teacher/child-managed) to peer interactions (peer-managed) to children working independently. Overall, this dimension captures who is focusing the child's attention on the learning task. For example, the teacher discussing a book with the students would be teacher/child-managed. Students working independently on seat work would be child-managed. Students working in groups or buddy reading would be peer-managed (a type of child-managed instruction). There is evidence that all three (teacher/child, child, and peer) contribute to student learning although children who struggle with reading generally require more time with the teacher (i.e., teacher/child-managed instruction).

The dimension code- versus meaning-focused instruction has been well established throughout the extant literature and finds its roots in the Simple View of Reading (proficient reading is the product of decoding and comprehension) and the Reading Wars (phonics vs. whole language). Code-focused instruction is designed to help children grasp the alphabetic principle, to gain phonological awareness, to blend and segment words, to learn spelling and phonics, and to read words fluently. Meaning-focused instruction is designed to support students' efforts to understand what they read and includes vocabulary, reading aloud, reading independently, writing, grammar, and comprehension strategies.

If we consider two dimensions – teacher-versus child-managed and code versus meaning-focused – these dimensions together form a grid upon which any literacy activity can be placed (**Table 2**). So, for example, children reading together in the library corner would be considered peer-managed meaning-focused instruction. The teacher explaining to children how word families work (b-at, c-at, h-at) would be an example of teacher/child-managed code-focused, and children doing phonics worksheets at their desks would be an example of child-managed code-focused instruction.

The classroom- versus student-level dimension considers the extent to which instruction is the same or different for each child in the classroom. When the teacher is reading aloud or conducting a phonics lesson to the entire classroom, this would be classroom level. All of the children are being provided essentially the same information. Even if children are working in small groups or individually (e.g., seat work), if they are all doing substantially the same thing (e.g., reading the same book), then that is classroom-level instruction. In contrast, when children are engaged in substantially different activities at the same time, this is considered student-level instruction. A key characteristic is that student-level instruction is individualized and may be provided in small groups or when children work individually (e.g., centers with different activities, tutoring one child while the rest do other activities). Specific types of activities, for example, book reading, can occur on both the classroom and student levels. For example, in one classroom, a teacher might read aloud to the entire class (teacher/child-managed, meaning-focused, classroom-level), while in another, a teacher might read aloud to a small group of children (teacher/child-managed, meaning-focused, child-level) while the rest of the children engage in substantially different activities such as writing in their journals (child-managed, meaning-focused, child-level).

The dimension change over time addresses the amount of time spent on specific instructional activities from grade to grade, as well as during the school year. Literacy instruction in second grade differs substantially from instruction in first or third grade. At the same time, many teachers change their instructional emphasis over the course of a single school year. For example, a teacher might begin the year with a strong focus on explicit, teacher-managed decoding instruction that decreases by winter and spring as children master basic skills. Researchers have also found that for first graders with weaker vocabulary scores, small amounts of child-managed, meaning-focused (e.g., independent reading and writing) activities at the beginning of the school year that decreased over the first grade year was associated with stronger decoding skill growth. The opposite pattern

Table 2 Examining two dimensions of instruction simultaneously

	Teacher-managed	Child-managed	Peer-managed
Code-focused	• Alphabet instruction • Letter–sound correspondence • Phonological awareness	• Alphabet worksheets • Letter–sound correspondence activities • Phonological awareness activities	• Alphabet practice • Letter–sound correspondence activities • Phonological awareness
Meaning-focused	• Phonics • Word fluency • Vocabulary instruction • Comprehension strategies • Connected text fluency • Read aloud • Discussion • Model writing	• Phonics • Word fluency • Vocabulary practice • Comprehension strategies • Independent fluency practice • Sustained independent silent reading • Independent writing	• Phonics • Word fluency • Vocabulary activities • Comprehension strategies • Connected text fluency buddy reading • Read aloud pairs • Discussion • Buddy writing or writer's workshop

held for children with strong vocabulary skills, for whom consistently high amounts of child-managed meaning-focused instruction related to stronger decoding skills.

Using these dimensions provides a better representation of the complexity of teaching and learning (although not fully) because, as research shows, even in whole-language classrooms, some time is spent in code-focused activities and any code-focused core curriculum includes opportunities for children to read connected text (a meaning-focused activity). Effective teachers individualize instruction (i.e., provide student-level instruction), balancing the amounts and types of reading instruction, across multiple dimensions, based on children's assessed learning needs. Viewing reading instruction multidimensionally rather than as 'whole-language' or 'skill-based' has been instrumental in revealing that the impact of any given instructional strategy depends on the vocabulary and reading skills students bring to the classroom (i.e., child-by-instruction interactions).

These child-by-instruction interactions reinforce the reciprocal nature of teaching and learning. This means that there is not one 'best way' to teach reading. Although, as we have discussed, children must master the alphabet principle on their path to proficient reading, providing intensive instruction in the alphabetic principle to students who can already read *Charlotte's Web* will probably not advance their reading skills. In the same way, providing sustained opportunities to read *Charlotte's Web* independently for a child who has not mastered fluent phonological decoding will most likely lead to frustration and less learning. As discussed, research shows that instruction that takes into account the unique constellation of skills children bring to the classroom is more effective than the traditional 'one size fits all' and 'every child on the same page' approaches. Moreover, as research continues, we are becoming more sophisticated in developing ways to predict and recommend optimal patterns of instruction for children based on their language and literacy skills.

Individualizing student instruction and new definitions of reading disabilities

The need for strengthening early reading instruction is underscored when we consider that the incidence of students identified as having a learning disability, which includes children with dyslexia (i.e., specific reading disability), during elementary school has grown exponentially (by over 200%) since the establishment of the learning disabilities (LD) category in 1977. Moreover, most LD students are identified because they are experiencing difficulty learning to read.

The modal age at which children qualify for services as LD is 11 years old, by which time reading difficulties become increasingly difficult to remediate. There is a critical need for more effective early reading interventions especially considering that, as we discussed, current data indicate that 36% of students in the US cannot meet basic standards of reading competence by the end of fourth grade. The NAEP data indicates that the situation is even more critical for poor and minority students because 56% of low-SES, 61% of African American, and 57% of Hispanic students (noting that many African American and Hispanic students are also low-SES and that these percentages overlap) were not able meet the fourth grade basic reading standards.

There is a vital need for effective early identification and interventions for students who struggle to read, keeping in mind that past and current research clearly demonstrates that remediating reading difficulties is more difficult after students have struggled in learning to read for several years. Torgesen reports that once students fall behind in reading fluency, even the most powerful remedial interventions are not able to help most of them to catch up. Other negative consequences of early reading difficulties include weak vocabulary growth, less motivation to read, and fewer opportunities to develop or practice reading comprehension strategies. Moreover, several longitudinal studies have shown that reading trajectories are distressingly stable: children who are poor readers at the end of first grade almost never acquire average level reading skills by the end of elementary school.

Response to intervention (RTI) has largely been conceptualized as a general education initiative to reduce the incidence of students identified as having LD with a focus on prevention, by providing students, who fail to progress in learning to read, with evidence-based instructional services immediately, rather than waiting for children to fall far enough behind to qualify to receive special education services. RTI stems from widespread concern about the number of children not reading at grade level, which has led researchers and practitioners to question the validity of using the traditional IQ–achievement discrepancy to identify students with LD. Proponents of RTI have criticized this discrepancy approach, which requires students to demonstrate up to two standard deviations of difference between their IQ and their reading achievement, for several reasons: (1) the large increase in the numbers of students with reading disabilities and variability in state-to-state prevalence figures, (2) the disproportionate representation of diverse students among those labeled with LD, (3) instructional needs of students labeled with LD are not reliably different from poor readers without the label (i.e., LD is essentially the low tail on a bell-shaped curve), and finally (4) that without the label, many children who need early literacy intervention, especially children from high poverty backgrounds, do not receive it.

Although there is no single RTI model, broadly speaking, all RTI models include a multilayer process that often involves extensive school reform. Teachers receive professional development that precedes or coincides with implementation of RTI that aims to support implementation fidelity and instructional effectiveness. There are some differences in how response to intervention has been conceptualized and operationalized. At one end of the continuum of current RTI models, students with similar reading deficits are given evidence-based interventions that have been shown to 'work' for other students with the same deficits. Teachers or interventionists are then expected to follow a standardized treatment protocol and implement the intervention with fidelity. At the opposite end of the continuum are models that address these deficits by individualizing instruction based on a problem-solving model. Between the two ends of the continuum are models that provide a combination of standardized and individualized intervention – often beginning with what works and increasingly tailoring instruction based on progress monitoring. A useful conceptualization presents RTI instruction in three tiers.

RTI begins with effective Tier 1 classroom intervention, which presupposes that this instruction will result in almost all children becoming literate. However, as we discussed, the research suggests that the effect of instruction depends on the language and literacy skills children bring to the learning opportunity. Thus, what is effective for a student with strong language and reading skills may be ineffective for the student with weaker language and literacy skills. For Tier 1 instruction to be effective, the strategies used should be tailored to each student's strengths and weaknesses. One encouraging development is the 'Individualizing Student Instruction Project'. This study by Connor and colleagues uses a web-based software program called Assessment-to-Instruction or A2i, to help teachers provide effective individualized instruction to all the children in their classroom. The software uses algorithms to recommend specific amounts and types of instruction for each child in the classroom using each student's assessed vocabulary and reading skills. In a random field trial, after 4 months, children demonstrated significantly stronger growth in letter-word skills when their teacher individualized instruction (i.e., used small groups with appropriate learning goals and planned instruction using A2i) compared to a control group and to children whose teachers had access to the software but did not use it consistently. By the end of the school year, children in the treatment group achieved stronger reading comprehension skill growth, overall, than did children in the control classrooms.

Next, students not making adequate progress receive Tier 2 – more intensive (3–5 days per week for 15–30 min) supplemental small group intervention delivered by classroom teachers, reading specialists, or other interventionists (i.e., research staff); student progress is monitored more frequently. One example of a successful Tier 2 intervention that may be delivered by well-trained paraprofessionals or community mentors is Tutor-Assisted Intensive Learning Strategies, or TAILS developed by Al Otaiba. TAILS was field tested in a randomized field trial involving 12 kindergarten classrooms in four high-poverty elementary schools. Al Otaiba and colleagues found that children who participated in TAILS 4 days per week achieved significantly stronger letter-word, phonological awareness, and passage comprehension growth compared to children in the control classrooms. Moreover, the effect sizes were large.

Lastly, students still not making adequate progress receive Tier 3 interventions, provided in even smaller groups (one to three children) by a skilled intervention specialist, such as a special education teacher, speech-language pathologist, or reading specialist. Tier 3 sessions may be conceptualized as a mix of general and special education that is more responsive to individual children's needs and might include up to 1 hour of extra instruction per day.

Conclusion

In this article, we have conceptualized literacy as a construct comprised of multiple dimensions, which cross the boundaries between oral and written language, that affect each other reciprocally, and that are greatly influenced by the learning opportunities provided to children as they develop into proficient readers. Accumulating and compelling evidence reveals that proficient literacy requires children to have a strong foundation in oral language including lexical and semantic knowledge, metalinguistic awareness including phonological awareness, and strong overall language skills, coupled with explicit and systematic instruction in decoding, comprehension, and writing. Time to practice these skills using engaging text also contributes to proficient reading. Any part of the system that breaks down undermines this complex and dynamic system and children fail to become proficient readers. Moreover, children themselves are active agents in this system. The language, literacy, temperament, self-regulation, motivation, and other characteristics children bring to literacy learning contribute significantly to their success or failure in learning to read by influencing how they respond to learning opportunities and by shaping how parents and teachers may respond to them.

Rigorous educational research establishes the causal impact of various literacy interventions on children's learning and incorporates randomized studies. Underlying most recent efforts is the notion that we will never find a silver bullet – the perfect curriculum or the high-quality program that will meet the needs of all children. Emerging evidence that child-by-instruction interactions are causal in nature, means that school- and classroom-based programs that are high quality for one child (i.e., positive outcomes) may be poor quality for another (negative outcomes) with a different set of skills and attributes. Systematic application of research that takes into account the links between language and literacy, the strengths and weaknesses children bring to classroom, individualizing instruction and monitoring children's response to this instruction, will help us better understand the complex and dynamic construct of literacy and support all children as they become literate members of our society.

See also: Grammar; Language Acquisition Theories; Preverbal Development and Speech Perception; School Readiness; Semantic Development; Speech Perception.

Suggested Readings

Adams MJ (1990) *Beginning to Read: Thinking and Learning about Print.* Cambridge, MA: The MIT Press.

Al Otaiba S, Schatschneider C, and Silverman E (2005) Tutor assisted intensive learning strategies in kindergarten: How much is enough? *Exceptionality* 13: 195–208.

Chall JS (1967) *Learning to Read: The Great Debate.* New York: McGraw-Hill Book.

Connor CM, Morrison FJ, and Katch EL (2004) Beyond the reading wars: The effect of classroom instruction by child interactions on early reading. *Scientific Studies of Reading* 8(4): 305–336.

Connor CM, Morrison FJ, Fishman BJ, Schatschneider C, and Underwood P (2007) The early years: Algorithm-guided individualized reading instruction. *Science* 315(5811): 464–465.

Ehri LC (2002) Phases of acquisition in learning to read words and implications for teaching. In: Stainthorp R and Tomlinson P (eds.) *Learning and Teaching Reading,* pp. 7–28. London: British Journal of Educational Psychology Monograph Series II.

Morrison FJ, Bachman HJ, and Connor CM (2005) *Improving Literacy in America: Guidelines from Research.* New Haven, CT: Yale University Press.

Neuman SB and Dickinson DK (2001) Handbook of early literacy research. In: Dickinson DK and Neuman SB (eds.) (2006) *Handbook of Early Literacy Research,* Vol. 2. New York: Guilford Press.

NRP (2000) *National Reading Panel report: Teaching children to read: An evidence-based assessment of the scientific research literature on reading and its implications for reading instruction* (No. NIH Pub. No. 00-4769). Washington DC: U.S. Department of Health and Human Services, Public Health Service, National Institutes of Health, National Institute of Child Health and Human Development.

Snow CE (2001) *Reading for Understanding.* Santa Monica, CA: RAND Education and the Science and Technology Policy Institute.

Snow CE, Burns MS, and Griffin P (eds.) (1998) *Preventing Reading Difficulties in Young Children.* Washington, DC: National Academy Press.

Relevant Websites

http://isi.fcrr.org – Individualizing Student Instruction.

http://www.nrp.org – Making Minneopolls Neighborhoods Better Places to Live, Work, Learn and Play.

http://www.fcrr.org – The Florida Center for Reading Research.

http://www.ed.gov – US Department of Education, Promoting educational excellence for all Americans.

Marital Relationship

M J Cox, N Heilbron, W R Mills-Koonce, A Pressel, and C W Oppenheimer, University of North Carolina at Chapel Hill, Chapel Hill, NC, USA
D E Szwedo, University of Virginia, Charlottesville, VA, USA

Glossary

Affect – Mood or emotion.

Constructive conflict – A type of marital conflict characterized by positive behaviors and outcomes such as problem solving, support, humor, and conflict resolution.

Co-parenting – Coordination between adults of their parenting roles.

Destructive conflict – A type of marital conflict characterized by negative behaviors such as physical aggression, verbal hostility, defensiveness, contempt, and withdrawal.

Emotion – A mental state that arises spontaneously and is often accompanied by physiological changes.

Emotional security – A child's sense of emotional well-being and safety within the family system.

Externalizing symptoms – Symptoms characterized by deviant, disruptive, or aggressive behavior. Conduct, attention deficit hyperactivity, and drug abuse problems are examples of externalizing symptoms.

Internalizing symptoms – Symptoms characterized by negative cognitions and behaviors directed toward the self. Depression, anxiety, and somatic problems are the primary types of internalizing symptoms.

Marital discord – Conflict between partners characterized by behaviors typically defined as negative, such as disagreement, criticism, and complaining.

Negative reciprocity – Responding to a negative behavior with a negative behavior.

Scapegoating – A process by which parents transfer their own conflict toward one another to their child, so that the child becomes the focus for the problems and the object of aggression and criticism.

Self/emotion-regulation – The ability to control emotional and behavioral responses in response to stimulating events or experiences.

Introduction

Historically, the study of marital relationships was primarily the domain of family sociologists, but over the last several decades there has been growing interest among psychologists who study infant and early childhood development in understanding how marriage and other relationships in the family are associated with children's development. Development of young children almost universally occurs in a family context, and we now know that the relationships in the family which young children observe and in which they participate have a significant impact on the course of their development. Marital relationships have been studied by individuals interested in the development of young children because of the power of the marriage relationship to support or undermine important parenting processes, and because the marital relationship itself is observed by the child and can be a critical source of learning about adult relationships, modeling of behaviors related to conflict or emotional display, and security or fear to a child when either reassuring or frightening behaviors are displayed by marital couples.

Much of the research in the US on marital relationships and children's development has involved middle-class individuals from European American families. The emphasis of most of this research has been on 'marital quality', usually measured by an individual's self-reported satisfaction or happiness with the marriage. To date, considerably less research has focused on marital processes among minority groups or among individuals living in poverty. The relatively narrow focus on samples comprised of middle-class, European American individuals and the general reliance on self-reports of marital satisfaction has limited our understanding of marital relationships.

The lack of research on minority families is especially unfortunate at a time when demographics in the US are changing dramatically such that minority groups constitute larger and larger percentages of families raising young children. It also is a time when marital roles are changing and marriage itself is becoming increasingly uncommon as cohabitation without marriage increases among couples raising young children. Future research will be important in considering the variety of adult relationships in families raising young children, and the implications of those varying adult relationships for children's development within various broader community and cultural contexts.

In this article, we will briefly describe the history of psychological research on marriage and consider the findings regarding how marital relationships affect other family relationships and the social and emotional development of young children. We have focused on research on marriages in which couples are raising their biological children.

Psychological Research on Correlates of Marital Quality

For several decades, the study of marital relationships has garnered considerable interest among psychologists and sociologists. The earliest published research on marriage addressed the fundamental question of what factors differentiate happily married couples from unhappily married couples. The scientific literature on marital functioning began with a conceptual model largely guided by individual personality theory. Accordingly, early research studies were aimed at identifying personality traits that correlated with satisfaction in marriage. Numerous studies demonstrated that certain personality characteristics are significant predictors of relationship satisfaction. For example, extraverted, agreeable, and highly conscientious individuals report greater marital satisfaction when compared to individuals who are less likely to be characterized by these personality dimensions. In contrast, individuals who are highly neurotic are likely to report less relationship satisfaction than are individuals who are less neurotic.

More recently, research stimulated by attachment theory has considered how attachment style, assumed to develop in childhood as a result of experiences in one's family, influences the quality of adult romantic relationships. Attachment theory posits that an individual's relationship with parents or parent-figures provides a foundation for the way an individual understands and behaves in human relationships. A warm and consistently responsive parent figure is believed to promote a secure attachment whose hallmark is a sense that others can be trusted and that one is worthy of love, whereas an aloof or inconsistently responsive caregiver is believed to promote an insecure attachment with the sense that others cannot be trusted to meet one's needs. Securely attached individuals tend to be comfortable in interpersonal relationships and are more able to employ adaptive strategies when dealing with relationship stress. In contrast, adults who experienced an inconsistently responsive parent in childhood are thought to develop an insecure, preoccupied style and may be more likely to fear rejection from their partner and tend to be anxious and clingy. Adults who experienced an aloof and distant parent in childhood are thought to develop an insecure, avoidant attachment style and as a result are more likely to typically distance themselves emotionally, preferring to be independent rather than close with a partner. The research support for this notion that individuals possess an adult attachment style that is unchanging and is derived exclusively from childhood attachment relationships and affects all other close relationships is mixed. Attachment style seems to vary across time in adulthood and probably reflects an individual's experiences in adult relationships as well as childhood experiences. However it arises, there is some evidence that a secure attachment style is protective in both men and women under conditions of stress or challenge; that is, individuals with a secure attachment style tend to remain more committed to their marriages when faced with other stressors such as parenting or financial difficulties than do individuals with an insecure attachment style.

In addition to the research considering how individual personality or attachment style correlate with marital satisfaction or stability, there has been a growing literature on how specific aspects of the way married individuals interact with each other are associated with marital satisfaction and stability. Beginning in the 1950s, researchers proposed that assessing characteristics of the interaction between marital partners, rather than simply isolating qualities of the individual members of the dyad, would provide important insights into marital satisfaction and stability. To test the hypotheses generated from this perspective required the advent of observational research methods to systematically evaluate interactions. Thus, by the late 1950s and early 1960s, there was a burgeoning interest in observational methods designed to capture verbal and nonverbal behaviors in marital interactions. Researchers have since created observational coding systems to provide metrics for measuring specific problem-solving and communication behaviors, supportive skills, and emotional behaviors when a couple is interacting. These methodological approaches are assumed to capture qualities of the relationship between married partners rather than individual characteristics such that behaviors seen in these interactions are specific to the relationship and do not completely represent personality qualities (i.e., one person might behave quite differently in the same kind of interaction with different people). Microanalytic coding strategies enable researchers to examine occurrences of specific behaviors or facial affect on a second by second basis, whereas macroanalytic coding strategies provide opportunities to assess the occurrence and quality of a variety of behaviors using global ratings of these behaviors over several minutes of interaction. Recently, investigators also have begun to also measure psychophysiological variables during couple interaction.

The emphasis on interactional processes in the study of marital and family functioning paralleled conceptual and theoretical advances in what came to be known as general systems theory. First formally proposed by von Bertalanffy as early as the 1930s and widely disseminated in an influential publication in 1968, the application of systems theory to understanding marital relationships and family functioning has had a significant influence on contemporary psychological and sociological research. The application of systems models to the family highlight the family as a complex and organized system with interdependent components and a hierarchical structure. Thus, the family system is thought to be comprised of different interdependent subsystems, including the marital subsystem and the parenting subsystem, and these subsystems are embedded within larger systems, such as the broader community. Influence across these levels of the system flows both ways such that subsystems within the family like the marital subsystem and the parenting subsystem show mutual influence, and these aspects of the family are affected by and affect the broader environment of the family. Thus, for example, unsupportive marriages can make parenting more difficult, but difficulties with parenting also can put stress on a marriage. Additionally, qualities of a marriage may be influenced by the accepted ways of interacting in marriages in the community, and those accepted ways of interacting can be changed over time by individual marriages. In accordance with the basic tenets of systems theory, it would be expected that the way in which the marital subsystem functions would have implications for the functioning of the individual members of a marital dyad, the quality of parent–child relationships, and the psychological adjustment of children.

These theoretical views led to considerations of not only how individual functioning affects marriage, but also the way in which the marriage functions affect individual adult functioning over time. The research has documented that the quality of marriage can have a powerful effect on adult functioning. Research findings have linked positive marital functioning to longevity and a variety of health-buffering effects. In contrast, marital relationships characterized by high conflict have been associated with a number of negative health outcomes including cancer, cardiac disease, chronic pain, and suppressed immune system. Marital conflict has also been identified as a predictor of multiple psychological outcomes including depression, eating disorders, and alcoholism.

The marital research that involves observations of couple's interactions has produced some important findings also. Observational studies revealed that interactions of couples who had high levels of satisfaction differed in predictable ways from the interactions of those who were distressed. A variety of standard situations have been used in this literature, but most involved having couples discuss and try to resolve a disagreement. Observational studies of couples engaged in these problem-solving discussions have demonstrated that interactions characterized by negative reciprocity (i.e., a negative behavior leads to a negative behavior) and escalation are associated with relationship distress and dissatisfaction. Specific negative behaviors, such as contempt, withdrawal, and defensiveness have been identified as particularly deleterious to relationship satisfaction, and ultimately predictive of future relationship dissolution. Observational studies have also demonstrated that the verbal content of messages exchanged by partners is not always as important as the underlying emotion conveyed by the messages. Careful study of nonverbal expressions of emotion has repeatedly found that the affective quality of the interaction alone is a powerful indicator of relationship distress. Indeed, negative affect predicts relationship dissolution. However, the absence of positive affect also predicts later relationship dissolution, whereas the presence of positive affect is a predictor of happiness and stability in a marriage. Moreover, the balance between positive and negative emotion seems to be important for marital satisfaction and stability. Some researchers suggest that positive exchanges need to occur five times more often than negative exchanges for marital satisfaction to be maintained. To make it more complicated, it appears that negative exchanges serve an important purpose, so that the complete absence of negative exchanges (avoidance of conflict) undermines marital satisfaction. For example, research has found that wives who have a low threshold for negativity in the husband early in marriage (i.e., it takes less negativity in the husband for the wives to respond negatively) are more likely to be stably married over time, and the couple is more likely to show higher marital satisfaction. Negative exchanges when handled properly (i.e., resolved and repaired to positive exchanges) help spur needed changes in marriages that maintain the satisfaction of both partners.

In addition to studying the ways in which partners interact, scientists have explored partners' perceptions of their interactions. By combining observational methods with various forms of self-report methods, researchers can uncover adaptive as well as maladaptive cognitions that accompany patterns of behavior. For example, a procedure developed by John Gottman and colleagues known as the 'talk table' requires each individual to rate how negative or positive a statement is before it is spoken, and the partner then rates the valence of the statement immediately after it is heard. Studies using this procedure have found that individual members of a distressed couple are much more likely to perceive a partner's message as discourteous or insulting, even if the partner did not intend it to be negative. Other research has provided support for a phenomenon known as attribution theory, which states that individuals in distressed relationships tend to make negative attributions for a partner's actions, whereas nondistressed couples are more likely to make positive attributions for similar actions. Specifically, distressed couples make internal, stable, and global attributions for negative behaviors, and external, unstable, and specific attributions for positive ones. The opposite is true for nondistressed couples. According to attribution theory, an individual in an unhappy relationship would likely view a partner's curt response as intentional, customary, and representative of the person's inconsiderate behavior in general. In contrast, an individual in a nondistressed relationship would be more likely to blame external factors such as a hectic day at the office, and believe it to be an isolated incident that is out of character.

Over the last couple of decades, there has been increased interest in how distressed marriages may resonate through the family and influence parent–child relationships and child development. This literature also considers whether children and the qualities of children affect marriages, and there is indeed a literature demonstrating that marital satisfaction tends to decrease when a child is born to a couple. Systems theory would suggest that effects flow both ways in a family, so that difficulties in parenting also would adversely affect a marriage; however, most of the existing research has focused on the way marriages affect parenting and child development, rather than the reverse.

A considerable body of literature establishes the importance of the quality of the parent–child relationships during the early childhood years for healthy emotional development in children. If marital processes undermine parenting, it is likely that the early emotional development of the child would be influenced. In fact, for many decades, family therapists have noted that children's behavioral and emotional problems were often associated with disrupted marital relationships.

Marital Relationships, Parent–Child Relationships, and Child Development

By conceptualizing families as systems, it follows that the quality of marital relationships exerts an influence on the well-being of the members of the marital dyad, as well as on children's adjustment within the larger family unit. Although the vast majority of research examining links between marital distress and child adjustment has focused on school-age children, many studies have demonstrated effects of marital distress on children in infancy and early childhood. These effects are seen in the success of the child in meeting developmental tasks of early childhood, especially in areas of early self-control and self-regulation.

Parent–Child Relationships and Early Emotional Development

During the first 3 years of life a child experiences amazing growth in the domains of self-control and self-regulation. During this time, it has been noted by Alan Sroufe, a leading researcher on early emotional development, that children develop the ability to manage frustration, accept delays and disappointments, operate effectively as self-reliant individuals, cooperate and coordinate in communicating with others, emotionally engage and interact with others, and regulate tensions that always will arise in complex social interactions. He further notes that these abilities require that children remain open to a range of emotional experiences, learn to recognize and regulate their own emotions, have confidence in their ability to regulate their emotions, and have positive expectations regarding their relationships with others, particularly relationships with their primary caregivers.

In the first year of life, the quality of a child's relationship with a primary caregiver or others in the family is of particular importance for emotional development. Although self-regulation is possible during the first year life, the ability to self-regulate is contingent on the child being supported by a sensitive and responsive caregiver. During this time, children are completely reliant on their caregivers for comfort and security. Furthermore, a child's willingness to explore the environment and interact with both inanimate objects and other people is dependent on the child's expectation that the caregiver will be both attentive and available when the child needs emotional support or assistance. This is seen both behaviorally and physiologically in young children. A child who has a secure relationship with a parent figure is more likely to exhibit active and more complex play and is less likely to be physiologically overaroused during frustrating tasks or when they are separated from the caregiver. In contrast, children who experience insensitive care or who are exposed to violence or other stressful living situations at home are more likely to show a low quality of play, increased social inhibition, and physiological dysregulation in response to challenging situations.

As children move into the second year of life, finding balance between the need for proximity to the caregiver and the need to explore the environment becomes more salient. Children who have a history of receiving sensitive and supportive care are more likely to function autonomously and actively explore their environment. However, as they physically distance themselves from their parents, they regularly maintain visual and often vocal contact, checking in periodically to ensure that the parent is still available and not emotionally distant. If in the process of exploring the environment the child becomes frightened or upset, he or she will then immediately return to the caregiver or signal a need for assistance. On the other hand, children who have experienced insensitive or unreliable parenting from their caregiver are less likely to explore their environment and can be less effective at using their caregiver as a source of comfort when distressed. Despite having the physical ability to move about and engage the social world, these children are likely to lack the psychological ability and confidence necessary to begin functioning as autonomous individuals.

The emergence of a stable sense of autonomy and confidence in self-regulatory abilities is based on a history of well-coordinated and responsive interactions between the child and the caregiver and the child's exposure to well-regulated emotions within the family. During the first three years of life, the confidence secured in the parent–child relationship eventually develops into self-confidence, which ultimately evolves into self-reliance and self-regulation. In contrast, children who have experienced chaotic households and inconsistent parenting do not have the positive regulatory experiences necessary to guide their own forays into the social world, nor do they have confidence in the caregiver to rely on her for comfort and soothing if necessary. Often times these children will either fail to develop self-reliance and effective autonomous functioning, or they will develop overly rigid styles of self-regulation because they have been forced to adapt to constant insecurity due to emotionally unavailable caregivers. Children in the former group fail to develop confidence in their abilities to cope with changes in their environment, and thus remain socially inhibited and fearful of leaving the immediate presence of the caregiver. The latter children do not learn to trust and use others as sources of regulation and comfort, leading them to be constantly vigilant and in states of high arousal. In both scenarios, an early sense of insecurity in the parent–child relationship leads to a compromised sense of self-reliance, distrust of others, and ultimately ineffective self-regulatory abilities. This has longer-term implications in that those children who acquire early self-regulatory abilities are more likely to go on to show greater self-reliance in the classroom, better ability to delay gratification, less inclination to become distressed in the face of challenge, and greater flexibility and complexity in their play and interactions with other children.

Many studies show a link between marital quality and the parenting needed to promote self-regulation in the child. Parents who report higher satisfaction with their marriage and more support from their spouse in their marriage also are more satisfied and involved with parenting, show more sensitivity and responsiveness to their child, and have children who are more securely attached.

Marriage and Parent–Child Relationships

Much of the work considering the link between marriage and parenting involves marital conflict. A considerable body of literature documents the relation between marital conflict and emotional and behavioral problems in young children. Much of the theorizing about why marital conflict affects children's development has centered on the parent–child relationship, and numerous studies have examined whether marital conflict influences child development because of its impact on the parent–child relationship.

An important distinction in this work is between constructive and destructive conflict. Marital conflict occurs in most families; however, marital conflict is not necessarily negative in a family, particularly when conflicts are resolved or dealt with constructively. Because conflict can be a way to resolve differences that may cause resentment, anger, or negative emotions and withdrawal, parents who engage in constructive conflict may actually be better able to parent than those who withdraw from conflict. Moreover, constructive conflict can help children learn appropriate ways to handle interpersonal difficulties.

The negative effects of marital conflict on parent–child relationships and on children's development seem to be limited to destructive conflict, that is, conflict that is not resolved, is not dealt with constructively, and may escalate into verbal and physical aggression in couples. Destructive marital conflict may influence the quality of parent–child relationships, as parents may be less sensitive and responsive to the needs of their children. Effects also may be seen in the harshness with which parents treat children, particularly with respect to discipline. Destructive marital conflict may also affect the quantity of the child's interactions with parents in that unresolved marital conflict may result in parents spending less time with their children. Parents may be less focused on their children and may provide less supervision and monitoring. Current investigations have suggested a variety of pathways or mechanisms through which marital processes and parent–infant relationships may be linked.

There is some empirical support for the 'spillover hypothesis', which refers to the idea that the emotion experienced and expressed in one relationship can be transferred or carried over to other relationships; that is, negative affect arising in marital conflict is thought to spread to and contaminate or disrupt interactions between the parent and the young child. Parents who are angry, exhausted, or demoralized from marital conflict may simply be less emotionally available or attuned to their infants. At the most basic level, they may be unable to perceive or detect their children's emotional needs. Even if such needs are detected, parents may be unable to respond in a supportive fashion if they are preoccupied with their own marital problems.

Parent–child relationships may be even more seriously threatened when the anger or withdrawal engendered by marital conflict leads parents to be actively rejecting, hostile, or physically aggressive with their young children. A parent who experiences marital conflict may show insensitivity or poor attunement to their child's emotional states. The insensitivity or poor attunement impedes the child's development of emotional regulation skills, as it is through the empathic and supportive responses of a parent that a child learns to regulate his or her own affective states as noted earlier in this article. Additionally, if conflicted parents transfer harsh or angry feelings onto their children, then parents may come to represent a source of fear rather than a source of comfort. Several studies have documented an association between marital conflict and children's insecure attachments to their parents. The infant may not learn to trust the parent as a source of comfort and have a secure sense of the parent's availability for comfort when the infant is frightened or distressed because of frightening, angry behavior in the parent either in interaction with the child or spouse.

Researchers also have highlighted other aspects of caregiving that may suffer in the wake of marital conflict. Parents who are preoccupied with their own marital problems may withdraw from their children, and this withdrawal may be evident in a lack of 'cognitive room' allocated to their children as noted by one researcher. Parental withdrawal may be evident in parents' failure to perform instrumental caregiving tasks for their children.

Concepts from the family therapy literature also have been useful in understanding the processes by which marital conflict may disrupt the parent–child relationship. Family systems theorists have long noted the dynamics of 'scapegoating' wherein the child takes on symptoms of the family pathology and becomes identified as the problematic member of the family system. Rather than directing anger or criticism toward one another, parents focus the negativity on the child, and the problems with the child serve to distract from the tension in the marital subsystem. This process can be seen even with infants and toddlers.

Researchers also have proposed that modeling may represent another mechanism by which marital conflict and child difficulties are linked. Studies show that many infants are quite content merely observing their parents interact, and that successful interparental interaction helps infants to regulate their own state. In contrast, children whose parents model poor affect regulation during marital interactions may be more vulnerable to poor regulation themselves. This lack of self-regulation in the child, in turn, may heighten the risk for negative parent–child interactions.

Parental Discipline

One aspect of the link between marital and parent–child relationships that has received attention is the way in which marital conflict may compromise parental discipline. A parent who is experiencing discord with a partner may exhibit harsh, permissive, or inconsistent discipline. Harsh discipline has been associated with a broad range of problems in adjustment for young children. Harsh parenting may be a function of the parent's displaced anger onto the child, or alternatively, a sense that the parent must compensate for the chaos or disruption created by the marital conflict by 'buckling down' on the child.

Permissive and inconsistent parenting also has been associated in research with the development of behavioral problems in the child. Permissive parenting is more likely in families where parents experience marital distress and may reflect the parent's absorption in their own marital difficulties, leaving little energy to devote to more careful monitoring of the children. Inconsistent parenting may be exhibited by parents who are disorganized by problems with their spouse and have difficulty sustaining a consistent approach to discipline. Alternatively, a parent's inconsistency may result from a parent behaving one way toward the children when their spouse is present, and another way when the spouse is absent. Additionally, parents who are experiencing a great deal of marital conflict and are having difficulty communicating in general may also have difficulties communicating about discipline and child rearing, and thus may have more disagreements about how the children should be raised.

Effects on Co-Parenting

Researchers interested in the manner in which marital conflict may lead to inconsistencies between parents have highlighted the importance of co-parenting as a distinct family construct. Co-parenting processes, or those involving direct interactions between the parents regarding the child, may become hostile and competitive in the context of marital discord. One parent may actively interfere with or undermine the other parent's interactions with the child, perhaps trying to engage the child in a more appealing task or making covert disparaging comments about the other parent's behavior or character. Alternatively, difficulties in overt co-parenting may be reflected in discrepancies in levels of mothers' and fathers' involvement in family interactions.

The Compensatory Hypothesis

Although there is a wealth of both empirical and theoretical work examining the ways in which marital conflict may adversely affect the parent–child relationship, there has been speculation that, in some families, parents may compensate for marital discord by focusing their efforts on their relationships with their children. The compensatory hypothesis suggests that parents may seek fulfillment in the parent–child relationship to make up for dissatisfactions they experience in their marriage. Some empirical evidence suggests a negative association between marital and parent–child relationships. The challenge in testing the compensatory hypothesis, however, is to distinguish genuinely positive parent–child relationships from seemingly positive relationships that actually meet the needs of the adult, rather than the child. There may be positive parent–child relationships that truly withstand and rise above the strain of marital conflict. In contrast, there may be parent–child dynamics in which a parent appears to be very involved with and devoted to their child, but where such involvement or devotion has become intrusive or burdensome to the child, or is largely motivated by efforts to win the child as an ally against the other parent. It is questionable whether a close relationship fueled by a parent's negative relationship with his or her spouse is truly positive. Thus, to date, there is not a great deal of empirical support for the compensatory hypothesis. However, there may be families in which parents can truly overcome the strain of marital conflict and provide sensitive, responsive parenting that remains focused on the child's needs. There also may be families in which there is little negative marital conflict in the family, but there is also little positive in the marriage, and parents instead invest in their children.

Direct Effects of Marital Conflict on Children

Most of the research on marital conflict has considered the indirect effect that marital conflict has on children via its effects on parenting as discussed above. Less research has focused on the direct impact on children of exposure to and involvement in parents' conflicts with each other. Additionally, much of the research on the effects of marital conflict on children focuses on school-age and adolescent samples, marital conflict may be a particularly important facet of the family system to evaluate in families with younger children. Parents of infants and toddlers may be more likely to expose their young children to marital conflict than older children because some parents believe their children are too young to be aware of or understand conflict. However, even very young children have demonstrated the ability to distinguish between friendly and angry exchanges between adults. A growing body of research has shown that marital conflict can have direct effects on children's adjustment in the early years and repeated exposure may increase the risk for poor emotional regulation, internalizing and externalizing symptoms, and problematic peer relationships later in childhood and adolescence.

Research by Mark Cummings and Patrick Davies and colleagues has been particularly important in demonstrating that conflict between parents in a family is a stressor for children. Their work shows that conflict can induce emotional distress in children, enmesh them in their parents' problems, elicit angry or aggressive behavioral displays, and can contribute over time to the development of dysfunctional behavior patterns in children. Cummings initiated a series of studies in which he used situations analogous to home situations where children were exposed to angry interchanges between adults. These involved contrived situations in the laboratory where adults showed anger toward each other in front of children. Even infants and toddlers showed distress and preoccupation with the adult anger. Young preschool children showed negative emotions, freezing, facial and postural distress, verbal concern, and anger. Older preschool children, who were able to report their emotions, reported anger, fear, sadness, and distress in response to the adult anger. Further, these investigators and others were able to show that changes in children's physiological response systems occur during exposure to this adult background anger, including changes in heart rate, systolic blood pressure, and skin conductance. Studies of children's reactions to angry parents in the home indicate a similar picture of responding. These investigators have concluded from this well-designed series of studies that background anger in the home induces distress and anxiety in children and that this response to adults' angry behavior begins as early as the first year of life.

Further, studies have found a link between this arousal in children from their exposure to marital conflict and increased aggression in children, even for children as young as toddler age. This may occur because arousal translates into aggression because of excitatory processes or because interadult anger provides models for children of aggressive behavior. At any rate, a number of studies demonstrate a link between interadult anger and child anger and aggression. The research suggests that this occurs regardless of parenting practices or other aspects of family functioning.

Another direct effect of conflict between marital partners in homes involves the tendency for children to become involved in parent's disputes. Research has shown that children from discordant homes, even as young as toddlers, show attempts to intervene in parental disputes by comforting or distracting parents or trying to resolve the problems for parents. Taking on this responsibility for the welfare of their parent's marriage has been associated with dysfunction in children and may result in children who subjugate their own feelings in favor of the feelings of others.

Context of Conflict and Effects on Children: The Emotional Security Hypothesis

Research has established that certain forms of conflict are apparently viewed as more upsetting than others by children and are more likely linked to child adjustment problems. Conflict that involves aggression and spouse abuse between marital partners leads to more distress in children than verbal aggression, and children who witness violence between parents are more likely to develop a wide range of adjustment problems than children just exposed to verbal aggression. Children's distress may also be greater when conflicts involve child-rearing issues.

Cummings and colleagues found that resolution of conflict lessens the negative impact of conflict on children's adjustment. Children's aggression and distress reactions to anger between adults return to baseline levels when children observe a complete resolution, and there is evidence that even when adults resolve their differences out of sight of children, there is benefit. These studies suggested that children do not just react to the conflict, but rather also to the meaning and message about how adults feel toward each other and how well they are getting along. Even preschool children engage in an appraisal of conflicts between their parents that includes the meaning of the conflict for the future stability of the family and their own well-being. An important goal for children is the maintenance of a sense of emotional security in the family so that a threat to the child's feeling of being emotionally secure will motivate behaviors to maintain emotional security, such as intervening in marital arguments. When parents resolve their own conflicts, the child's appraisal may be that the conflict is not that threatening to the family or to their own well-being, and thus child attempts at intervening, for example, occur less frequently. In short, the evaluation children make of conflict seems important in the implications for their adjustment. Children seem to evaluate resolved conflicts quite differently from unresolved ones, with unresolved conflicts more likely to lead to the children's appraisal that the conflict is a threat to the family and their well-being.

Marriage in Ethnic Minority Groups

Although there have been considerable advances in marital research methodology over the last 40 years, scientists have only recently begun to investigate marital processes in minority families. Much of the current understanding of the correlates of marital satisfaction and stability has been shaped by studies examining the marital relationships of middle-class European Americans, with a smaller body of research on African Americans couples. Less than 10% of studies on marriage include African American participants, and this happens more often when studies involve physical violence. Studies that include Hispanic or Asian couples are even rarer, such that the discussion to follow focuses mostly on marriage in African American families and how social and cultural context may play a role in differences between African American and European American groups. It is unfortunate that the discussion must be so limited given that demographic projections suggest that by 2050 the US population will be 8% Asian American, 15% African American, 24% Hispanic, and only 50% non-Hispanic White. Moreover, because marital research has typically focused almost exclusively on European American, middle-class couples as the normative population, the idea that marriages themselves operate within specific social contexts has remained relatively unexplored. The importance of context has gained considerable attention during the past decade as scientists have begun to discover that marriages among people of minority racial groups are impacted by contextual variables that not only affect the quality and stability of these marriages, but of family relations as well.

The importance of understanding the implications of social context for marital relationships has been made salient by research indicating significant ethnic group differences for a number of factors associated with marriage. Census data, for example, reveal that the percentage of African Americans aged 15 years and older who are currently married (31.5%) is considerably less than that of the general population (51.7%). In addition to this lower marriage rate, African Americans also are significantly more likely to experience marital dissolution than European Americans despite findings that African Americans are no less approving of marriage than European Americans and actually appear to be more disapproving of divorce. Although rates of marital conflict appear to be generally similar in the two groups with perhaps higher conflict in early marriage for African American couples, a few national studies have found that African Americans are more likely to report engaging in spousal violence than European Americans. Controlling for income and social class inequalities reduces, but does not eliminate, the relationship between ethnicity and spousal violence.

With regard to the greater conflict early in African American marriages, recent research suggests that this may be related to different roles and responsibilities in marriage for African Americans and European Americans. African American couples seem to be more likely to adopt nontraditional gender roles than European American couples. Studies have shown that African American men have more positive attitudes toward working wives than European American men, and African American women have historically higher rates of labor force participation than European American women resulting in more equality in African American couples. For example, one study found that among African American couples, but not among European American couples, marriages were less stable when wives felt that there was inflexibility in the marriage with regard to household task responsibilities and when husbands perceived more power imbalance in decision-making. Some studies have shown higher marital conflict for African American spouses in the early years of marriage and have speculated that the higher rates of marital conflict may be related to the greater difficulty of negotiating equity and sharing of role responsibilities in African American couples. When roles and responsibilities are adopted along more traditional lines, there may be less need for negotiation. In support of this, studies have found that in stable marriages African American and European American wives tend to be supportive in different ways, with European American wives adopting a more submissive, compliant style and African American wives adopting a more equitable, collaborative approach. The use of the collaborative style has been described as a reflection of the cultural value that African Americans place on the strength and independence of women.

With regard to the greater incidence of spousal violence and the lower marriage rate, community structural variables may partially explain ethnic group differences. Recent research has identified several community variables that seem to exacerbate marital difficulties for African Americans, including poverty and residential instability. Poverty, which affected an estimated 24.6% of African Americans living in the US in 2004, has been associated with poorer marital quality for African American couples. This effect has been explained in terms of the family stress model, which contends that adverse experiences, including financial strain, contribute to lower quality of interactions between family members. Additionally, impoverished communities often lack accessible health resources which prevent couples from obtaining services (i.e., counseling) that may help to maintain their marriages. Poverty also is associated with high unemployment rates and high rates of incarceration among African American men, and both factors have been further cited as reasons for the declining rate of marriage among this group. Research has shown that both imprisonment and low economic potential are negatively related to African American men's desirability as marriage partners. These factors create a smaller pool of potential spouses for African American women. Moreover, the inability to find work may make men more unwilling to marry because they are unable to fill their desired role as family provider.

Residential instability also has been shown to have a negative effect on African Americans' marital quality.

Unstable communities may lack adequate housing, reliable transportation, and a safe environment. Together with the constant movement of families in and out of the neighborhood, such conditions may facilitate the deterioration of marriages because they provide contexts from which behaviors may spill over into the marital relationship. Couples living in dangerous neighborhoods, for example, may encounter hostile behaviors on a daily basis which they may transfer to their marital interactions. Such neighborhoods are also less likely to have stable families to serve as positive role models for their residents.

Finally, one of the few studies to consider spousal violence predictors within African American couples has shown that lower income, younger couple age, shorter residence in a community, husband unemployment, being hit as an adolescent, and witnessing violence between parents were all significant predictors of husband-to-wife violence.

There is speculation that when violence occurs in marital relationships, different attributions may be made in African American women as compared to European American women. Researchers have speculated that African American women whose husbands are physically violent are more likely than European American women to see the cause for the violence as attributed to the larger society and the treatment that African American men receive in the larger society including a greater likelihood of arrests and police maltreatment than for other men. It has been suggested that to the extent that these ethnicity-related attributions are communicated to children, the emotional responses of children to spousal violence may vary with less adverse impact expected when these outside explanations are offered.

Marriage and the Development of Ethnic Minority Children

There is some preliminary evidence that marital discord and dissolution is more strongly associated with negative outcomes for European American children than for African American children. Scholars have speculated that the fact that more African American children grow up in extended family circumstances and have access to other adults may lead to buffering of the effects of the marriage for the child. However, a recent study found that when parents are married, African American children are unlikely to live in an extended family situation. Still, these children may have more access to extended family than European American children. It may also be that African American mothers are less negatively affected in general in their own functioning as a result of marital relationship difficulties as a number of studies report better psychological functioning among African American women than European American women following separation and divorce. If the mother is functioning well, there may be less of a negative effect on the quality of her parenting behavior. Of course, maternal psychosocial functioning may also relate to the greater access of African American mothers to the support of extended family members. A less-positive explanation, however, is that ethnic minority children are more likely to be subjected to an abundance of stressful events in their environments, and so the stress of marital distress or dissolution is less significant relative to other stressors. Because African American children are more likely to be raised in poverty, with reduced economic and employment opportunities for adults in the family, and in poor and unsafe neighborhoods, the argument is that this convergence of risk factors is likely to mute any unique effects of marital discord or dissolution.

Conclusions

Much of the research on families and child development during the last several decades has really been focused on parent–child relationships and has failed to recognize the broader network of relationships in the family and their importance, including the marriage of adults. It is well established that young children's relationships with parents are important for their social and emotional development. However, those parent–child relationships are situated in the context of the larger family, and in many families, the marital relationship is important in either undermining or supporting parent–child relationships. The marital relationship also is influenced by what happens in the parent–child relationship. Children observe their parents interacting together, and these observations are related to what they learn about how to resolve conflict and express affection in adult relationship. Children's observations also contribute to their sense of safety and security in the family. Thus, understanding the linkages between the marital relationship and other relationships in the family as well as understanding linkages between marital relationships and the functioning of individual family members is critical to a complete understanding of child development in the social institution of the family.

Although a great amount of literature has accumulated on the aforementioned topic, it is mostly a literature that involves middle class European American families. The lack of research on minority families limits our understanding of the way marital distress or happiness serves to support parenting and family relationships in different family and community contexts. Our theories would suggest that families make adaptations to their environments, and relationships may take different forms in different environments because these alternate forms are more suited to the demands of the environments. On average, minority families in this country are more likely to be living in poverty. Extended family support may be an adaptive response to the challenges of raising children in the riskier environments that poorer families encounter. Because fewer men who can support families are available because of incarceration and joblessness rates among African American men compared to European American men, it is perhaps understandable that the rate of marriage is lower among African American women than among European American women. However, it does not appear that strong marriages are valued less in African American women than in European American women. In fact, hesitancy to marry perhaps reflects the reality of the pool of marriageable men. Because the context of marriage is different in African American families, it is also likely that the influence on children's development is different, and there is some evidence of that in the literature. However, more research is needed to establish the linkages between marital processes and children's development in varied environmental contexts.

See also: Attachment; Divorce; Emotion Regulation; Family Influences; Independence/Dependence; Parenting Styles and their Effects; Self-Regulatory Processes; Social Interaction; Social and Emotional Development Theories.

Suggested Readings

Bryant CM and Wickrama KAS (2005) Marital relationships of African Americans: A contextual approach. In: McLoyd VC, Hill NE, and Dodge KA (eds.) *African American Family Life: Ecological and Family Diversity*, pp. 111–134. New York: Guilford.

Cummings EM and Davies PT (2002) Effects of marital conflict on children: Recent advances and emerging themes in process oriented research. *Journal of Child Psychology and Psychiatry and Allied Disciplines* 43: 31–63.

Davies PT and Cummings EM (2006) Interparental discord, family process, and developmental psychopathology. In: Cicchetti D and Cohen DJ (eds.) *Developmental Psychopathology: Risk, Disorder and Adaptation,* 2nd edn., vol. 3, pp. 86–128. Hoboken, NJ: Wiley.

Gottman JM and Notarius CI (2000) Decade review: Observing marital interaction. *Journal of Marriage and the Family* 62: 927–947.

Gottman JM and Notarius CI (2002) Marital research in the 20th century and a research agenda for the 21st century. *Family Process* 41: 159–197.

Kerig PK (2001) Children's coping with interparental conflict. In: Grych JH and Fincham FD (eds.) *Interparental Conflict and Child Development: Theory, Research, and Applications*, pp. 213–245. New York: Cambridge University Press.

McLoyd VC, Cauce AM, Takeuchi D, and Wilson L (2000) Marital processes and parental socialization in families of color: A decade review of research. *Journal of Marriage and the Family* 62: 1070–1093.

Sroufe LA (1995) *Emotional Development: The Organization of Emotional Life in the Early Years.* New York: Cambridge University Press.

Maternal Age and Pregnancy

R C Fretts, Harvard Vanguard Medical Associates, Wellesley, MA, USA
C Zera, Brigham and Women's Hospital, Boston, MA, USA
L J Heffner, Boston Medical Center, Boston, MA, USA

Glossary

Advanced maternal age – Maternal age at delivery 35 years or older.

Aneuploidy – A condition of having more or less than the normal number of chromosomes, the most frequently observed cytogenetic abnormality.

Chromosomes – The individual packages of genetic materials containing many genes. A full complement of chromosomes is required for normal development.

Down syndrome – Trisomy 21 (also Down syndrome) is a genetic disorder caused by the presence of all or part of an extra chromosome 21.

Ectopic pregnancy – A pregnancy that implants outside of the uterine cavity, most commonly in the fallopian tubes. Ectopic pregnancies are hazardous to the health of the mother and can be associated with intraabdominal bleeding and maternal death if not recognized and appropriately treated.

Fetal death *in utero* – The death of a baby in the uterus before it is born. This event may also be referred to as an *in utero* fetal demise (IUFD) or stillbirth.

Gestational diabetes – Diabetes that is diagnosed during pregnancy. The majority of cases are secondary to a lack of sufficient insulin to counter the increased circulating glucose induced by the pregnancy; however, some cases are actually undiagnosed diabetes that was present before pregnancy.

Human female reproductive life span – The time period between the onset of menses (menarche) and the end of menses (menopause). In developed countries, normal menarche occurs as early as age 9 years, and menopause, as late as age 50+ years. Over 99.5% of births occur in women aged 15–44 years.

Infertility – A couple's inability to conceive a pregnancy with regular sexual intercourse for one year in the absence of contraception or sterilization.

Low birthweight – Any newborn whose weight is less than 2500 g (5 lb 9 oz), either due to the fact that they were born early or did not gain adequate weight in the uterus.

Maternal age – The mother's age at the estimated or actual time of delivery.

Perinatal mortality – The death of a fetus or neonate within a specified period after birth is used to calculate the perinatal mortality rate. There are variations in the precise definition of perinatal mortality that specifically concern the issue of inclusion or exclusion of early fetal and late neonatal fatalities. The World Health Organization defines the perinatal period to include deaths occurring during late pregnancy (i.e., 22 completed weeks' gestation and over), during childbirth and up to 7 completed days of life, although this definition is not universally accepted. The perinatal mortality is the sum of the fetal mortality and the neonatal mortality.

Preeclampsia – A type of pregnancy-induced hypertension in which there are additional signs and/or symptoms beyond the high blood pressure. These include the symptoms of swelling of the hands and face, severe headaches, upper abdominal pain, and visual disturbances. The most common sign is the presence of protein in the urine. Preeclampsia can progress to eclampsia, or seizure, and can involve multiple organ systems.

Pregnancy-induced hypertension – The new onset of high blood pressure during the second half of pregnancy in a woman who is known not to have had high blood pressure prior to pregnancy.

Spontaneous abortion – Also known as a miscarriage, it is the unintended loss of a pregnancy in the first half of pregnancy.

Introduction

In developed countries, it is routine for women 35 years of age or older to consider having a baby, often their first. Thus, the management of these women has become central to the practice of obstetrics. This article will review the effects of age on fertility, pregnancy, and delivery.

Incidence and Epidemiology

The global total fertility rate has fallen from five children per women lifetime in the early 1950s to 2.7 children in the early 2000s. Within the US, as well as in other developed countries, the overall fertility rate (i.e., the number of live births per 1000 women aged 15–44 years) has dropped from 106.2/1000 to 64.8/1000. Although overall birth rates for older women have decreased, there is evidence that women are merely delaying childbearing. In developed countries during the 1960s, women 35 years of age were more likely to be completing their families, while today women are more often starting their families. At ages 40–44 years, for example, the number of women who had not had at least one birth was 15.8/1000 in 2002, compared with 15.1/1000 in 1960. However, at every other age group the number of women who had not yet had a live birth was significantly higher in 2002 than in 1960. For example, 66.5% of women aged 20–24 years had not had a child yet in 2002 vs. 47.5% in 1960; similarly, at ages 25–29 years, 41.3% in 2002 vs. 20% in 1960 had not yet given birth. These data clearly indicate that women in developed countries are having fewer children, often later in life, rather than opting not to have children at all.

The reasons for this shift toward later childbearing are many. The primary reason is that women are attaining higher educational levels than in previous decades. Within developing countries, the age of first birth and the interval between births increases as a woman's educational status increases. Educational level correlates with a more sophisticated knowledge and use of contraception, age at first birth, and total number of children. The changing role of women in the workplace, with more career opportunities available, has undoubtedly affected childbearing. Control of fertility with increased contraceptive options plays a part. The downside of women completing advanced degrees and establishing their career is that they are more likely to need to use fertility treatments in order to conceive.

Preconception Issues

Infertility

The biggest obstacle for women who have delayed childbearing is their reduced fertility. There are multiple factors, both physiologic and acquired, that contribute to this diminished fertility. Acquired pathologies that contribute to infertility include fallopian tube disease, often a result of sexually transmitted infections, and endometriosis, which is the presence of uterine lining cells elsewhere in the pelvis. The impact of both of these processes can worsen with time. The role of structural lesions that increase with advancing age, such as uterine fibroids and endometrial polyps, is unclear but may also play a part in decreasing fertility. The greatest contributor to the age-related decline of fertility is the decline in ovarian oocyte (egg) reserve, which leads to an increasing number of anovulatory cycles. Clinically, this results in a steep

decline in fertility rates for women in their late 30s. This is true now and is largely unchanged from information gleaned from historical cohorts, as reported by Menken and colleagues, who have summarized the rates of having a child in eight historical cohorts based on the age of marriage (**Figure 1**). The current fertility rates for women aged 35–39 years are 41.4/1000, for women aged 40–44 years, 8.3/1000, and for women aged 45–54 years, 0.5/1000 as compared to 103.6/1000 for women aged 20–24 years and 113.6/1000 for women aged 25–29 years.

This decreased ability of the ovary to recruit multiple preovulatory follicles is further illustrated by data from assisted reproductive technology clinics. In 2002, according to data from the Center of Disease Control Reports of Assisted Reproductive Technologies, the number of cancelled *in vitro* fertilization (IVF) cycles in women aged 41–42 years was estimated to be about 20%, whereas women under 35 years old had only a 9% cancellation rate. This higher cancellation rate reflects the decreased ability of the ovary to respond to ovulation induction with medication as women age.

Finally, oocyte quality diminishes over time, thereby contributing to a less 'competent' oocyte both in terms of an increasing risk of aneuploidy with advancing maternal age and fertilization potential. The first phase of reproduction begins prior to birth. In the fetal period, the oocytes reach metaphase I, and remain aligned on the metaphase plate until the oocyte is stimulated to divide just prior to ovulation. At the typical age of first menstruation (11 years), the oocytes within the ovary have

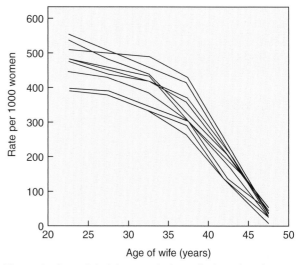

Figure 1 Age-related decrease in fecundity based on the age of marriage in eight historical cohorts. This figure displays the chance that women within a historical cohort would have a child based on the age at which she married. If she married at 35 years of age, their chances of having a child were between 30% and 45%. Reprinted from Menken J, Trussell J, and Larsen U (1986) Age and infertility. *Science* 233: 13899. Reprinted with permission from AAAS.

been sitting in metaphase I for 11.5 years. As maternal age increases, the number of opportunities for errors to occur increases and accumulates over time. A very important error that occurs and appears to be related to aging of the egg is nondisjunction. When nondisjunction occurs, the number of chromosomes present in the egg is different than the necessary 23. Following fertilization by the sperm with its 23 chromosomes, the embryo has too many or too few chromosomes. This condition, called aneuploidy, reduces implantation rates and results in abnormal development in implanted embryos. Estimates of the rates of aneuploidy have become more precise recently with the advent of preimplantation genetic diagnosis (PGD). Studies evaluating embryos prior to transfer back into the mother show consistently that the rates of aneuploidy are high (30–50%). The observed rates are even higher among older women with a history of recurrent miscarriage. The majority of aneuploid conceptions result in miscarriage, resulting in a higher rate of miscarriage in older women. The number of conceptions affected with nonlethal aneuploidies (including trisomy 13, 18, or 21, Turner's syndrome and Kleinfelter's syndrome) is also much higher in women of advancing age, as will be further discussed below.

The options for treatment of infertility are somewhat dependent on the cause, but as women age, they increasingly must turn to assisted reproductive technologies (ART). While these treatment options improve the likelihood of achieving pregnancy when compared to expectant management, current state-of-the-art reproductive technologies cannot compensate for the entire natural decline of fertility with advancing age (**Figure 2**). Thus, as maternal age increases, the success of IVF using fresh, nondonor eggs decreases at every stage of ART. The likelihood of a successful response to ovarian stimulation and progression to egg retrieval decreases and cycles that have progressed to egg retrieval are slightly less likely to reach transfer. The percentage of cycles that progress from transfer to pregnancy decreases and cycles that have progressed to pregnancy are less likely to result in a live birth because of the greater risk for miscarriage. Miscarriage rates for women in their late 40s approach 90%.

For older women without sufficient ovarian reserve to successfully undergo ovulation induction and retrieval for IVF, egg donation by younger woman represents the only option likely to succeed in achieving pregnancy. While this is technically feasible and has worked in women in their 50s and 60s, the routine practice of egg donation remains controversial. Egg donation is more costly than most adoptions, and the outcome of having a family is more certain with adoption than with egg donation. The harvesting of eggs from young women is not without risk and the motivation for egg donation usually occurs when there are significant monetary incentives. There has not yet been

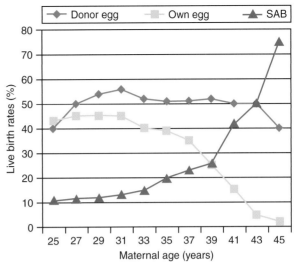

Figure 2 Live birth rates using fresh and donor eggs and the spontaneous abortion rate. SAB* Spontaneous abortion rate among women who had advanced reproductive technology cycles using their own eggs. Although the live birth rate using donor eggs was not influenced by the age of the recipient, the live birth rate using fresh eggs was significantly influenced by maternal age. Adapted from 2002 Assisted Reproductive Technology Success Rates, National Summary and Fertility Clinic Reports, Centers for Disease Control, 2002.

sufficient long-term follow-up of the egg donors to know if multiple ovarian stimulation and retrieval procedures place these women at increased risk for reproductive cancers later in life. Unused fertilized and frozen embryos of course can also be 'adopted' by infertile couples if it is acceptable to all parties. The success of these donor egg cycles is similar to other reproductive procedures (in the range of 40% per cycle depending on the donor's age). There is considerable appeal to extend a woman's reproductive span with the use of egg donation, since the success of egg donation in recipients does not significantly decline up to age 50 years, after which the success rate declines slowly due to lower rates of implantation. While the risk of aneuploidy is related to the age of the egg donor, the risks of third trimester pregnancy complications such as gestational diabetes and hypertension remain elevated consistent with the recipient's age. Therefore, there is still much debate about using donor embryos for women of significantly advanced maternal age.

Another option involves cryopreservation of ovarian tissue for women who are young, with the eventual goal of utilizing oocytes for fertilization when the woman desires pregnancy. Many hope that harvesting ovarian tissue prior to the age-related decline of oocytes will preserve a women's reproductive potential. However, the technology remains experimental at this time and the number of successful pregnancies following ovarian cryopreservation has been few.

First Trimester Complications

Although it is difficult to truly quantify the number of spontaneous abortions, it is well established that older women are at increased risk (**Figure 3** and **Table 1**). In the Nybo-Anderson *et al.* linkage study, they reported the overall clinical miscarriage rate to be 13%, but at the age of 42 years, nearly half of the clinically recognized pregnancies ended in miscarriage, and for women 45 years of age or older, nearly 75% ended in a spontaneous loss. Additionally, the leading cause of death in early pregnancy, ectopic gestation, remains one of the most significant obstetric complications. There is evidence associating advancing maternal age with increased risk for ectopic pregnancy. Older data suggest up to four- to sevenfold increased risk of ectopic pregnancy in women aged over 35 years compared to younger women (**Table 1**).

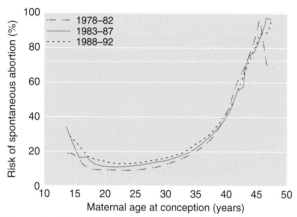

Figure 3   The rate of clinically diagnosed spontaneous miscarriage by maternal age. The cohorts 1978–82, 1983–87, 1988–92 all had similar rates of miscarriage. Reproduced from Nybo Anderson A, Wohlfahrt J, Christens P, Olsen J, and Malbye M (2000) Maternal age and fetal loss: Population based register linkage study. *British Medical Journal* 320: 1708, with permission from the BMJ Publishing Group.

Chromosomal Anomalies and Options for Prenatal Screening and Diagnosis

Advancing maternal age is associated with an increased risk of bearing a child with a major chromosomal abnormality. The population incidence of major chromosomal abnormalities is approximately 1 in every 140 live births or about 0.7%. The risk of having a child with a chromosomal abnormality increases with age from a low of 0.2% at age 20 years to 12.5% at age 49 years (see **Table 2**).

Individuals born with chromosomal abnormalities often have anatomic malformations, stunted growth, and mental retardation. The most common and widely appreciated chromosome abnormality is Down syndrome. Down syndrome has an overall incidence of one in 730 live births and is caused by the presence of an extra chromosome 21 (trisomy 21) in each cell of the affected child. The excess genetic information typically causes characteristic facial abnormalities and mental retardation. Serious structural heart defects and an increased risk for childhood leukemia are also associated with Down syndrome. As may be seen in **Table 2**, women in their 40s carry a risk of Down syndrome that increases from 1% to 9% over the decade.

The second most common chromosomal abnormalities involve the sex chromosomes, X and Y. Fertile individuals have two sex chromosomes: women are XX and men are XY. Sex chromosome abnormalities such as XO (Turner syndrome), XXY (Klinefelter syndrome), XYY, and XXX occur with a frequency of approximately one in 800–1000 male or female live births. Individuals with sex chromosome abnormalities are typically sterile and may have structural abnormalities as well. Interestingly, the risk for bearing a child with Turner syndrome (XO) does not increase with advancing maternal age. Instead, it is the only major chromosomal abnormality that is more prevalent among young women than older women.

In addition to Down syndrome, two other trisomies (one extra chromosome) are seen in live born infants: trisomy 13 and trisomy 18. The incidence of these

Table 1   Percent loss by maternal age at conception

Maternal age	Spontaneous abortions (%)	Ectopic pregnancies (%)	Stillbirths rate/1000
12–19	13.3	2.0	5.0
20–24	11.1	1.5	4.2
25–29	11.9	1.6	4.0
30–34	15.0	2.8	4.4
35–39	24.6	4.0	5.0
40–44	51.0	5.8	6.7
≥45	93.4	7.0	8.2

Adapted from Nybo Andersen A, Wohlfahrt J, Christens P, Olsen J, and Malbye M (2000) Maternal age and fetal loss: Population based register linkage study. *British Medical Journal* 320: 1708, figures 2, 4, and 5. This estimates the total spontaneous abortion rate under the assumption that only 80% of women with abortions in recognized pregnancies were hospitalized.

Table 2 Age-specific risk for major chromosomal abnormalities in live born infants

Maternal age at delivery	Risk of trisomy 21	Risk of any chromosomal abnormality
20	1/1667	1/526
22	1/1429	1/500
24	1/1250	1/476
26	1/1176	1/476
27	1/1111	1/455
28	1/1053	1/435
29	1/1000	1/417
30	1/952	1/385
31	1/909	1/385
32	1/769	1/322
33	1/602	1/286
34	1/485	1/238
35	1/378	1/192
36	1/289	1/156
37	1/224	1/127
38	1/173	1/102
39	1/136	1/83
40	1/106	1/66
41	1/82	1/53
42	1/63	1/42
43	1/49	1/33
44	1/38	1/36
45	1/30	1/21
46	1/23	1/16
47	1/18	1/13
48	1/14	1/10
49	1/11	1/8

Data modified from maternal age-specific rates by Hook EB (1981) Rates of chromosome abnormalities at different maternal ages. *Obstetrics Gynecology* 58: 282; and Hook EB, Cross PK, and Schreinemacher DM (1983) Chromosomal abnormality rates at amniocentesis and in live-born infants. *Journal of the American Medical Association* 249: 2034.

chromosomal abnormalities is much lower than either Down syndrome or the sex chromosome abnormalities. Both of these trisomies also increase with advancing maternal age. Trisomy 18 occurs in one in 5500 live births. Trisomy 13 occurs in one in 17 000. Children born with these genetic conditions usually do not survive, as they typically have lethal structural abnormalities of the heart and brain that result in death or devastating mental retardation.

The presence of a chromosomal abnormality or aneuploidy can be detected in an embryo or fetus before birth. The techniques by which this is done each involve removal of a small amount of placental tissue (chorionic villus sampling, CVS) or amniotic fluid (amniocentesis) followed by cell culture, staining, and counting of the chromosomes in a specified number of cells. Because of the risk of pregnancy loss from either technique, most clinicians feel that their use should be restricted to women whose risk of a chromosomal abnormality is at least as great as the risk of the procedure. Screening programs

for chromosomal abnormalities use a combination of ultrasound and maternal serum analytes in either the first or second trimester (9–11 weeks or 15 + weeks, respectively, since the last menstrual period). Women whose estimated risk is equal to or greater than one in 280 are offered a diagnostic test. The prevalence of chromosomal abnormalities detected by CVS or amniocentesis is higher than that seen among liveborn infants by about 30%. The reason for the difference is that chromosomally abnormal fetuses are at increased risk for intrauterine death. The syndrome with the highest risk of embryonic or fetal loss is Turner syndrome where the loss rate approaches 75%. Because of the unusual association of Turner syndrome and younger maternal age, prenatal diagnosis is based exclusively upon ultrasound findings of anomalies suggestive of the syndrome rather than testing schemes based upon advanced maternal age.

The impact of prenatal screening and diagnostic programs on pregnancy outcomes is complex. Universal screening will identify about 90% of fetuses with Down syndrome while subjecting 5% of women to an invasive procedure. Depending on the type and timing of the invasive procedure, the pregnancy loss rate is quoted from between 1/100 and 1/1000. How these risks are viewed by a given pregnant woman or couple is extremely complex. While socioeconomic status, educational level, and ethnicity influence the observed utilization of the programs, attitude surveys indicate the most important variables in determining whether a given woman undergoes screening or diagnosis are feelings about having a child with Down syndrome, moral beliefs, family and social influences, perceptions of one's own health, the difficulty of becoming pregnant, willingness to put the fetus at elevated miscarriage risk, trust in the medical system, and available resources. Whether women over the age of 35 years are offered invasive diagnostic testing by CVS or amniocentesis based only on their age related risk of aneuploidy without adjustment for the serum analytes varies from one healthcare system to another.

While cardiac malformations, clubfoot, and diaphragmatic hernia are relatively rare, they do appear to be more common in offspring of older women. As these abnormalities are structural and usually unrelated to aneuploidy, they are generally diagnosed in the second trimester by ultrasound. Indeed, the increased risk of congenital anomalies in offspring of older women has been demonstrated by several large series. Hollier and colleagues in one series that included over 100 000 abortions, stillbirths, and live births reported that cardiac defects were four times more common in infants of women 40 years of age and older compared to those 20–24 years of age. The FASTER trial, a trial of pregnancy outcomes which prospectively followed 30 000 singleton pregnancies, reported congenital anomaly rates for women under 35 years, 35–39 years, and 40 years of age of 1.7%, 2.8%, and 2.9%, respectively.

The presence of an increased risk of an abnormality is typically anxiety producing and, for some women, affects their attitude toward the pregnancy. The decision whether to undergo a diagnostic test and risk loss of the pregnancy or not often has to be made in a relatively short time interval. The wait for the results of the diagnostic test is stressful. Receipt of 'good news' does not totally alleviate anxiety for some. Although it has not been formally studied, it is very likely that these pregnancy experiences carry over into the postpartum period for some women. Given that postpartum depression and anxiety can interfere with the relationship between mother and infant and affect the child's emotional, behavioral, and cognitive development, psychologic trauma associated with prenatal testing and diagnosis may have long-term consequences.

The decision to terminate an otherwise wanted pregnancy because of fetal abnormalities is difficult for most parents. Termination rates are related to the type and severity of the abnormality with the highest rates ($\sim$90%) observed for trisomic fetuses and intermediate rates ($\sim$50%) for fetuses with sex chromosome abnormalities. Not unexpectedly, termination rates for structural malformations unassociated with chromosomal abnormalities appear related to the availability of postnatal therapy. Over 90% of parents will terminate a pregnancy complicated by a severe central nervous system malformation such as anencephaly (absence of the brain) or encephalocoele (brain tissue outside of the skull) for which there is no therapy. In contrast, 90% of women carry the pregnancy when diagnostic or therapeutic uncertainty exists and 'hope for the best'.

Late Pregnancy Issues

As women age they have a greater opportunity to acquire conditions that can influence their health and the health of the fetus. Typically women 35 years of age will have twice the risk of complications during pregnancy which can lead to twice the rates of antepartum hospitalization, induction, and Cesarean delivery than her younger counterparts (**Tables 3** and **4**). While it is perceived by many that older women having their first pregnancy are at a greater risk for complications, older women having the second or greater pregnancy have similar complications as women having their first baby. Women having their first birth later in life are more likely to report a higher rate of infertility, where as multiparous women have had a higher rate of having a miscarriage (**Tables 3** and **4**). Minority women who have accumulated medical conditions such as hypertension and diabetes fare somewhat worse than their white counterparts during pregnancy. While some of this may be related to access and quality of care, stress, and diet, biological factors may also play a role, so their pregnancies are at a higher risk for adverse outcomes.

Table 3 Demographic characteristics and medical history by parity and maternal age

	First birth (nulliparous)		Second or greater birth (multiparous)	
	20–29 years (%)	40+ years (%)	20–29 years (%)	40+ years (%)
History of infertility	3.6	20.3	1.3	6.8
History of IVF use	0.3	8.7	0.2	2.3
History of SAB*	11.8	34.4	19.5	41.1
Hypertension	0.5	0.9	0.6	2.1
Diabetes	0.3	0.5	0.5	0.8
Cardiac	2.2	3.9	1.9	4.1
Leimyomas	1.1	10.1	1.1	4.6

IVF, in vitro fertilization; SAB, spontaneous abortion.
Hypertension and diabetes as pre-existing conditions.
Adapted from Bianco A, Stone J, Lynch L, et al. (1996) Pregnancy outcome at age 40 and older. *Obstetrics and Gynecology* 87: 917–922.

Hypertension

High blood pressure (hypertension) is the most frequent medical problem encountered in pregnancy with older women. Their risk is doubled that of younger women. The incidence of preeclampsia in the general obstetric population is 3–4%. It increases to 5–10% in women over the age of 40 years and as high as 35% in women over the age of 50 years. With careful monitoring and appropriately timed intervention, maternal and fetal morbidity and mortality can be reduced, although even when contemporary practice guidelines are followed, hypertension remains associated with an increase in pre-term birth, small for gestational age infants, stillbirth and Cesarean delivery.

Diabetes Mellitus

The prevalence of diabetes increases with maternal age. The rates of both pre-existing diabetes mellitus and gestational diabetes increase three to six-fold in women 40 years of age or older compared to women aged 20–29 years. Pre-existing diabetes is associated with an increased risk of congenital anomalies, perinatal mortality, and perinatal morbidity, while the most common complication from gestational diabetes is macrosomia.

Obesity

Maternal obesity is a condition increasingly affecting women in developed nations. In 2004, more than 60% of women of childbearing age in the US were overweight or obese by the Center for Disease Control and Prevention's criteria for body mass index. As women age, they tend to gain weight and therefore more women of advanced maternal age are obese. Although obesity is also associated with a higher prevalence of underlying

Table 4 Antepartum complications by maternal age and parity

	Nulliparous			Multiparous		
	20–29 years (%)	40+ years (%)	P	20–29 years (%)	40+ years (%)	P
Gestational diabetes	1.7	7.0	<0.01	1.6	7.8	<0.01
Preeclampsia	3.4	5.4	<0.01	1.0	2.7	<0.01
Placenta previa	0.03	0.25	<0.01	0.13	0.05	<0.01
Prematurity	9.1	14.1	<0.01	10.3	13.7	<0.01

Adapted from Gilbert WM, Nsbitt TS, and Danielsen B (1999) Childbearing beyond 40: pregnancy outcome in 24,032 cases. *Obstetrics Gynecology* 93: 9–14.

medical conditions including hypertension and pregestational diabetes, it remains an independent risk factor for pregnancy complications. Obesity is associated with higher rates of infertility and miscarriage, hypertensive disorders of pregnancy, gestational diabetes, Cesarean delivery, macrosomia, and stillbirth.

Abnormal Placentation

Placental abnormalities include placenta abruption and placental previa. Placental abruption, in which the placenta separates from the wall of the uterus prematurely and both fetal and maternal hemorrhage can occur, is a serious complication of pregnancy and can lead to both fetal and maternal death. Placenta previa, or placenta covering the cervix, which predisposes to hemorrhage as cervical dilation occurs, also represents a serious concern. Both of these conditions do occur more commonly in older women, although a large portion of this additional risk is associated with increasing parity. Nonetheless, Gilbert *et al.* found a 10-fold increased risk of placenta previa in women 40 years of age having their first birth when compared to women ages 20–29 years, although the absolute risk of this was small (0.25% vs. 0.03%). The increased risk of abruption may be somewhat explained by the increased frequency of hypertensive disorders of pregnancy in older women.

Low Birthweight

The prevalence of low birthweight has increased 11% over the past 10 years, despite efforts to improve maternal nutrition and reduce the rates of pre-term delivery. Low birthweight is defined as weight less than 2500 g regardless of gestational age at delivery. According to the March of Dimes, in 2004 8.1% of infants were below this threshold. Advancing maternal age is strongly associated with low birthweight; among women over 40 years of age, 10.9% of infants weighed less than 2500 g. Very low birthweight infants, or those weighing less than 1500 g at delivery, are also substantially increased in older women, with a rate of 2.1% in women over 40 years of age. Pre-term delivery accounts for a substantial proportion of low and very low birth weight infants born in the US. In women of advanced maternal age, much of this risk is associated with the use of

assisted reproductive technology, which increases the rates of multiples (twins or more), for whom the rates of pre-term delivery were 61.4% in 2004. As already discussed, other risk factors for indicated pre-term delivery, including high blood pressure and abnormal placentation, are also increased in older women. The well-known adverse effects of smoking on pre-term birth and fetal growth are also seen disproportionately more often in women 35 years of age or older. Intrauterine growth restriction (weight less than tenth percentile for gestational age) is also somewhat increased in older women, likely due to the associated risk factors including acquired maternal conditions such as increased propensity to form blood clots and hypertension, use of assisted reproductive technology, and higher rates of fetal chromosomal anomalies.

Macrosomia

High birthweight, or macrosomia, is defined as a birthweight greater than 4000 g. Risk factors for macrosomia include diabetes (gestational or pre-existing) and maternal obesity, both of which are increased in women of advanced maternal age. Macrosomic infants face more complications during labor, delivery, and the period immediately following birth. During labor and delivery, macrosomia is a risk factor for prolonged labor, need for Cesarean delivery, and varying degrees of difficulty delivering the fetal shoulders after the head has appeared, which can lead to permanent nerve injuries in the neck and arm, central nervous system damage, or death. Macrosomic infants are also at risk for low blood sugar and have an associated higher risk of admission to the neonatal intensive care unit. There is some concern that macrosomic infants, like growth restricted infants, also have higher risks of long-term metabolic derangements including obesity, diabetes, and cardiovascular disease, although this relationship is not yet clearly defined.

Perinatal Mortality

Historically, the increased perinatal mortality seen in older women was distributed evenly among neonatal and fetal deaths, with the greater number of perinatal deaths related to lethal congenital and chromosomal anomalies. Since the initiation of routine prenatal screening of women 35 years of age or older and the availability of abortion, the number of perinatal deaths due to anomalies has decreased to the rate experienced by younger women. In singleton gestations, the increased perinatal mortality is largely during the fetal period, with a higher rate of otherwise unexplained stillbirths. These stillbirths occur more often in older women with the rate of stillbirth in those left undelivered rising significantly after 37 weeks of gestation, so that potentially these could be prevented with early delivery if there were reliable screening tools (**Figure 4**). To date there is no proven screening tool for appropriately grown fetuses. It is a relatively common practice to perform antepartum testing in women of advanced maternal age, (such as monitoring the fetal heart and evaluating the heart rate patterns, and by ultrasound). While this strategy might be helpful to determine the timing of delivery in patients who are deemed to be at increased risk of stillbirth, it also carries with it an increase in the induction and Cesarean section rate.

Multiple gestations, especially higher order multiples conceived spontaneously or with assisted reproduction, contribute significantly to perinatal morbidity and mortality losses in older women. Reducing the number of embryos transferred during IVF is one important strategy to reduce these losses.

Dysfunctional Labor and Cesarean Delivery

Women 35 years of age or older are more likely to be delivered by Cesarean section. The Cesarean delivery rate in the general obstetric population of the US is almost 30%, compared to almost 50% in women over age 40–45 years and almost 80% in women age 50–63 years. The reasons for this are multifactorial, and while there appears to be a linear relationship between dysfunctional labor and maternal age, other factors also come into play, such as the increased risk of medical complications, induction of labor, and malposition as often seen in older gravida. Physicians and patients alike probably have a lower threshold to perform a Cesarean delivery in older women because they have fewer reproductive opportunities, and thus there is a growing acceptance of primary elective Cesarean deliveries.

Maternal Mortality

In developing nations, where the maternal mortality rates are many fold higher than in developed nations (**Table 5**), the lack of adequate prenatal and perinatal care contributes substantially to these maternal losses, but nevertheless maternal characteristics such as increasing age and parity also remain significant contributors. In sub-Saharan Africa and in regions of South Central Asia, maternal death in childbirth is a real phenomenon, with a lifetime risk of dying estimated to be as high as one in 16. Within the US and in other developed countries, the leading cause of maternal mortality is trauma. Nonetheless, rates of death are higher in older women. The death rate for obstetric causes in the US from 1991 to 1997 for women ages 26–29 years, was 9/100 000 live births. The rate for women 35–39 years was 21/100 000 live births, and for women 40 years of age or older, the rate was 46/100 000. The most common causes of death were related to hypertension, hemorrhage, and thromboembolism.

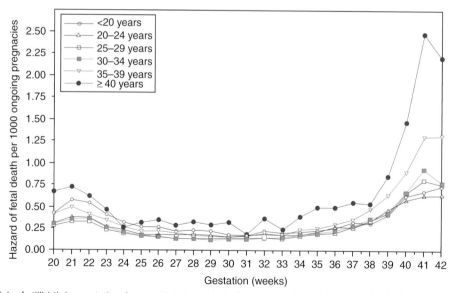

Figure 4 The risk of stillbirth by gestational age and maternal age. The risk for stillbirth for singleton births without congenital anomalies by gestational age, 2001–02. Reproduced from Reddy U, Ko C, and Willenger M (2006) Maternal age and the risk of stillbirth throughout pregnancy in the US. *American Journal of Obstetrics and Gynecology* 195: 764–770, with permission from Elsevier.

Table 5 Maternal mortality estimates by United Nations MDG Regions, 2000

Region	Maternal mortality ratio, maternal deaths per 100 000 live births	Number of maternal deaths	Lifetime risk of maternal death
World total	400	529 000	1:74
Developed regions	20	2 500	1:2800
Europe	24	1 700	1:2400
Developing regions	440	527 000	1:61
Africa	830	251 000	1:20
Northern	130	4 600	1:210
Sub-Sahara	920	247 000	1:16
Developing regions			
Asia	330	253 000	1:94
Eastern	55	11 000	1:840
South-central	520	207 000	1:46
South-eastern	210	25 000	1:140
Western	190	98 000	1:120
Latin America and the Caribbean	190	22 000	1:160
Oceania	240	530	1:83

Maternal Mortality 2000 Estimate Developed by WHO, UNICEF and UNFPA. http://www.who.int/reproductive-health/publications/maternal_mortality_2000/index.html.

Summary

In spite of the many advances of modern medicine, age still matters in obstetrics. While many women in the developing world have limited reproductive choices, in the US and some European countries, delayed childbearing has become a common phenomenon. Although late pregnancy may be a significant hazard for women, if recognized and appropriately managed, the dangers of childbearing can be minimized so that the outcomes are good. The greatest obstacle for women of advanced maternal age who are planning a family is infertility. Once pregnancy is achieved, obstetricians can help minimize the complications of maternal age including hypertension, diabetes, and pre-term delivery.

See also: Birth Complications and Outcomes; Birth Defects; Demographic Factors; Depression; Developmental Disabilities: Cognitive; Developmental Disabilities: Physical; Down Syndrome; Genetic Disorders: Sex Linked; Genetic Disorders: Single Gene; Intellectual Disabilities; Mortality, Infant; Nutrition and Diet; Obesity; Postpartum Depression, Effects on Infant; Screening, Newborn and Maternal Well-being; Screening, Prenatal.

Suggested Readings

Bianco A, Stone J, Lynch L, *et al.* (1996) Pregnancy outcome at age 40 and older. *Obstetrics Gynecology* 87: 917–922.

Centers for Disease Control and Prevention (2002) Assisted Reproductive Technology (ART) Report. http://www.cdc.gov/ART/ART02/download.htm (accessed on 16 July 2007).

Cleary-Goldman J, Malone FD, Vidaver J, *et al.* (2005) Impact of maternal age on obstetric outcome. *Obstetrics Gynecology* 105: 983–990.

Fretts RC, Elkin EB, Myers ER, and Heffner LJ (2004) Should older women have antepartum testing to prevent unexplained stillbirth? *Obstetrics Gynecology* 104: 56.

Gilbert WM, Nesbitt TS, and Danielsen B (1999) Childbearing beyond 40: Pregnancy outcome in 24,032 cases. *Obstetrics Gynecology* 93: 9–14.

Hollier LM, Leveno KJ, Kelly MA, MClntire DD, and Cunningham FG (2000) Maternal age and malformations in singleton births. *Obstetrics Gynecology* 96: 701–706.

Hook EB (1981) Rates of chromosome abnormalities at different maternal ages. *Obstetrics Gynecology* 58: 282.

Hook EB, Cross PK, and Schreinemachers DM (1983) Chromosomal abnormality rates at amniocentesis and in live-born infants. *Journal of the American Medical Association* 249: 2034.

Maternal Mortality (2000) Estimate Developed by WHO, UNICEF and UNFPA. http://www.who.int/reproductive-health/publications/maternal_mortality_2000/index.html (accessed on 16 July 2007).

Martin JA, Hamilton BE, Ventura SJ, *et al.* (2002) *National Vital Statistics Report, Vol. 51, No. 2: Births: Final Data for 2001.* Hyattsville, MD: National Center for Health Statistics.

Menken J, Trussell J, and Larsen U (1986) Age and infertility. *Science* 233: 1389.

Moyer A, Brown B, Gates E, Daniels M, Brown HD, and Kupperman M (1999) Decisions about prenatal testing for chromosomal disorders: Perceptions of a diverse group of women. *Journal of Women's Health and Gender-Based Medicine* 8: 521–531.

Nyobo AA, Wohlfahrt J, Christens P, Olsen J, and Malbye M (2000) Maternal age and fetal loss: Population based register linkage study. *British Medical Journal* 320: 1708.

Practice Committee of the American Society for Reproductive Medicine (2002) Aging and infertility in women: A committee opinion. *Fertility and Sterility* 78(1): 215–219.

Pryde PG, Druga A, Johnson MP, Isada NB, and Evans MI (1993) Prenatal diagnosis: Choices women make about pursuing testing and acting on abnormal results. *Clinical Obstetrics and Gynecology* 36: 496–509.

Reddy U, Ko C, and Willenger M (2006) Maternal age and the risk of stillbirth throughout pregnancy in the United States. *American Journal of Obstetrics and Gynecology* 195: 764–770.

Relevant Website

http://www.marchofdimes.com – March of Dimes Foundation.

Maternal and Paternal Employment, Effects of

W A Goldberg and R Lucas-Thompson, University of California, Irvine, Irvine, CA, USA

Glossary

Labor force – As used by the Bureau of the Census, the labor force includes people, who at the time of the Current Population Survey, were employed as civilians, unemployed, or in the Armed Forces. People who are neither employed nor seeking employment are not included in the labor force.
Maternal employment – Work performed for pay by mothers of minor children (under 18 years of age): includes full-time and part-time work.
Selection effects or selection bias – When random assignment to groups is not possible, this threat to validity is a concern. Includes concerns that treatment effects are confounded with pre-existing differences between groups and that outcomes differ due to prior differences between groups.

Introduction

One of the most dramatic social changes in the last half of the twentieth century was the marked increase in the number of women employed for pay outside the home or actively seeking employment. Indeed, some have dubbed this change 'a social revolution'. In 1950, about one in three women participated in the labor force. In 1975, almost half of women (47.4%) with minor children were in the labor force. By 2003, this figure had increased to 71.1% – an employment rate similar to that for women without children. Single mothers with minor children had an even slightly higher labor force participation rate: 78.1% in 2003. Today, maternal employment is normative in the US. Its impact on children is the focus of the current article.

Mothers in the US Labor Force

Often acknowledged to be the most remarkable aspect of the demographic changes in women's employment has been the rise in labor force participation by women with young children. In the mid-1970s, less than one-third of women with children under 6 years of age were working or seeking work; indeed, the Census Bureau only started recording labor force participation rates of mothers with infants in 1976. By the turn of the new millennium, a new profile emerged of the mothers of infants: the majority of women with young children were in the labor force. Interestingly, there is some indication that the labor force participation rate for mothers of infants may have already peaked: it reached a high of 58.7% in 1998, receded to 54.6% in 2002, and to 53.7% in 2003. The reasons for this plateau are not well understood, but may include a slowing economy and weaker demand for labor, increased costs of childcare, and a decision by some women to 'opt out' of the labor force given partner wages and work–family issues. Recent declines in labor force participation rates have been most striking for new mothers over 30 years of age who are Caucasian and who have at least one year of college. Adult mothers with infants are more likely than other women to work part-time, but as a whole, they still are twice as likely to work full-time as part-time. However, new mothers who have higher levels of education return to work sooner after birth and are more likely to return full-time. Overall, labor force participation rates for single mothers of infants have remained steady at 55% between 2000 and 2002, but variation in rates by race and level of education has been observed.

Why Parents Work?

As Scott Coltrane delineated when he wrote a book about men and the family, fathering is synonymous with first providing the necessary biological raw material for conception and then providing financial support for the family. Mothering, in contrast, connotes ongoing care and nurturing of children. For mothers, but not for fathers, the employment role is considered to be a discretionary role. Although for many mothers, paid employment is a financial necessity, the fact that not all mothers of young children work for pay suggests that there may be differences between those women who choose employment, to the extent that it is a choice, and those who do not.

Women in their 20s and 30s who are committed to a career have been characterized as seeing paid work as identity-affirming; they value advancement, income, and maintaining job skills; they gain pride and affirmation from employment, perceive negative consequences from a full-time homemaking role, and see maternal employment as providing more benefits than costs to children. Women who choose full-time homemaking hold certain convictions central to their identities: they believe no one can do childrearing as well as a mother; if married, they hold traditional gender role values; they believe that the homemaker role offers variety and accomplishment, and they believe that maternal employment conveys more costs than benefits for children.

In a study that compared employed mothers and homemakers, there were no differences on major mental health indicators (e.g., depression, anxiety, self-esteem) when the children were 1 year of age. Although employment status *per se* was not significant, further analyses revealed that the 'fit' between the beliefs/preferences of women and their actual work status was important for maternal distress. For example, anxiety and anger were greatest among women whose employment status did not match their preferences. These findings underscore the importance of considering individual differences among adults as they make decisions about work and family. Recognizing that children benefit most from having emotionally healthy parents who are able to identify their needs and actualize their ambitions, it is important to reiterate that the flexibility to align preferences and behaviors concerning work and family is not an option for many parents.

Although women constitute a substantial portion of the labor force in the US, the picture of employment does not look the same for women and men, even today. A considerable amount of the well-documented 'wage gap' between the sexes is due to occupational sex segregation and the concentration of women in lower-paying jobs. The gender gap in labor force participation is greatest among Hispanic adults (20–64 years of age), smaller for Asian and Caucasian adults, and smallest between African American adult men and women. Women are slightly less likely than men to have flexible schedules at work. Ironically, women without minor children are more likely to have flexible schedules than women with children under age 18 years, whereas the reverse trend holds for men. However, parents are more likely than nonparents to work from home at least once a week.

Effects of Maternal Employment

There are several pathways through which maternal employment is expected to affect children's development. At the most macro level, the 'economic pathway' suggests that the added income brought by maternal employment will augment the home environment and standard of living, thereby conferring benefits to children, especially those in socioeconomically disadvantaged circumstances. Drawing on the interplay between extrafamilial settings in which parents find themselves (e.g., the workplace) and the dynamics of family functioning, the 'parenting stress' pathway posits that job conditions (e.g., stability, schedules, hours, complexity, autonomy) on the one hand may induce personal stresses and strains that then compromise the quality of parenting and lead to adverse child outcomes. On the other hand, job characteristics that

enhance individual well-being (e.g., contact with people, opportunities for self-direction and control) may also boost the quality of parenting and be associated with positive child outcomes.

At the psychological level, within the family, the 'maternal deprivation' pathway conjectures that children's socioemotional and cognitive development will be adversely affected when they are separated from their mothers for lengthy periods of time. The security of attachment is seen as especially vulnerable when infants and toddlers experience regular, extended maternal absence. Lack of supervision brought about by maternal absence due to employment is seen as detrimental to the behavior and achievement of older children. As predicted by these pathways, both beneficial and adverse effects of maternal employment on children are expected. In most psychological research in the area, maternal employment is operationalized either categorically (employed vs. nonemployed or full-time/part-time/not employed) or continuously, in terms of weekly hours of employment.

The Child–Parent Attachment Relationship

Of particular concern to many researchers, practitioners, and parents is the possibility that the separation of mother and infant caused maternal employment is detrimental to the mother–infant relationship. A primary question has been whether maternal employment is associated with the child–parent attachment relationship, a dyadic connection between a child and a caregiver who provides safety and security, particularly in times of stress.

As the theoretical basis of a secure attachment relationship is sensitive and responsive parenting, researchers have questioned whether maternal employment affects these qualities of maternal behavior. Studies based on observations of mother–infant interactions suggest, however, that there are very few differences in the caregiving behaviors of employed and nonemployed mothers. In addition, one study found that, in a sample of Caucasian mothers and their toddlers, greater hours of work were actually associated with more responsive parenting as observed both in the home and the laboratory.

Although it does not appear that maternal employment renders mothers less sensitive or responsive to their infants, it is possible that maternal absence for several hours each day prevents infants from developing expectations that their mothers will respond quickly and sensitively in times of stress. Research examining whether maternal absence due to employment is in fact associated with increased attachment insecurity has typically relied on the Strange Situation, a laboratory task designed to activate the attachment behavioral system by exposing infants to events of increasing anxiety and distress. Few studies of maternal employment and attachment have used alternate methods, despite indications that the maternal separations and reunions during the Strange Situation may not be as stressful for children who have experienced nonmaternal care.

In general, research suggests a small effect of maternal employment on the security of the attachment relationship, such that mothers who work outside the home are more likely to have infants who are insecurely attached than mothers who are not employed. Studies that have failed to find such an association have often relied on smaller samples, which may lack the power to detect the small difference in attachment security based on employment status. More problematically, the use of small samples often requires that the subtypes of insecure attachments be combined to increase power; however, there are theoretical and empirical indications that maternal employment is differentially associated with the insecure subgroups.

However, research suggests that it is not necessarily employment *per se* that has a negative influence on the attachment relationship, but instead specific factors that characterize employment such as attitudes about work, the timing of a return to work, and the number of hours worked that impact attachment security. A particularly consistent finding has been the role of maternal attitudes: mothers who are less satisfied with their work roles or time spent outside of work, more concerned or anxious about separating from their infant to go to work, less committed to returning to work, and more anxious about utilizing childcare are all more likely to have infants with insecure attachments.

The timing of a mother's return to work also appears to be an important factor to consider. Researchers have expected that a later return to work (after infants have firmly established attachments) would be more likely to lead to insecurity than an earlier return. In particular, researchers theorize that an early return to work will influence the 'development' or emergence of a secure attachment, whereas a later return will influence the 'maintenance' of a secure attachment. Essentially, a later return to work can disrupt the existing attachment relationship – even a secure attachment between an infant and a sensitive, responsive caregiver. Indeed, in general, mothers who return to work during the second year of their child's life, as compared to mothers who return during their child's first year, are more likely to have insecurely attached infants. In addition, changes in work status later in infancy appear to be associated with changes in the attachment relationship.

An additional employment characteristic that has been associated with attachment security has been the extent of employment. When significant differences in attachment security based on employment status are found, it appears that greater hours of employment are associated with an increased likelihood of insecure infant–mother attachments. Specifically, infants whose mothers work full-time appear to be at the greatest risk for developing

insecure attachments, as compared to infants of mothers who do not work or who work part-time.

In the early days of research in this area, few studies distinguished between the effects of maternal employment and the effects of childcare. While admittedly these two constructs are difficult to disentangle as maternal employment necessitates nonmaternal care, research indicates that both the nature and quality of the childcare arrangement and maternal work influence the attachment relationship. In fact, these two elements appear to work together to make infants more or less vulnerable to an insecure attachment. Mothers who work longer hours and place their children in lower-quality childcare appear to expose their infants to the greatest risk for developing an insecure attachment.

Independence and Autonomy

A major developmental achievement during the early years of childhood is the emergence of independent and autonomous behavior. Children who are independent and autonomous feel a strong sense of efficacy and control and exhibit behaviors characterized by activity and initiative. Parents who support their young children's independence and autonomy encourage their children to be active participants in problem-solving and decision-making within the context of parental guidelines.

In studies of maternal employment and young children's independent and autonomous behaviors, researchers typically employ parent questionnaires (including Q-sorts) and naturalistic or laboratory-based observations, often videotaped, of the child and parent (usually the mother). Structured observations commonly feature the parent and young child engaged in play, teaching, or discipline situations. Teacher ratings of children's behavior sometimes supplement these measures. Small samples of majority Caucasian, middle-class families dominate the research in this area.

Although more studies in this domain have been conducted with older children, some interesting findings have emerged from research with toddlers and preschoolers. In some, but not all, studies with white, middle-class toddlers, more dependence on adults has been observed in families with nonemployed mothers; employed mothers are less likely to include dependency characteristics in their descriptions of their securely attached toddlers. More initiative-taking in talking to teachers has been evinced by girls in the nonemployed-mother samples but more initiative-taking with peers and greater self-sufficiency has been reported by teachers for toddler boys and girls with employed mothers.

These differences could reflect higher levels of maturity in the children of employed mothers or different values and family dynamics. Employed mothers may accentuate independence and autonomy in the rearing of their children; although this generalization is fairly robust, it belies the variability within and across studies. Illustrative in the extant research are findings of no difference between employed and nonemployed mothers of toddlers in attitudes related to independence training, findings of greater independence and flexibility ('ego resilience') among boys with employed mothers, and a finding of greater emphasis on independence for school-aged daughters of low-income single mothers.

When older children are the focus, the greater emphasis on independence and taking responsibility by employed mothers is sometimes understood as a practical response to time pressures and an attempt to enlist greater involvement from other family members. At other times, the fostering of independence and autonomy is a deliberate, essential component of the parents' socialization values. Mothers who work outside the home for pay tend to place a high value on self-reliance and autonomy and look to instill these values in their children.

Characteristics of mothers' work, such as the degree of autonomy on the job and the amount of job-related stress, also condition the association between maternal work and parenting attitudes and behavior. Moreover, family structure interacts with childrearing values; one study that compared mothers in two-parent and divorced families found a greater emphasis on independence in the divorced group than the intact group, but a greater sense of self-efficacy among children in two-parent families. The nontraditional gender role attitudes that are more common in families with employed mothers also may contribute to different childrearing values and patterns of behavior.

Yet another mechanism for the association between maternal employment and children's independence and autonomy draws on social learning theory. Employed mothers can serve as role models for their children, especially daughters, inspiring them by their example to be independent. Daughters of employed mothers do seem to incorporate independence as part of their self-concept.

Lastly, lessened maternal availability due to employment away from home can result in less supervision and monitoring of children, which *de facto* leads to greater independence. This mechanism has been called into play to explain the negative associations that are not infrequently found for boys' behavior and academic performance when mothers are employed. The reasoning is that boys, who, across the board, tend to be granted more independence than girls, and who have been found in some studies to receive less attention than girls in employed-mother families, may have too much freedom and too little supervision when mothers are employed outside the home. However, qualifications to this generalization may be in order; recent research indicates variation in maternal levels of supervision and monitoring depending on social class and child gender.

Physical Health

Studies of maternal employment in relation to children's physical health have been bidirectional. Research from the perspective of the effects of maternal employment on children has concentrated on children's feeding and dietary routines. These studies indicate both competitive and beneficial relations between mothers' paid employment and healthy feeding practices. Research from the reverse direction has focused on the impact of childhood disabilities on maternal participation in the labor force.

Breastfeeding is seen as optimal for infant health, growth, and development, and is recommended as the exclusive means of feeding infants through the first 6 months of life. However, rates of breastfeeding decline rapidly between 2 and 3 months after birth, a time when many previously employed mothers return to work. Maternal employment is usually portrayed as posing obstacles for breastfeeding, although actual research on the topic is limited. The research that does exist is noteworthy for its cross-cultural breadth. Surveys, interviews, and medical records are the usual measures in these studies.

The timing of return to work, and the availability and length of maternity leave exert an impact on the duration of breastfeeding. The number of hours that mothers work upon return figures into the duration of breastfeeding, with 'low' part-time employed mothers breastfeeding longer than those employed full-time at 35 h per week or more. The intensity of work appears to constrain the intensity of breastfeeding rather than vice versa. The initiation and duration of breastfeeding also are affected by factors other than maternal work, such as maternal age, education, geographic location, and social support. As well, the introduction of solid foods or formula bears on the early cessation of breastfeeding.

In 1997, the American Academy of Pediatrics released a policy statement strongly supporting breastfeeding for the first 6 months of life, although that recommendation can be difficult for working mothers to follow. In the late 1990s, there was growing evidence that workplace environments that support and facilitate breastfeeding have lower rates of healthcare costs and employee absenteeism, as well as higher productivity, company loyalty, and morale. In response to this increasing recognition of the benefits of breastfeeding and family friendly policies supporting it, the *New Mothers' Breastfeeding and Promotion and Protection Bill* was introduced to the US House of Representatives in 1998. Research indicates that both personal attitudes toward breastfeeding as well as structural characteristics of the workplace such as flexibility influence how long new mothers continue to breastfeed. Therefore, increasing recognition by policy-makers and employers about the importance of workplace environments that support breastfeeding should encourage and make it easier for new mothers to both return to work and breastfeed their infants.

Maternal employment has even been discussed in relation to the current 'obesity epidemic'. Work schedules that require that parents be away from home at mealtimes can affect the type of food that is prepared and consumed and contribute to the number of meals eaten outside the home. The few studies on the association between maternal employment, the frequency of family meals, and the nutritional value of consumed food have produced inconsistent results and usually conclude that the child's age and other facets of family life must be considered because maternal employment only explains a small amount of the variance.

Maternal employment appears to interact with social class in terms of its benefits and risks for children's weight. The added income that maternal employment provides can benefit children's nutrition by providing the means to purchase fresh, healthy food.

The negative effect between the intensity of maternal work (work hours) and obesity is greater for children from high socioeconomic status (SES) backgrounds compared to those from lower SES environments. In a recent analysis by economist Ruhm, the risks of being overweight or obese are rather low for advantaged 10- and 11-year-olds, except when mothers are employed full time.

Characteristics of the child can influence maternal work activities. A nontrivial percentage of young children suffer from physical or mental conditions that limit their ability to learn, ambulate, and/or participate in usual childhood activities. Low-income families are more likely than other families to have a child with a serious health problem.

Studies of maternal employment and child health problems utilize a wide variety of definitions of childhood disability, which contributes to a mixed set of findings. Small sample studies tend to find that having a child with major physical or developmental disabilities impedes mothers' full participation in the labor market. Not only are small sample studies hampered by the relatively low incidence rate for childhood disabilities, most of these studies fail to examine the impact of factors such as family structure and maternal health. More recent studies, such as those by economist Powers, indicate that simple estimates overstate the negative impact of children's disabling conditions on mothers' employment. Mothers with young children with major activity limitations lag behind their counterparts in increasing their work hours but this effect is more pronounced for mothers who are head of households than for married mothers.

Providing care for a child with a chronic disabling condition is difficult under the best of circumstances. Children with disabilities often require additional parental time and suitable alternate care may not be available or affordable. It is particularly stressful for single mothers who are the primary economic providers and who lack other avenues of income and support. According to some research, among married women, having a child with a disability affects the decision to be employed or not (i.e., work status) more than it impacts work hours. Longitudinal studies on the associations between maternal labor activity and children's health would be valuable as children's conditions can change over time as can mothers' means of adapting to these altered conditions.

Social Competence and Peer Relations

If the skills necessary for competent peer interactions are first observed and learned during parent–child interaction, and maternal employment decreases the amount of time infants spend with their mothers, it is possible that there may be differences in social competence based on maternal work status. Children of employed mothers may spend more time with their peers than the children of mothers who do not work outside the home. On the one hand, this increased time with peers could facilitate children's autonomy and social competence; on the other hand, it could lead to more aggressive behavior. However, children of employed mothers may also need to do more work around the home, which may decrease the time they have available for interacting with peers and participating in group activities.

The above are all theoretical questions posed by those studying maternal employment. To investigate these associations, researchers have typically utilized questionnaires, and the judges of social competence have included mothers, teachers, peers, and the children themselves. Mothers and teachers rate aspects of social competence such as prosocial behavior, aggression, and social withdrawal, whereas peers rate how much they like the target child or how often he/she does things like act shy, be mean, or hit others. Studies of older children and adolescents have made use of self-reports of time spent in various activities and with whom time is spent, in addition to questionnaire-based measures of perceived social competence.

These studies suggest a weak, somewhat inconsistent association between social competence and maternal employment. Boys of mothers who are married and employed part-time are better liked by their peers than other boys; there are no such differences based on employment, however, for girls or for children of single mothers. Children of mothers who returned to work in the first year after birth are more likely to be rated by teachers as acting out more and, for boys in particular, by peers as one who hits and is mean. However, this last association disappears when the number of childcare arrangements is taken into account. Other studies suggest no association between maternal employment and social adjustment, empathy, sociability, or cooperation. The results are similarly mixed when older children and adolescents constitute the target population. Children of employed mothers spend more time with peers than do children of nonemployed mothers, but no differences are found in social competence or social interaction based on maternal employment.

What about the effects of maternal employment on the development of positive child behaviors such as prosocial behaviors that are intended to help others? Strong, positive mother–child relationships affect moral behavior by setting the stage for the child's internalization of maternal values and expectations. In turn, moral internalization promotes the manifestation of prosocial behavior. Do employed mothers have adequate contact with and 'quality' time with their children to promote the development of prosocial behaviors and inhibit the development of problem behaviors? Evidence from several small studies indicates that employed women engage in more direct interactions with their children during their childcare time than do full-time homemakers. Other studies have confirmed that maternal employment is not associated with teacher ratings of prosocial behavior.

Although employment status is not associated with social competence, characteristics of the employment appear more consequential. Of particular importance appears to be maternal attitudes about employment. Those women who are 'unemployed' but feel that they should be working have children who are rated by their teachers as lower in their consideration for others. Early research by Lois Hoffman suggested that mothers who enjoyed working had children who were less assertive and effective in their interaction with peers, and mothers who did not enjoy working had children who were more assertive and hostile in their peer interactions. However, these findings were based on data collected when maternal employment was not normative and have not since been replicated. In addition, the anxiety that mothers report about being separated from their child and having others care for their child is not associated with children's social competence.

Behavior Problems

Substantial proportions of the American public persist in their belief that children whose mothers are employed exhibit more negative and undesirable behaviors than children of full-time homemakers. They believe that teenagers whose mothers work outside the home are more vulnerable to experimentation with drugs, alcohol, and sex, and conversely, that teenagers get into less trouble with the law when their mothers do not work full-time outside the home. Underlying these beliefs are assumptions that maternal employment compromises parenting by reducing the amount and quality of contact and interaction between mothers and their children and leaves children vulnerable to problem behaviors.

Problem behaviors include both internalizing (e.g., 'troubled' behaviors such as anxiety, withdrawal) and externalizing behaviors (e.g., 'troublesome' behaviors such as acting out, conduct disorders), and issues of both overcontrol (inhibited, dependent behaviors) and undercontrol (impulsive, attention problems, aggressive behaviors). As constructs, there is overlap between indices of internalizing behaviors and measures of children's emotional and psychological well-being. Externalizing problem behaviors that have been studied vary in severity, from minor disruptive or noncompliant behaviors to major acts of deviance and truancy.

Examination of the links between maternal employment and children's behavior sometimes relies exclusively on maternal reports but more frequently, the studies have been multimethod, incorporating two or more of the following: maternal interviews, parent questionnaires, standardized child behavior checklists, and videotaped structured and unstructured observations in the home and/or lab. Parents, teachers, and observers are typical informants; in older samples, children also provide self-report data. Although there is general consensus about what constitutes a problem behavior, sometimes there are disagreements about terminology in the interpretation of findings. Is noncompliance to adult directives an act of disobedience or is it assertiveness, greater social maturity, or precocious independence? The answer to this question remains unresolved.

Some studies report results that corroborate the public's concerns about maternal employment and indicate, for example, higher noncompliance by children whose mothers were employed full-time, starting in the child's first or second year of life. However, direct, significant associations between maternal employment and young children's problem behaviors are not commonly found. Moreover, when direct associations emerge, they do not explain much variance and often disappear when control variables are added. Some effects are larger for older children from advantaged compared to disadvantaged backgrounds.

Positive, direct associations between maternal employment and children's behavior also have been found. In one study, less maternal negative control and more child compliance were exhibited by full-time employed mothers and their toddlers when compared to full-time homemaker–toddler dyads. Toddlers of full-time employed mothers also were more compliant during dinnertime, maybe reflecting the mutual pleasure of being reunited at the end of the day. Employed mothers appear to have adequate contact and 'quality' time with their children to prevent or inhibit the development of problem behaviors.

More common than direct effects are indirect associations between maternal employment and children's problem behaviors. Personal strain and parenting behaviors act as mediators between work experiences and child behavior. They operate by affecting maternal mood and attention/arousal levels and the quality of parenting, which in turn, affects children's behavior. For example, single mothers perceive more problem behaviors in their children when divorce was recent, when they believed that maternal employment had greater costs for children, and when they were concerned about the quality of their children's alternate care.

Work conditions and mothers' experience of work and family roles also are related to problem behaviors. Complex occupations that provide opportunities for self-direction – jobs that involve people more than things, have opportunities for mastery, and include high physical activity – are associated with fewer child behavior problems. Job satisfaction also matters: when mothers are satisfied with their jobs, their young daughters are reported to have fewer problems with self-control and conduct. Instability of employment and the experience of interrole conflict contribute to increased levels of childhood behavior problems. The extent of maternal satisfaction with family and work roles, and the amount of strain experienced due to work experiences, insufficient social support, and financial difficulties affect mothers' use of power-assertive strategies.

Characteristics of the child also figure into the equation. When gender differences were found in the Hoffman and Youngblade study of several hundred third graders, for example, boys with employed mothers were more likely to engage in defiant behaviors than were boys with nonemployed mothers or girls in both employment conditions. These gender differences are typical of those noted in other studies, with boys showing more externalizing, problem behaviors than girls. These child gender effects are sometimes moderated by socioeconomic class and ethnicity: middle-class boys with full-time employed mothers have been found to act out more than other boys; maternal employment has been associated with teacher ratings of frustration tolerance for Caucasian but not for African American children. Gender-of-child differences may reflect differential socialization of boys and girls by mothers who are employed and not employed as well as different reactions from boys and girls to the same parental treatment.

With older samples of children, research has examined associations between maternal employment and juvenile delinquency. The presumptive pathway is that employed mothers, by virtue of their absence from the home after school, are less able to supervise, discipline, and nurture their adolescent children, who therefore are more likely to engage in deviant, truant, substance-abusing behaviors. Recent analyses of the National Longitudinal Survey of Youth (NLSY) sample with young adolescents, many of whom had young mothers, failed to support a direct connection between early employment and youth delinquency or engagement in risky behaviors. One study detected a small (in magnitude) indirect path through

the influence of work conditions on maternal supervision. Based on the meager support of a connection between maternal employment and delinquency coupled with nonsignificant findings from other studies, these researchers concluded that the connection between maternal employment and delinquency is a socially constructed problem.

Gender-Related Behaviors and Ideas

An empirical question often posed by researchers interested in the sequelae of maternal employment is whether maternal work outside the home influences the development of children's gender-typed behavior or gender ideology. Mothers who work outside the home model less traditional behavior and more egalitarian attitudes than mothers who do not work; each type of mother presumably provides a role model for her children about acceptable gendered behavior. Employed mothers also may socialize their children differently than nonemployed mothers. A survey of public opinion about the consequences of employment for children indicates that a sizable majority of college students and adults believe that 'benefits' of having a working mother for both sons and daughters include being a good role model for leading a busy and productive life, and for daughters in particular, preparing them how to combine work and motherhood.

Researchers investigating the association between maternal employment and children's gendered behavior and ideas vary their methods depending on the age of children being studied. Older children and adolescents provide information about their beliefs about gender and maternal employment via questionnaires; often younger children are observed or interviewed using picture cards about their beliefs about what is acceptable for men and women or their own vocational aspirations.

Work in this area has been relatively free of the inconsistencies prevalent in other areas of the maternal employment literature. One of the most consistent findings is that children of employed mothers have more egalitarian ideas about gender, are less likely to endorse sexual stereotypes, and are less likely to respond in stereotyped ways in interviews than the children of nonemployed mothers. These associations are particularly consistent for the daughters of employed mothers, plausibly because children are more likely to be influenced by their same-sex role model. Although it is not always evident that the gendered behavior and ideas of the sons of employed mothers are affected in the same way as the daughters of employed mothers, there is evidence that boys behave in less sex-typed ways and have more flexible sex-role concepts when their mothers are employed.

The association of a more flexible, egalitarian gender ideology with maternal employment extends well into adulthood; again, this finding is particularly strong for females as compared to males. As older adolescents, both genders appear to have slightly more conservative opinions about women's work outside the home when their mothers are not employed. Across the lifespan, females whose mothers were or are employed tend to have more egalitarian ideas about gender, including endorsing increased political freedom for women and de-emphasizing the importance of traditional gender roles. In older childhood, girls of employed mothers are more likely to report aspirations to work in a field traditionally dominated by men. Furthermore, women whose mothers were employed are more likely to work outside the home themselves.

Research also suggests that decreases in traditional ideas about gender are most likely when mothers re-enter the workforce early in their children's lives. The younger children are when their mother returns to work, the more likely they are to endorse maternal employment; this association remains after various demographic controls. Other characteristics of a mother's employment are also significant for her child's career aspirations. Mothers who are employed in jobs that are traditionally dominated by men have children who are less likely to show gender-typed vocational aspirations and daughters who endorse less feminine careers. In addition, mothers who are satisfied with working outside the home are more likely than dissatisfied mothers to have daughters who emulate them in terms of employment outside the home and ideas about gendered behavior.

Welfare-to-Work

Prior research that has found either beneficial or neutral effects of maternal employment on children in low-income families has focused on women who were employed voluntarily. Women may have been un- or underemployed involuntarily, but the decision to be employed was personal and not legislated. Maternal employment that is voluntary, even if financially necessary to make ends meet, is qualitatively different than employment that is mandated by the government. The Family Support Act of 1988 and the enactment of the Personal Responsibility and Work Opportunity Act (PRWORA) in 1996 were intended to reform welfare by moving welfare-dependent mothers into the paid labor force. These acts initiated the phenomenon of mandatory employment.

Welfare-to-work programs target poor mothers with young children, and success is measured by the cessation of dependence on public assistance and by the number of hours of paid employment. States can set the length of time that families can receive welfare benefits and require women to participate in education, training, job searches, or employment activities. With the new laws, women with young children have fewer options than before to combine work and public assistance, and are limited in how long they can rely on welfare alone.

Assumed, but not often tested in research on the effectiveness of welfare-to-work programs, is the impact of these shifts on the women themselves and on their children. Not only does the issue of mandatory vs. voluntary employment arise, but the required work may differ in important ways (hours, wages, stability, complexity) from jobs that are sought voluntarily. Initial assumptions were that the increased income and opportunity for mothers to serve as role models would bring benefits of maternal work into children's lives. In other words, both an economic pathway and a family-level pathway were expected to operate to benefit children. From other quarters, worries arose that mandated maternal employment would increase parental stress, impair parenting abilities, and leave children vulnerable to being unsupervised or placed in low-quality or unsafe care arrangements.

In an analysis of a large, national data set of very low-income families conducted before mandatory work requirements went into effect, maternal employment during the child's first three years of life, controlling for family income, did not yield negative effects on children's cognitive performance or behavior problems at age 5–6 years. However, controlling for income, children of mothers who were solely dependent on welfare (no paid income) had lower cognitive test scores and less-stimulating home-learning environments. Highest behavior problems were found for children of mothers who had neither employment nor welfare.

Before PRWORA went into effect, several states were granted federal waivers to test innovative welfare reform programs. One such experimental welfare program was conducted in Minnesota and its impact on children was evaluated by Gennetian and Miller. Single mothers of children aged 2–9 years were randomly assigned to three different research conditions to allow separate tests of various components of the programs. A distinguishing feature of this program was a financial incentive that made work for pay better than welfare and gave the women more choices as they sought to incorporate paid work into their lives. Children whose mothers were in the experimental program exhibited fewer behavior problems, performed better and were more engaged in school, were more likely to have continuous healthcare coverage and more stable childcare than children whose families received welfare only. Although both economic and family socialization pathways may have been operative, the researchers believed that increased economic resources contributed most to the positive child outcomes.

Results from a very large, longitudinal study of low-income families suggest that mothers' transitions from welfare to work are not associated with negative outcomes for preschoolers or young adolescents. However, according to a recent study by the Children's Defense Fund

(CDF), when welfare-to-work programs result in reduced family income, children are more likely to suffer adverse effects such as poor mental and physical health, school problems, behavior problems, and a greater likelihood of being removed from their mothers' care. Programs that are most helpful to children are those that raise family income and economic security in addition to boosting maternal employment. The CDF cautions that welfare-to-work programs must be developed thoughtfully to help families avoid poverty as they move toward economic self-sufficiency. Recommendations include putting in place supports such as childcare, after-school activities, and income support to make the transition from welfare to work an effective one.

Time Spent with Children

Most of the concerns about the negative influences of maternal employment on infant and child development are rooted in the absence of mothers due to work outside the home. An empirical question is whether employed mothers do in fact spend less time with their infants than nonemployed mothers. Results from a large national study show that despite being away from their children on the average of 500 min (8 h) a day, full-time employed mothers spend only about 100 min less a day with their children than do full-time homemakers. According to time-use studies, employed mothers compensate for their time away by reducing time in housework, leisure, organizational, and social activities and thereby protect the time with their young child. In fact, employed mothers spend a greater proportion of their 'free' time (time not at work) with their children than do nonemployed mothers. Although employed mothers spend less time with their infants during the week, they spend significantly more time with their young children on the weekends. Employed- and nonemployed-mother families do not differ in the time spent as a family, that is, time with mother, father, and children together.

Employed mothers use their time with their child somewhat differently, engaging in more mother–child social interaction than do nonemployed mothers. Employed mothers are also more interactive with their infants than nonemployed mothers. To the extent that maternal time with the child is related to negative outcomes for children – and many studies do not support this link, as seen in the preceding sections – employed mothers do not appear to be disadvantaged in terms of direct time engaged with the child, nor do they appear to be compromised when the content and quality of that time are the focus.

With increasing technological developments that allow 'telecommuting' or 'telework', parents with children may increasingly work from home. Currently, about 15% of men and women work at home at least once per week as part of their main job; this arrangement is more common for parents than nonparents. Although there is little research to date on how these more flexible employment options influence families and children, one can speculate that it may have both negative and positive repercussions. On the one hand, flexible employment options may allow working parents to spend more time at home with their children. On the other hand, there are concerns that mothers who work at home may experience increased role strain due to the unclear boundaries between family and work life. Relatedly, working from home may decrease the quality of time parents and children spend together; for instance, parents who work from home may have more difficulty 'protecting' the time they spend with their child. Available empirical data from recent studies conducted in the US and Western Europe indicate that working from home seems to lessen work–family role conflict for women and enables men to participate more fully in childcare activities. Some of these studies report that other factors are important to consider, such as the nature of the job held by the teleworker, the employee's health, and number of children.

Paternal Employment

Unlike mothers, whose employment is the source of public and research concern, when fathers' work is the focus, concern centers on the impact of their unemployment on children. Glen Elder's classic 1974 book on the children of the Great Depression brought the problem of unemployment and financial loss into the limelight. Prolonged paternal unemployment was associated with lower educational attainment and less occupational mobility for the children. In addition to financial hardship for the family, unemployment also has been associated with a greater incidence of infant health problems, behavioral and emotional problems in children and adolescents, lower self-esteem among adolescents, and a greater risk of depression and drinking among adolescents.

When mothers are not in the labor force, the common reason is to care for home and family. For the 1 million married fathers with minor children who were out of the labor force in 2003, their unemployment was more often due to illness or disability rather than care for home and family. When men take off time around the birth of a new baby, they usually use vacation or sick days, although more large corporations have begun providing fathers with paid parental leave.

Most married and single fathers of minor children are employed, as paid work is heavily socialized for males in our culture and work is central to men's identity and family roles. The high percentage of paternal employment has inspired researchers to look beyond employment status to examine characteristics and conditions of fathers' work in relation to parenting, and to a lesser extent, to children's well-being and development.

Complex jobs that entail opportunities for self-direction and autonomy, that involve people more than things, and that are not highly routinized enhance the functioning of the employee both at work and at home. Working-class fathers of school-aged children who had positive job experiences (e.g., more autonomy, clarity, innovation, support) were more likely to have enhanced self-esteem, which was the path through which they held more accepting parenting styles and used less psychological control. In previous sections, we saw that mothers' occupational complexity was associated with more favorable parenting values and behaviors and child outcomes. In one study of about 50 families, middle-class fathers who worked at more complex jobs valued self-direction over conformity for themselves. Job complexity was related to the extent of their nurturing parenting of preschool-aged children, but job complexity was not significantly predictive of the child's depression and aggression scores as reported by mothers on a child behavior checklist. Other research indicates that characteristics of fathers' jobs influence their childrearing values, parental expectations for children's behavior, and children's cognitive performance.

In a model analogous to the one reported for mothers, Barling and colleagues suggested that fathers' work-related experiences (decision-making autonomy and initiative, competing job demands, job insecurity, work–family interrole conflict) influence children's behaviors indirectly, through their impact on men's moods and parenting behaviors. Empirical evidence with elementary-school-aged children and adolescents supports this indirect process model and confirms the importance of examining men's work–family role conflict and role overload, topics too often neglected in the study of fathers. A national survey study conducted in the Netherlands points to the salience of men's job stress and job satisfaction for fathers' level of strain and their sense of parenting as a burden. Time pressures are especially exaggerated for men whose jobs involve extended absences from home (e.g., trucking, commercial fishing). Indirect effects extend to mothers in these situations: the more hours that fathers put in at work, the more the childcare burden falls on mothers, a problem exaggerated when the child has special needs.

Married fathers are differentially involved with their preschool and school-aged children depending on whether their wives also work outside the home and depending on fluctuations in the economy (e.g., recession or nonrecession years). Analysis of the NLSY data set by Parcel and Menaghan points to the importance of considering fathers' work schedules when examining the effects of paternal work conditions on children. Young children displayed more behavior problems when their fathers worked less than full-time during their early years; however, overtime work hours (>40 h per week) conferred

negative associations with children's performance on a verbal test. Other research indicates that it is the time of day and days of the week in which fathers work that contribute most to their involvement in the care of children. The shift in the economy to more service-based jobs has meant more nonstandard work schedules. When fathers work evenings or weekends, they are more involved in the care of their preschoolers. Wives' schedules, too, have an impact on father involvement. When men work different hours than their wives, they are most likely to take care of the youngest child (child under 5). Fathers also are more involved in care of their preschool children when their wives work on the weekends or nights.

Work appears to 'spillover' to men's family life – their parenting, their relations with their children – in both positive and negative directions. Jobs with more desirable conditions, such as higher autonomy, initiative, and support, are associated with positive parenting. Jobs that bring more strain and less satisfaction seem to compromise the quality of parenting. Economic conditions affect employment status, the availability of full-time work, work schedules, and the affordability of nonparental care, which in turn affect how families organize the care of their children. Although characteristics of fathers' employment are receiving more attention in recent years, and the study of the work–family relations is no longer just about mothers, we still know far more about fathers' jobs in relation to parenting than we do about the direct and mediated impact on children's development in a variety of domains.

Moderators

As can be seen from the preceding review, in general, there are few 'direct' associations between maternal employment and child outcomes. Instead, there are a variety of factors that moderate these relations; in other words, maternal employment is associated with infant and child outcomes only under certain conditions. Therefore, in order to understand the implications of maternal employment for child development, one needs to take into account a host of other factors.

Child Gender and Socioeconomic Status

As mentioned previously, a particularly important moderator appears to be child gender. One of the most consistent findings in the maternal employment literature is that of more positive consequences for girls and more negative consequences for boys. However, even this relatively well-established relation appears to be moderated by variables such as race and socioeconomic status. In terms of social competence, for instance, daughters (but not sons) of employed mothers are rated as better liked by their peers than are daughters of nonemployed mothers, but this association holds only for Caucasian girls. In addition, children from working-class families with mothers who return to work in the first year of their child's life are significantly more likely to be nominated by peers for being mean and hitting than are children from working-class families with nonemployed mothers or children from middle-class families.

Another oft-cited example of the interaction between child gender and socioeconomic status is in the field of achievement: maternal employment in the middle- and upper-socioeconomic classes appears to be detrimental to the achievement of sons, but not to the achievement of their working-class counterparts or to daughters in either class. Interactions between employment, parenting behaviors, and class are also evident. In general, employed mothers appear to use parenting and discipline styles that are associated with greater competence and adjustment in their children; however, this relation is particularly evident in the working as compared to the middle-class families, regardless of family structure. The economic pathway is believed to explain these findings: maternal employment in working-class families generates invaluable financial resources and benefits that outweigh the loss of time and supervision due to the mother's employment outside the home. In contrast, maternal employment in middle- and upper-classes is not always a financial necessity; therefore, the 'maternal deprivation' pathway may be operative as these children potentially suffer from decreased maternal attention, supervision, and availability, especially if the alternate-care setting is less enriched than the home environment.

Quality of Alternate Care

Another essential factor that influences the associations between maternal employment and child outcomes that is being increasingly recognized by researchers is the quality of alternate-care arrangements. As discussed previously, the negative consequences of employment for children, in particular their security of attachment to mother, are more pronounced when they are placed in lower-quality childcare. Conversely, it also appears that the positive consequences of maternal employment for children are enhanced when children are in high-quality childcare. In addition, quality and number of alternate-care arrangements can interact with other factors, such as child gender, to influence outcomes for children.

Selection Factors

In addition to considering how various factors produce conditions that facilitate or buffer the influence of maternal employment on child outcomes, it is essential to recognize that better outcomes for children of employed mothers may reflect pre-existing differences between employed and nonemployed mothers. Employed and nonemployed women often differ on a variety of measured and unmeasured characteristics – socioeconomic, demographic, and psychological – that may contribute to what are called 'selection effects' or selection bias. Socio-economic and family-level factors can shape who is employed and who is not and contribute to selection effects. In addition, these differences themselves may render children more or less vulnerable to the outcomes discussed throughout this article. Mothers who are employed typically have higher levels of education, are part of families with greater income, and have fewer children than nonemployed mothers. In addition, maternal attitudes about work and mothering are different between the two groups of women in ways that likely influence parenting styles and practices and thereby child development.

Unless these factors are controlled, differences in children's development attributed to maternal employment might instead reflect selection processes that are related to mothers' labor force participation and children's development. A number of studies have found that when they control for a host of potentially confounding variables, the first-order significant findings are diminished. The difficulty in controlling for all likely confounding sources of influence should remind us to exercise caution before concluding that there is a cause and effect relation between maternal employment and children's development.

Summary

Despite the normative status of maternal employment in Western societies, it remains an area replete with controversy and mixed findings. Although the bulk of public opinion focuses on negative consequences of maternal employment for children, research points to both positive and negative associations and the need for more complex, ecologically sensitive models. The emphasis in this article has been on maternal employment and child development, but we also have seen that conditions of fathers' employment are consequential for their parenting and for the development of their children.

Research indicates that maternal employment may render infants slightly more vulnerable to developing insecure attachments to their mother, but that maternal attitudes about work, the timing of work in the infant's life, and the hours a mother worked outside the home play a more important role in terms of the mother–infant attachment relationship. Often cited as a benefit of maternal employment, particularly for girls, is the association between greater independence among children with employed mothers. Gender-of-child differences may reflect not only differential treatment of boys and girls by employed and nonemployed parents, but differences between boys and girls in how they react to the same treatment and in terms of what treatment they elicit from their parents.

In terms of young children's physical health, the timing of return to work and the hours of work can impede the breastfeeding process. Maternal employment status alone explains little variance in childhood obesity. The added income supplied by working mothers can benefit childhood nutrition, but extensive work hours that interfere with family mealtimes may contribute to poor eating behavior particularly in economically advantaged families. Having a child with a physical disability does have a negative impact on mothers' labor force activity, and the effect is stronger for families with a female head of household.

There is only weak, inconsistent evidence for an association between maternal employment and social competence with peers, although maternal attitudes about work may predict positive child behaviors with peers. Some research suggests that boys of employed mothers are better liked by their peers, but that children of employed mothers are also more likely to be rated by the teachers as acting out. There is little evidence for links between maternal employment and prosocial or cooperative behaviors. Despite public beliefs that maternal employment will lead to greater behavior problems in children, there is inconsistent evidence about work outside the home and measures of compliance and non-compliance. Personal strain and parenting behaviors mediate most of these associations. Girls and boys seem to respond differently to maternal behaviors that are consequential for children's display of uncooperative or defiant behaviors.

A consistent finding in the maternal employment literature is that children of employed mothers have fewer stereotypes and more egalitarian ideas about gender. It appears that females are especially likely to be influenced by maternal work outside the home, perhaps because of the potency of a same-sex model of egalitarian behavior.

The impact of fathers' employment on children has received less attention than has investigation of the consequences of paternal unemployment. When fathers are unemployed, negative effects accrue for the families' economic health as well as for children's physical health, behavior, and psychological development. Characteristics of the jobs held by employed fathers, such as autonomy and complexity, are related both to their parenting and to their children's cognitive performance. There also is evidence that fathers' work influences children indirectly, operating through paternal well-being and parenting values as well as through its effects on mothers.

The body of research suggests that work conditions are more relevant for children's behavior than parental work status *per se*, which explains little variance. There is considerable variability across and within studies, often explained by moderators such as child gender, SES, family structure, and quality of alternate care. Particularly important mechanisms to explain associations between mothers' and fathers' work and children's behavior are personal strain and parenting behaviors. Ecological variables, such as income, family structure (i.e., single parent, two-parent families), and work conditions affect the employment–child associations.

Improvements over time have been apparent in the way that researchers approach the study of parental employment. Increasingly, research in this area has incorporated larger and more diverse samples as well as more ecologically based models that consider demographic selection factors and conditions of parental employment. Continuing these trends can only further our understanding of the mechanisms through which parental employment affects children's development.

See also: Attachment; Independence/Dependence; Child and Day Care, Effects of; Demographic Factors; Family Influences; Family Support, International Trends; Parental Leave; Parenting Styles and their Effects.

Suggested Readings

Chase-Lansdale PL, Moffitt RA, Lohman BJ, *et al.* (2003) Mothers' transitions from welfare to work and the well-being of preschoolers and adolescents. *Science* 29(5612): 1548–1552.

Dye JL (2004) *Fertility of American Women,* Current Populations Reports P20–555. Washington, DC: US Census Bureau.

Gottfried A and Gottfried AW (2006) A long term investigation of the role of maternal and dual-earner employment in children's development. *American Behavioral Scientist* 49: 1310–1327.

Hoffman LW and Youngblade LM (1999) *Mothers at Work: Effects on Children's Well-Being.* New York: Cambridge University Press.

Perry-Jenkins M, Repetti R, and Crouter AC (2000) Work and family in the 1990s. *Journal of Marriage and Family* 62: 981–998.

Waldfogel J (2006) *What Children Need.* Cambridge, MA: Harvard University Press.

Zaslow MJ, Brooks JL, Moore KA, Morris P, Tout K, and Redd Z (2001) *Impacts on Children in Experimental Studies of Welfare-to-Work Programs.* Washington, DC: Child Trends.

Relevant Websites

http://wfnetwork.bc.edu – Sloan Work and Family Research Network.

http://www.bls.gov – US Department of Labor, Bureau of Labor Statistics, Current Population Survey, Women in the Labor Force: A Databook.

Mathematical Reasoning

K McCrink and K Wynn, Yale University, New Haven, CT, USA

Glossary

Accumulator model – A proposed system which underlies an organism's ability to represent approximate magnitudes.

Core systems – A suite of conceptual systems which are responsible for specific evolutionarily advantageous cognitive tasks.

Dyscalculia – A selective impairment in number processing. Can be either acquired (through strokes or lesions in the brain) or are developmental (present from birth).

Evolutionary continuity – The idea that traits and capacities found in common ancestors will likely be found in all subsequent evolutionary branches.

Habituation – The technique of repeatedly presenting a certain stimulus until the observer has thoroughly processed the item of interest.

Intermodal – Going from one sense, or modality, to the other.

Object file – A mental 'tag' placed on a visually presented object, which helps track the object in case of occlusion or disappearance.

Weak-Whorfian view of number – The learning of number words, and the particular native language, influences the already developing exact number calculations in children.

Weber fraction limit – The ability to discriminate two stimuli is dependent not on the absolute difference between the two values, but rather their proportionate difference. The amounts 20 and 10 are the same 'mental distance' away as 2000 and 1000, because these pairs share a Weber fraction of 2.0.

Introduction

Number and the Core Systems View

Numerical comprehension is thought by many psychologists to be part of a suite of domains that comprise our 'core systems'. These conceptual systems, originally proposed by Elizabeth Spelke, correspond roughly to the major academic subjects (such as physics, geography, math, and psychology) and, at least in the evolutionary environment, provided a platform for relatively inexperienced organisms to quickly grasp critical aspects of incoming information. These systems predate our current evolved state, are by and large shared with our common mammalian ancestors, and are present during infancy. They are automatically engaged, largely impervious to explicit second-guessing, and specific to the domain and task of interest; they represent only a circumscribed set of entities (such as magnitudes or faces) and use these representations to address a certain set of tasks (such as enumeration, deciding whom to approach, etc.).

The benefit of having a sensitivity to number and an ability to compute over numerical values is apparent when one examines the literature on animal cognition. Although many of the current methods and models take place in an artificial learning environment, some of the most striking evidence for the ecological utility of a number system comes from studies that capitalize on natural surroundings. American coots who are able to count the number of eggs in their nest can avoid devoting resources to extraneous eggs deposited by local parasitic birds. The foraging literature on species as varied as ducks and rats illustrates a number- and time-based ability to maximize the yield of depleting food sources. These findings highlight the significant survival advantage that would be conferred to individuals who happened to possess these numerical abilities.

A General Model of Numerical Processing

There has been overwhelming evidence for two main distinct systems that support numerical cognition, each of which has its own neural circuitry. The first component is the ability to represent and operate over approximate numerical magnitudes. This ability to represent inexact magnitudes is found not only in adult humans, but also in infants and animals. Although there are several models one could posit to account for magnitude approximation, a prevalent model with empirical support is the 'accumulator model' proposed by Warren Meck and Russell Church. This model, originally developed to account for perceptual and numerical competencies in rats, postulates a mechanism composed of a sensory source for a stream of impulses, a pulse former that gates this stream of impulses to an accumulator for a fixed duration (around 200 ms) whenever an object or event is counted, an accumulator that sums the impulses gated to it, and a mechanism that moves the magnitude from the accumulator to memory when the last object has been counted. The output of the accumulator can be either magnitude-based ('roughly 10') or time-based ('roughly 10 s'). (Because this article focuses on number alone, we will for the purposes of brevity set aside the dual nature of this mechanism. It is, however, a vital aspect of the full model and there are major similarities between counting and timing processes). This mechanism is subject to psychophysical laws, namely Weber's fraction limit, which states that the variability of perception of magnitude increases with the amount to be represented (i.e., representation becomes more approximate and discrimination between quantities less exact as the magnitude in the accumulator increases). The accumulator can enumerate both large and small amounts across several different modalities, during both sequential and simultaneous presentations. In adult humans, the intraparietal sulcus is thought to house the mechanism for approximating magnitudes; it is active when quickly estimating a large number of visually presented objects, and also when approximating the result of an addition problem (but not when calculating the exact solution). Much of the research on infant number is assumed (either explicitly or implicitly) to be tapping into this evolutionarily ancient magnitude system. Critically, this mechanism is thought to give rise to a sense of magnitude that is conceptual and ultimately independent from the sensory modality in which it was perceived. A scene of 10 objects will activate the same circuitry that represents 10 incoming tones, yielding an identical 'number sense' across the two modalities.

The second component of a mature numerical system is, in actuality, not inherently arithmetical at all but rather language-based. Located in the left angular gyrus, its main role is to serve as a retrieval system for facts that are stored in verbal memory, such as automated small number addition facts or the multiplication table. In tandem with the approximate magnitude system, it aids the exact, uniquely human calculations of complex math problems such as counting to precisely 10, discriminating 100 from 101, determining derivatives, and solving for 'x'. As children's linguistic skills develop, so does their ability to comprehend and keep track of precise amounts and verbally manipulate these magnitudes.

There is some evidence that, in addition to these two central components, a third non-numerical mechanism contributes to mature number processing. This system is found in the posterior superior parietal lobule, is responsible for orienting attention, and was originally thought to be mainly active during visuo-spatial tasks. This has led to speculation that the numerical estimation system is somehow spatially oriented, perhaps corresponding to a mental 'number line'. Recent adult work on operating over approximated numbers and numerical judgments by hemispheric-neglect patients has provided evidence that there is indeed a link between space and number, mediated by attentional processes. However, there is to date very little work in the developmental literature on this third

system. Consequently, in this article we will focus on the developmental origins of the two primary components of number comprehension: the approximate magnitude system and exact verbal numerical representations.

Developmental Origins of Number Processing

The Approximate Number System in Infancy and Early Childhood

Research on approximate magnitude representations in infancy is a relatively new topic. Classic psychophysical work looking at numerical representation in animals has been present for over 50 years in the animal literature. With the popularization of the concept of 'evolutionary continuity', infant researchers began in earnest to study number across multiple populations and age groups. Beginning in the early 1980s, experimental evidence that preverbal infants also possess an inherent capacity to represent and manipulate numerical magnitudes began to emerge. Infants are able to discriminate between two numbers of items (such as 8 and 16) if the values are sufficiently disparate. These numerical representations are independent from perceptual variables (such as area or contour length), are highly salient to infants, and are represented in an abstract and sensory-independent fashion.

In one of the first studies on approximate magnitude representation in infancy, Fei Xu and Elizabeth Spelke habituated 6-month-old infants to displays containing either 8 dots or 16 dots. At test, the infants were given alternating trials of 8 dots and 16 dots. The infants dishabituated to the novel number, showing successful discrimination of these larger values. In a second experiment using an identical design, infants failed to discriminate 8 from 12. Subsequent research illustrates that infants this same age also succeed at discriminating 16 from 32, but fail to discriminate 16 from 24. These results indicate that young infants' representations are highly imprecise. Interestingly, the discrimination function obtained in these studies displays the Weber fraction signature of scalar variance, in that the ratio of the two values rather than their absolute difference determines their discriminability. This scalar variability, or 'noisy' representation, is a hallmark of the accumulator model outlined above, suggesting that both infants and animals use a similar mechanism for approximating magnitudes.

The ability to discriminate between two represented amounts is not restricted to the visual domain. Jennifer Lipton and Elizabeth Spelke studied 6- and 9-month-old infants in a tone discrimination task. After habituation to a set number of sounds, both groups of infants were able to discriminate a test item consisting of a novel number of sounds. However, as with previous studies, this ability to represent sounds was inexact, and it also sharpens with age; younger infants could only tell apart items that differed by a factor of 2 (such as 16 and 8), while older infants were able to discriminate items both at a factor of 2 (16 and 8) and a more difficult discrimination ratio of 1.5 (12 and 8). Infants also have been shown to represent other units besides visual objects and sounds. After being habituated to a set number of puppet jumps, 6-month-old infants will look longer to a moving puppet when it is jumped a novel number of times, as compared to a number that was previously shown to the infant. The children are able to make this discrimination on the number of jumps alone, since extraneous perceptual variables such as duration and tempo of the sequence were controlled. Further, these infants are able to tabulate these distinct countable units despite the presence of continuous extra motion, such as head waggling, that the puppets were performing. Infants are also able to discriminate between distinct numbers of moving objects and collections of objects.

Some of the most compelling evidence for an abstract number sense is work that addresses the intermodal nature of these representations. In an early study, Prentice Starkey, Elizabeth Spelke, and Rochel Gelman presented 6–8-month-old infants with visual displays of either 2 or 3 objects while 2 or 3 drumbeats played in the background. The infants looked preferentially to the visual displays that matched the auditory input. Although the replicability of this study has been controversial, several recent studies, using somewhat different methods, have clearly shown a similar capacity to detect magnitudes that are identical across the senses. For example, 5-month-olds who are given 2 or 3 objects to handle (while a sheet prevented them from viewing the objects) exhibit a preference for displays that contain a novel number of objects relative to the previous tactile phase. To summarize, the number mechanism that infants possess can be used to: (1) tabulate many types of countable units, (2) produce representations that can be matched across sensory modalities, and (3) yield an inexact representation of magnitude which gets sharper throughout the first year of life, such that discriminability of the two values rests on the proportionate difference between them.

The Special Case of Small Numbers of Objects: Object Tracking and the Object–File System

The research program on infants' numerical capacities has not always revealed a clear-cut competence with respect to discriminating two magnitudes. Indeed, there are experiments that show a lack of numerical understanding in a domain that would be, intuitively, the easiest – small sets of objects. This has led some researchers to suspect that infants' numerical competence is a result not of a numerical representation system, but rather of an automatic and precise system for tracking and reasoning about

individual objects in the world, via 'object files' or other object tracking mechanisms. According to the strong version of this account, each individual object in an array is mentally tagged as an open 'file', and any numerical differences between two sets are detected by a one-to-one correspondence function. Thus, when faced with two sets that mismatch, the infants look longer not because of a difference in magnitude, but because there is an open (and now missing) object file. These object files are used to establish location and track individuals as they move about the world. Critically, just as the accumulator mechanism has a distinct failure point (the Weber fraction limit), so too does the object-tracking mechanism. It shows a set-size limit of roughly 3 to 4 objects, and is disengaged when dealing with a large number of objects.

There are several pieces of evidence that support the presence of this system. Lisa Feigenson, Susan Carey, and Marc Hauser presented 10- and 12-month-old infants with two amounts of graham crackers, placed one at a time in separate containers, and tested which container the children crawled to. The infants were able to choose the container that had more when the number of crackers was less than four, easily telling apart 1 from 2, and 2 from 3. When one container held four or more crackers, the infants chose randomly (even failing to discriminate 1 cracker from 4). Furthermore, the infants did not attend to number when the overall amount of cracker 'stuff' was controlled for, and crawled evenly to both buckets, showing a lack of sensitivity to number. The authors took this finding as support for a numerical system that was not really numerical at all, but rather based on tracking and discriminating individuals in a display. Fei Xu found that when continuous extent variables in a display were controlled for, 6-month-old infants were able to discriminate 4 objects from 8, but not 2 from 4. This failure is also found with respect to discriminating action units. Infants (6-month-olds) can discriminate 4 from 8, but not 2 from 4, puppet jumps when all available perceptual variables are controlled for (such as sequence duration, jump duration, jump rate, and extent of jumping motion). Some research has even found that infants habituated to a small number of objects (either two or three squares) look longer to test displays that exhibit a new amount of contour length relative to that previously seen, and fail to look longer to a new number of objects when contour length was controlled. When infants are habituated to a set of either 1, 2, or 3 items whose sizes vary systematically, longer looking is only exhibited to the test displays that contain a new amount of surface area, and looking continues to decline at test when an array containing a new number of objects is shown.

So how can one reconcile the massive literature on successful number discrimination, the majority of which is well controlled, with this new evidence of failure? One hypothesis is that this special case of tracking small numbers of objects engages a system in addition to the magnitude approximation mechanism that is constantly churning in the background. This tracking system does its job in a very accurate and task-specialized fashion. It knows where objects should be and can predict where they are going, keeps tabs on continuous extent variables such as summed area and contour length, and uses this information to guide the infants' behavior. In a hierarchy of systems that interpret incoming information, the object-tracking system was built for a specific situation and takes precedence when a certain condition, like the presentation of a small number of objects, is met.

Evidence for the approximate magnitude estimation system still abounds. The proposed object tracking mechanism cannot be the entire story of infants' enumeration capacities, as one sees arithmetic prowess in areas not covered by this mechanism. For example, the set-size limit of object tracking means that any well-controlled study that goes beyond these limits of 3–4 objects is tapping into an inherently numerical system. There is also evidence for discrimination of small numbers of entities that are not visual, such as tones. Seven-month-old infants are able to distinguish between two sets of tones, even when these tones are in the small number range (such as 2 tones vs. 4), and this discrimination function is nearly identical to the Weber fraction limit found in work on large number discrimination.

This controversy has two main consequences: it highlights one of the main challenges to studying number in infancy, and it leads to a fuller understanding of how exactly our numerical processing works. These studies show us that, in addition to the broader methodological issues one deals with when studying a nonverbal population, the variable of interest, numerosity, is naturally confounded with purely perceptual variables. These continuous extent variables, such as area and contour length, are an additional cue to perceived number. If participants in these tasks behave differently to a test item, it may be because of a change in these linearly related dimensions, such as a new amount of brightness, or a differing amount of area than previously shown. When experimenters took care to control for these perceptual dimensions, they uncovered the possible presence of an alternative system (the object-tracking mechanism) which is so attuned to the qualities of the individuals that it trumps the processing of numerical information. This 'two-systems view' (recently outlined by Lisa Feigensen and colleagues) is still in the early stages of being developed, but is promising as a key to reconciliation of the curious pattern of successes and failures in the developmental literature.

Going Beyond Discrimination: Using the Approximate Number System in Arithmetic Operations

Although discriminating two numerical sets is undoubtedly a critical ability, many of the advantages of numerical capacity identified by researchers (e.g., foraging calculations) rest on the ability not only to represent numerical values, but to compute over them. We can now examine the child's ability to go beyond simple discrimination and use these represented magnitudes as parts of an arithmetic computation. Here too the developmental origins are located in early infancy, indicating an unlearned basis that serves as the foundation of our arithmetical capacity. For example, 11-month-old infants are able to order numerosities in either a descending or ascending manner. Infants habituated to a sequentially presented set of carefully controlled arrays of objects (4, 8, and 16 objects for the ascending group, or 16, 8, and 4 for the descending group), then tested with a new sequence of arrays in either a novel ascension (3, then 6, then 12), or a novel descension (12, then 6, then 3), look significantly longer when the type of ordering at test is a mismatch for what they had been habituated to. They are able to extract from the habituation scenario a concept of 'small → big' or a concept of 'big → small' and generalize on the basis of that criteria. This ability, like the majority of findings outlined here, is not unique to humans. In an earlier study, rhesus monkeys had been trained to respond in an ascending ordinal fashion to 1, 2, 3, and 4 objects (1 → 4), while varying perceptual factors such as size, shape, and color. These monkeys were given displays during a testing phase that showed novel large numbers (5, 6, 7, 8, and 9), and they responded by ordering these new magnitudes in an ascending fashion (5 → 9).

Karen Wynn tested 5-month-olds' simple addition and subtraction capacities by using a small set of objects to act out a computation (such as 1+1 or 2−1). The infants in the addition condition saw a single Mickey mouse doll hop onto the stage, and a rotating screen rose to occlude it. A hand from the side of the stage came out and moved a second doll to join the first behind the screen, then exited the stage as an empty hand. A second group of infants saw a complementary action played out, where instead of addition the operation was subtraction. Two dolls were placed on the stage, and covered. A hand came and took away one of the dolls, leaving the stage with one doll. The screen then came down to show either a correct outcome, or an incorrect outcome produced by manipulating a trap door behind the screen. Infants who witnessed the addition event were more likely to look longer to the outcome of 1 doll over 2 dolls, while infants who saw subtraction looked longer to 2 dolls than to a single doll. This 'flip' in looking time preference was driven by the preceding operation; each group of infants looked longer to the wrong outcome, despite this outcome being different across groups. This experiment has recently been replicated and extended using an intermodal addition paradigm. First, infants are familiarized to a display of a doll hitting the bottom of the stage and producing a tone. They are then shown several arithmetic events involving the addition of tones and objects (such as 1 object + 1 tone = 2 or 3 objects), and are able to detect the incorrect outcomes of these problems. Infants appear to compute the basic arithmetic operation of addition across sensory modalities.

There were several criticisms to the Wynn study, and to some extent all studies that use a similar paradigm and number of objects. In the case of the original study, the amount of continuous extent (area of the dolls) was confounded with the total number. Melissa Clearfield and Kelly Mix performed several follow-up studies which hypothesized that this confound was responsible for infants' performance, and that if these variable were manipulated there would be no significant effect of number. They habituated infants to two or three squares of the same size, and then showed the infants test displays which had either a novel number of objects, or a novel total area. The authors found that infants looked longer to the test displays that showed a novel surface area compared to those displays that showed a novel number of objects. This experiment has been replicated to show that this pattern of preference for novel continuous extent variable also holds when the child is tested with a novel contour length as well. These results, while interesting, are limited in interpretation due to the fact that the variables at test are not merely controlled for, but rather 'pitted against' each other. This research raises the invaluable point that babies are indeed very sensitive to continuous extent variables, and perhaps may even give higher priority to detecting them than to detecting numerical violations. The research as to whether this is truly the case is still ongoing, with researchers such as Elizabeth Brannon finding that, in fact, infants in her studies have a bias toward numerical discrimination over area and contour length discrimination.

The sheer fact that small numbers of visual objects were being manipulated in Karen Wynn's original addition and subtraction study makes it difficult to disentangle claims about represented magnitudes from hypothesized object-tracking systems. Even in the case of intermodal addition and subtraction, the possibility remains that the familiarized pairing of objects and tones resulted in the engagement of the object-tracking system. One simple way to get around the possible engagement of this alternate system is to take the identical paradigm and methodology of Wynn, but move them out of the domain of small number. One has reason above and beyond the small-number work on addition and subtraction to believe that infants would be able to perform operations over large nonverbally represented magnitudes, as animals as varied as monkeys and pigeons have shown this ability in numerous studies. Rhesus macaques are able to spontaneously compute the outcome of both small- and large-number addition problems (such as $2+2$, or $4+4$) and the limit on this ability is set by the Weber fraction of the possible outcomes. Pigeons are able to compare a constant number of flashes with the number remaining after a numerical subtraction of two comparison magnitudes of flashes.

To look at infants' ability to perform these large-number operations, we presented 9-month-old infants with a computerized display of addition or subtraction events. Half the infants saw displays in which 5 objects dropped down from above, constantly changing shape and gradually moving to the right side to become occluded. Five more objects dropped down and went behind the occluder. The other half of the infants saw the complementary subtraction movies in which 10 objects fell down, an occluder rose, and 5 objects moved off screen. All infants then saw two alternating test displays of either 5 objects or 10 objects. These test displays had the same amount of summed area and overall contour length, leaving only number as the difference between the two sets. The addition group looked longer when presented with test displays of 5 objects, the incorrect outcome of $5+5$. The subtraction group showed the opposite pattern, and looked longer at the test displays of 10 objects (the incorrect answer to $10-5$). This study establishes that performing computations such as addition and subtraction do not only occur in the non-numerical context of object-tracking; rather, the systems that provide an approximate sense of magnitude are able to provide representations for use in arithmetic operations. Follow-up studies have confirmed that the representations used in these computations are inexact. While the infants were generally quite good at determining incorrect vs. correct outcomes (even succeeding at $4+5=6$ or 9, and $10-4=6$ or 9), their performance suffered when trying to discriminate two outcomes that were very close together. When presented with difficult problems such as $7+5=12$ or 9, or $14-5=9$ or 12, the infants looked similarly to each outcome irrespective of whether it was correct or incorrect.

Hilary Barth and colleagues have conducted several studies on young children using a similar computerized addition and subtraction paradigm. In one such study, 5-year-old children were shown arrays of large numbers of objects and given the two tasks of comparison and addition. In the comparison task, a group of blue dots comes from offscreen and becomes occluded. A group of red dots then comes down from offscreen and the children are asked whether there are more blue dots, or red dots. In the addition task, a group of blue dots goes behind an occluder, and a second group of blue dots moves to join the first set. A group of red dots comes from off screen, and the child is again asked if there are more blue dots or red dots. In both these tasks, the children were able to correctly answer, above chance performance, which array was larger. Five-year-olds have also been found to correctly compare and add two sets of items across different sensory modalities. Barth also found that children could perform both the comparison and addition tasks when given a combination of objects and tones, and that their performance was just as accurate when dealing with multiple modalities than their performance in a single-modality version of the tasks. Thus it appears that this magnitude information was put into an abstract numerical code, distinct from the sensory code through which it was initially perceived.

But what of more complicated operations, assumed to come online later in life via schooling and experience? These computations, such as multiplication, division, and statistics have only recently been indirectly tested in young infants. For over 50 years animal theorists have noticed that animal foraging behavior appears to rely on computational processes that use time, amount, and discrete number as relevant variables in operations that are analogous to division and multiplication. For example, in a case alluded to earlier, many animals will 'rate match' when foraging. Mallard ducks will distribute themselves to two experimenters at opposite ends of a pond in a proportion that is equivalent to the relationship between the size, number, and rate of tossed bread morsels. Although it is of course impossible to perform these sorts of experiments with infants, it is a reasonable hypothesis that such an evolutionarily critical computation will be present from early on in our development, and can potentially manifest itself in other ways through careful testing.

To examine this hypothesis, we presented 6-month-old infants with a test of proportional understanding, by habituating them to a series of slides displaying a constant ratio of object type A (pellets) to object type B (pacmen). At test, the infants were shown either an entirely new ratio of pellets to pacmen, or a new example of the old ratio. If infants dishabituate to the never-seen ratio, but not the new example of the old ratio, this would be evidence for an ability to extract a common proportion and generalize on the basis of this relationship. Several manipulations were performed within this basic design, and examined whether infants can detect a change in proportion of perceptual variables (such as area), conceptual variables (such as number), the difference between ratios that are quite disparate (such as 4:1 vs. 2:1), and the difference between ratios that are closer together (such as 3:1 vs. 2:1). Incredibly, these young infants readily distinguish between scenes that contain a different numerical proportion of object A to object B. They can also tell the difference between scenes that contain a different proportion of pellet area and pacmen area. This ability to equate proportions disappeared when we decreased the disparity between the two ratios; the infants looked similarly to test outcomes of 2:1 and 3:1 irrespective of what they were previously habituated to.

This ability to comprehend ratios has also been found in early childhood. Children with the age of 4 and 5 years tested with a variety of stimuli (such as animals with varying degrees of head-to-tail ratio, or two line segments that exhibited a particular length ratio) are able to reliably determine which test stimulus exhibits the same proportion as the standard when they have the comparison readily available. This research, as well as the infant research outlined above, is in stark contrast to earlier work by classic developmental scientists such as Piaget on ratios and proportions which does not find competence when testing schoolchildren. In fact, many schoolteachers and students say that understanding of fractions and proportions is one of the hardest basic math lessons to learn. Although there is very little research that directly tests hypotheses that could reconcile these two findings, one idea is that the use of implicit measures such as looking time (in the case of the babies) or direct comparison of perceptual ratio (in the case of the competent schoolchildren) taps into a slightly different, less-conscious system than those commonly used when testing or teaching ratios. When one learns about ratios in school, it is in a very concrete, exact way that does not necessarily recruit the same representations that are being used in the experiments on estimated ratios.

This ability to understand proportion is, to our knowledge, one of the most computationally complex operations shown in infants to date. It is also a finding that confirms that attention to ecological validity (here, in the evolutionary sense of the term) is a critical component to establishing and elucidating the suite of possible processes that infants possess. Using the wealth of animal literature will be critical to pinpointing those abilities that are most likely to be found as part of our underlying cognitive architecture.

The Role of Language in Numerical Development

Learning to Count

With the immense competence shown by preverbal infants, one would have very little reason to think that a mature numerical understanding would be an arduous process. This is, however, exactly the case. As with many of the core knowledge systems, the aspects of the world that are salient to nonverbal organisms do not necessarily manifest themselves in the explicit day-to-day behaviors children perform as they develop. One of the very first steps in transitioning from a nonverbal representation of quantity to a mature verbal system is learning to count. Rochel Gelman and Randy Gallistel outlined three basic principles that must hold in order to successfully count a set. The child must understand that as an ordered list of words is applied to the items, each linguistic tag applies only to a specific item in the set (the one-to-one correspondence principle). The stable-order principle states that the count list must be applied the same way across different counting situations. The cardinal principle states that the final word used when counting the set represents the total number of items (the cardinal value). In order to successfully count, children must map the number of the set represented by their magnitude system to these ordinal, symbolic terms used by the linguistic system.

Rochel Gelman performed a classic series of 'magic' studies with young children. In these experiments, children were presented with two plates, each of which had a differing number of toys. Half the number of children were trained that the plate containing a greater number of toys was the 'winner', and the plate with the smaller quantity the 'loser'. The other half were trained on the reverse labels, with small-quantity plates being 'winners' and large-quantity plates 'losers'. After training the children to distinguish winners from losers, the experimenter covered the plates and surreptitiously transformed the plates. These transformations were either numerical in nature (such as changing 2 objects to 3), spatial (rearranging where each object was on the plate), or identity-based (changing the type of object on the plate.) When the plates were uncovered, the experimenter asked them to distinguish anew the winner and loser plate, and justify their decision. Children as young as 2.5 years of age appealed to concepts of numerosity and were not 'fooled' by other numerically extraneous transformations. Gelman concludes that children, even if they are counting poorly, understand that this counting process gives a representation of number that lends itself to arithmetic reasoning, and are able to apply these counting principles from a very early age.

Other researchers believe that, although young children are giving the appearance of competence, they are actually performing the task without true comprehension of what it means to count. Karen Wynn tested children ranging from 2.5 to 4 years of age and asked them to give a certain number of toys from a pile (the give-a-number task). They were also given a counting task, and were asked to count sets ranging from two to six items and then report how many there were to the experimenter (the how-many task). Although some children were able to count to correctly perform the give-a-number task (the Counters, whose average age was 3.5 years), the younger children (the Grabbers) failed to count in order to solve the task, instead grabbing several dolls to hand to the experimenter. This failure is more striking when one considers that these children had in place a very solid counting routine, and could count the six items in the pile with no problem. The Grabbers failed to understand that the count list they happily produce is what determines the specific number of a collection of items. Counters and Grabbers also exhibited different behavior in the how-many task. Children who counted in the give-a-number task were able to distinguish between their own correct and incorrect counts, and were three times as likely to reply with the last number word they produced after a correct count than they were when their initial count was incorrect. The Grabbers were equally happy to give whatever number word they had stopped at as their answer to the experimenter, irrespective of whether this count was correct or not. Through this study, and other studies that examine the protracted development of counting,

Wynn posits that a true conceptual understanding of the count list, and the principles that guide counting, is only available to children come early childhood (roughly 3–4 years of age.)

There is evidence to suggest that it is the particular linguistic context of differing types of number words that scaffold the child into a mature understanding of number. Children are able to determine that a particular word picks out a specific quantity of items (and therefore, it is a number word) if that word occurs in certain syntactic frames and not others. For example, in a database that examines naturalistic speech to young children, adults speaking to 1- and 2-year-olds used number words to apply over individuals, when denoting discrete unchangeable values, and when describing the quality of a set of objects. These syntactic frames correspond to the level of knowledge described by the Grabbers in the give-a-number task above. Thus, it follows that how these number words are presented in the syntax of the child's language will interact with pre-existing numerical systems to guide children toward a greater understanding of arithmetic principles.

Linguistic Effects on Number Comprehension and Encoding

The impact of language on arithmetic development is more striking when one examines cross-cultural studies that map the linguistic idiosyncrasies of a language to altered patterns of numerical development. A well-established example in the developmental literature is that of the Chinese language. The construction of the first ten counting words is completely arbitrary (yi, er, san is equivalent to one, two, three), as in English and most other languages. The numbers that follow ten, however, are perfectly regular and embody the structure of the base-10 system. For example, 35 is expressed as Three-Ten-Five, or $3 \times 10 + 5$. This intuitive system, markedly different from the relatively opaque English counting system, is thought to contribute to the superior performance of Chinese-speaking pupils over English-speaking pupils. Children (4-, 5-, and 6-year-old) who speak Chinese are able to count higher and more competently than an age-matched group of US children. First-graders in San Francisco who know the Chinese counting system are more likely to represent numbers in base-10 form (by segregating a collection of 35 objects into groups of 10, 10, 10, and 5 for the experimenter) than English-system first-graders, who simply present 35 objects. The idea of place value, a concept that many American children struggle with in school when learning precise computations, is inherent to the way Chinese number words are expressed.

In addition to symbolic number words, the Chinese language is more transparent with respect to mathematics terms used for complicated domains such as algebra and trigonometry. For example, the literal translation for the symbol of 'mode' from Chinese to English is 'frequent number'. In an ingenious study on the conceptual differences between Chinese and English numerical systems, and how this may prompt differential learning, Yi Han and Herbert Ginsburg created a set of 'Chinglish' words by literally translating Chinese symbols into the English words for those symbols. These Chinglish terms were rated to be more conceptually clear, as the inherent compound structure is well-suited to portray complicated mathematical ideas. The authors then examined three groups of junior-high-school students, all of whom were ethnically considered Chinese: monolingual English speakers, bilingual English/Chinese speakers, and monolingual Chinese speakers. The students who could speak Chinese performed better on a test of mathematical concepts, and level of Chinese reading ability correlated positively with performance level during the test. This was not merely a situation in which underlying cognitive factors drive success in both math and language, as the level of English-speaking ability was not correlated with performance on the math test in the bilingual and English-speaking groups.

Olivier Houde and colleagues have studied the relative influence of several languages on early arithmetic development. In one study, they found that the dual use of the word 'un' in the French language as both an indefinite article ('an') and a number word ('one') led to a phase of development in which qualitative differences in arithmetic performance could be observed between French-speaking children and English-speaking children. Using a task that mimicked Karen Wynn's violation-of-expectation experiment with young infants, the experimenters performed a puppet show of the arithmetic problems $1 + 2 = 2$, 3, or 4, and $2 + 1 = 2$, 3, or 4. The children were then asked if each outcome was 'okay' or 'not okay'. English-speaking, but not French speaking, 2-year-olds were able to correctly determine the outcome of all the addition problems. The French 2-year-olds were selectively impaired on those problems that start off with 'un' object on the stage. By 3 years of age, both groups of children were able to do both types of problems. The authors argue that this shows an effect of language on the child's conceptualization of the situation at a fundamental, arithmetic level. The child could not compute the answer to the problem, because the mental application of the tag 'un' put the child in a situation that was syntactic, and not numeric. Follow-up studies by the same group have found an identical pattern of results with Spanish and Finnish children. Spanish-speaking children, whose word for 'an' overlaps with their word for 'one' (*uno/una*), showed a performance deficit relative to Finnish-speaking children (whose language does not conflate the article with the number word) when given addition problems that start off with a single object on stage. These findings support a weak-Whorfian view that some aspects of language influence the pattern of conceptual development in the numerical domain.

Evidence for this weak-Whorfian view also comes from the literature on how adults behave when placed into a new learning situation. Bilingual students who were taught a set of new numerical operations, new exact equations, and novel numerical or non-numerical geography and history facts show a lag when tested for exact calculation problems ('$86 + 26 = 112$ or 102' ?) or numerically based facts ("After which election did the King execute several governors?") outside of the language in which they had encoded them. However, this discrepancy is not present when the students retrieve information on approximate numbers (such as determining the approximate logarithm or cube-root of a value) or recall non-numerical facts ("Where did the band of farmers meet?") that they had learned in the other language. Thus, language appears to play a critical role in the encoding and storage of particular types of numerical information but not others, and this role corresponds nicely with the proposed number systems of approximate magnitude representation and exact verbal calculation.

Abnormal Numerical Development

In the condition of developmental dyscalculia (DD), a child with otherwise normal mental abilities shows a deficit in mathematical abilities. Brian Butterworth, via the 'defective number module hypothesis', posits that this deficit arises from a genetic defect in the specialized numerical systems common to all humans. Evidence for a genetic component of DD comes from studies with twins. While the baseline rate of the disorder is somewhere around 6% of the general population, dizygotic twins (who share half of genetic material) have a 39% concordance rate and monozygotic twins (whose genetic material is identical) have a remarkably high 58% concordance rate. DD is frequently comorbid with other learning disabilities, such as dyslexia and attention deficit hyperactivity disorder (ADHD). Although this is suggestive of an across-the-board deficit in processing information, there is evidence that cases of pure dyscalculia exist. One investigation into 8- and 9-year-old children with dyscalculia, dyslexia, or no learning disability found that children with dyscalculia had deficits specific to math that extended qualitatively and quantitatively beyond those shown in the other two groups. These cases provide us with the opportunity to examine what exactly it means to represent and manipulate number, and the limits of the supplementary systems used in arithmetic tasks.

There are many different types of DD, with widespread deficits seen in some patients, and other patients who suffer only from specific deficits. These specific deficits tend to roughly correspond with the circuits outlined above, namely the approximation system and the rote verbal calculation system. In several case studies on 'acquired dyscalculia' (a deficit that came about as a result of injury to the developed brain), Stanislas Dehaene and colleagues have found a dissociation between magnitude approximation and exact calculation. One patient, N.A.U., was able to determine whether a simple approximated arithmetic calculation was incorrect (such as $2 + 2 = 9$), but was unable to say if exact, small-number calculations were correct or incorrect, judging such rote, precise, arithmetic problems as $2 + 2 = 3$ to be correct. Two other dyscalculiac patients who exhibited a double dissociation between the systems of approximation and exact calculation have been studied. A patient with a lesion of the inferior parietal lobe was impaired in tasks that tested the manipulation of approximate quantity, but was able to perform rote, exact tasks such as the multiplication problems one finds on a grade-school multiplication table. Another patient, who had a lesion of the left subcortical region, was impaired on operations that involved rote, verbal calculations and unimpaired on tasks that involved the manipulation of magnitudes.

These studies, while generally supportive of the outlined component model of number processing, are not able to address questions of numerical development *per se*, as they study adult humans who had many years of schooling and experience before impairment. It is entirely possible that outside cultural norms regarding how to classify number concepts had come to shape the organization of numerical knowledge. In order to examine the way in which our minds are initially organized, the population of children with dyscalculia is of interest. These children have been impaired from birth (assuming the defective number module hypothesis is correct), with official diagnoses generally given as they started schooling and failed to progress normally. And they too, show deficits that are specific to the proposed number components. Children with DD exhibit immature strategies for dealing with basic arithmetic, such as counting on their fingers instead of retrieving rote facts. These children do not exhibit difficulties on just the verbal tasks of recall, however. Butterworth also discovered a reverse distance effect in children who had severe DD. Normally, it is much easier to determine that magnitudes that lie far apart on the number line (such as 4 and 12) are different, and this task gets more difficult when deciding if magnitudes that are on roughly the same area of the number line (such as 10 and 12) are different. Children with severe DD sometimes exhibit the opposite pattern; they are better able to determine the difference between numbers that are similar (15 and 14) than numbers that are disparate (15 and 10), presumably because they are using a non-magnitude-based counting process. Although there are only a handful of neuroimaging studies done with DD patients, they are suggestive of brain abnormalities analogous to that found in adult patients with acquired dyscalculia. If one examined two groups of adolescents, one of which was unimpaired and the other which exhibited specific deficits on numerical operations, the impaired adolescents would have overall significantly less gray matter in the left intraparietal sulcus, an area that is found to be selectively active during magnitude approximation and calculation tasks in adults.

On the strongest possible account of the defective number module hypothesis, children who are impaired have been impaired since birth. An intriguing way to test this hypothesis would be to use the early tests of mathematical understanding outlined previously to pinpoint which children may have problems in the future. One can do this in an 'educated-guess' manner by studying the relatives (siblings or children) of those who have already been diagnosed with dyscalculia. If scientists are able to correlate later numerical competence based on their performance as infants, this would be extremely important at both the theoretical and applied level. First, it would suggest that the abilities we see in infants are indeed related to our adult arithmetic abilities and are recruited later on in development. Second, it would confirm the idea of a genetic basis for developmental dyscalculia. Third, it would allow psychologists to pinpoint those children who would benefit the most from an intervention to improve their arithmetic skills.

Sex Differences in Arithmetic Development

The idea that males are superior to females on arithmetic tasks has been omnipresent for quite a long time, both scientifically and anecdotally. There are many different types of claims about sex differences and mathematics. Some people believe that there are intrinsic differences from birth with respect to male and female competence. Others believe the differences are indeed present, but have come about as a function of socialization or only happen as hormone levels fluctuate. The developmental literature on mathematical ability is therefore extremely relevant to this debate, as it has the ability to pinpoint if and when differing capabilities arise.

First and foremost, there is no compelling evidence from the developmental literature on number systems in infancy that the genders innately differ on any of the tasks relevant to this debate. Although some work has shown a tendency for male infants to focus more on objects (thus, presumably, leading to a more mechanical and mathematic way of thinking) and female infants to focus more on faces (suggesting a predisposition for socializing), the specific experiment of interest has not been replicated and, in fact, goes against several other well-replicated studies that show equal levels of interest to both objects and faces by female and male infants. There is a tendency, by around adolescence, for boys to outperform girls on such standardized tests as the math portion of the SATs.

This difference grows larger as one moves up the age range. David Geary and colleagues posit that the main factor mediating this difference between genders is not mathematical reasoning ability *per se*, but rather a sex-based difference on how each sex chooses strategies-when faced with different tasks. Females are more likely to solve complicated problems by using verbal calculations, whereas males resort to a strategy of spatial imagery. It is true that spatial imagery is, on average, stronger in men than women, but only as hormonal levels fluctuate in the female body. Non-ovulating females show similar performance to an average male. This unreliability is, perhaps, a reason for females to adopt a non-spatial strategy as a first pass at arithmetic problem solving. Because the SAT-M is composed of questions that are more easily solved by using spatial imagery, a difference in overall mathematics scores emerges.

The psychological processes of socializing girls and boys with respect to math achievement reveals a lopsided picture of parental influence on arithmetic development. Parental justifications of their childrens' success in mathematics courses have been examined by researchers in several cultures (such as America, Finland, and Israel). These experiments have found that parents of boys are more likely to attribute success to inherent, natural ability, while parents of girls believe their child's success is due to effort. People tend to associate effort with diligence and, unflatteringly, conformity. Thus, a boy who does well in math is considered to possess a very highly valued trait (natural ability), while a girl who performs similarly is seen as having the less-admirable trait of a good work ethic. (Ironically, the parents of the boys are doing their children no favor, as attributions of natural ability in the classroom yield a less motivated student than attributions of effort.) To summarize, it appears that eventual sex differences in mathematical ability are due to many factors, including socialization, test construction, and deployment of differing problem-solving strategies in a mathematical context.

Conclusion

The above review of the current and classic literature on numerical understanding shows a deep continuity between nonhuman animals, infants, and adults. By informing our infancy research with established phenomena in the animal literature, we are closer to discovering the 'fundamentals' of our nature. The capacity to represent amounts, and to productively use these representations, indicates an important and rich network of systems that have evolved to support a core capacity of arithmetic understanding. This line of research starts to address the broader issue of how humans process and organize information from our environment, and how this activity changes across development.

Although the mechanisms outlined above are undoubtedly critical to a mature number system, they are only a small step toward the entire package of complicated mathematical discovery. There are some concepts that do not lend themselves to being represented as a magnitude, an object, or even a word. Concepts such as infinity, zero, derivatives, and *pi* are unique to the world of theoretical math. The systems outlined above must be built upon and improved throughout development, and meshed with other core capacities such as physics, mechanics, biology, and linguistics. It is through this combination of domains that we are able to use our mind to its fullest extent.

See also: Habituation and Novelty; Neonativism.

Suggested Readings

Barth H, La Mont K, Lipton J, and Spelke ES (2005) Abstract number and arithmetic in preschool children. *Proceedings of the National Academy of Sciences USA* 102(39): 14116–14121.

Butterworth B (1999) *The Mathematical Brain.* London: Macmillan.

Dehaene S (1997) *The Number Sense: How the Mind Creates Mathematics.* Oxford: Oxford University Press.

Dehaene S, Piazza M, Pinel P, and Cohen L (2003) Three parietal circuits for number processing. *Cognitive Neuropsychology* 20(3–6): 487–506.

Feienson L, Carey S, and Hauser M (2002) The representations underlying infants' choice of more: Object files versus analog magnitudes. *Psychological Science* 13: 150–156.

Feigenson L, Dehaene S, and Spelke E (2004) Core systems of number. *Trends in Cognitive Science* 8(7): 307–314.

Gallistel CR (1990) *The Organization of Learning.* Cambridge, MA: MIT Press.

Geary DC (1996) Sexual selection and sex differences in mathematical abilities. *Behavioral and Brain Sciences* 19: 229.

Gelman R and Gallistel CR (1978) *The Child's Understanding of Number.* Cambridge, MA: Harvard University Press.

Han Y and Ginsburg H (2001) Chinese and English mathematics language: The relation between linguistic clarity and mathematics performance. *Mathematical Thinking and Learning* 3: 201–220.

Hubbard E, Piazza M, Pinel P, and Dehaene S (2005) Interactions between number and space in parietal cortex. *Nature Reviews Neuroscience* 6(6): 435–448.

Kimura D (1999) *Sex and Cognition.* Cambridge, MA: MIT Press.

Lipton J and Spelke E (2003) Origins of number sense: Large-number discrimination in human infants. *Psychological Science* 14(5): 396–401.

McCrink K and Wynn K (2004) Large-number addition and subtraction by 9-month-old infants. *Psychological Science* 15: 776–781.

Meck W and Church R (1983) A mode control model of counting and timing processes. *Journal of Experimental Psychology: Animal Behavior Processes* 9(3): 320–334.

Spelke ES (2000) Core knowledge. *American Psychologist* 55: 1233–1243.

Wynn K (1990) Children's understanding of counting. *Cognition* 36: 155–193.

Wynn K (1992) Addition and subtraction by 5-month-old human infants. *Nature* 348: 749–750.

Xu F (2003) Numerosity discrimination in infants: Evidence for two systems of representations. *Cognition* 89(1): B15–B25.

Xu F and Spelke E (2000) Large number discrimination in 6-month-old infants. *Cognition* 74(1): B1–B11.

Memory

H Hayne, University of Otago, Dunedin, New Zealand
J Richmond, Harvard University, Boston, MA, USA

Glossary

Classical conditioning – A form of learning in which a previously neutral stimulus (conditioned stimulus or CS) is presented in conjunction with another stimulus (unconditioned stimulus or US) that elicits a particular response (unconditioned response or UR). Over successive pairings of the CS and US, the CS begins to elicit the same response (conditioned response or CR).

Encoding – The process by which information is stored in memory.

Habituation – A decline in responding to the repeated presentation of the same stimulus.

Memory retrieval – The process by which information that is stored in memory is accessed.

Reminder treatment – The presentation of a stimulus prior to the retention test; presentation of this stimulus facilitates memory retrieval and improves retention.

Retention – A term that is analogous to memory or remembering; retention interval refers to the delay between the end of the learning session and the outset of the test session.

Introduction

Relative to other primates, human infants enter the world in a relatively altricial, or immature, state. Although most of their senses are well developed at birth (e.g., hearing, taste, touch, and smell), their visual acuity is initially very limited. The newborns' motor skills are also very immature and it will take years before they attain the motor milestones that their other primate cousins attain at or around the time of birth. If we look at the nature of the human brain, we can begin to understand the source of the human newborn's immaturity. Unlike other primates whose brain growth peaks during mid-gestation, human brain growth peaks at about the time of birth; thus, at the time they are born, human infants are more neurologically immature than other primates. After birth, the human brain continues to mature for at least another 20 years (and perhaps even longer), but changes in the brain occur very rapidly during infancy and early childhood.

What are the consequences of this brain growth on infants' cognitive skills, particularly on their memory? How does the infant's memory skill change as he or she matures? Begins to crawl? Acquires language? These are some of the questions that we will try to answer here.

The task of measuring memory in human infants is one that is fraught with difficulty. Unlike human adults, pre-verbal infants cannot draw on language to express their memory for a past event. As a result, researchers must rely on infants' overt nonverbal behavior as an index of their memory. In other words, researchers must find ways for infants to 'show' us rather than 'tell' us what they remember. In addition, infants are often unpredictable research participants; their attention span is typically short and their emotional state can change very rapidly. For these reasons, tasks that are designed to assess memory during infancy must be brief; when the experimental session is long, attrition rates are often very high. Studying age-related changes in memory across the infancy period is also particularly challenging because the changes that occur in language, motor skill, and attention that take place over the first 2 years of life make it difficult to design a single task that can be used with infants of different ages. Despite these challenges, researchers have developed a number of experimental techniques that have allowed us to study memory development over the first 2 years of life.

Newborns

At the time of birth, the average human newborn weighs approximately 3400 g or 7.5 lbs. Despite excellent auditory, olfactory, and taste capability, newborn infants' visual acuity is extremely limited. Based on three different assessment methods, newborn visual acuity is estimated to be about 20/640. In terms of gross motor skill, human newborns cannot sit, crawl, or roll over and they do not have the fine motor control required to reach for or grasp objects. In fact, most newborns cannot support the weight of their own head for more than a few seconds.

Historically, many researchers believed that because of their physical immaturity, infants were unable to learn or remember during the first few months of life. Initial research on learning and memory in newborns confirmed this belief. When newborns were tested using habituation or classical conditioning procedures that were originally developed to study nonverbal memory in human adults or other animals, researchers consistently found that newborns were incapable of retaining information for more than a few seconds at best.

Gradually, however, researchers began to take a different approach to studying the memory ability of newborns. Rather than focusing on the newborns' inability to learn and remember arbitrary relations between novel stimuli and their consequences, researchers began to examine what newborns might learn and remember about meaningful stimuli in their environment. This shift in focus has challenged the claim that newborns lack memory skill. In fact, the results of these experiments have uncovered some remarkable memory abilities in human newborns.

The first step in studying memory in newborns is to find a way for infants to demonstrate that they remember. In order to do this, researchers must harness a behavior that newborns can master. Although the range of behaviors that they exhibit is somewhat limited, researchers have been able to capitalize on newborns' ability to suck, look, turn their head, and stick out their tongue.

High-Amplitude Sucking

The high-amplitude sucking task capitalizes on a behavior that newborns do exceptionally well – sucking. In this task, infants learn to suck on a non-nutritive nipple; by changing the pattern of their sucking, infants can produce changes in the environment. In a landmark study, DeCasper and Fifer used the high-amplitude sucking procedure to study newborns' memory for their own mother's voice. In that study, a standard baby bottle nipple was placed in the infant's mouth. One end of a piece of flexible tubing was connected to the nipple and the other end was connected to a recording device. This arrangement allowed the researchers to measure and record the pattern of the infant's sucking bursts. In addition to sucking on the nipple, the infant was also fitted with a set of headphones that allowed the experimenters to present the infant's mother's voice or the voice of another, unfamiliar woman.

For each infant, baseline suck rate was established during a 5-min period in which no voices were presented. Following this baseline period, some infants were required to increase the duration of the pause between successive sucking bursts and some infants were required to decrease the pause between successive sucking bursts. When infants met their target criterion (i.e., increased or decreased pause length), their mother's voice was played through the headphones. When they did not meet their target criterion, another woman's voice was played through the headphones. DeCasper and Fifer found that although the infants were less than 3 days old at the time of the test, they altered their suck rate to maintain contact with their mother's voice. The results of this study showed that these newborns had already learned something about the characteristics of their mother's voice and that they would alter their own behavior to maintain contact with it.

These data raise another interesting possibility. On the basis of their findings it is tempting to conclude that the infants' preference for their mothers' voice was based, at least in part, on their experience with her voice prior to birth. We know that infants can hear *in utero* and that the volume of their mother's voice is sufficient to reach their ears, but is there any evidence that they learned the characteristics of her voice during the prenatal period? Because all of the infants in the DeCasper and Fifer study had at least some postnatal contact with their mothers, it was impossible to rule out the role of postnatal learning in their findings. In an attempt to study what infants might remember about a 'prenatal' auditory stimulus, DeCasper and colleagues conducted another study in which he asked pregnant women to read one of three prose passages out loud to their fetus, twice a day during the last 6 weeks of their pregnancy. Two to three days after these infants were born, they were given the opportunity to alter their suck rate to produce the passage that their mother had read during her pregnancy or to produce another passage. DeCasper found that infants altered their suck rate to maintain contact with the familiar story irrespective of who read it during the test (i.e., their mother or another unfamiliar woman). Taken together, studies conducted by DeCasper and colleagues clearly show that the ability to remember emerges at the time of birth, if not earlier!

Visual Preference

Despite their limited visual acuity, research has shown that newborn infants do learn and remember the basic characteristics of their mother's face within the first few days after birth. In the visual preference task, for example, infants are given the opportunity to look at their mother or at an unfamiliar woman when both women are presented simultaneously. Both women are silent during the task so that infants cannot use their mother's voice as a cue. Under these conditions, newborns spend more than twice as much time looking at their mother relative to the other, unfamiliar woman. Furthermore, when the women change their right/left position during the test, infants track their mother's position and continue to look longer at her face. Additional research has shown that newborns' recognition of their mother's face depends, at least in part, on her hair line. When the women's hair is covered by a towel, for example, newborns show no visual preference for their mother over another unfamiliar woman during the test.

Head Turning

Although most human newborns cannot support the weight of their own head for long periods of time, if the weight of their head is supported by a hand or a pillow, they can (and do) turn their head from side-to-side. A number of researchers have capitalized on this behavior to study newborns' memory for both olfactory and auditory stimuli. For example, newborn infants will turn their head in the direction of odor cues from their mother's body or breast milk when they are pitted against similar cues from another infant's mother.

Presumably, infants learn and remember the characteristics of their mother's smells on the basis of their prolonged daily contact with her. What about other stimuli that are encountered less often? Can infants learn the characteristics of these stimuli as well? To answer these questions, some researchers have used head turning procedures to study newborns' memory for stimuli encountered for the first time during the experimental session. In one experiment, for example, researchers examined habituation of head turning in 1–2-day-old newborns. During the habituation phase of the experiment, the experimenter, supporting the infant's head, positioned the infant midway between two speakers. One of two words (beagle or tinder) was played from the speakers, one at a time. On the initial trials, infants turned their head toward the speaker from which the word was played. Over trials, however, the infants presumably became bored with the word and they started to turn away from the speaker. The next day, when infants were tested again, those infants who were tested with the original word were less likely to turn toward the speaker than infants who were tested with a new word or than infants who had never heard the original word before. In short, these newborns exhibited some memory for their brief experience with the word the day before.

Imitation

Imitation is a monkey-see, monkey-do activity in which a child copies a behavior that he or she has seen performed by someone else. Imitation is an important way by which children acquire a wide range of new behaviors during the course of their daily lives and researchers have capitalized on this opportunity to develop more standardized procedures that can be used to study imitation in the laboratory. In these experiments, an infant watches as an adult performs an action or series of actions, and the infant's ability to reproduce that action or actions is assessed immediately or following a delay.

Research conducted using imitation procedures has shown that even newborns readily learn by watching and repeating the actions of others. In one study with 6-week-old infants that was conducted by Meltzoff and Moore, an adult demonstrated a particular facial gesture (e.g., sticking out his tongue) and the infants' ability to imitate this gesture was assessed both immediately and after a 24 h delay. They found that these very young infants not only imitated

the model's action at the time of the original demonstration, but they also repeated the action when they encountered the model again the following day.

Summary

In contrast to the view that newborns have little or no memory ability, a large body of research has now shown that newborns learn and remember a great deal about biologically relevant stimuli that are associated with their survival – they learn the basic characteristics of their mother's voice, face, and smell and they remember this information when they are tested after a delay. Furthermore, newborns also exhibit some, albeit limited, ability to learn and remember information about new stimuli and new actions that are not intimately tied to survival. Over the next several months, however, the ability to accomplish these memory tasks improves dramatically.

3–6-Month-Olds

Human infants undergo some remarkable changes between 3 and 6 months of age. Their visual ability increases dramatically, and by the age of 6 months, their average visual acuity is roughly equivalent to that of adults (e.g., 20/40). In terms of gross motor skill, most infants begin to roll over sometime between 2 and 4 months of age, and they begin to sit unsupported by approximately 5 months. Infants begin to engage in visually guided reaching by about 4 months of age and they rapidly get better and better at holding and manipulating objects. Consistent with these changes in perception and motor skill, infants also make great strides in their ability to learn and remember about the world around them.

Visual Recognition Memory Paradigm

The visual recognition memory (VRM) paradigm that researchers now use to study infant memory evolved from experimental procedures that were originally designed to study visual perception in human infants and nonhuman primates. In this task, the infant is typically seated on the mother's lap facing a pair of computer screens or video monitors (see **Figure 1(a)**). The VRM procedure typically involves two phases; a familiarization phase and a test phase. During the familiarization phase, infants are presented with a visual stimulus, either for a fixed period of time, or until a fixed amount of looking time is accumulated. Following a delay, infants are presented with a pair of stimuli, one that is the same as the familiarization stimulus and one that is new (see **Figure 1(b)**).

Infants' visual behavior is recorded during the test phase of the VRM procedure and it is analyzed to determine the amount of time that they spend looking at the

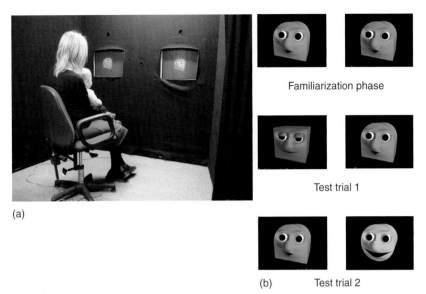

Familiarization phase

Test trial 1

(b)   Test trial 2

Figure 1   (a) An infant during the familiarization phase of the visual recognition memory (VRM) paradigm. (b) Sample stimulus presentation schedule during the familiarization and test phases of the VRM paradigm.

novel stimulus and the familiar stimulus. Memory is inferred if infants exhibit a novelty preference, spending a greater proportion of time fixating the novel stimulus than the familiar stimulus. Forgetting is inferred when infants exhibit a null preference, fixating the novel and familiar stimuli equally during the test.

Novelty preferences in VRM performance have been reported in infants from birth; however, the amount of familiarization time that is required for infants to exhibit novelty preferences changes with age. Susan Rose and colleagues have shown that with limited familiarization time, infants will initially exhibit a preference for the familiar stimulus. This preference shifts toward novelty with longer familiarization times. For example, Rose reported that while both 3- and 6-month-olds exhibited familiarity preferences when they were allowed only 5 or 10 s familiarization, 6-month-olds required only 15 s of familiarization to exhibit a novelty preference, while 3-month-olds required 30 s of familiarization. These results illustrate significant age-related changes in the speed of encoding across this age range.

The maximum retention interval after which infants will exhibit a novelty preference in the VRM procedure also changes with age. Although young infants typically exhibit retention on the VRM task after delays ranging from minutes to days, by 6 months of age, infants may exhibit novelty preferences after delays as long as 2 weeks. Although testing is most commonly discontinued after the retention interval at which infants exhibit a null preference (i.e., forgetting), some researchers have tested infants on the VRM task after delays ranging from 1 min to 3 months. Lorraine Bahrick and colleagues have shown that 3-month-olds may exhibit novelty preferences when tested after short delays, null preferences when tested after intermediate delays, and familiarity preferences, which can also be interpreted as evidence of retention, when tested after long delays. Bahrick argues that performance on the VRM task may be best characterized along a continuum from novelty preference to familiarity preference.

There is now considerable evidence that the VRM task may measure a fundamental component of cognitive ability that is continuous across development. Individual differences in the magnitude of infants' novelty preference have been shown to predict childhood intelligence quotient (IQ) at age 11 years. In addition, VRM performance is sensitive to a number of risk factors for developmental delay, including prematurity, prenatal drug exposure, and Down syndrome.

Operant Conditioning Procedures

The mobile conjugate reinforcement procedure is an operant conditioning task that was originally developed by Carolyn Rovee-Collier. In this task, infants learn to kick their foot to produce movement in an overhanging mobile, which is attached to their foot by a ribbon. The term 'conjugate reinforcement' refers to the fact that the rate and vigor of reinforcement (i.e., movement in the mobile) is directly proportional to the rate and vigor of the infant's responding (i.e., kicking). In other words, the more or harder the infant kicks, the more the mobile moves.

Infants are typically trained in the mobile procedure in two 15 min sessions that take place on consecutive days. During each session, infants are placed on their back in their crib and a mobile is suspended from a flexible mobile stand. Each training session begins with a period of nonreinforcement (see **Figure 2(a)**). During this period, a ribbon is tied around the infant's ankle, but

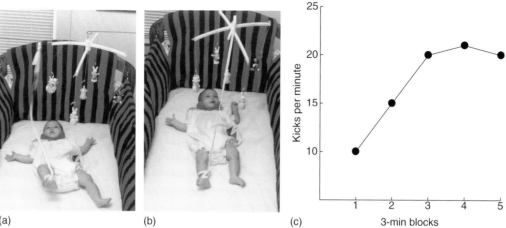

(a)   (b)   (c)   3-min blocks

Figure 2 (a) A 3-month-old infant during the nonreinforcement phase of the mobile conjugate reinforcement paradigm. One end of the ribbon is tied to the infant's ankle and the other end is secured to an empty mobile stand. In this arrangement, the infant can see the mobile and feel the tug of the ribbon when she kicks, but her kicks are ineffective in producing mobile movement. (b) A 3-month-old infant during the reinforcement phase of the mobile conjugate reinforcement paradigm. During this phase, the ankle ribbon is attached to the stand supporting the mobile. In this arrangement, kicks of the infant's foot produce corresponding movement in the mobile. (c) The mean number of kicks per min by a group of 3-month-old infants trained in the mobile conjugate reinforcement paradigm.

rather than being attached to the active mobile stand, it is attached to an empty mobile stand. In this way, the mobile is visible to the infant, but kicks do not produce movement in the mobile. The purpose of this nonreinforcement phase is to measure the infant's baseline kick rate, before the contingency between foot kicks and mobile movement is introduced. Following this baseline phase, there is a period of reinforcement. During this phase, the ribbon is attached to the stand containing the mobile, and the infants' kicks produce movement in the mobile (see **Figure 2(b)**). Each training session ends with another brief period of nonreinforcement. During this period, the ribbon is again attached to the empty mobile stand, and infants do not receive reinforcement for foot kicks. The period of nonreinforcement at the end of each session provides a measure of immediate retention. Learning in the mobile conjugate reinforcement paradigm is operationally defined as a kick rate that exceeds the baseline kick rate by a factor of 1.5 during 2 out of any 3 consecutive minutes of reinforcement. A number of studies have shown that infants as young as 3 months meet or exceed this kick rate within the first session of training (see **Figure 2(c)**).

The mobile conjugate reinforcement paradigm can be used to study memory simply by inserting a delay between the end of the final training session and the beginning of the test that is scheduled days or weeks later. Memory in the mobile conjugate reinforcement task is assessed during another period of nonreinforcement at the outset of the test session. Retention is inferred on the basis of two relative response measures. First, the baseline ratio expresses the degree to which the infant's kick rate during the test exceeds his or her kick rate prior

to learning. Memory is typically inferred if the baseline ratio is significantly greater than 1.0. Second, the retention ratio expresses the degree to which the infant's kick rate during the test matches his or her kick rate at the end of training, prior to the retention interval. Retention ratios that approach 1.00 indicate that little or no forgetting has occurred over the delay.

Although the mobile conjugate reinforcement task is suitable for use with infants from 2 to 6 months of age, it is necessary to adjust the task to account for age-related changes in motor skill and speed of learning. Because they are more likely to roll over during the training and test sessions, 6-month-old infants are placed in an infant seat during each session. Furthermore, the duration of the training sessions varies slightly as a function of age. For example, while 3-month-old infants are typically trained in two sessions that are 15 min in duration, 6-month-old infants only require 6-min training sessions to learn the same task, so their training sessions are typically abbreviated.

Research conducted using the mobile conjugate reinforcement paradigm has clearly documented that the duration of infant memory increases linearly as a function of age. For example, 2-month-olds exhibit memory for 1 day, 3-month-olds exhibit memory for 8 days, and 6-month-olds exhibit memory for 14 days (see **Figure 3**, open circles). The duration of retention in an analogous task, the train task, continues to improve over the next 12 months.

Although infants eventually forget in the mobile conjugate reinforcement paradigm, Rovee-Collier and colleagues have shown that the memory may still be retrieved and expressed if infants are exposed to a brief reminder treatment prior to the test. In the initial demonstration of this phenomenon, Rovee-Collier found that

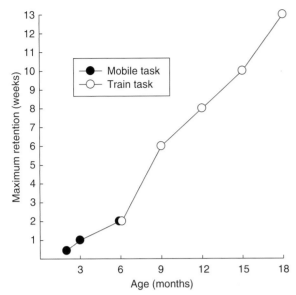

Figure 3 Age-related changes in the maximum duration of long-term retention by 2–18-month-old infants who were tested in either the mobile conjugate reinforcement paradigm (open circles) or in the train paradigm (closed circles). As shown here, 6-month-olds perform equivalently on both tasks. This figure was redrawn from Hartshorn *et al.* (1998) and has been reprinted with permission from John Wiley & Sons, Inc.

when 3-month-old infants were briefly exposed to the moving mobile 24 h prior to the test, forgetting was alleviated after a 2–4-week delay. During the reminder treatment, infants were placed in an infant seat to restrict movement of their legs. During the test, however, infants were again placed supine in the crib. In the absence of a reminder treatment, infants did not kick during the test; when infants were given a reminder, their kick rate during the test was virtually identical to their kick rate at the end of the final training session 2–4-weeks earlier. Furthermore, infants continued to exhibit memory in the task for several days after the reminder treatment.

Subsequent research has shown that if 6-month-old infants are given a 2-min exposure to the moving mobile 20 days after the conclusion of training, they also exhibit retention when tested 24 h later, and will continue to remember for 14 days, the same length of time that 6-month-olds typically remember the task in the first place. Taken together, these studies show that although forgetting occurs very rapidly at 3–6 months of age, the memory is not always permanently lost and, given the appropriate conditions, the memory can be restored, allowing infants to profit from their prior experiences over very long delays.

Research using the mobile conjugate reinforcement paradigm has also shown that young infants form remarkably detailed memories of the mobile that is present during training as well as detailed memories of the context in which training occurs. Studies in which researchers

have manipulated aspects of the mobile or the testing environment have shown that relatively small changes in the cues that are available at retrieval will disrupt infants' memory for the mobile task. For example, 3–6-month-old infants will not exhibit retention if they are trained with one mobile and tested with a different mobile. In fact, at 2 and 3 months of age, memory for the mobile is so specific that infants do not exhibit retention during the test if more than one out of the five objects that make up the mobile is changed during the test.

Memory performance by 3–6-month-olds is also highly context-specific; memory retrieval is impaired if aspects of the incidental learning environment are changed between training and the test. Rovee-Collier has shown that infants do not exhibit retention if they are trained in one room of their house but are tested in another, or if they are trained in the presence of one distinctively colored crib bumper but are tested with a different crib bumper. These results suggest that young infants encode a considerable amount of detail about the mobile and the testing environment; however, the specificity of the memory representation prevents infants from generalizing their memories if aspects of the cue or context are manipulated. In the end, the highly specific nature of infants' memories may actually work against them because, in the real world, cues and contexts rarely occur the exact same way twice. As we will see below, a major hallmark of memory development during the second year of life is an increase in the flexibility of memory retrieval.

Electrophysiology

Event-related potentials (ERPs) represent transient changes in the brain's electrical activity that occur in response to the presentation of a stimulus. Electrophysiological measures of memory are particularly useful in studies with infants because ERPs can be measured from the scalp (see **Figure 4**). Furthermore, although ERPs may be correlated with behavior, they do not require an overt motor or linguistic response. As such, ERPs may be recorded from infants of different ages using the same paradigm, or may be recorded from the same infant tested on an ERP paradigm at a number of different ages. Although ERP techniques have poor spatial resolution (it is difficult to localize where the electrical activity recorded at the scalp is generated in the brain), the temporal resolution is very high. This feature allows researchers to precisely assess the timing of the neural events that underlie the memory processes in the brain.

There are a number of characteristic components of the infant ERP waveform that have proven to be of interest in the study of memory development. The Nc (negative central) is a mid-latency negative component that is evident in electrodes that are positioned over the central front of the scalp. This feature of the infant ERP waveform is thought to reflect obligatory attention. Although it is not considered a direct index of memory, the Nc is often modulated by stimulus novelty. In contrast, late slow wave activity is thought to index memory processing more directly. Following the Nc, the infant ERP response may take one of three forms: a positive slow wave (PSW), negative slow wave (NSW), or return to baseline (see **Figure 5**). The PSW is thought to index memory updating of a partially encoded or forgotten stimulus. The NSW is often seen in response to a novel stimulus that is presented in the context of familiar stimuli and is thought to reflect novelty detection. A return to baseline is interpreted as evidence of a fully encoded stimulus that does not require additional processing.

ERPs are used to study infant memory using one of two different paradigms. Researchers sometimes record ERPs in response to stimuli with which the infant is presumably very familiar, and compare the ERP waveform to that elicited by stimuli that the infant has not yet experienced. For example, in some studies, researchers record ERPs in response to pictures of the infant's mother's face relative to the face of an unfamiliar woman. These studies have shown that in 6-month-old infants, the amplitude of Nc component is larger in magnitude in response to the mother's face relative to the stranger's face. Following the Nc, the ERP in response to the mother's face returns to baseline, indicating complete encoding. The response to a stranger's face, however, takes the form of a PSW, indicating

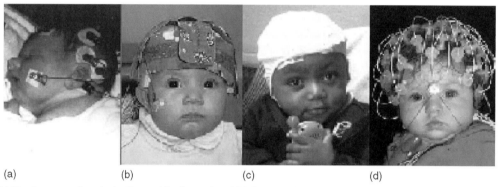

(a)   (b)   (c)   (d)

Figure 4   (a) Newborn wearing single disposable electrodes; (b) infant wearing 16 electrodes held in place with adhesive foam pads and Velcro headbands; (c) infant wearing a 32-channel electro-cap; and (d) infant wearing a 64-channel electrogeodesic sensor net. From C. A. Nelson.

• No (negative component)

   – middle latency response occurring 400–800 ms after stimulus onset attentional response

• PSW (positive slow wave)

   – later latency response occuring 800–1700 ms after stimulus onset memory updating

• NSW (negative slow wave)

   – later latency response occuring 800–1700 ms after stimulus onset detection of novelty

• Return to baseline
   – later latency response occuring 800–1700 ms after stimulus onset
   – present for stimuli not requiring memory updating and not detected as novel

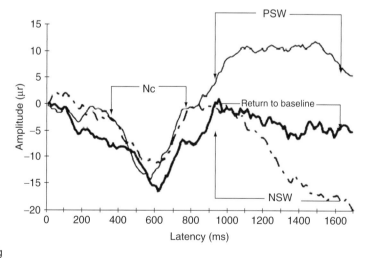

Figure 5   Example of the components observed in the infant event-related potential during a visual recognition memory task. From de Haan M and Nelson CA (1997) Recognition of the mother's face by six-month-old infants: A neurobehavioral study. *Child Development* 68: 187–210.

that the infant may be encoding new details of the stranger's face during the course of the testing session. Similar studies using auditory paradigms with younger infants have shown that the Nc and slow wave components also differentiate between mother's voice and that of a stranger. In 6-month-old infants, these components also differ when infants are presented with pictures of their favorite toy and a novel toy. Collectively, these results have led researchers to suggest that the brain systems that are necessary for infants to form representations of people and objects in their environment and to discriminate novel and familiar stimuli are functionally mature during the first months of life.

Given the extensive experience that infants have with their mother's face (or even their favorite toy), ERPs recorded in response to such stimuli can only tell us so much about the neural correlates of infant learning and memory. For these reasons, the majority of infant ERP studies have used a modified oddball paradigm in which infants are familiarized with new stimuli at the outset of the session and they are tested for recognition of these newly familiar stimuli relative to a novel stimulus. In the oddball paradigm, infants are familiarized with two stimuli. Following familiarization, one of these stimuli is presented on 60% of the test trials (frequent familiar) and the other is presented on 20% of the test trials (infrequent familiar). A novel stimulus is presented on the remaining 20% of trials.

Studies using the oddball paradigm have shown that while the Nc is evident in the ERP waveform of infants across a wide range of ages, there is considerable change in the pattern of slow wave activity in response to novel and familiar stimuli across the first year of life. For example, in 4-month-old infants, slow wave activity does not differentiate between frequent familiar, infrequent familiar, or novel stimuli; in 6-month-old infants, frequent familiar stimuli elicit a return to baseline, indicating complete encoding, while infrequent familiar stimuli elicit a PSW, indicating some kind of updating. In 8-month-old infants, familiar stimuli, whether presented frequently or infrequently, elicit a return to baseline. This pattern of results indicates a gradual improvement in memory capabilities between 4 and 8 months of age. While 4-month-olds are unable to distinguish between any of the stimulus categories, 6-month-olds maintain a representation of a familiar stimulus provided that the stimulus is presented relatively frequently. If the familiar stimulus is presented infrequently, the representation is forgotten rapidly, and requires additional updating. Eight-month-old infants, however, are able to maintain a representation of the familiar stimulus even when it is presented infrequently, as evidenced by a return to baseline for both the frequent familiar and infrequent familiar stimulus presentations.

Electrophysiological measures of infant memory are often more sensitive than behavioral measures. Several studies have now shown that the Nc and slow wave components differentiate between novel and familiar stimuli under conditions in which infant's looking behavior on tasks such as the VRM paradigm does not. In addition, ERP studies of infants at risk for neurodevelopmental delay (i.e., pre-term infants, infants of diabetic mothers, infants who have suffered hypoxic injury) have yielded memory deficits in the absence of detectable differences in standardized measures of cognitive development.

Summary

Infant memory between 3 and 6 months of age is typically measured by assessing changes in infants' behavior (i.e., looking, kicking) or brain response (i.e., event-related potential) as a function of their prior experience. Infants of this age are able to demonstrate memory; however, there are age-related changes in the speed with which infants learn and the delay after which they will exhibit retention. In addition, infant memory during this period is characterized by extreme specificity; small changes in the stimuli or learning environment disrupt memory retrieval.

6–12-Month-Olds

Developmental changes in motor abilities continue during the second half of the first year of life, expanding the range of behaviors that can be used to index infant memory. Between 6 and 12 months of age, infants are increasingly able to grab and manipulate objects using their hands. Researchers have capitalized on this ability in the design of operant conditioning and deferred imitation tasks that are typically used to measure memory during this period.

Operant Conditioning – Train Task

Although the mobile conjugate reinforcement paradigm is ideally suited for infants up to 6 months of age, changes in motor capabilities, interests, and motivation render the task less interesting for older infants. To continue the study of memory development in infancy, Carolyn Rovee-Collier designed an equivalent task that can be used with 6–18-month-olds. In the train task, infants learn how to press a lever to produce movement in a toy train (see **Figure 6**). Like the mobile task, training begins with a brief period of nonreinforcement before the contingency between lever presses and train movement is introduced. Each training session also ends with a period of nonreinforcement. Retention is typically tested after a delay and memory is inferred from infants' response rate during the nonreinforced test period, relative to response rates during baseline (baseline ratio) and following training (retention ratio).

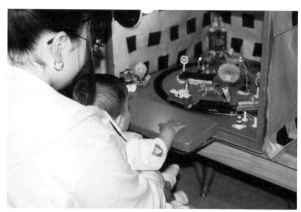

Figure 6 A 6-month-old infant being tested in the train paradigm.

Although reinforcement in the train task is not 'conjugate' like it is in the mobile task, in every other sense the two tasks are equivalent. Six-month-old infants learn the train task at the same rate and remember it for the same length of time that 6-month-olds remember the mobile task. At this age, memories for the train task are similarly disrupted by a change in train set (i.e., cue) or testing room (i.e., context). Forgotten memories for the train task may be also reinstated by administering a brief reminder treatment.

Infants' ability to exhibit long-term retention continues to improve gradually between 6 and 12 months of age. For example, while 6-month-olds will remember the train task for 2 weeks, 9-month-olds will remember the task for a maximum of 6 weeks, and 12-month-olds will remember the task for 8 weeks (see **Figure 3**, closed circles). Similarly, the rate at which infants learn about the contingency between their behavior (i.e., lever presses) and its consequences (i.e., train movement) continues to improve during this period, requiring researchers to adapt the learning phase of the task to suit the age of the infant; for 6-month-olds, the training involves 6-min periods of reinforcement, however, 9- and 12-month-olds will learn the task with only 4-min periods of reinforcement.

Infants' memory for the train task becomes less susceptible to changes in cue and changes in context as infants approach 1 year of age. Six-month-olds will not exhibit retention if the train set (i.e., cue) or testing room (i.e., context) is changed between the learning and test phases. Older infants, however, will generalize responding to a new train set or a new context provided that they are tested after a short delay. At the extreme end of the forgetting function however, infants' memories continue to be disrupted by changes in the retrieval cues at the time of the test well into the second year of life.

Deferred Imitation

Although neonates will exhibit imitation for facial gestures, it is not until the second half of the first year of life that infants' motor skills are sufficiently developed to allow them to imitate actions that can be performed with objects. In the deferred imitation task, the experimenter demonstrates a sequence of actions using novel objects. During this demonstration phase, the experimenter does not label the objects or describe the actions verbally; infants are allowed to watch but are not allowed to touch the objects or practice the actions. Following a delay, infants are given the opportunity to reproduce the actions that the experimenter performed earlier. Memory is inferred if infants in the demonstration group produce the target actions at a higher rate than do infants in a control group who had the same amount of experience with the objects, but did not see the actions demonstrated.

When defined in this way, infants as young as 6 months of age will exhibit deferred imitation after a 24-h delay; however, younger infants require more encoding time than older infants to exhibit the same level of performance after a delay. Using a deferred imitation task in which a set of novel actions are demonstrated with a hand-held puppet, Hayne and colleagues have shown that following a 30 s demonstration period, both 6- and 12-month-old infants will imitate the actions immediately, however, only 12-month-olds will do so after a 24-h delay. If 6-month-olds are shown the actions for a 60 s demonstration period, however, they too are able to demonstrate retention when tested after a delay. These results point to age-related changes in both the speed of encoding and the duration of retention across this period.

Like performance on the train task, deferred imitation between 6 and 12 months of age is characterized by extreme specificity (see **Figure 7**). During this period, small changes in the objects (i.e., cue) or learning environment (i.e., context) can disrupt infants' retrieval of imitation events. For example, 6-month-olds fail to exhibit retention when the demonstration occurs in their home but the test occurs in the laboratory (or vice versa). This retrieval failure occurs irrespective of the cue present at the time of the test (see **Figure 7**, context change). In contrast, 12-month-old infants exhibit the same level of retention irrespective of whether they are tested in the same or a different context. At both 6 and 12 months of age, changes in the cue (i.e., puppet) disrupt memory retrieval and impair performance (see **Figure 7**, cue change). Both 6- and 12-month-old infants do not exhibit retention after a 24-h delay if they are shown the target actions with one puppet (i.e., a pink rabbit) but are tested using a different one (i.e., a gray mouse). In fact, 12-month-old infants do not exhibit retention if the test puppet differs from the demonstration puppet in color only (i.e., a pink mouse to a gray mouse) or in form only (i.e., a pink mouse to a pink rabbit). It is not until well into the second year of life that infants begin to use their memories in a flexible manner to perform a deferred imitation task across changes in cue (see **Figure 7**, 18-month-olds).

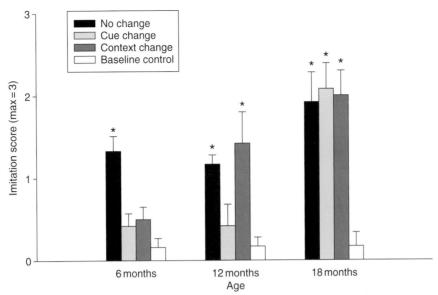

Figure 7 Age-related changes in generalization across cues and contexts by 6-, 12-, and 18-month-old infants who were tested in the deferred imitation paradigm. Asterisks indicate scores significantly greater than baseline.

Infants' experiences influence their emerging ability to use their memory flexibly. With the onset of independent locomotion, infants begin to learn that objects work in a similar way even when they are moved to a new environment. Research has shown that 9-month-old infants who are crawling and 12-month-old infants who are walking are more likely to exhibit generalization across changes in cues and contexts than are their noncrawling and nonwalking counterparts. Although it is tempting to argue that individual differences in motor skill simply reflect individual differences in maturational status, the relation between motor development and cognitive development is quite specific. For example, infants with higher levels of motor skill perform equivalently to infants with lower levels of motor skill on standard tests of deferred imitation; the difference between the two groups only emerges when infants are asked to solve problems that involve changes in cues and contexts (i.e., that require representational flexibility).

Even stronger evidence that the relation between motor skill and cognitive development reflects maturation alone, is derived from studies of the relation between motor ability and language skill. For example, infants with higher levels of motor skill perform equivalently to infants with lower levels of motor skills on global tests of language, but they outperform infants with lower levels of motor skill when it comes to the comprehension and production of prohibitive language in particular. We know that as infants begin to crawl, parents begin to use more prohibitive language (e.g., "Stop." "Don't touch."); apparently this experience facilitates language learning in this specific domain. Although it is not possible to rule out maturation entirely, the highly specific nature of the differences in

representational flexibility and language skill has lead many researchers to argue that the ability to crawl or walk provides new experiences and poses new challenges. It is these experiences and challenges that ultimately drive changes in both representational flexibility and language skill during the infancy period.

Summary

There continues to be a gradual improvement in infants' encoding and retention during the second half of the first year of life. Although memory during this period continues to be highly specific to the conditions that were present at encoding, coincident with the onset of independent locomotion, there are some improvements in infants' ability to use their memory flexibly. Independent of the task that is used to measure memory, 12-month-old infants are able to exhibit retention even when aspects of the learning context have been changed. The ability to generalize memory across changes in cue continues to develop into the second year of life.

12–24-Month-Olds

The second year of life is characterized by two major changes in infant development. First, most infants take their first tentative steps sometime around their first birthday. Second, infants' ability to both comprehend and produce language increases dramatically between their first and second birthdays. How do these changes in motor development and language acquisition influence memory ability? As described above, the onset of upright locomotion, like the onset of crawling, influences the flexibility of memory retrieval. When chronological age is held constant, for example, infants who can walk show more flexible memory retrieval than do infants who cannot yet walk.

Second, language acquisition also plays a major role in memory development during the second year of life. Most of the research on the relation between language development and memory development has relied on the deferred imitation paradigm described above. Even before they can produce many words themselves, infants can use an adults' language to facilitate their memory performance in the deferred imitation task. For example, when the demonstration and the test sessions are narrated by an adult who labels the objects and describes the actions and the outcome of the event, 18-month-olds infants exhibit superior memory performance than they do when the demonstration and the test session do not include these linguistic cues (see **Figure 8(a)**).

By 24 months of age, infants can use an adult's language to facilitate generalization to novel test cues. For example, when tested with more complex stimuli and target actions, memory retrieval by 24-month-olds is impaired by changes to the stimuli at the time of the test (see **Figure 8(b)**). If the experimenter provides a unique verbal label for the stimuli during the demonstration and uses the same label to refer to the new stimuli at the time of the test, then infants exhibit the same level of memory performance irrespective of whether the test stimuli are the same as or different from the stimuli present at the time of the demonstration (see **Figure 8(b)**).

Summary

Although the speed of encoding and the duration of long-term retention continue to increase between 12 and 24 months of age, the most important change in memory development during this period is an age-related change in the flexibility of memory retrieval. Between 12 and 24 months, infants begin to retrieve and use their memories in a wider range of circumstances. They also begin to exploit new retrieval cues, including words provided by an adult.

Conclusions

Taken together, the research outlined here supports three general principles of infant memory development. First, the speed of original encoding increases as a function of age. Data collected using the VRM paradigm, the mobile conjugate reinforcement paradigm, the train paradigm, and the deferred imitation paradigm have all confirmed that older infants learn faster than younger infants. Put another way, if encoding time is held constant in any of these procedures, older infants learn more during a given episode than younger infants.

The second general principle of memory development is that the duration of long-term retention increases as a function of age. Even when the level of original encoding is held constant by increasing exposure time to the stimulus or by extending the duration of the training session, older infants remember longer than younger infants. This age-related increase in retention allows older infants to profit from their prior experience over longer periods of time. Greater retention also allows older infants more opportunity to accumulate information over successive learning episodes, particularly if those episodes are separated in time.

Third, the flexibility of memory retrieval increases as a function of age. During early infancy, infants can retrieve and use their memories if and only if they re-encounter

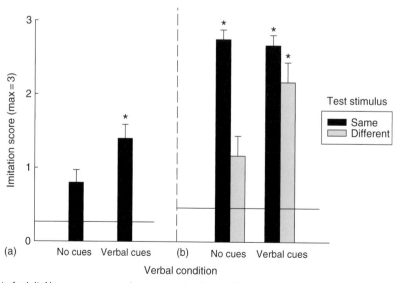

Figure 8   (a) The effect of adults' language cues on long-term retention by 18-month-old infants. (b) The effect of adults' language cues on generalization by 24-month-old infants. In both parts, the imitation score of the baseline control group is indicated by the solid line.

the original cue in the original learning context. If either the cue or the context is different, then retrieval suffers. As a function of both age and experience, however, infants gradually begin to exploit cues that are different from those encountered during original learning. Clearly, both language acquisition and motor development play an important role in this process. Age-related changes in the flexibility of memory retrieval allows older infants to use their memories in a wider range of circumstances and it may also allow them to learn from a wider range of sources including picture books, television, and photographs.

Age-related changes in encoding, retention, and retrieval that take place during the infancy period continue to take place throughout early childhood. By the end of the infancy period, children begin to acquire their native language and as they do, they also begin to express the contents of their memories linguistically. It is important to note, however, that children's ability to use language in the service of memory pales by comparison to their nonverbal memory skill or to their ability to use language in the here-and-now. Furthermore, children do not readily map their emerging language skill onto their nonverbal representations which means that most of the memories that we form during the infancy period do not survive the transition to language. It has been argued, for example, that the failure to translate our early, pre-verbal memories into language may be one source of childhood amnesia – the universal inability of adults to recall events that took place during their infancy and early childhood.

For decades, many researchers expressed a relatively dim view of mnemonic capacity during the infancy period. Based on a substantial body of research, we now know that infants can and do exhibit sophisticated memory skills beginning at birth. The next new challenge for research on infant memory development will be to establish the critical link between age-related changes in memory performance and maturation of the human central nervous system. Thirty years ago, this goal was little more than a pipe dream, but as our ability to study the human brain in action becomes increasingly more sophisticated using electrophysiological and imaging techniques, we are slowly moving closer to making this dream a reality.

Acknowledgments

Preparation of this article was supported by a Marsden Grant from the Royal Society of New Zealand to Harlene Hayne.

See also: Amnesia, Infantile; Attention; Brain Development; Habituation and Novelty; Hippocampus; Language Acquisition Theories; Language Development: Overview; Milestones: Cognitive; Motor and Physical Development: Locomotion; Motor and Physical Development: Manual.

Suggested Readings

Bahrick L and Pickens J (1995) Infant memory for object motion across a period of three months: Implications for a four-phase attention function. *Journal of Experimental Child Psychology* 59: 343–371.
de Haan M and Nelson CA (1997) Recognition of the mother's face by six-month-old infants: A neurobehavioral study. *Child Development* 68: 187–210.
DeCasper AJ and Fifer WP (1980) Of human bonding: Newborns prefer their mothers' voices. *Science* 208: 1174–1176.
Hayne H (2004) Infant memory development: Implications for childhood amnesia. *Developmental Review* 24: 33–73.
Meltzoff AN and Moore MK (1994) Imitation, memory, and the representation of persons. *Infant Behavior and Development* 17: 83–99.
Rose SA and Feldman JF (1997) Memory and speed: Their role in the relation of infant information processing to later IQ. *Child Development* 68: 630–641.
Rovee-Collier C (1997) Dissociations in infant memory: Rethinking the development of implicit and explicit memory. *Psychological Review* 104: 467–498.

Mental Health, Infant

P D Zeanah, M M Gleason, and C H Zeanah, Tulane University Health Sciences Center, New Orleans, LA, USA
M M Gleason, Brown University School of Medicine, Providence, RI, USA

Glossary

DC:0–3R – The revised edition of the *Diagnostic Classification of Mental Health and Developmental Disorders of Infancy and Early Childhood*, published by Zero to Three in 2005. This document was developed by an advocacy and professional development organization to specify criteria for disorders of early childhood because of the belief that DSM-IV-TR did not adequately describe the problems seen in young children.

DSM-IV-TR – The fourth edition (text revision) of the *Diagnostic and Statistical Manual of Mental*

Disorders, published by the American Psychiatric Association in 2000. This document specifies criteria used in the diagnosis of psychiatric disorders. The criteria are developed by expert committees who review relevant research and use it to inform the criteria.

Neuronal synapses – The connections between the axon of one neuron (nerve cell) and the dendrite of another in which neurotransmitters are released and taken up as electrical impulses are discharged.

RDC-PA – This document, the 'Research diagnostic criteria – preschool age', was published in the *Journal of the American Academy of Child and Adolescent Psychiatry* in 2003 and describes criteria for early childhood disorders. The purpose was to modify existing DSM-IV-TR criteria so that they could be applied to young children with a degree of specificity that would help investigators achieve uniformity in studies of early childhood disorders.

Strange situation procedure – A laboratory paradigm involving a young child, a caregiver (parent), and an adult who is unfamiliar to the child (the stranger). The procedure involves a series of episodes in which the child's behavior with the caregiver (parent) is compared with the child's behavior with the stranger. Based on the child's behavior, the child's attachment to the caregiver (parent) is classified as secure, avoidant, resistant, or disorganized. Each of these types or patterns of attachment is preceded by certain patterns of interaction and predictive of subsequent outcomes in the child. The attachment classification may vary with different caregivers (parents) and is thought to reflect a characteristic of the relationship rather than a characteristic of the child.

Strengths perspective – In clinical work, the conscious attempt to discover strengths in individuals, families, and situations that may be used as the clinician attempts to reduce or eliminate problems or risks. This does not mean overlooking problems, vulnerabilities, or weaknesses, but rather, not focusing on them exclusively.

Introduction

There is more interest at present in infant mental health than ever before. In part this is because enhanced infant survival in the developed world has shifted focus to quality of life issues. This interest has been bolstered by

unprecedented gains in scientific advances in our understanding of early life experiences and the impact of these early experiences on later social, emotional, and cognitive development. Neuroscientific advances have begun to address how experiences affect brain development (and vice versa), increasing interest in the kinds of experiences that lead to adaptive and maladaptive outcomes.

Definitions

Although there are a number of ways to think about infant mental health, it is usually considered to be essentially synonymous with healthy social and emotional development. It has been defined as the developing capacities to experience, regulate, and express emotions; to form close interpersonal relationships; to explore the environment; and to learn in the first 3 years. In this definition, infant mental health must be considered in the context of family, community, and cultural expectations for young children. This definition incorporates a broad range of risk and protective factors that impact current and future functioning and development.

In addition, infant mental health is relationship-focused; that is, the infant's dependence on the caregiver means that any interventions undertaken to either enhance development or address problems must consider the caregiver's capacity to care for the infant, as well as the psychological 'fit' between the infant and caregiver. Infant mental health is also intergenerational in approach. In addition to attending to both parent and infant, the parents own sense of their childhood relationships, as well as ongoing interactions with their family of origin are often central to work with infants and their families. Clinical efforts are likely to be aimed at parents or extended family members in addition to the infant. Further, infant mental health is culturally bound, with different values defined by different cultures about childrearing.

Infant mental health is also prevention-oriented; activities are aimed at enhancing normal development and preventing problems from getting worse or from disrupting normal developmental trajectories. In this sense, it may be considered health promoting as well as distress alleviating.

Infant mental health has traditionally been transdisciplinary – enriched by the frameworks and perspectives of numerous professional disciplines that contribute to our understanding of the early experience of children. As an integrative discipline, infant mental health involves all professionals who work toward strengthening social and emotional development of young children and their families, and it is not synonymous with any specific discipline.

For some, the term infant mental health – if not the idea mental health in infancy – is objectionable. The discomfort may come from several sources: a negative association of mental health with major mental illnesses, a more general cultural issue of stigma related to mental health (e.g., many hospitals now have behavioral health units rather than mental health or psychiatric units), or a belief that the earliest years are carefree and innocent.

It is likely that even those who object to the term can agree on a shared goal of fostering healthy development for our youngest and most vulnerable citizens. Nevertheless, there are those who find it difficult to imagine that infants and toddlers can have mental health problems. They discuss risk factors for later disorders rather than disorders *per se*, or prefer to focus on problem behaviors rather than psychiatric symptomatology. Some suggest using the term infant well-being as a strengths-based approach to describe early childhood social–emotional development. Well-being, however, does not capture the actual experience of many young children who do suffer, nor is it particularly helpful in guiding us in how to enhance early experience. Thus, this article is written from the perspective that the construct of infant mental health is both clinically useful and developmentally important.

Further definition of some terms is necessary to facilitate this discussion. In infant mental health, infancy is considered the first 3 years of life or so. Typically in American culture, infancy is considered to be the first year of life, so infant mental health requires a broadening of that view. While we recognize that influences on the child's early development begin prior to birth, and extend through adolescence, the first 3 years represent the period of the most rapid developmental gains in the human life span. The term developing capacity refers to the enormity and rapidity of growth and development during the first 3 years of life. Finally, we emphasize that an exclusive focus on the infant alone is untenable, as the needs of parent and child in their many family, environmental, and cultural contexts are all a part of the focus of infant mental health.

Development

As noted above, the developmental gains during the first three years of life are exceptional. Normal newborns are capable of recognizing their caregiver (at a sensory level), and have basic modes of communicating with their caregiver. Over the first few months of life, they begin to discriminate caregivers, express a variety of emotions, and are increasingly able to communicate needs. By age 3 years, they have developed strategies for learning, and are able to engage in complex interactions with peers, including cooperating with and showing empathy for others, and have some abilities to initiate and to resolve conflicts.

Though there is a wide range of what is considered normal, there is also increasing understanding of how delays and deviations impact the pathway for normal development, and the implications for current and future mental health. For example, research shows that infants in the first few years of life who experience serious adversity (i.e., exposure to violence, trauma, or multiple medical procedures) are more likely to show abnormal patterns in the expression of emotions, unusual or deviant behaviors including increased motor activity, distractibility and inattention, disruptions in feeding and sleeping patterns, and/or developmental delays in motor and language skills. Many of these problems are not transient but herald the onset of longstanding problems.

Contexts of Infant Mental Health

Context refers to all of the many factors that influence infants' development. Intrinsic, or internal, factors include biological, genetic, and constitutional make-up. Extrinsic, or external, factors include the infants' caregiving relationship, family, culture, and social class. These intrinsic and extrinsic characteristics are risk and protective factors that dynamically interact with each other. Risk factors increase the probability of adverse outcomes, and protective factors decrease the probability of adverse outcomes.

Biological Context

The biological context includes all of the intrinsic factors that affect an infant's development: genetic influences, temperament, constitution, physical health, and physical attributes. These factors are considered 'within the individual'; they may or may not be modifiable. Much of primary healthcare is devoted to ensuring that the infant is off to a healthy start and addresses some of the modifiable intrinsic factors by using interventions such as nutritional education, developmental surveillance, and early intervention for various health and developmental problems. Clearly, development depends in part on biological dimensions of the individual's experience of the world.

Important contributors to the infant's mental health are evident in the biological context. In addition to genetic dispositions, many nongenetic biological factors may be important. From the third trimester of pregnancy to the second year of life is the most rapid period of brain development in the human life cycle, though brain development begins in the first few weeks after conception and continues well into adulthood. Much of the structural development of the brain occurs prenatally, but circuitry continues to be elaborated after birth, as a result of experiences. Functional development depends on making connections between distal and local neural circuits through the formation and pruning of neuronal synapses – believed to occur in part as a result of prenatal and postnatal experiences. Thus, numerous prenatal experiences such as poor nutrition or poor maternal health may directly affect brain growth. Prenatal exposure to pharmacological agents may result in the newborns showing withdrawal symptoms at birth, and prenatal maternal stress has been associated with changes in infants' stress-regulation abilities.

Physical health impacts the type of care needed by the infant, how his caregivers respond to him, and his capacity for normal physical as well as mental growth and development. The infant's temperament (e.g., behavioral inhibition or effortful control), as well as the infant's physical attributes (e.g., resembling a family member or disfiguring anomalies) can powerfully impact the caregiver's perceptions of and responses to the infant. Physical or temperamental characteristics may result in the caregiver feeling drawn to, protective of, or disconnected from the infant. Infants' physical or behavioral attributes may facilitate positive or negative interactions and further exacerbate negative interactions. For example, a fussy infant may be off-putting for a disengaged caregiver leading the infant to cry more in an effort to elicit attention.

Cultural Context

Culture provides norms for parenting beliefs and behaviors, defining how to care for infants and young children, as well as expectations about the roles of mothers, fathers, and extended family members. Although different cultural and ethnic groups develop different child-rearing practices, there are certain values that are evident in cultures around the world: (1) ensuring the child's safety and health, (2) ensuring the child becomes capable of economic self-maintenance, and (3) ensuring the child will be able to maximize societal values. Finally, the family exerts a strong influence on the day to day experience of the infant, particularly the type and availability of support for the parent. Culture also influences the parents' expectations, hopes, and values regarding the infant, and in turn, how the parent cares for and experiences the infant.

Social Context

Social class confers access to resources. Increasing availability and use of external supports for families with young children are associated with higher social classes. Living environment impacts the needs of the infant and the family as well as the prioritization, type, and availability of resources. Rural or isolated areas, inner cities with crowded living conditions and unhealthy living spaces, and even extreme climate or physical terrain, all confer unique needs and limit families' access to resources. Lower social class also is associated with probability of the individual encountering environmental risk factors. For example, poverty exerts a strong negative influence on the early experience of many young children because

of the myriad of associated environmental and psychosocial stresses, including an increased risk of community violence and mental health issues.

Relationship Context

The most crucial interpersonal context for the developing infant is the small number of caregiving relationships that the child encounters. Through these relationships the infant begins to understand his world, learns how to interact with others, and begins to develop a sense of his competence and self-worth. After all, the impact of infant's experiences of environmental risk factors, such as poverty, maternal mental illness, and partner violence is primarily via their effects on the infant–parent relationship. Further, intrinsic risk factors, such as biological difficulties, are moderated by the infant–parent relationship. For example, infants with complications of prematurity have better outcomes when their caregiving environments are supportive, and more problematic outcomes when their caregiving environments are less supportive. Also, difficult temperaments can be moderated through a responsive, nurturing, and consistent caregiving experience.

The attachment relationship is a biologically based process that motivates the young child to seek comfort, support, nurturance, and protection in times of distress from discriminated attachment figures – providing the basis for psychological security as well as physical safety. The attachment relationship develops over the course of the first year of life through the myriad of daily interactions between the infant and the primary caregiver(s). The quality of the infant–caregiver relationship is a risk or protective factor for infants' later development. A warm, nurturing, sensitive, responsive, and consistent pattern of interactions between the infant and caregiver leads to a 'secure' attachment; through these interactions, the infant learns that he is worthy of being taken care of, that he can count on his caregiver to be there when he needs her, and he develops a sense of self-competence in that his actions (i.e., signals, cues, behaviors, communications) can be understood and are effective in getting his needs met. Conversely, interactions that lack these positive qualities and are inconsistent, unpredictable, harsh, or punitive lead to insecure or disorganized attachments. Preferred attachment appears in the latter part of the first year of life, heralded by the appearance of separation protest and stranger wariness. Infants become attached to caregivers with whom they have a significant number of interactions. If more than one attachment figure is present, infants develop a hierarchy of preferred caregivers to whom they turn for comfort, support, nurturance, and protection.

During these early months, the infant appears to develop a set of expectations, termed 'working models', of what it is like to be in an intimate relationship with another person. These models are relationship specific, so that the infant's experiences with each caregiver determines the nature of the expectations that the infant develops for his or her relationship with each caregiver. This relationship specificity has significant implications for assessment and treatment.

Psychopathology in Infancy

The idea of psychiatric diagnoses of infants and young children often makes us uncomfortable. We prefer to think of infancy as a carefree time with unlimited possibilities for the future. Faced with infants who are distressed or who have impairments in functioning, we may prefer to think about them as having risks for subsequent disorders rather than discrete psychiatric disorders. Nevertheless, in clinical practice, examples of patterns of severe psychopathology are impossible to avoid. Young children present with consistent patterns impairing symptoms which affect their functioning and development.

As early as the first year of life, some infants demonstrate significant behavioral or emotional problems, including odd behaviors or unusual social or emotional responses in certain situations. Even when an infant has a mild or subclinical problem, the dynamics of the interaction between caregiver and child may be altered: the caregiver may become more or less attentive, more nurturing or annoyed at the difficulties the infant presents. While such problems may not be disorders they do affect the relationship between the infant and caregiver, and when the relationship is altered or stressed, the infant is likely to react.

Of course, real challenges exist in the psychiatric diagnosis of disorders in young children. Because infants and preschoolers develop social, emotional, communication skills at such a rapid rate, there are developmental differences in presentation of disorders across this age range. Furthermore, the major nosology-describing criteria for psychiatric diagnoses, the DSM-IV-TR, was developed without attention to young children. Many researchers and clinicians have been concerned about the usefulness of DSM-IV-TR diagnostic criteria in evaluating the symptoms of infants and toddlers because the diagnoses were primarily derived from studies of adults and used limited empirical data related to children, much less very young children. Alternative diagnostic systems have been proposed and the field continues to finetune the definition of disorders in young children.

Diagnostic Classification Systems

Specific symptoms or symptom clusters become problematic in children when they interfere with normal development or functioning; for example, in infants and young children, this may include disturbances in interactions between peers or with caregivers, impediments to play and learning, or negative impacts on health, growth, emotional, or behavioral development. Diagnostic classifications allow effective communication with parents and colleagues about our understanding of the problem and provide a common foundation for research to understand the validity, prognosis, intervention effects of the identified symptom constellations.

An alternative to the DSM approach was first developed in 1992, when the Zero to Three organization published the *Diagnostic Classification of Mental Health and Developmental Disorders of Infancy and Early Childhood (DC:0–3)*. *DC:0–3* was revised in 2005. It uses a clinically driven set of developmentally derived criteria and a multidimensional approach to diagnostic classification to attempt to capture both developmental issues and contextual features of psychopathology. The diagnostic classifications include descriptions of relationship psychopathology as well as the infant's functional emotional level.

A third diagnostic approach was created in 2003, when a group of investigators developed the Research Diagnostic Criteria – Preschool Age (RDC-PA) to facilitate communication and additional research on the reliability and validity of early childhood disorders.

Although only preliminary data exist, it appears that overall prevalence of disorders in young children is similar to rates in older children, that is, roughly 10–20%. Disorders with prominent externalizing symptoms, such as inattention/hyperactivity, oppositional defiant disorder, and aggressive behavior disorders are common diagnoses in most referred and nonreferred populations in mental health settings. Trauma-related disorders also are prominent, though the rates of other internalizing disorders, such as depression and anxiety disorders, vary in different reports, perhaps a reflection of limited data related to their use. In primary care settings, on the other hand, regulatory problems, such as feeding and sleeping problems, are most commonly reported particularly in infants.

Types of Disorders

Disorders of regulation
The earliest-appearing disorders in infancy are those that disrupt basic regulatory functions such as feeding and sleep.

Feeding disorders
In early infancy, feeding is a major activity involving parent and child, and feeding continues to be central in the lives of toddlers. In some diagnostic classification systems, feeding disorders are grouped under a single heading but in others they are split into many types. Most feeding disorders involve an inability to eat or food refusal, sometimes associated with an inability to maintain appropriate weight gain. Feeding disorders can present

in the context of caregivers who are disengaged from the infant during feedings, or with intense conflict between infant and caregiver during feedings. Although some feeding disorders can be related to specific events (e.g., nasogastric feedings or traumatic intubations), most feeding disorders appear to have multifactorial etiologies. Sensory-processing abnormalities, attachment-relationship disturbances, state-regulation difficulties, and complicated medical conditions all may play a role in the development or perpetuation of feeding disorders. Regardless of the etiology, feeding disorders are generally stressful both for parents and for the parent–child relationship. These disorders often create feelings of inadequacy in parents. Of most concern is when feeding problems impair growth (failure to thrive), since malnutrition is particularly pernicious as an influence on brain development.

Sleep disorders

Sleep is a central index of infant state regulation. Newborns spend up to 18 h of every 24 h sleeping. As children get older, they begin to develop a diurnal sleep pattern, sleeping in the evening and being awake during the daylight. This developmental process provides for the opportunity of a varied developmental course, and some researchers have suggested that sleep patterns be classified specifically by their frequency and duration, as some sleep problems are part of a normal developmental course. Disorders of sleep in young children can occur around sleep onset (primary insomnia or sleep refusal) or during sleep in the form of night wakenings or parasomnias (nightmares and night terrors). In toddlers and preschoolers, enlarged tonsils and adenoids can lead to obstructive sleep apnea symptoms, including night-time snoring and daytime drowsiness and sometimes irritability. Sleep disturbances may affect children's attention and behavior, as well as impact family sleep practices and relationships.

Behavioral disorders

Behavioral disorders are characterized by externalizing symptoms, such as aggression, tantrums, oppositional/ defiant behavior, and inattention/hyperactivity. They are uncommon in the first 18 months of life but are commonly described in preschool children. Aggressive behavior is the most common presenting sign in children in the third year of life who are brought for mental health evaluations. It is important to distinguish true signs and symptoms of disorders from variants of normal development. The challenge of diagnosing these disorders in young children involves determining the developmental appropriateness of some of the symptoms. As children develop an enhanced sense of autonomy and they test the limits of their emotional and physical dependence, parental report of oppositional behaviors often

increases. Parental reports of aggression and externalizing behaviors peak at about age 2 years and then begin to decrease to some extent. Even in the context of developmentally typical behaviors, parental distress in response to these behaviors must be acknowledged and addressed. However, there are also clearly cases in which a child's behaviors reflect an impulsivity and dysregulation out of proportion for the normal developmental phase.

The three major behavior disorders described the diagnostic classification systems include attention deficit hyperactivity disorder (ADHD), oppositional defiant disorder (ODD), and, less commonly, conduct disorder (CD). These diagnoses are among the best-validated disorders in the preschool age group, and they show significant stability over time.

Attention deficit hyperactivity disorder

ADHD is defined as a maladaptive and developmentally inappropriate level of inattention, hyperactivity, and impulsivity. Like older children with ADHD, preschoolers with ADHD present primarily with hyperactive, impulsive symptoms or with notable inattention and disorganization, or both. Because of the diagnostic challenges of assessing young children with these symptoms, it is especially important to obtain information about the child's behavior in multiple settings and from various caregivers, especially day care providers to rule out differential diagnoses like anxiety disorders, learning disorders, or relationship-based disorders.

Oppositional defiant disorder

In most clinical settings, aggressive and negativisitic behavior problems are commonly seen, especially in boys. ODD is characterized by a pattern of negative, hostile, and defiant behaviors including arguing with adults, losing temper, refusing to follow directions and seeming angry, resentful, or spiteful. Children with ODD often have associated ADHD. In those cases, the outcome 2 years later is significantly less favorable than in children with ADHD only.

Conduct disorder

Conduct disorder, a more extreme disorder of disruptive, aggressive, and destructive behaviors, is less common in the preschool population. Nevertheless, not only have signs and symptoms associated with conduct disorder been identified in young children (e.g., aggression, bullying, and cruelty to others), but also dispositions associated with conduct disorder symptoms at older ages, such as callous unemotional traits, also have been identified in preschoolers.

Not all children who present with aggression or negativistic and defiant behaviors as their chief complaints have a disruptive behavior disorder. Assessing the biological, emotional, relationship, and environmental contexts of the symptoms can guide the diagnosis. Children presenting with externalizing behaviors may have mood or anxiety disorders, including post-traumatic stress disorder (PTSD).

Emotional disorders

The category of emotional disorders includes disorders of mood, that is depressive disorders, and anxiety.

Depression

Depression in young children looks similar to depression in older children and adults. In young children, irritability or sadness can be the core symptom of depression. In addition, depressed children can have notable sleep, appetite or concentration disturbances, as well as preoccupation with death or excessive guilty feelings. Unlike adults, preschoolers with depression may not demonstrate the consistent presence of daily symptoms for 2 weeks. Recent data indicate that somatic symptoms may occur, but depressive symptoms and anhedonia (lack of interest in usual activities) dominate the clinical picture.

Anxiety

Anxiety symptoms normally are prominent in early childhood, with the fears peaking in the toddler years and then usually decreasing over time before entering school. It is during this time that young children can develop fears of the dark and of monsters. However, it is also possible for children to present with impairing anxiety symptoms. Young children can present with specific phobias during this period. It is not yet clear if young children present with social phobia (though they may be extremely shy, or behaviorally inhibited), panic disorders or acute stress disorders. It is clear that young children can experience post-traumatic stress disorder (PTSD) after traumatic events such as witnessing violence, being in motor vehicle accidents, or experiencing physical or sexual abuse. Among preschoolers, trauma reactions commonly include re-experiencing symptoms such as distress in response to a reminder of the trauma and/or repetitive play related to the traumatic event; avoidance of reminders of the trauma (e.g., not wanting to go in the car); and increased arousal as evidenced by increased irritability and temper tantrums, hypervigilance (increased scanning and attention to perceived threats in the environment), and increased startle response. The context of the traumatic event is an important mediator in the development of PTSD. Children who experience a single major traumatic event are more likely to develop PTSD than those who experience chronic traumas, such as ongoing abuse or neglect, although chronic traumas increase children's risk for other disorders. The ability of the child to feel safe and return to normal activities after a traumatic event can help to minimize the child's reactions.

A secure, supportive parent–child relationship may provide the most important way to ameliorate children's symptoms related to a traumatic event.

Relationship disorders

Although psychiatry and psychology traditionally have considered disorders to be within-the-individual, the unique dependence of infants on their caregiving context have led some to suggest that disorders may exist between individuals – in this case, infant and parent. This approach is bolstered by clinical observations and research evidence of relationship specificity. What this means is that the young child may be symptomatic in the context of one relationship but not others.

In young children, a relationship with a nurturing, sensitive, responsive caregiver is one of the most important contributors to healthy development. In nonreferred children, the formal attachment classifications based on the strange situation procedure provide a way to understand various relationship patterns. A secure attachment is found in children who have had warm, sensitive, responsive caregiving, and can be observed when young children are able to seek and respond to comforting in a stressful situation. Three types of insecure attachment have been described. Insecure–avoidant is seen when young children respond to stress by not seeking, or actively avoiding, help from their caregiver. Insecure–resistant attachment is characterized by the young child who can signal his distress but has great difficulty getting effective comfort from the caregiver. The disorganized attachment classification is found in dyads in which the young child does not have coherent, reliable ways of signaling distress to the caregiver, often associated with bizarre or unusual behaviors.

The insecure attachment classifications can be predictive of later psychopathology, but these classifications do not necessarily indicate current pathology. For example, children who exhibit avoidant attachment behaviors in the strange situation are at risk of developing anxiety disorders, and those children with disorganized attachments have an increased chance of developing preschool behavior problems. These characterizations of the parent–child relationship also are associated with later behavior problems and social–emotional difficulties.

In some dyads, disordered patterns of behaviors as well as distortion of perceptions about the other in the relationship can impair the child or dyadic functioning at the level of a disorder. Attachment disorders are considered to reflect a significant disturbance in the relationship between the infant and his or her primary caregiver, such that it interferes with the child's ability to develop normally in other domains, including cognitive, physical, behavioral, as well as social–emotional development.

Controversy remains about how best to diagnose attachment disorders. The DSM-IV-TR contains only criteria for the diagnosis of reactive attachment disorder (RAD).

The diagnosis requires a total lack of an attachment relationship and requires a known history of maltreatment to make the diagnosis. However, even in situations of profound deprivation, it is rare for a child not to develop some type of attachment with a caregiver, most likely to be a disturbed type of relationship. In contrast to DSM-IV-TR, the RDC-PA provides an alternative means of concretely operationalizing the concept by clearly describing behaviors of disordered attachment, even in the context of an attachment relationship. Unlike the DSM IV, the RDC-PA does not mandate that the child has been maltreated. DC:0–3R has similar criteria for attachment disorders as RDC-PA, but also uses Axis II for diagnosis of problematic relationship patterns which do not meet the standards for reactive attachment disorders and/or which are not focused specifically on the attachment portion of the relationship.

Whatever the specific diagnostic criteria used, it is clear that clinically relevant disturbances in children's attachment behaviors exist. A healthy attachment allows for a balance between the toddler's developmentally appropriate exploratory drive and need for emotional reassurance and support. Children with healthy attachments to a caregiver or parent can use that person in an effective manner for comfort and are able to successfully begin to explore their environment in a safe way. Children with attachment disorders generally demonstrate two major patterns of behaviors: inhibited and disinhibited behaviors. Children with the inhibited form of RAD tend to be emotionally restricted, are overly cautious, and do not seek out comfort effectively, if at all. In the disinhibited type, children do not have the usual wariness of new situations and new people. They are excessively and indiscriminately friendly with unfamiliar adults and rarely check back with their parent, even in new environments where they may not know anyone. These two patterns of attachment disorders are not mutually exclusive; children can present with features of both patterns. Indiscriminate behaviors, but not inhibited behaviors, appear to persist in young children who have been raised in institutions such as orphanages, even after a child has been adopted and has developed a new attachment relationship with a committed caregiver. Although it is clear that disturbances of attachment may continue to put children at risk for other disorders, attachment disorders have not been studied in children older than 5 years, and the current descriptions of these disorders may not be helpful in the older age group.

Summary of disorders

While different categories of diagnosis for infants and toddlers exist, significant psychopathology can exist within children and their relationships with their primary caregivers. The field continues to move toward further validation of the disorders of early childhood. These disorders can impair children's emotional, physiologic, and diurnal regulation as well as children's abilities to function within the structured rules of family and school and peers. Because of the critical role of the primary caregiving relationship, recognition of disorders of this relationship – whether because of parent psychopathology, child disorders or a relationship disorder – should be evaluated and, if necessary, diagnosed to provide intervention.

Assessment of Infants and Caregivers

We use the term assessment to describe the process of gathering data about an individual child and family for purposes of determining if intervention is needed and what the nature of that intervention should be. In this framework it subsumes diagnosis and includes an inventory of strengths and stressors that may affect both caregivers and child. Although we diagnose disorders, we assess individuals and families as a way of developing a comprehensive and coherent plan of intervention.

Infant mental health assessments are multimodal evaluations which often take place over a number of appointments and in different settings. A thorough history, careful observations, and collateral information are critical components of the assessment. Formal assessments including structured questionnaires, observations, and interviews, developmental assessments, and relationship assessments can add additional understanding to the child and the relationships which define his or her world.

One of the most important principles of assessment in infant mental health is that the infant–caregiver relationship is the most important focus of assessment rather than the infant as an individual. This principle derives largely from the extraordinary dependence of the human infants on their caregivers in the first several years of life and is bolstered by research demonstrating the following: (1) relationship patterns are more stable than individual characteristics of infants and they are important predictors of individual characteristics in later childhood and beyond, (2) the infant–caregiver relationship moderates the effects of intrinsic biological risk factors (e.g., complications of prematurity or adverse temperamental characteristics) on the infant, (3) the infant–caregiver relationship mediates the effects of extrinsic risk factors (e.g., poverty or partner violence) on the infant, and (4) there is often a remarkable degree of relationship specificity in signs and symptoms of disturbance in young children, suggesting that many problems in early childhood are most usefully conceptualized as relationship disorders rather than within the individual disorders. For all of these reasons, the usual assessment of the individual must be supplanted by a more comprehensive relationship assessment of young children in all of their important contexts.

Conventionally, two components of the relationship are assessed. These are (1) the recurring patterns of observable interactions between infant and parent, and (2) the subjective experience of each member of the dyad with regard to the 'other' and the relationship. Assessment of these two components allows one to evaluate both patterns of behavior and also of the meaning of behavior for the dyad.

Interactions between young children and their caregivers may be observed in unstructured, in naturalistic settings, such as during home visits or visits to child-care settings, or they may be observed in structured clinic visits during which prescribed tasks are given to the dyad. Common activities in more structured assessments are free play, problem-solving tasks, feedings, and brief separations and reunions. Most useful, even among more structured tasks, are those which do not overconstrain or prescribe parental behavior in order to allow the dyad to reveal to the evaluator how they negotiate different situations and challenges. Different paradigms of interaction have been used in clinical assessments and these are usually modified based on infants' ages or cognitive levels.

Parents' subjective, or internal, experience of the dyad may be assessed directly but the infant's perceptions must be inferred. Several structured interviews for assessing parents perceptions of their infants exist. Although these typically have formal coding systems for use in research, some have been used extensively in clinical settings without strict use of the formal coding system. An important contribution of these structured interviews was the demonstration that qualitative features of the parents' narrative accounts of their infants are important predictors of their behavior with their infants; that is, what the parent says about their infant may be important, but how they say it may be even more important. Of course, a parent's subjective experience of their infant also may be assessed in less formal ways, such as through listening carefully to parents' descriptions of their infant's behavior or personality or how the baby makes them feel, during the assessment process.

Domains of the parent–child relationship are the usual targets of assessment in both history taking and observations. These domains include parent characteristics that are conceptually linked with emerging infant behaviors and qualities. Thus, parents' emotional availability is associated with infants' patterns of emotion regulation. Parents' nurturance and warmth are associated with infants' sense of trust and security. Parents' response to distress is related to infants' learning to seek comfort for distress. Further, parents' protection of their infants is related to the infants' feelings of safety and the later development of the capacity for self-protection. Parents are important play partners for their infants, and play is an important domain of the infant–parent relationship. Parents also are teachers of their infants, and these efforts relate to infants' curiosity, sense of mastery, and interest in learning. Parents provide structure, routines, and instrumental care in order that their infants develop a sense of predictability and the capacity for self-regulation.

Finally, parents set limits and discipline as needed to assist young children to develop self-control and a reasonable degree of compliance and cooperation. Parents may have strengths in some areas, but difficulties in other areas of parenting; likewise, infants may experience difficulties in one or more domains, but not others. By assessing all of these domains of parent–infant relationship using both the external, observable pattern of interaction and the internal, subjective experience of who the infant, it is possible to construct an understanding of the relationship. Once the strengths and concerns of the relationship have been identified, it is important to appreciate them within contexts of caregiver functioning, and family, community, and environmental resources, including culture and class.

A comprehensive infant mental health assessment includes assessment of the caregivers' abilities to care for and understand the infant. Issues such as depression, substance abuse, a history of trauma, abuse, or significant losses, ongoing domestic violence, and isolation and/or lack of a supportive family system can all contribute to the caregiver's ability to engage in treatment and care for the infant. Furthermore, any other environmental factors that could contribute to difficulties in the relationship or that could interfere with treatment, such as lack of stable housing, also must be identified as part of the assessment process.

A comprehensive assessment must also include identification of the strengths of the infant, caregiver, and family. Including strengths in the assessment gives a fuller perspective of the infant's experience and can help build the treatment alliance between family and professional. Knowledge of strengths also can provide the building blocks for intervention.

Finally, any interventions must be congruent with a parent's cultural belief system. Because social class typically determines access to resources, enhancing a family's access to needed services is a critical step toward enhancing the young child's development. The overall goal is to design an intervention that is appropriate for whatever problems exist, uses the family's strengths, and will be acceptable and useful for the family.

Intervention in Infant Mental Health

Levels of intervention in infant mental health vary from the level of treating the individual infant/family through more comprehensive systems approaches aimed at changing policies to better address the needs of our most vulnerable citizens. They also may be arrayed along a continuum from universal, to focused, to selected (i.e., treatment). The overall goals of infant mental health services across universal, focused/targeted, and selected approaches are similar. They involve enhancing the ability of caregivers to nurture young children more effectively, expanding the ability of nonfamily caregivers to identify, address, and prevent social–emotional problems in early childhood, and minimizing or averting suffering, and ensuring that families in need of more intensive services can obtain them.

Preventive Interventions

Universal approaches are aimed at improving child development, parenting knowledge, and behavior. These approaches often are applied in primary healthcare settings, in early childhood education and childcare, and in family support settings. Strategies generally include health and behavioral promotion, screening and assessment, education and guidance, and referral for more intensive assessment and intervention services when needed.

Focused, or targeted approaches are aimed at specifically identified groups considered at risk for developing potentially serious social or emotional problems. These approaches may be administered in any setting serving at risk infants and their families. Examples include early intervention for premature or low birthweight babies, home visiting services for first-time mothers, or preventive interventions for abused or neglected children. Family support interventions include income assistance, adult basic and secondary education, parenting education to promote positive parent–child interaction, and interventions that address other environmental risk factors associated with poverty. The nurse home visiting program developed by David Olds, for example, has shown longlasting effects on children's emotional well being, child abuse, and even adolescent delinquent behaviors, even though the intervention extends only from late pregnancy to the child's second birthday.

Intensive, or selected services serve infants and caregivers experiencing current difficulties, and also attempt to prevent or lessen future problems. These services are most likely to develop from mental health programs, and may be provided for those infants currently experiencing distress, such as those who have experienced significant trauma, or for whom there are serious parent–infant relationship problems.

Treatment (Selected Interventions)

Treatment of infant mental health disorders may be focused primarily on changing the infant's behavior, the parents' behaviors, or the infant–parent relationship. Although each of these therapeutic 'targets' use different strategies, all are concerned with changing the infant–parent relationship as a way of changing infant behavior and ensuring that the changes are enduring.

Working with parent and infant together on changing their relationship requires the establishment of a good 'working alliance' between parents and therapist. This is a shared commitment to work together in the best interest of the child. The relationship between the therapist and the parent becomes an important component of treatment. In the context of this relationship, therapy focuses on appreciating the parent's emotional experience of the young child, and the young child's experience of the parent.

Examples of effective treatment strategies in infant mental health include infant–parent psychotherapy, in which patterns of intimate relationships and communication are explored using a psychodynamic approach, and interaction guidance, which uses videos of the dyad to identify and strengthen positive interactions within the dyad.

All successful treatment strategies with infants require active parent participation. Furthermore, caregivers must be able to function effectively in order to care appropriately for the child. Thus, it is often the case that treatment of the caregiver for problems such as maternal depression, substance abuse, domestic violence, or other issues occurs simultaneously with dyadic treatments. Coordination of services, as well as availability of services for caregivers, can be impediments to effective infant mental health treatment.

Finally, treatment of established problems aims to resolve current symptoms and distress and to prevent or minimize the detrimental effects of the symptoms on infants' later development. For these reasons, infant mental health treatments are concerned simultaneously with present and future adaptation of the child, and treatment of infants is always concerned with prevention.

Systems Intervention

When considering how to support infant mental health through a comprehensive system of services, it is important to think strategically. One important strategy is the development of a workforce with a continuum of expertise. A growing consensus holds that infant and early childhood mental health requires specialized training and that there are far too few mental health clinicians with requisite skills given the number of young children who could benefit from provision of services. It is equally important to better equip healthcare and other nonmental health service providers, such as child-care providers and preschool teachers, to promote infant mental health and serve as efficient and effective sources of screening and referral. Tertiary providers, such as adult mental health or substance abuse services, may not be familiar with the impact of such disturbance on the parenting ability of their client, and thus, they also need education to work effectively with such clients.

Another set of strategies focuses on the environmental factors that impact infant mental health. For instance, improving the financial well-being of families and communities will help to relieve the myriad of stresses associated with poverty and other environmental factors. The data are clear that the negative consequences of poverty are cumulative, pervasive, longlasting, and impact all aspects of physical, cognitive, and socioemotional development. Relief of poverty-related stressors can directly improve the health and social situations of young children and their families, ease stress on the parent–infant relationship, and directly and indirectly improve the social and emotional development of young children.

Summary of Principles of Infant Mental Health

Infant mental health is considered synonymous with healthy social and emotional development. Warm, nurturing, protective, sensitive, stable, and consistent relationships provide the fundamental building blocks to infant mental health. Important indicators of infant mental health include the young child's capacity for emotion regulation, the ability to communicate feelings and needs to caregivers, and active exploration of the environment. These behaviors lay the groundwork for later social and emotional competence, readiness to enter school, and better academic and social performance.

Risk and protective factors have been clearly identified that relate to current and later function. Risk factors predispose to subsequent psychopathology, but most clinicians also believe that infants can experience psychological disorders in the first 3 years of life. Protective factors are important especially when they can be mobilized to prevent or minimize adverse outcomes in high-risk infants.

The central focus of infant mental health assessment is on the infant–parent relationship. Any factors that impact the relationship between the infant and caregiver have the potential to impact the infant's mental health. The strengths perspective, as well as inclusion of cultural influences, provides a full picture of the infant's experience, and can provide the foundations for intervention. For these reasons, the usual infant-focused assessment must be supplanted by a comprehensive assessment of infant and young children that examines functioning across physical, developmental, environmental, family, and relationship contexts.

A continuum of services is needed to address prevention and treatment in infant mental health. Programs that address infant mental health must focus on relationships, be based in current developmental knowledge, and be supportive of the family. It is important that whenever possible, families are involved in the planning and delivery of infant mental health services.

See also: ADHD: Genetic Influences; Attachment; Autism Spectrum Disorders; Depression; Emotion Regulation; Failure to Thrive; Feeding Development and Disorders; Mental Health, Intervention and Prevention; Nutrition and Diet; Risk and Resilience; Sensory Processing Disorder; Separation and Stranger Anxiety; Shyness; Sleep; Social Interaction; Social-Emotional Development Assessment; Temperament.

Suggested Readings

American Psychiatric Association (2000) *Diagnostic and Statistical Manual of Mental Disorders,* 4th edn. – Text revision (DSM-IV-TR-TR Washington, DC: Author

Gleason MM and Zeanah CH (2006) Infant mental health. Comprehensive handbook of personality and psychopathology. In: Hersen M and Thomas JC (eds.) *Child Psychopathology,* vol. 3, pp. 173–191. Wiley: New York.

Sameroff A, McDonough S, and Rosenblum K (eds.) (2003) *Treatment of Infant–Parent Relationship Disturbances.* New York: Guilford Press.

Task Force on Research Diagnostic Criteria: Infancy and Preschool (2003) Research diagnostic criteria for preschool children: The process and empirical support. *Journal of the American Academy of Child and Adolescent Psychiatry* 42: 1504–1512.

Zeanah CH (ed.) (2000) *Handbook of Infant Mental Health,* 2nd edn. New York: Guilford Press.

Zeanah PD, Stafford B, and Zeanah CH (2005) *Building State Early Childhood Comprehensive Systems Series, Vol. 13: Clinical Interventions in Infant Mental Health: A Selective Review.* Los Angeles, CA: National Center for Infant and Early Childhood Health Policy.

Zeanah P, Stafford B, Nagle G, and Rice T (2005) *Building State Early Childhood Comprehensive Systems Series, Vol. 12: Addressing Social–Emotional Development and Infant Mental Healthin Early Childhood Systems.* Los Angeles, CA: National Center for Infant and Early Childhood Health Policy.

Zero to Three (2005) *Diagnostic Classification of Mental Health and Developmental Disorders of Infancy and Early Childhood,* revised edition. Washington, DC: Zero to Three.

Mental Health, Intervention and Prevention

H E Fitzgerald, Michigan State University, East Lansing, MI, USA
L M McKelvey, University of Arkansas for Medical Sciences, Little Rock, AR, USA

Glossary

Additive risk model – Concept that the total number of risk factors predicts developmental outcomes, rather than the particular type of risk.

Effectiveness trials – Application of effective programs evaluated with efficacy trials, to broader real-world settings to determine if efficacy findings hold up.
Efficacy trials – Well-controlled demonstration studies with strong experimental designs, and

sound and comprehensive assessment of outcomes.

Infant mental health approach – An approach to therapy or home-visiting interventions that emphasizes building trusting relationships between interventionist and parent, and parent and infant.

Probabilistic risk model – Concept that poor developmental outcomes are predicted by the interplay of risk factors, not necessarily the total number of factors.

'Speaking for the baby' – An expression used to represent one of the tasks of a home visitor, to reflect and comment on the infant's behavior in order to enhance parental understanding of infant development and the meaning of infant behaviors.

Introduction

Infants develop in a wide range of environments that differ in family composition, family resources, supplemental child-care, socioeconomic conditions, endemic health, and cultural contexts. Infant mental health focuses on the social and emotional well-being of infants within the context of their relationships with their caregivers and their caregiving environments. Characteristics of the infant such as premature birth, perinatal complications, physical appearance, difficult temperament, and physical or mental disability, as well as characteristics of parents such as inadequate prenatal care, single parenthood, parental psychopathology and/or substance abuse, parental stress, abusive parenting, and marital conflict can have negative impacts on the relationship between parents and their infants. Finally, parent–infant relationships can also be affected by the the family's financial resources, work demands, religious practices, social support networks, and neighborhood quality. It is the intersection among all of the factors that potentially influences the quality of the parent–infant relationship that challenges the infant mental health specialist to design an effective intervention strategy.

Infant Mental Health Defined

The key idea is that infant mental health reflects all of the events that contribute to normative social–emotional development, or push infants onto developmental pathways that optimize negative developmental outcomes. Infant mental health is first and foremost anchored in the normal social and emotional development of infants and reflective of their relationships to caregivers. The Maine Association for Infant Mental Health captures

this focus well in their definition of infant mental health as, "the ability of infants to develop physically, cognitively, and socially in a manner which allows them to master the primary emotional tasks of early childhood without serious interruptions caused by harmful life events. Because infants grow in a context of nurturing environments, infant mental health involves the psychological balance of the infant–family system."

Infant mental health encompasses all of the forces that may induce, facilitate, or maintain infants and their caregivers along a life-course pathway that will enhance the infant's vulnerability and risk for poor developmental outcomes or strengths and protective factors related to optimal developmental outcomes. The core message of infant mental health is that social–emotional development involves emergent, active systems of relationships that (1) influence the organization of the child's mental representations of self, others, and the self–other relationship, (2) modulate self-regulatory systems, and (3) influence adaptive functioning later in the life course. **Figure 1(a)** portrays a heuristic model that reflects this dynamic system and **Figure 1(b)** provides an illustration of how one might conceptualize the relationship between maternal characteristics and negative child outcomes. The illustration posits that the relationship between maternal depression and child attachment and self-regulation is influenced by child characteristics (e.g., difficult temperament, colic, and autistic behavior), the mother's own prior rearing environment, as well as family and social network variables. One could just as easily substitute paternal antisocial behavior or alcoholism, abuse, or abandonment as the factor(s) that might move an infant away from a normative pathway onto one leading to poor developmental outcomes.

Historical Influences

Two key individuals, Rene Spitz and Selma Fraiberg, sparked the development of the interdisciplinary field of infant mental health. Spitz was the first one to propose a classification of infant psychiatric problems formally. Today, the prevailing diagnostic classification system for infant mental health is that developed by Zero to Three. Revised in 2005, this system posits five axes (clinical disorders, relationship classification, medical and developmental disorders and conditions, psychosocial stressors, and emotional and social functioning) (see **Table 1**). Axis I, clinical disorders, is further broken down into nearly 20 separate diagnostic conditions. The classification system was revised through the work of an international and interdisciplinary panel of experts.

Spitz contributed innovative ideas that helped scientists and clinicians to break away from the prevailing theoretical tradition of the day. Drawing attention to the

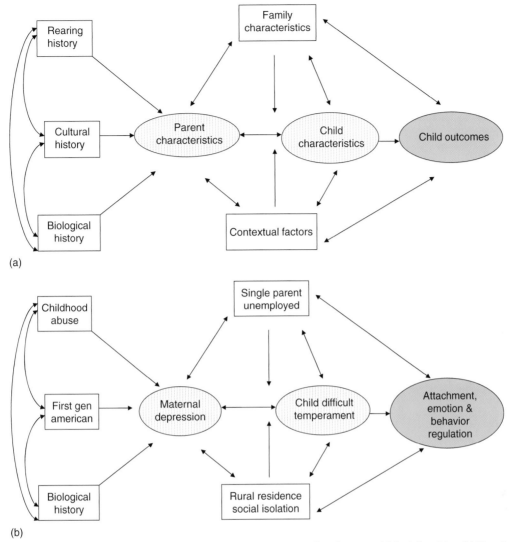

(a)

(b)

Figure 1 (a) Heuristic model of infant mental health: factors affecting the quality of parent–child relationships. (b) Hypothetical model of the impact of maternal depression on infant/toddler emotional and self-regulatory systems.

dynamic relationship between mother and infant, he noted that such interactions were constructions from the actions and reactions of the participants: mother smiles, baby coos; mother vocalizes, baby smiles. The flow of such action sequences reveals the dynamic processes that trigger transformations both in the infant's growing awareness of self and self–other relationships (subject–object relations).

Around the late 1970s, Selma Fraiberg and colleagues developed an approach to strengthen the emotional well-being of infants and young children, an approach that most often is referred to as the infant mental health model. The approach was embedded within the tenet that secure and stable parent–child relationships are critical for optimal child development. The Fraiberg approach represented a significant shift in the focus of clinical practice as it existed at the time. It focused on relationships

between the mother (caregiver) and infant/toddler as central to the establishment of healthy patterns of development for children. Within this framework, relationships between other members of the family and between the family and the intervention, a therapist or home visitor, are also viewed as significant influences on positive child developmental outcomes. This attention to the parent–child relationship, the child, and the parent required intensive and comprehensive treatment activities that included early relationship assessment and support, infant–parent psychotherapy, emotional support, developmental guidance, concrete assistance, and advocacy. Over time, this work generated a set of standards of practice for infant mental health specialists. Regardless of whether a home visitor is involved in intensive therapeutic sessions with families, is involved with brief interventions, or is part of a large-scale prevention program, the strategies described in

Table 1   DC: 0-3R. Diagnostic classification of mental health and developmental disorders of infancy and early childhood

Axis 1: Clinical disorders
  Post-traumatic stress disorder
  Deprivation/maltreatment disorder
  Disorders of affect
  Prolonged bereavement/grief reaction
  Anxiety disorders of infancy and early childhood
    Separation anxiety disorder
    Specific phobias
    Social anxiety disorder
    Generalized anxiety disorder
    Anxiety disorder
  Depression of infancy and early childhood
    Type I: Major depression
    Type 2: Depressive disorder
  Mixed disorder of emotional expressiveness
  Adjustment disorder
  Regulation disorders of sensory processing
    Type A: fearful/cautious
    Type B: negative defiant
  Hyposensitive/underresponsive
  Sensory stimulation-seeking/impulsive
  Sleep behavior disorder
  Sleep-onset disorder (protodyssomnia)
  Night-waking disorder (protodyssomnia)
  Feeding behavior disorder
  Disorders of relating and communicating
  Multisystem developmental disorder
  Other disorders (DSM-IV-TR or ICD-10)
Axis II: Relationship classification
  The parent–Infant relationship global assessment scale
  The relationship problems checklist
Axis III: Medical and developmental disorders and conditions
Axis IV: Psychosocial stressors
Axis V: Emotional and social functioning
  Capacities for emotional and social functioning

Adapted from ZERO TO THREE (2005) *Diagnostic classification of mental health and developmental disorders of infancy and early childhood*. Revised Edition (*DC: 0–3R*). Washington, DC: ZERO TO THREE Press.

Table 2 optimize success for building strong parent–infant relationships. The quality of such relationships is presumed to provide a key building block for development of positive child outcomes.

Need for Infant Mental Health Programs and Services

Despite the fact that the level of public knowledge concerning the importance of the earliest years of life for brain growth and development, for cognitive stimulation, self-regulatory skills, and the formation of relationships is unprecedented in human history, an extraordinary number of infants and toddlers are exposed to circumstances that prevent them from forging positive developmental pathways. Ten per cent of children experience a mental health problem, but few of them receive treatment.

The number of children with learning disabilities, speech and language handicaps, mental retardation, autistic spectrum disorders, emotional disturbance, poor self-regulatory skills, aggressive behavior, antisocial behavior, substance abuse disorder, and poor school achievement is increasing at alarming rates. Seventeen per cent of all children in the US have one or more developmental disabilities; 20% of all school-age children have attention problems; and the age of first onset of drug use, smoking, and sexual activity continues to spiral downward. Moreover, increasing numbers of children experience the detrimental and insidious effects of poverty. Although many of these problems present overtly at ages older than infancy and early childhood, most have their origins in the individual's biological and life-course history. Therefore, most mental health problems can be understood better, treated, and/or prevented if they are conceptualized as developmental disorders with origins tracing back to birth, if not before.

Life-Course Risk and Change

Significant numbers of the world's youngest children are at risk for poor developmental outcomes. One of the most widely used indexes of risk, developed by Arnold Sameroff, proposes that any three of the following 10 life-course events placed individuals at high risk for poor developmental outcomes: (1) history of maternal mental illness; (2) high maternal anxiety; (3) parental perspectives that reflected rigidity in the attitudes, beliefs, and values that mothers had in regard to their child's development; (4) few positive maternal interactions with the child observed during infancy; (5) head of household in unskilled occupations; (6) minimal maternal education; (7) disadvantaged minority status; (8) single parenthood; (9) stressful life events; and (10) large family size. While acknowledging that risk factors may add up over time, other investigators propose a probabilistic dimension based on the interplay between the individual's genetic history, level of environmental risk, and the length of exposure to familial and other structures that serve to maintain poor developmental pathways (see **Table 3**). The probabilistic approach is consistent with the concept of multifinality. Multifinality refers to the fact that the same circumstances may lead to different outcomes. For example, very young children reared by alcoholic parents may develop the same disorder, some other disorder, or may have no maladaptive outcomes at all. Maternal depression may or may not have a negative impact on children, because parental characteristics are only one component of the equation linking parent behavior to child effects.

Infants with biological risk factors who are exposed to high-risk environments are among the most vulnerable and in greatest need of infant mental health interventions. Regardless of whether one operates from an additive or a

Table 2   Overview of intervention strategies and tasks for infant mental health specialist home visitors

Strategy	Tasks for infant mental health specialist
Building an alliance	Visits regularly in the home; provides telephone support; observes, listens, accepts, nurtures; provides stable, consistent relationship; identifies and meets material needs.
Meeting material needs	Facilitates access to community agencies, provides transportation to services, discusses safety issues.
Supportive counseling	Observes, listens, feels, responds; identifies and reinforces feelings, sets limits for behavior, establishes expectation for change.
Developing life coping skills and social support	Helps parent to: resolve conflicts with family members, understand need for social support and obligations involved, identify possible friends, community groups and services, use anticipatory role-play to rehearse use of social support, models and teaches problem-solving and decision-making skills, supports parent is using skills.
Developmental guidance	Provides information about infant growth and development (uses formal assessment to show infant's capacities and next steps; shares literature if appropriate): Encourages parents to interact positively with infant (encourages observation and interaction, speaks for the infant; models, reinforces or shapes appropriate interaction; provides toys and books.
Infant–parent psychotherapy	Observes patterns of interaction, defines issues of clinical concern, assists parents to: identify feelings and put them into words; understand reactions, defenses, and coping strategies; find words to understand, grieve, forgive, and heal; develop new, healthier patterns of interaction.

Adapted from Weatherston D and Tableman B (2002) *Infant Mental Health Services: Supporting Competencies/Reducing Risks*, p. 81. Southgate, MI: Michigan Association for Infant Mental Health.

Table 3   Probabilistic model of risk for poor developmental outcomes

	Environment	
	High risk	Low risk
Genotype		
High risk	Vulnerable	Resilient
Low risk	Troubled	Nonchallenged

Adapted from: Zucker RA, Wong MM, Puttler LI, and Fitzgerald HE (2003) Resilience and vulnerability among sons of alcoholics. In: Luthar SS (ed.) *Resilience and Vulnerability: Adaptation in the Context of Childhood Adversities*, p. 79. Cambridge, UK: Cambridge University Press.

probabilistic model of risk, the key to resolving negative outcomes lies in the strategies employed to prevent the formation of negative pathways or to intervene with sufficient power so that the infant will be guided to a more positive developmental life course.

Ideally, infants and toddlers are reared in supportive, nurturant, loving environments and parents receive whatever assistance is required through relatives, parents, friends, and others in their social support system. However, when confronted with situations that challenge parental capacity to provide nurturant environments, various formal interventions can help them to resolve their conflicts and modify their relationships with their infants. Brief psychotherapy often is sufficient, but in other instances, longer-term treatments may be required. Researchers have identified scenarios associated with heightened risk for poor developmental outcomes. For example, it is generally accepted that most developmental outcomes are the result of gene-environment interactions.

Table 3 provides one illustration of the relationships between the continua of genetic and environmental risks. From this perspective, families experiencing heightened risk factors are prime candidates for prevention programs. The level of intervention or prevention will be guided by the severity of risk. Vulnerable children/families will require the most intense intervention or prevention efforts. Troubled children/families will require moderate intervention or prevention efforts and resilient and non-challenged children/families most likely will benefit from natural support networks and interactions with significant others over the life course. Whatever approach is used to intervene with development or to prevent negative pathways, the goal is to shift infants and their families toward resilient and nonchallenged developmental pathways. Intervention and prevention are the two major approaches to change relationship patterns early in development. Intervention approaches are designed to change an existing program, whereas prevention approaches are designed to prevent problems from emerging.

Intervention

When Should Intervention Begin?

Investigators often refer to magic moments when linking interventions to developmental stages. For example, human development is characterized by a sequence of dynamic and systemic reorganizations beginning at conception and continuing throughout postnatal development. These reorganizations occur at well circumscribed intervals: 1–3 postnatal months (shift from external regulation to internal regulation); 7–9 postnatal months (emotional and cognitive reorganizations accompanied by significant changes in memory processes); 12–14 months (transition to upright locomotion); 18–24 months (transition to language as the major form of communication); 5–7 years (transition from preschool to formal schooling); 9–14 years (changes associated with puberty, influence of peers and the shift to if–then thinking); and 18–25 years (identity, independence, and the transition to adulthood). Each of these transitions involves systemic change processes and each is embedded within the context of the individual's experiential world. If the infant has maximum plasticity in neurobiological-behavioral development and if the parent–infant relationship contains the same degree of plasticity, then it follows that the earlier one intervenes the more likely one will be able to effect change. Similarly, intervening during a transitional period may maximize that the reorganization achieved with be based on strengths.

Dosage Effects

A key issue in early preventive interventions concerns how much of a treatment may be required in order to effect long-term change. There are two aspects of dosage, the first concerns the length of time involved in each home visit, and the second concerns the number of sessions (months) that are required to bring about changes in the infant–parent relationship. For infants with colic, one might measure the sensitive period in terms of months, with only a few sessions of educational intervention required in order to build parenting skills and knowledge about the infant's transitional states. For clinically depressed or schizophrenic mothers, mothers with substance abuse problems, or who may be in marriages with high conflict, a much higher regime of intervention may be required, ranging from formal psychotherapy, marital therapy, or infant mental health-focused preventive-intervention programs.

It is reasonable to ask how much intervention is necessary to enhance child development to the point that anticipated outcomes can be achieved. Is a dosage level of 1 h per week adequate to effect changes in parenting behavior, parent–child relationships, and child development outcomes? Or, is a more intensive intervention required? Studies investigating dosage effects do not provide clear answers to this question, although it is clear that home visits that are scheduled at regular times and are more intensive in the beginning of intervention and decrease over time, provide the kind of routine and decreased dependence that can lead to successful changes in parenting skills and parent–child relationships. Most home-visiting programs are based on a minimum 1h visit, with an outside maximum of 3 h. Brief interventions generally involve about 10–15 sessions, but can be as little as several sessions. Longer programs tend to provide evidence of stronger long-term effects, perhaps because they are more likely to mirror the consistency and availability of natural rearing situations.

Another determinant of success concerns the quality of the staff involved in the intervention. For traditional psychotherapy, this almost always involves highly trained mental health professionals. For many preventive-intervention programs, however, there is a broader range of expertise among intervention staff, with extensive use of paraprofessionals and other individuals who are trained to deliver various program segments either in the context of an educational setting, or at home. Among these approaches, the most extensive involves the use of home visitors.

Home Visitors: Key to Infant Mental Health

Home visitors are typically professionally trained interventionists or are paraprofessionals who work in concert with professionals to deliver services. Among professionals, home visitors are mostly likely to be nurses, social workers, psychologists, early childhood educators, or child development specialists. For paraprofessionals, the key qualifications center around some degree of higher education and/or rich life experience. Home visitors are typically responsible for more components of intervention than just direct work with caregivers and infants. Researchers and infant mental health clinicians have developed a set of practices that optimize the development of parental competency skills apropos of their knowledge about child development. **Table 4** summarizes practices that will enable home visitors to enhance parenting skills as well as provides an inroad for development of criteria to assess the effectiveness of home-visiting programs.

Investigators have distinguished five approaches to early intervention with specific concerns for mental health issues: service-based, information-based, behavior-based, and relationship-based (two versions). In practice, however, many interventions utilize combinations of these approaches (see **Table 5**). For relationship-based approaches, a key to success lies in the quality of relationship established between the home visitor and the parent. One problem with brief interventions is that ordinarily the length of commitment to intervention does not allow sufficient time for the development of a trusting relationship between the parent and home visitor. In many situations it may take months to establish trust. Building a trusting relationship is essential to maintain outcomes once the intervention regime begins to decrease in frequency.

Prevention

The field of prevention research has received much attention and made great advances in the last decade. The concept of prevention is deeply connected to the field of public health. Public health professionals argue that no disease has ever been completely conquered by treatments,

Table 4   Task-focused intervention through home visiting: building parent knowledge about child development and enhancing parenting skills

Promoting parental self-efficacy
  Teach problem solving skills by focusing on basic needs, child care decisions, and relationship stresses
    Promote goal setting, step by step
  Engage in life planning with emphasis on delaying the next birth, completing high school, obtaining employment
  Developing social skills and social networks, by encouraging relationship development with family, neighbors, friends, and
    community groups
Promoting the parent–infant relationship
  Observer infant and parent to assess their responsiveness to one another, and quality of interaction
  Interpreting the infant's behavior and needs to the parent (referred to as 'speaking for the baby')
    Pointing out the infant's responses to the parent.
  Videotaping parent–infant interaction during play or feeding situations to discuss the interaction with the parent as an 'observer.'
  Guiding parents to understand the importance of their relationship to their infant's development.
  Guiding parents toward sensitive and emotionally responsive caregiving when interacting with their infant
  Supporting the parent's abilities to listen, observe, understand and respond appropriately to the infant
Modeling appropriate interactions
  Encouraging observation, play, speaking, singing, and reading to infants and toddlers
    Allow parent a safe place to express negative emotions
  Help the parent to understand how present life experiences and past history affect and influence the quality of parent–infant
    relationships
Encouraging good child care practices
    Facilitate access to services for healthcare for parent and infant
    Connect family with primary healthcare provider
    Accomplish well-baby-visits and immunization
    Encourage good child care practices in feeding and sleeping
    Attend to safety issues in the home
    Encourage continuity and appropriateness in substitute caregivers
Understanding developmental stages/promoting development
  Communicating Information about brain development and the importance of a stimulating environment and learning opportunities
  Communicating the importance of speaking often and positively to young children
    Interpreting the meaning of the infant's behavior
  Using assessments to indicate what the infant is currently capable of now and what parent can expect in the months to come
    Promoting play and exploratory experiences for the infant
    Promoting limit setting and appropriate discipline
    Promoting the father's role as a parent and for providing learning opportunities

Adapted from: Tableman B (ed.) (1999–2000) *Best Practice Briefs No. 19: Effective Home Visiting for Very Young Children, No. 2,* p.10. East Lansing, MI: Michigan State University Outreach and Engagement.

Table 5   Five approaches to intervention during infancy and early childhood

Service-based: Designed to reduce life stressors and support infant development by enhancing access to resources and community
  services.
Information-based: Designed to enhance maternal knowledge about caregiving and infant development, as well as the level of parenting
  skills.
Behavior-based: Designed to parent–infant interaction via observation of the infant's behavior, interpretation of its meaning, and
  shaping the quality of the mother's response to the infant.
Relationship-based: Supportive counseling: designed to guide the parent and support her in reflecting on her relationship with her
  infant. Places emphasis on creating a trusting relationship between the home visitor and the parent.
Relationship-based: Psychotherapy. Designed to help the parent to understand past and present relationships in the context of the
  parent–infant relationship. Emphasis on creating a trusting relationship between the home visitor and the parent.

Adapted from Tableman B (ed.) (1999–2000) *Best Practice Briefs No. 19: Effective Home Visiting for Very Young Children, No. 2,* pp. 2–4. East Lansing, MI: Michigan State University Outreach and Engagement.

but only through involvement of prevention. Utilization of this public health model leads social scientists to seek out the causes of pathology and act to prevent them, either by strengthening the infant's resilience or by modifying the infant's rearing environment. The primary goal of prevention research is to reduce the incidence or recurrence of behavioral or mental disorders and to increase the likelihood of mental and/or physical health for individuals over the life course. This mission requires the identification and targeting of the antecedent protective or risk factors to enhance or inhibit their influence on developmental outcomes.

Infant Mental Health and Prevention

The concept of prevention offers an alternative perspective for the timing and focus of intervention. Prevention seeks to determine how and in what way action might be taken prior to the onset of maladjustment. A unique aspect of early development is that intervention and prevention are so inextricably linked. So much of early development is dominated by the rapid differentiation of brain structures, rich plasticity of neural networks, and the organization of functional abilities that nearly any intervention is by definition a prevention, when viewed against potential downstream outcomes.

The efficacy of prevention has been the subject of debate over the past few decades. According to early prevention researchers, there were two factors that hindered understanding of the efficacy of prevention, namely inconsistent definition and the absence of a sound research base. A review and analysis of prevention research, conducted by the National Institute of Mental Health, generated five central themes to the conceptual framework of prevention science. These five themes include: (1) the expanding understanding of risk and protective factors at the individual and environmental level, the interaction of these factors, and their importance in the development of psychopathology or maladaptive behaviors; (2) the role of developmental processes in influencing the impact of risk and protective factors on adverse or beneficial mental health outcomes across the lifespan; (3) the increasing knowledge of how psychological, biological, and social contexts interact to create variations in developmental processes and trajectories; (4) the use of multidisciplinary perspectives to control selection bias in sampling and to assess variations in risk and protective factors and in responses to preventive interventions; and (5) the design and implementation of interventions designed to alter developmental processes in order to decrease risk, increase protective factors, and reduce the incidence or recurrence of psychopathological or maladaptive outcomes.

Promotion or Strengths-Based Approaches to Prevention

To this point the discussion on the theory of prevention extends to efforts to promote positive and prevent negative developmental outcomes. Traditionally, human service agencies as well as researchers and scientists have focused on needs, deficits, and problems demonstrated at the individual and environment level. Infant mental health approaches focus on identifying and enhancing parental strengths. The premise behind the strengths-based approach to human service delivery and empowerment ideology is to refocus attention on the strengths and capacities present in individuals. An assumption of strengths-based or empowerment ideology is that people have knowledge that is critical in defining their situations: the problematic aspects as well as the potential solutions. This refocus on human capital and assets may alleviate feelings of inadequacy and helplessness at the individual level and foster independence.

Strengths-based or empowerment ideology grew from one of the major paradoxes evident from applied research. This paradox, put simply, arose from the recognition that attempts to help people may be harming them through such practices as labeling, which tends to generate stigma as well as victim-blaming. Empowerment suggests both individual determination and sense of personal control; furthermore, it is a multilevel construct applicable to individuals and communities. Empowerment is a process through which individuals, organizations, and communities gain mastery over their affairs. The strengths-based or empowerment research and service paradigm assumes that humans have strengths and capacities that can be exploited and that, given access and control over personal and community resources, individuals can prosper and thrive throughout the course of their development. This approach fits the infant mental health model well, because it focuses on building strengths in the caregiver, the infant, the caregiver–infant relationship, and connecting families to community resources.

During the middle of the twentieth century many studies of child-care programs appeared in scientific and professional literature. Often these studies described programs that were narrowly focused and guided by a particular theoretical model. Rarely did studies involve random assignment of participants, use sophisticated quasi-experimental designs, or collect outcome data over time. Moreover, they seldom involved sample sizes sufficient to generate reasonable statistical power. Near the end of the century, significant funding from several government agencies established large-scale, longitudinal evaluations of the impact of large-scale national prevention efforts, such as Early Head Start. Nearly all of these studies emphasized child development, parent involvement, and community networking; some utilized random assignment evaluation designs, some were center-based, some home-based, and many combined home- and center-based models while others used infant mental health-focused home-visiting strategies.

A few well-designed longitudinal studies have provided impressive results indicating that high-quality preventive-interventions can have positive outcomes. Most of these target families where living conditions increase chances that an infant will be at high risk for developmental delays because of an excess number of risk factors. The following brief descriptions of programs provide some insight into the variety of efforts designed to prevent the occurrence of poor developmental outcomes for very young children.

Preventive-Intervention Programs for Families with Infants and Toddlers

Access to Services

Ready, set, grow: Passport

The Passport Initiative was a communitywide collaboration, originally was focused on the US city of Flint, Michigan designed to build a broad-based system of support through connecting families with existing services and teaching families about the importance of the earliest years of life. The primary goal of the program was to enhance the social development and well-being of children birth to six throughout a large county in Michigan. The program sought to increase positive social development in children by providing (1) parents with knowledge about child development, (2) incentives to participate in activities with their children that promote positive social and cognitive development, and (3) family advocacy to identify family needs and provide connections with community agencies, services, and programs to meet those needs. At its peak, approximately 9000 children were enrolled in the Passport Program.

The effects of parent knowledge of child development on child outcomes have been less frequently documented than have the effects on parent outcomes. The literature concerning the parent factors of knowledge of child development, parent confidence, and parent behaviors indicates that these factors are related to the child's social, cognitive, and physical development. In addition, research supports the notion that a parent support program such as Passport would positively influence these parent factors and, thus, indirectly influence child development. It is expected that Passport services positively relate to parental knowledge of child development and confidence, and that these attributes relate to more positive behaviors and activities with their child, and ultimately the child's social competence. Preliminary results support the effects of the program on parents and indicate that those who use Passport educational materials are more likely to have higher levels of knowledge of child development, have more confidence in their parenting, and engage more frequently in positive activities with their children. Parents who utilize the program's support services more frequently also engage in positive activities with their child.

Starting Early Starting Smart

Starting Early Starting Smart (SESS) attempted to integrate substance abuse and mental health services into primary health and early childhood education for low-income children birth to 5 years of age. A total of 2907 children and families (1598 were assigned to the treatment and 1309 to the control group) in 12 projects participated in the study. Common to each of the project models was an effort to put the family at the center for services and to provide careful need assessments in order to link program services to actual family needs and resources. A case coordinator was assigned to each family with an objective of forming a stronger connection between participants and service providers. At some project sites regular home visits were made by the case coordinator in hopes of maximizing communication and engagement; however, the extent of case coordination and home visitation varied by site.

The evaluation of SESS showed some small positive impacts on parents, specifically on parental drug abuse, and parenting behaviors such as reduced verbal aggression toward their children, more positive interactions with them, and declines in parenting stress through 18 months of program participation. In addition to the impacts on parents, some small positive impacts on children in the areas of problem behavior and language competence were also evidenced.

Comprehensive Child Development Program

The Comprehensive Child Development Program (CCDP) was developed to assess whether community service delivery programs could identify high-risk families and orient them to existing services in order to improve child development outcomes. The program objectives were to intervene early, involve all family members, and ensure delivery of services continuously through the child's entering the first grade. Twenty-one programs serving 4410 (2213 assigned to CCDP and 2197 assigned to a control group) low-income, ethnically diverse families, participated in a random assignment evaluation. Mothers in the programs were often (more than one-third) teenage mothers and over half did not complete high school.

Evaluation of the programs produced no evidence that exposure to community services has positive effects on families. There were no differences evidenced between control and CCDP families in parenting skills or family economic self-sufficiency, nor were there differences for children on measures of cognitive or social–emotional development. Findings suggest that providing community-based referral systems without any parent-education intervention component is inadequate to positively impact extremely low-income families.

Houston Parent–Child Development Center

The Houston Parent–Child Development Center (PCDC) targeted primarily Mexican American parents and their 12-month-old children in an effort to enhance the positive affective relationships between mothers and their children. During the first year of services families received home visits from trained neighborhood peer-educators and weekend family workshops that focused on issues of communication and support. When the children were 24 months of age, they attended a nursery school program while their mothers participated in classes on home management, personal development, and child development. After the 2-year intervention, PCDC mothers had more supportive interactions with their children than did comparison mothers. PCDC children scored better on the Stanford-Binet Intelligence Scale than the comparison children. Follow-up studies were conducted when children were 4–7 years of age and were 8–11 years of age. At the first follow-up, mothers of children in the comparison group reported higher levels of behavior problems than did mothers of children in the PCDC group, especially for boys. At the second follow-up, teachers rated children in the comparison group, especially boys, to have more behavior problems than boys in the PCDC group, suggesting continuity in behavior problems across contexts for non-PCDC boys.

Information-Based Approaches

Parents as Teachers

Parents as Teachers (PAT) is rapidly become one of the most extensively used home-visiting approaches to encourage more effective parenting, particularly with a focus on children's education and cognitive development. Parent educators typically have some college education, although education is not the sole criterion for selection. All parent educators receive a 5-day training program with some follow-up in order to be certified as a PAT educator. Program dosage varies, and can be as frequent as weekly and as infrequent as monthly. Parents must participate in one group meeting per month. Home visits are guided by the curriculum, 'Born to Learn', which teaches parents how to interact with their children. Paper materials are available to expand or reinforce lessons. Linking families to community support services is an additional responsibility of the home visitor and, as needed, families were referred to children's health services for hearing and vision screening and general health.

Studies using random assignment designs generally tend to show small gains in child cognitive functioning and social development. Children of teen mothers show advances in cognitive development and are less likely to experience abuse. A statewide program in Michigan, modeled after PAT, was designed to enhance school readiness by enhancing parenting skills, improving the quality of parent–child interactions, and facilitating family access to community services. The program utilized home visitors trained in child development in 23 demonstration sites varying in geographic areas. A total population of 274 545 children and their families were eligible for services with 44 691 receiving home visits, parent education groups, and parent–child play groups. Although state funding difficulties caused the initiative to be cut short, outcome indicators were moving in the right direction; children with developmental delays in personal–social or problem-solving skills benefited from parent–child play groups, were less likely to evidence delays at a second assessment, and were more likely to improve in communication skills after receiving a hearing screening.

Healthy Families America

The purpose of Healthy Families America (HFA) is to promote positive parenting, reduce child abuse and neglect, and ultimately enhance child health and development. The program started in 1992 and serves families with risk factors similar to those experienced by low-income families in other early intervention programs: low income, less than high school education, history of substance abuse, mental illness, and family stress and conflict. HFA programs are extensive, with over 400 communities in the US and Canada involved. The service delivery model uses paraprofessionals as home visitors, with selection criteria based on personal characteristics. Families are recruited during pregnancy with a goal of enrolling them in the program during the first postnatal trimester. Often, HFA paraprofessionals receive training in PAT and Infant Mental Health relationship-based approaches as well. Home visitors provide referrals to a range of community services, including child-care, job training, food and housing assistance, substance abuse treatment programs, and domestic violence shelters. Educational information is given concerning child development, parenting, discipline, food preparation, and parent–infant relationships. All program services are linked to the family's level of functioning and efforts toward goal attainment are made to build family supports with relatives. Studies of program effectiveness produce variable but generally positive results. Some studies show improvement in parent responsiveness to their children, more enriched home environments, and reduction in child abuse potential scores as well as actual incidence of child abuse. Children are more likely to have immunizations than control group children.

Behavior-Based Approaches

Interactive Guidance

Interactive Guidance, developed by Susan McDonough at the University of Michigan, focuses heavily on play interactions between infants and family members. It also embraces the principles of infant mental health: focus on relationships, presenting symptoms, and the mother's representations of her infant. The interventionist is a mental health professional with special training in the core components of the infant mental health model. It is conceptualized as a brief psychotherapeutic intervention, as much a component of any other therapeutic process being employed or any other prevention program in which the family is participating. The goal is to allow the family to begin to engage their infant or young children positively by discovering child behavior and development through play interactions.

Initially, all family members are invited to participate in a discussion about the child in order to understand how the family views their situation, what they can expect to happen in the interactive guidance sessions, and to decide whether they wish to participate. They are asked to tell their 'family story', an example of how components of family systems theory permeate McDonough's approach. In 1 h, weekly sessions, the therapist focuses on family strengths, explores the history of family relationships with their infant, and helps set family treatment goals. Six-minute video clips of play interactions are viewed after play sessions and provide the basis for building positive behaviors or behaviors that need to be changed toward more positive interactional styles. Random design studies of the effectiveness of interactive guidance provide evidence of effectiveness. Mothers showed improvement in relationship indicators, less intrusive and controlling behaviors, and improvement in mental health symptoms. Failure-to-thrive infants showed weight gain and reduced hospitalizations, while their parents improved in their parenting skills and social support networks.

Relationship-Based Approaches

National Institute of Child Health and Human Development Study of Early Child Care

The National Institute of Child Health and Human Development (NICHD) Study of Early Child Care (SECC) was designed to assess the impact of nonparental caregivers on a broad range of child outcomes, including social–emotional, cognitive, linguistic, achievement performance, physical development, and health. Nonparental caregivers included relatives (kinship care) and nonrelatives. The context for caregiving varied from in-home, in the provider's home, and at child-care centers.

The SECC study tracked the effectiveness of four models proposed to account for the way in which early care experiences impact later child behavior (Cumulative, Endurance, Sleeper, Fade). The Cumulation model suggests that child-care contributions aggregate over time such that children in child-care should show progressively stronger effects over the course of their exposure. The Endurance model proposes that the effects of child-care consolidate and persist over time regardless of changes in the child's educational context. The Sleeper model predicts that child-care effects are least likely to be evident during the time that infants and toddlers are enrolled in child-care, but emerge downstream at later points in developmental time. The Fade model suggests that the effects of child-care are transient over time. The SECC study not only provided an opportunity to assess these models, but also allowed investigators to examine the relationship between child-care experiences and concurrent psychological and health outcomes, the effects of the home environment on child outcomes, and the linkages between demographic and family characteristics and child development.

Participants in the study were recruited from 24 designated hospitals at ten data collection sites across the US. By 12 months of age, 84% of the infants in the study had entered some form of nonparental child-care, with the majority starting care before age 4 months. When they first entered care, 25% of the infants were cared for by their father or their mother's partner, 23% were cared for by other relatives, and only 12% were enrolled in child-care centers.

Observations of the quality of care at 6 months indicated that more positive caregiving occurred when children were in smaller groups, child–adult ratios were lower, caregivers held less authoritarian beliefs about child-rearing, and physical environments were safe, clean, and stimulating. Observed quality of care for poor children was generally lower than for nonpoor children when they were cared for by an unrelated caregiver, with one exception: poor children in centers received better-quality care than near-poor children, perhaps because they were more likely to be in subsidized settings.

Analyses of the effects of family and child-care on child outcomes indicated that, in general, family characteristics and the quality of the mother's relationship with her child were stronger predictors of child outcomes than were child-care factors. Family factors predicted child outcomes even for children who spent many hours in child-care. Family factors that predicted child outcomes included income level, education, maternal attitudes, and behavior. In addition, children whose mothers reported feeling depressed performed more poorly on measures of cognitive-linguistic functioning at 36 months and were rated as less cooperative and more problematic.

When observed quality of caregivers' behavior was high, children had better cognitive and linguistic abilities, showed more cooperative behavior with the mother during play, and had fewer behavior problems. Children in center care at 36 months had fewer behavior problems and higher scores on language comprehension and school readiness when classes met more of the guidelines recommended by experts for ratios, group sizes, and teacher training and education. Higher-quality child-care was also associated with higher-quality mother–child interaction among the families who used nonparental care.

Steps toward Effective Enjoyable Parenting

Steps toward Effective Enjoyable Parenting (STEEP) is a well-developed infant mental health relationship-based intervention program developed at the University of Minnesota by Martha Erickson and colleagues. Its goal is to promote positive parent–child relationships and to prevent the development of social and emotional problems in very young children. Although targeting low-income mothers many of who report intergenerational abuse, the program has been used with low-income fathers as well. STEEP is a home-visit program supplemented with parent–infant group sessions. Home visitors are well-educated, experienced in working with low-income families, and engage in weekly reflective supervision. Enrollment occurs during pregnancy and services are provided through the end of the first postnatal year. Follow-up checks continue until preschool age. For families in severe crisis, program intensity is increased.

Home visitors attempt to build a trusting relationship with parents and provide information about positive caregiving practices as well as the importance of parent–infant interactions. In this context, home visitors practice 'speaking for the baby'. Home visitors also assist mothers with everyday needs and problems, particularly those involving education, work, and access to community services. In the Fraiberg tradition, mothers are helped to explore issues related to the way they were raised, and they are encouraged to build support networks including networks with family members. Videotaping is used to illustrate effective and ineffective forms of parent–infant interaction.

Randomized studies of program effectiveness are encouraging. Findings indicate that STEEP mothers tend to be less depressed and anxious, have better coping skills for daily life events, are more sensitive in reading infant cues, and provide a richer home environment than are control mothers. STEEP mothers also have longer intervals between pregnancies than control mothers. Program effects related to the quality of the mother–infant relationship are less certain.

The UCLA Family Project

The UCLA Family Project (FP), developed by Christoph Heinicke and colleagues, is a home-visiting program supplemented with weekly mother–infant group sessions. The program is designed to enhance parenting skills, improve child development, and strengthen the quality of parent–child relationships. The program focuses on first-time low-income mothers with poor social support systems. Home visitors are mental health specialists with training in child development and family systems. Home visitors receive special training and weekly reflective supervision. Enrollment occurs during pregnancy and home visits occur weekly through the end of the first postnatal year and continue twice monthly thereafter until age 2 years. Telephone and follow-up contacts can continue through age 4 years. The program also involves fathers and other family members.

Home visitors provide comprehensive family services, promote sound parenting skills, explore family history issues, assist with resolution of marital conflict, encourage goal setting, and help mothers with work, education, healthcare, and child-care issues. Random assignment studies indicate good success in quality of the marital relationship, extent of social support, responsiveness to infant needs, and use of positive discipline techniques. Infants developed more secure attachment relationships and enhanced

attentiveness during play situations; however, changes in infant cognitive development are less clear-cut.

Nurse Family Partnership

The Nurse Family Partnership (NFP) was developed by David Olds and has become one of the most widely used evidence-based early intervention programs in the US. First developed in Elmira, New York, subsequent large-scale studies of the NFP were conducted in Memphis and Denver. Home visitors are nurses, selected because of their formal education in women's and children's health and their skills at managing the complexities of life situations facing at-risk families. Nurses' training in issues related to pregnancy and infant health present a natural setting from which to build a trusting relationship with mothers. Home visits focused on enhancing maternal and family behaviors that would improve pregnancy outcomes, building strong familial and other social support networks, and linking families with available community resources. Nurses were extensively involved pre- and postnatally with families and with an extraordinary range of parenting and child development issues. In all three major studies, women were randomly assigned to receive either home-visitation (lasting throughout the pregnancy and the first 2 postnatal years) or to receive community services. Families received regularly scheduled visits and, when needed, more frequent visits to deal with particular issues.

Overall, studies of NFP provide strong and positive evidence of the effectiveness of home-visiting to reduce risky maternal behaviors during pregnancy (smoking, fewer pregnancies, and increased delay in having another child reduced substance abuse). Child abuse and neglect rates decreased and mothers expressed greater empathy and more realistic expectations for their children's behavior. Because NFP studies involved longitudinal designs, it was possible to follow children through at least 15 years of age. Adolescents whose mothers received home-visiting were less likely to be runaways, had fewer arrests and convictions, fewer lifetime sex partners, and were less likely to use tobacco and alcohol. Parents reported that their children had fewer behavior problems related to alcohol and other drug use. The Denver study provided an opportunity to contrast the effectiveness of paraprofessionals and nurses as home visitors. Although paraprofessionals were associated with positive outcomes, they were less than half as effective as nurses.

Administration for children and families: Early Head Start

Early Head Start (EHS) is a two-generation program that serves both children and parents, and seeks to promote positive development in children directly by providing services to the children, supporting parents in their parenting, and promoting family self-sufficiency and healthy functioning. The impact study followed 3001 children from enrollment to age 3 years. When the families applied to the EHS program, half were randomly assigned to a comparison group and half were assigned to EHS programming. There were 17 research sites, not selected at random, but rather to reflect geographic and racial/ethnic diversity, different program approaches (home-based, center-based, and mixed). Program options for the 17 sites in the evaluation were based on needs of families and community. Home-based programs included weekly home visits and a minimum of two group socialization experiences per month, center-based programs also included a minimum of two home visits per year, and mixed model programs provided a combination of both home- and center-based approaches. Over time, however, many programs were using home-visiting program components extensively, favoring relationship-based infant mental health interventions alone or in combination with educational child development interventions.

Nationally, EHS had positive impacts on child cognitive, language, social–emotional, and physical development. Children who participated in EHS as compared to comparison group children scored in the normal range on indicators of cognitive development, had higher average scores on indicators of cognitive development, had larger receptive vocabularies, scored in the normal range on indicators of language development, had lower levels of aggressive behavior, had greater sustained attention with objects, were more engaging of their parents during play, demonstrated less negativity toward their parents, reported fewer emergency room visits for accidents and injuries, and had current immunizations.

EHS had positive impacts on parenting and family self-sufficiency as well. Parents who participated in EHS when compared with those in the comparison group demonstrated greater warmth and emotional supportiveness during semistructured play with their children, demonstrated less detachment during semistructured play with their children, reported playing with their children more frequently, provided more stimulating home environments, demonstrated more supportiveness of their children's language and learning, were more likely to read to their children daily, reported less spanking (both mothers and fathers), and were more likely to be involved in educational or job training activities.

Economic Benefits of Early Prevention

Correlations between socioeconomic status and the quality of healthy life styles are well documented. High socioeconomic status families engage in more health-promoting behaviors, and low socioeconomic status families engage in more health-damaging behaviors. Early prevention programs are designed to alter the lifestyle choices of low-income families so that the life-course events that negatively impact society can be reduced, and family lives can be altered. Demonstration projects designed to determine the efficacy of preventive-intervention programs generally are expensive. Efficacy trials are well controlled, generally involve randomized designs, meticulous data collection, well-educated home visitors, and careful management of program implementation and program dosage. Positive results encourage policy makers to fund large-scale implementation, often circumventing a critical second step in the scientific development of successful prevention programs. This step involves effectiveness trials. Do effectiveness trials involving large-scale real world settings generate the same outcomes that were produced by highly controlled, well-funded efficacy trials? Demonstrating effects in situations where there is greater variation in program implementation, dosage, family involvement, and turnover of personnel, provides even stronger evidence of program effectiveness.

One approach to the analysis of the effect of early intervention programs is to assess their impact from an economic perspective. What is the relative impact or rate of return society can expect from investments in early preventive-intervention programs? In recent years, economists have been examining this question with surprising results. Using data from several of the most prominent longitudinal efficacy studies of early interventions, estimates of rate of return range from $3.00 to much as $9.00 per dollar invested in the program. Enhancing family stability, reducing crime and substance abuse, increasing graduation rates, and stable employment histories dramatically offset the costs to steer infants and their families onto positive developmental pathways. What is needed now are similar studies of the effectiveness of programs for low-income families when implemented on a national scale without the guiding hands of dedicated researchers, random assignment models, strict research methodologies, and highly trained home visitors. Whether such study results will mirror those obtained from efficacy trials remains to be determined. However, results from efficacy trials provide clear evidence that high-quality early intervention, sustained from pregnancy through at least the kindergarten years, can have profound effects on the life course for children in low-income families.

Summary

There are many contexts in which optimal child mental and physical health and development is difficult to achieve. Intervention and prevention programs for infants and young children seek to dampen the deleterious effects of negative social and environmental influences on health and developmental outcomes. Overall, findings suggest that intervention in infancy and early childhood is effective for promoting more optimal parent and family environments and, ultimately, child developmental outcomes. Programs such as the CCDP, which sought to connect families to existing community resources, demonstrated that service referral is not sufficient for altering the developmental trajectory of at-risk children. The studies reviewed attempted to alter infant development by enhancing the quality of experiences very young children had with their caregivers and the caregiving environment. Features of the service-, information-, behavior-, and relationship-based models for programming are utilized in many home-based interventions, such as in EHS or in the NFP. The findings from programs that utilize a more holistic or systemic approach to services are the most positive and overarching. Nevertheless, findings from these interventions are relatively modest, and little information exists to support their effectiveness in broad-based effectiveness studies. There is an ongoing dialog among researchers and policy experts as to the meaning of modest impacts of programs for children in high-risk developmental trajectories. Some argue that resources that go into programs with modest impacts could be better utilized, while others argue that even small changes in the developmental context for at-risk children can protect them from some of the negative effects of risk exposure. Findings from existing research have taught much about which interventions produce the greatest change for children and families. Further studies will allow investigators to untangle the individual differences in effects of intervention for infants and young children.

See also: Attachment; Demographic Factors; Family Influences; Head Start; Mental Health, Infant; Preschool and Nursery School; Risk and Resilience.

Suggested Readings

Fitzgerald HE, Lester BM, and Zuckerman B (eds.) (2006) *The Crisis in Youth Mental Health, Vol. 1: Childhood Disorders.* Westport, CT: Praeger Press.

Landy S and Menna R (2006) *Early Intervention with Multi-Risk Families: An Integrative Approach.* Baltimore: Paul Brookes.

Osofsky JD and Fitzgerald HE (2000) *WAIMH Handbook of Infant Mental Health,* vols. 1–4. New York: Wiley.

Tableman B (ed.) (1999–2000) *Best Practice Briefs: Effective Home Visiting for Very Young Children, Nos. 17–20.* East Lansing, MI: Michigan State University Outreach and Engagement.

Tableman B (ed.) (1999–2000) *Best Practice Briefs No. 19: Effective Home Visiting for Very Young Children, No. 2,* p. 10. East Lansing, MI: Michigan State University Outreach and Engagement.

Tableman B (ed.) (1999–2000) *Best Practice Briefs No. 19: Effective Home Visiting for Very Young Children, No. 2,* pp. 2–4. East Lansing, MI: Michigan State University Outreach and Engagement.

Weatherston D and Tableman B (2002) *Infant Mental Health Services: Supporting Competencies/Reducing Risks,* p. 81. Southgate, MI: Michigan Association for Infant Mental Health.

Zeanah CH, Jr. (ed.) (2000) *Handbook of Infant Mental Health,* rev. edn. New York: Guilford.

ZERO TO THREE (2005) *Diagnostic Classification of Mental Health and Developmental Disorders of Infancy and Early Childhood, Revised Edition (DC:0-3R).* Washington, DC: ZERO TO THREE Press.

Zucker RA, Wong MM, Puttler LI, and Fitzgerald HE (2003) Resilience and vulnerability among sons of alcoholics. In: Luthar SS (ed.) *Resilience and Vulnerability: Adaptation in the Context of Childhood Adversities,* p. 79. Cambridge, UK: Cambridge University Press.

Milestones: Cognitive

M W Daehler, University of Massachusetts, Amherst, MA, USA

Glossary

Analogical problem solving – Transfer of a solution principle applicable for solving one problem to another problem that can be solved using the same solution principle.

Explicit memory – Recall of information that had been acquired at a specific time and place.

Habituation – Gradual decline in intensity, frequency, or duration of a response over repeated or lengthy occurrences of the same stimulus.

Implicit memory – Recognition or recall of information not available to conscious reflection or awareness of its having been acquired at a specific time or place.

Means-ends behavior – Deliberate actions that must be performed prior to achieving a goal.

Norms – Measures of average values and their variations for the onset or display of some aspect of development.

Object identity – Ability to anticipate an object's reappearance after a brief interval of time.

Object permanence – Realization that objects continue to exist and can be retrieved even when not in view.

Psychological causality – Recognition that the actions of humans or other agents are influenced by intentions or other mental, emotional, or motivational factors.
Scripts – Organized memories for commonly experienced events.

Introduction

The major milestones or markers indicating various cognitive achievements in infants and young children during specific developmental ages (0–1 month, 1–6 months, 6–12 months, 12–18 months, 18–24 months, and 24–36 months of age) are identified and described. These milestones provide useful practical information about important intellectual changes and challenge researchers and theorists to explain the mechanisms underlying how cognitive structures and processes are acquired and develop.

Virtually everyone who studies children and their development would agree that there are momentous changes in attention and memory, planning, problem solving, language, reasoning, and a host of other intellectual domains over the first 3 years of life. Developmental psychologists have long been enamored with describing these changes. Even the efforts of some of the earliest observers, those who maintained a diary of their own children's developmental progress, typically focused on documenting when their children accomplished some task or demonstrated some level of competence. For example, Charles Darwin reported that his 5-month-old son already seemed to be making connections among events in his world; at that age he would become upset if not taken outdoors soon after being dressed in a hat and cloak. At 7 months of age this same child looked around to find his nurse upon hearing her name, and Darwin noted that one of his children readily imitated a variety of actions at 11½ months of age. Furthermore, at a little over 3 years of age one of Darwin's children recognized a picture of his grandfather and remembered a series of events that had taken place upon visiting him 6 months earlier. If psychologists are to understand the processes and mechanisms responsible for development in any domain, it is imperative that an accurate assessment of the child's progress in achieving various cognitive skills be obtained.

Milestones most frequently have been linked to the first appearances of various motor behaviors, for example, the ability to roll over from back to stomach, to sit upright without support, to crawl on all fours, or to walk without assistance. In a similar vein, the onset of various language skills such as babbling, first words, and the appearance of two-word utterances have been viewed as milestones. The idea of milestones applied to the emergence of cognitive skills has been less frequently voiced by developmental researchers, perhaps because behaviors that unambiguously signal a new-found cognitive skill often must be inferred from performance on tasks designed to measure such an accomplishment rather than being directly observed as they are exhibited in the child's day-to-day behaviors. As a consequence, the ingenuity and creativity of the researcher in devising procedures that assess a particular cognitive ability is often a major factor in determining when infants or very young children have reached a specific level of accomplishment.

Norms, measures of average times and their variability among children for achieving some aspect of development, are exceedingly useful for a number of reasons. Norms often serve a practical function. Knowing that an infant or young child is demonstrating satisfactory progress in a domain that typically undergoes change can signal whether biological or experiential factors are hindering, or perhaps promoting, some cognitive capacity. For example, several reflexes routinely displayed by the 1 month old are no longer exhibited by the healthy 6 month old. These changes are generally accounted for in terms of the maturation of various regions of the cortex; failures in this normal progression may be an indicator of brain damage. From a similar perspective, precocious intellectual advances may signal the benefits of certain kinds of experience for development.

Documenting the emergence of new cognitive abilities may also serve a theoretical function. A child who demonstrates the capacity to use symbols or representational insight, for example, awareness that a word, a picture, a map, or a model can stand for or serve in the place of a real object or event, reveals a new level of conceptual understanding that needs to be considered within any explanation of cognition and its development. For Piaget, the transition from being able to act upon objects and events in the world to using symbolic representations in place of those objects and events served as the key cognitive advance to distinguish two stages of intellectual competence differentiating the child older than 18–24 months of age from the infant or younger child. If researchers are to recognize theoretically important changes and fully understand the processes underlying some developmental capacity, they must begin by documenting when that capacity has emerged.

Keep in mind, however, that variability is an essential aspect of measuring the onset of intellectual markers in development. Although an age may be identified when children, on average, are capable of some ability, this average is based on information obtained from many different children. Any single child may be several weeks or months younger or older than another child before exhibiting some cognitive ability, yet fall well within the range of acceptable deviation from the so-called 'typical' child. Thus although we can describe milestones or, perhaps more appropriately, markers for intellectual development, when they are exhibited is probably better considered within a broader conceptualization regarding age than at time X or time Y.

Variability in displaying some capacity may even be found when observing the same infant. For example, variability can occur if a procedure is modified, that is, the task or situation used to assess some level of competence is changed. Thus in one context the infant may be said to have some cognitive skill but if evaluated with a different procedure, for example, when the processing load becomes too great, he or she may not appear to have the skill or to even have lost it. Nevertheless, this variability can be the impetus for further efforts to understand what processes and mechanisms are central to the emergence of cognitive markers.

Table 1 summarizes, within relatively broad age ranges, some of the major cognitive achievements demonstrated by infants and very young children who are described in additional detail here. Developmental researchers, however, are not always in agreement concerning the time these various capacities emerge. Nevertheless, these disagreements can have positive consequences in that they provide additional challenges for investigating and understanding the basic processes and structures that comprise cognition and its development in humans.

0–1 Month of Age

Before developmental psychologists began to study carefully their behaviors and had established procedures for asking questions that would shed light on their capacities, the general view was that infants were quite limited in terms of their cognitive skills. Research carried out, particularly beginning in the 1960s and continuing at a rapid pace yet today, has refuted this historical assumption and has revealed surprising competencies at far younger ages than ever anticipated. For example, even the newborn shows evidence of some cognitive skills.

Table 1   Summary of major markers in cognitive development from birth to 3 years of age

Age[a]	Cognitive capacity
0–1 Month	Demonstrates recognition memory for simple visual arrays for short durations
	Capable of being operantly conditioned using behavioral systems such as sucking and head turning
	Responsive to classical conditioning
1–6 Months	Able to recognize events experienced days and weeks earlier
	Possesses object identity, memory for the location and movement of a briefly occluded stimulus
	Displays some core physical knowledge of objects (e.g., solidity; need for support)
	Makes inferences about the continuity of an object when portions are occluded (object unity)
	Aware of numerosity (1–4 objects)
	Exhibits perceptual categorization (based on perceptual attributes)
6–12 Months	Shows consistent increases in the durability of short-term memory
	Demonstrates explicit recall memory for a sequence of actions over several weeks
	Searches for a hidden object (object permanence)
	Infers causality between physical objects (mechanical causality)
	Begins to understand goal-directed and intentional actions
	Shows planning and means–ends problem solving
	Operates with an egocentric frame of reference in terms of spatial tasks
	Comprehends the meaning of a few common words
	Demonstrates conceptual categorization (based on role, function, or meaning)
12–18 Months	Shows long-term recall involving a series of action over several months' duration
	Exhibits an awareness of intentionality and psychological causality
	Produces single word utterances that reflect overextensions, underextensions, or overlap with typical concepts
	Initiates pretense activity initially involving self, then includes another person or toy
	Differentiates pictures from objects
	Succeeds in solving simple analogical problems
18–24 Months	Provides first indications of strategic behavior to assist memory
	Acquires a concept of self
	Understands that the desires of others may differ from one's own
	Reaches goals through the appropriate selection of and use of tools
	Uses interesting objects (e.g., models) as representations for other objects
24–36 Months	Recalls conventional scripts for routinely experienced events
	Reorients pictures as well as objects to be upright
	Begins to use maps and models as symbols
	Able to employ arbitrary substitute objects in play and demonstrates simple kinds of sociodramatic play

[a]Infants and very young children often show individual differences in the ages at which they display the various developmental achievements summarized in this table.

Recognition Memory

Newborns have basic recognition memory capacities. When shown the same object over and over again, they will look at it for less and less time. They are displaying habituation, that is, a decline in intensity, frequency, or duration of a behavior. This decline is not due to fatigue or some other processing limitation since infants often display recovery of attention when a new stimulus is presented. Instead, newborns must be recognizing (remembering) that the repeatedly presented object is the same and that a new one is different. Recognition memory is even possible for events to which the infant was exposed prenatally. Newborns and very young babies respond differently to music that they have repeatedly heard while in the uterus compared to music that they have not heard before. In addition, they discriminate and prefer their mothers' voices over the voices of strangers. For example, a neonate is more likely to engage in sucking at a particular rate that results in the opportunity to hear the voice of his or her mother reading than sucking at another rate that has the consequence of hearing a stranger reading that same passage. Recognition memory for simple visual objects, their size, shape, and color, begins to be evident typically within the first month after birth.

Basic Learning Processes

Infants also show the capacity to learn shortly after birth. Within a matter of hours or days after delivery, newborns can modulate their rate or manner of sucking to more successfully ingest milk or to obtain some other reinforcer such as visual or auditory stimulation. For example, as already indicated, they will quickly learn to suck at a faster or slower rate depending on whether it results in hearing the mother's voice rather than a stranger's voice. Very young infants also display the capacity to be classically conditioned. For example, they learn to turn their head toward the sound of a tone that has repeatedly signaled the availability of milk. Not surprisingly, 1- and 3-month-olds are likely to display such learning more consistently and in fewer numbers of conditioning trials than the newborn whose central nervous system is less fully mature.

1–6 Months of Age

Recognition Memory

Recognition memory for visual events experienced days and weeks earlier becomes evident beginning around 2–3 months of age. For example, if 3-month-olds are given the opportunity to make brightly colored elements of a mobile move and produce sound by kicking a leg to which a ribbon from the mobile has been attached, they learn to do so in a matter of minutes. When shown the mobile again 2–8 days later, but with the ribbon no longer attached to their leg, they display more active kicking than when the mobile is not present; they appear to remember that the kicking would make the mobile move. If presented the opportunity to learn the contingency between the mobile and their kicking on more than one day, retention of the relation is extended several more days. Perhaps not surprising is that memory for the specific elements of the mobile such as the particular shapes and colors of the items in it, tends to be lost fairly quickly over that time; any similar mobile, even with somewhat different elements, is sufficient to increase kicking rate. More surprising, however, is that surrounding aspects of the setting in which the learning has taken place such as the colors and patterning of the crib bumper are important cues to remembering; memory is less likely over short periods of time when these contextual features change. Even more remarkable is that a reminder of the mobile, such as showing infants its movement independent of their kicking activity many days after memory for the array has apparently been lost, encourages some infants as young as 2 months of age, and most infants at 3 months of age, to remember the kicking activity for nearly 1 month. Thus infants at a very early age display competence in performing behavioral responses that have had consequences on their environment over surprisingly long durations of time. Moreover, by 5 months of age, even after only briefly seeing a visual array, infants will recognize it as long as 2 weeks later.

Knowledge of Objects and Events

Infants around 3–4 months of age also begin to display knowledge of core principles of some of the physical characteristics of objects. One core principle is object identity. Object identity refers to the ability to remember and to anticipate an object's reappearance after being hidden for a brief period of time. Thus, a representation of at least some of its properties such as its location and direction of movement has been formed. As one illustration of this capacity, if shown an object passing behind an opaque barrier, babies attend to it more, as if surprised, if it reappears at some position other than the edge of the barrier where expected to re-emerge than if it reappears at the edge where it should re-emerge. As another illustration, an opaque barrier whose forward edge rotates upward in front of an object so as to hide it from view, but then continues to rotate as if the object is no longer behind the barrier to stop its continued motion, draws more attention from 4-month-olds than when the barrier stops its motion about the point where the hidden object normally would prevent its continued movement.

Infants this young may have some awareness of other properties of objects. For example, they attend longer, again as if somewhat surprised, when a solid object appears to pass through another solid object than when it does not. Moreover, they seem to understand that an object will fall if it is pushed past the edge of a supporting surface. Yet at 3 months of age, they accept any contact with the surface as sufficient to uphold the object; it is not typically until about 7 months of age that they seem to appreciate that a substantial proportion of the object needs to be supported by a surface to prevent it from falling. In addition, at about 2–3 months of age, infants infer that a rod whose two ends can be seen protruding from behind a barrier comprises a unified object, that is, a continuous rod rather than two separate segments. This knowledge of object unity becomes evident when the two visible ends show various kinds of coordinated movement; newborns do not make this inference and seem to interpret the end segments as two separate, unconnected objects even though there are coordinated movements between the visible ends.

Even 1-month-olds may have some capacity for representing numerosity. When repeatedly shown the same number of items in different arrays, say two, they show increased attention if three items are shown. However, the evidence infants process numerosity for between one and three items is especially compelling beginning around 5 months of age. At about this same time, infants may also have some basic understanding of addition and subtraction, again among small numbers of items. For example, if infants are shown one object before it is covered by a screen, then watch as a second is placed behind the screen, they respond differently when the screen is removed if they see only one object than if they see the expected two objects. Similarly, if they see two objects before they are covered by the screen and observe one being removed from behind that barrier, they look longer, when the screen is removed, if two objects come into view rather than only one perhaps an indication of being somewhat surprised by two still being there. This finding, however, has been difficult to replicate consistently; explanations for these behaviors based on perceptual processes rather than a conceptual understanding of arithmetic may provide an alternative, more parsimonious explanation for some of these results.

Perceptual Categorization

A major question that has prompted considerable research throughout infancy is how soon after birth babies conceptualize different objects as members of the same category. Considerable evidence supports the conclusion that infants by around 3 months of age recognize different exemplars of cats or dogs or horses as belonging together and some findings show that they process exemplars of broader classes such as mammals or birds or furniture as belonging together. But substantial disagreements continue over whether this recognition is driven by an understanding of conceptual representations or is better considered in terms of the similar perceptual attributes that category members may share such as specific features, that is, color, shape, movement, and so on. Infants as young as 3 months are able to notice the correlation among simple features of stimuli such as color and shape; thus perhaps from repeated experience with exemplars belonging to a category, infants this young are beginning to abstract commonalities or prototypic components that serve to promote a conceptual representation for that category. Not surprisingly, however, at this age these representations are likely to be implicit and developed without any conscious awareness on the part of infants.

6–12 Months of Age

Short-Term Memory

Short-term memory in infants after about 6 months of age is often assessed by a measure of its durability, that is, the length of delay the infant can withstand in order to successfully find a hidden object from among one of several different locations. Research generally reveals that infants of about 7 months of age can remember where an object was hidden for only a couple of seconds but that their short-term memory increases on the order of about 2 s per month over the next several months; thus by about 12 months of age they can tolerate delays of about 12 s. This ability may, of course, be affected by any number of methodological factors and the above estimates should be considered conservative since some studies report somewhat greater durability of memory in infants of this age.

Recall and Long-Term Explicit Memory

Some evidence exists that an implicit memory for a particular event experienced around 6 months of age may still be retained up to about 2 years later. But explicit memory, the conscious recall of information linked to the specific occurrence of an event, now becomes evident during the second 6 months of life. Explicit memories are typically measured by verbal recall in older children. However, infants under 18–24 months of age do not have the verbal abilities needed to report explicit memories. Thus imitation of actions performed on objects provides some of the best evidence for explicit memory in infants. For example, a sequence of three or four actions with a toy may be modeled for the child. If the infant imitates those actions in the same order as they were modeled, he or she is displaying a kind of recall very similar to that of an older child who remembers a short series of words verbally. In comparison to 6-month-olds who show little evidence of recall of such a sequence of actions, a substantial proportion of 9-month-olds reproduce the multistep actions with the toy even when tested up to 1 month later.

Object Permanence

Knowledge about the properties of objects shows further advances in children 6–12 months of age. Infants begin to display object permanence, or the realization that objects continue to exist and can be retrieved even when out of sight. For example, at about 8 months of age, infants actively implement searching for an attractive object that they have just been shown but which has then been hidden behind a cloth. For many developmental psychologists, this search behavior is theorized to signal the onset of a more sophisticated level of representation or a more active type of memory than that associated with object identity for which 3-month-olds demonstrate competence.

Object permanence undergoes a protracted developmental progression. Eight-month-olds may search for a toy that has been hidden under a single cloth. However, if they retrieve it from that location several times and it is then hidden under a second cloth, they are not likely to initiate a correct search for it, returning instead to the original location in which they had repeatedly found it during their previous efforts to retrieve the toy. This incorrect search, described as the 'A-not-B' error, usually is no longer made by infants as they approach 1 year of age and may be due to an increasing ability to inhibit an inappropriate response or the development of greater memory strength for the more recent event relative to repeated earlier events.

Causality

Philosophers have long speculated about when children begin to understand causality. An appreciation of physical causality or awareness that one object can influence another may occur as early as 6 months of age at least when simple launching events are observed. For example, infants may be repeatedly shown a moving object that makes contact with a second object which, in turn, moves as if in response to its contact with the first object. At some point the causal sequence is reversed; the second object moves to make contact with the first which then moves. Infants shown this display demonstrate a substantially greater increase in attention when this sequence is reversed compared to a reversal of a sequence where the first object is shown stopping short of making contact with the second before the second appears to move on its own. Infants appear to have recognized something unique about the relationship between the two objects in the first context, that is, when they make contact with each other, but not in the second where the movement takes place independent of direct contact. This understanding of causality, however, is quite fragile at 6 months of age. For example, when the objects are simple such as balls that strike one another the effect is found around 6–7 months of age, but behaviors suggesting an understanding of causality involving more complex, toy-like objects are not evident

in infants until they are several months older. This delay presumably stems from the greater amount of information involved in processing the more complex stimuli which leaves fewer cognitive resources for imputing a causal relationship between them. By the end of the first year infants seem to understand additional aspects of causality, for example, a larger object striking a smaller one will normally have a greater impact than a smaller object striking a larger one.

Goal-Directed and Intentional Action

In addition to an early understanding of causality, infants around 6 months of age begin to infer that some actions, especially those associated with humans, are directed toward a goal. The basic procedure involves infants observing a person repeatedly reaching for and grasping one of two different objects. Each object appears in its same location on each trial so that the person is always reaching in the same direction. Once the attention of the infants to this repeated action declines to a predetermined level, a change is introduced. The location of the two objects is reversed and the person then either reaches to grasp the same object (now in a different location so that the path of reaching has changed) or reaches in the same direction as on preceding trials to grasp the object that had not been acted on before. Infants from 6 to 12 months of age show far greater recovery of attention when the direction of reach stays the same and a different object is grasped than when the direction of reach changes in order to grasp the same object. The novelty of reaching for and grasping a different goal object appears to attract far more attention than the perceptual change introduced by changing the direction of reaching. Moreover, this difference is more typically found when the actions are initiated by a human; infants are less likely to display the same kind of response when an inanimate claw or ambiguous agent is used in the sequence of events.

Evidence that infants at about 9 months of age have a somewhat more sophisticated understanding of goal-directed behavior comes from research in which a person attempts to hand small toys to the child. In some cases the initiator accidentally drops a toy before the baby can take it, but in other cases, he or she pulls the toy back out of reach as if belatedly deciding not to give it to the infant. Nine-month-olds seem more frustrated by the latter condition than the former, whereas 6-month-olds do not respond differently to these two events. These findings suggest that underlying the child's conceptualization of goal-directed behavior may be some early appreciation of intentionality in human agents. Other research provides further support for this view. For example, 12-month-olds who watch a sequence in which a larger ball rolls toward a barrier and then appears to 'jump' over the barrier to make contact with a second, smaller ball respond in a manner suggesting that the first ball's actions are intentional. Adults watching this scenario often describe it in terms of a 'mother' (the larger ball) intending to get to its 'baby' on the other side of the barrier. Infants seem surprised when the barrier is no longer present but the larger ball continues to jump gratuitously, that is, no longer has to perform this action as part of its 'intention' to reach the small ball.

Planning and Means–Ends Problem Solving

A major achievement associated with problem solving is the ability to plan for and initiate the sequence of steps that may be necessary to reach a goal. This capacity, often termed means–ends behavior, is first clearly displayed by infants between 8 and 12 months of age. Prior to this time infants who are shown an attractive toy placed out of reach, but on a cloth that is within reach, will typically initiate a 'direct action attack' toward the object, completely disregarding the possibility that the cloth could serve as a tool for obtaining the toy. These actions may include extending their reach and leaning as far forward toward the object as possible, perhaps even attempting to crawl on the table or hard surface supporting the cloth and the toy if that is an option. Should these behaviors fail to achieve the goal, infants may be left with one final recourse, entreating their caregivers to serve as instruments for obtaining their goal. However, around 8 months of age babies are far more likely to reach for and grab the edge of the cloth on which the toy has been placed and pull it (and the toy) toward themselves. By 12 months of age they can combine several means–ends steps that may be necessary to reach the goal. For example, if shown a toy on a cloth to which a string is attached, but the string cannot be reached because of a barrier, babies will first knock over the barrier, reach for the string, and use it to pull the cloth supporting the toy in order to retrieve it.

Egocentric Spatial Framework

The 6- to 12-month-old's understanding of space is often described as egocentric, that is, heavily weighted toward the use of their own body for determining the location of an object. For example, 9-month-olds will have little difficulty repeatedly finding an object hidden in a well located on either the left or right side of their body. But if the baby is then moved to the opposite side of the room, he or she will typically choose the well on the same side of the body, that is, the incorrect location, instead of updating spatial information based on his or her having been repositioned. Frame of reference for infants this age is heavily governed by the body.

Nevertheless, this limitation is not absolute; for example, if distinctive landmarks or features differentiate the two locations such as the color of the wells, infants this age may be able to override their egocentric orientation and correctly locate an object after being repositioned.

Meanings of Words

Word production typically will not begin until about the end of the first year. Nevertheless, understanding the meaning of commonly spoken words that the infant hears is probably well underway by this time. For example, by about 6 months of age infants will look in the direction of their mother or father when they hear 'mommy' or 'daddy', respectively, but not to an unfamiliar woman or man. Similar responses to objects for which infants have repeatedly heard the name before become evident by about 9 months of age and they are able to respond to simple requests spoken by another person. Thus word comprehension is possible well before word production.

Conceptual Categorization

Whereas debate continues with respect to whether children younger than 6 months of age have concepts or are able to classify different members of a category together on the basis of more than their perceptual similarity, there is consensus that categorization clearly has become meaning-based or conceptual by 12 months of age. Infants now apply actions that they have seen someone perform on one member of a category, such as pretending to feed a toy dog, to other toy animals but not to vehicles or exemplars of other categories. Since infants may not yet be producing verbal utterances by this time, these early concepts are likely image-based. Nevertheless, even though the members of different categories may share considerable overlap in their perceptual features, the behavior of infants of this age provides considerable ammunition for concluding that inferences are being made on the basis of the similarity in role or function of objects identified as belonging together. These early concepts may also be relatively global, for example, at the superordinate level such as mammals, vehicles, furniture, and food or even at higher levels such as animate objects and artifacts as well as at more basic levels such as dogs, cats, chairs, and tables.

12–18 Months of Age

Advances in Long-Term Recall

Noteworthy during the first half of the second year of life is the increase in recall memory over longer and longer periods of time. For example, at 16 months of age, most infants are not only capable of reproducing an ordered sequence of three or four actions on objects when shown the objects 1 month later, but even when tested 3 and 6 months later. If the sequence is seen at 20 months of age, infants recall them as much as 12 months later.

Intentionality (Human Agency)

Although infants very likely begin to understand some aspects of goal-directed behavior and intentionality in others before they reach a year of age, this knowledge shows further development during the first half of their second year. Before 1 year of age infants will often use another person's gaze to redirect their own looking. However, now they begin to appreciate that looking at an object has a goal-directed quality on the part of that other person. Using procedures similar to those designed to explore their understanding of goal-directed reaching at 6–12 months of age, 1-year-olds respond more when another person looks at a different object located in the same place as the object at which he or she had been gazing than when the individual redirects his or her attention to the original object now repositioned in a different location. The same can be said for pointing which may be understood as an intentional behavior even before 1 year of age. Moreover, the emergence of and understanding of the message being communicated by pointing is correlated with the child's initiating his or her own pointing to direct the attention of another.

These findings do not necessarily mean that children this age have a complete understanding of intentions in others, for example, that some mental state is motivating the other person's behavior. However, these and other accomplishments do suggest that among the toolbox of cognitive resources becoming available at this time is an appreciation of psychological causality. For example, in one study 14-month-olds observed adults performing a simple activity. However, the demonstrations were accompanied either by a verbal comment that suggested that the activity was completed as intended ('There!') or that the outcome was accidental ('Whoops!'). The children were more likely to imitate the activity when the adult's comment suggested it was intentional. Moreover, 18-month-olds are as likely to complete a simple activity that they see an adult complete successfully as one that they see the adult attempting to complete, but not being successful at; they seem to have recognized the intention of the adult even though they did not observe the goal being achieved since, if just given the materials on their own, infants this age generally did not produce these activities. Nor are they as likely to imitate these activities when mechanical devices are shown performing them. Inferring the intentions, goals, and plans of a human agent seems essential to infants imitating these activities and this understanding may provide an important stepping stone for the very young child in eventually learning to regulate their social interactions based on the mental states of others.

Word Production

Few milestones in development are met more enthusiastically by parents than the production of their children's first words. Such utterances typically emerge toward the end of the first year of development and generally increase to about 50 different words by about 18 months of age. Although the production of words is an interesting behavioral milestone in itself, realizing that an arbitrary symbol such as a word can represent an object or event reflects a major advance in cognitive development. The beginnings of comprehension of the meanings of some words very likely came about sometime between 6 and 12 months of age; now that understanding extends to infants' production of their own words.

Not surprisingly, the meanings for early words may not quite match up with typical adult meanings for those words. Children at this age and for several more years may overextend the meaning of their initial words, that is, apply them to far more referents than normally acceptable. For example, the word 'ball' may initially be used to label an orange, the moon, or any other round object. They may also underextend their meaning, that is, provide the label to far fewer referents than normally considered appropriate by adults standards. For example, they may apply the word 'dog' to only those that walk through their yard and not to those seen riding in a car. Perhaps even more frequently, they may both overextend a word to some inappropriate referents yet at the same time underextend them by failing to include some typical referents of the concept. One culprit underlying these kinds of errors may be an overemphasis on the similarity in perceptual features of categorically different referents (when overextension occurs) or insufficient similarity in perceptual features (in the case of underextension). Errors based on similarity (or lack of similarity) of functional characteristics may occur as well. Finally, most of the earliest words that are acquired refer to things (i.e., are nouns) rather than actions (i.e., verbs) or other parts of speech.

Pretense

In addition to the use of words to represent some object, other clear signs that children are beginning to understand that one thing can represent another is evident in the onset of pretend behavior. The earliest appearance of this activity varies widely from one child to another, but many children display simple forms of pretending soon after 1 year of age, for example, simulating drinking from an empty toy cup. At this age, children are unlikely to have any appreciation that pretense involves a mental activity; moreover, the pretense behavior often appears as an extension of well-learned sensorimotor behaviors applied to similar, thus not completely arbitrary objects. As they near 18 months of age, toddler's make-believe activity often begins to include a cohort, another person or toy such as a favored doll, who becomes the recipient of feeding or combing or comforting activities that children, at a younger age, only might have applied to themselves.

Pictorial Competence

Infants less than 1 year of age attempt to treat pictures of objects somewhat the same way as the objects themselves.

They may rub the picture and make finger and hand motions as if attempting to grasp the depicted object and as if confused about the differences between the physical properties of two-dimensional and three-dimensional stimuli. These responses diminish with development so that by 18 months, infants are displaying them very infrequently. In response to pictures, infants are now much more likely to apply labels or verbal expressions. In addition, a label learned for a pictured object can be readily generalized to its three-dimensional referent. Two-dimensional sequences of actions such as those presented via television are imitated and remembered just as when real people serve as models indicating that information can be gained from two-dimensional stimuli as well as three-dimensional stimuli.

Analogical Problem Solving

Analogical problem solving refers to the ability to extend some principle for solving a problem to another problem which, at least in terms of its specific features, seems very different. For the most part, even adults are not always very good at analogical problem solving, but the beginnings of this ability can be observed during the first half of the second year. As already indicated, infants around 12 months of age will knock over a barrier to reach a string attached to a cloth on which an attractive toy has been placed, pulling the string and attached cloth toward themselves to reach the toy. But even those who do not spontaneously demonstrate this problem-solving skill will often perform it if it is modeled for them by a parent. Moreover, once they have demonstrated competence on one task of this type, they are able to transfer it to others that require the same solution even though barrier, string, cloth, and desired goal are quite different from the one on which they first learned this solution principle; they seem to understand that the problems are analogous to one another. However, children under 1 year of age are less successful in demonstrating transfer and only do so if there are substantial perceptual similarities among the elements of the various problems.

18–24 Months of Age

Strategic Memory

The development of various strategies for assisting memory accounts for much of the improvement in recall throughout later childhood; nevertheless, the earliest implementation of one rudimentary strategy can be seen beginning around 18 months of age. At this time, if shown an object hidden at a particular spatial location but not allowed to search for it immediately, toddlers begin to point to or look toward that location on occasion as if to reconfirm that the object is still there even though they are engaged in other activities during the delay. In contrast, if the object is clearly visible

during the delay, they initiate such actions far less frequently. Although children this age are unlikely to be consciously aware of its benefits to memory, such behavior is a primitive manifestation of far more sophisticated mnemonic strategies children acquire as they become older.

Self-Recognition

Evidence from several different types of observations converge in suggesting that by 18 months of age toddlers form a concept of themselves as individuals different from other individuals. The household mirror has become a valuable tool for demonstrating the earliest evidence of this accomplishment. For example, if a spot of rouge is surreptitiously placed on the nose or forehead of children, toddlers between 15 and 18 months of age are much more likely to touch or rub the spot on their own body whereas younger infants touch or rub the spot on the image they see in the mirror. Even children who have no experience with mirrors typically display such self-recognition activity before they reach 24 months of age. In addition, by 2 years of age, children respond differently, smiling and verbalizing about themselves, when they see their own photograph as opposed to the photograph depicting another child of a similar age. Common, too, at this time, is the onset of personal pronouns such as 'I' or 'me' when talking about themselves.

Desire in Others

As already indicated, infants recognize some aspects of intentionality in the behavior of others well before 18 months of age. However, toward the end of their second year, they start to display a greater appreciation for psychological factors that underlie the actions and goals initiating behaviors. By the age of 2 years, toddlers realize that they themselves have desires or emotional states and that the desires or emotional states of others may not match their own. If given a choice between a preferred or a nonpreferred food, children are highly likely to choose the preferred. However, if informed by the facial or verbal expressions of another person that this individual would rather have the nonpreferred food, children will offer that alternative to him or her. Although at this age toddlers are unlikely to understand that others have mental representations of desires, the realization that the actions of others are governed by motivations that do not always correspond to their own serves as an important step to acquiring a fuller understanding of the psychological states of others.

Tool Use

Children's tool use becomes far more sophisticated at this time. For example, if shown how a tool such as a rake can be used or alternatively, if given a hint to use it to retrieve a toy that is too far away to reach, toddlers now readily generalize such information to other problems by choosing a tool that is rigid, long enough, and contains a feature permitting the toy to be pulled toward themselves from among the various alternatives.

24–36 Months of Age

Scripts as Organizational Underpinnings for Autobiographical Memory

Beginning around 30 months of age; undoubtedly facilitated by their burgeoning verbal abilities, children begin to recount events that have been commonly experienced such as eating out at a restaurant or getting ready for bed. These scripts, or organized descriptions for commonly experienced events, usually lack specific details but highlight the key, routine components often involved in recurring activities and appear to serve as the basis for much of autobiographical memory. Children this young do not normally recall specific events that have occurred to them, that is, they still show infantile amnesia or the inability to remember the details of any particular experiences, but they nevertheless have clearly begun to organize their retention of general information around sequential, context-specific routines.

Advances in Pictorial Competence

Although children recognize that pictures of objects are different from the three-dimensional objects they represent, they continue to have limited appreciation of the spatial orientation governing how to view pictures. If shown a picture book, it typically matters little to them if a parent is holding the book upside down nor do they show preferences for pictures of objects that are upright vs. upside-down; in contrast, clear preferences for uprightness are displayed for real objects. However, by 30 months of age, even pictures are perceived as having an appropriate orientation.

Models as Symbols

Although infants, perhaps even before the end of their first year, seem to understand symbols, for example, that a word can be used to represent some external referent, the range of symbols that can serve this representational capacity expands between 24 and 36 months of age. Objects that are meaningful and interesting in themselves now can serve as representations. Consider pieces of furniture in a room in a dollhouse. For young children these items are usually items interesting in and of themselves, for example, things to play with. However, the furniture and room can also serve as a representation of a normal, life-size room. Thus, if told that a toy is located behind a piece of furniture in the dollhouse, and that a similar toy is located behind the equivalent piece of furniture in the regular room, we would have little difficulty finding it in the regular room. However, it is not until children are typically nearly 36 months of age, that they are successful on such a task. They appear to lack the capacity to form two different representations for the dollhouse, one as an interesting array in and of itself and one as a symbol for the regular room. Not surprisingly, when using photographs depicting the dollhouse furniture to indicate the location of the toy, children at 30 months of age are already successful presumably because the primary function of pictures is to serve as a representation of something else.

Pretense and Sociodramatic Play

Pretend activities now become substantially more complex. For example, beginning around 2 years of age arbitrary objects (e.g., a block or a stick) can be incorporated into make-believe play; toddlers are not limited to using somewhat realistic representations of objects as part of their play adventures. In addition, an agent such as a doll may become actively engaged in participating in a pretend routine; it takes on a separate role in the play activity, for example, it is used to feed itself or another doll. Finally, by about 30 months of age, these advances contribute to the onset of modest forms of sociodramatic play where the child begins to coordinate roles among themselves and others (parents, siblings, dolls) in their imaginary world, a skill that becomes far more sophisticated and frequently displayed as children move into the preschool years.

Challenges and Opportunities

As these examples illustrate, memory, understanding of the physical and social world, conceptual development, representational abilities, and planning and problem solving undergo tremendous changes in infants and young children during their first 3 years. Identifying and determining when these new cognitive accomplishments first emerge has been one outcome of the enormous efforts of many developmental researchers engaged in ingenious and creative approaches enticing infants and very young children to provide answers about what they know and understand. The description of these milestones and indicators of early cognitive development remains incomplete. In the years to come newly discovered methods for gaining insights into the major achievements occurring in infancy and early childhood will undoubtedly provide a more accurate, more complete, and more informative picture of when and under what circumstances various markers of intellectual development are exhibited. These advances are likely to provide further distinctions and refinements to complete the many gaps that remain unfilled concerning this topic.

In contrast to other areas such as physical and language development where milestones in development are often of interest, the research on cognition has provided little information concerning the range and variation among children with respect to when various intellectual accomplishments are achieved. Developmental psychologists have, for the most part, carried out their research on samples of European or American children growing up in middle- or higher-income families. Within these populations, little attention has been given to what proportion of children display various cognitive abilities weeks, or even months, earlier or later than the 'average' child. In other words, we know little about how much variability exists from one child to another in displaying various cognitive accomplishments. This information is important since it can inform us about whether caregiving practices or factors associated with cultural, socioeconomic, or other family variables have an influence on the development of these capacities.

In closing this discussion of milestones pertaining to cognitive development one further idea needs to be emphasized. Such descriptions should not be the endpoint but rather the beginning of our explorations into cognitive development. Describing when infants and young children accomplish various cognitive skills tells us very little about how these structures and processes came about or the practical implications and theoretical importance of their acquisition. In fact, many other articles included in other sections of this encyclopedia address these kinds of issues and should be considered an important additional step to understanding the remarkable changes in cognition that take place during infancy and early childhood.

See also: Bayley Scales of Infant Development; Brain Development; Categorization Skills and Concepts; Cognitive Developmental Theories; Cognitive Development; Developmental Disabilities: Cognitive; Mathematical Reasoning; Memory; Object Concept; Piaget's Cognitive-Developmental Theory; Reasoning in Early Development; Self Knowledge; Theory of Mind; Vygotsky's Sociocultural Theory.

Suggested Readings

Bauer PJ, Burch MM, and Kleinknecht EE (2002) Developments in early recall memory: Normative trends and individual differences. *Advances in Child Development and Behavior* 30: 103–152.

Cohen LB and Cashon CH (2006) Infant Cognition. In: Damon W, Lerner RM, Kuhn D, and Siegler R (eds.) *Handbook of Child Psychology: Vol. II. Cognition, Perception and Language,* 6th edn., pp. 214–251. Hoboken, NJ: Wiley.

Flavell JH, Miller PH, and Miller SA (2002) *Cognitive Development,* 4th edn. Upper Saddle River, NJ: Prentice-Hall.

Pelphry KA and Reznick JS (2003) Working memory in infancy. *Advances in Child Development and Behavior* 31: 173–227.

Siegler RS and Alibali MW (2005) *Children's Thinking,* 4th edn. Upper Saddle River, NJ: Prentice-Hall.

Troseth GL, Pierroutsakos SL, and DeLoache JS (2004) From the innocent to the intelligent eye: The early development of pictorial competence. *Advances in Child Development and Behavior* 32: 1–35.

Woodward AL (2005) The infant origins of intentional understanding. *Advances in Child Development and Behavior* 33: 229–262.

Milestones: Physical

W O Eaton, University of Manitoba, Winnipeg, MB, Canada

Glossary

Cephalocaudal – Along the long axis of the body, from head to tail.

Developmental milestone – A near-universal age-related accomplishment.

Gestational age – Interval between the first day of the mother's last menstrual cycle and birth, typically between 38 and 42 weeks.

Prone – Lying with the stomach down.

Proximodistal – From the center to the periphery.

Skeletal age – Age as determined by degree of bone maturity.

Introduction

All human lives share at least one ordered set of universal events – namely, conception, birth, and death. Other ordered events may not be universal, but physical accomplishments like learning to walk are nearly so. These physical achievements during infancy and early childhood are very rapid, and major motor accomplishments such as sitting, crawling, and walking are apparent to nearly everyone. They are also age-related in their appearance. Because such events are ubiquitous, easily observed, and regular in their emergence, they are viewed as markers along life's path, which is probably why they are referred to as milestones, a term originally used for distance markers placed at regular intervals along roadsides.

The focus here will be on those milestones that have been most studied, physical milestones. Such milestones generally refer to a set of developmental changes that result in the infant's improved ability to coordinate and control voluntary movements, and are often differentiated into fine and gross motor categories. Fine motor milestones are typically those related to arm, hand, and finger movements that allow for the grasping and manipulation of small objects. Gross motor milestones, in contrast, comprise a series of attainments that enable the infant to go from being relatively immobile to being capable of bipedal locomotion, a major evolutionary adaptation and a defining characteristic of our species.

Early Research

The foundation for our modern understanding of milestones was laid in the 1920s and 1930s when pioneering early researchers such as Arnold Gesell, Mary Shirley, Myrtle McGraw, and others began to carefully describe and catalog infant motor skills. This early work was primarily empirical, descriptive, often qualitative, and highly detailed. For example, Gesell was one of the first researchers to use motion pictures to study infants in the laboratory. With the filmed vignettes he could do frame-by-frame analyses that were exhaustively described and presented in his *Atlas of Infant Behavior*, published in 1934. Taking a different approach, Mary Shirley and coworkers sought to study babies in their natural environments, so they made 1370 weekly visits to the homes of 25 infants, who were studied for the first 2 years of their lives! From such painstaking work came schedules of what babies did and at

what age. For example, **Figure 1** is the ordered summary Shirley produced in 1931 of the median ages for the emergence of various milestones observed with her infants.

The milestones studied by Shirley, Gesell, and other early researchers have been used, with variations, in many subsequent studies. For example, in developing a set of milestones for use cross-nationally, the World Health Organization (WHO) selected six gross motor milestones, all of which have close parallels in Shirley's **Figure 1**. Incidentally, one of the WHO's milestones is 'hands-and-knees-crawling', which would have been called 'creeping' by Shirley and other early researchers. The critical difference between creeping and crawling is whether or not the baby's abdomen is in contact with the floor as forward movement occurs. Here the term crawl will follow contemporary usage and will to refer to forward, generally prone locomotion with the stomach raised off the floor (called 'creeping' in older work).

Shirley's sequence in **Figure 1** reveals a general progression by which the baby's motor development reduces the amount of contact with the supporting surface while raising the body's center of gravity (see **Figure 2**). A characteristic feature of the sequence is that the baby first gains control of his head, then upper trunk and arms, followed by control of the trunk, which leads to sitting. Then active locomotion is initiated in a prone posture (e.g., crawling), followed by more active control of the legs and feet. This head-to-tail sequence is an example of cephalocaudal development, which is apparent in many features of embryology.

A second principle of milestone development is more apparent in the development of grasping and reaching where control is gained first over the shoulder, then the lower arm, and finally the hand and fingers. The grasp of objects, itself, shifts from a crude grasp that stabilizes

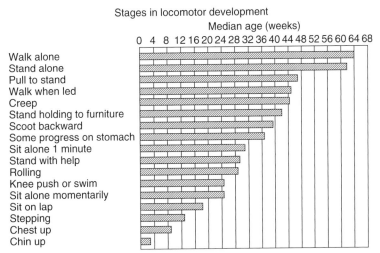

Figure 1   Shirley's list of locomotor milestones, which is ordered by the median ages at which they were reached by a sample of 25 infants. Reprinted from Shirly MM (1931) *The First Two Years: A Study of Twenty-Five Babies, Vol. 1, Postural and Locomotor Development*. Minneapolis: University of Minnesota Press, copyright © 1931 by the University of Minnesota Press, renewed 1959.

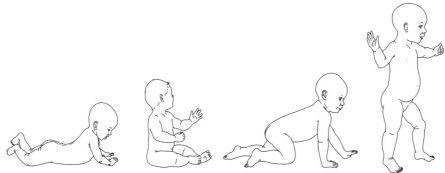

Figure 2   Milestone composite illustration of the raising of the center of gravity and the decrease in surface contact through postural changes. Adapted from Harcourt Health Sciences.

an object between the heel of the hand and the little, ring, and middle fingers. Control later shifts to the finger tips, first through the involvement of the base of the thumb, and then to the tips of the opposed thumb and first finger. This sequence of increasing fine motor control illustrates the principle of proximodistal development (development from the center to the periphery). This developmental principle, like that of cephalocaudal development, had parallels in embryology, from which early researchers drew inspiration.

Descriptions of what babies do, in what sequence, and when, do not provide an explanation for what causes those changes. Most of the earlier researchers emphasized the apparent universality of the sequence of events and the stage-like features of motor milestone attainment. If the sequence of development is universal, as they believed, it was reasonable to conclude as they did that underlying biological and maturational mechanisms are responsible. The early emphasis on maturation as a theoretical explanation for milestone appearance was probably, in part, a response to radical environmental theories of the time, promulgated by John Watson, who characterized infants as highly malleable. In any event, the early workers highlighted the universality of sequences of development, which they attributed to endogenous maturational and neurological processes.

Developmental Tests

Milestones were integrated as items in early tests of infant development by Gesell and colleagues, who pioneered such tests. Their approach owed much to the earlier work of Alfred Binet who, with Theodore Simon, developed the modern intelligence test. Binet's measurement strategy was to identify a large number of age-graded pass/fail items. In essence, passes on these items could be summed to create a summary score, and a child's performance could be interpreted by comparing her or his summary score to the average summary score from other children

of the same chronological age. Gesell adapted this approach and used physical milestones as pass/fail items, for example, whether or not an infant lying prone (stomach down) can use her arms to lift her head and shoulders up off the surface. Criteria for passing each item were specified in a way so that the examiner could readily score a baby has having passed or not. Because physical milestones are relatively easy to observe and are related to age, they were well suited for inclusion in developmental tests.

Milestones appropriate to infants of different ages were included so that coverage of a broader age range could be addressed by the test, and the number of milestones passed contributed to a composite picture of the baby's developmental status. Through comparison of an individual's score with those of others the baby's developmental progress could be characterized as advanced, typical, or delayed. Thus, physical milestone items became an important part of infant development tests. Nancy Bayley later improved on and refined Gesell's work to produce the Bayley Scales of Infant Development, a test which, through several revisions, has been in widespread use for more than 45 years.

The psychometric approach used by Gesell, Bayley, and others required the assessment of many infants so that reference norms could be described. The search for norms was also of interest to neurologists, who sought specific clinical diagnostic items that could be used to predict later developmental outcomes. Consequently, one continuing goal of the early work was the development of age norms for developmental tests and for the various milestones that they included. For the most part, such normative work involved cross-sectional studies in which infants of different ages were assessed. Such designs are useful for snapshots of development but they do not involve the repeated measurement of individuals, nor do they provide information on how well the attainment of one milestone predicts when a later one will be reached. The prediction of when a later milestone will be reached from when an earlier one was reached required the longitudinal study of many infants, and such studies are quite rare.

Theoretical Considerations

Once milestones were identified and tested in normative samples, scientific attention waned, and for many years little milestones work has been published. The descriptive emphasis of the pre-World War II years was replaced by emphases on experimental, process-oriented research. Certainly there were various reports of environmental factors that might have an influence on when key milestones were reached (e.g., birth weight, socioeconomic status), but such factors were seen as noise around the signal provided by a maturational blueprint. Beginning in the late 1980s research on motor development was dramatically altered by the work of Esther Thelen and colleagues, who argued that motor skills were not so much the product of a central genetic blueprint, but were constructed from the interactions of many more peripheral processes, for example, limb biomechanics, surfaces, etc. This dynamic systems perspective inspired the detailed study of infants who were not simply observed, but observed under experimentally altered conditions. By manipulating the conditions, a better understanding of the underlying process could be inferred. So, for example, a baby's balance might be altered by a weighted backpack, or the shoe worn on one foot might have a Velcro sole that made it harder to move. By studying experimentally induced disturbances in the developmental system could be better understood at a basic level.

The emergence of the new, dynamical systems approaches to the study of motor development led to a re-evaluation of milestone attainment. Instead of an emphasis on a maturational blueprint that controlled an invariant, unfolding sequence of stages, the newer approach has emphasized the specifics of each new motor attainment. Which specific muscle groups are used? How are they constrained by the biomechanics of joints, etc.?

Such close examination of the processes involved with a milestone attainment generally reveals a series of gradual changes in various constituent components (e.g., muscle strength and limb size). Consequently, newer explanatory models have tended to focus on continuous, incremental change and to invoke explanatory processes like practice and experience. This contemporary emphasis on developmental specifics and gradual change contrasts with the traditional milestone emphasis on sequence universality and abruptness of milestone onset. The observation that a milestone is attained quite suddenly suggests a stage-like process that could have a maturational base. Indeed, early investigators like Shirley viewed the abrupt milestone appearance as evidence for the key role of maturation in physical development.

New theoretical approaches have changed the focus from broad normative questions in the older work to the details of the process of development. In part, the difference of focus is a difference in level of analysis.

Milestones, when viewed from afar, display considerable regularity in their appearance and sequencing. In contrast, when the motor developments of a given milestone such as crawling are viewed in detail over a short time-frame, many factors are seen to influence the outcome. Regularity at the global, or macroscopic, level appears less ordered at the local, more microscopic, level. The two perspectives are not necessarily incompatible because the attainment of a new milestone may seem sudden and qualitatively distinct, even while it represents the emergent product of many specific events. From one perspective the change is gradual, yet from another, it is sudden and stage-like.

Despite their differences in emphasis, the global and local perspectives can complement each other. The microscopic, process-oriented approach informs us about the factors that can influence attainment. The macroscopic approach, in contrast, is better suited to studying the natural variability of factors in play outside the lab; it informs us about the factors that do correlate with milestone attainment. After reviewing how milestones have been measured, we will turn to a review of those factors that have some value in predicting when infants reach milestones.

Measurement Considerations

Gesell's early work was an exhaustive approach to milestones measurement in that infants visiting his laboratory were extensively recorded in various settings designed to elicit milestone-related behavior. This laboratory approach has the advantage of scientific rigor but the disadvantages of considerable expense and heavy demands on the infant's parent, who must be willing to come to the laboratory. A single visit is not unreasonable, but because of the rapid changes in infant motor skills during the first 2 years, frequent return visits would be necessary to collect sensitive longitudinal data. Consequently, longitudinal laboratory studies are uncommon. However, in some jurisdictions parents make frequent clinic visits for infant monitoring during the first year. Milestone data have been collected on such visits, and these clinic-based longitudinal studies have provided valuable information.

Outside the laboratory, there have been three approaches to the assessment of milestones. One is to have trained individuals visit the home to observe an infant in various postures and to categorize the baby's status as a pass or fail on the various milestones under consideration. By using trained observers, the researcher can maximize reliability and obtain milestone information at a lower cost than the laboratory approach entails. The major disadvantage is that much information about infant variability is lost because it is only possible to get a snapshot of development. One baby may have just reached the milestone, whereas another may have passed the same milestone weeks or months earlier. Both would have the same score. The loss of information due to dichotomization greatly reduces the statistical power of tests of the data, and may lead to an underestimate of the individual variability in attainment and reduced possibilities for linkage to other variables.

A second approach is to ask the parent, usually the mother, to recall when a specific milestone was reached. This recall approach is better able to capture variability in attainment age, but has some important disadvantages. The time between the parent report and specific milestones will vary, and it is plausible to assume that more recent milestone attainments will be more reliably reported than more distant ones. Furthermore, some milestones are much more salient than others. For example, independent walking is easy to observe and viewed as highly important by most parents. In contrast a more subtle milestone, like the use of a pincer grip to hold an object is likely to be missed by the parent. For this reason, retrospective parent reports after several years have passed have generally been restricted to the most highly salient milestones like first walking. Mothers have quite accurate recall of when their child first walked, whereas their memories of other milestones like teething and smiling are much poorer. The quality of recall may be related in part to the practical significance of the event for the caregiver. A newly crawling or walking infant poses caretaking challenges that may make the attainment event particularly memorable.

A third approach requires longitudinal measurement and involves parents completing a daily (or regular) checklist of milestone attainments. From such daily checklists it is possible to more precisely estimate when a milestone is reached. This approach has also been validated by comparing parents' recent checklist records against the observations of home visitors. A disadvantage of the checklist approach is that it requires ongoing commitment and involvement on the part of the parent.

Regardless of how information about the milestone event is obtained, the metric of milestone progress is the same – the age at which a milestone is reached. Most questions about milestones involve age. For example, at what age can we expect a baby to first sit without support? Are there factors that speed or delay this achievement? Age as a measure of milestone attainment is familiar and understandable to nearly everyone. It also has an important, implicit advantage, which is that the age of attainment reflects rate of development. For example, a baby who walks at 11 months has mastered a particular set of motor skills more quickly than a peer who walks at 13 months. Why does the first infant get to the milestone before the second? What causes the difference? Does the difference have immediate or long-term implications? Answers to such questions are drawn from studies in which variability in the ages of milestone attainment are correlated with other factors, and it is to those factors that we now turn.

Predictors of Developmental Progress

Many important physical skills are age-related in appearance and ubiquitous, so the number of potential milestones to be predicted is potentially quite large. This would not be a problem if babies were uniformly advanced or delayed on all milestones; attainment of one would be highly predictive of progress on another, and any milestone would do. How closely tied are milestone attainments? We do not know a great deal about this because the degree to which attainment of one milestone predicts another has received little attention, probably because extensive longitudinal measurement is required. When the correlations ages of attainment for different milestones are considered, they are generally positive but variable in magnitude. As a consequence we cannot assume that timing on one milestone will serve as a proxy for timing on another. To further complicate matters, the specific importance of a milestone can be influenced by local concerns and cultural practices. For example, the child's ability to get up from a squatting position without help is a relevant milestone in India, but is not in North America. Despite such cultural variability, there are motor milestones that have considerable generality. The WHO identified for its Multicentre Growth Reference Study six milestones (see **Table 1**) because they were viewed as simple to evaluate, critical for erect self-locomotion and universal. There are many variations in how these milestones are specifically defined, but nearly all research on physical milestones considers one or more of these six key milestones.

Predicting Milestone Attainment

Parents and healthcare workers view timely milestone attainment as reassuring sign of normal development because marked delay can be the result of disease (e.g., HIV and muscular dystrophy) or malnutrition. Fortunately for most children in economically developed countries such hazards are relatively uncommon, yet healthy well-fed babies still vary considerably in their trajectories of milestone attainment. What variables contribute to this variability? It is to that question that we turn next.

Genetic Factors

Because traditional approaches to milestones emphasized maturation, the role of genetic influences on milestone attainments has long been of interest. Early researchers like Gesell were among the first to conduct twin studies of infants, and they measured milestone timing. By exposing identical (monozygotic) twins to different training experiences, they sought to hold genetic factors constant while varying experiential influences. With only one set of

Table 1   World Health Organization Multicentre Growth Reference Study gross motor milestones

Milestone	Performance criteria
Sitting without support	Child sits up straight with the head erect for at least 10 s. Child does not use arms or hands to balance body or support position.
Hands-and-knees crawling	Child alternately moves forward or backward on hands and knees. The stomach does not touch the supporting surface. There are continuous and consecutive movements, at least three in a row.
Standing with assistance	Child stands in upright position on both feet, holding onto a stable object (e.g., furniture) with both hands without leaning on it. The body does not touch the stable object, and the legs support most of the body weight. Child thus stands with assistance for at least 10 s.
Walking with assistance	Child is in upright position with the back straight. Child makes sideways or forward steps by holding onto a stable object (e.g., furniture) with one or both hands. One leg moves forward while the other supports part of the body weight. Child takes at least five steps in this manner.
Standing alone	Child stands in upright position on both feet (not on the toes) with the back straight. The legs support 100% of the child's weight. There is no contact with a person or object. Child stands alone for at least 10 s.
Walking alone	Child takes at least five steps independently in upright position with the back straight. One leg moves forward while the other supports most of the body weight. There is no contact with a person or object.

Reproduced from Wijnhoven *et al.* (2004) from the World Health Organization.

twins, Gesell's seminal study was a case study, and one in which the zygosity status was cloudy. Recent studies have used much larger samples of twins and have had better information on zygosity. At its simplest these more recent twin studies take advantage of the fact that identical (monozygotic, MZ) twins share the same genotype, whereas fraternal (dizygotic, DZ) twins and non-twin siblings share, on average, half of their genotypes. If genetic factors are causal and if certain assumptions about the equivalence of environments for the two types of twins hold, then MZ twins should be more similar in their milestones attainments than their less genetically similar DZ counterparts.

By also including nontwin siblings, contemporary behavior genetics studies can also estimate family environment effects. In general, the few studies available have found greater MZ than DZ similarity, and greater DZ than nontwin sib similarity. Such a pattern of results implicates roles for both genetic and environmental influence on the age of milestone attainment. A genetic role is implied because differences in genetic similarity (the MZ–DZ comparison) are associated with differences in milestone similarity. An environmental role is implied because DZ twins are more similar than nontwin sibs even though their degree of genetic similarity is the same. This latter result is interesting because there must be something about the twins' shared environment that makes their milestone attainments more similar than those of full siblings. Shared environments could include anything from shared fetal environment (e.g., mother's age) to features of the household that makes twins more alike in the timing of their milestone attainments.

Prenatal Influences

Both fine and gross motor achievements of infancy build on a foundation of prenatal movements, and there is considerable continuity in the types of movements that are observable *in utero* through ultrasound, and those extra-uterine movements and reflexes visible to the delighted parents of a newborn. However, little is known about whether, or if, prenatal movements predict variation in later milestone attainment.

Gestational Age and Birth Size

Several studies have reported that babies who are gestationally more mature at birth reach milestones at a younger chronological age. Such a result could occur when the samples of infants include prematurely born babies, who typically have a variety of medical problems. However, the influence of gestational age is also found in studies of healthy infants, all of whom were born within a couple of weeks of the expected due date for a full-term pregnancy. Variation in gestational age around a full-term pregnancy is also predictive of early milestone attainment (e.g., for sitting). Perhaps conceptual age (the sum of gestational age and chronological age) is the crucial determinant, which would suggest that an older gestational age is offset by younger chronological age at attainment. However, there is not a simple one-to-one correspondence between the earliness of the birth and the lateness of milestone attainment. The lack of such a correspondence implies that differences between the prenatal and postnatal environments are important in influencing when a baby reaches key gross motor milestones.

Birth weight and birth length are positively and strongly related to gestational age, which makes it very difficult to disentangle their influences from those of gestational age. Gestationally older babies are longer and heavier, so in light of the association between gestational age and age of attainment it is not surprising that heavier and longer babies newborns tend to reach milestones sooner. However, measures of infant chubbiness (a combination of length and weight) are not so strongly correlated with gestational age, and it is to these body composition measures that we turn next.

Body Composition

One variable thought to influence when babies would reach milestones like walking is the infant's body composition. For example, it was popularly believed in the 1940s that chubbier babies would walk later. This makes some sense logically, because the process of gross motor development enables the infant to raise the center of gravity as crawling, and then walking, develops. Other things being equal, a heavier body would be harder to lift than a lighter one. Other things are rarely equal, and one can distinguish among different components of body weight, such as the skeleton, muscles, internal organs, and fat. More muscle mass could facilitate early attainment, whereas relatively more fat could delay it. Little research has been done on this topic, and one of the few studies in which careful physical measurements of length and weight were collected along with milestone data was that of Shirley. She reported that muscular, thin babies tended to walk earlier than round or heavy babies. This finding was replicated once, though both Shirley's study and the replication were based on very small samples of babies.

As Shirley noted, the lean–early idea is complicated by the fact that leanness and earlier attainment may both be the result of greater infant motor activity. An infant who is strongly motivated to move could be leaner due to greater activity and could reach milestones early because of more motor practice. To argue that lean motor mass is a cause of early attainment requires that one show that the leanness preceded the attainment. Such research would require ongoing longitudinal measurement of both infant size and milestone attainment, and such research is almost nonexistent. This situation may change because current theoretical conceptualizations attach much importance to biomechanics, and the infant's limb size, weight, and dimensions are important from this perspective.

Nutrition

Milestone attainment is affected, not just by malnutrition, but also by undernutrition. Infants and young children reared in nutritionally at-risk communities have been found to be delayed on age of milestone attainment for milestones such as crawling and walking. Physical growth delays occur concurrently, which suggests that milestone attainment and physical growth are intimately connected. However, the effects of poor nutrition may be apparent in milestone delays before physical growth is measurably affected. Indeed, nutrition researchers often use milestones attainments as an outcome measure for assessing nutritional interventions. One feature of nutrition that has received considerable attention is breastfeeding, and

clinical trials done in nutritionally at-risk communities have reported that extended breastfeeding is associated with earlier crawling and walking.

Sex Differences

Although some studies have reported statistically significant sex differences in the ages of milestone attainment, these magnitude of these effects have been very small. It must be remembered that statistical significance tells us that a difference is unlikely to have occurred by chance, which does not necessarily mean that the difference has practical importance. For example, a study could find that, on average, girls reach a given milestone a day or two before boys do. If a large number of babies have been studied, a difference of a couple of days would be unlikely to be found if there truly is no gender difference. However, one might reasonably conclude that such a developmental advantage for girls is too small as to be practically important.

The fact that size of sex differences in milestone attainment is very small is somewhat surprising because girls are skeletally more mature than are same-aged boys at birth and throughout infancy. Skeletal (or bone) age is a measure of how advanced the development of the bones are, and can be determined from X-rays. A pattern of large sex differences in skeletal age, coupled with very small milestone sex differences suggests that skeletal age is not a critical influence on milestone attainment.

Experience and Training

Acquiring a motor skill takes practice, so infant opportunity for practice is a prime predictor candidate of attainment variability. Circumstantial evidence for the role of practice opportunity emerged in the 1990s after public health campaigns to reduce the incidence of sudden infant death syndrome emphasized the importance of positioning babies for sleep on their backs (supine) or in a side-lying position. These campaigns were effective, but in subsequent years various practitioners began to report that infants were delayed in their gross motor attainments. Subsequent studies found supine sleeping postures to be associated with delays on gross motor milestones like holding the head up and crawling.

More recent research has focused on the time babies spend in different postures when awake. In general, babies who spend more time in the prone position while awake display earlier crawling attainment. Parents may mistakenly over apply the advice about avoiding the prone position during sleep and avoid placing their awake babies on their stomachs. In effect, the avoidance of the prone position would limit the baby's practice on skills needed for various forms of crawling.

One applied implication from the preceding link between time in prone and milestone attainment is that parents could encourage earlier milestone attainment by placing their awake baby in prone play positions. However, some of the studies that reported delays associated with posture also found these delays to be transient – prone and supine groups did not differ in when they walked. This raises the more general question of the lasting effects of variation in milestone attainment. Does variation predict any subsequent outcomes of importance? If not, such attainment variability could be of minor importance.

Socioeconomic Influences

Income, education, and occupational prestige variables are the major components in most measures of socioeconomic status (SES), and in many developmental domains SES is positively related to developmental outcomes (e.g., better child outcomes co-occur with more parental education and income). Motor milestone attainment appears to be an exception to this general pattern, however. Studies that have looked at social class and milestone achievement have generally reported no significant findings. Moreover, those that have reported SES effects have found an attainment advantage for babies raised in lower SES households. This result may be due in part to the confounding of SES and race in North American samples. Black infants, who have been more likely to experience low SES conditions, have been reported to be younger in their ages of attainments than white infants on various motor milestones.

Cultural Differences

Caregiving practices are influenced by cultural beliefs, and cultural variations in infant care may influence rate of milestone attainment through variations in the way babies are handled. This possibility may have explained the observation made in the 1960s that American babies, who were more likely to be placed for sleep in a prone position, were more advanced on milestones than babies in the UK, who were more likely to be placed in the supine position. Culture is associated with many other variables (e.g., race, nutrition, climate, etc.), so it is very difficult to isolate the effects of culture on milestone attainment.

One cultural variable of relevance to milestone attainment is physical stimulation. Parental stimulation and arousing environments have been associated with motor acceleration. In Zambia, for example, mothers emphasize arousal of their infants and stimulate them by picking them up under the arms and tossing them up and down. Vigorous bouncing is used to calm babies, and infants are transferred to a back-worn sling by grasping the infant at the elbow and swinging the baby into position on the mother's back. Babies are also frequently carried in upright postures without much head support. Motor acceleration has been observed in Zambian and other African cultures, and this may be a consequence of such vigorous childcare practices.

Cultures differentially value specific milestones. In cultures in which sitting is valued, rolling and crawling may not be. Consequently, parents may actively discourage the appearance of some milestones and encourage others. Such parental attitudes and expectations will affect training opportunities for the infant and contribute to variation in the ages at which specific milestones are reached.

Season of Birth

One of the more unusual correlates of milestone attainment is season of birth. An isolated report of such a relation could be discounted as spurious, but several independent studies have found that babies born in the late summer and fall later crawl and walk later than babies born in the later winter and spring. A number of variables covary with season (e.g., light levels, temperature, and nutrition) so it is not clear what factors might be responsible. One suggestion has been that summer and fall-born babies, who are working on their crawling skills during the following winter, may have less opportunity to practice the building-block skills than their spring-born counterparts who are working on crawling during the warmer part of the year.

Does Milestones Attainment Have Predictive Value?

It seems clear from the preceding review that a variety of factors may influence how soon babies sit, crawl, and walk, but does early or late physical milestone attainment have any predictive value for subsequent development? An answer to that question depends, in part, on whether all or most babies are consistent in their sequence of milestone attainment. If they are, then prediction is simpler because being early on one milestone would mean being early on another, and individual differences in rate of development would be most likely to persist and predict. Early milestone researchers were inclined to see a single common sequence of milestone attainments for all infants, and if one examines the average ages for milestones attainments (e.g., see **Figure 1**) one gets the impression that there is only one sequence for all infants. However, we have since learned that there can be individual variation in which milestones are reached first. This is most likely to occur for milestones that are reached at about the same age (e.g., sitting unsupported and standing with help). Even though one milestone is usually passed before another, it is not difficult to find individual exceptions. One baby will sit first and stand second, whereas another baby may stand first and sit second. A related complexity arises because some infants may skip a milestone (e.g., 5–10% of babies walk without crawling first). Such individual variation in patterns of attainment works against simple predictions.

An additional complexity arises because developmental progress in one domain (e.g., physical development) may not be closely connected to progress in another domain (e.g., cognitive development). If development is indeed domain-specific, rapid progress through physical milestones does not necessarily imply advanced development in other domains. Traditional models of milestone attainment emphasized the interconnectedness of various domains, which led to the expectation that early development in one domain would predict developmental advance in another. Contemporary models, in contrast, see the many threads of development as less tightly woven, so there is less of an expectation that advance or delay in one domain will predict corresponding advance or delay in another. Nevertheless, individual differences in the rate of progress toward bipedal locomotion may be a signal for the timing of later developmental events, and it is to an overview of the predictive value of milestones that we turn next.

Developmental Screening

As noted earlier, one major use of milestones information is for the identification of children who are at risk developmentally. Many milestones items are included in infant tests such as the Bayley Scales of Infant Development, and they contribute substantially to the summary scores from such tests. Norms developed for such tests allow for the early identification of children who may be developmentally delayed and who may benefit from early interventions. When embedded in developmental tests, milestones are scored on a dichotomous pass/fail basis and aggregated, and it is not possible to determine specific patterns of milestone attainment from composite developmental tests. However, milestone attainments contribute in important ways to the summary scores of tests used for developmental screening.

Single milestones, for example, age at walking, have been considered as possible screening tools for predicting later outcomes, but the results have not been strong enough to be diagnostic for the individual. Such a result is unsurprising from a measurement perspective because a single item will normally be much less reliable than a composite score like that produced by a comprehensive developmental test. Still, individual milestone items are included in several pediatric assessment tools designed for use by physicians as preliminary screening tools.

Predicting Cognitive Ability

Cognitive abilities build upon motor accomplishments, so individual differences in infant motor milestone attainment might plausibly predict later cognitive abilities. Indeed, Joseph Campos and colleagues have argued that self-produced locomotion in the form of crawling has positive consequences for various cognitive skills. For example, self-produced locomotion can enhance

perspective-taking skills. These ideas have historical parallels. Bayley and Shirley both considered whether the age of first walking was predictive of preschool mental ability, and both reported that it was; later walking was associated with lower ability scores. However, the strength of the relationship, though statistically significant, was not large, and critics subsequently argued that the relation was due primarily to the influence of a small number of cases where development was greatly delayed. There is little doubt that extreme delays in infant motor development are predictive of poorer later outcomes; the more contentious issue is whether variation in the normal range of motor development predicts later outcomes.

More recently medical researchers considered the potency of individual milestone attainment for predicting later developmental deviations or delays. Like Bayley and Shirley they found a small-to-moderate negative correlation between age of attainment and scores on later intelligence tests. However, the size the relation was too small for clinical diagnostic use (i.e., for predicting individual outcomes).

Another relevant literature has to do with the predictive value of infant development tests for predicting later cognitive abilities. As noted earlier, physical milestones are an important part of infant development tests, so the predictive success of infant development tests bears on whether or not milestone variability has any predictive utility. Generally, scores on infant tests were predictive, but the relationships were too small to allow for predicting later individual outcomes. These findings, together with those discussed above, consistently suggest that individual differences in milestone attainment have some relation to later individual differences cognitive ability. Although there is a relationship, it is too small to allow for individual prediction.

Other Outcomes

Some recent epidemiological studies have linked milestone attainment in infancy (age at standing and walking) to later child and adult outcomes. For example, infants who had been late in reaching milestones were more likely, as adolescents, to be in special classrooms for those performing below age level. In a similar vein, earlier standing in infancy was a predictor of greater educational achievement in adulthood. Results from such population-level studies do provide some evidence that early individual differences in the rate milestone attainment may have long-term consequences. However, infant milestone attainments and cognitively relevant measures in adolescence and adulthood are far removed from each other in time. Many intervening events undoubtedly play important roles. Nevertheless, it seems clear that variability in the timing of milestones attainment is not independent of later developmental events and may have more relevance than is commonly believed.

Conclusions

Descriptive and normative work on the attainment of major physical milestones was an important task of early scientific work on infant and early child development. Early explanations for the course of milestone attainments emphasized genetically based maturational factors and universal stage-like features of development. In subsequent years, research moved away from description to more process-oriented, experimental approaches, and basic-science interest in the study of milestones waned. However, the child's status on specific milestones was integrated into most tests of infant development, many of which are in widespread use today. Various pediatric screening tools also have made use of examiner assessments and parent reports of milestone status.

Variability among infants in the ages at which they reach motor milestones is substantial, and comparisons of different cities and countries have revealed differences in the ages at which specific milestones are reached. The causes of such differences are not clear, but several correlates of attainment age have been identified, some obvious and some surprising. An obvious one is that disease and disability are associated with later milestone attainment. Likewise, poor nutrition and prematurity predict the delayed appearance of milestones. Variation in gestational age at birth seems to be particularly important, because even gestational age variation in full-term samples is predictive: younger gestational age predicts later attainments, particularly for early milestones. Some experiential factors appear to be important, and a good deal of circumstantial evidence suggests that the time that a pre-crawling baby spends in a prone position in the first half year predicts earlier crawling. One of the more surprising correlates of variation in age of milestone attainment is season of birth; several studies have reported that birth in the late summer and fall is associated with later crawling and walking. The mechanisms responsible for such a pattern are not well understood.

Although milestone-attainment differences between babies are widely believed to be unrelated to later development, both old and new evidence shows that earlier milestone attainment is associated with better performance on childhood cognitive measures. Some large-scale epidemiological studies have even linked infant milestone variability to adolescent educational achievement and adult cognitive functioning. The strength of such longitudinal linkages is too modest to allow predictions about individual outcomes, but they reveal that variation among babies in physical milestones attainment is an important thread in the larger fabric of infant and early child development.

See also: Bayley Scales of Infant Development; Motor and Physical Development: Locomotion; Motor and Physical Development: Manual; Nutrition and Diet; Physical Growth; Prenatal Development; Reflexes; Self Knowledge.

Suggested Readings

Campos JJ, Anderson DI, Barbu-Roth MA, Hubbard EM, Hertenstein MJ, and Witherington D (2000) Travel broadens the mind. *Infancy* 1: 149–219.
Malina RM (2003) Motor development during infancy and early childhood: Overview and suggested directions for research. *International Journal of Sport and Health Science* 2: 50–66.
Piper MC and Darrah J (1994) *Motor Assessment of the Developing Infant.* Philadelphia, PA: Saunders.
Shirley MM (1931) *The First Two Years: A Study of Twenty-Five Babies, Vol. 1, Postural and Locomotor Development.* Minneapolis: University of Minnesota Press.

Relevant Websites

http://www.marchofdimes.com – March of Dimes.
http://www.milestoneshome.org – Milestones Study Center.
http://www.zerotothree.org – ZERO TO THREE.

Mortality, Infant

K M Andrews, D B Brouillette, and R T Brouillette, McGill University, Montréal, QC, Canada

Glossary

Infant mortality rate (IMR) – The number of deaths of children less than 1 year of age per 1000 live births.
Intrauterine growth restriction (IUGR) – Reduced fetal growth due to caloric, nutrient, and/or developmental deficiencies of the fetus or mother that results in low birth weight.
Low birthweight (LBW) – Infants weighing less than 2500 g at birth.
Low birthweight rate – The number of infants born with a weight less than 2500 g per 1000 live births.

Neonatal infant mortality rate (N-IMR) – The number of deaths between birth and 27 days per 1000 live births.

Perinatal mortality rate – Number of late fetal deaths plus infant deaths within 7 days of birth per 1000 live births.

Postneonatal mortality rate – The number of deaths between 28 days and 1 year per 1000 live births.

Prematurity rate – The number of infants born at less than 37 completed weeks of pregnancy.

Stunting – Below minus two standard deviations (SD) from median height of reference population.

Very low birthweight – Infants weighing less than less than 1500 g at birth.

Very pre-term – Parturition at less than 32 weeks' gestation.

Wasting – Below –2 SDs from median weight of reference population.

Introduction

Each year over 10 million infants and children die before their fifth birthday. Ninety-nine percent of these deaths occur in developing countries and most could be prevented with relatively inexpensive interventions such as improved sanitation, access to clean drinking water, and immunizations against infectious diseases. Poverty, malnutrition, and wars prevent access to these very basic public health measures and are, therefore, important risk factors for infant and child deaths.

National rates of infant and child mortality span a wide range. In 2005, 12 countries had mortality rates for children under 5 years of age of 200 deaths per 1000 live births or higher. By contrast, 22 developed countries had mortality rates of 3–5 deaths per 1000 live births, demonstrating what is possible.

In 1990, world leaders came together to agree on a set of 'millennium development goals' to improve the health and well-being of people worldwide. The fourth millennium goal was to decrease the under-5 mortality rate by two-thirds: from 95 deaths per 1000 live births in 1990 to 31 deaths per 1000 live births in 2015. With only 10 years left until 2015 the under-5 mortality rate was still 76 deaths per 1000 live births in 2005.

In the current article we will first examine infant mortality from a global perspective, focusing on issues of most importance to the developing world. We will then consider the very different challenges that developed countries face in reducing infant mortality.

Causes of infant death vary greatly according to postnatal age. Mortality within 28 days postpartum is classified as neonatal, or newborn, death and is usually attributable to inadequate access to basic medical care at, and immediately following, birth. Postneonatal infant mortality occurs between 29 days and 12 months of age and is largely explained by malnutrition, infectious disease, and home environment. Perinatal mortality describes death in the late fetal period, typically after 28 weeks' gestation and in the first week postpartum. Infant mortality rate (IMR) is the number of deaths under 1 year of age per 1000 live births. Another widely used metric is the mortality rate for infants and children under 5 years of age – under-5 mortality rate. The top 10 causes of under-5 mortality are depicted in **Figure 1**.

Infant Mortality Rate: Disparities Mirror Socioeconomic Development

National under-5 and infant mortality rates are effective proxy measures for national aggregate quality of life, and accordingly, vary markedly by nation. As depicted in **Figure 2**, a nation's under-5 mortality rate relates inversely to its degree of socioeconomic development and integration into global economy. IMRs for the 48 most developed countries are less than 10 deaths per 1000 live births (developed regions comprise Europe, North America, Australia/New Zeland, and Japan) and causes of mortality are overwhelmingly due to premature birth, sudden infant death syndrome (SIDS), and congenital conditions. In contrast, developing countries comprise a heterogeneous group with widely ranging rates and causes of infant mortality. The least developed countries suffer the highest IMRs, typically due to socioeconomic factors such as war, poverty, government corruption, endemic infectious disease, and lack of access to basic healthcare.

Political Will

The importance of political will cannot be overstated regarding infant mortality reduction. According to the international organization Save the Children, to reduce maternal and infant mortality through cultural and medical initiatives in sub-saharan Africa (SSA) would cost $1 billion (dollar equivalents) per year and save an estimated 740 000 newborns. In South Asia, $1.2 billion (dollar equivalents) could save up to 1.13 million newborns – a small expenditure when compared to the Southeast Asia gross national product for 2004: $2.5 trillion (dollar equivalents).

Access to affordable, professional healthcare remains a limiting factor for most developing countries. In industrialized countries, government-financed health expenditure is never less than 5% of gross domestic product (GDP). The case is quite different for most developing countries. For instance, China's government-financed health expenditure is less than 1% of GDP and India's is 2%.

There are important links between public education and health. Mothers with secondary-level education are

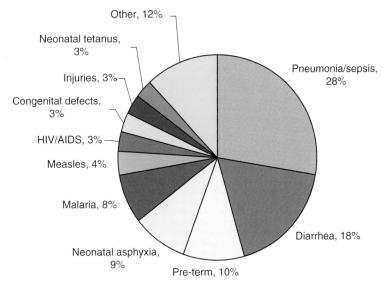

Figure 1   Top 10 causes of under-5 child mortality. Adapted from Bryce J, Boschi-Pinto C, Shibuya K, Black RE, and WHO Child Health Epidemiology Reference Group (2005) WHO estimates of the causes of death in children. *Lancet* 365: 1147–1152.

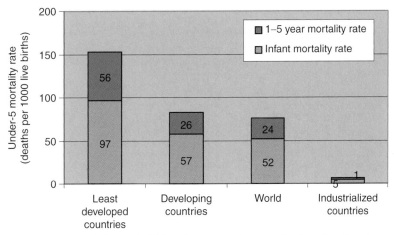

Figure 2   Under-5 mortality rates with the infant and childhood components according to national socioeconomic status. Adapted from *United Nations Report on the State of the World's Children* (2007).

far more likely to begin having children at a later age and to seek out medical care during and after pregnancy. Developed countries usually spend no less than 4.5% of GDP on universal primary and secondary education. As with healthcare, only a handful of developing countries publicly finance education to this degree. Thus, political will and effective health and education policies, even more than national income, determine the level of infant mortality in developing areas.

An economically disadvantaged country can attain a relatively low national IMR through policies that address the combined need for education, nutrition, and access to basic maternal and infant health services. In Niger, gross national income (GNI) per capita is $230 (dollar equivalents) and the IMR is 152 deaths per 1000 live births. Less than 5% of Niger women use modern contraception. Niger's total adult literacy is approximately

14% and only 1 in 10 women are literate. By comparison, Viet Nam's GNI per capita is $550 but the IMR is 17 deaths per 1000 live births. Government-sponsored health programs ensure that 90% of Viet Nam mothers are vaccinated for tetanus and 85% receive prenatal care and medical birthing assistance. Viet Nam's literacy rate is approximately 90%. The GNI of these two countries differs only by $300. Factors such as literacy and national healthcare programs explain much of the IMR gap.

Infant Mortality in Developing Countries

The developing world experiences 99% of global infant mortalities. **Figure 3** illustrates the 10 developing countries with the highest IMRs. Nine countries out of the top 10 are in SSA and all have recent histories of extreme poverty, epidemic, and endemic infectious diseases (lower respiratory infections, diarrhea, malaria, measles, tetanus, pertussis, and HIV/AIDS), low levels of access to maternal and child healthcare, and/or political unrest or war. The highest IMR is shared by Sierra Leone and Afghanistan, with 165 deaths per 1000 live births.

Figure 4 depicts the 10 developing countries with the most infant deaths in 2004. This figure depicts the interplay of IMR and population size. Of note is the fact that India and China are among the top three contributors to infant deaths globally although they have IMRs of 62 and 26 deaths per 1000 live births, respectively. The large populations of these countries contribute to a significant portion of global infant mortality. Given their global and regional importance, India, China, Nigeria, and Brazil will be discussed as case studies below.

Neonatal Mortality in Developing Countries

Of the 10 million children who die each year, 4 million are newborns (less than 1 month of age). Another 3 million pregnancies end in stillbirth and 500 000 mothers die per year in labor. While global child mortality has declined by 14% during the 1990s, neonatal IMRs (N-IMRs) have held constant at 30–31 deaths per 1000 live births. Seventy-five per cent of neonatal mortality occurs within the first week postpartum. As shown in **Figure 5**, 86% of newborn deaths in developing countries are due to infections, prematurity or its complications, and perinatal asphyxia and birth injuries. As discussed below, most such deaths are preventable with low-cost measures.

In developing countries where financial and material resources are lacking, birth takes place in cultures of apprehension that tolerate high levels infant death. Babies often

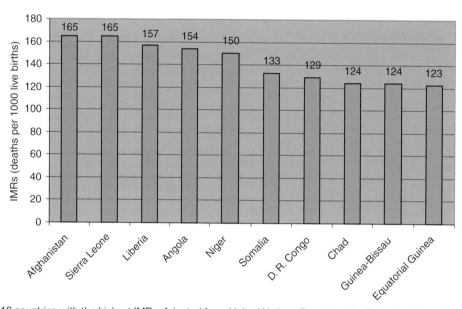

Figure 3   The 10 countries with the highest IMRs. Adapted from *United Nations Report on the State of the World's Children* (2007).

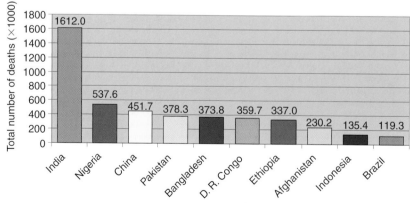

Figure 4   The ten countries with the highest total number of infant deaths in 2004. Adapted from *United Nations Report on the State of the World's Children* (2006).

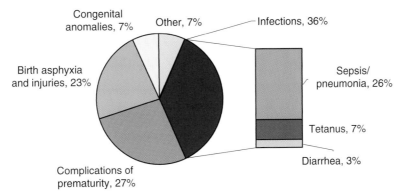

Figure 5 The top causes of infant death in developing countries. Most of these are treatable or preventable with properly trained medical personnel. Adapted from Lawn JE, Cousens S, and Zupan JE (2005) 4 Million neonatal deaths: When? where? why? *Lancet* 365: 891–900.

remain unnamed until they survive 1–6 weeks of life. Previous public health initiatives by the World Health Organization (WHO) and other nongovernmental organizations have proved that such fears are surmountable through culturally sensitive, low-cost educational campaigns employing community leaders and school-based initiatives. Once a community becomes aware that death by sepsis, measles, diarrhea, or tetanus is preventable, family members seek out professional healthcare and practice prophylaxis such as sanitation and exclusive breastfeeding.

A misconception with regard to neonatal mortality is that the advanced technologies of the developed world are necessary for newborn mortality rate improvement. On the contrary, high-intensity neonatal intensive care units (NICU) are not required in developing countries working to reduce neonatal mortality. For example, in England, as with most developed countries, the greatest drop in neonatal mortality (from 30 to 10 deaths per 1000 live births) occurred with the introduction of free antenatal care, improved provision of skilled birth attendants, and increased availability of antibiotics – not with the advent of NICU facilities. In their 2005 study, Adam *et al.* found that the most cost-effective measures for reducing neonatal and maternal mortality in both SSA and Southeast Asia were:

1. community-based newborn care;
2. antenatal care (obstetric care involving tetanus immunization, preeclampsia screening, treatment of asymptomatic bacteriuria and syphilis);
3. presence of skilled birthing attendants, with the availability of level I perinatal care; and
4. emergency obstetric and peri- and postnatal care.

These neonatal health initiatives become more cost-effective if they are implemented together in a coordinated fashion that maximizes both the diversity and the total coverage of services within a regional health system. The Adams *et al.* study projected that 95% coverage by community-level interventions could halve the number of newborn and maternal deaths in regions with elevated IMRs.

Causes of Infant Mortality in Developing Countries

Low birthweight – risks and causes

Low birthweight (LBW) is common in developing countries and a significant risk factor for infant mortality. Between 60% and 80% of newborn deaths are among LBW infants and worldwide 99% of all LBW infants are born in the developing countries of Africa, Asia, Central and South America. Risk factors for LBW include pre-term birth, poor maternal nutritional status, lack of antenatal care, maternal sickness during pregnancy, and an unhygienic home environment.

Unplanned pregnancies exacerbate the risk for LBW and elevate risks for both mother and child. Birth intervals of less than 24 months present excessive energy demands on the mother without opportunity for postpartum recovery. Resulting intrauterine growth restriction (IUGR) leads to LBW, delivery complications, and increased morbidity for the first year of life.

Small women tend to have small, LBW babies, and in developing countries this cycle is often self-perpetuating. Patriarchal norms, food taboos, and young pregnancy, common to many developing countries, promote female stunting and compromise maternal nutrition. Stunted, malnourished women are less capable of safe and full-term delivery and are more likely to deliver LBW and small for gestational age (SGA) infants who then grow into small adults, perpetuating the cycle.

Malnutrition

Well-nourished infants and children have stronger immune systems, bones, and muscles, as well as improved brain function. They are more readily able to combat infectious disease and possess greater energy stores to support recovery. According to the WHO, 50% of the children under 5 years in the least developed countries are stunted due to protein-energy malnutrition and/or micronutrient deficiency. Undernourishment contributes to more than half of all under-5 mortality. Acute diarrhea illness kills infants not only by dehydration but also by predisposing to malnutrition. In Indonesia and India, diarrhea is responsible for 60% of childhood wasting and protein-energy malnutrition. Undernutrition thus presents a significant compromise to child and infant health.

Breastfeeding

The high-energy fats, vitamins, minerals, and iron in human milk are matched perfectly to infant nutritional requirements. Extranutritional advantages of breast milk include prevention of gastrointestinal tract infections, allergies, and obesity. The mother's antibodies, particularly secretory immunoglobulin A, resist digestion by the infant and inhibit bacterial and viral replication in the intestine. Breastfeeding also delays the return of fertility, allowing the mother to devote more energy to feeding and caring for the infant.

Risks of malnutrition to the infant are minimized with exclusive breastfeeding for the first 6 months of life. Ideally, breastfeeding continues up to 2 years of age, with solid foods becoming more dominant over time. Certain cultural taboos in developing countries, particularly India, discourage breastfeeding immediately after birth. For such cases, the infant misses the nutritious and antibody-rich colostrum milk delivered with the first lactation, as well the warmth of the mother and a chance to bond.

Vitamins and micronutrient deficiency

Deficiencies of iron, folic acid, zinc, iodine, and vitamin A pose significant health risks to mother and child. About 250 million children worldwide are affected by vitamin A deficiency, leading to stunting, blindness, and increased mortality. Iron-deficiency anemia is present in 40% of women in developing countries, and is responsible for elevated maternal and infant death rates, stillbirth, LBW, premature delivery, and fetal brain damage. Iodine deficiency causes stunting, cretinism, and mental retardation in regions with low abundance of iodine in local soils and available foods. Folic acid supplementation for women prevents neural tube defects for the fetus, but must be taken regularly prior to conception for maximum efficacy. Public health measures such as iodized salt or drinking water, vitamin A or multivitamin supplements, and food fortification with folic acid have proved to be successful and extremely cost-effective where implemented.

Protein-energy deficiency

Stunting due to protein-energy malnutrition presents an intergenerational risk. As of 2006, an estimated 450 million women in developing countries were classified as stunted due to childhood malnutrition. In cultures and countries where resources are scarce and girls are made to eat least

or last, underdeveloped female bodies experience higher rates of obstructed pregnancy and IUGR. Infants also suffer with low-quality breast milk as caloric and nutrient deficiencies increase susceptibility to infectious disease.

Infectious diseases

The WHO estimates that 7 in 10 childhood deaths are due to acute respiratory infections (ARI), diarrhea, measles, malaria, and/or malnutrition. Most childhood illness in the developing world involves multiple diagnoses of more than one of these conditions. Improving child and infant health will thus require integrative approaches to reduce the prevalence of multiple infectious diseases in addition to malnutrition. Coordination of Health systems remains the primary obstacle to prevention.

Pneumonia/lower respiratory infections

Nearly 30% of under-5 deaths are attributable to acute lower respiratory infections (pneumonia, bronchiolitis, and bronchitis) and sepsis. Whether severe or nonsevere, supportive care includes rehydration therapy, antipyretic therapy, and continued feeding. Even when severe, pneumonia can often be treated without hospital care, if there is access to antibiotics. Infants with signs of both pneumonia and malnutrition (signs of malnutrition include severe wasting and edema of lower extremities) require hospital care and are at very high risk of death. Children with sickle cell anemia are at greater risk even with prophylactic antibiotic treatment and full immunization.

Developing countries experience 95% of the world's childhood pneumonia cases. According to the WHO Child Health Epidemiology Reference group data, the global incidence of pneumonia is 150.7 million cases per year with 7–13% of these cases requiring hospitalization.

Diarrhea

As the second greatest cause of child death in the world, diarrhea is responsible for 17% of under-5 mortality and 3% of neonatal mortality. Both bacterial and viral agents can be curtailed though basic sanitation, food protection, and clean drinking water. Mortality has been reduced by use of oral rehydration therapy for dehydration, an inexpensive therapy not requiring inhospital or advanced medical intervention. Prevention and treatment of diarrhea and dehydration is a simple, low-cost measure with proven public health benefits.

Malaria

Malaria causes 11% of all under-5 mortality. The malaria parasite's vector, *Anopheles* mosquito, is primarily active at night and in the early morning. As such, malarial infection is readily preventable through the use of pesticide-coated sleeping nets, which cost only $5 (dollar equivalent), avoiding outdoor activities at dawn and dusk, and reducing the amount of adjacent standing water. Pharmacologic prophylaxis is also effective, albeit more expensive. Case management includes treatment of malarial infections and anemia.

In countries with endemic malaria, women are most likely to be infected by the parasite during pregnancy. Although causes for increased susceptibility remain unclear, suppressed immunity during gestation has been implicated. Perinatal malaria increases the incidence of LBW, miscarriage, and stillbirth. Risk of maternal death during delivery is also elevated due to severe anemia.

Measles

Measles is the fifth greatest cause of infant and child death in developing countries. Almost all children lacking immunity to measles will catch the disease, which is transmissible through aerosolized droplets and direct contact. The measles vaccine is available for less than $1 (dollar equivalent) – one of the most cost-effective preventive measures known to public health. Consequently, routine immunization with the measles vaccine is a cost-effective step toward United Nations Millennium Development Goal 4, to reduce global childhood mortality by two-thirds. Between 1999 and 2003 worldwide measles mortality decreased by 39%.

Mortality due to measles is usually attributable to the associated complications especially pneumonia and diarrhea. Proper treatment of measles includes case management of pneumonia and other infections, rehydration, and vitamin A supplementation.

Case fatality rates due to measles are relatively low at 1–5% but jump to 25% in populations with compromised immunity due to other diseases (e.g., HIV/AIDS) or nutritional deficiency (especially, vitamin A). War, political unrest, and natural disasters offer footholds for measles epidemics. Damage to infrastructure prevents scheduled immunizations, while squalor among the displaced increases rates of transmission. SSA and South Asia account for 99% of deaths due to measles.

Tetanus

Neonatal tetanus results in 7% of all neonatal mortality, accounting for about 250 000 deaths per year. Risk factors for neonatal infection with *Clostridium tetani* include unsterile delivery and treatment of the umbilical cord stump with animal dung. Neonatal tetanus is readily preventable with two vaccinations – costing a total of 40 cents – given to the mother before or during pregnancy. Other simple precautions against tetanus include clean delivery and umbilical cord care. Mandatory DPT (diphtheria, polio, tetanus) immunization in India since 1981 has been cited as a major factor in lowering N-IMR from 110 deaths per 1000 live births in 1981 to 71 deaths per 1000 live births in 1997.

HIV/AIDS

Almost 70% of those newly infected with HIV are living in Africa; however, heterosexual and intravenous drug transmission rates are rapidly rising in China, Southeast Asia, and Eastern Europe. In nine countries, eight of which are in SSA, the HIV/AIDS pandemic has been responsible for 'increasing' child mortality to levels observed in the 1980s. Sixteen countries have reverted to the under-5 mortality rates of 1990.

The threat to infants from HIV is twofold. First, there is a 35% chance an untreated HIV-positive mother will pass the virus to her fetus. Simultaneous maternal infection of HIV and malaria further increases the risk of viral transmission to the infant. A short round of antiretroviral treatment can reduce the chances of such transmission by 50% yet only 1% of pregnant women in heavily affected countries receive the preventive treatments necessary to stem maternal transmission.

In addition, parental illness and death orphans infants and children, placing the younger generation at extreme risk for poverty, exploitation, and malnourishment. According to Save the Children, 12 million children were orphaned in SSA due to AIDS in 2003. By 2010, that number is expected to rise to 25 million. Indeed, in many countries an entire generation of children is growing up without parents. Young people 15–24 years old are the fastest-growing population of newly infected persons and represent nearly half of all new infections. In some SSA nations, females are five times more likely than males to become infected – a serious obstacle to the delivery and care of healthy infants. The cultural practice of female teenage marriage to older men exposes these women to the risks of teen pregnancy, sexually transmitted infections (STIs), and exposes their infants to maternal HIV transmission.

Environmental health risks
Polluted water

Universal access to clean drinking water could literally save millions of infant lives each year. Water-borne pathogens are responsible for diarrhea, hepatitis, and a host of parasitic and microbial infections. Surmountable obstacles to prevention include inadequate plumbing infrastructure, and squalor among urban poor and displaced populations. Drought, flood, and lack of natural resources due to local geography and climate often present great challenges to delivery of clean water supplies. In areas where infrastructure overhaul is not presently feasible, home-based technologies must suffice and include chlorination, filtration, solar disinfection, and improved storage in homes.

In regions where women and children must walk several miles daily to fetch clean water, exhaustion and malnutrition compound the problem of potable water. Furthermore, the time spent *en route* to and from the water source becomes unavailable for education or economic pursuits, thus exacerbating longer-term risk factors for infant and maternal mortality, such as illiteracy, poverty, and marginalization.

Air pollution

Poor air quality in dwellings due to the burning of inefficient fuels doubles the risk for acute lower respiratory tract infections for children under 5 years of age. Burning biomass such as wood, dung, and coal for energy pollutes the living environment with particulate and noxious byproducts of incomplete combustion (aerosolized byproducts include nitrogen oxides, benzene, butadiene, formaldehyde, poly-aromatic hydrocarbons, sulfur, arsenic, and fluorine). Improving indoor air quality would alleviate child and infant pneumonia and help protect the developing fetus from stillbirth, perinatal conditions, and LBW.

Maternal benefits of clean fuel include less energy expenditure in search of adequate cooking fuel and less polluted air during pregnancy and birth. As with water scarcity, time spent by women and children in search of firewood is lost time for education and social development, exacerbating health risks and reinforcing the poverty gap. One-third of child deaths attributable to indoor smoke take place on the African continent and the African poor are at greatest risk of dying due to indoor pollution.

Female education as an indicator of infant health

Efforts to curb infant mortality in developing countries rely heavily on improving female health and social status. The most effective policies fulfill basic nutrition requirements and increase female access to basic healthcare and contraception, relying heavily on female education to disseminate health information. Female literacy and education are effective indicators of and protectors against maternal and child mortality in a number of ways:

In developing nations, children of uneducated mothers are twice as likely to die in childbirth or to suffer malnutrition as those whose mothers have completed a secondary education. Women who finish at least a primary-level education have improved nutrition, medical care, information access, and economic autonomy, and provide healthier environments in which to raise their children. Prolonging education increases the level of personal income, increases the age of marriage and/or first pregnancy, and decreases parity and the risk of unplanned pregnancy.

Where women lack access to education and health services, girls often marry during or before adolescence and become pregnant at a young age. The bodies of young adolescents are not yet matured and thus less capable of safe, full-term pregnancy. Further exacerbating the risk to poor, young mothers in many developing countries is a lack of trained medical birthing assistants. Unattended delivery of a young mother increases the risks for perinatal asphyxia and birth trauma. Birth complications and LBW are common for this group. Teenage maternal mortality is twice that of older women.

Greater utilization of basic and professional medical care for self and children

Educated women are more likely to give birth with the help of a skilled birth attendant (doctor, nurse, or midwife) who can diagnose, manage, and refer high-risk cases. In Nigeria, 88% of women with higher education give birth with medical assistance, whereas only 15% of uneducated women do. Skilled birth attendants are essential in preventing neonatal mortality for even low-risk labor, as they are trained to maintain clean delivery, perform resuscitation in the case of asphyxiation, and keep both mother and infant dry and warm. Mothers with secondary education are also more likely to breastfeed their infants immediately and exclusively, resulting in the benefits described earlier.

Increased use of family planning and birth spacing

Teaching girls and women to read is a relatively simple measure for preventing unplanned births, short birth intervals, LBW, and large family size. Women with higher levels of education, higher socioeconomic status, and access to contraception are more likely to have planned families, birth intervals of at least 24 months, and fewer children.

Decreased risk of HIV and other sexually transmitted diseases

Blindness, stillbirth, and LBW are just a few of the complications of maternal STIs that are readily preventable through syphilis and gonorrhea screening and treatment. Educated women are more likely to understand the causes and risks of STIs. They are more likely to encourage the use of barrier methods such as male and female condoms, as well as the use of abstinence and medical screening examinations. Female education is imperative for stemming the HIV/AIDS epidemic, as newly infected women between the ages of 15 and 24 years are the most rapidly growing group with HIV.

Case Studies

Four countries have been chosen to exemplify the challenges faced by, and progress achieved in, regions with traditionally high IMRs. Latin American, East Asia, South Asia, and SSA are represented by Brazil, China, India, and Nigeria, respectively. Together these four nations comprise 60% of global infant mortality. The following descriptions serve to contextualize some of the factors leading to these countries' high infant mortality numbers and rates without attempting to generalize trends to the particular regions discussed. See **Table 1** for selected health and demographic information from these countries.

Table 1 Health and socioeconomic demographics from Brazil, China, India, and Nigeria

	Brazil	China	India	Nigeria
Infant mortality rate, 2002	33	30	65	103
World rank for IMR	59	62	41	23
Usage of modern contraception	70%	83%	43%	9%
Female illiteracy	11.9%	19.6%	51.7%	39%
% Females enrolled in primary education	88%	95%	75.7%	NA
Under-5 malarial mortality[a]	2	0	6	49
Gross national income (GNI) per capita	7510	4980	2880	930
Maternal mortality[b]	260	60	440	800
Infants immunized for measles	99%	84%	67%	35%
Population undernourishment	9%	11%	21.4%	9.3%
Tuberculosis mortality[c]	7.9	20.9	34.8	62.3
Access to safe water	87%	76%	83%	62%
Rural access to sanitation	35%	29%	18%	30%
Urban access to sanitation	83%	69%	58%	48%

Data adapted from http://globalis.gvu.unu.edu/.
[a]Number of malaria-related deaths of those under-5 years of age per 1000 live births.
[b]Maternal mortality measures the number of deaths per 100 000 among women who are either pregnant or within 42 days of pregnancy termination.
[c]Deaths per 100 000.

Brazil

Latin America and the Caribbean as a region saw a dramatic decrease in infant mortality between 1960 and 2001 as the IMR dropped from 102 to 28 deaths per 1000 live births. Occupying half of South America's landmass and containing the world's fifth largest population, Brazil is no exception to this trend. Known for its abundant natural and agricultural resources and tapping an extensive labor force, Brazil is a South American economic powerhouse. Between 1970 and 2000, Brazil has decreased its IMR by an impressive 72%. Yet despite its economic prowess and recent statistical accomplishments, the country possesses an IMR that remains unimpressive when compared to other countries with similar GNPs or at similar levels of industrialization. This unexpected delay in IMR reduction has been attributed to the unequal distribution of resources within the country. Disparities have driven disproportionate reductions in healthcare services.

Access to healthcare

Between 1968 and 1981 Brazil's IMR had actually increased from 72 to 92 deaths per 1000 live births. This period was known as Brazil's 'economic miracle', but counterintuitive to notions of development and healthcare growing together, few people were benefiting from the increases in GNP. National-level economic success was subsequently related to diminished public health. Beyond this quick phase of economic growth there is further evidence of unequal distribution amongst regions in the country. In 1970, the difference in IMRs between the top-scoring region and the worst-scoring region of the country was 11-fold. In 2000, despite the national IMR being much lower, this differential grew to 20-fold.

Underinvestment in social infrastructure and services has been cited as a determinant for Brazil's elevated IMR. Although Brazil has a mandate to provide public healthcare to all, an underfunded public healthcare delivery system, an immense demand for care, and the availability of private healthcare for the affluent have resulted in unequal access to preventive and treatment services and disparate IMRs according to income.

Targeting populations and care

Government targets for improving child health include communicable disease prevention, addressing malnutrition, focusing on maternal health, and providing adequate sanitation. The effects of poverty are being stemmed with increased prenatal care. Since 1995, poor municipalities have been targeted specifically according to a national agenda. Despite these efforts, there remains low attendance and a lack of appointments for adolescent mothers seeking prenatal care. A synergistic effect of poverty, adolescent pregnancy, and low levels of education has been suggested to explain undesirably high IMRs in urban settings. Of note, fertility rates have been diminishing in all age groups except the 10–19 years category. Teenage birth may 'transmit' poverty, as young mothers are more likely to drop out of school, have less potential for finding well-paying employment, and will be less able to provide necessary educational opportunities for their children.

Delays in care additionally depend on geographical and cultural situations. Travel time and distance are major determinates for the utilization of medical services. Language barriers between rural communities and service areas can also deter families from seeking healthcare. Within remote communities, traditional healing methods may also be sought instead of evidenced-based medical interventions. This may be compounded by economic factors whereby families with sick children perceive the children as 'doomed' and are less likely to seek costly medical assistance. To remedy these actions, fusing western beliefs into traditional practices has been suggested.

National factors for infant mortality

Many basic aspects of the Brazilian landscape influence infant mortality. The level of education of mothers profoundly affects infant mortality. The children of mothers with 1, 4, 5–8, 9–11, or 12, or more years of schooling have IMRs of 93, 42, 38, 28, and 9 deaths per 1000 live births, respectively. In addition, race is an associated factor. The children of black women have an IMR twice as large as those of white mothers.

Region of residence significantly impacts IMR. The highest rates of mortality are in the north and northeast regions of the country. The 1996, northeast IMR was 64 deaths per 1000 live births, nearly 2.5 times greater than that in the south. These disparities may be attributed to urban–rural differences as the north, comprising 45% of the landmass, contains only 7% of the population. From 1986 to 1996, urban areas experienced a decline in IMR from 51 to 32 deaths per 1000 live births while rural areas had only a reduction from 69 to 61 deaths per 1000 live births. This divide may be explained partially by postneonatal mortalities as they are declining significantly in urban areas yet still account for two-thirds of infant deaths in the countryside.

China

Overall health conditions in China are improving and infant mortality is no exception. Between 1960 and 2003 IMR decreased from 150 to 30 deaths per 1000 live births. Maternal mortality rates have also decreased dramatically but still three-quarters of maternal mortality are attributable to the largely preventable or treatable conditions of hemorrhage, hypertension, embolism, and sepsis.

Access to healthcare

Healthcare access and insurance have improved since the mid-1990s, but further progress remains necessary. The greatest improvement was made in the rural sector: 22% of deliveries took place in a hospital in 1992 and 62% in 2002. Around 88% of pregnant women had at least one prenatal examination in 2003. Although the rate of hospital delivery has increased by 30% since 1993, it exhibits a sharp urban–rural disparity in access: 92.6% and 62%, respectively. Both figures fall short of the Chinese Children and Women Development Compendium goal of 96% hospital delivery.

Lack of insurance coverage remains an important problem for most Chinese mothers and infants, particularly rural residents. Eighty per cent of the rural population is without any form of medical security. Major improvements in insurance are also needed among urban residents – only 55% of the urban population is medically insured.

National programs to improve rural health infrastructure aimed to provide 40% of counties with subsidized insurance coverage at $5 (dollar equivalents) per person by 2006. Efforts to increase total funding and rural health practitioner training are also in place. In 2004, 88% of central finance subsidies went to rural areas to help meet these goals. Urban care policy is restructuring fund allotment away from level-III hospitals and toward community-based health services offering low-cost preventive screening and perinatal care. The number of urban community health centers grew by 70% between 1993 and 2003 and further decentralization of care is in progress.

National mortality factors

Communicable disease burden is on the rise in China. In reaction to these trends, a State Department order in 2005 enacted a plan for government-funded universal payment of vaccination expenses and an integrated reporting system for communicable diseases to be developed for all 31 provinces. Vaccination rates are already relatively high at 80–95%.

With respect to HIV/AIDS prevention, current policy provides antiretroviral drugs, consultations and screenings, maternal transmission blocking drugs, government-provided care of AIDS patients, and AIDS orphans' schooling. Between 2003 and 2005, 310 000 pregnant women were tested for HIV and 387 positive cases identified – all of whom received transmission-blocking drugs. China's adult AIDS prevalence is presently low, at 0.07%.

Population growth in this country of 1.3 billion people will remain a significant impediment to health in the coming century. Although birth rates have been limited by China's stringent family planning policy, population continues to increase due to the large percentage of individuals in their child-bearing years and to increasing life expectancy. Even more significantly, as China moves from a developing to a developed country, resource utilization will dramatically increase. Health expenditure for 2003 amounted to $81.6 billion US (dollar equivalents) and, as with most countries, is growing at a faster rate than annual GDP. China's health sector is expected to experience increasing strain. Out-of-pocket spending by patients rose from 36% to 56% of national health expenditure from 1990 to 2003. United Nations reports conclude there is a shortage of government investment in China's health sector and that resource allocation is inefficiently targeted.

Targeting care

Leading causes of neonatal death in China remain largely preventable and include: asphyxia, pneumonia, premature birth, and LBW. Most infant deaths occur in rural settings. Urban IMR was 10 deaths per 1000 live births in 2004; rural IMR was 25 deaths per 1000 live births. Western provinces are among the poorest and so require the greatest amount of policy intervention and healthcare reform. Targeting those most at risk – the rural, poor, and/or migrant populations will improve national averages significantly.

Perinatal health is becoming of greater importance to China's health system and the percentage of hospital visits due to pregnancy and childbirth complications are on the rise. This rise indicates a change in access to perinatal care, rather than need. As more mothers are able to seek out professional medical care during delivery, the strain on Chinese health infrastructure will continue to grow. Increased funding and additional services for third-trimester pregnancy are necessary to reduce further China's infant mortality.

India

With a large and mostly rural population lacking access to healthcare, India is the largest single contributor to global infant deaths. There were 2.2 million deaths among Indian children under 5 years of age in 2004. National IMR dropped from 146 deaths per 1000 live births in 1960 to 63 per 1000 live births in 2003. Stark IMR inequalities among India's states have been noted.

Interstate disparities generally fall along a north–south divide. The states with better socioeconomic status are not those with the lowest IMR, but more often possess rigid caste systems that enforce inequality and undermine regional infant survival. As of 2000, the four states of Bihar, Uttar Pradesh, Madhya Pradesh, and Rajasthan were home to 45% of the Indian population and accounted for 66% of infant deaths in India. Fewer than 25% of children in these states were immunized. A startling 26% of India's infant deaths occurred in Uttar Pradesh alone. By contrast, southern Indian states have higher rates of literacy and public healthcare access and consistently lower IMRs than do northern states.

Access to healthcare

Access to medical care during delivery plays a crucial role in decreasing neonatal mortality. Stark interstate disparities are partially attributed to differing rates of institutional delivery. In Kerala where 90% of all births take place in a hospital, neonatal IMR was only 10 deaths per 1000 live births. In Rajasthan, Bihar, and Uttar Pradesh, where only 12% of deliveries are in-hospital, neonatal IMR was over 40 deaths per 1000 live births.

Family planning centers in India offer community-specific approaches to intermittent and terminal contraception, maternal care, and STI prevention. Indian households with access to low-cost healthcare have smaller families and lower IMRs. Improving public healthcare access and addressing rural/urban disparities need not entail massive overhaul of facilities, but may be as simple as providing shuttle-bus service to the area in need.

Targeting populations and care

For reducing the number of preventable child mortalities Jones et al. highlight the importance of a few community – and individual-based interventions listed in **Table 2**. In the primarily rural state of Maharashtra, a neonatal IMR reduction of nearly 50% was noted after the introduction of these interventions delivered through state-trained female village healthcare workers. Equivalent programs that target low cost and widespread interventions to high-risk groups have been effective not just in other Indian states, but throughout the developing world.

In a largely rural area, lacking rapid transport systems, such as Maharashtra, it often proves impossible to effect inhospital delivery for unexpected delivery complications. However, reductions in neonatal mortality can be achieved by arranging for high-risk mothers to deliver in a hospital with obstetric and at-least primary-care neonatal services.

National factors for infant mortality

Over one-third of Indian infants are LBW and nearly 70% of perinatal deaths occur among LBW infants. As with IMR, the national average conceals much higher rates among specific regions and groups. Around 40% of all infants born in rural towns and in urban slums are classified as LBW.

The capabilities of Indian healthcare facilities have been a limiting factor for decreasing national IMR. In 1987, only

Table 2 Childhood conditions and deaths are considered preventable if they can be avoided or treated with the interventions listed below

Prevention measures
Breastfeeding 6–11 months
Measles vaccine
Vitamin A supplementation
Skilled attendant at birth
Tetanus toxoid
Clean water, sanitation hygiene
Breastfeeding exclusively for the first 6 months
Nutrition – moderately and severely underweight
Newborn temperature management
Antibiotics
Nivirapine and replacement feeding
Antenatal steroids
Haemophilus influenzae vaccine
Malaria prevention and control during pregnancy
Zinc
Complementary feeding

Treatments
Vitamin A
Antibiotics – pneumonia
Antibiotics – dysentery
Antimalarias
Oral rehydration therapy
Antibiotics – sepsis
Newborn resuscitation
Zinc

Adapted from Jones G, et al. (2003) How many child deaths can we prevent this year. *Lancet* 362: 65–71.

four hospitals possessed the equipment and staff to be considered intermediate (level II) neonatal units. There are now over 50 of these facilities, 12 of which provide level III neonatal intensive care. More basic, preventive interventions, such as improved nutrition and vaccination, will also go a long way in decreasing IMR.

Adult female literacy, caste, and gender inequality are also determinants of IMR in rural India. Indian female literacy is currently 52%, with a significant range. Ninety-nine per cent of women in Kerala can read and write at least at a primary school level whereas only 35% and 43% can in Bihar and Uttar Pradesh states, respectively. Owing to patriarchal norms and marriage customs of certain groups, membership in a scheduled caste and tribe increases a woman's risk of experiencing infant mortality. Female infant mortality among members of such castes is higher than national averages due to preferential treatment of males. Sex-selective abortion and infanticide also favors male births and has resulted in the loss of millions of potential female infants.

Nigeria

SSA has the world's highest regional IMR and has exhibited the least improvement since 1990. Under-5 mortality dropped from 188 per 1000 live births in 1990 to 171 in 2004. Infant mortality improved from 112 deaths per 1000 births to 102 deaths per 1000 live births in the same time period. Not all countries of SSA are experiencing simultaneous, identical phenomena, for each faces its own myriad of social, economic, environmental, and health condition. (e.g., HIV/AIDS, war, poverty, and famine). Thus, improvements in some countries are masked by worsening conditions in others.

Nigeria, the most populous African nation, is among those where child and infant mortality have recently risen. Nigeria has a history of colonization, ethnic and religious tension, and class differentials and can therefore serve to illustrate many of the sources of high IMR in SSA. The country's IMR was estimated at 98 deaths per 1000 live births in 2003. Infectious disease and malnutrition are the most significant influences. Malaria alone accounts for 25% of infant mortality, and malnutrition contributes to 50–60% of under-5 child deaths.

Access to healthcare

Despite the transition to democratic rule from a military dictatorship in 1999, reductions in the IMR have decreased only 0.3% annually. Lack of organization, infrastructure, healthcare professionals, and financial security have all been identified by the WHO as key factors for the poor state of the Nigerian health system. These factors are further compounded by environmental, social, and political problems.

The proportion of the population residing 10 km or less from a health facility ranges from 67% in the northwest to 88% in the southwest. Despite this apparent access poorly supported facilities reduce the efficacy of treatments available. In 2001, only 42% of primary healthcare centers offered antenatal and delivery services. Of these centers, 60% did not use midwives and nearly 20% operated without senior health workers or midwives.

Targeting populations and care

Healthcare is procured in several ways ranging from public federal, state and local initiatives to nongovernmental organisations and private funding. With a growing proportion of Nigerians living below the poverty line (43% in 1985 and 70% in 2005) inclusive public policy is a necessity. Recent trends do not support this logic as the per capita government health expenditure decreased between 1980 and 2000. This trend has been mainly attributed to rapid population growth. As such, fertility rate reduction has been sought. A reduction in fertility rate from 6.4 to 5.5 births per woman has been obtained between 1992 and 2002, but this falls short of the envisioned goal of 4 births per woman. For comparison, the US fertility rate was 2 births per woman in 2004.

Other initiatives for improving infant survival have been implemented including malaria reduction, monitoring and reducing malnutrition, breastfeeding awareness, immunizations, LBW care, vitamin A supplementation, and programs to reduce mother-to-child HIV/AIDS transmission. Pluralistic in nature, these programs combine different levels of government and nongovernmental bodies. The control strategy against malaria, for example, includes lowering or eliminating taxes and tariffs on bed nets and insecticides, educating caregivers to symptoms, providing insecticide-treated nets to high-risk groups (children under 5 years of age and pregnant women), prophylaxis for pregnant women, increased qualified personal in medical institutions and clinics, and an expanded network of community-based practitioners in rural communities.

National factors for infant mortality

Regional, educational, and wealth factors all contribute to substantial variations in the IMR in Nigeria. The first and second poorest quintiles in the country have IMRs of 133 and 140 deaths per 1000 live births, respectively, whereas the richest quintile stands at 52 deaths per 1000 live births. The northeastern region of the country has an IMR of 125 deaths per 1000 live births while the southeast is under half of that figure at 66 deaths per 1000 live births. These regional differences stem from unequal antenatal care, expertise, and assistance at delivery. An urban–rural divide is also present as urbanites have an IMR of 81 deaths per 1000 live births compared to an IMR of 121 deaths per 1000 live births for those living in the countryside. N-IMR are nearly twice as large outside the cities as in urban centers (60 vs. 37 deaths per 1000 live births).

Infant Mortality in Developed Countries

Temporal Changes

In the developed world very low IMRs have been achieved. Rates as low as 2–5 per 1000 live births are present in Japan and a number of European countries. The US has a rate of 7 per 1000, substantially higher. It is instructive to consider temporal changes in IMRs. Many of these concepts are applicable to the developing world today.

In Europe in the middle of the nineteenth century IMRs ranged from 100 to 250 deaths per 1000 live births with the lowest rates in the Scandinavian countries and higher rates in eastern and southern Europe. Throughout the twentieth century infant mortality declined continuously but at different times in different countries and regions. Again in the twentieth century the northern European countries had the earlier declines and eastern European countries and Portugal lagged farthest behind.

Early twentieth century declines in IMRs were primarily due to improved standards of living and associated reductions in deaths due to infectious diseases. These gains have been so impressive that many doctors practicing today have never seen an infant dying of measles, diphtheria, or tetanus. Smallpox, once one of the most important causes of general and infant mortality has been eradicated worldwide since 1980. These improvements were largely observed in their effect on postneonatal mortality such that a higher proportion of infant deaths occurred in the neonatal period.

Decreases in postneonatal mortality in the late nineteenth and twentieth century were associated with important social and environmental improvements: improved sanitation, access to clean drinking water, improvements in personal hygiene, and promotion of breastfeeding. Improvements were more dramatic and occurred earlier in higher social classes who had the benefits of these improvements sooner. In the late nineteenth and early twentieth century, overcrowding, poverty, and poor sanitation made urban and industrial centers substantially more dangerous for infant health than traditional rural settings.

There is substantial evidence that increased breastfeeding reduced infant mortality. For instance, French and Italian data from the late nineteenth and early twentieth century show that abandoned infants who were breastfed by wet nurses had a higher survival rate than those who were bottle-fed.

Figure 6 demonstrates the twentieth century changes in the US IMR. Beginning in the 1960s and 1970s, advances in the organization of perinatal care contributed to reduced neonatal mortality. In regionalized centers, high-risk pregnancies are treated by specialist obstetricians and high-risk neonates, such as those born at very LBW, are treated in NICUs. These specialist centers have been instrumental in developing new effective therapies targeted at the high-risk fetus and infant. In obstetrics, prenatal ultrasound and fetal heart rate monitoring have provided key diagnostic tools. Maternal treatment with corticosteroids for threatened preterm labor has proved to be effective in reducing the severity of respiratory distress syndrome and thereby improving

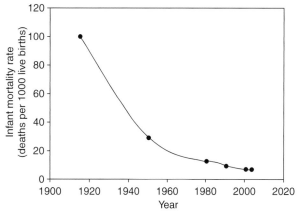

Figure 6 US IMR 1915–2003. Adapted from Hoyert DL, *et al.* (2006) Annual summary of vital statistics: 2004. *Pediatrics* 117: 168–183.

chances for survival of pre-term infants. Likewise, important therapies that have facilitated survival of pre-term and severely ill term-infants include total parenteral nutrition, positive pressure ventilation, surfactant treatment for respiratory distress syndrome, inhaled nitric oxide for pulmonary hypertension, and advances in pediatric surgery.

Infant mortality in developed countries will be approached by examining recent data from the US. In 2002 there were just over 4 million live births and nearly 28 000 infant deaths resulting in an IMR of 7 deaths per 1000 live births. As discussed above, infant mortality has been continuously falling in developed countries, including the US. However, the US IMR is over twice that of several other developed nations and within the US there are important determinants. About two-thirds of infant deaths occur in the neonatal period.

Tables 3 and **4** list the 10 most common causes of death for neonates (less than 28 days old), and for postneonatal infants (from 1 month to 1 year) in the US for 2002. The causes of death for neonates and for postneonatal infants are quite different. Only disorders related to short gestation (prematurity) and LBW and congenital malformations are among the top 10 causes of death in both age groups. We will therefore first discuss causes of death of neonates and then those of postneonates.

Causes of Death–Neonatal Period

Prematurity and low birthweight

Infant mortality increases exponentially as birthweight and the length of gestation decreases (**Figure 7**). Of importance, a higher proportion of infants is being born prematurely recently. The pre-term rate was 12.5% in 2004 up from 9.4% in 1981. Normal weight infants born at term have a 1 in 500 chance of dying in infancy. By contrast, infants weighing 1.5–2.5 kg had an IMR of 15 deaths per 1000 live births and infants born weighing

Table 3   Neonatal deaths, US, 2002

Rank	Cause of death	Number	Percentage of total deaths
	All causes	18747	100.0
1	Disorders related to short gestation and low birthweight, not elsewhere classified	4538	24.2
2	Congenital malformations, deformations, chromosomal abnormalities	3976	21.2
3	Newborn affected by maternal complications of pregnancy	1695	9.0
4	Newborn affected by complications of placenta, cord, and membranes	1011	5.4
5	Respiratory distress of newborn	875	4.7
6	Bacterial sepsis of newborn	705	3.8
7	Intrauterine hypoxia and birth asphyxia	543	2.9
8	Atelectasis	379	2.0
9	Neonatal hemorrhage	379	2.0
10	Birth trauma	339	1.8
	All other causes	4307	23.0

Causes of neonatal death USA, 2002.
From Anderson RN and Smith BL (2002) *Deaths: Leading Causes for 2002. Division of Vital Statistics*. http://www.cdc.gov/nchs/data/nvsr/nvsr53_17.pdf (accessed on 14 August 2007).

Table 4   Postneonatal infant deaths, US, 2002

Rank	Cause of death	Number	Percentage of total deaths
	All causes	9287	100.0
1	Sudden infant death syndrome	2110	22.7
2	Congenital malformations, deformations, chromosomal abnormalities	1647	17.7
3	Accidents (unintentional injuries)	851	9.2
4	Diseases of the circulatory system	432	4.7
5	Septicemia	296	3.2
6	Chronic respiratory disease originating in the perinatal period	259	2.8
7	Assault (homicide)	253	2.7
8	Gastritis, duodenitis, and noninfective enteritis and colitis	231	2.5
9	Influenza and pneumonia	230	2.5
10	Disorders related to short gestation and low birth weight, not elsewhere classified	99	1.1
	All other causes	2879	31.0

Causes of postneonatal infant deaths, USA, 2002.
From Anderson RN and Smith BL (2005) *Deaths: Leading causes for 2002, Division of Vital statistics*. http://www.cdc.gov/nchs/data/nvsr/nvsr53_17.pdf (accessed on 14 August 2007).

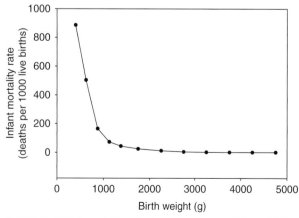

Figure 7   Infant mortality rates increase exponentially as birth weight and/or gestational age decreases.

less than 1.5 kg have a one in four chance of dying. Infants weighing less than 500 g at birth rarely survive intact. The current borderline for survival is a gestational age of about 23–24 weeks.

An infant may be born at a LBW either because of prematurity and/or IUGR. It is important to distinguish between prematurity and growth restriction as causes of LBW because these two processes are associated with different disease entities and have different prognoses.

There have been major improvements in birthweight-specific and gestational age-specific mortality rates since the mid-1970s. These improvements are thought to relate to improved obstetrical and neonatal care. Particularly important has been the regionalization of high-risk perinatal and neonatal care so that the sickest infants are cared for in specialized facilities. In obstetrics, treatment of mothers with threatened pre-term delivery with corticosteroids has improved the respiratory status of the pre-term newborn. Starting in the 1960s the development of newborn intensive care has allowed sicker infants to survive. Particularly remarkable have been the use of mechanical ventilation, parenteral nutrition, and surfactant for respiratory distress syndrome of the premature.

Opposing the improved birthweight-specific mortality has been the increasing percentage of infants born LBW in pre-term. In 2004 12.5% of US infants were born pre-term. LBW rates are substantially higher amongst Blacks than Caucasians or Hispanics and are higher in urban centers than in rural environments. Infant mortality is accordingly 2.4 times higher for Blacks than Caucasians.

Over half of twins and over 90% of triplets are born pre-term and the incidence of multiple gestations has been rising, now accounting for over 3% of live births. A substantial part of the increase in multiple gestations has been due to the use of assisted reproductive technologies. This has led a number of experts and organizations to recommend limiting implanted embryos to one or two. The tendency of mothers to have pregnancies later in life has also contributed to the increase in multiple births.

Progress in preventing prematurity has been disappointing and it seems likely that research will have to provide new insights into the causes of pre-term labor and premature rupture of the membranes before prematurity rates can decline substantially.

Infants born pre-term have immature organ systems and disorders and dysfunction of specific systems account for the elevated mortality rates seen in premature infants. After an infant is born, the lungs must immediately assume respiratory gas exchange, a function performed by the placenta in fetal life. In the pre-term infant, the lungs are not fully formed and until about 34 weeks, do not have the key chemical surfactant that allows easy expansion and contraction during the breathing cycle. Respiratory distress syndrome of the newborn used to be the most important cause of mortality for the pre-term infant. With the discovery that treatment of the mother with corticosteroids can induce surfactant and 'mature' the fetus' lungs and with the availability of postnatal surfactant treatment, survival of premature infants has improved.

Other important disorders contributing to excess mortality for pre-term infants include: intraventricular hemorrhage, neurologic; necrotizing enterocolitis, gastrointestinal; sepsis, infection/immunity; and patent ductus arteriosus, cardiovascular.

Congenital malformations

Congenital malformations, deformations, and genetic abnormalities apparent at birth represent the first or second most common cause of infant mortality in industrialized countries and many other malformations impose significant burdens on the infants and their families. These malformations vary according to organ system, severity, and etiology. Some are associated with genetic abnormalities or environmental exposures and others are due to intrauterine positional deformation. There has been an 18% decline in infant deaths due to congenital malformations, deformations, and chromosomal abnormalities from 1994 to 2002. This suggests that preventive programs such as folate enhancement of maternal diet have been effective and/or that there has been an increase in elective termination of pregnancy when major fetal abnormalities are recognized.

Mortality rates for congenital malformations vary widely. For many malformations mortality rates are not increased. For some major abnormalities, such as anencephaly, and some chromosomal abnormalities, such as trisomy 13 and trisomy 18, mortality rates approach 100%. For many abnormalities there is a spectrum of severity that impacts chances of survival. For instance, abdominal wall defects vary from tiny to massive with mortality increasing as a size of the defect and severity of associated abnormalities increase. Diaphragmatic hernia can vary from asymptomatic or presentation with mild respiratory distress to reduced pulmonary function incompatible with life. Many causes of infant mortality are caused by genetic abnormalities and/or are associated with the defects of the cardiovascular, respiratory, gastroenterologic, or neurologic systems. Among cardiovascular malformations, hypoplastic left heart has the highest mortality rate. With improvements in medical and surgical care of newborns and infants, mortality rates for specific malformations have improved. As an example, infants with gastroschesis, an abdominal wall defect, rarely survived before the advent of parenteral nutrition. Infants with diaphragmatic hernia presenting in the delivery room usually have an associated severe hypoplasia of the ipsilateral lung. Recent advances in neonatal cardiorespiratory support, including high-frequency ventilation, and inhaled nitric oxide, have allowed these infants to be stabilized before surgical repair with a concomitant improvement in outcome.

Race/ethnicity/gender

Within the US in 2002, IMR was 4.8, 5.6, 5.8, 8.6, and 13.8 deaths per 1000 live births amongst Asian or Pacific Islander, Hispanic, white, American Indian, and black mothers, respectively. The two groups with the highest IMRs have high rates of prematurity and SIDS. IMR is 17% lower for girls than for boys.

Maternal risk factors

Teenage mothers and mothers older than 40 years have about a twofold increased risk of having their infant die. Infant mortality for infants of smokers is also increased due to prematurity/LBW, SIDS, and other problems.

Other demographic markers or risk factors for infant mortality include poverty, unmarried status, single-parent household, and late or absent perinatal care.

Causes of Death–Postneonatal Period

The most frequent causes of death in the postneonatal period are SIDS (accounting for 23% of infant mortality in 2002 in the US) and congenital malformations, deformations and genetic abnormalities (18% of infant mortality). Accidents accounted for another 9%. Congenital malformations, deformations, and genetic abnormalities have been discussed above.

Sudden Infant Death Syndrome

SIDS is defined as the sudden death of an infant under 1 year of age, which remains unexplained after a thorough case investigation, including performance of a complete autopsy, examination of the death scene, and review of the clinical history. SIDS represents the most common cause of postneonatal mortality. By definition, the cause of SIDS is unknown. However, epidemiologic studies have indicated risk factors and national campaigns based upon these associations have resulted in dramatic decreases in SIDS incidence. In the late 1980s and 1990s, many countries introduced 'back to sleep' campaigns that emphasized the importance of placing an infant supine to sleep. These campaigns also promoted use of safe cribs, firm mattresses, avoidance of over bundling, and avoidance of maternal smoking prenatally and exposure of the infant to secondhand smoke postnatally. In the US the SIDS rate has decreased from 1.2 deaths per 1000 live births to 0.4 deaths per 1000 live births. Similar declines were seen in other countries worldwide when safe sleeping campaigns were instituted. More recently, additional recommendations have been forthcoming. Evidence has suggested that infants should sleep near the parents but not in the same bed. For reasons that are still not understood pacifier use seems to be associated with over a 50% decrease in the SIDS rate.

SIDS rates in the US are two to three times higher in black people and American Indians than in white people. A portion of these increased rates may be due to modifiable risk factors. For instance, black infants are about twice as likely to be placed prone to sleep as white infants and are more likely to bed share and to sleep in a makeshift bed. As a group, American Indians have high rates of maternal smoking and binge drinking that are risk factors both prenatally and postnatally.

Summary

Over 10 million infants and children under 5 years of age die each year. Over 99% of these deaths occur in the developing countries and the least developed countries. Under-5 mortality rates range from 3 deaths per 1000 live births in Iceland and Sweden to over 250 deaths per 1000 live births in Afghanistan, Niger, Angola, and Sierra Leone. In 2000 the United Nations Millennium Declaration established a goal of a two-thirds reduction in under-5 mortality rate between 1990 and 2015. With only 10 years left the rate had been reduced from 95 deaths per 1000 live births to 76 deaths per 1000 live births in 2005, a 20% reduction. Latin American and East Asian countries have shown a 43% decline; the Middle East and North African countries and South Asia have had declines of 33–35%; by contrast, SSA has had a decrease of only 10%.

Most infant and early childhood deaths can be prevented by inexpensive measures such as nutritional support to the pregnant mother, access to clean water, immunization against childhood infectious diseases, provision of a skilled attendant at birth, treatment of diarrhea and dehydration with oral rehydration fluid, and implementation of malarial control measures including insecticide-pregnated bed nets. Improvement in socioeconomic status results in improvement in infant in childhood mortality but just as important is the political will within a nation to provide support for women and children. Conversely, war, sociopolitical deterioration, and the HIV/AIDS epidemic have increased infant and childhood mortality from 1990 to 2005 as exemplified by Iraq, Zimbabwe, and Botswana.

Historically, infant mortality in developed countries first improved when standards of living increased and infectious disease mortality decreased. More recently advances in obstetric and neonatal care for high-risk pregnancies and premature infants have reduced neonatal mortality rates to as low as 3 deaths per 1000 live births. Back to sleep and other risk reduction strategies have cut the incidence of SIDS by 50% and more since 1990. Despite these advances, even in developed countries there remain disadvantaged subgroups and high-risk populations with significantly higher infant and child mortality rates.

See also: AIDS and HIV; Birth Complications and Outcomes; Birth Defects; Breastfeeding; Demographic Factors; Failure to Thrive; Healthcare; Maternal Age and Pregnancy; Newborn Behavior; Nutrition and Diet; Parental Chronic Mental Illnesses; Premature Babies; Prenatal Care; SIDS.

Suggested Readings

Anderson RN and Smith BL (2005) *Deaths: Leading Causes for 2002, Division of Vital Statistics.* http://www.cdc.gov/nchs/data/nvsr/nvsr53_17.pdf (accessed on 14 August 2007).
Black RE, Morris SS, and Bryce J (2003) Where and why are 10 million children dying every year? *Lancet* 361(9376): 2226–2234.

Bryce J, Boschi-Pinto C, Shibuya K, and Black RE (2005) WHO Child Health, Epidemiology Reference, Group WHO estimates of the causes of death in children. *Lancet* 365: 1147–1152.

Corsini CA and Viazzo PP (1997) *The Decline of Infant and Child Mortality*. Dordrecht: Martinus Nijhoff Publishers.

Hoyert DL, Mathews TJ, Menacker F, Strobino DM, and Guyer B (2006) Annual summary of vital statistics: 2004. *Pediatrics* 117(1): 168–183.

Jones G, Schultink W, and Babille M (2006) Child survival in India. *Indian Journal of Pediatrics* 73: 479–487.

Jones G, Steketee RW, Black RE, Bhutta ZA, and Morris SS (2003) The Bellagio, Child Survival Study Group how many child deaths can we prevent this year? *The Lancet* 362: 65–71.

Lawn JE, Cousens S, and Zupan J (2005) Lancet Neonatal Survival, Steering Team 4 million neonatal deaths: When? where? why? *Lancet* 365: 891–900.

Pelletier DL, Frongillo EA, and Habicht JP (1993) Epidemiologic evidence for a potentiating effect of malnutrition on child mortality. *AMJ Public Health* 83: 1130–1133.

Relevant Websites

http://globalis.gvu.unu.edu – Globalis is an interactive world.

http://marchofdimes.com – March of Dimes. Saving babies, together.

http://www.savethechildren.org – State of the world's mothers 2006.

http://www.unicef.org – UNICEF The state of the world's children 2007, women and children: The double dividend of gender equality.

Motor and Physical Development: Locomotion

K E Adolph, New York University, New York City, NY, USA

Glossary

Affordance – A term drawn from Gibson's perception–action theory referring to the fit between the physical properties of the environment and an animal's physical abilities that makes a given action possible. Affordances exist regardless of whether they are detected or used.

Crawling – Moving in a prone position, either with the belly on the floor or with the abdomen in the air. Infants may crawl using hands, arms, elbows, knees, feet, belly, and head for support and they may coordinate their limb movements into countless combinations.

Dynamic balance – Keeping the body in equilibrium against gravity while the body is in motion (as in crawling or walking).

Newborn reflexes – Movements produced by neonates in response to stimulation (e.g., stepping, grasping, sucking). Typically, these movements disappear after a few months. The movements are not truly reflexive because infants produce them spontaneously and they can be deliberately controlled and modified.

Posture – Stationary and dynamic positions of the body that characterize a form of stance or locomotion (e.g., sitting, crawling, standing, cruising, walking). All postures except lying flat on the ground require balance control.

Prospective control – Planning movements ahead of time based on perceptual information about upcoming obstacles and goals.

Walking – A form of independent, upright locomotion with the body facing forward. Infants achieve independent walking when they do not need to hold onto furniture or caregivers for support. In contrast to running, where both feet are off the ground for brief periods, in walking, at least one foot is always on the ground. In the swing phase, one foot is on the ground while the other foot swings forward. In the double support phase, both feet are on the ground.

Introduction

The development of locomotion begins prenatally with spontaneous fetal movements. After birth, infants learn to cope with gravity and the continual flux of physical growth and variations in the terrain. Balance and strength are the critical factors for the emergence of new forms of locomotion and for improvements in proficiency. Experience is the critical factor for promoting adaptive responding to changes in body dimensions and variations in the environment. However, experience does not generalize from one postural milestone to the next. Independent mobility both requires and facilitates developments across multiple psychological domains.

The Psychological Significance of Independent Mobility

Locomotion is a landmark developmental achievement. Independent mobility offers new opportunities for learning about the environment, the self, and the relations between them. Before the onset of mobility, infants are dependent on their caregivers for gaining access to new vistas and places. Without transportation by their caregivers, infants' view of the world is limited to the scenes revealed by turning the eyes and head. Exploration of objects and surfaces is restricted to the things within arms' reach. After the onset of mobility, infants are less dependent on their caregivers for making contact with the environment. They can change their vantage point to peer over the top of the coffee table or to explore beneath it. They can retrieve objects and transport them from place to place. They can choose to move away from their caregivers or to follow after them.

Locomotion requires infants to master dynamic balance control. Long before the onset of mobility, infants can produce the patterns of limb movements used for crawling, walking, and other forms of locomotion. The really impressive achievement in the onset of mobility is the ability to produce coordinated limb movements while in a state of dynamic balance. In stationary postures such as sitting and standing, the body must be stabilized to allow the head and arms to move. In contrast, for dynamic balance during locomotion, the body must be destabilized in conjunction with movements of the arms and legs. To propel the body forward, infants must create the conditions of a fall and then recapture their balance on the fly from step to step.

The advent of mobility provides new possibilities for action. However, detecting possibilities for locomotion requires infants to perceive the surface layout and the friction and rigidity of each surface relative to their own physical abilities. To make their way safely through the surrounds, infants must decide whether the ground is sufficiently flat, continuous, and clear of barriers to maintain balance and fit the body, and whether there is sufficient friction and rigidity to grip the surface and to support body weight. Selecting and modifying locomotor movements to suit the constraints of the current situation requires infants to generate and use new sources of perceptual information for controlling their motor actions adaptively.

Compared with other motor actions, infants' success (and failure) at locomotion is easy to see. Movements of the eyes during visual tracking, the arms and hands during reaching and grasping, and the torso while keeping balance in stationary postures are typically so small and rapid that observations require special motion recording equipment. In contrast, displacements of the whole body during locomotion are relatively large and slow and can be seen with the naked eye or on videotape. Missteps and falls are obvious (as are their consequences when infants cry or incur injury). Given the psychological significance of locomotion and the accessibility of locomotor movements to observation, it is no wonder that parents commemorate infants' first steps in 'baby books' and home movies, and that researchers have been formally documenting the development of locomotion for more than a century.

Classical and Contemporary Approaches to Locomotor Development

Early Pioneers

By the early 1900s, amazing stop-action photography techniques were available for recording objects in motion such as horses galloping, birds flying, and human locomotion. In the 1930s and 1940s, developmental psychologists co-opted and greatly expanded new recording technologies and research on locomotor development entered its heyday. The early pioneers, Mary Shirley, Myrtle McGraw, and Arnold Gesell, are best known for their detailed, normative descriptions of locomotor development and their emphasis on neuromuscular maturation as the agent of developmental change. Equally important, however, is their legacy of elegant and meticulous recording methods for capturing motor actions in real time, and their precedent of back-breaking microgenetic methods for documenting changes over development. With a diligence and persistence that set the modern standard, homely, everyday materials were combined with the finest film techniques of the day.

Shirley, for example, laboriously scored the x–y coordinates of footprints made from olive oil sprinkled with graphite to track the development of upright locomotion over the first 2 years of life. McGraw traced infants' body position from still frames of high-speed film to observe locomotor development from birth until independent walking. Gesell built a 'research hotel' in his laboratory so that he could observe infants continuously for several days.

What became of all this meticulous descriptive data? The writings of the early pioneers are full of quantitative data that chart improvements in the proficiency of crawling, walking, and other forms of locomotion and changes in the frequency of various precursory and locomotor movements. However, the prevailing adherence to a theory of neuromuscular maturation led the early pioneers to emphasize qualitative descriptions of stage-like changes in the development of locomotion and to ignore the immense intra- and intersubject variability that was apparent in the real-time performance and developmental appearance of each type of locomotor movement. The development of locomotion was viewed as an outward illustration of endogenous changes in the brain and body. In their view, locomotor behavior 'grows' as an accompaniment to infants' maturing brains and bodies. Because motor behaviors are more accessible to observation than neuromuscular maturation, growth in locomotor development could provide insights into the corresponding growth of the nervous system.

Thus, the variable developmental trajectories in the original datasets were depicted as invariant developmental sequences. McGraw, for example, identified seven stages in the assumption of an erect posture. With a tenacity unrivalled before or after his time, Gesell identified 23 ordered stages in the development of locomotion. Their quantitative data have withstood the test of time, and the practice of cataloging motor achievements, identifying onset dates, and assigning stages to ages continues today with popular developmental screening inventories such as the Bayley Scales. Most developmental textbooks contain a chart that features infants' postural milestones (**Figure 1**).

Contemporary Approaches

Between 1950 and 1980, research on locomotor development was dormant. Possibly, the early pioneers had done their work too well. With reams of data recording infants' locomotor movements at various points in development and volumes of published works describing the ages and stages of locomotor development, there seemed little else for investigators to do. Beginning in the 1980s, contemporary researchers led by Eleanor Gibson and Esther Thelen resurrected the study of locomotor development. New theories were proposed (perception–action and dynamic systems theories for Gibson and Thelen, respectively), new motion recording technologies became available (including videotape which allowed any researcher or parent to capture infants' movements, and sophisticated,

high resolution devices such as force plates and automatic motion capture systems), and once again research took off.

Whereas the early pioneers depicted locomotor development as universal and decontextualized from the surrounds, the starting assumption for most current work is that motor actions are embodied and embedded. The perception–action concept of 'affordances' captures the functional significance of embodiment and embeddedness: Possibilities for performing locomotor movements depend on the biomechanical facts of infants' bodies and the physical properties of the surrounding environment. The dynamic systems tenets of nested subsystems and emergent outcomes highlight the multiply determined nature of locomotor movements and the inter-related nature of the relevant components. The size, shape, mass, strength, flexibility, and coordination of infants' various body parts affect the biomechanical constraints on locomotion. Reciprocally, possibilities for locomotion depend on the conditions of the environment in which infants' bodies are embedded: the effects of gravity acting on the body and the surfaces and media that support the body.

From a dynamic systems account, no component, including the brain, has logical priority for driving locomotor development. New forms of movement emerge in development when all of the component subsystems are at a state of readiness. Locomotor movements are stable or variable depending on the levels of each component. The

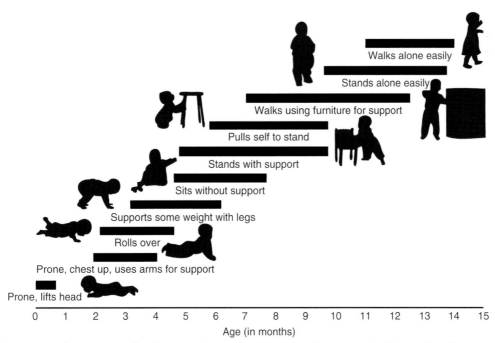

Figure 1 Infant motor milestone chart showing range of ages for achieving various postural and locomotor milestones. Source: from Siegler R, DeLoache J, and Eisenberg N (2003) *How Children Develop*, 1st edn. New York: Worth Publishers; Santrock J (2006) *Life-Span Development*, 10th edn. New York: McGraw-Hill; Frankenburg W, Fandal A, Sciarillo W, and Burgess D (1981) The newly abbreviated and revised Denver Developmental Screening Test. *Journal of Pediatrics* 99: 995–999, Copyright (1981), with permission from Elsevier.

critical component at a given point in development or in a particular situation might be the status of the central nervous system, or it might be leg strength, balance control, the effects of gravity, the slope or friction of the ground surface, or some other peripheral factor.

From a perception–action account, the development of locomotion cannot be divorced from function. For locomotion to be adaptive, infants must select and modify movements to suit the affordances of the current situation. Moreover, movements should be planned prospectively before stepping over the brink of a cliff or losing balance on a slippery patch of ground. Given the relatively slow rate of neural conduction, reactive adjustments are only a strategy of last resort. Thus, for infants to control locomotion adaptively, they must gather perceptual information about upcoming affordances in sufficient time to plan their next steps. For perception–action researchers, the study of locomotor learning and development is also the study of perceptual learning and development.

The data that were so troubling for the neuromuscular maturation theory – the fact that infants' locomotor movements are variable, idiosyncratic, and context dependent, and the finding that infants frequently straddle stages, skip stages, and backslide to earlier stages – are not problematic for contemporary theories. A guiding principle in current research is that unique moves can lead to common outcomes. The question is how. Dynamic systems researchers examine how multiple routes can converge on the same developmental pathway. Perception–action researchers study how individuals update their assessment of their own abilities from step to step and from one developmental period to the next.

A challenge for developmental researchers from both dynamic systems and perception–action frameworks is to identify the relevant aspects of infants' bodies and environments that create affordances for locomotion, even while these features are continually changing. The facts of embodiment vary due to developmental changes in body growth and abilities. Similarly, the features of the environment vary as infants' developing bodies and skills introduce them to new surfaces and places.

Precursors of Locomotion: The Case of Newborn Stepping

Since the early pioneers, researchers have located the developmental precursors to independent locomotion in infants' first, spontaneous limb movements. From the instant that their rudimentary muscles are enervated, fetuses exhibit limb and body movements. By 10 weeks of gestation, fetuses move their arms and legs singly, simultaneously, or in alternation, sometimes moving their limbs in conjunction with whole body activation as when they alternate their legs to turn a somersault. In the first weeks after birth, neonates continue to exhibit spontaneous limb and body movements.

As in the fetus, some of these resemble locomotor patterns such as swimming, crawling, and walking. Of course, fetuses and neonates are not maintaining balance or trying to go someplace, but the propensity for coordinated, locomotor-like patterns is there.

Newborn stepping is the best-known example of precursory locomotor limb movements because it shows a fascinating U-shaped developmental trajectory. Also known as the 'stepping reflex', when newborns are held upright under their arms with their bare feet touching a hard surface, they respond with alternating leg movements that look like exaggerated marching (**Figure 2(a)**). Stepping movements typically disappear by the time infants are 8 weeks old and then reappear at around 8 months of age when infants begin to walk with caregivers holding their hands to provide balance.

From the traditional neural maturation account, first proposed by McGraw and adopted by many modern researchers, maturation of the central nervous system drives the disappearance and subsequent reappearance of stepping. Neonates' reflexive movements are subcortical

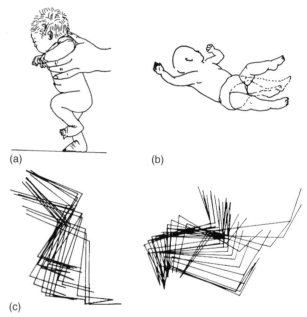

(a)   (b)

(c)

Figure 2 Alternating leg movements in newborn infants. Figure reprinted from Adolph KE and Berger SE (2006) Motor development. In: Damon W and Lerner R (eds.) *Handbook of Child Psychology: Vol. 2: Cognition, Perception, and Language*, 6th edn., pp. 161–213. New York: Wiley. (a) Upright stepping. Courtesy of Adolph KE, New York University. (b) Supine kicking. Reproduced from Thelen E (1979) Rhythmical stereotypies in normal human infants. *Animal Behavior* 27: 699–715, with permission from Elsevier. (c) Stick diagrams of leg movements in upright stepping and supine kicking in a representative 2-week-old infant. The lines chart the movements of one of the infant's legs at toe, ankle, knee, and hip every 33 ms. Thelen E and Fisher D Newborn stepping: An explanation for a 'disappearing reflex'. *Developmental Psychology* 18: 760–775, 1982. Copyright © 1982, the American Psychological Association, reprinted with permission.

(anencephalic infants step). Increasing myelinization of the corticospinal tract suppresses the stepping reflex, and allows stepping to reappear under cortical control toward the end of the first year. Continued maturation of neural structures and circuitry increases information processing speed and efficiency so that infants walk independently at approximately 12 months of age.

Several lines of evidence argue against the traditional account. First, early stepping movements may not be reflexive. Fetuses and neonates exhibit stepping movements without an eliciting stimulus; they step with their legs dangling in the amniotic fluid or in the air, and they step upside down in the uterus or with their feet on the ceiling. Second, early leg movements can be cortically controlled; infants move a leg singly, alternate their legs, and move legs simultaneously when the appropriate leg movements are linked with the jiggling of an overhead mobile in operant conditioning experiments.

Third, Thelen and colleagues showed that alternating leg movements do not disappear; they are only masked when infants are held in an upright position. Throughout the first year of life, infants move their legs in an alternating pattern when they lie on their backs (**Figure 2(b)**). In fact, supine kicking movements have the same pattern of muscle activations and time-space trajectories as upright stepping movements. As shown in **Figure 2(c)**, when leg movements are plotted as overlaying stick figures, supine kicking looks like upright stepping if the plots are turned 90°.

Thelen proposed that leg fat rather than the central nervous system is responsible for the U-shaped trajectory of upright stepping. Normal gains in leg fat over the first few months of life typically outstrip gains in muscle strength. Alternating leg movements disappear in an upright position but not in a supine position because of the differential effects of gravity. While held upright, infants must work against gravity to flex their legs at the hip. While lying supine, gravity assists hip flexion by pulling the bent thigh toward the chest. Gravity, inertia, and the spring-like quality of the muscles and tendons help to extend the hip and spring the leg straight again. By 8 months of age, infants have sufficient muscle strength to lift their fat legs in an upright position.

In line with Thelen's body-based account, infants with thinner legs continue to display upright stepping movements at the same ages when infants with fatter legs stop stepping. Infants who normally take steps stop stepping when their legs are weighted to simulate the leg fat gained over the first 2 months of life. Infants who normally have stopped taking upright steps step once again when their legs are submerged in a tank of water to alleviate the effects of gravity. Finally, with a few minutes of daily exercise moving the legs in an upright position, infants do not show the usual decline in stepping movements at 8 weeks.

Prerequisites for Locomotion: The Importance of Posture

Both classical and contemporary researchers view postural control as the central prerequisite for locomotion. The stage-like progressions depicted by the early pioneers were really a series of distinct postural stages. Each subsequent posture marked the next triumph over gravity in an orderly march toward erect locomotion. It is easy to see that upright walking requires postural control. But, as the early pioneers recognized, every form of locomotion requires postural control, including the forms that typically precede walking (cruising, crawling, bum shuffling, crabbing, rolling, etc.) and the forms that follow it (running, skipping, sliding, stair climbing, walking backward, etc.). In any position except lying flat on the ground, postural control is required to fight the pull of gravity.

Terms like static balance and stationary posture refer only to the fact that the body is not changing location. Even while sitting or standing, the body is always slightly in motion, swaying gently within a cone-shaped region of permissible postural sway. To keep balance in stationary and dynamic postures, infants must keep their bodies within the region of permissible postural sway. The size of the sway region depends on infants' available muscle torque relative to the size of the gravitational and inertial forces pulling the body over.

Typically, infants achieve stationary postures before they achieve sufficient control over destabilizing forces to deliberately create the necessary disequilibrium to change locations without falling. They lift and turn their heads before they can roll. They prop on all fours before they can crawl on hands and knees. They stand upright before they walk. In the first few months after walking onset, infants' strategies for deliberately inducing disequilibrium are variable and idiosyncratic. For example, they may stand up on tiptoe and allow themselves to fall forward, or wind their trunk like a spring and then use the angular momentum to bring their swinging leg around. Adult-like anticipatory control of gait initiation takes years to acquire. Stopping at the end of a gait sequence is also problematic. Initially, infants collapse to the ground after a crawling step or two, and their walking sequences end when they crash into caregivers' open arms. After several weeks of experience, infants can maintain a steady pace, modify their speed at will, and come to a controlled stop at the end of a sequence.

Crawling and Walking

Prone Progression

McGraw described prone progression as the most variable and idiosyncratic of all of infants' motor behaviors. Contemporary researchers would agree. The typical precursors to crawling involve changes in body position and orientation without moving to a new location. Infants roll front to back and vice versa, transition from sitting to prone, pivot in circles on their stomachs, swim in place, and rock back and forth on hands and knees. Before they begin propelling themselves forward, some infants propel themselves backward by pushing with their arms, keeping their legs extended in the mermaid position.

Approximately half of the infants who eventually crawl display a period of 'belly crawling', in which the abdomen rests on the floor at some point during each crawling cycle. Some infants drag their abdomens along the floor like a marine, and some repeatedly launch themselves from hands (or elbows) and knees (or toes) onto their bellies during each step. The other infants who eventually crawl skip the belly crawling period of development. Their first success at forward prone progression is with their abdomens raised in the air during each crawling cycle, termed hands-and-knees crawling. Former belly crawlers also display a period of hands-and-knees crawling and they do so at the same age, on average (8 months), as the infants who skip belly crawling.

Because belly crawling involves less stringent balance constraints, infants show tremendous intra- and intersubject variability in the body parts used for balance and propulsion and in the patterns of coordination between the limbs. From cycle to cycle, infants use their arms, legs, bellies, and heads in various combinations, sometimes pushing with only one limb in a girdle and dragging the lame arm or leg behind, sometimes pushing with first the knee then the foot on one leg, sometimes resting on their belly and sometimes on their cheek, and so on (**Figure 3**, rows for 'Army' and 'Inchworm' crawling). Interlimb timing is equally variable. Infants move arms and legs on alternate sides of the body together like a trot, ipsilateral limbs together like a pace, lift front then back limbs into the air like a bunny hop, and so on. Belly crawlers simply power up their limbs and allow whatever idiosyncratic and arduous patterns to emerge.

Even the prototypical hands-and-knees pattern is variable in terms of body parts used for balance and propulsion (**Figure 3**, rows for 'Standard' and 'Bear' crawling). Infants may crawl by balancing on a knee on one side and a foot on the other, balancing on two feet with the knees in the air like a bear, or using both the knees and feet in succession during each cycle. Variability in interlimb timing, however, shows a dramatic decrease in the developmental transition from belly crawling to hands-and-knees crawling. Within 1 or 2 weeks after learning to keep their abdomens off the floor, infants converge on a diagonal, near-trot gait: The right arm moves and then the left knee, followed by the left arm and then the right knee. Presumably, the diagonal pattern provides the most stability while balancing on hands and knees.

Despite all the variability and regardless of the body parts used for support and propulsion, infants' proficiency

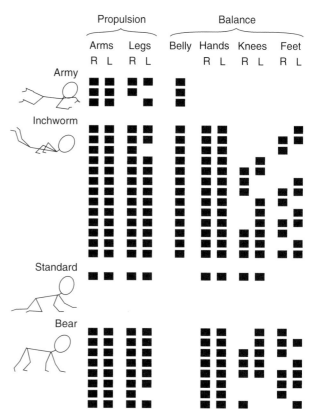

Figure 3 Some of the many individual variations in infants' crawling patterns. Left column illustrates four types of increasingly erect crawling postures: 'army' belly crawls, 'inchworm' belly crawls, 'standard' hands-and-knees crawling, and 'bear' crawls on hands and feet. Columns represent combinations of arms, legs, and belly used for propulsion and balance. Each row represents a unique crawling pattern displayed by at least one infant. Reproduced from Adolph KE, Vereijken B, and Denny MA (1998) Learning to crawl. *Child Development* 69: 1299–1312. Copyright (1998) by the Society for Research in Child Development, with permission from Blackwell Publishing.

at crawling increases with each week of experience: Crawling steps become larger and faster. Infants who belly crawl show an advantage in proficiency compared with infants who skip belly crawling. From their first week on hands and knees, former belly crawlers take larger, faster steps, and the belly-crawling advantage persists for several weeks. Moreover, the duration of infants' experience with any of the prone skills – even pivoting, rocking, and skills that do not involve traveling somewhere – predict their proficiency at crawling on hands and knees. In summary, practice executing the variety of movements involved in belly crawling has beneficial effects on movements that use different parts of infants' bodies in different temporal patterns once they have sufficient strength to move on hands and knees. Experience with precursory forms of prone progression provides infants with practice initiating disequilibrium and stabilizing their torso while moving their extremities.

Upright Locomotion

Walking upright is a unique accomplishment compared with other motor milestones. It is a developmental rite of passage marking the transition from infant to toddler, and like infants' first words, walking is emblematic of human culture. However, achieving an upright posture can take infants several months. With increasing leg strength, infants pull to a stand gripping furniture, but fall back to their bottoms as their legs tire; when caregivers prop them against furniture, they bear weight momentarily with their legs hyperextended. Eventually, infants can stand with softly flexed knees while holding furniture or caregivers' hands for support. When infants acquire sufficient strength to hold part of their weight on one leg, they display 'supported walking' (facing forward with caregivers holding onto both hands or supporting them under the arms) and 'cruising' (moving sideways, using the arms for balance by holding onto furniture for support).

Most infants take their first independent walking steps around their first birthday, but the normal age range is extremely wide – from 9 to 17 months in Western cultures. Typically, infants' first walking steps are shaky and inconsistent. Infants point their toes out to the sides, take tiny forward steps, and plant their feet so wide apart laterally that their step width may be larger than their step length. Velocity is slow, punctuated by relatively short periods with one leg in the air and relatively long periods with both feet on the ground. Movements at the hip, knee, and ankle joints are jerky and variable. Infants' feet contact the ground on the toes or flat-footed. Their arms are flexed at the elbow in a frozen 'high-guard' position.

The first 4–6 months of independent walking show the most rapid improvements in walking proficiency (**Figure 4**). Rather than responding *ad hoc* to the outcome of their last step, infants' movements are uniform and consistent over the whole path of progression. Their toes point more forward, their steps are longer, and their feet are closer together laterally. Overall velocity increases; the proportion of the gait cycle with one leg in the air increases and the proportion with both feet on the ground decreases. Joint angles become smoother and more consistent and infants' feet contact the floor with a heel–toe progression. Infants' hands are down at their sides and their arms swing reciprocally with the leg on the opposite side of the body. Walking patterns continue to improve, albeit more slowly, until 5–7 years of age, when children's walking becomes truly adult-like.

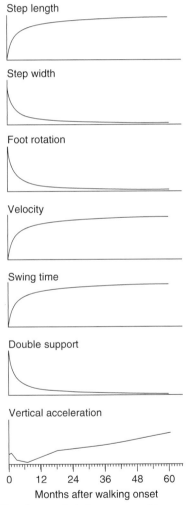

Figure 4　The characteristic time course of improvement in several measures of children's walking gait over the first 60 months of independent walking. Figure reprinted from Adolph KE and Berger SE (2006) Motor development. In: Damon W and Lerner R (eds.) *Handbook of Child Psychology: Vol. 2: Cognition, Perception, and Language*, 6th edn., pp. 161–213. New York: Wiley. Step length, distance between consecutive steps; Step width, lateral distance between steps; Foot rotation, absolute value of in/out-toeing from path of progression; Velocity, overall distance/time; Swing time, percent of gait cycle with one foot moving through the air; Double support, percent of gait cycle that both feet are on the floor; Vertical acceleration of the center of mass, rate of change in velocity of the center of mass along the vertical axis. Adapted from Bril B and Ledebt A (1998) Head coordination as a means to assist sensory integration in learning to walk. *Neuroscience and Biobehavioral Reviews* 22: 555–563, with permission from Elsevier. Curves for step length, step width, and foot rotation drawn from data presented in Adolph KE, Vereijken B, and Shrout PE (2003) What changes in infant walking and why. *Child Development* 74: 474–497, reproduced with permission from Blackwell publishing. Curves for velocity, swing time, and double support derived from data presented in Garciaguirre JS, Adolph KE, and Shrout PE (2007) Baby carriage: Infants walking with loads. *Child Development* 78: 664–680 and Garciaguirre JS and Adolph KE (2006) Infants everyday locomotor experience: A walking and falling marathon. *International Conference of Infant Studies*, Kyoto, Japan. Curve for vertical acceleration drawn from data presented in *Journal of Motor Behaviour* 24: 105–116. Reprinted with permission of the Helen Dwight Reid Educational Foundation. Published by Heldref publications, 1319 Eighteenth St, NW, Washington, DC 20036-1862. Copyright © 1992.

As in crawling, however, group averages mask tremendous intra- and interindividual variability. The typical developmental progression is only a rule of thumb. Some infants initially conquer dynamic balance by plunging forward and catching themselves before they fall; their first walking steps are long, their feet are pointed to the front, and one or both arms swing wildly. Although infants' average step length is short and average double support period is long relative to those of mature walkers, occasionally they can take steps longer than their leg length and display short periods with both feet on the floor.

Both the early pioneers and contemporary researchers agree that the characteristic deficiencies and variability in infants' early walking patterns stem from the same problem that hinders walking onset: sufficient balance control to support the body on one leg while the other leg swings forward. In fact, infant walkers fall downward into each step; the vertical acceleration of their center of mass is negative when their foot contacts the floor. In contrast, adult walkers propel upward at each step; the vertical acceleration of their center of mass is positive at foot contact. In essence, new walkers sacrifice balance to solve the problem of forward propulsion. They allow their bodies to fall forward while they stand on their stationary foot and then catch themselves mid-fall with their moving foot. Adult walkers control balance during forward propulsion by pushing upward with the foot supporting their body.

Since the early pioneers, researchers have debated the underlying factors that give rise to developmental improvements in balance control. From a brain-based account, changes in neural structures and circuitry facilitate dynamic balance by increasing information-processing speed and efficiency and by expanding infants' ability to sequence their movements. From a body-based account, more slender body proportions and the lowering of infants' center of mass facilitate dynamic balance control by mitigating the size of destabilizing torque pulling the body over. Thus, infants require less strength to keep their bodies within the region of permissible postural sway. Moreover, an increased muscle to fat ratio provides infants with more strength to combat gravitational and inertial forces. From an experience-based account, practice moving in an upright position facilitates dynamic balance control by providing infants with opportunities to detect the perimeter of their sway region. In addition, lifting their legs against gravity provides rigorous strength training in the leg muscles.

Correlational and experimental evidence is consistent with all three explanations. In support of a neural maturation account, infants' brains increase from 30% to 70% of adults' brain weight over the first 2 years of life, and neural fibers become increasingly myelinated in the corticospinal tract. Other psychological functions that require combinatorial sequences (language, symbolic play) appear at approximately the same age as walking. Infants' high-guard arm position co-occurs with a return to two-handed reaching, suggesting underlying brain linkages. In support of a body-based account, chubbier, more top-heavy infants tend to begin walking at later ages than slimmer, more maturely proportioned babies. Experimentally simulating more babyish body proportions and decreased strength by dressing infants in lead-weighted shoulder packs causes them to fall more frequently; when they manage to stay upright, infants wearing lead-loaded packs display less proficient walking patterns. In support of an experience-based account, both controlled laboratory studies and natural cross-cultural experiments show that exercising infants' legs in an upright position facilitates walking onset.

To date, the three putative underlying factors have only been pitted against each other statistically. When experience (indexed by the number of days since walking onset), brain changes (indexed by infants' chronological age), and body changes (measures of body proportions) are compared statistically, experience independently predicts improvements in walking proficiency, accounting for statistical effects above and beyond those exerted by age and body proportions. Neither age nor body dimensions exert statistical effects above and beyond those produced by experience. However, the traditional indices of experience, brain, and body are too crude to provide satisfying explanations of development.

Although the state of the art in relating changes in the brain, body, and experience to locomotor development is still in its own infancy, new developments may inspire current research. For example, researchers have discovered that infants' skeletal growth is episodic. Height, for example, stays constant for several weeks, then in the course of a single day, infants can grow up to 1.65 cm. New video-tracking measures of experience suggest that infants accumulate truly massive amounts of experience with balance and locomotion. A typical 14-month-old may travel the length of 39 football fields per day and incur 90 minor falls. Advances in understanding the relation between brain changes and locomotor development may await a technology that can image brain activity while infants' bodies are in motion.

Historically, brain-based explanations are maturational accounts, experience-based explanations are learning accounts, and body-based explanations are agnostic regarding the respective roles of nature and nurture. Nonetheless, the historical compartmentalization of theories does not reflect researchers' sensitivity to the bidirectional nature of development. Both early pioneers and contemporary researchers agree that brain, body, and practice are likely to be inter-related. For example, maturation of the central nervous system and of infants' various body parts might spur infants to engage in more practice. Alternatively, practice might hone the neural circuitry and slenderize infants' bodies.

Walking is the most recognized of infants' locomotor achievements, but it is not infants' final locomotor milestone.

Although new walkers can carry objects in their arms and loads in tiny packs on the back, front, and sides of their bodies, infants' load carrying strategy differs dramatically from that of adults. Infants accommodate to the disruption in balance by leaning with the load and adapting their footfall patterns as best they can. Older children and adults compensate for loads by leaning in the opposite direction of the added weight (e.g., leaning forward while carrying a heavy backpack). As a consequence, their footfall patterns are less disrupted.

Turning in circles and walking backward typically appear after forward walking. Jumping and running take even longer because, for both skills, both feet leave the ground simultaneously. Before infants can display a flight phase during running, they may Groucho run, where they speed-walk on bent knees like the famous actor, Groucho Marx. Initial success at walking up stairs typically requires use of a handrail or caregiver's hand. Infants mark time, meaning they bring both feet to one stair before lifting a leg to move to the next riser. A smooth, alternating gait for stair climbing can take years. Milestones for walking down stairs follow those for walking up. New patterns of interlimb timing (skipping, galloping, etc.), new ways to change body orientation (twirling, front and back somersaults, etc.), and incorporation of external devices into locomotion (tricycles, scooters, bicycles, etc.) appear during the preschool and grade school periods.

Cultural Effects and Historical Changes

The idea that infant locomotion is primarily the development of crawling and walking is an invention of twentieth century Western culture. Gesell and McGraw first transformed it into scientific fact, and contemporary researchers have perpetuated the idea. Although all healthy infants eventually walk, crawling is not universal. In some cultures, infants walk before they crawl or skip crawling altogether. Mothers in Jamaica and Mali, for example, view crawling as dangerous, primitive, and unnecessary, and infants in these cultures are likely to skip crawling. To encourage walking, which they view as the outcome of training and exercise, caregivers submit their infants to daily massage and vigorous exercise routines consisting of stretching, massaging, stroking, and shaking (**Figure 5**). They throw newborns up in the air and catch them. They hold infants by an arm or leg, and support them at the torso rather than the head. The idea that infants must be handled like a carton of fragile eggs with the head always supported is also a Western invention.

In accordance with cultural differences in mothers' expectations and childrearing routines, infants in Jamaica and Mali typically walk months earlier than infants in Western cultures. Similarly, mothers in Western Kenya exercise their infants' upright stepping and jumping movements and mothers in some East African tribes exercise

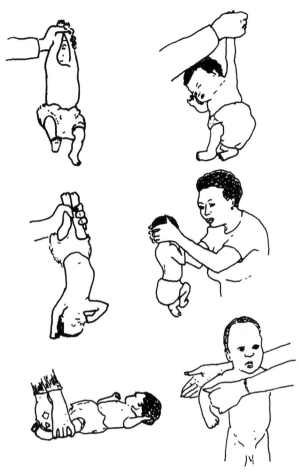

Figure 5 Some groups of African and Caribbean mothers engage in elaborate daily handling routines to massage and stretch their infants' muscles. These special exercises may contribute to the cultural differences in the ages at which motor milestones are achieved. From *Genetic, Social and General Psychology Monographs* Vol. 114, 379–408. Reprinted with permission of the Helen Dwight Reid Educational Foundation. Published by Heldref Publications, 1319 Eighteenth St., NW, Washington, DC 20036-1802. Copyright © 1988.

their infants' prone postures; accordingly, infants in these cultures walk and crawl sooner than infants in cultures that do not exercise their infants' locomotor skills.

Even within a culture, historical changes in daily childrearing practices affect the structure and schedule of locomotor development. For example, in 1900, 40% of Western, middle-class infants skipped crawling. Instead, they hitched along in a sitting position, crabbed on their backs, or logrolled. Hitching and so on may have been infants' solution to the long dresses that hampered their movements in a prone position. When infants tried to crawl, their knees caught at the edge of their long gowns pinning them in place.

More recently, researchers noted another link between historical changes in childrearing and infant crawling. For decades, Western pediatricians recommended that parents put infants to sleep on their stomachs to prevent aspiration of regurgitated milk. In 1994, the American Academy of Pediatrics launched a 'Back to Sleep' campaign recommending that infants sleep on their backs to reduce the incidence of sudden infant death syndrome (SIDS). Although doctors advise parents to give their waking infants 'tummy time', back-sleepers tend to fuss when they are placed prone. Among back-sleepers, more tummy time is related to earlier onset ages for sitting, crawling, and pulling to a stand, presumably because the prone position facilitates muscle strength in the arms and shoulders. Moreover, compared with infants who sleep on their stomachs, back-sleepers display more hitching, they sit, crawl, and pull to stand at later ages, and they score lower on measures of gross motor skill.

Beyond Muscles and Gravity: Locomotion in the Environment

How infants cope with gravity and inertia addresses only part of the story of locomotor development. Functional locomotion involves movement over variable terrain. In infants' typical environment, objects are strewn in the path. Changes in elevation create an up-and-down landscape. Ground surfaces can be high traction or slippery, rigid or deformable. The legacy of abstract stages from the early pioneers does not capture the embodied and embedded nature of locomotor development. As exemplified in **Figures 6** and **7**, a functional characterization of locomotor development illustrates how infants adapt their movements to variations in the surface layout (the arrangement of the environment in three dimensions) and to changes in the friction and rigidity of the supporting surface. From a functional account, navigation over irregular terrain involves a decision process – which movements to do and how to execute them – and consequently, locomotor development involves changes in the accuracy of infants' locomotor decisions.

Variations in Surface Layout

The most famous paradigm for testing infants' response to variations in the surface layout is the 'visual cliff' (**Figure 6(a)**), first devised by Eleanor Gibson and Richard Walk. The apparatus is a large glass table, divided in half by a narrow starting board. On the 'deep' side, a patterned surface lies on the floor far below the glass, creating the illusion of an abrupt drop-off. The 'shallow' side serves as an experimental control: The patterned surface is placed directly beneath the glass, providing visual information for a solid surface. Infants are placed on the center starting board and encouraged to cross by caregivers standing at first one side then the other. Animals descend from the starting board to the side of their choosing.

Since the initial report in 1957, dozens of experiments have yielded fascinating but conflicting findings regarding when and why human infants and other animals avoid locomotion over the deep side of the visual cliff. An early view was that adaptive avoidance responses depend on depth perception and that depth perception is innate. However, the problem is not lack of depth perception because human infants can see the drop-off months before they begin crawling.

A widely cited, but controversial claim is that infants avoid the apparent drop-off when they have acquired fear of heights and that fear, in turn, depends on the duration of infants' locomotor experience. However, behavioral indices of fear yield discrepant findings. For example, some researchers have found accelerated heart rate – a measure associated with fear – when crawling infants are lowered toward the deep side. However, other researchers found decelerated heart rate – a measure associated with interest – when crawling infants are lowered toward the deep side. Moreover, infants display positive or neutral facial expressions, not fearful expressions, when they avoid crawling over the apparent drop-off.

Findings are equally discrepant with regard to locomotor experience. Although some studies found that crawling experience predicts avoidance on the deep side, other studies showed the opposite result – that crawling experience predicts crossing onto the deep side. Longitudinal data are inconclusive because infants learn from repeated testing that the safety glass provides support for locomotion. In fact, infants who have prior experience playing with Plexiglas boxes, do not avoid crossing the visual cliff. In some studies, locomotor experience appears to be posture-specific: Crawling infants who avoid the deep side when tested on their hands and knees will readily cross when tested in an upright posture in a wheeled baby-walker. In other studies, locomotor experience appears to generalize: More 12-month-old walkers avoid locomotion over the deep side than 12-month-old crawlers.

Albeit the most famous test paradigm, the visual cliff is not optimal. Discrepant findings may result from methodological problems stemming from the design of the apparatus. The safety glass presents mixed messages: The visual cliff looks dangerous, but feels safe. In fact, because infants quickly learn that the apparatus is perfectly safe (albeit creepy), avoidance attenuates, and they can only be tested on one or two trials. Moreover, the dimensions of the visual cliff are fixed so that researchers cannot test the accuracy of infants' responses or ask whether infants scale their locomotor decisions to the degree of the challenge.

To circumvent the methodological problems with the visual cliff, researchers have devised other paradigms with real drop-offs using apparatuses with adjustable dimensions and no safety glass (a spotter follows alongside

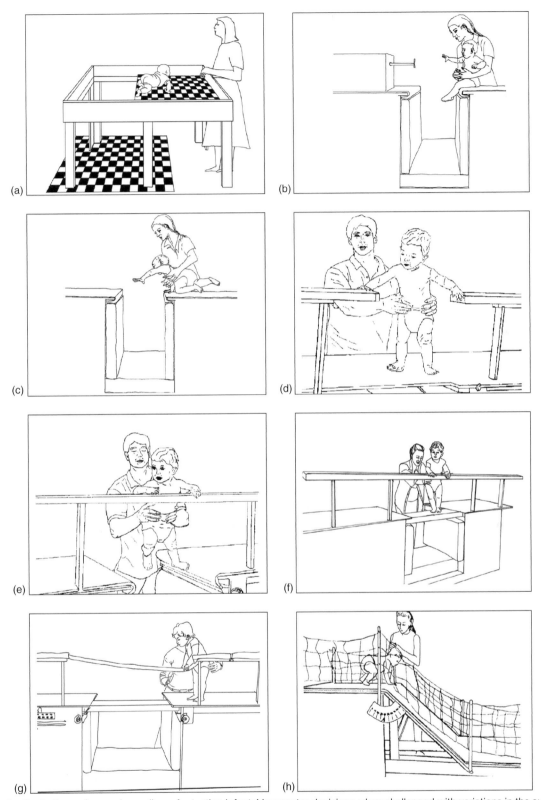

Figure 6 Illustrations of several paradigms for testing infants' locomotor decisions when challenged with variations in the surface layout. Figure partially adapted from Adolph KE and Berger SE (2006) Motor development. In: Damon W and Lerner R (eds.) *Handbook of Child Psychology: Vol. 2: Cognition, Perception, and Language*, 6th edn., pp. 161–213. New York: Wiley. (a) Crawling infant approaching an apparent drop-off on a visual cliff. From Walk RW and Gibson EJ (1961) A comparative and analytical study of visual depth perception. *Psychological Monographs: General and Applied* 75 (15, Whole No. 519), 1961, © American Psychological Association, adapted with permission. (b) Infant leaning forward over an adjustable gap in the surface of support in an experienced

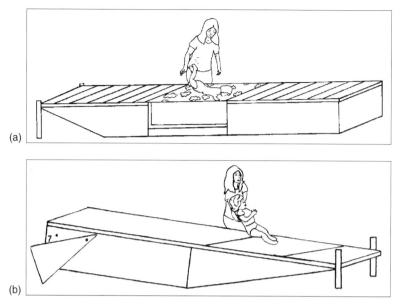

Figure 7 Illustrations of paradigms for testing infants' locomotor decisions when challenged with variations in rigidity and friction conditions. (a) Infant falling into deformable foam pit. Reproduced from Adolph KE and Joh AS (2007) Multiple learning mechanisms in the development of action. In: Woodward A and Needhan A (eds.) *Learning and the Infant Mind*. New York: Oxford University Press. By permission of Oxford University Press. (b) Infant slipping on a walkway interrupted by a low-friction Teflon floor. Courtesy of Joh AS and Adolph KE, New York University.

infants to ensure their safety). The gaps paradigm is one such alternative to the visual cliff (**Figures 6(b)** and **6(c)**). The apparatus challenges infants with a 'veritable cliff', a moveable platform abutting a deep precipice.

On the gaps apparatus, the duration of infants' everyday experience maintaining balance and locomotion predicts whether they avoid falling into the drop-off. However, learning does not transfer from an earlier developing postural control system to a later developing one. For example, at 9 months of age, most infants have been sitting for a few months, but have just begun crawling. In both postures, infants are encouraged to lean forward over the gap to retrieve a toy on the far side of the precipice. When facing gaps as experienced sitters, infants perceive precisely how far forward they can lean without falling into the precipice. However, when the same infants face the

same gaps as novice crawlers, they show poorly adapted decisions: They fall into impossibly risky gaps on trial after trial, even on the widest, visual-cliff sized gap.

A similar pattern of results regarding the role of locomotor experience holds for other action systems and test situations. For example, at 11 months of age, most infants are experienced at cruising sideways along furniture but they have not yet begun to walk independently. When challenged with a gaps task relevant for keeping balance with their upper extremities as in cruising – a solid floor, but an adjustable gap in the handrail they are holding for support – their locomotor decisions are highly accurate: They attempt to cruise over safe gaps and avoid cruising over risky gaps. However, when challenged with a situation relevant for keeping balance with their lower extremities as in walking – a solid handrail, but an adjustable gap in the

sitting posture. Adapted from Adolph KE (2000) Specificity of learning: Why infants fall over a veritable cliff. *Psychological Science* 11: 290–295 (c) Infant approaching an adjustable gap in the surface of support in an unfamiliar crawling posture. Adapted with permission from Adolph KE (2000) Specificity of learning: Why infants fall over a veritable cliff. *Psychological Science* 11: 290–295. Copyright (2000) by American Psychological Society, with permission from Blackwell publishing. (d) Cruising infant deciding whether to span an adjustable gap in the handrail used for support. (e) Cruising infant deciding whether to span an adjustable gap in the floor. (d) and (e) Adapted from Adolph KE and Joh AS (2007) Multiple learning mechanisms in the development of action. In: Woodward A and Needhan A (eds.) *Learning and the Infant Mind*. New York: Oxford University Press. By permission of Oxford University Press. (f) Infant crossing narrow bridge using a handrail as a tool to augment balance. Berger SE and Adolph KE. Infants use handrails as tools in a locomotor task. *Developmental Psychology* 39: 594–605, 2003, Copyright © the American Psychological Association, reprinted with permission. (g) Infant deciding whether a wobbly handrail will aid in walking over a narrow bridge. Reprinted from Berger SE, Adolph KE, and Lobo SA (2005) Out of the toolbox: Toddlers differentiate wobbly and wooden handrails. *Child Development* 76: 1294–1307, Copyright (2005) by the Society for Research in Child Development, with permission from Blackwell publishing. Reprinted with permission. (h) Crawling infant at the top of an adjustable slope. Adapted from Adolph KE (1997) Learning in the development of infant locomotion. *Monographs of Society for Research in Child Development* 62(3, Serial No. 251), with permission from Blackwell Publishing.

floor – their locomotor decisions are grossly inaccurate: They attempt safe and risky gaps alike, despite viewing the obstacle at the start of each trial (see **Figures 6(d)** and **6(e)**). Newly walking 11-month-olds err in both conditions, as if they do not know how many steps they can take before reaching the ending handrail and they do not realize that they need a solid floor to support their bodies.

At 16 months of age, when most infants are experienced walkers, they use a handrail as a tool to augment their balance (**Figure 6(f)**). When encouraged to cross wide and narrow bridges spanning a deep, wide precipice, infants refuse to walk over narrow bridges on trials when a handrail is not available, but successfully walk over the same bridges when they can hold onto a handrail to keep balance. They run straight over wide bridges regardless of whether a handrail is available. When the substance of the handrail varies, infants walk over narrow bridges when the handrail is made of sturdy wood, and avoid crossing when the handrail is made of wobbly foam (**Figure 6(g)**).

In contrast to cliffs, gaps, and bridges that present an abrupt discontinuity in the visible surface texture, sloping ground is continuous between the summit and the base and infants can feel the intervening slope with their hands and feet (**Figure 6(h)**). In both cross-sectional and longitudinal studies using a slope paradigm, experienced crawling and walking infants display exquisitely fine-tuned prospective control of balance. As they approach the slope, they slow down, peer over the edge, probe the sloping surface by rubbing it with their hands and feet, and generate torque at the relevant joints by making small stepping and swaying movements and rocking back and forth with their hands or toes at the brink. On safe slopes, infants crawl or walk down. On risky slopes, they adopt alternative locomotor strategies (sliding down in sitting, backing, or prone positions) or avoid descent.

Experienced 14-month-old walking infants can even update their risk assessment after experimental manipulation of their body dimensions with a lead-loaded vest. While carrying lead loads in shoulder packs, infants' bodies are more top-heavy and immaturely proportioned. Infants recalibrate their judgments of risky slopes to their new, more precarious balance constraints. They correctly treat the same degrees of slope as risky while wearing the lead-weight shoulder packs but as safe while wearing the featherweight shoulder packs.

As in the gaps paradigm, infants require a protracted period of learning before demonstrating adaptive locomotor decisions on slopes, and experience with balance and locomotion is posture-specific. In infants' first week of crawling they repeatedly plunge headfirst down impossibly steep slopes. Over weeks of crawling, locomotor decisions gradually hone in to infants' actual ability. The decrease in errors reflects increased powers of calibration because, like the toddlers wearing lead-weighted shoulder packs, each week brings about naturally occurring changes in infants'

body dimensions and locomotor skill. A risky slope one week might be perfectly safe the next week when crawling skill improves. A safe slope for belly crawling might be impossibly risky for crawling on hands and knees.

Learning to gauge threats to balance in a crawling posture, however, does not transfer to walking. Despite months of testing and hundreds of trials on slopes, the same infants who had avoided risky slopes as crawlers show no evidence of generalization after they begin walking. Errors are just as high in infants' first week of walking as in their first week of crawling, and learning is no faster the second time around. Learning is so posture-specific that new walkers who avoid descent of an impossibly steep slope in their experienced crawling posture plunge down the same slope moments later when tested in their inexperienced walking posture.

The evidence suggests that a protracted period of everyday locomotor experience facilitates learning to gauge novel threats to balance, not fear of heights. Experience traversing slopes is not required for adaptive responding. Few infants in everyday life have experience descending slopes on their own, and in the laboratory, infants in control groups matched for age and experience behave similarly to infants tested repeatedly on slopes. As on the visual cliff, fear does not mediate adaptive responding. Infants do not display fearful or negative affect as they approach the brink, regardless of whether they plunge down or avoid risky slopes (although they sometimes fuss after they fall).

Finally, similar results regarding experience are obtained in studies that do not involve falling from a height. For example, psychophysical assessments show that walking experience is a better predictor of infants' ability to step over barriers placed at different heights from the ground than infants' age and body dimensions. As in the gaps experiments, infants show specificity of learning between sitting and crawling postures when asked to reach around barriers in their path. When tested longitudinally, crawling infants reach around a barrier to retrieve a desired object while in a sitting position several weeks before they retrieve the object by crawling around the barrier. In studies with cross-sectional designs, 10- and 12-month-olds are more successful at retrieving objects from behind a barrier when they are tested in a sitting position than when they must detour around the obstacle by crawling. As in the slopes experiments, infants show specificity between crawling and walking postures when asked to learn a location based on repeated trips to their mothers' hiding place: Experienced crawlers fare better than younger novice crawlers and better than older novice walkers.

Specificity of learning between sitting, crawling, cruising, and walking postures suggests that each postural milestone operates as a distinct perception–action system. Indeed, each posture involves very different parameters, including different regions of permissible sway, key pivots about which the body rotates, muscle groups for balance and forward propulsion, vantage points for viewing the ground, correlations between visual and vestibular information, and so on. With each postural milestone, infants must identify the new parameters for the new balance control system and then learn to calibrate the settings of each parameter as they approach novel ground surfaces.

The functional dissociation between postural milestones calls into question the widespread notion of functionally linked stages in a continuous march toward increasingly erect postures, first popularized by the early pioneers. Similarly, cultural differences and individual differences in the timing and appearance of various locomotor milestones belie the notion of obligatory stages in the development of locomotion. Although sitting, crawling, and cruising typically precede upright locomotion, apparently these precursory postures are functionally distinct postural control systems rather than obligatory prerequisites for walking.

Variations in Friction and Rigidity

Variations in friction and rigidity present a different sort of problem for infants compared with variations in the surface layout. In contrast to slopes, gaps, cliffs, and the like, novel changes in friction and rigidity are not specified by reliable visual cues from a distance. Instead, friction and rigidity are resistive forces that emerge only when two surfaces come into contact, such as when the foot presses against the ground during walking. Because friction and rigidity result from the interaction between two surfaces, the appearance of a single surface cannot serve as a visual cue for friction and rigidity conditions. The same shiny floor, for example, may be slippery or resistive, depending on walkers' footwear and the velocity and angle of the foot as it touches the ground.

As a consequence, when approaching a novel patch of slippery or squishy ground, infants, like adults, are likely to step onto the offending surface and fall. Unlike adults, however, infants require multiple falls before they realize that a particular surface is too slippery or squishy to support locomotion. For example, on their first encounter with an unexpectedly squishy surface, 15–39-month-old children and young adults walk straight over a flat, rigid platform into a bumpy, deformable foam pit, and fall (**Figure 7(a)**). Visual cues for the foam pit – the bumpy surface and rounded edges of the foam blocks and the coincident change in the color, pattern, and texture of the material covering the foam pit – are not sufficient to elicit hesitation or focused exploration on the first encounter with the obstacle. In fact, across all ages, participants gasp when they fall, indicating that the consequences were unexpected. Although 15-month-olds fall face-first into the foam pit, most require multiple trials before they avoid falling and some infants never show evidence of

learning. Older children learn faster, and many, like adults, learn after only one trial. Similarly, when 15-month-olds approach an unexpectedly slippery surface – a large, white, shiny piece of Teflon – all of them fall on the first trial (**Figure 7(b)**). Some infants require several repeated trials to show evidence of learning and the other infants fall over and over, never showing any evidence of learning.

Infants' everyday experiences may explain why learning to link arbitrary visual cues (e.g., bumpy or shiny surfaces) with loss of balance is so difficult. Falling is commonplace in infants' everyday experience. A typical 14-month-old falls 15 times an hour in the course of free play. Most falls, however, are not elicited by a change in the ground surface. Infants do not slip, trip, or topple over because the ground is slippery or deformable. Although these challenges will induce falls, most frequently, infants slip and trip when they misplace their swinging foot on perfectly level, rigid, high-traction ground and they topple over when they turn their heads or lift an arm. Everyday experience may lead to learned irrelevance. That is, infants may learn to ignore the visual appearance of the ground surface because bumpy or shiny ground does not predict falling.

Feeling a questionable surface provides infants with the information they need for prospective control, but it does not allow them to extrapolate to future conditions. For example, if infants stop at the edge of a squishy foam pit, deformable waterbed, or slippery Teflon patch and feel the obstacle with their hands or feet, they are most likely to avoid traversal or to select an appropriate alternative method of locomotion for navigating it safely. Similarly, if they stop at the brink of a slippery slope and probe it with their hand or foot, they detect affordances (or lack of them) and respond adaptively. After touching the slope and feeling the lack of resistive forces, they recognize that their threshold is much shallower under slippery conditions than under high-friction conditions.

However, the feeling of slip underfoot as infants approach a slippery slope is not sufficient to induce hesitation or exploration at the brink of the slope. Although a continuous surface covers the flat starting platform and slope, and despite the fact that infants must struggle to retain balance on the slippery starting platform, they walk straight down shallow slopes and fall. Adults also fail to extrapolate information from friction underfoot to an upcoming sloping surface. Despite feeling themselves slip on a flat platform adjoining the slope, they grossly overestimate their ability to walk down.

Conclusions: Travel and the Mind

The development of locomotion is one of infants' greatest achievements. It is accomplished little by little as infants learn to cope with gravity, the constraints of their growing bodies, and variations in the terrain. Initially unique solutions in crawling and walking (and the myriad other forms that infants invent to move themselves from place to place) tend to converge on common patterns of inter-limb coordination. But, common patterns of movements do not imply rigidity in the face of adversity. Infants take each encounter with everyday obstacles as an opportunity to employ a boundless repertoire of exploratory procedures, to discover new ways of modifying ongoing movements, and to construct alternative solutions when the current method of locomotion is impossible.

Thus, the development of locomotion reflects important changes across many domains of development – physical growth and biomechanics, as well as perceptual learning and cognitive development. For infants, carrying objects involves developmental changes in the biomechanics of balance. Navigation through a cluttered environment involves perceptual exploration in the service of prospective control. Finding a new sliding position to descend a steep slope and using a handrail as a tool to augment balance are dramatic examples of means-ends problem solving.

Moreover, the development of locomotion facilitates change across many domains of development. The ability to go somewhere, to move and retrieve objects, and to leave caregivers behind creates new sources of information about the self in relation to places, surfaces, objects, and other people. Independent mobility has system-wide effects on psychological development. Indeed, as Campos and colleagues remind us, travel broadens the mind.

Acknowledgments

Work on this article was supported by National Institute of Health grants HD-33486 and HD-42697.

See also: Milestones: Physical; Motor and Physical Development: Manual; Perception and Action; Physical Growth; Reflexes.

Suggested Readings

Adolph KE (1997) Learning in the development of infant locomotion. *Monographs of the Society for Research in Child Development 62(3).* Serial No. 251.

Adolph KE (2000) Specificity of learning: Why infants fall over a veritable cliff. *Psychological Science* 11: 290–295.

Adolph KE and Berger SE (2005) Physical and motor development. In: Bornstein MH and Lamb ME (eds.) *Developmental Science: An Advanced Textbook,* 5th edn., pp. 223–281. Mahwah, NJ: Lawrence Erlbaum Associates.

Adolph KE and Berger SE (2006) Motor development. In: Kuhn D and Siegler RS (eds.) *Handbook of Child Psychology, Vol. 2: Cognition, Perception, and Language,* 6th edn., pp. 161–213. New York: Wiley.

Adolph KE and Joh AS (2007) Multiple learning mechanisms in the development of action. In: Woodward A and Needhan A (eds.) *Learning and fue Infant Mind.* New York: Oxford University Press.

Adolph KE, Vereijken B, and Denny MA (1998) Learning to crawl. *Child Development* 69: 1299–1312.

Berger SE and Adolph KE (2003) Infants use handrails as tools in a locomotor task. *Developmental Psychology* 39: 594–605.

Berger SE, Adolph KE, and Lobo SA (2005) Out of the toolbox: Toddlers differentiate wobbly and wooden handrails. *Child Development* 76: 1294–1307.

Bertenthal BI and Clifton RK (1998) Perception and action. In: Kuhn D and Siegler RS (eds.) *Handbook of Child Psychology, Vol. 2: Cognition, Perception, and Language,* 5 edn., pp. 51–102. New York: Wiley.

Bril B and Breniere Y (1992) Postural requirements and progression velocity in young walkers. *Journal of Motor Behavior* 24: 105–116.

Bril B and Ledebt A (1998) Head coordination as a means to assist sensory integration in learning to walk. *Neuroscience and Biobehavioral Reviews* 22: 555–563.

Campos JJ, Anderson DI, Barbu-Roth MA, Hubbard EM, Hertenstein MJ, and Witherington DC (2000) Travel broadens the mind. *Infancy* 1: 149–219.

Frankenburg W, Fandal A, Sciarillo W, and Burgess D (1981) The newly abbreviated and revised denver developmental screening test. *Journal of Pediatrics* 99: 995–999.

Gesell A (1946) The ontogenesis of infant behavior. In: Carmichael L (ed.) *Manual of Child Psychology*, pp. 295–331. New York: Wiley.

Gibson EJ and Schmuckler MA (1989) Going somewhere: An ecological and experimental approach to development of mobility. *Ecological Psychology* 1: 3–25.

Hopkins B and Westra T (1988) Maternal handling and motor development: An intra-cultural study. *Genetic, Social and General Psychology Monographs* 114: 379–408.

Joh AS and Adolph KE (2006) Learning from falling. *Child Development* 77: 89–102.

McGraw MB (1935) *Growth: A Study of Johnny and Jimmy.* New York: Appleton-Century Co.

Santrock J (2006) *Life-Span Development,* 10th edn. New York: McGraw-Hill.

Siegler R, DeLoache J, and Eisenberg N (2003) *How Children Develop,* 1st edn. NY: Worth Publishers.

Thelen E (1984) Learning to walk: Ecological demands and phylogenetic constraints. *Advances in Infancy Research* 3: 213–260.

Thelen E and Fisher D (1982) Newborn stepping: An explanation for a 'Disappearing reflex' *Developmental Psychology* 18: 760–775.

Thelen E and Ulrich BD (1991) *Monographs of the Society for Research in Child Development, Vol. 56(1) Serial No. 223: Hidden Skills: A Dynamic Systems Analysis of Treadmill Stepping during the first year.* Chicago: Blackwell Publishing Limited.

Walk RD and Gibson EJ (1961) A comparative and analytical study of visual depth perception. *Psychological Monographs* 75(15), Whole No. 519.

Relevant Websites

http://www.hhp.umd.edu – Dr. Jane Clark's page at College of Health and Human Performance, University of Maryland.

http://psych.nyu.edu – Dr. Karen E. Adolph's page at NYU Department of Psychology, New York University.

http://www.anthropology.emory.edu – Dr. Michelle Lampl's page at Department of Anthropology, Emory University, Atlanta, GA.

http://www.psychology.uiowa.edu – Dr. Scott Robinson's page at Laboratory of Comparative Ethogenesis, University of Iowa.

http://www.babycenter.com – Toddler milestone: Walking, Developmental milestones: Crawling reviewed by Paul Young, MD, BabyCenter LLC.

Motor and Physical Development: Manual

C von Hofsten, Uppsala University, Uppsala, Sweden

Glossary

Oculomotor – The motor system or nerves and musculature of the eyes.
Ontogeny – The development of an individual organism.
Otoliths – An organ in the inner ear (a part of the vestibular system) for the sensing of linear acceleration.
Proprioception – Sensing the positions and orientations, and movements of the different bodyparts in relation to each other.
Prospective – Future directed.
Shuffling – Propelling forward by sliding on the bottom.
Synergy – The combined action of several muscles.
Vertebrates – Animals with a spine.

Introduction

The motor performance of the child gives the clearest evidence of how children develop. Parents notice with joy the first time their children roll over, when they succeed in reaching for and grasping an object, or when they take their first step. These changes are so predictable that motor development has often been described in terms of milestones. A child is expected to grasp objects at a certain age, and walk at another. This simplified description makes motor development appear to be rather uneventful and mostly the result of maturation. The true story is much more fascinating. At all stages of life, children are agents who act on the world. Actions reflect all the different aspects of development, including perception, cognition, and motivation. Even in the newborn child, the movements are never just reflexes, but purposeful goal-directed actions. Furthermore, motor development is not just a question of gaining control over muscles; equally important are questions such as why particular movements are made, how the movements are planned, and how they anticipate what is going to happen next.

Actions have to deal with the fact that events precede the feedback signals about them. Relying on feedback is therefore nonadaptive. The only way to overcome this problem is to anticipate what is going to happen next and use that information to control ones behavior. Furthermore, most events in the outside world do not wait for us to act. Interacting with them requires us to move to specific places at specific times while being prepared to do specific things. This entails foreseeing the ongoing stream of events in the surrounding world as well as the unfolding of our own actions. Such prospective control is possible because events are governed by rules and regularities. The most general ones are the laws of nature. Inertia and gravity for instance apply to all mechanical motions and determine how they evolve. Other rules are more task specific, like those that enable a child to grasp an object or use a spoon. Finally, there are rules that facilitate social interaction and enable us to communicate and exchange information with each other. Some of those rules like the facial expressions of emotion have deep biological roots, while other rules have been agreed upon for practical reasons. Knowledge of these different rules makes smooth and skilful actions possible. It is accessible to us through our sensory and cognitive systems.

Infants begin to move much before they are born as every mother is aware. These movements are not just startles or twitches of muscles. They are organized movements requiring the coordination of several groups of muscles. Already in the third month of pregnancy, the first movements are produced. Some of them are rather complex, like swallowing, yawning, sucking, and the movements that are later used for breathing. In the fourth month, the child moves around in the uterus, touches the walls of the amniotic sack, grasps the umbilical cord, and puts the thumb in his or her mouth. All these movements require some kind of sensory guidance. In fact, the sensory system and the motor system develop together. The activities of the child in the uterus are most probably of crucial importance for preparing the child for a life outside the uterus. At birth, infants are ready to act on the world, although their movement repertoire is still quite limited.

Preparations for Action

The most obvious way in which the child has been prepared for action is the design of its body. It is obvious that hands are made for grasping and manipulating objects, feet are made for walking, and eyes are made for looking. However, there is no grand plan for evolution. It just optimizes what is at hand. Therefore the same body-part may look rather different in different species depending on its function. For instance, the limbs of horses, lions, and humans differ for obvious functional reasons. It is also true that different body parts may have evolved to serve the same function. The trunk of elephants and hands of humans are both examples of how the morphology of the body has been altered in special ways in order to facilitate object manipulation.

What is less obvious but equally valid is that each of these body parts contributes to a perception–action system that also includes specially designed perceptual and neural mechanisms. The design of the body of any animal, its sensory and perceptual system, its motor system, and indeed its neural system have been tailored to each other for solving specific action problems. The changes in the morphology through evolution of the body also include adjustments of the perceptual system to improve extraction of information for controlling specific actions. For instance, the frontal positions of the eyes in primates give access to better information for controlling manual movements. In lower vertebrates, it often appears as if action systems have evolved independent of each other. Thus the frog seems to possess independent perceptual mechanisms for extracting spatial information needed for catching flies and for negotiating barriers. In higher vertebrates, movement patterns are more flexible and the perceptual skills more versatile. When new skills evolve, the animal may re-use some of the mechanisms already evolved for other tasks instead of developing completely new ones. This leads to more general mechanisms and more generalized skills. A similar trend seems to be going on in ontogeny. The earliest appearing skills seem more task specific than those appearing later.

Although perception and action are mutually dependent, there is an asymmetry between them. Perception is necessary for controlling actions and every action requires specific information for its control. Without perception there will be no action. Action is a necessary part of perceiving but only in a general sense. Specific actions are not required for producing specific percepts and actions do not tell perception what to perceive. It only provides opportunities for perceiving and guides the perceptual system to where the information is. This has clear consequences for development. The ability to extract the necessary information must be in place before actions can be organized. Before vision can guide looking, there must be a correspondence between the position in the visual field where a stimulus appears and the kind of eye movements evoked to refocus gaze on that stimulus. Such correspondences are present in the newborn child. In order to localize significant objects to look at, the visual system must divide up the visual field into object defining entities. Although little is known about when these processes of perceptual structuring start to emerge in development, the object-directed actions performed by newborn infants indicate that neonates can visually segregate objects from their background.

All sensory systems are available from birth and can be used to guide basic forms of actions. Most of them have been available in the uterus where the child has had opportunities to use them. Tactile and proprioceptive information become available when the child moves and sounds penetrate the uterus. The sensory system that has been least exercised is the visual system because the light that reaches the eyes in the uterus is only minimally structured. At birth the visual acuity is only 3-5% of the adult one. However, this enables the children to see their hands and the gross features of another person's face. The newborn child can also crudely guide his or her arm movements by vision. Such visual–motor maps could be innate but it is also possible that the unborn child detects the luminance changes when they move an arm in front of the eyes and in this way begin to develop a visual–motor map.

Neonatal Behavior

The movements of newborn infants have traditionally been described in terms of reflexes. The reflex concept was defined over 100 years ago by the British physiologist Charles Sherrington. It refers to a sensory–motor arc organized at a spinal level such that when the sensory part is activated by a stimulus, a simple and stereotyped motor response is elicited. A typical example is the stretch reflex. When the position of a limb is perturbed and certain muscles are stretched, a reflex is activated that regains the original position of the limb. Thus, a reflex is not spontaneously activated by a motivated subject but automatically elicited by a stimulus. An increasing number of studies of the movements performed by newborn infants show that their behavior cannot appropriately be described as reflexes. This is not to deny that neonates have reflexes. They have them just like adults. However, to describe normal neonatal behavior as expressions of reflexes is wrong. Most movements of newborn infants are driven by motives, their structures are flexible, and they anticipate future goal states.

Take, for instance, sucking. It is traditionally described as a reflex but is in fact a very complex behavior with very little in common with reflexes. Controlled measurements of sucking in newborn infants show that they anticipate the upcoming flow of milk and adjust their sucking ahead of time to produce the most efficient behavior. In a typical sucking cycle, the vacuum in the mouth increases up to a point where the milk is released. If the child is not ready for this influx of milk, the vacuum will drastically decrease and the flow of milk will stop. This does not happen because the child changes its sucking action ahead of time and maintains the pressure as the milk is released (see **Figure 1**). Newborn infants will also alter their sucking rate to achieve advantages. If one arranges the situation such that they will hear their mother's voice when they suck with a slower or faster pace, they will discover this contingency and change the sucking rate to produce the voice more often.

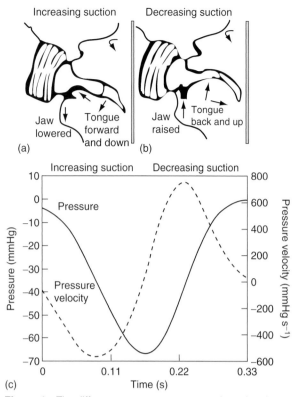

Figure 1 The different movement processes that take place within a newborn infant's mouth to bring about smooth changes in the intraoral pressure. (a) The increasing suction period, where the tongue moves forward and down as the jaw is lowered. The culmination of these processes brings about an increase in suction, which facilitates the flow of milk from the bottle into the mouth. (b) The decreasing suction period, where the tongue moves upwards and backwards as the jaw is raised. These movements help to propel the milk expressed during the increasing suction period to the back of the mouth, where it waits to be swallowed. (c) Actual recorded sucking pressures from inside the mouth of a feeding infant. The first part corresponds to the increasing suction period and the second part to the decreasing suction. From Craig CM and Lee DN (1999) Neonatal control of nutritive sucking pressure: Evidence for an intrinsic t-guide. *Experimental Brain Research* 124: 371–382.

Another example of neonatal behavior traditionally considered as a reflex is rooting. When the cheek or chin of the newborn infant is touched, the child tends to turn the head as to center the touching object on his or her mouth. This behavior is, however, by no means automatic or stereotyped. When the child is hungry the response is elicited more reliably and when the child happens to touch him or herself on the chin or side of the mouth, no rooting response is produced. A more functional description of this behavior is thus that the children turn toward things that touch face and that they obviously cannot see, in order to explore them with their mouth. During, at least, the first 6 months of life, infants have a great tendency to explore objects in this way.

A third example of functional neonatal behavior is imitation. Newborns tend to imitate facial gestures. The most reliable observations have been obtained from mouth opening and protrusion of the tongue. Although contingent on the model's behavior, this is not a reflex. The tongue protrusion of the model does not just elicit the tongue protrusion of the child. It changes the frequency and the appearance of spontaneously performed tongue protrusions. The movements are by no means just elicited or stereotyped. The infant might wait for a while before repeating them and the repeated movements are different every time they are performed. If the adult model opens the mouth instead of sticking the tongue out, the child will increase the frequency of mouth openings but not the frequency of tongue protrusions. Neonatal imitation provides important information about newborn capabilities. It shows that neonates have a visual acuity good enough to identify the mouth among other facial features and that they can discriminate different mouth movements. It also shows that neonates apply differentiated and appropriate behaviors to the seen facial patterns. It makes sense for nature to invest in such innate abilities. Neonatal imitation has great social significance. It provides a means for social contact between the mother and her newborn child. However, it is also the embryo of a social communication system based on gestures.

A fourth example is visually guided arm movements. When an attractive object is moved slowly and irregularly in front of a newborn infant, he or she will extend the arms toward it. It is not a very precise movement, but if several such movements are considered, the mean direction is toward the object in front of them. The immediate function of this reaching behavior cannot be to grasp and manipulate objects, because the infants do not yet control their hands independently of their arms. On the contrary, the arm and the hand movements are coupled in such a way that when the arm extends the hand opens up and vice versa. The successful grasping of an object necessitates flexion of the hand while the arm is extended. However, newborn reaching has another very important function. When the hand moves toward the object of interest it enters into the visual field and its movements may then become controlled by visual information. Closing the visual–manual loop in this way is of crucial importance for the development of manual control. This is precisely what is needed for the system to develop. It makes it possible for the infant to explore the relationship between commands and movements, between vision and proprioception, and discover the possibilities and constraints of manual movements.

Newborn infants also find it attractive to view their own hands and they are able to move them into the visual field. Audrey van der Meer at Trondheim University performed the following interesting experiment. She placed newborn infants in a semi-dark room and had a beam of light shine across their visual field. When the infants happened to put their hand into the beam of light, it was seen brightly against the dark background. The subjects quickly learnt to move their hands to where the beam of light was and when the spotlight itself was moved the infants adjusted their arm position to the new location.

The question whether to regard the movements of newborn infants as reflexes or actions has important implications. If they are seen as reflexes, then the child is no more than a complex mechanical device. If the movements are seen as purposeful, however, the child becomes an agent that acts and explores. Grasping is a good illustration of this point. If you place an unseen object in the hand of a newborn child, he or she will probably close the hand around it. Is this a reflex or a voluntary action? The traditional account says that it is a reflex. If you instead place an unseen object in the hand of an adult, he or she will also most probably close the hand around it. In this case, however, the traditional account says that it is a voluntary action. What the accumulating evidence of today tells us is that both the adult's and the newborn infant's closing of the hand should be regarded as voluntary actions.

What makes the movements of newborns special is the fact that the nervous system is still quite undeveloped and many of the mechanisms necessary for controlling movements are not yet established. Although newborn infants scan their surrounding, fixate attractive objects including other people, and follow moving objects with their eyes, they do not track moving objects with smooth eye movements because the neural structures necessary for doing that are not yet established. Newborn infants do not stand alone or walk because the necessary neural mechanisms for maintaining balance are not yet developed. However, when newborn infants are held in an upright position and lowered toward a surface they move their legs in walking movements. This behavior is also traditionally regarded as a reflex although it is never stereotypical or just automatically elicited. An interesting observation is that the walking movements of neonates are organized in the same way as those of 1.5-year-old infants who walk successfully. At both ages, infants, step with the toes first just like other mammals. Striking with the heel first only develops gradually over childhood.

Finally, the attention of newborns is unstable and the children seem to wander off into own world every now and then. However, this does not change their basic way of functioning. Like any other biological organism, they are agents that spontaneously act and their movements are planned and goal directed. The function of neonatal actions is primarily explorative. By moving, children can begin to find out about the relationship between the different senses, between commands and movements, and discover the possibilities and constraints of their actions.

The Developmental Process

Infant development is most clearly reflected in motor behavior. These developmental changes can indeed be dramatic. Sometimes, they almost occur from one day to the next. Suddenly, the parents observe that the child stands up without holding onto something. The processes that lead up to these changes may be more continuous but they are not necessarily less dramatic. They are a function of both the developing nervous system and the activities of the child. Together they constitute a self-organizing dynamical system. When certain thresholds are attained, this can lead to radically new modes of functioning.

The brain, undoubtedly, has its own dynamics that makes neurons proliferate in certain ways and at certain times. Once a critical mass of connections is established, a self-organizing process begins that results in new forms of perception, action and cognition. As new pathways open up in the central nervous system and new connectivity emerges, new modes of control become possible. There are a number of such programmed changes in the CNS that have great impact on the organization of actions.

The emerging capabilities, however, are also crucially shaped by the subject's interactions with the environment. Without such interaction there would be no functional brain. Perception, cognition, and motivation develop at the interface between neural processes and actions. They are a function of both and arise from the dynamic interaction between the brain, the body and the outside world. A further important developmental factor is the biomechanics of the body: perception, cognition, and motivation are all embodied and subject to biomechanical constraints. Those constraints change dramatically with age, and both affect and are affected by the developing brain and by the way actions are performed. Therefore, there is not an exact sequence or schedule for motor development that is set in advance. What is optimal for one child raised in one environment may not be optimal for another child raised in a different environment. Every child does not need to crawl. Sliding on one's bottom, for example, is an excellent mode of locomotion in an apartment with polished floors but rather inefficient in a house with wall-to-wall carpets.

Two kinds of developmental processes are distinguishable. The first has to do with coordinating muscle activations to make efficient movements and assembling those movements into functional synergies. When infants begin to extend the arms toward objects in front of them early in life, the movements consists of several small submovements with little overall organization. At around 4 months of age, the hands consistently get to the object but the grasping is still not an integrated part of the reach. Reaching and grasping will only be integrated into a fluent integrated whole toward the end of the first year of life. Building functional synergies is also about coordinating perception and action. In the case of reaching it is about integrating the movements of eyes and head with reaching. The second process has to do with acquiring prospective control. Actions are directed into the future and must anticipate what is going to happen next. This is possible because the world is governed by natural laws, rules, and regularities. For instance, if a ball rolls, it will continue to roll in the same way unless something interferes with its motion. This is the law of inertia. When infants reach and grasp objects successfully at 5 months of age, they correctly perceive the upcoming motion of the object. At that age they catch moving objects, and in doing so they aim for a future position of the object. Anticipation of what is going to happen next is also necessary for being able to control ones own movements. Because newborn infants can control some of their movements, a part of this knowledge is obviously innate, but most of it is has to be acquired. The relationship between muscle contractions and movements, however, is too complex to make it possible to completely determine every movement ahead of time. Continuous perception is always needed to guide actions to their goals.

Looking

Although each perceptual system has its own privileged procedures for exploration, the visual system has the most specialized one. The whole purpose of movable eyes is to enable the visual system to explore the world and to stabilize gaze on objects of interest. The development of oculomotor control is one the earliest appearing skills and marks a profound improvement in the competence of the young infant. It is of crucial importance for the extraction of visual information about the world, for directing attention, and for the establishment of social communication. Controlling gaze may involve both head and eye movements and is guided by at least three types of information: visual, vestibular (the semicircular canals in the ear sensing head rotation), and proprioceptive (receptors in the neck sensing head movements). How do young infants gain access to these different kinds of information, how do they come to use them prospectively to control gaze, and how do they come to coordinate head and eyes to accomplish gaze control? Two kinds of tasks need to be mastered, moving the eyes to significant visual targets and stabilizing gaze on these targets. Each of these tasks is associated with a specific kind of eye movement. Moving the eyes to a new target is done with high speed, saccadic, eye movements and stabilizing them on a moving target is done with smooth pursuit eye movements. The second task is, in fact, the more complicated one. In order to avoid slipping away from the fixated target, anticipations of its forthcoming movements is required. When the subject is moving relative to the target, which is almost always the case, the smooth eye movements need to anticipate those body movements in order to compensate for them correctly.

Shifting gaze

The ability to shift gaze is of crucial importance for the development of visual perception, because it turns the visual sense into an efficient instrument for exploring the world. The saccadic system for shifting gaze develops ahead of the system for smooth tracking. It is functional at birth and newborn infants turn their eyes to fixate significant visual stimuli such as faces and moving objects. Newborns, however, cannot track moving objects smoothly.

Stabilizing gaze on a moving object

From about 6 weeks of age, infants begin to track objects smoothly. von Hoften and Rosander have studied the development of smooth pursuit eye tracking and found that the improvements in smooth pursuit tracking are very rapid and consistent between individual subjects. Smooth pursuit attains adult-like levels from around 14 weeks as can be seen in **Figure 2**. In normal infants, smooth pursuit is always predictive, that is, it never lags the object it is geared to.

Before 3 months of age, the head is minimally engaged in the tracking of moving objects. However, head tracking increases very rapidly from then on. At 5 months, the amplitude of the head tracking is often as large as the amplitude of the object motion. However, the head lags the target at that age (0.3 s or more). In order to stabilize gaze on the object of interest, the eyes must therefore lead. This creates a phase differences between the eyes and the head that may be so large that the eye

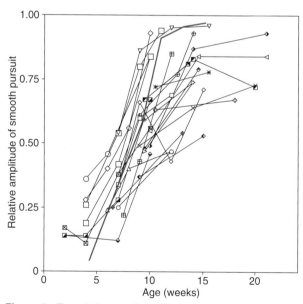

Figure 2 The relative amplitude of smooth-pursuit eye movements in 26 infants followed longitudinally over parts of the first 5 months of life. Zero means that no smooth pursuit is produced and 1.0 that all eye movements are smooth pursuit. As a comparison, the development of sensitivity to direction of motion is indicated by the blue line.

tracking and the head tracking counteract each other. Instead of contributing to stabilizing gaze on the fixated moving object, head tracking may then deteriorate gaze stabilization. **Figure 3** shows an example of a 5-month-old infant tracking a fast target with large head movements. It can be seen that the head lags substantially. The eye-tracking record shows that in order to keep the gaze on the target, the eyes must make large and fairly complicated movements to compensate for the head lag. In fact, the task would be much simpler if the head had not moved at all. The reason why infants persisted in engaging the head can only be because infants are internally motivated to do so. Just as in the early development of reaching this is an expression of important developmental foresight because in the end, the ability to engage the head will result in much more flexible tracking skills.

Stabilizing gaze while moving

When infants turn the head or move in other ways, the direction of gaze is perturbed. In order to maintain the original gaze direction, the eyes must move to counteract those body movements. Such compensatory eye movements are primarily controlled by the vestibular system. They are present in newborn infants and attain adult level

of performance within a few weeks. When infants begin to track objects with the head a problem arises, because the sensory signals from the vestibular system tell the eyes to compensate those head movements. Thus, while the head moves with the object, the eyes turn in the opposite direction leaving gaze unaffected. This paradoxical effect can sometimes be observed in 2-month-old infants and demonstrates an important problem that the oculomotor system must solve before functioning appropriately. It has to distinguish between head movements that are a part of the tracking effort and head movements unrelated to it. This requires that the head tracking commands are available to the oculomotor system ahead of time, so that the tracking movements can be separated from other head movements. By 4 months of age, they obviously are.

Posture and Locomotion

Basic orientation is a prerequisite for all functional activities and purposeful movements are not possible without it. This includes balancing the body relative to gravity and maintaining a stable orientation relative to the environment. Gravity gives a basic frame of reference for such

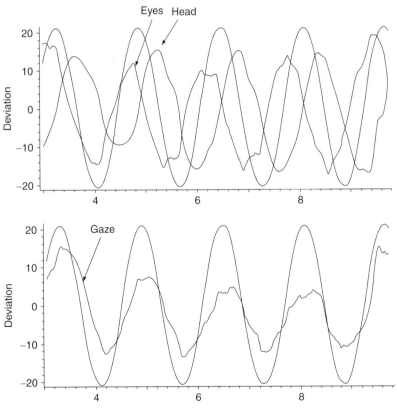

Figure 3 An example of a 5-month-old infant tracking a rapidly moving object with large head movements. The vertical axis shows the deviation from straight ahead. The object oscillates on a horizontal path with 0.63 Hz which means that one cycle was completed in 1.6 s. The top diagram shows that the head lags very much and that the eyes lead with about the same magnitude. The time difference is so large that gaze amplitude suffers. Instead of contributing to the tracking, the head movements counteract the smooth pursuit eye movements.

postural stability and almost all animals have a specialized mechanism for sensing gravity (in humans it is the otoliths). In addition, vision and proprioception provide excellent orientational information.

Gravity is also a potent force and when body equilibrium is disturbed, posture becomes quickly uncontrollable. Therefore, any reaction to a balance threat has to be very fast and automatic. Several reflexes have been identified that serve that purpose. For instance, when one slips on a patch of ice, ongoing actions are interrupted, and a series of fast automatic responses are elicited that serve the purpose of regaining balance. However, disturbances to balance are better handled in a prospective way, because if the problem can be foreseen there is no need for an emergency reaction and ongoing actions can continue uninterrupted.

The newborn child cannot control posture very well. Even lifting the head is a great challenge to the child at this age. Maintaining the head in an erect posture, raising the trunk by stretching the arms, sitting, and crawling are all major steps in the development of postural control, but the greatest challenge of them all is standing and walking. At around 3 months, infants show the first signs of being able to actively control gravity. When in a prone position they will lift their head and look around. To hold the head steadily, its sway must be correctly perceived and used to control head posture. Such control seems to be attained over the first few weeks of head lifting. The next step in mastering postural control is controlling the sitting posture. This is normally accomplished around 6 months of age and requires the child to control the sway of both head and trunk in relation to each other.

Toward the end of the first year of life, infants begin to control their erect posture. The difficulty of maintaining balance in this position is dependent on the length of the body. Contrary to what is intuitive, it is more difficult to keep a short body in balance than a long one. To convince yourself, try the following experiment. Take a short rod, like a pencil, place it vertically on you index finger tip, and try to balance it. It is almost impossible. Now, try instead to do the same thing with a walking stick. It is rather easy. This is because balancing is a question of controlling sway. The natural sway frequency decreases with the length of the rod. This is also valid for the body. The shorter the body, the faster does it sway and the faster it sways, the quicker does it get out of control. For instance, a child who is only half the size of an adult will sway with a frequency which is 40% higher than that of the adult and will consequently have 40% less time in which to react to balance disturbances. Thus, when the child for the first time can stand alone, he or she has mastered a problem that is more difficult than ever after.

Everything that the child does will perturb balance in one way or another. Just reaching out to grasp an object will displace the point of gravity of the body and if the reach is fast the momentum of it will push the body column out of its equilibrium. All these disturbances need to be dealt with ahead of time if ongoing activity is to be maintained. When the child starts to walk, the problem of maintaining balance becomes really difficult, because then the body is systematically pushed out of equilibrium. In fact, walking has been described as controlled falling. A child who has just started to walk looks like he or she is about to fall at every step.

Postural control is crucially dependent on anticipations of what is going to happen next. Balance is maintained through continuous adjustments of body sway. These adjustments must be made ahead of time and before balance is threatened. If they are not, the control of the body is lost and the ongoing activity is interrupted. Recent research has shown that at the same time as children gain control of their erect posture, they begin to compensate disturbances to their balance ahead of time.

A nice example of how this prospective mode of control emerges as the child gets to master upright stance was provided by Barela, Jeka, and Clark. They examined how infants used a supporting contact surface (a handrail) during the acquisition of upright stance. The infants were studied at four developmental epochs: pulling to stand (10 months), standing alone (11 months), walking onset (12 months), and walking mastery (13.5 months). The subject's body sways and the forces applied to the contact surface by the subject were measured. They found that the subjects up to walking onset applied forces to the contact surface as a reaction to or as a physical consequence of their body sway whereas the oldest infants applied forces to the contact surface in anticipation of body sway.

Because of its central role in movement production, postural control becomes a limiting factor in motor development. If the infant is given active postural support, goal directed reaching can be observed at an earlier age than is otherwise possible. For these reasons, development of reaching and other motor skills should be studied in the context of posture.

Reaching and Grasping

Although newborn infants have some ability to visually control their arm movements, they cannot grasp objects successfully. One important reason is that the extension and flexion of the arm is coupled to the extension and flexion of the fingers, usually referred to as flexion and extension synergies. Thus, when the arm is extended the hand usually opens up and when the arm is flexed the hand closes. This synergistic mode of moving the upper limbs facilitates the overall control of the limb but prevents independent use of the hand. Therefore one of the major challenges that infants face at the transition to functional reaching is to gain separate control of the arm and the hand. It has been found that the extension-flexion synergy is broken up at around 2 months of age and infants then begin to fist the hand when the arm is extended. At the same time the movements also appear more voluntary, as if the child really tries to reach out and get to the object. A month or so later, the forward extended arm movements become more fluent again and the hand opens and closes in the extended state. That hand control is a limiting factor in pre-reaching is supported by the work of Needham and associates. They provided 3-month-old infants with Velcro mittens and Velcro-covered objects. Thus, when the infants reached out, the objects got attached to their hands. The infants became quite excited by this sudden ability to retrieve objects. The experienced infants became focused on objects, and showed more sophisticated object exploration strategies compared to their inexperienced peers.

In addition to being able to independently control the arm and hand movements, a number of other developments are required for functional reaching to appear. First, infants must be able to control their posture while reaching. Otherwise the forward extension of the arm might upset the balance of the trunk. By 3–4 months of age, infants can sit upright with support. Second, the exact position of the object in space relative to the body must be perceived. This prerequisite is fulfilled with the emergence of binocular space perception at around 3–4 months of age. Finally, the child must have a motivation to reach for and grasp objects. Accordingly, at around 4 months of age infants begin to devote much of their waking time to such activity.

Early reaching is accomplished thorough a series of sub-movements (movement units) that during development merge into a more continuous and fluent sequence. To begin with the average duration of these movement units is about a quarter of a second. They can be thought of as feed-forward packages. A new goal can be defined at the beginning and evaluated at the end of each unit. With age, the number of such units decreases and, one unit comes to dominate the reaching movements (the transport unit), and the units by the end become rather small (grasping units). Toward the end of the first year of life, most reaches consist of one approach unit and one grasp unit.

When infants first begin to reach for and grasp objects, they cannot independently control the movements of the fingers. On the contrary, objects are grasped with the whole hand in a power grasp. It is only toward the end of the first year of life that infants begin to use the fingers in a differentiated way. At around 9–10 months of age, infants begin to pick up small objects with just their index finger and thumb in a precision grip. This is made possible by the maturation of a direct pathway between the motor cortex and the hand (the cortico-moto-neuronal pathway). Kuypers showed that when he lesioned this pathway

in very young monkeys they never developed an ability to control the fingers independently as measured by their ability to pull out a peanut from a depression in a board. The ability to control the fingers in this differentiated way marks the beginning of tool use in infants.

In the act of reaching for an object there are several problems that need to be dealt with in advance, if the encounter with the object is going to be smooth and efficient. The reaching hand needs to adjust to the orientation, form, and size of the object. The grasp must be timed in such a way that the hand starts to close around the object in anticipation of and not as a reaction to encountering it. Such timing has to be planned and can only occur under visual control. A grasp that is initiated after contact will induce an interruption in the reach-and-grasp act. The reach–grasp action is most efficient if the opening and closing of the hand is an integrated part of the approach. While grasping is almost always controlled visually, it takes until around 1 year of age until infants integrate the approach and the grasping into a fluent single action.

From the age when infants start to reach for objects they have been found to adjust the orientation of the hand to the orientation of the object reached for. For instance, when reaching for a rod, they grasp it around the longitudinal axis. Adjusting the hand to the size of a target is less crucial. Instead of doing that, it would also be possible to open the hand fully during the approach. This would lessen the spatial end point accuracy needed to grasp the object. Adults use this strategy when reaching for an object under time stress. The disadvantage is the additional time it takes to close a fully opened hand relative to a semi-opened hand.

A remarkable ability of infants to time their manual actions relative to an external event is demonstrated in early catching behavior. Claes von Hofsten and colleagues found that infants reached successfully for moving objects at the very age they began mastering reaching for stationary ones. Eighteen-week-old infants were found to catch an object moving at 30 cm s^{-1}. The reaches were aimed toward the meeting point with the object and not toward the position where the object was seen at the beginning of the reach. Eight-month-old infants successfully caught an object moving at 120 cm s^{-1}. **Figure 4** shows an 8-month-old infant who tries to catch an object moving at 60 cm s^{-1}. In this trial the object suddenly stops and the infant reaches for a position of the object where is should be if the motion had continued.

When infants begin to reach, they do not have a clear hand preference. It gradually emerges over the first year of life and is most apparent in demanding tasks. Rather than just providing an absolute preference of hand, laterality determines the role of each hand in bimanual tasks. For instance when trying to get something out of a jar, one hand is used to hold the jar and the other to poke.

Figure 4 An 8-month-old infant attempting to grasp a fast moving object that abruptly stops. Upper left: The object approaches from the right. The infant prepares to catch the object. Upper right: The object stops.Lower Left: The infants closes the hands around the position where the object should have been if the motion had continued. Lower right: The infant discovers the true position of the object.

Manipulation

During the second year of life, infants become fascinated by problems of how to relate objects to each other. For instance, they find it very attractive to pile objects, put lids on pans, and insert objects into holes. The ability to solve such problems reflects infants' developing spatial perception and cognition in addition to their dexterity. To pile blocks on the top of each other in making a tower requires increasingly delicate visual control of the hand as the tower gets taller. To fit an object into an aperture, infants must understand how the two-dimensional aperture is related to the three-dimensional object form. Finding this relationship requires the subject to see or imagine different projections of the objects. Planning the fitting action in a prospective and economical way also requires the subject to imagine how to rotate the object in order to make it fit. These are rather sophisticated expressions of spatial cognition. They include mental rotation, as well as, the ability to imagine goal states and understand means-end relationships. Thus, manipulation tasks provide a window both for learning about the development of these spatial abilities and how children develop their motor skills when solving them.

Örnkloo and von Hofsten studied young children's ability to fit object of various forms into snugly fitting apertures. They found that infants from around 1 year of age just loved this task although they only solved a minority of the object placements. Fourteen-month-olds understood that the objects should go into the apertures but had little understanding of how to orient the objects in order to make them fit. When they failed, they often used brute force and tried to press the object through the lid. Clearly, they lacked an understanding of the spatial relationship between the object and the aperture. In contrast, the 26-month-old infants moved the objects into the correct position before or during the approach of the aperture and turned the objects appropriately before the hand arrived at the lid. What characterizes the development between these two endpoints? The results showed that the infants could not solve the problem of inserting the object into the aperture by just moving it around. Success was associated with appropriate pre-adjustments before the hand arrived with the block to the aperture. Such pre-adjustments require the child to somehow imagine the goal state of the action before it is carried out. The results show how these pre-adjustments become more sophisticated with age.

What Determines Motor Development?

Although motor development may seem to be the simplest aspect of development, it is also the most complex one. To plan and perform motor movements, children do not only need to acquire control over muscles. They must also learn to perceive and anticipate the sensory consequences of those movements not only for the body part that is moved, but also for the postural stability of the whole body. Motion planning requires the child to be able to perceive the spatial layout of the surrounding and what it offers. In order to manipulate objects, their form and function has to be correctly perceived. To understand and predict the movements of objects in the surrounding, children must distinguish object motion from their own movements, and the movements of other people. Social development is a fundamental aspect of motor development. To be able to communicate with and learn from other people, the child must both be able to understand their gestures and speech and be able to perform those gestures and speech movements. Thus, motor development is not an independent entity. It is, in fact, at the heart of development and reflects all the developmental processes of the child, such as the physical growth of the body, the development of sensory and perceptual processes, the growing ability to reflect on the world and foresee future events, and the changing motives and preferences of the child.

In order to develop new modes of action, infants must solve the specific problems associated with those modes and this can only be accomplished through their own activity. The persistence and effort invested in developing new modes of actions is one of the greatest enigmas of development. Long before infants master reaching, they may spend hours trying to attain an object in front of them and although they fail most of the time, they persist and seem to enjoy it. Another example is walking. At a certain time in development, infants will try to take their first step. To begin with, they will fail repeatedly. Why bother to try this new mode of locomotion when they most certainly already possess a different and more efficient mode? It cannot be that they realize that walking in the end will be superior to crawling. The motivating force has to come from within. It seems that infants find it very pleasurable to explore their action capabilities and to find out about new ways of moving.

Apart from learning new action skills from moving around, children also learn them from observing others perform the actions. A special devoted system in the brain, the mirror neuron system, helps us to perceive and understand other people's actions. It is a distributed system with one part situated close to Broca's area, one in the rostral part of the parietal cortex and one part in the temporal cortex (STS). The mirror neuron system enables us to simulate other people's actions in our own motor system through a direct matching process in which observed actions are mapped onto the observer's motor representations of those actions. This enables us to understand the motives and goals of the observed actions and to repeat those actions ourselves. It is important to note that the mirror neuron system does not create new motor competences. An infant does not learn to stand alone or walk simply by observing other people do it. The motor

representations of the observed actions correspond to what is spontaneously generated during everyday activities and whose outcome is known to the acting individual. Thus, imitation learning has to do with learning new instances of actions including their purposes and goals. Therefore, infants are not expected to predict others' action goals before they can perform such actions themselves. Infants begin to master important socially based manual competences such as imitation, and communication by means of gesture at around 8–12 months of life. It is, thus, expected that the mirror neuron system begins to function for such actions during this period of life.

When we perform visually guided actions, action plans encode proactive goal-directed eye movements, which are crucial for planning and control. We also spontaneously look at the goal of an observed action when it is performed by others, indicating that action plans guide the oculomotor system also in action observation. Falck-Ytter, Gredebäck, and von Hofsten studied 6- and 12-month-old infants' tendency to fixate the goal of an observed manual action before the hand arrived there. We found that the 12-month-olds consistently shifted gaze to the goal of the observed action before the hand arrived there, but the 6-month-olds did not, thus supporting the mirror neuron hypothesis.

Individual Differences

Parents often ask what makes one child develop a specific motor competence early and another late. Because motor competence is the final common path for several different developments, there are also several different reasons for such variability. The body can grow fast or slow and a fat child may develop at a different pace than a thin one. The development of the nervous system may be slower in one respect and faster in another. Infants tend to focus on one aspect of their motor competence at a certain period and on another at a different period and this will also produce variability. Thus, if an infant is very much engaged in object manipulation or speech, he or she may delay the onset of walking or vice versa. An efficient crawler may delay the onset of walking in comparison to a child who has not found an equally efficient mode of crawling. If motor development is much delayed, however, there is reason to suspect neurodevelopmental disturbances. This does not mean that the problem is easy to identify. Injuries and impairments in the neural structures that control movements usually do not only result in delays but also in abnormal movements. Impairments in the sense organs that supply the motor system with information will also result in developmental delays. Visually impaired children, for instance are usually delayed in their postural development as well as in the development of reaching and manipulation. Finally, delays can be caused by impairments to the motivational system of the child because normal motor development requires the child to actively explore the world and their own action capabilities.

Acknowledgments

The author was supported by grants from The Swedish council of Research (VR) and EU integrated project FP6-004370 (Robotcub).

See also: Breastfeeding; Future Orientation; Imitation and Modeling; Milestones: Physical; Motor and Physical Development: Locomotion; Perception and Action; Perceptual Development; Reflexes; Suckling.

Suggested Readings

Adolph KE and Berger SA (2006) Motor development. In: Damon W and Lerner R (eds.) *Handbook of Child Psychology. Vol 2: Cognition, Perception, and Language,* 6th edn., pp. 161–213. New York: Wiley.

Barela JA, Jeka JJ, and Clark JE (1999) The use of somatosensory information during the aquisition of independent upright stance. *Infant Behavior and Development* 22: 87–102.

Craig CM and Lee DN (1999) Neonatal control of nutritive sucking pressure: Evidence for an intrinsic t-guide. *Experimental Brain Research* 124: 371–382.

Falck-Ytter T, Gredebäck G, and Von Hofsten C (2006) Infants predict other people's action goals. *Nature Neuroscience* 9: 878–879.

Gazzaniga (ed.) *The Cognitive Neurosciences*, pp. 165–179. Cambridge, Massachusetts: MIT Press.

Örnkloo H and Von Hofsten C (2006) Fitting objects into holes: On the development of spatial cognition skills. *Developmental Psychology* 43(2): 404–416.

Van der Meer ALH (1997) Keeping the arm in the limelight: Advanced visual control of arm movements in neonates. *European Journal of Paediatric Neurology* 4: 103–108.

Von Hofsten C (1993) Prospective control: A basic aspect of action development. *Human Development* 36: 253–270.

Von Hofsten C (2003) On the development of perception and action. In: Valsiner J and Connolly KJ (eds.) *Handbook of Developmental Psychology*, pp. 114–140. London: Sage.

Von Hofsten C (2004) An action perspective on motor development. *Trends in Cognitive Science* 8: 266–272.

Von Hofsten C (2005) The development of prospective control in looking. In: Lockman J and Rieser J (eds.) *During Learning and Development. Minnesota symposium on Child Psychology, Vol 33: Action as an Organizer of Perception and Cognition.* Florence, KY: Lawrence Erlbaum Associates.

Music Perception

S E Trehub, University of Toronto at Mississauga, Mississauga, ON, Canada

Glossary

Contour – Overall shape of a melody in terms of the direction of pitch changes – up, down, or staying the same – without regard to the magnitude of such changes.

Interval – Pitch distance between two successive notes (melodic interval) or between two simultaneous notes (harmonic interval).

Melody – A succession of notes of varying pitch that have a recognizable shape. Melody is considered the horizontal dimension of music because the notes or pitches follow one another, in contrast to harmony, which involves the vertical dimension or simultaneous sounding of notes.

Meter – The underlying pulse of music and pattern of strong and weak beats.

Rhythm – Pattern of notes in time.

Transposition – Change in the pitch level of a musical piece (i.e., higher or lower) while retaining all other features of the piece.

Introduction

Infants' music perception skills are similar, in many respects, to those of adults. For example, infants are sensitive to the pitch and timing relations that define specific melodies. Moreover, they prefer consonant to dissonant music, and they remember music for extended periods. In the case of foreign music, they detect some pitch and timing changes that adults fail to detect. Infants' precocious music perception skills are useful in everyday life. Mothers everywhere sing to infants in the course of providing care, and their singing has important consequences for infant attention and arousal

General Perspectives on Music

Scientists as well as laymen are inclined to view music as a frill – a vocation for the talented few, a hobby for others, and one of many pleasant pastimes for the general population. This conception, which may characterize music in contemporary industrial cultures, is at odds with musical practices in different cultures and eras. In many cultural contexts, music is not merely decorative art or entertainment. Instead, it is inextricably linked to ceremonies that mark rites of passage (e.g., birth, puberty, marriage, and death) and religious rituals and to numerous commonplace activities such as caregiving. These various uses of music across cultures modulate affect, solidify group identity, enhance interpersonal relations, ease the burden of work, and relieve suffering. Because songs, in particular, remain relatively intact over extended periods, they provide a means of transmitting knowledge across generations. For example, songs in oral cultures have been used to delineate land boundaries, family histories, social obligations, and agricultural routines. Even in literate societies, songs often encode information of interest or importance to children (e.g., ABC song, counting songs) and adults (e.g., national anthems, prayers, protest songs).

Despite differences in its nature and role across cultures, music is ubiquitous at present, as in the past. Moreover, its roots are ancient, predating language, by several accounts. Just as specific languages are distinguished from language in general, musics, or different musical idioms, are distinguished from music in general. Competence in a musical idiom is thought to necessitate specialized training and practice, but musically untrained adults display implicit knowledge that is similar, in many respects, to that of musicians. With few exceptions, untrained adults recognize hundreds of familiar tunes, and they can sing many of these tunes from memory, which implies that incidental exposure to music results in basic proficiency in the everyday music of one's culture. By contrast, mastering the technical and expressive aspects of performance requires intensive effort or training.

Scholars posit an underlying capacity that enables us to achieve basic musical competence on the basis of unsystematic exposure. Some aspects of the capacity for music perception are likely to overlap with skills required for speech perception. Music involves sounds, largely within the frequency range of speech, that unfold over time. In both domains, the sound stream must be segregated from other sounds in the environment, and sounds within a stream are grouped on the basis of their proximity, similarity, or continuity. Beyond these obvious similarities between speech and music lie numerous differences. Whereas simultaneous speech interferes with intelligibility, aspects of the temporal and pitch patterning of music permit, even invite, simultaneity. Group music-making and listening are facilitated by the pulsed, predictable temporal frame of most familiar music. Even in the case of unfamiliar material from a familiar musical idiom, groups of listeners have little difficulty dancing, clapping, or tapping synchronously.

With respect to the pitch structure of music, simultaneous tones separated by an octave (frequency ratio of 2:1)

tend to fuse, creating the impression that the same note is being sung or played. Simultaneous notes related by other small-integer ratios (e.g., 3:2 or perfect fifth; 4:3 or perfect fourth; 5:4 or major third) sound consonant or blend well, in contrast to those related by large-integer ratios (e.g., 45:32, or tritone), which sound dissonant or blend poorly. Note, however, that the vertical or simultaneous blending of notes (i.e., harmony) is a relatively recent addition to musical practice (i.e., hundreds of years).

The horizontal dimension of music – involving note sequences or melodies – has superficial similarities to the intonation patterns, or melodies, of speech. Whereas speech moves continuously, gliding upward or downward in pitch, with relatively few constraints, music moves in a highly constrained manner from one steady-state pitch level to another. In general, the music of a culture is based on a relatively small set of distinct pitches – usually five to seven – that carve up the octave into unequal rather than equal steps, as with the whole-steps (e.g., between *do* and *re*) and half-steps (e.g., between *ti* and *do*) of the Western major scale. Moreover, musical pieces typically move in small pitch steps (commonly, one or two semitones or half-steps), with each pitch heard in relation to a central pitch, known as the 'tonic', which provides a stable frame of reference or anchor for the other pitches. Musical pieces typically begin and end on this central, or stable, pitch, which is considered the musical key of the piece in question. Perceiving or producing the small pitch steps of music requires considerably greater precision than that required for speech prosody (intonation, in particular). Perhaps it is not surprising, then, that a small number of healthy adults exhibit impaired perception and production of melodies but intact perception and production of intonation patterns. There are also cases of brain-damaged individuals who exhibit impaired perception of speech but preserved perception of music, raising the possibility of separate as well as overlapping neural resources for speech and music.

Developmental Perspectives on Music Processing

Although competence in a specific musical idiom necessarily depends on long-term exposure, aspects of the general capacity for music predate such exposure. Indeed, a number of musical or musically relevant skills are evident in infancy, which implies that the initial musical slate is not blank or that learning proceeds rapidly in this domain. In principle, newborn skills could provide optimal evidence of the initial musical state. Unfortunately, newborns are notoriously uncooperative participants in music perception experiments because of their propensity to sleep or cry, their limited response repertoire, and the potent endogenous stimuli that compete for their attention. The usual compromise is to test older infants, acknowledging that their perceptual skills could be influenced by prior exposure to patterned auditory input. Nevertheless, music perception skills that are evident early in life could be considered to reflect perceptual or learning biases for music.

Methods of Testing Infants

Music perception in infancy is typically assessed with conditioning or preference procedures. The operant head-turn procedure, used with infants 6 months and older, can reveal which aspects of a recently heard musical pattern are encoded and retained on a short-term basis. Infants 6 months or older listen to repetitions of a musical pattern, with or without variations, that are presented from a loudspeaker on one side. To maintain infants' attention at midline, an observer manipulates puppets directly in front of them. If infants turn to the sound source immediately after a change in the musical pattern, they are rewarded by the presentation of an interesting mechanical toy or video. Turns at other times have no consequence. In short order, infants learn to maximize the available entertainment by turning for changes and otherwise watching the puppet show. The observer, who is unable to hear the sound stimuli, maintains a continuous electronic record of infant visual fixation (i.e., directly ahead, turning toward the loudspeaker) throughout the test session to ensure appropriate delivery of test trials (i.e., only when infants are looking directly ahead) and rewards (i.e., only when turns occur within 3 s of a change). The occurrence of significantly more turns on test trials with a change than on those with no change indicates that infants can detect the change in question and that they consider the change salient.

Infants' ability to detect specific changes also provides information about features encoded and retained from the original pattern. For example, infants would be unable to detect a change in the pitch or duration of one note unless they encoded the relevant pitch or timing features of the original pattern. Task difficulty can be increased in various ways, for example, by requiring infants to differentiate a category of musical patterns (e.g., different melodies that conform to a specific rhythmic structure) from another (e.g., melodies with a contrasting rhythmic structure) or by lengthening the retention interval between standard and comparison patterns.

The head-turn preference procedure evaluates listening preferences, usually between two musical patterns that contrast in familiarity, surface details, or underlying structure. In the most common version of the procedure, infants' attention is attracted to one location (e.g., rightward), and a musical pattern is presented until they look away. Then their attention is attracted to another location (e.g., leftward), and the contrasting pattern is presented

until they look elsewhere. Visual fixation times to each of the two loci are accumulated over successive, alternating trials. Significantly greater looking time during the presentation of one of the two patterns implies not only that infants differentiate the patterns but also that they prefer one to the other. Because the preference procedure minimizes cognitive demands, it can be used with infants considerably younger than those tested with the operant head-turn procedure. In addition, the preference procedure can be preceded by a brief or extended familiarization period, either immediately before testing or days or weeks earlier. Such prior familiarization makes it possible to determine which features of the original stimulus are remembered over short delays (seconds, minutes) or over long delays (days, weeks).

Prerequisites for Music Processing

Obviously, music listening requires adequate pitch and timing resolution. Although 6-month-old infants have poorer pitch resolution than adults, they detect differences smaller than a semitone (i.e., frequency ratio of roughly 1.06:1), which is the smallest meaningful pitch distance in the musics of different cultures. Their temporal resolution is also poorer than that of adults, but 6-month-olds detect the smallest distinctions required for structural or expressive aspects of musical timing. They notice such pitch and timing differences whether they are comparing isolated notes or note sequences (i.e., melodies). As anyone knows, however, the essence of music listening is not the resolution of fine auditory details. Rather, it is about perceiving relations between successive notes, groups of notes, and comparing the current input to representations of previous input. Moreover, affective and esthetic reactions are central features of musical engagement. Finally, unless listeners perceive the unfolding musical sequences as coherent rather than unrelated auditory events, they would not hear them as music.

Pitch Patterns

Transposition

Perhaps the most fundamental pitch relation in music is that of transposition. A melody retains its identity regardless of its starting pitch level (within the range of pitch audibility) so long as the internal pitch relations remain invariant. This enables listeners to recognize familiar tunes when they are hummed or sung by men, women, or children, or played on different musical instruments. In principle, the perceptual equivalence of transposed tunes could arise from frequent exposure to different renditions of the same tunes. This experiential interpretation is inconsistent with the evidence of comparable skills in infant listeners. In the operant head-turn procedure, for example, infants 6 months of age and older respond to changes that result from reordering the notes of the original melody or from changing the identity of a single note. In general, however, they do not respond when the melodies are simply transposed, that is, when all notes are altered but the pitch relations are preserved. Infants' failure to respond to transpositions in such cases does not result from discrimination failure, as can be demonstrated experimentally, but rather from their recognition of the invariance or equivalence of melodies across transposition. In this respect, infants are rather similar to adults.

Contour

For adults, the melodic (i.e., pitch) contour of a musical passage, which refers to the pattern of successive directional changes in pitch (i.e., up, down, same), lends a distinctive shape to the melody line and contributes to its esthetic appeal. The melodic contour is also the most memorable aspect of the passage. Upon hearing a novel melody, adults generate a global representation that features relatively accurate information about contour but imprecise information about intervals (i.e., exact pitch distances between adjacent notes). As a result, they often confuse recently heard melodies with others that have the same contour, especially when the comparison melody starts on a different pitch. Like adults, infants often confuse same-contour patterns, but they readily distinguish melodies with contrasting contour. For example, after hearing repetitions of a melody, either at the same pitch level or in transposition (i.e., at different pitch levels), 5–10-month-old infants readily notice changes in contour, whether the retention interval is very brief (e.g., 1 s) or relatively long (e.g., 15 s). It seems, then, that contour processing is largely unaffected by musical experience.

Intervals

Musical experience should have a greater impact on precise aspects of relational processing such as those involving intervals. In the case of highly familiar or overlearned melodies (e.g., 'Happy Birthday'; national anthems), adults retain considerable detail, including the intervals or exact pitch distances between adjacent notes. Precise representation of intervals allows adults to distinguish in-tune from out-of-tune renditions and to sing the tunes themselves. Even for novel tunes that conform to familiar musical conventions, most adults notice interval errors in the performances of others, revealing their implicit knowledge of the note sequencing rules in their musical culture.

In general, musicologists consider melodic intervals (i.e., involving successive notes) to be entirely arbitrary or conventional, in contrast to harmonic intervals (i.e., involving simultaneous notes), which are constrained by sensory consonance (i.e., harmonious blending) or dissonance (i.e., inharmonious blending or roughness). Some

psychologists contend that perceptual constraints account for the universality or near-universality of some melodic intervals, including the octave (12 semitones), the perfect fifth (seven semitones), and the perfect fourth (five semitones), all of which exemplify small-integer ratios (2:1, 3:2, and 4:3, respectively). Not only do adults show enhanced encoding and retention of these ubiquitous musical intervals, which could arise from long-term exposure, but infants do as well. For example, after 9-month-olds listen briefly to a consonant five- or seven-semitone melodic interval that repeats in transposition (i.e., at different pitch levels), they can detect a change to the dissonant interval of six semitones (45:32). If they listen, first, to the six-semitone interval repeating in transposition, then they are unable to detect a change to a five- or seven-semitone interval. These findings imply that some intervals are inherently easier to encode and retain than others. Interestingly, the dissonant six-semitone interval, or tritone, has had an illustrious musical history. In medieval Europe, for example, it was considered to manifest the devil in music.

Processing advantages for consonant intervals are not restricted to situations involving decontextualized intervals. They are also evident in the context of melodies. Consider the simple standard and comparison melodies in **Figures 1** and **2**, each of which has the same rising–falling (up–up–down–down) contour. The comparison melody in each case starts on a different pitch level, and the middle (third) note, which is also the highest in pitch, has been raised by a semitone. After listeners hear repetitions of the standard pattern in transposition (i.e., at different pitch levels), their task is to detect the alteration (i.e., a one-semitone change). Because the repetitions and comparison patterns are transposed, listeners must use relative rather than absolute cues to solve the task. Assume that, for the standard melody in **Figure 1**, the pitch distance between first and second notes (and between fourth

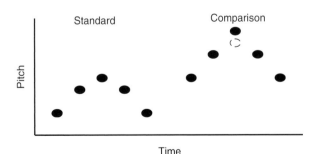

Figure 1 Schematic version of two melodies presented at different pitch levels. Note that the pitch difference between the first and second notes of the standard melody is larger than the pitch difference between the second and third notes of that melody. Aside from the difference in pitch level, the comparison melody differs from the standard by having its top note raised in pitch. Without that change, the pitch level of the top note would be as indicated by the open symbol.

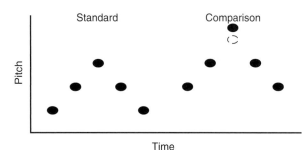

Figure 2 Schematic version of two melodies presented at different pitch levels. Note that the pitch difference between the first and second notes of the standard melody is equivalent to the pitch difference between the first and second notes. Aside from the difference in pitch level, the comparison melody differs from the standard melody by having its top note changed in pitch. Without that change, the pitch level of the top note would be as indicated by the open symbol.

and fifth notes) is four semitones, and the pitch distance between the second and third notes (and between third and fourth notes) is three semitones. The component notes of this pattern are the familiar *do mi sol*, and the ratios among their frequencies are relatively simple (4:5:6). Indeed, this pattern, which is known as the major triad, is fundamental to Western music. Assume that the standard melody in **Figure 2** has four-semitone intervals separating all of its notes, which are related by more complex frequency ratios (16:20:25). After hearing the standard melody in **Figure 1**, 7-month-old infants and adults detect the interval change in the comparison melody, but they fail to do so after hearing the standard melody in **Figure 2**. This pattern of performance has been replicated with other melodies whose intervals exemplify simple (small-integer) or complex (large-integer) frequency ratios.

Because of the special status of the major triad in Western music, adults' performance could be based on mere familiarity. Could infants' performance also be based on familiarity with aspects of Western musical structure? A more likely explanation involves inherent biases for small-integer ratios, which would account for infants' enhanced performance on melodies that embody such ratios and for the prevalence of intervals with small-integer ratios across musical cultures. When common melodies from other cultures are simplified in ways that are acceptable to informants in those cultures, the resulting melodies tend to sound familiar, even Western, to Western ears.

Enhanced processing of consonant musical material has its counterpart in clear preferences for consonant over dissonant music on the part of infants and adults. When given a choice of consonant or dissonant music, newborns and older infants listen significantly longer to the consonant music. Some scholars dispute the notion of inherent preferences for consonant music, arguing instead that exposure to consonant speech sounds, even in the prenatal period, could underlie the observed preferences.

This perspective is inconsistent with the robust preferences for consonance that have been observed in hearing newborns of deaf, signing parents who would have had limited prenatal exposure to consonant sounds. Indeed, the preference for consonant sounds may be uniquely human. Although tamarin monkeys demonstrate clear preferences in the laboratory for species-specific food calls over distress calls and for low rather than high levels of white noise, they exhibit no preference for consonant over dissonant intervals. What is more telling is their preference for silence over various kinds of music. In short, the motivation for music, which has been demonstrated across age level and culture, may be a defining feature of our species.

Foreign music

It comes as no surprise that adults outperform infants on many music perception tasks because of their overwhelming advantages in cognitive skill and musical knowledge. At times, however, implicit musical knowledge interferes with accurate perception of foreign or unconventionally structured music, just as expertise in one language can interfere with the perception of some foreign speech sounds. Experienced listeners often assimilate what they hear to culture-specific expectations. This phenomenon has been documented extensively for speech and, to a more limited extent, for music. For example, adults detect subtle melodic changes (e.g., mistuned notes) more readily in the context of Western melodies than in Indonesian melodies. By contrast, 6-month-old infants perform equally well in Western and Indonesian melodic contexts, which implies that one change is not inherently easier than the other. By 12 months of age, however, infants perform better on Western melodies than on Indonesian melodies, which reflects increasing sensitivity to pitch regularities in their musical environment. For many culture-specific aspects of melody and harmony, however, the course of development is protracted, extending into the school years.

Scale structure

Scales involve the specification of pitches that fill an octave and the relations among those pitches. Although scales are not formalized in many cultures, they can be inferred from the component pitches of melodies in those cultures. An examination of scale structure across cultures reveals similarities as well as differences. Aside from a limited number of pitches in a scale (usually five to seven) and the prevalence of specific ratios (e.g., 3:2), pitch steps (i.e., pitch distances between one scale step and the next) of more than one size are typical of non-Western as well as Western scales. For example, the Western major scale consists of whole-steps (two semitones in size), as from *do* to *re* or *re* to *mi*, and half-steps (one semitone in size), as from *ti* to *do*. In principle, scales could be based on equal steps, but there is no confirmation of such scales in any of the world's musics. Perhaps the widespread use of scales with unequal steps stems from processing advantages or predispositions favoring that feature. In fact, 9-month-old infants and adults have been tested on three types of scales – the major scale, with its seven whole- and half-steps, an invented scale with seven whole- and half-steps based on a division of the octave into eleven units (rather than twelve semitones), and a scale that divides the octave into seven equal steps. When adults were required to detect a very small pitch change in the sixth step of each scale, they succeeded only in the context of the familiar major scale. By contrast, infants succeeded on the major scale and on the invented, unequal-step scale, but not on the equal-step scale. These findings support the view that unequal steps in scales facilitate music processing, which has influenced their prevalence across cultures. Undoubtedly, adults' failure to profit from this design feature stems from interference caused by robust representations of familiar Western scales. The latter interpretation is consistent with adults' documented difficulty with foreign or unconventionally structured musical materials.

Absolute pitch processing

Although relational processing is central to music, this does not imply that absolute aspects of music are irrelevant. For example, the pitch level of a musical performance contributes to its distinctiveness, as do other absolute features such as its tempo (i.e., rate or speed) and timbre (i.e., instrument or voice quality). The encoding of such features enables adults to identify well-known recordings from fragments as brief as 100 or 200 m, well before aspects of the melody or voice become recognizable. Indeed, there is increasing evidence that listeners retain absolute as well as relational details of well-known musical material. For example, children and adults not only recognize the music that accompanies their favorite television programs, but they also distinguish authentic versions – those presented at the original pitch level – from versions that have been pitch-shifted by one or two semitones.

Some scholars contend that absolute pitch processing dominates in infancy, with experience prompting a shift to relational processing late in the preschool period. As supportive evidence, they cite 7-month-olds' focus on absolute rather than relative features of pitch when exposed to a 2 min sequence of pure tones of equal duration. In such impoverished contexts, which exclude the rich temporal and pitch patterning of typical music, infants may show undue reliance on absolute cues. Indeed, the nature of the musical material has an enormous impact on the amount and type of information encoded. As the ecological validity of the music increases, information retained about its relational and absolute features also increases.

Other scholars claim that tone language exposure in infancy or early childhood could reinforce infants' predisposition for absolute pitch processing, generating a lifelong enhancement in pitch memory. Such experience is thought to account for Asian adults' superior memory for musical pitches as compared with their North American counterparts. Although Japanese is not a tone language, Japanese adults also exhibit the characteristic Asian enhancement in musical pitch memory. It is notable, however, that children of Asian origin who are reared in North America exhibit pitch memory comparable to that of non-Asian children, even if the Asian children are regular users of tone languages. In short, there is no definitive evidence of enhanced pitch memory from tone language exposure alone. Moreover, pitch relations rather than absolute pitch levels are the defining features of lexical tones (i.e., tones that signal a difference in word meaning). It is likely, then, that the reported differences in pitch memory among Asian and non-Asian individuals arise from different pedagogical techniques across cultures that emphasize absolute aspects of pitch (e.g., Asian countries typically use *do* to label a specific note, C, and its replication in different octaves) or relative aspects (e.g., non-Asian countries typically use *do* to label the starting or tonic pitch of a musical piece). In addition, absolute pitch processing biases in early life are questionable. Rather, there is every reason to believe that listeners engage in absolute and relative pitch processing through all stages of development, deploying skills that are relevant to the task at hand.

Long-term memory

Obviously, infants have relatively limited exposure to specific songs or musical pieces compared to older children or adults. Nevertheless, they remember aspects of music that they hear repeatedly. For example, after 7-month-old infants hear portions of two Mozart sonatas at home over the course of 2 weeks, they listen longer to novel Mozart sonatas than to the original sonatas, confirming their memory for the music heard at home. Similarly, 1 week of at-home exposure to an instrumental rendition of an unfamiliar folk tune leads 6-month-old infants to listen longer to a novel tune than to the original, confirming their long-term memory for relative pitch patterns.

In addition to remembering the tune, infants may also remember aspects of the original performance heard at home, such as its tempo and timbre (instrument). Nevertheless, infants' long-term memory is thought to exclude information about pitch level. As noted, however, the nature of the music affects the information encoded and retained. When the music consists of expressively sung lullabies rather than synthesized folk tunes, then 7-month-old infants exhibit long-term memory for its pitch level. The relative contributions of vocal and affective cues to enhanced learning and memory remain to be determined. It would not be surprising if affective cues enhanced infants' processing of music, as they do for speech. This facilitation could be mediated by favorable mood, which is known to improve performance on a variety of tasks.

Timing Patterns

Time in conventional Western music is commonly organized into a regular pulse or beat and into groups of two or three (or their multiples). The pattern of accents, or strong beats relative to weak beats, defines the meter. For example, a march is characterized by repeating patterns of 'one'–two–three–four, 'one'–two, three, four; and a waltz is characterized by repeating patterns of 'one'–two–three, 'one'–two–three. Rhythm, by contrast, is concerned with the pattern of relative durations (i.e., long and short notes) and their grouping into units. Thus, for each of the two main metric categories in Western music (i.e., groups or two or three and their multiples), there can be many different rhythms. Just as listeners encode relative aspects of pitch, so they encode relative aspects of timing. As a result, they recognize the same rhythm, or pattern of successive durations (e.g., short-short-long, as in *Three Blind Mice*), at different speeds or tempos so long as the relative durations remain unchanged. They also recognize specific rhythms (e.g., the familiar shave-and-a-haircut rhythm, or dum-da-da-dum-dum—dum-dum) across changing pitch patterns, and they notice correspondences between simple auditory and visual rhythms.

Grouping

Perhaps the most fundamental temporal process involves the segmentation of a tone sequence into groups or subsets of tones. Grouping tendencies are so strong that listeners tend to experience the illusion of groups even with repeating tones of uniform pitch, duration, and loudness (i.e., subjective grouping). For example, they may hear groups of two, three, or four elements, with accents on the initial note of each group. In general, however, there are explicit cues to grouping, including pitch, duration, intensity, and timbre. Consider the standard sequence in **Figure 3**, which is isochronous, or equally timed, and consists of six tones – the first three at one pitch level and last three at a different pitch level. The added silent increment between third and fourth tones of the comparison sequence disrupts the isochrony or equal timing of the original sequence, but it preserves the grouping structure (i.e., two groups of three). In **Figure 4**, however, the added silent increment in the comparison sequence occurs between the fourth and fifth tone, which disrupts the original grouping structure. After adults and 6-month-old infants are exposed to an isochronous standard sequence such as that depicted in **Figures 3** and **4**, they are more accurate at detecting alterations that disrupt the original grouping structure than those that preserve it. The effect is more pronounced

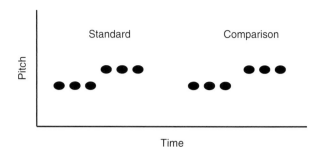

Figure 3 Schematic version of a sequence consisting of three notes at one pitch level followed by three notes at another pitch level. In the standard sequence, all notes are equally spaced. In the comparison sequence, the time interval between the third and fourth notes (i.e., between groups of notes) is longer than the other internote intervals.

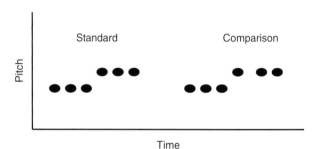

Figure 4 Schematic version of a sequence consisting of three notes at one pitch level followed by three notes at another pitch level. In the standard sequence, all notes are equally spaced. In the comparison sequence, the time interval between the fourth and fifth notes (i.e., within a group of notes) is longer than the other inter note intervals.

for larger pitch differences between tones, and it is also evident for tones contrasting in intensity or timbre.

Long durations signal the boundaries of groups for infants, as they do for adult listeners. As a result, infants have more difficulty detecting silent increments that follow long-duration tones (i.e., preserving the grouping structure) than those that follow short-duration tones (i.e., disrupting the structure). Sensitivity to such grouping cues aids in the recognition of phrase boundaries in music, which are typically cued by notes that are longer and lower in pitch than the preceding notes. In fact, when infants are given the choice of listening to versions of a Mozart minuet with 1 s pauses 'between' musical phrases or comparable pauses 'within' phrases, they prefer the former with its intact phrases.

Grouping processes generally increase the coherence and memorability of auditory sequences. At times, however, they disrupt the perceived temporal order of tones by reorganizing the sequences along other lines. For example, when a repeating sequence of sounds is presented at a very rapid rate, listeners may experience it as two or more parallel streams, each composed of elements that are similar in pitch, timbre, or some other feature.

In such situations, listeners can track the order of tones within each stream but not across streams. Comparable processes of auditory stream segregation or scene analysis have been observed in listeners as young as 7 weeks of age.

Meter

The metrical structure of music, which concerns our sense of patterned strong and weak beats, enables individuals to synchronize their rhythmic behavior, as in dancing, singing, clapping, tapping, or marching. In principle, listeners could tap to every note that they hear, but they usually tap less frequently, perhaps on every second, third, or fourth note, and on some elements more strongly than others. Meter is hierarchically organized, which allows listeners to tap faster (i.e, at lower or less abstract metrical levels, as in 'Twin'-kle, 'Twin'-kle, 'Li'-ttle 'Star', 'How' I 'won'-der 'what' you 'are'), or more slowly (i.e., at higher metrical levels, as in 'Twin'-kle, Twi-nkle, 'Li'-ttle Star, 'How' I wonder 'what' you are). Because of their greater understanding of the temporal organization of music, trained listeners tend to tap more slowly, or at higher metrical levels, than do untrained listeners.

Metrical structure is salient for infants as well as adults. For example, after 7-month-old infants are familiarized with different rhythms that induce a common meter, they respond preferentially to a novel rhythm that induces a novel meter than to a novel rhythm that induces the same meter. Concurrent movement also influences infants' encoding of musical meter. After 7-month-old infants hear 2 min of an ambiguous rhythm while they are bounced on every second or third beat (i.e., corresponding to duple or triple meter), they respond preferentially to a test rhythm with intensity accents that match the pattern of bouncing during the familiarization period.

In line with inherent preferences for simple or small-integer frequency ratios in music, there are presumptions of inherent preferences for small-integer duration ratios (e.g., 2:1, 3:1) and for the simple, isochronous meters (i.e., equally spaced accents) that prevail in Western music. Although simple meters of this nature are widespread, many regions of the world, including Eastern Europe, Southern Asia, the Middle East, and Africa, have complex meters in addition to simple meters. In much Balkan dance music, for example, the primary metrical level (i.e., the level at which listeners usually tap) is not isochronous, consisting instead of alternating short- and long-duration notes in a 3:2 ratio. When Western adults hear such music, they tend to assimilate it to conventional Western metrical structures. As a result, they fail to detect changes in metrical structure that are readily detected by adults of Balkan origin. Western 6-month-olds not only detect the changes that Western adults do (i.e., those involving simple meters); they also detect changes that adults fail to detect (i.e., those involving complex meters). These findings provide evidence against the claim of inherent processing biases for simple meters.

Instead, adults' implicit knowledge of the temporal structure of Western music seems to interfere with their perception of foreign rhythms, just as their knowledge of the pitch structure of Western music interferes with their perception of foreign melodies.

Western 12-month-olds can detect metrical changes in the context of the simple meters that are characteristic of Western music. Unlike 6-month-olds, however, they are unable to do so in the context of the complex Balkan meters. On the basis of their limited exposure to music, they have become sensitive to its temporal regularities, with consequent narrowing of their former perceptual focus and skill. Nevertheless, after 2 weeks of brief daily exposure to Balkan music, 12-month-olds succeed in detecting subtle changes in the context of complex meters. When Western adults receive comparable exposure, they are still unable to detect metrical changes in these foreign rhythms. Perhaps adults would succeed with additional exposure, but the fact remains that 12-month-olds acquire the relevant perceptual skills more rapidly than adults do. One consequence of infants' relatively weak representations of music may be enhanced perceptual flexibility and ease of learning about music.

Music in Everyday Life

Maternal Speech

Speech to preverbal infants, not only from mothers but also from others involved in infant care, is notable for its distinctive, sing-song style. Compared to typical speech, infant-directed speech is higher in pitch, more variable in pitch and loudness, slower and more rhythmic, and considerably more repetitive. Addressed as it is to a noncomprehending audience, infant-directed speech generates sound effects that convey the speaker's positive feelings as well as her playful or soothing intentions. Although there are common elements in speech to infants, both within and across cultures, there are also individually distinctive aspects or specific tunes (i.e., precise interval sequences) that set one mother apart from another. Each mother seems to use a small repertoire of unique melodies or intonation frames that she fills with different speech content, both within the same interaction and across interactions separated by a week or more. Perhaps these signature tunes contribute to infants' differentiation of the mother's voice from other voices. In any case, infants exhibit more sustained attention to such melodious speech than to adults' usual speech regardless of whether the speaker and language are familiar or unfamiliar.

Maternal Singing

Across cultures, mothers and other caregivers sing to their infants in the course of caring for them. Some of the sound effects that appear in infant-directed speech are muted and some are intensified in singing. Unlike infant-directed speech, which is relatively unconstrained in its pitch and temporal patterning, the pitches and rhythms of songs are prescribed. Nevertheless, those who sing to infants tend to differentiate their infant-directed singing from their usual singing in a number of ways. For one thing, they select material from a special genre of music, which includes lullabies and play songs. In contrast to play songs, which appear in a subset of cultures, lullabies are universal. Moreover, lullabies across cultures share a number of properties that enable listeners to distinguish foreign lullabies from nonlullabies matched on tempo and culture of origin. The style of infant-directed singing also differs from that of other informal performances by the same singer in having higher pitch and slower tempo as well as greater emotional expressiveness. Because the songs that mothers and other caregivers typically sing have well-known words, the singers are free to focus on the expressive quality of their performances. At times, however, caregivers alter the lyrics, adding the baby's name or airing complaints about their life to the noncomprehending infant.

Despite the fact that mothers generally know several nursery songs, they sing a handful of those songs repeatedly. Their performances of the same song on different occasions are surprisingly uniform or stereotyped. For example, measurements of the same singer performing the same song for her infant on different days reveal virtually identical pitch level and tempo. In principle, such uniformity could facilitate infants' recognition of the mother's singing voice. Mothers' performing style is also influenced by the maturity and mood of her audience. For example, when mothers sing the same song separately for their infant and preschool child, the performances differ in pitch level (i.e., higher for infants) and articulation of the lyrics (i.e., clearer for preschoolers).

Singing also provides an effective means of maintaining emotional contact with infants, even when visual or physical contact is precluded (e.g., darkness, driving a car). When the mother is unable to touch her infant, she intensifies her speech prosody by raising her pitch level and expanding her pitch range, but she maintains her characteristic infant-directed singing style. The comparability of maternal singing across touch and no-touch contexts implies that such singing is effective in bridging the distance between mother and infant.

Just as infants prefer infant-directed to adult-directed speech, so they prefer infant-directed to non-infant-directed singing. In fact, this preference for the maternal singing style is evident from the newborn period. Although the features that underlie infants' preference for sung performances have not been identified to date, it is likely that the emotional intensity and valence of performances are relevant. A cluster of performance cues may be implicated rather than any specific cue, and the relevant cues may change from one context to another. There are suggestions, for example, that infants prefer higher-pitched performances of play songs (more playful, perhaps) but lower-pitched performances of lullabies (more soothing, perhaps), the preferred pitch level in each case intensifying the singer's expressiveness.

Although infants are clearly captivated by their mother's speech, they are even more captivated by her singing. When given a choice between audio–visual samples of maternal singing or speech, infants remain engaged for substantially longer periods by the singing. The intensity of their engagement is reflected not only in very long fixations on the mother's image during her singing episodes but also in substantial reductions of body movement. Singing also modulates infants' mood and arousal level. Nevertheless, similar sung performances can have different consequences for different infants and for the same infants at different times. For example, maternal singing generates subtle increases in arousal for infants with low initial arousal and subtle decreases in infants with higher initial arousal, as indicated by concentrations of a stress-related hormone (i.e., cortisol) in their saliva. It is possible, then, that singing optimizes arousal and attention in early life. Maternal speech also has arousal-modulating consequences, but the effects of singing on arousal are more enduring Infants' sustained responsiveness to such singing is likely to reinforce maternal effort and encourage further singing.

Some scholars consider the universality, nature, and consequences of musical caregiving as potential clues to the adaptive significance of music. In this regard, arousal regulation, involving the soothing consequences of lullabies and the energizing consequences of play songs, is especially important for a species with an extended period of helplessness or dependence. This so-called caregiving hypothesis is compatible with the proposal that vocal protomusic – pleasant but meaningless sound sequences that cement relationships – preceded music as we know it as well as language.

Summary

Infants' music perception skills are similar, in many respects, to those of adults. For example, infants recognize melodies at different pitch levels provided the pitch relations among notes are preserved. They also recognize musical patterns across changes in tempo or speed, and they group the component tones of music much as adults do. Infants detect some interval changes, but they have difficulty with others, notably those that pose difficulty for adults. Like adults, infants prefer consonant music to dissonant music, and they remember specific melodies and performance features over extended periods. In the case of foreign music, 6-month-old infants sometimes notice subtle pitch and timing changes that adults fail to notice. By 12 months of age, however, they exhibit differential sensitivity to culture-specific aspects of pitch and temporal patterning. Nevertheless, limited exposure to foreign music leads 12-month-old infants but not adults to notice changes that are otherwise imperceptible. Infants' keen music processing skills are put to use in the early months of life. In the course of providing infant care, mothers perform a special repertoire of songs in a distinctive manner. These performances, which have favorable consequences on infant attention and arousal, may provide clues to the adaptive significance of music.

Acknowledgments

The preparation of this article was assisted by grants from the Natural Sciences and Engineering Research Council and the Social Sciences and Research Council of Canada.

See also: Auditory Perception; Memory; Perceptual Development; Preverbal Development and Speech Perception; Speech Perception.

Suggested Readings

Fitch WT (2005) The evolution of music in comparative perspective. *Annals of the New York Academy of Sciences* 1060: 29–49.
Jackendoff R and Lerdahl F (2006) The capacity for music: What is it, and what's special about it? *Cognition* 100: 33–72.
Trehub SE and Hannon SE (2006) Infant speech perception: Domain-general or domain-specific mechanisms? *Cognition* 100: 73–99.
Trehub SE and Trainor (1998) Singing to infants: Lullabies and play songs. *Advances in Infancy Research* 12: 43–77.

Relevant Websites

http://www.psychology.mcmaster.ca/ljt – McMaster University, Auditory Development Lab.
http://www.waisman.wisc.edu/infantlearning – University of Wisconsin, Infant Learning Lab.
http://www.utm.utoronto.ca/5726.0.html – Infant and Child Lab, University of Toronto Mississauga.

N

Nature vs. Nurture

B M D'Onofrio, Indiana University, Bloomington, IN, USA

Glossary

Allele – One variant of a gene at a particular location (or locus) on a chromosome.

Behavior – The response of an individual or group of individuals to their environment.

Emigration – The act of leaving one's original country.

Endophenotype – An intermediate observable trait that contributes to a phenotype.

Epigenetic – The situation in which nongenetic factors influence the action of genes.

Gene – A set of DNA bases that code for specific proteins.

Gene–environment correlations – The situation in which one's genetic predisposition is associated with environmental factors.

Genetics – The science of heredity, which accounts for similarities and differences among organisms due to the environment and/or genes.

Genotype – The genetic identity of an individual that does not show as outward characteristics.

Heritability – The percent of variation in a trait that is due to genetic factors.

Immigration – The act of moving into a new country.

Locus – The place on a chromosome where a specific gene is located.

Lod score – An estimate of whether two positions on a chromosome are near each other, suggesting they have been inherited together.

Mendelian inheritance – The situation in which a particular gene is sufficient to account for a trait.

Microarray – A research technique that measures the activity of many genes simultaneously.

Multifactorial inheritance – The situation in which a phenotype is influenced by many genes and environmental factors (also referred to as polygenic inheritance).

Nature of nurture – A term referring to gene–environment correlations, when genetic predispositions are associated with environmental factors.

Phenotype – An observable trait or behavior.

Pleitropy – When one gene influences more than one phenotype.

Polymorphism – A common variation in the sequence of DNA among people.

Proband – The primary or first person identified in a research study.

Quantitative trait loci (QTL) – One gene, among many that influence a trait is normally distributed.

Transcription – The process of making of an RNA copy of the DNA sequence from the chromosome, the first step in gene expression.

Translation – The process by which RNA directs the production of amino acids and polypeptides, which ultimately form proteins.

Introduction

Historically, the field of psychology has generally discounted the importance of genetic factors. Early psychological theories and research were heavily influenced by environmentalism, the notion that experience accounted for all traits. Gregor Mendel's research on inherited patterns of traits in pea plants and Charles Darwin's theories of the importance of evolutionary influences for the selection of traits were, by and large, not incorporated into psychological research. Studies that explored genetic and environmental influences on humans were also disregarded. Francis Galton was the first person to systematically study the influence of genetic and environmental factors for a human behavior; he published a family study of genius (intelligence) in 1869. It was not until the mid-1900s, however, that the field of psychology as a whole began to consider the importance of genetic factors. Based on a number of influential animal studies of learning and twin and adoption studies of behavior, the field of psychology gradually accepted that genetic factors were important for psychological traits. The recognition of the role of genetics by the field of psychology can now be seen by the number of psychologists conducting research on the influence of genetic factors and the number of genetics papers that are published in psychology journals. Most psychologists, thus, currently accept the importance of both genetic and environmental factors. Yet, many researchers continue to ask whether genetic or environmental factors are more important, which is the very premise of the nature vs. nurture debate.

This article provides a brief description of a number of topics related to genetics and psychology in order to facilitate a greater understanding of the nature vs. nurture debate. First, the article describes the types of psychological traits and behaviors that are studied by the field of behavior genetics, the controversial field that explores genetic and environmental influences on behavior. Second, the text will include a brief review of human genetics to provide the necessary background for the discussion of the nature vs. nurture debate. Third, it will explain the types of environmental influences that need to be considered when reviewing behavior genetic findings. Fourth, the article will go on to provide an overview of the basic behavior genetic findings that are relevant to psychological traits. Fifth, the importance of the interplay of genetic and environmental factors will be emphasized. Sixth, an overview of the research methods behavior geneticists use to simultaneously study environmental and genetic factors will be included. Finally, the text addresses some of the social concerns surrounding behavior genetic research. This article stresses the importance of moving beyond the debate over the relative importance of genetic and environmental influences. Instead, the text highlights the need to study how genetic and environmental factors act and interact to influence psychological traits.

The Study of Individual Differences in Behavior

The research field that explores genetic and environmental influences is generally referred to as 'behavior genetics'. However, it is essential to define what researchers mean by the term behavior because the term can be misleading. Behavior certainly refers to actions that an individual takes, such as dropping out of school, getting into fights, or filing for a divorce. But, there is a much broader understanding of the term. 'Behavior' is defined as any response to environmental stimuli, so that any traits in which people

differ are considered to be 'behavior'. Behavior genetic research explores the variation that exists among people, which is referred to as the study of individual differences. Intellectual abilities (why are some people smarter than others?), personality traits (why are some people outgoing but others shy?), susceptibility to psychological problems (why do some people get depressed but not others?), physical health (why are some people overweight or more sensitive to pollen?), and a host of other traits are all considered to be behaviors. It is important to note that the broad definition of behavior also means that animals and plants 'behave'. The nature vs. nurture debate, in fact, has frequently relied on animal and plant studies to provide important insights. The broad definition of behavior may seem as if it includes every characteristic of humans, animals, and plants. But, behavior genetic research solely focuses on traits or behaviors that vary among individuals and does not study characteristics that are common to all people. For example, behavior geneticists do not study characteristics that everyone shares, such as normative psychological and physical development. Additionally, many people assume that the field is primarily focused on genetic factors. That is not true. What distinguishes the field of behavior genetics from other social sciences is the use of genetically informed methods (see section titled Behavior genetic methods), which are designs that can help answer the nature vs. nurture debate.

Human Genetics

To help aid the review of the nature vs. nurture debate, it is important to understand some basics of human genetics. The human genome is the complete set of human genetic material. Offspring receive a set of 23 chromosomes from each of their parents, for a total of 46 chromosomes. Chromosomes are composed of deoxyribonucleic acid (DNA), which is made of smaller units called bases. There are four bases: adenine, cytosine, thymine, and guanine. The bases are paired with each other so that DNA is in the shape of a double helix. The shape was first discovered by James Watson and Francis Crick in 1953. The human genome has approximately 3 billion base pairs. The nucleus of each cell in the body contains a copy of each chromosome. The bases are ordered along each chromosome so that a number of bases work as a unit. These units are referred to as genes, and each gene has a specific location, or locus, on a chromosome. Because humans are diploid – everyone receives two sets of chromosomes – each gene exists in two alternate forms, or two alleles. Recent estimates suggest that the human genome includes as many as 30 000 genes. Genes are important because they are the template for the building of proteins, which are essential molecules in the body. They are involved in every process that occurs within the cells of our body – they provide the structure, influence the function, and regulate each of the body's cells. The order of the base pairs of a gene is copied by ribonucleic acid (RNA) in the process of transcription. RNA then specifies the synthesis of amino acids and polypeptides via the process of translation. When strings of polypeptides are linked together in three-dimensional (3D) structures they form proteins. Thus, the particular ordering of base pairs in each individual's DNA (referred to as their genotype) provides the guidelines for the building of proteins.

There are different patterns of genetic influences, but they are typically separated into two main categories: Mendelian (or single-gene) inheritance and multifactorial inheritance. Mendelian inheritance refers to the situation in which a particular set of alleles at a gene is sufficient to completely account for a trait or disorder. It is referred to as Mendelian inheritance because the one-to-one connection between an individual's genotype and their phenotype (or observable properties of an individual) follows the pattern Gregor Mendel originally found in his plant studies. In contrast, multifactorial inheritance (also referred to as polygenic inheritance) describes the situation in which a phenotype is influenced by many genes that each have a small effect and numerous environmental influences. Traits that follow a pattern of multifactorial inheritance are referred to as complex behaviors. Genes that influence these traits are referred to as susceptibility genes or quantitative trait loci (QTLs). The influence of multiple genes could be additive, meaning that each gene influences the phenotype without the influences of other genes. An allele at one gene can also affect the expression of an allele at another gene, so that there is a gene by gene interaction. Dominance refers to the situation in which a particular allele at a gene more heavily influences the phenotype than the other allele or alleles. Although there are some instances in which psychological traits are influenced by Mendelian disorders, most traits studied by developmental psychologists are polygenic. The remainder of the article will, therefore, focus on polygenic phenotypes, traits that are influenced by multiple genetic and environmental factors.

But, what does it mean to have a genetic effect on a complex behavior? How can there be genetic influences on complex behaviors, such as intellectual abilities, personality traits, conduct problems, social attitudes, etc.? Is there a gene for getting into a fight or a gene for being shy? No, genes provide the template for building proteins. Genes do not directly influence one's behavior. When research states that there are genetic influences on complex traits, the findings suggest that individual differences for a trait (or the underlying risk for a disorder) in a given population are partially influenced by differences in individuals' genotypes. Any genetic effect on behavior is mediated by biological processes in the body. Therefore, genetic influences on multifactorial traits are only probabilistic in nature; they are not deterministic. Finding susceptibility genes for disorders or QTLs for various measures of individual differences is, therefore, only informative in as much as they can help researchers understand the underlying biological and environmental process that ultimately influence the behavior. In fact, it is imprecise to describe the effects of one gene on a complex multifactorial behavior as a gene for 'x'. For multifactorial traits, the influence of any one single gene on an individual's phenotype will probably be quite small, meaning the gene will not be associated with much variation in the trait. Plus, the same phenotype may result from different genes or a different set of genes, a condition referred to as heterogeneity. Furthermore, a gene may influence more than one phenotype (called pleitropy.) Ultimately, the effect of one's genotype on one's phenotype involves a complex number of processes and interactions (see section titled Gene–environment interplay). Studying genetic factors provides one a powerful research tool for analyzing the underlying causes of psychological traits, including the role of environmental factors in a person's 'behavior'.

What Constitutes the 'Environment?'

Understanding what is considered to be the environment is also crucial for the nature vs. nurture debate. When referring to environmental influences, psychologists typically include factors such as parenting practices, family-wide variables, and characteristics of larger communities. Researchers also frequently associate genetic effects with the influence of all biological factors. However, behavior genetic studies consider all nongenetic and biological influences to be 'environmental' in origin. Therefore, the availability of nutrients in the body and prenatal and postnatal insults are also considered to be environmental influences in behavior genetic studies, in addition to the traditional psychosocial factors that are more familiar to psychologists and other social scientists.

Just as there are rare conditions that are completely accounted for by single-gene disorders (Mendelian disorders), there are also extreme environmental circumstances that can completely overcome genetically influenced variation in traits. Instances of severe deprivation or abuse are some examples. As highlighted by the famous case of Victor, the 'wild boy of Averyron', extreme environmental experiences can markedly influence psychological development. Victor had no human contact until he was 12–13 years old. Due to intensive interventions he was able to write a few words and respond to others, but he was never able to speak. The example of Victor and other documented cases of severe early neglect or abuse high-light the importance of the environment. But, do more normative environmental experiences play a role in the development of psychosocial traits?

Findings from Behavior Genetic Studies

In addition to the major advances in our understanding of molecular genetics over the past century, researchers in the field of population genetics have also made great strides in understanding the factors that influence psychological traits. Population genetics explores the patterns of inheritance – the importance of genetic and environmental influences – in populations. Using various research designs (see section titled 'Behavior genetic methods') behavior genetic studies explore how much of the variation in a certain trait is due to genetic factors. The percentage of variation accounted for by genetic factors is referred to as the heritability. Heritability is an index of the extent to which individual differences in a phenotype reflect genetic differences among the people in a certain population. Behavior genetic research designs also measure the importance of environmental influences. Environmental influences are frequently separated into two types based on the impact the environment has on individuals. The first type of environmental factor is referred to as the shared environment. Shared environmental influences are environmental factors that make siblings in the same family similar. In contrast, nonshared environmental influences make siblings in a family different. Both of the estimates of environmental influences are presented as the percentage of the total variation for a trait in a population.

There are a number of important caveats that must be considered when interpreting the estimates of heritability, shared environmental influences, and nonshared factors. First, the estimates of the importance of each are based on the sample from which they are drawn. The estimates from behavior genetic studies (heritability, shared environmental factors, and nonshared environmental factors) are not invariant, meaning that the influence of genetic factors for multifactorial traits can change. If environmental conditions change or differ across samples or time, the estimates of heritability are susceptible to change. Like-wise, a large change in the make-up of a population (i.e., the frequency of alleles changed through immigration or emigration) could also influence the estimates of the importance of environmental factors. Second, the estimates of heritability do not state what should or could be true. Rather, the estimates of behavior genetic studies simply provide a snapshot of importance of genetic and environmental factors at the time of the study. Third, the magnitude of the heritability is not necessarily indicative of whether a trait would respond to environmental interventions. The well-known example of phenylketonuria

(PKU) supports this notion. PKU is a metabolic disorder that is caused by a Mendelian genetic mutation that makes it impossible for the body to break down dietary phenyl-alanine (certain amino acids). The condition results in severe mental retardation. However, genetic tests can now identify infants with the genetic mutation, and providing children with a phenalanine diet prevents the cognitive problems associated with the disorder. Finally, the estimates are population-based percentages and cannot be applied to specific individuals within the population. If the heritability of a certain trait, say delinquent behavior, is 50%, researchers cannot claim 50% of the variation in a specific individual's delinquent behavior is due to genetic factors.

Are Genetic Factors Important?

One of the most surprising results from behavior genetic research is the extent to which genetic factors influence all areas of psychology. Behavior genetic research over the past 50–75 years has shown that genetic factors influence nearly every psychology trait. Behavior genetics studies have shown high heritabilities for psychological disorders such as schizophrenia, bipolar depression, and autism. But research has also shown that genetic factors influence individual variation in behaviors that were once thought to be completely influenced by social forces. Behavior genetic studies have documented heritabilities for intellectual abilities, school performance, personality traits, substance use and abuse, self-esteem, television watching, and social attitudes, just to name a few areas of research. Genetic factors are not restricted to extreme conditions, but also influence normal variation in the traits. For example, there are heritable influences in normal variation in mood and major depression. The magnitude of genetic influences on psychological traits has also shocked many researchers. Genetic factors sometimes account for as much as half of the variance in some traits, if not more. In sum, behavior genetic research has shown that genetic differences among people influence almost every area of psychology.

Are There Specific Genes Associated with Psychological Traits?

There have also been great advances in the design and analysis of molecular genetic studies (see section titled Behavior genetic methods). Therefore, studies reporting associations between specific genes and measures of behavior are frequently being reported. A proper understanding of the issues related to finding genes associated with psychosocial traits is important when considering the nature vs. nurture debate. First, many of the initial research articles that claimed to find a particular gene associated with psychosocial traits, such as intellectual abilities or homosexuality, were subsequently not replicated. Researchers and the public should, consequently, not draw conclusions about the importance of a specific genetic finding based on the results from only one study. Second, studies reporting associations between specific genes and some psychological traits have been replicated. For instance, findings for specific susceptibility genes have been replicated in studies of schizophrenia, alcohol dependence, and measures of attention/impulsivity problems. So, yes, there are specific genes associated with some psychological traits. Third, the magnitude or relative importance of the genes identified so far are not large (the genes do not account for a lot of the variation in the trait). Fourth, it is important to remember that identifying a gene is not informative about the underlying causes of a trait. Researchers can only gain a better understanding of the underlying causes by exploring the processes through which the gene influences protein-formation and biological functioning.

Finally, it has been difficult to identify susceptibility genes or QTLs for psychological traits. One possible reason may be that the magnitudes of the effects of individual genes are smaller than were originally expected. This has required researchers to collect DNA from very large samples (rather than studying hundreds of people or thousands of people, new studies are including tens of thousands of individuals or more). Another complication stems from the fact that researchers frequently have difficulty assessing many psychological traits accurately. This is to say that if one wants to measure depression, is it best to have subjects in a study complete a questionnaire, be assessed by a psychologist, or complete one of the many other measures of depression? Another strategy researchers are using is to include measures of endophenotypes, which are phenotypes related to the complex behaviors (such as depression) but are measured at more biological levels. For example, researchers interested in studying psychological traits hope that measuring brain functioning may provide an outcome measure that is more directly affected by specific genes. In sum, genetic research is just beginning to identify specific genes that are associated with psychological traits but the search for specific genes represents the start of a research endeavor, not the final step.

Are Environmental Factors Important?

Although the breadth and magnitude of genetic influences on psychological traits may be somewhat surprising, behavior genetic research has also highlighted the importance of environmental influences. Estimates of heritability for many traits, including severe psychological disorders such as schizophrenia, are below 100%, meaning that environmental influences do play an important role. In fact, most estimates of heritability are around 50% or lower. Thus, behavior genetic studies have clearly demonstrated that environmental factors are crucial for understanding individual differences in psychological traits. The type of environmental influences that are important, however, was largely unexpected. Environmental factors that make siblings different appear to be the most influential. Most psychological traits (with some notable exceptions, such as religiosity) are not influenced greatly by shared environmental influences. There has been great confusion concerning the meaning of the environmental estimates (shared and nonshared) that are found in behavior genetic studies. Because estimates of shared environmental influences are frequently small or nonexistent, some researchers have suggest that environmental factors that siblings share, such as parental divorce, family socioeconomic status, and neighborhood characteristics, are not important. But this is an incorrect interpretation of the results. Behavior genetic studies that show large nonshared environmental influences (and no shared influences) illustrate that environmental factors make siblings in the same family different, not more similar. To put it a different way, it appears as if environmental factors, such as parenting practices and family socioeconomic status, influence children in the same family differently.

The fact that most environmental influences are nonshared also has profound implications for our understanding of why siblings in the same family are similar. Because shared environmental factors influence few psychological traits, the reason why individuals in a family are similar is mostly due to the fact that they share similar genotypes. The results of behavior genetic studies (and other research approaches) have, therefore, caused psychologists to change their theories regarding familial influences. It is, therefore, important for psychologists to study how multiple children in a family react to environmental factors. Research is also starting to focus on the importance of sibling interactions and the role of peers, which are factors that may be unique to each sibling. With respect to the nature vs. nurture debate, behavior genetic studies have highlighted the importance of the environment, but the way in which environmental factors operate appears to make children within a family different rather than similar.

Are There Specific Environments Associated with Psychological Traits?

Researchers have repeatedly claimed that behavior genetics would highlight the importance of specific environmental factors. But has behavior genetic research identified specific environments that are associated with complex behaviors? Again, the answer is yes. For example, studies that compared lung cancer rates in twins who were dissimilar in the habit of smoking cigarettes (one twin smoked and one did not) provided some of the most compelling early research that tobacco smoking causes lung cancer. The comparison of identical twins (who share 100% of their genetic make-up) can provide a powerful study of environmental risks because the design controls for genetic risk and other risky environmental factors. Behavior genetic studies have recently highlighted the importance of divorce, prenatal alcohol exposure, and numerous other measures of the environment. In fact, more behavior genetic research that is focused on studying specific environmental risk factors is currently being conducted.

What Happens When Studying Multiple Behaviors at One Time?

By exploring the genetic and environmental influences on multiple traits at the same time, behavior genetic research can also study why different traits are correlated or frequently occur together. These models are referred to as multivariate models, in contrast to univariate models that only explore one variable at a time. The analyses can study the extent to which the same genetic and environmental factors influence different traits. Again, the situation in which the same genetic factors influence more than one behavior is referred to as pleiotropy. For instance, individuals with mood disorders, such as major depressive disorder, are also frequently diagnosed with an anxiety disorder. What explains why these two disorders commonly co-occur? A number of behavior genetic studies have illustrated that the same underlying genetic factors related to the personality trait of neuroticism (negative emotionality) largely explain why these disorders frequently co-occur in the same individual. Multivariate behavior genetic research can therefore help guide the psychological/psychiatric classification of diseases and our understanding of complex psychological traits.

What Happens to Genetic and Environmental Influences over Time?

Instead of merely documenting genetic and environment influences on psychological traits at one time point, behavior genetic studies also seek to ask questions about possible changes during development. Genes can be turned on and off (see section titled 'Epigenetic influences') or the same genetic factors could have different effects across the lifespan. If changes occur, maybe heritable traits are more influential during infancy than during adulthood because children have not experienced as many environmental experiences? The findings for cognitive abilities actually follow the reverse pattern. McGue and colleagues found that the importance of genetic influences increase from childhood through adolescence and into adulthood. What could account for these findings? One possibility is that genetic propensities for intellectual abilities are actually correlated with environmental experiences. Individuals

with greater intellectual abilities may also experience more environments that foster their intellectual abilities (see the explanation in the section titled Gene–environment correlation). Behavior genetic analyses can therefore explore developmental changes in the importance of genetic and environmental influences rather than only providing one snapshot at a time.

Are There Genetic Influences on the Environment?

Individuals greatly differ in their exposure to negative life events and harmful environments (and positive/nurturing environments). Could genetic factors influence the underlying risk for experiencing negative environments? Behavior genetic studies can analyze environments as extended phenotypes. In one of the most surprising findings of behavior genetics, numerous studies have found a heritable component for exposure to environmental risk and protective factors, such as parenting practices, divorce, stress, and social support. Genetic influences on environments are referred to as the nature of nurture. Again, the question arises – how could genetic factors influence a behavior as complex as exposure to risky environments? Simply put, there are no genes that code for the selection of dangerous environments. There are, however, psychological traits and personal characteristics that are related to risky environments. For example, individuals who exhibit high levels of the personality trait sensation-seeking are more likely to expose themselves to dangerous environments, and behavior genetic research has consistently shown that personality traits are influenced by genetic factors. Consequently, one's exposure to many environments does not occur at random. Rather, genetically influenced individual differences (in addition to environmental factors) affect how individuals select and construct their environments. The findings of genetic influences on a range of environmental measures also highlight the important point that genetic and environmental factors may not operate independently. In fact, the field of behavior genetics is increasingly studying the interplay of genetic and environmental factors.

Gene–Environment Interplay

The nature vs. nurture debate has generally relied on a view that the two types of influence are largely independent of each other, which results in the question of whether genetic or environmental factors are more important. However, research has found that genetic and environmental effects are largely intertwined. The interplay of genetic and environmental influences can be broken down into three basic phenomena: gene–environment correlation, gene–environment interaction, and epigenetic influences.

Gene–Environment Correlation

Gene–environment correlations (rGE) occur when there are genetically influenced differences in exposure to environmental risk factors (described earlier). There are three main types of rGE: passive, active, and evocative. Passive gene–environment correlation occurs when genetically influenced traits in parents constitute the environment for their children. Because parents provide the environment and pass along their genes to their offspring, genetic influences in the offspring are correlated with exposure to measures of the family environment. Take the example of maternal depression, a well-known risk factor for offspring adjustment. Depression is partially heritable and leads to poorer parenting practices. Parents could pass down risk for depression genetically to their children. The genetic factors that influence depression in the children would correlate with the greater likelihood of receiving inconsistent parenting.

Active gene–environment correlation occurs when an individual selects environments based on genetically influenced traits. For example, students with greater intellectual abilities may select classes that are more challenging, which further increases their knowledge. Evocative gene–environment correlation comes about when genetically influenced traits elicit or evoke environmental responses from others. Recent research suggests that children's oppositional behavior toward their parents, which is influenced by genetic factors, elicits parents' use of spanking as a parenting technique. There are no genes for being spanked, but a child's behavior may create more opportunities when parents feel the need to use corporal punishment. In both active and evocative gene–environment correlation, genetically influenced traits differentially influence the exposure to experiences/environments.

The presence of gene–environment correlation creates major difficulties for research studying environmental risk and protective factors. Many studies in the social sciences have shown that various environments are correlated with psychological traits, meaning that exposure to the environment is associated with some behavior. Although measures of the environment may be correlated with psychological or behavioral outcomes, the association does not mean that experiencing the risk factor actually causes the traits. A fundamental lesson in every statistics class in the social sciences is that correlation does not mean causation. If an environment 'x' is correlated with outcome 'y' there could be a third factor that explains the correlation. The presence of gene–environment correlation suggests that genetic factors may be a third factor, or confound, that actually explains why an environmental risk factor is associated with negative outcomes. A common genetic liability between parents and offspring (reflected by passive gene–environment correlation) may account for the association between parenting practices and children's adjustment. Genetically

influenced behaviors may account for selection into risky environments (active or evocative gene–environment correlation). This is critical for the study of environmental influences for the reason that there could be a reciprocal effect ('y' could cause 'x'). Because genetic influences on environmental experiences are so pervasive, studies that do not consider the role of gene–environment correlation cannot adequately test the consequences of most environmental risk factors. For example, every family study of parenting practices using traditional samples is confounded by gene–environment correlation.

Two important cautions are in order. First, other environmental risk factors can also act as confounds. Genetic factors do not represent every third variable in the study of measured environmental risk factors. Second, just because there are genetic factors influencing exposure to an environmental risk factor does not necessitate a genetic explanation for all negative outcomes associated with the environment. For instance, risk-taking and impulsivity (personality traits that have been shown to be partially heritable) may lead an individual to drive recklessly. But, a car crash that resulted from the dangerous driving would specifically cause the bodily harm that occurred in the crash. The presence of genetic influences on exposure to environments, the 'nature of nurture', requires researchers to use genetically informed research designs and other approaches. The methods allow researchers to test alternative hypotheses that would explain why people who experience specific environmental risk factors have poorer functioning.

Gene–Environment Interaction

Gene–environment interactions occur when genetic factors affect sensitivity to environmental risk factors making some people more susceptible to environmental risks. They can also be considered environmental control of genetic expression. Gene–environment interactions occur when nature influences nurture and nurture influences nature. The same genotype may lead to different phenotypes depending on the environmental circumstances. Likewise, the importance of the same environment may also depend on one's genotype. The role of gene–environment interaction is crucial for understanding the nature vs. nurture debate. In the presence of gene–environment interaction the study of genetic and environmental influences separately would provide inaccurate results. Researchers interested in environmental risk factors would have to also know about genetic risk to properly understand how the environment actually influences individuals. The flip side is also true; researchers interested in understanding how genetic factors operate would have to have an understanding of an individual's environmental context.

Plant and animal studies have been very informative about the gene–environment interaction because researchers have the power to randomly assign plants and animals with different genotypes to different environmental conditions (see section titled Behavior genetic methods). Human behavior genetics studies will be highlighted here. Researchers generally use two primary methods to explore gene–environment interaction: (1) testing whether the heritability of a condition differs in various environments and (2) investigating whether the association between a specific measured gene and a phenotype varies in different settings.

Heritability by measured environment interactions

As described earlier, heritability indexes the importance of genetic factors, but estimates of heritability are not set; they can vary depending on environmental context. A study by Turkheimer and colleagues that explored the genetic and environmental influences on children's intellectual abilities recently highlighted differences in heritability among different environmental conditions. When the researchers explored whether the family's socioeconomic status influenced the estimates of heritability, the shared environment, and the nonshared environment, a dramatic pattern resulted. In children from poor families, genetic factors were very small or nonexistent; rather, shared environmental factors accounted for most of the variation in children's intellectual abilities. In contrast, genetic factors accounted for an overwhelming majority of the variance in children's intellectual abilities in richer families. The estimate of the shared environment was zero in the families who were better-off. Thus, the importance of genetic and environmental factors depended on the socioeconomic status of the children, an example of gene–environment interaction. Other studies have shown that the importance of genetic factors on alcohol problems depends on marital status and the heritability of smoking cigarettes in females has increased as smoking has become more common for women, to describe two more examples. The study of heritability by specific environment interactions supports the notion that genetic and environmental factors do not act in isolation.

Measured gene by measured environment interactions

Researchers are now studying the influence of specific genes and specific measured environments to gain a better understanding of the genetic processes (and environmental influences) that influence psychosocial outcomes. Do alleles in specific genes confer greater risk for a trait under certain environmental conditions? A number of recent studies have found that the answer appears to be yes.

Researchers across numerous disciplines have explored the underlying causes for behavior problems and aggression because of the societal implications of such behaviors. Child maltreatment is a known environmental risk factor for later aggressive behavior, although there is great variability in how children respond to abuse. Neuroscience studies have also documented that numerous neurotransmitters (chemicals in the brain that help brain cells communicate with each other) are also associated with conduct problems. Caspi and colleagues studied whether a gene that influenced neurotransmitter activity in the brain would make children more vulnerable to maltreatment. In fact, the study revealed that individuals who had alleles associated with low neurotransmitter activity and experienced maltreatment exhibited many more aggressive and criminal problems than individuals who only experienced maltreatment or only had the 'at-risk' allele. Multiple research teams, using samples from around the world and various measures of abuse and behavior problems, have replicated the finding. The research illustrates the interdependence of specific genetic and environmental influences by identifying how genetically influenced neurotransmitter-functioning made some children more vulnerable to the risks associated with abuse. The research illustrates how the influences of genetic and environmental processes depend on each other.

Epigenetic Influences

The interplay between environmental and genetic factors also occurs at a more basic level. The process through which DNA sequences code for proteins is often described as a straightforward process that only goes one way (from gene to protein). However, there are many factors that influence the activity of a gene, referred to as gene expression. Proteins, growth factors, hormones, and other molecules affect the action of genes without altering the sequence of the base pairs in DNA. These factors can influence which genes gets transcribed into RNA, which RNA gets translated into amino acids, and how the amino acids combine to form proteins, to name a few possibilities. The term epigenetics refers to a myriad of factors, including environmental stimuli, that influence gene expression. What is crucial for the nature vs. nurture debate is the fact that environmental factors can influence the expression of genes. The exact mechanisms through which environmental factors influence gene expression represent an exciting new area of research that are not well understood at this time.

Overall, the interplay between environmental and genetic factors is now a central focus of behavior genetics. It is not enough to claim that both genetic and environmental factors are important. Thus, current research is actively pursuing how specific environmental factors act and interact with genetic predispositions to influence behavior. What is becoming more apparent is the interrelationship among factors that were once considered to be separate. Because of the interplay between environmental and genetic factors, research needs to use designs and analytical techniques that can specify the influence and interactions of multiple factors from various levels of analysis (e.g., biological and societal). It is therefore important to understand the different approaches that behavior geneticists use to study nature and nurture.

Behavior Genetic Methods

Unfortunately, the nature vs. nurture debate has been fueled, in part, by the fact that researchers on both sides do not understand the methods or substantive findings of research on the other side. The following review includes the primary behavior genetic methods that address the nature vs. nurture debate.

Plant and Animal Studies

The ability to experimentally control both genetic and environmental factors represents the greatest strength of plant and animal research. Through selected breeding, the crossing of animals or plants based on particular phenotypes over many generations, researchers can determine whether a trait is heritable. For example, cows with high milk output have been bred to produce more milk, which suggests that milk production is influenced by genetic factors. Selected breeding over many generations can also create inbred strains, populations of animals that share near-identical genotypes. Any variation in the behavior or traits within a population of inbred animals, therefore, reflects environmental influences. Animals from inbred populations can also be randomly assigned to different environmental conditions. The studies can explore the importance of environmental effects and the role of gene–environment interactions. Animal studies have also become increasingly important because researchers can study gene expression in specific areas of an animal's brain. The procedures frequently require the postmortem evaluation of the animal's brain.

Knockout studies represent another key area of animal research. In knockout studies, researchers use newly developed laboratory techniques to deactivate a specific gene in the embryos of mice. The procedure produces a line of mice that are missing the target gene. Mice with and without the gene are then compared to study the role of the targeted gene. New techniques also provide the opportunity for researchers to 'knock in' particular genes. The ability to experimentally control genetic and environmental conditions in plant and animal studies has shed great light on the nature vs. nurture debate. The greatest limitation of animal and plants study, however, is the ability of researchers to generalize the findings to human populations.

Family Studies

Family studies explore whether specific behaviors or traits run in the family, for instance, alcohol problems. Family studies begin by identifying a proband, an individual who has the identifiable trait (in this case alcohol dependence). Researchers then assess the proband's first-degree relatives (the parents, siblings, and children) and second-degree relatives (grandparents, aunts, uncles, grandchildren, etc.). Even more distant family members can be included. If alcohol problems are more prevalent in the family members of probands than in the family members of individuals without alcohol problems, researchers can conclude that alcohol problems run in families. Family studies cannot, however, effectively determine whether genetic or environmental factors are responsible because family members share similar genotypes and environmental circumstances.

Adoption Studies

Adoption studies are based on families in which genetic or environmental similarity among relatives has been separated. That is, the genetic and environmental factors that co-occur in traditional families are split by the adoption process. Researchers analyze adoption studies from a number of perspectives. Three will be highlighted here. First, adopted children can be compared to their biological and/or adoptive parents. The influence of genetic factors on a phenotype would be supported if the adopted child was similar to their biological parents. The importance of environmental influences would be supported if adoptive children are similar to their adoptive parents. Second, adoptive children can be compared to the biological children of the adoptive parents. Adoptive and biological children are not genetically related, so any similarity between the siblings would be due to environmental factors. Third, adoption studies can analyze gene–environment interactions. Measures of traits in the biological parents can be used as a proxy for genetic risk in adoption studies. If children with greater genetic risk are more susceptible to the influence of environmental risk factors, the findings support the presence of gene–environment interaction.

Adoption studies are difficult to conduct because of confidentiality requirements of adoption records, the difficulty obtaining information about the biological parents, and the drop in adoptions, especially within-country adoptions. Adoption studies are also based on a number of assumptions, which may partially limit the conclusions that researchers can draw. These include the limited range of environmental risk factors in adoptive homes (adoptive parents are screened for major risk factors) and the assumption that the adoptive parents are not similar to the biological parents. The latter is violated when children are adopted by family members, although these families are typically removed from adoption studies.

Twin Studies

Twin studies are based on the fact that identical or monozygotic (MZ) twins share all of their genes, while fraternal or dizygotic (DZ) twins share, on average, half of their genes. Twin studies assess the resemblance of MZ and DZ twins, measured by concordance rates (the degree to which twins share the same discrete trait) or correlation coefficients (the degree to which twins resemble each other for continuously measured phenotypes). If MZ twins are more similar than DZ twins, genetic factors are implicated because the only difference between the two types of twins (given some assumptions) is in their degree of genetic relatedness. If MZ twins are not perfectly similar or correlated, then nonshared environmental factors are important. Finally, if both MZ and DZ twins are similar and there is not much difference between the resemblance of MZ and DZ twins, shared environmental factors influence the phenotype. As described earlier, twin studies can explore whether heritability estimates differ across environments, a finding that supports gene–environment interactions. It is important to note that twin studies are based on a number of assumptions. The 'equal environments' assumption assumes that there are no unique environmental experiences that make MZ twins more similar than DZ twins. The design also assumes limited risks due to the process of twinning compared to being a singleton (i.e., there are no lasting problems associated with prenatal crowding in the uterus).

As discussed briefly earlier in the article, the twin design can also be used to study the importance of specific environmental risk factors. The twin design is an especially useful approach for studying experiences that are unique to individuals in a family. In the co-twin control design, twins who differ in their exposure to environmental risk factors are compared (one twin smoked and the other did not, one got divorced and the other did not, etc.). The design controls for genetic factors that could confound the association between the environment and the outcome (gene–environment correlations) and environmental factors that influence both twins.

Extended Family and Combined Designs

Family, adoption, and twin studies can also be combined to provide more accurate estimates of genetic and environmental influences. For example, identical twins adopted into separate homes have been compared. Similarity between the separated twins provides strong evidence for the importance of genetic factors. The parents of twins, their spouses, and the children of twins can also be included in studies. Statistical model fitting with the extended designs can provide informative tests of the genetic and environmental processes that account for similarity between parents and children. The designs can also test the importance of environmental risk factors that all siblings in a family share.

Linkage Studies and Association Studies

Great advances in computational ability, the processing of DNA, and the completion of the human genome project have made it possible to begin looking for specific genes associated with psychological traits. Linkage studies explore whether an area of a chromosome contains a gene for a trait. The studies explore how often a measured trait is 'linked' with a genetic marker, a gene whose precise loci is already known. Linkage studies provide a statistical measure, referred to as a lod score (logarithmic odds), that measures the probability that the genetic marker is closely associated with the measured trait. A high lod score suggests that the genetic marker and a gene for the trait are located close to each other on a chromosome. Linkage studies have helped identify genes associated with single-gene disorders, but, in general, the approach cannot identify the precise location of genes and are better suited to finding genes with large effects on traits. Using more genetic markers, especially in a small section of a chromosome, can help researchers better identify the location of a gene that is associated with a trait. Because of recent advancements, researchers can now complete whole genome scans with many, precise genetic markers.

Association studies are another approach to finding specific genes that influence traits. In contrast to linkage studies, association studies start with one gene, which is referred to as a candidate gene. Researchers explore whether there is a statistical association between alleles at the candidate gene and the trait of interest. Candidate genes can be identified through linkage studies, the known function of the gene through biological studies, animal studies, findings from the human genome project, and other sources. Association studies have helped identify specific genes related to Parkinson's disease and smoking behavior, to name just two of the many examples.

Microarray Studies

Microarray studies provide the opportunity for researchers to study the expression of thousands of genes at once. The procedure involves placing an organism's genome on a specialized chip. The chip is then placed in a solution that has RNA extracted from one of the organism's cells. The RNA contains a dye that becomes highlighted if the RNA binds to a gene. The stronger the dye appears on the chip for each gene, the more the particular gene is expressed. As a result, researchers can explore the expression of thousands of genes in a cell or multiple cells. Microarray studies provide a great deal of information that will hopefully shed light on the genetic influences related to various phenotypes, including psychological traits.

Experimental and Natural–Experimental Studies

Although experimental studies and research based on natural experiments are not frequently considered to be behavior genetic studies, the designs can shed light on the nature vs. nurture debate. Because experiments are based on random assignment to different environmental conditions, differences among the intervention groups at the end of the study are due to the environmental conditions. In natural experiments, researchers do not randomly assign people to different conditions. Rather, researchers compare individuals who randomly experienced a naturally occurring event. Again, the approach can highlight the importance of environmental factors.

As the list of behavior genetic methods demonstrates, researchers can explore the etiology or causes of psychological traits from various perspectives. No one method can provide the answer; but combining the results from different research approaches gives researchers great insight into the nature vs. nurture debate.

Social and Ethical Concerns Related to Behavior Genetic Research

Behavior genetic research raises a number of concerns. One concern is related to the dangers of reductionism, the belief that everything at one level can be explained by some lower level. Some researchers are concerned by an overemphasis on biological and genetic findings (biological reductionism) that ignores other levels of analysis, such as familial and societal factors. However, behavior genetic research considers the interplay of multiple factors at various levels (see the section titled Gene–environment interplay). The search for genetic influences can provide greater insights for psychology, but the research should not preclude the study of important variables at all levels of analysis and the interactions among them. Second, behavior genetics is frequently associated with eugenic practices, particularly the sterilization of Americans against their will in the 1930s and the abhorrent practices of the Nazis before and during World War II. The leaders of eugenic movements used genetic research to support their actions, and some geneticists supported the activities. However, the practices were based on a great misrepresentation of genetic findings. Discriminatory eugenic practices are not supported by behavior genetic researchers and they do not 'naturally' flow from research into genetic influences on behavior. There are concerns, nevertheless, associated with research looking for genes that are related to complex behaviors. What does society do with the information? Can parents screen embryos to select children with or without particular traits? Can insurance companies use the information? These are serious issues that are being addressed by a number of institutions and agencies throughout the world.

Summary

The very title of this article (Nature vs. Nurture) is a dichotomy, which implies that one influence wins and one loses. Initial behavior genetic studies tested which side was more important, with proponents on both sides of the nature vs. nurture debate making heated (and sometimes extravagant) claims. The field of behavior genetics has moved away from trying to declare a winner or a loser. Rather, researchers are trying to study how genetic and environmental processes act and interact to better understand the underlying causal processes related to individual differences in behavior. Studies are also considering the developmental context of genetic and environmental processes to examine how the mechanisms transpire over time. Most researchers, if not all, now conclude that both genetic and environmental factors are important. However, a lot more research needs to be done to highlight the specific mechanisms. The findings will have significant implications, and society will have to grapple with important ethical decisions that result from the research. But, the debate over nature vs. nurture is not 'either/or'. The debate is now 'both/and/with/depending' plus a lot more.

See also: Behavior Genetics; Genetic Disorders: Sex Linked; Genetic Disorders: Single Gene; Genetics and Inheritance; Perceptual Development; Television: Uses and Effects; Twins.

Suggested Readings

Baker C (2004) *Behavior Genetics: An Introduction to How Genes and Environments Interact through Development to Shape Differences in Mood, Personality, and Intelligence.* Washington, DC: American Association for the Advancement of Science.

Carey G (2003) *Human Genetics for the Social Sciences.* Thousand Oaks, CA: Sage Publications.

Nuffield Council on Bioethics (2002) *Genetics and Human Behavior: The Ethical Context.* London: Nuffield Council on Bioethics.

Plomin R, DeFries JC, McClearn GE, and McGuffin P (2001) *Behavior genetics,* 4th edn. New York: Worth Publishers.

Rutter M (2006) *Genes and Behavior: Nature–Nurture Interplay Explained.* Oxford: Blackwell Publishing.

Relevant Websites

http://www.apa.org – American Psychological Association, Genetics in Psychology.

http://www.bga.org – Behavior Genetics Association.

http://www.genome.gov – National Human Genome Research Institute, National Institutes of Health.

Neonativism

A Needham and K Libertus, Duke University, Durham, NC, USA

Glossary

Canalization – Extent to which the development of a process is constrained by environmental factors. Highly canalized processes do not have a wide range of phenotypes available to them, whereas less highly canalized processes do.

Contrastive evidence – A type of evidence that comes from observing the outcomes of events in which a physical principle is in operation and when it is not (e.g., when an object receives adequate support it remains stable in space and when it receives inadequate support it falls down). Comparison of these two events within a physical principle may be essential for coming to understand the physical principle.

Core knowledge – Knowledge that is fundamental to reasoning about objects, events, and people. Many theorists consider this knowledge to be innate.

Experience-dependent – Term to describe a process that may or may not develop (or may develop in very different ways), depending upon the environmental input.

Experience-expectant – Term to describe a process that depends upon a certain kind of environmental input at a certain time in development in order for it to develop appropriately.

Interactionism – A range of approaches to explaining origins that all involve some amount of influence of factors intrinsic to a process and those extrinsic to it.

Introduction

Adult humans have remarkably complex cognitive skills. We can write novels in which we create whole worlds quite different from our own; we do the science to build rockets that take people into space, and have made discoveries that help us cure diseases that used to kill people. In recent years, we have also started to understand the basis of our cognitive skills, our brain, in more detail. For example, we have discovered areas in the brain that are specialized for particular functions. We believe there is a language area (or areas – one for production and another for comprehension); we believe there is a face area; we believe there is an area that processes biological motion.

Furthermore, we can also predict about where each of these areas is likely to be in any individual. Our brain may be one of the most complex structures on our planet and we are just beginning to understand how it is organized and how it functions. Indeed, it is still far from clear whether the organization of our brain that research has uncovered was destined to be this way because of factors that were established millions of years ago or whether it reflects the product of an active process that is shaped by the consistency in the environment in which it develops.

These and related questions are discussed within the context of the nature/nurture 'debate', which has probably garnered more attention and anger than any other question in developmental and cognitive science. Because of the unique opportunity to produce evidence that directly addresses the importance of nature and nurture, research on infants has provided a high-profile battleground for addressing these influences on knowledge. However, this opportunity comes with some challenges. Research with infants is notoriously difficult, as there are relatively few responses they can give. Typically, indirect measures are taken and interpretation is required to make conclusions of theoretical interest. Further, negative findings could always be interpreted in light of competence/performance differences – perhaps a suitably sensitive measure has not yet been found to tap into this underlying competence.

Some investigators remain enmeshed in the nature–nurture arguments while others have rejected these traditional views and have put forth the strong claim that this dichotomy is false because there is no way to separate these factors, even conceptually, and therefore no way to somehow estimate the effects of one in the absence of the other. An illustration of this view comes from Susan Oyama, who argues, "Since the genome represents only a part of the entire developmental ensemble, it cannot by itself contain or cause the form that results. But then, neither can its surroundings.". It is striking that, after so many years of study there remains such a multiplicity of views on this topic. It is a testament to the strength of the metaphors contained in the nature–nurture tug-of-war that so little agreement has been achieved and it shows the continued need for precise and clear definitions of what is meant by terms like innateness, nativism, and environment. As Oyama's quote demonstrates, many philosophers and researchers find that any conceptualization that partitions the developing system along the lines of internal/external, biological/environmental is inherently flawed, because the components of the developing organism have a recursive quality in which characteristics of the organism (typically thought of as nature) serve as environmental influences for subsequent developmental change. At different scales or levels of analysis, environment can be conceptualized very differently, and it is always possible to continue asking how earlier and earlier forms of the ability or organism came into being and whether that process could have been influenced by factors extrinsic to that particular developmental change. In sum, it is impossible to overestimate the complexity of development.

Explaining the Origins of Behavior and Knowledge

How can we think of these different influences on the body, on behavior, and on cognition? Specifically, when we think of the origins of our many skills, what kinds of explanations do we give and what kind of explanations are we willing to accept? In this essay, we first consider the historical foundations of nativism and then move on to the current issues influencing researchers' thinking about these basic notions.

A History of the Notion of Nativism

Where does our knowledge come from and how are we able to learn so many complex skills throughout our lifetime? The questions about the origins of knowledge and human behavior are maybe as old as the human species itself and whole branches of science and philosophy are still investigating this issue. Especially in philosophy, the epistemological question about where knowledge comes from and how it is acquired has a long-standing tradition. Two basic forms of knowledge can be distinguished: *a priori*, knowledge that is independent of experience, and *a posteriori*, knowledge that is derived from experience (empirical knowledge). Early philosophers used these terms to distinguish between knowledge that is acquired through experience and knowledge that is derived from basic principles that were assumed to be predefined (axioms).

Ancient times
The notion of *a priori* knowledge can be traced back to Socrates in Plato's dialog Meno (380 BC). In the course of this dialog Socrates proposes that it is not necessary for us to acquire new knowledge, instead we already have all knowledge and just need a reminder. To support this claim, Socrates demonstrates how a boy can produce a geometrical theorem even though this boy has never been taught geometry before. According to this line of reasoning, all knowledge is *a priori*. Along the same lines, the philosophical notion of rationalism argues that all

knowledge can be, in principle, derived from some basic principles and deduction alone. Assuming that these basic principles are in place (are axioms in the system) then no experience is required to obtain new conclusions. Similarly, the question about the origins of human behavior can be seen from this perspective. Are our behaviors and traits predetermined *a priori* or are they acquired *a posteriori*? Or in more modern terms: is our behavior defined by aspects of our biology (nature) or does our environment (nurture) define how we will behave?

An early account of the influence of nature on human behavior can be found from Hippocrates and thinkers of his time (around 400 BC). They suggested that four fluids (humors) can be found within the body and that the mixture of these fluids determines the personality of a person – essentially arguing that behavior is driven by intrinsic factors or nature. The two classic notions about knowledge (Socrates) and behavior (Hippocrates) described above can be subsumed under the heading of nativism. Both accounts share one important aspect: something is considered to be given, something in our body – nowadays preferably in the brain – is innately predisposed for a certain task.

Influences of early modern philosophers
These ancient versions of the nativist idea often referred to a divine source of the innate knowledge or behavior. This notion remained popular in the seventeenth century. The famous philosopher Rene Descartes (1596–1650) assumed the existence of a benevolent god that has created our bodies in a way that allows us to extract truthful information from our surroundings. Moreover, Descartes made a strong distinction between our mind and our body (Cartesian Dualism) that holds that our mind is different from our physical body. For Descartes our mind was nonphysical substance and its main function is thought (res cognitans). With respect to the mind, Descartes also expressed a strong nativist argument in that he claimed that some of the most basic truths (truths of reason) are innate, that there is a basis of innate knowledge in the human mind upon which all further knowledge can build. This idea stands in strong opposition to notions from empiricists.

Most famously, the British empiricist John Locke (1632–1704) described the human mind as a 'tabula rasa', a blank slate, at the onset and all knowledge is build onto this void. One of the ancient forefathers of this position is Aristotle who first introduced the empiricist principle that all knowledge about the real world is based on experience through the senses. Following Aristotle, the Stoics (around 300 BC) were the first to formulate the idea of the human mind as a clean slate but at the same time also maintained the notion that some universals are innately present in the mind of all humans. Later, Jean-Jacues Rousseau (1712–78) formulated a similar notion when he proposed that humans have an innate tendency to be good but that external experiences influenced this innate tendency and could eventually override it. These early accounts of a combination of empiricist and nativist ideas expressa general dissatisfaction with the idea of an *a priori* foundation of the human mind that derives from an unknown (probably divine) source but at the same time acknowledges the need to assume a foundation for our mind to grow on (even if our mind is a blank slate, there is still the slate that is innate).

Innate modules

In the early nineteenth century Franz Josef Gall (1758–1828) presented a new idea concerning the organization of the mind. His theory became known as 'phrenology' and is concerned with the localization of mental functions in the brain. Gall believed that the shape of the skull, the bumps on our head, reflects how pronounced certain character traits of cognitive abilities are in an individual. The theory of phrenology stated that the brain is the seat of our mind and that its size and shape directly reflects individuals' traits and personalities. More important, different cognitive functions or traits were believed to be localized in particular areas of the brain. Thus, the mind was seen as a modular system with specialized areas that subserve a specific trait. This idea provides arguments for a nativist position in that it suggests that the global organization of the mind into functional compartments is predefined by nature.

The idea of modules continues into the twenty-first century, as researchers have identified, in a surprisingly close parallel to Gall's general idea, specific areas of the brain (of course not apparent on the skull!) that are responsible for conducting different cognitive functions. For example, Jerry Fodor, in his well-known nativist treatise *Modularity of Mind*, proposes that functions like language and perception are accomplished via specialized processes or modules in the brain. These modules have specific characteristics, including that they conduct their computations very quickly and their processes are informationally encapsulated – in other words, we are not aware of the processes by which we perceive various components of the visual world, and these processes are typically not influenced by other knowledge we may have about the stimuli. Although it is of course possible that these areas of the brain are trained up through development to provide this automatic and quick processing, Fodor and others who share his perspective believe that these modules do not need training of any sort. Rather, these functional modules are in place prior to any relevant experience.

Advances in science eventually lead to the discovery of the genome and its role in heritability. Gregor Mendel (1822–84) first proposed the existence of genes and studied their role in inheriting traits from parents to offspring. The existence and idea of genes provided a new basis for nativist arguments by filling in the place that had been occupied by divine intervention before. Basic innate notions and predispositions of the mind could now be explained in terms of the 'blueprint' found in the genome. One of the first scientists to explore the role of genes with respect to human behavior was Sir Francis Galton (1822–1911). One of the goals of Galton's research was to identify the influences of environmental factors and hereditary factors on human development and to what extent one could act on the other. Galton was also the first to use the terms nature and nurture to distinguish between the genetic endowment and our experiences. However, Galton did not provide an answer to the question of whether nature or nurture defines human behavior. However, his research and his techniques foreshadowed future research that has been essential in the nature–nurture debate. In particular, Galton was one of the first scientists to methodically study twins in order to estimate the different contributions of shared genes or a shared environment. In his view, the evidence favored the influence of nature, the hereditary factors.

Behaviorism and nativism

Following the dawn of the twentieth century the psychologist John B. Watson (1878–1958) started the psychological movement of behaviorism. This train of thought would become most dominant in American psychology for the first half of the twentieth century. Most behaviorists favored the nurture side in the debate about nature and nurture. For example, Watson himself made a strong claim about the influence the environment can have on an organism:

> Give me a dozen healthy infants, well-formed, and my own specified world to bring them up in and I'll guarantee to take any one at random and train him to become any type of specialist I might select – doctor, lawyer, artist, merchant-chief and, yes, even beggar-man and thief, regardless of his talents, penchants, tendencies, abilities, vocations, and race of his ancestors. I am going beyond my facts and I admit it, but so have the advocates of the contrary and they have been doing it for many thousands of years. John B. Watson (1924, p. 82)

The learning mechanisms uncovered by behaviorism like classical or operant conditioning seemed to provide enough basis for nurture to fundamentally influence the behavior of an animal. However, another psychological movement around the same time, psychodynamics, provided a more balanced view where nature and nurture influenced each other. Carl Jung (1875–1961), for example, introduced the notion of innate archetypes that influence the personality of a person. In contrast, to uncover the reasons for a certain behavior, behaviorists claimed that an analysis of the current environment and the history of the environment and the animals' behavior are sufficient. According this view there was no or only little need for innate capabilities. However, exactly this point led to a now famous discussion about the mechanisms of language acquisition in Noam Chomsky's response to the book *Verbal Behavior* by Burrhus F. Skinner (1904–90). Chomsky challenged the behaviorist view and instead, with respect to language acquisition in particular, proposed the existence of linguistic universals that all languages have in common and therefore seem to be part of a universal grammar. Chomsky argued that a small set of rules is built into the human brain and that these rules help us to acquire a language – even in the presence of impoverished or incorrect models from which we learn. This form of nativism, for the first time, is highly specific about what is innate and why this innate knowledge is crucial for normal development and stands in contrast to classical nativism. This view suggests that children are biologically prepared for a certain task – like language acquisition – by their genes or the structure of their mind.

Constructivism

A different approach that provided the theoretical grounding for the systematic study of cognitive development was put forward by Jean Piaget (1896–1980). According to his theory, children construct their own cognitive structures over protracted periods of time interacting with objects (his theory is referred to as a constructivist theory). Piaget believed that a steady state or equilibrium of cognitive activity was present early in life and maintained throughout development via the processes of assimilation and accommodation. What the child experiences is compared with the existing knowledge structures, and is either consistent or inconsistent with these structures. If too much inconsistent evidence is collected, a disequilibrium results and the cognitive structures are reorganized through a process of accommodation. These processes of assimilation and accommodation lead to a progression to each successive developmental stage.

One critical component of Piaget's theory is that representational abilities were relatively late to develop. Indeed, he believed that infants must first construct the world of real, three-dimensional objects (through their actions upon these objects) and only then could begin the process of re-creating these objects in representational form in the mind. From this perspective, it was not until approximately 2 years of age that children could form 'true' representations of objects. Thus, infants lived in a very different world from adults – a world in which objects (and presumably people) were totally unpredictable. These strong claims, apparently supported by his observations, at first did not encourage researchers to study the abilities of infants. However, over the years researchers have developed new and more sensitive

methods to study infants and made some critical discoveries that provided new arguments for a new nativist position.

A new form of nativism

Gaining arguments from novel and carefully designed studies, a new form of nativism emerged. For this new form of nativism, the study of child development is of critical importance. Piaget was the first to create a comprehensive theory of cognitive development on the basis of his rich and detailed set of observations about children's abilities and behaviors at several ages. His theory included several different stages of development that were defined by the abilities of the child. In addition to being valuable for these reasons, Piaget's theory served as a framework against which new ideas were proposed. One way to test Piaget's theory is by asking if it is possible to see evidence for the presence of an ability earlier then predicted by Piaget. For example, a theoretical perspective called the competent infant or rational infant approach grew up in strong opposition to Piaget's theory. According to this approach, infants were substantially more sophisticated than Piaget gave them credit for. Presumably, if sensitive enough tests were devised, one could discover newborn competences abounding in every cognitive domain, making development a bit of a pointless process to study. However, the data that are now available from studies of early infant abilities are not consistent with this perspective. There are many changes that happen with development, and one might argue that it is these changes that are important to characterize and understand. The competent infant movement did have a lasting impact on the field, though, in the form of questioning some of the basic tenets of Piaget's theory that applied to infants' cognitive development.

Arguing with more subtlety and precision, researchers such as Renée Baillargeon and Elizabeth Spelke argued that success in Piaget's tasks required more than just conceptual competence – motoric competence and planning were also required. To be judged as having a representation of the existence of a hidden object, infants had to reach for and uncover a hidden object. This requires considerable skill in planning, problem solving, and motor control. Even though infants' goal is likely to play with the toy, they cannot fulfill that goal directly, they must first grasp the toy's cover and remove it. So, clearly infants could have the competence – a representation of that hidden toy – without being able to reveal this in their performance.

Piaget's high threshold for granting children cognitive skills coupled with a new interest in the subcomponents of the skills required to succeed in his tasks led researchers to investigate these subcomponents. Visual measures were used that did not require infants to plan an overt 'this is my answer' solution to the tasks. These visual tasks were hypothesized to be less demanding of infants' cognitive resources than Piaget's manual tasks were. These new tasks were built upon basic patterns of infant looking behavior, such as that they tend to look longer at novel or unexpected events than at familiar or expected ones. Thus, two events could be created that were superficially very similar but that differed in a component critical for the principle being tested.

For instance, two events could proceed in a nearly identical fashion, but one would contain a violation of object permanence and the other one would not. This procedure was used in one study where infants were shown a car that rolled down a ramp, traveled behind a screen and across the apparatus floor. Prior to seeing this event, infants had been shown what was behind the screen. All infants saw a toy behind the screen but for half of the infants the toy was positioned on top of the ramp, while for the other half it was placed behind or in front of the ramp. The rationale of the researchers was that if infants represented the existence of the toy on the track, they should look reliably longer when the toy was blocking the tracks and the car seems to pass through the space occupied by the toy, emerging unscathed from the far end of the screen. The results supported this conclusion with infants as young as 4.5-month-old of age.

These results and many others like them called into question Piaget's explanation of cognitive development in at least two ways. First, the timetable Piaget sketched out for the ages at which different cognitive structures develop was inconsistent with these new findings. Infants showed more and earlier understanding about the physical world than Piaget's theory predicted. Perhaps more importantly, the mechanism by which Piaget thought infants acquired these knowledge structures – self-produced actions on objects – was not fully functional at the point in development that these competences were discovered. Both of these factors, especially the second one, were problems for Piaget's theory and called for new theories and explanations.

These new approaches that attempted to more accurately understand infant behavior and development, often in contrast to Piaget's perspective, are referred to as neonativism. However, instead of postulating completely preformed innate abilities, here the focus is often on constraints on learning. These constraints are not learned themselves. Thus, there is a nativist component to these approaches, but in most cases, the emphasis is on how learning takes place and how abilities change over development. This could be at least in part because we do not yet have a good way to characterize or talk about unlearned components of behavior or skill.

The early abilities revealed by these measures that do not require overt behavior on the part of infants are sometimes referred to as core knowledge and are thought to provide the basis for future learning.

According to many core knowledge theorists, these core knowledge systems are thought to have developed through the evolution of our species and to be independent of input from the environment. Research with young infants has shown that infants have a concept of object permanence and a rudimentary understanding of number and numerical transformations. These findings and the interpretations offered for them have stirred a heated debate about infants' early cognitive abilities and the origins of these abilities. Specifically, there are some researchers who consider it likely that learning mechanisms that support rapid learning on the basis of relatively few observations are not learned but that content about objects, people, or language is learned. However, more extreme nativist perspectives hold that actual cognitive content is part of the innate endowment, built into the organism through evolution. This debate on the origins of cognitive skills continues to be one of the most discussed topics in developmental psychology.

What is Nativism?

Nativism assumes that some abilities or skills are 'innate'. Therefore, the first and most important point we need to consider when discussing nativism is the precise definition of 'innateness'. What do we mean when we use the word 'innate'? Researchers typically mean that a given structure, behavior, or ability cannot be learned or does not need to be learned and is not dependent upon exposure to environmental stimuli. On the one hand, that a behavior or ability is innate can be seen as a specific expectation already present in the animal's mind the first time he or she encounters a situation in the world. In such a case, the knowledge of the animal was truly independent of prior experience. On the other hand, it can also mean that a specialized learning mechanism or constraint is innate to the cognitive structure of the animal. In this case, experience is necessary for the ability to be learned or expressed but at the same time an innate mechanism is necessary to derive this ability from the experience. The former view represents a strong form of nativism that claims that actual substantive knowledge is innate. The latter represents an interactionist perspective that acknowledges the need for experience with the environment but at the same time assumes the existence of innate mechanisms that constrain learning from the environment.

As our discussion of the history of nativism has shown, the function and quality of innate abilities has become more and more concrete in the last century. Especially, research with infants has developed finer measures enabling us to study infants' expectations and beliefs as well as their brain function. In the following we consider some concrete instances from the developmental psychological literature. One recent example concerns the existence of a Spelke object early in infancy, named for

Elizabeth Spelke who has conducted much of this pioneering research. Evidence from Spelke's lab as well as from other labs studying early physical knowledge indicates that very early in life, infants have a tendency to assume that the world is populated with three-dimensional (3D) objects that are bounded, have substance, are lasting in time and space, and move in predictable ways. Spelke has argued that this knowledge is part of our genetic endowment. We do not need to learn about these properties of the physical world because we already have them built into our system to prepare us for the world we live in. It should be noted that these expectations are very basic, not complex or elaborate, and are probably required in order to learn anything about physics (because physics is in its essence about how objects move relative to each other).

Evidence for this claim comes from a variety of studies with infants. At the core of this research and similar research using habituation or violation of expectation paradigms is the finding that infants show a strong novelty preference. For example, when exposed to a series of photographs from one category (e.g., dogs) infants will show an increase in looking duration if a new category (e.g., cats) is shown after repeated exposure to the first category. Similarly, if infants have an already formed expectation about how the world works and functions (e.g., that objects fall without support) then they should be surprised and look longer if researchers present them with an event that violates this expectation (e.g., a floating box) as compared to an expected event (e.g., a box being supported by a hand). This basic finding about infants' novelty preference has been used repeatedly in infant research to study infants' understanding of the world. For example, several studies from Spelke's own lab investigate as directly as possible the ways in which infants expect objects to behave. In one of these studies, infants were shown events in which an object moves along a straight path from left to right or from right to left. Between the infant and this path of motion were two narrow screens. Infants were shown test events in which the object disappeared as it moved behind each screen. The difference between the two test events was in whether the object was visible between the two screens: in the possible event the object was visible between the two screens, whereas the object disappeared between the two screens in the impossible event. Thus, Spelke and colleagues asked whether infants expect objects to move along spatiotemporally continuous paths – do they expect that to get from point A to point B, objects must travel through every point between A and B? Alternately, infants could expect that objects can disappear at location A and reappear at location B, as has been initially suggested by Jean Piaget. Spelke's results, significantly longer looking at the impossible than at the possible event, supported the former of these two possibilities: infants do expect objects to travel along spatiotemporally continuous paths.

These and other results have led some researchers to speculate that object persistence (part and parcel of the Spelke object), the notion that objects are bounded, have substance, are lasting in time and space, and move in predictable ways, is innate.

Of course, showing that this is the case is quite difficult, especially given the concerns raised about the meaning of innateness discussed earlier. Ideally, one would want to show that the ability could not possibly have been learned. Two factors constrain if an ability can be learned, first its overall difficulty and second the time that is available to learn the ability. As we will see below, we must even consider the possibility that learning takes place prior to birth. While still in the uterus, the fetus has access to a surprisingly large amount of information (not necessarily visual, but certainly tactile and auditory) about the physical world. Thus, it is possible that an ability that is present at birth is not innate but learned by the fetus in the uterus. Therefore, it is important for a nativist argument to show that an ability is not learnable given the time and exposure to situations that would allow an infant to learn the ability.

The concept of learnability comes from formal learning theory and is a mathematical and computational framework. One domain where this framework has been used is language acquisition. The key issue of learning a first language is the question how it is possible for a child to extract the grammatical rules and structure of a language given the limited and often ill-formed language examples they are exposed to? One answer to this question is to assume that infants are prepared to learn languages that follow the general structure found in all human languages. Thus, infants are able to pay attention to the important properties of language that are needed for successful learning. Such learning could be based on the statistical properties of natural languages but it could also be aided by innate structures such as a universal grammar.

Baillargeon and colleagues have also addressed this issue of learnability. In their work on learning about the physical world in infants, Baillargeon and colleagues have shown that 'contrastive evidence' is an important source of information for infants to learn the critical components of any physical principle. Contrastive evidence refers to observing the outcome of an event when a physical principle is maintained and what happens when it is not maintained. For instance, when learning about support relations between objects, contrastive evidence is obtained when infants see the consequences when an object is adequately supported by another (i.e., it remains stable on top of that object) and they also see the consequences when an object is inadequately supported by another (i.e., it falls to the ground). Results from a variety of studies indicate that infants learn about the principles of support and other physical principles such as occlusion and containment when they have access to contrastive evidence.

However, Baillargeon points out that infants cannot observe contrastive evidence for object continuity as they watch parents interact with objects or as they do so themselves, because such evidence does not exist in our physical reality. There is never a clear-cut set of events in which objects are continuous in one case and not in another – this is essentially object implosion or disintegration, which are not physically possible and therefore not observable. Baillargeon's extensive body of research led her to conclude that this contrastive evidence, available for all other physical principles she has investigated and critical for learning, is not available for object persistence. Despite this, infants show evidence of expecting objects to be lasting in time and space in most every visually based paradigm used to test it. Taken together, these pieces of evidence lead to the logical conclusion that the persistence of objects need not be learned.

One possibility we will consider in more detail later is how learning in the prenatal environment could have an influence on postnatal ability. Here it seems as though the observations necessary for learning about the persistence of objects is not available in the visual environment postnatally, but perhaps the first learning done about objects actually occurs prenatally, in the dark fluid environment of the uterus. It is difficult to know what kind of relevant experiences fetuses might have in the uterus, because as far as we know, fetal learning about objects has not been studied at all. Until this has been studied, the cautious approach would be to not make assumptions about the origins of these abilities.

Perhaps this analysis has made clear how difficult it is to find unequivocal evidence for innateness in humans. Below we will consider other reasons why the use of the term innate is often at odds with producing findings, interpretations, and theoretical claims that are clear.

Struggling with Definitions

It turns out that exactly how to define 'innate' is nontrivial. Patrick Bateson has explained his concerns that there are different possible meanings for the word 'innate'. He puts forth six possible meanings: (1) present at birth; (2) a behavioral difference caused by a genetic difference; (3) adapted over the course of evolution; (4) unchanging throughout development; (5) shared by all members of a species; and (6) not learned. These different meanings or connotations are present throughout the literatures in different subfields of psychology, ethology, and biology, raising at least two major questions regarding meaning. First, if evidence for one of these conclusions is demonstrated, can another (or all six) be inferred? Certainly not. But this is a common logical error in the literature. Further, an author might use the term in one limited way, but readers may infer a different or broader use of the term. As a solution to this problem, Bateson

implores scientists to "Say what you mean (even if it uses a bit more space) rather than unintentionally confuse your reader by employing a word such as innate that carries so many different connotations." Thus, if a scientist has evidence that a given ability is present at birth, Bateson asks that he or she simply states that fact and not be tempted to make inferences beyond that actual finding. Employing this simple measure would reduce confusion about what precisely is meant by the claim that something is innate. Researchers must be aware that our findings have implications for other researchers from related or even unrelated disciplines. Furthermore, caution with this matter is warranted because an ability that is present at birth could have been learned in the uterus and therefore does not automatically support a nativist argument.

Why These Differences in Meaning Are Important

It may seem that some of Bateson's six meanings are just synonyms for each other. For example, isn't 'present at birth' the same as 'not learned'? One example will show how they can be quite different. Studies with humans and animals have shown that the sensory and cognitive systems of the fetus allow for learning to take place prior to birth. For example, a series of studies with human infants conducted by Anthony DeCasper and colleagues showed that newborn infants prefer listening to their mothers' voices to other female voices. Some researchers might have been tempted to make the conclusion that this ability is innate, after all 'present at birth' is one of the meanings ascribed to innate. Then, we would be tempted to make additional conclusions, such as this ability is not learned, that it is caused by a genetic difference, etc.

However, it turns out that this was just part of the story. The full story was that newborn infants did not just prefer their mothers' voices. They also preferred listening to a story their mother had read aloud everyday during her last 6 weeks of pregnancy (they showed this preference even when their mother was not reading either story). Thus, it was not just that the newborns preferred their mother's voice, they preferred things that she said! Now we can see more clearly that the preference newborns show for their mother's voice is very likely due to the experience they have with her voice while still in the uterus.

So, perhaps fetal learning is something special about early human cognition, but other animals would not show evidence of it. After all, we know that animals display species-specific action patterns that are sometimes quite elaborate, and perhaps these are truly not learned or influenced by experience. However, the research of Gilbert Gottlieb has shown that fetal experience influences ducklings' perceptual judgments, proximity-seeking behavior, and vocal behavior.

Fetal ducklings that do not hear themselves or their siblings vocalize prior to or immediately posthatching are different from ducklings with typical auditory experience in many ways. The ducklings that did not receive auditory input prior to hatching did not discriminate between their own species' maternal call and those of other similar species as well as ducklings who did hear these early calls. Although the ducklings with typical auditory experience only seek proximity to an audio speaker emitting their own species' maternal call, those without auditory experience with their species' maternal call seek proximity to the speaker when it emits many different calls. Thus, newly hatched ducklings without typical auditory experience fail to discriminate between their own species' call and other similar calls. They also failed to produce these calls as well as ducklings with typical auditory experience. These findings show that abilities that had typically been thought of as innate (identifying and producing their species' maternal call) are actually dependent upon certain experiences. Further, we see that it is not always straightforward to determine which prenatal experiences support which postnatal abilities.

Thus, early preferences and behaviors (and, presumably, cognitive skills) can be set up and traced back directly to experiences that were received prior to birth. However, these paths of influence are not always what we might expect them to be. At this point we do not yet know enough about the prenatal environment or about how human fetal experiences can set up particular expectations, thoughts, or behaviors in the newborn. Therefore, we cannot make claims about which of these skills are certainly not influenced by various experiences they have prior to birth.

Various Forms of Interactioninsm

Another account of the role of experience in development has been put forth by William Greenough and colleagues. According to this approach, there are some events that are so prevalent in the environment of the developing organism that the system develops in such a way that these events are 'expected' by the organism. Thus, the mammalian visual system is only partially developed at birth and requires a steady diet of patterned visual stimulation for normal development to continue. Once the organism leaves the uterus, patterned visual stimulation is available essentially whenever the eyes are open, as long as the infant is in a typical environment of any kind. These kinds of processes are called experience-expectant and will not develop into their typical form if certain experiences are not available at certain times. In addition, he proposes that other processes are experience-dependent – not so constrained by time and by appropriate input and likely resulting in more variability across individuals.

Another way researchers describe how much the environment contributes to the development of a trait or ability is by using the concept of 'canalization'. This term comes from Waddington's classic metaphor of trait development involving a ball rolling through a landscape that allows for more or less lateral movement from environmental influences or winds that might blow the ball to another portion of the landscape and a different instantiation of the trait. If the ball began in a deep canal or was highly canalized, presumably hurricane-force winds would be necessary to push it off track. A process is highly canalized if it is not very vulnerable to the influences of the environment. Less canalization means that more variability is expected from environmental influence. The appeal of this metaphor lies in its capturing the dynamics of the whole organism–environment system rather than trying to separate these two in ways that are untenable. Thus, this metaphor replaces the dichotomy of nature and nurture with a continuous scale of environmental and biological influences on development. Another strength of this view is that it makes no claims about the starting point or ending point of a developmental process. This avoids unnecessary confusion about origins and puts the emphasis on process.

Such accounts of development have been called interactionist approaches since the influences and interplay of both biology and environment are considered. However, even in this very general sketch of an interactionist approach different camps of researchers prefer to focus on different aspects of development. While researchers generally agree that some learning mechanisms are available relatively early in life to support further development, one can choose to focus either on understanding the learning mechanism itself or to focus on understanding what is learned. Even if researchers seem to agree on how the developing system works in general and which processes are necessary for development, they could still disagree on which process or learning mechanisms are employed first, are most important, are dependent on each other or just plainly most interesting. Thus, while a less rigid form of nativism that assumes only a limited number of core processes to be innate may be indistinguishable from a similar form of empiricism, the theoretical positions underlying these views can differ greatly on where they place their emphasis. Thus, among researchers there is also a graded continuum of views and perspectives on nativism and empiricism. Differences between two views are often quantitative rather then qualitative. New and highly sensitive methods in the cognitive neurosciences will allow researchers to identify more core processes in development. However, if these new findings are interpreted as evidence for nativism or for empiricism will remain a matter of the theoretical position of the researcher.

Conclusions

Nativism is an approach to understanding human cognition that has a long and rich history within philosophy and even today is considered by many to be an important component of how we explain human nature. Although nativist explanations have stirred many heated debates, we suggest that the utility of this term has to do with the level of analysis at which the argument is targeted. For more philosophical approaches to psychology and human nature, the concept of innateness may well be useful and appropriate. However, for more biologically oriented approaches that are in the realm of neuroscience, the concept of innateness is nearly impossible to define and impossible to use with precision. How to resolve this conflict in boundary areas that span these levels of analysis is a challenging question for the future of our disciplines. Often it is nearly impossible to make this distinction and in 1967 William Kessen pointed out that "... the division of he world of infant studies into naturist and nurturist is at best misleading ..." We agree and suggest that, for now, abandoning the use of the word 'innate' unless further clarification is also offered may be the most useful way to go forward.

See also: Cognitive Development; Cognitive Developmental Theories; Habituation and Novelty; Learning; Mathematical Reasoning; Nature vs. Nurture; Object Concept; Piaget's Cognitive-Developmental Theory.

Suggested Readings

Baillargeon R (1999) Young infants' expectations about hidden objects: A reply to three challenges. *Developmental Science* 2: 115–163.

Bateson P (1991) Are there principles of behavioural develoment? In: Bateson P (ed.) *The Development and Integration of Behaviour: Essays in Honour of Robert Hinde*, pp. 19–39. Cambridge: Cambridge University Press.

Fodor JA (1983) *The Modularity of Mind.* Cambridge: MIT Press.

Gottlieb G (1971) *Development of Species Identification in Birds: An Inquiry into the Prenatal Determinants of Perception.* Chicago: University of Chicago Press.

Oyama S (2000) *The Ontogeny of Information: Developmental Systems and Evolution.* Durham, NC: Duke University Press.

Spelke ES (1990) Principles of object perception. *Cognitive Science* 14: 29–56.

Spelke ES (1998) Nativism, empiricism, and the origins of knowledge. *Infant Behavior and Development* 21: 181–200.

Spelke ES (2000) Core knowledge. *American Psychologist* 55: 1233–1243.

Neurological Development

M C Moulson, Massachusetts Institute of Technology, Cambridge, MA, USA
C A Nelson, Harvard Medical School, Boston, MA, USA

Glossary

Axon – A long projection from a neuron that transmits information to other cells by conducting nerve impulses away from the cell body.

Dendrite – A protrusion from a neuron that receives information from other neurons.

Developmental plasticity – The ability of the brain to be modified by experience during development. A normative process that involves the formation and elimination of synapses.

Glia – Cells in the brain that perform supporting functions such as guiding neurons to their correct locations in the developing brain and speeding up the transmission of information between neurons. There are many different types of glia.

Myelin – A lipid protein substance composed of glial cells, which forms a sheath around axons to insulate them and speed transmission of nerve impulses.

Neural induction – The genesis of the nervous system approximately 18 days after conception, whereby cells of the dorsal ectoderm are specified to become neural tissue, forming a flat structure called the neural plate.

Neurulation – The process by which the neural tube, which gives rise to the central nervous system (CNS), is formed from the neural plate. It occurs between 3 and 4 weeks after conception.

Progenitor – A cell that gives rise to neuronal and glial precursors through cell division.

Programmed cell death (PCD) – A normative event in which approximately 50% of all neurons in the developing brain die.

Synapse – The miniscule gap between axons and dendrites through which information flows in the form of neurotransmitters.

Introduction

Over the course of development, the central nervous system (CNS) grows from a single sheet of undifferentiated cells into our most complex organ, the brain, and the processes by which it does so are nothing short of miraculous. Brain development begins approximately 18 days after conception and experiences an explosion of growth during the prenatal period. During this period, the brain takes on both the rudimentary form and function of the mature organ, but its development is not complete at birth. Rather, the brain undergoes a protracted period of development. Whereas other bodily organs are mature at birth, the brain continues to develop at least through the adolescent period. There is even some evidence that certain aspects of brain development continue into middle age.

The brain is composed of two major classes of cells: neurons and glia. In the mature brain, there are approximately 100 billion neurons and many more glia. Neurons communicate information throughout the brain by forming connections called synapses. Glia are the support cells of the brain, and perform numerous functions, including guiding neurons to their correct locations in the developing brain, and speeding up the transmission of information and stabilizing connections between neurons in the brain.

Neurological development, though heavily constrained by genetics, is not predetermined. Rather, the developing brain is an open system that is shaped by both genetic and epigenetic factors. That is, although genetically programmed influences induce the events that give rise to the mature nervous system, this does not mean that these events are impervious to exogenous influences. For example, it is well known that exposure to certain agents during prenatal development (e.g., mercury, alcohol, rubella) can have deleterious effects on the developing fetus. These agents are said to have teratogenic effects and are a clear example that the developing brain, even during very early stages of prenatal development, is not immune to the outside world. Moreover, during the later stages of brain development (e.g., circuit formation) the developing brain actually requires normative experiences in the form of sensory input in order to customize its connections and, correspondingly, to increase its information processing efficiency. The ability of the brain to be modified by experience is called plasticity, and different processes during the development of the brain are more or less plastic. Specifically, early events are less amenable to experience (i.e., less plastic), whereas later events including circuit formation are more amenable to experience (i.e., more plastic). Importantly, the major vehicles of plasticity during later stages of brain development are in fact regressive events, including programmed cell death (PCD) and the loss of synapses. These regressive events allow the brain to capture experience, an ability that will be described in more detail in the final section of this article.

An understanding of plasticity in the developing brain holds promise for researchers studying child development. We know that early experiences alter the course of behavioral development in both positive and negative ways depending on the nature of the specific experiences a child has; understanding neural plasticity will lead to an understanding of how these early experiences exert their effects. Thus, a thorough understanding of neurological development will permit researchers to move beyond the historical nature–nurture debate, and to address multifaceted questions regarding which behavioral systems are modifiable by experience, the nature of experiences required to alter the brain circuitry underlying these behavioral systems, and when these experiences must occur in order to have their effects.

Thus, the purpose of this article is to review the typical development of the human brain by describing the series of events that give rise to the mature nervous system and to investigate the role that experience plays in brain development. These events include neural induction and neurulation, proliferation, migration, and circuit formation. Each event will be discussed in terms of the timing and course of typical development and the resulting morphological changes of the developing brain. Additionally, errors that may occur during each major event and their consequences will be described. In the final section of this article, developmental plasticity will be discussed. It is important to note that although the events of brain development are described in sequence, they represent overlapping waves of development. That is, later processes are initiated before earlier processes are completed, which creates a complexity that is often difficult to study, especially in the human. This brings us to a significant limitation in our understanding of neurological development. Much of our knowledge of brain development in humans is extrapolated from work with animals and based on postmortem studies of small numbers of human brains. Thus, a full description and understanding of brain development has not yet been reached for humans, especially with regard to the molecular events that give rise to brain development. With this caveat in mind, we turn to a discussion of the major events that give rise to the mature brain, a summary of which can be found in **Table 1**.

Neural Induction and Neurulation

The human nervous system begins to form by day 18 postconception. Prior to this, the cells of the embryo have differentiated into three different layers. The endoderm is composed of cells that give rise to the gastrointestinal system, liver, and lungs; the mesoderm gives rise to the vascular system, muscle, and connective tissue; and the ectoderm gives rise to the nervous system and epidermis (skin). Neural induction is the process by which the dorsal

Table 1   Timeline of neurological development

Developmental event	Timing	Description of event
Neural induction	Prenatal day 18	Dorsal side of ectoderm becomes specified as neural tissue
Neurulation	18–26 prenatal days	Neural tube is formed
		Cells within the neural tube become the CNS
Proliferation	6–20 prenatal weeks	Progenitor cells within ventricular zone give rise to neuronal and glial precursors
		* In some areas of brain, neurogenesis continues until adulthood
Migration	6–24 prenatal weeks	Neurons migrate out of the ventricular zone along radial glia
		Six-layered cortex is formed in an inside-out manner
Programmed cell death	2nd and 3rd trimesters	On average, 40–60% of neurons undergo programmed cell death
		Helps establish optimal connectivity
Axon and dendrite growth	15 prenatal weeks – 2nd postnatal year	Chemical signals guide axons and dendrites to their correct targets
		Synapses are formed between outgrowing axons and dendrites
Synaptogenesis	23 prenatal weeks – 2nd postnatal year	Synapses are strengthened through neural activity
		* Experience-dependent synapse formation continues throughout life
Synaptic pruning	1st postnatal year – adolescence	Inactive and aberrant synapses are eliminated
		* Mechanism whereby brain 'captures' early experience
Myelination	3rd trimester – middle age	Glial cells form myelin sheath around axons
		Results in increased speed and efficiency of neural transmission

side of the ectoderm becomes specified as neural tissue. The mesoderm, although not composed of neural tissue itself, plays a vital role in this specification; proteins secreted from the organizer region of the mesoderm determine differentiation of the ectoderm into neural vs. epidermal tissue. Initially, this newly specified neural tissue forms a flat structure called the neural plate. Soon after the neural plate has formed, the process of neurulation begins. First, a crease is formed along the longitudinal axis of the neural plate. The neural plate buckles along this crease, the neural groove, causing the edges of the neural plate to rise up. Starting at gestational day 22, the edges of the neural plate begin to fuse together, forming the neural tube. Cells inside the neural tube become the CNS while cells trapped between the outer wall of the neural tube and the overlying ectoderm form the autonomic and peripheral nervous systems (ANS and PNS, respectively). The midsection of the tube fuses first, proceeding toward the rostral and caudal ends of the tube. The rostral end of the tube, which later becomes the brain, closes by gestational day 24, and the caudal end of the tube, which becomes the spinal cord, closes by gestatorial day 26.

Errors in neurulation, collectively called neural tube defects, have devastating consequences on the developing fetus. Craniorachischisis totalis, or the complete failure of neurulation, most often results in spontaneous resorption of the embryo, and therefore its incidence cannot be estimated. More common are defects in neural tube closure. Anencephaly, which has an incidence of approximately 0.2 per 1000 births, occurs when the rostral end of the neural tube (the part which later becomes the brain) fails to close. Of fetuses that suffer anencephaly, 75% are stillborn and the others generally die within several weeks of birth. Myelomeningocele, which has an incidence of

approximately 1 per 1000 births, occurs when the caudal end of the neural tube (which later becomes the spinal cord) fails to close. Also called spina bifida, this defect results in portions of the spinal cord protruding unprotected from the back of the fetus. Infants affected by myelomeningocele generally survive, and the defect can be fixed surgically. However, myelomeningocele results in paralysis, with the extent of paralysis being determined by the location and size of the spinal lesion. Although genetic factors may predispose a fetus to neural tube defects, the environment can also play a pivotal role. For example, neural tube defects have been associated with a deficiency of folic acid in the maternal diet, and supplementing the maternal diet with folic acid seems to reduce the incidence of neural tube defects.

Proliferation

As the neural tube closes, cell proliferation within the tube takes off at an astonishing rate. Between the second and fifth month of prenatal life, the vast majority of all neurons that make up the adult nervous system are born in a process called neurogenesis. Prenatal cell proliferation also gives rise to glial cells, the support cells of the brain, on a timeframe that lags somewhat behind neurogenesis (although radial glial cells, discussed in a later section, are among the first cells to be produced). As one might imagine, cell proliferation dramatically alters the anatomical form of the developing nervous system.

Initially, the cells within the neural tube are all progenitor cells, meaning that they undergo mitosis (cell division) and can give rise to either neurons or glia. These cells reside in the innermost layer of the neural tube, an area called the ventricular zone. During mitosis, progenitor cells migrate from the luminal (inner) surface to the pial (outer) surface of the ventricular zone through a process called interkinetic nuclear migration. As they travel to the pial surface, they undergo DNA replication. They then migrate back to the luminal surface of the ventricular zone where they undergo cell division. Progenitor cells can divide either symmetrically or asymmetrically. During symmetric cell division, which starts at approximately the sixth prenatal week, progenitor cells give rise to two identical daughter cells that are themselves progenitors capable of undergoing cell division. Thus, symmetric cell division causes an exponential increase in the number of progenitor cells (i.e., after only 10 rounds of cell division, one progenitor cell gives rise to 1024 new progenitor cells). Asymmetric cell division on the other hand results in two daughter cells that are not identical. Rather, one daughter cell is a progenitor, as in symmetric cell division, whereas the other daughter cell is now a precursor to a neuron or a glial cell. These daughter cells that are destined to become neurons or glia are postmitotic (they do not undergo further rounds of cell division), and begin the process of migration and differentiation (see the following section). Between prenatal weeks 8 and 10, an additional zone of cells forms above the ventricular zone. This zone, called the subventricular zone, also contains progenitors that give rise to neurons and glia through the prenatal period and into the second year of postnatal life.

Neurogenesis, through asymmetric cell division, is largely complete by the end of the fourth postnatal month, while glial cell production continues until at least the second postnatal year. However, in certain regions of the brain, including the olfactory bulb and the dentate region of the hippocampus, neurogenesis continues into adulthood. Be that as it may, the vast majority of the 100 billion neurons that comprise the human brain are prenatal in origin.

This exuberant proliferation beginning in the sixth week of prenatal life in the human leads to considerable morphological change in the developing CNS. As the neural tube closes, uneven cell division along different parts of the tube leads to three distinct swellings at the rostral end of the neural tube – the prosencephalon (forebrain), mesencephalon (midbrain), and rhombencephalon (hindbrain) – that are apparent by 22 days postconception (see **Figure 1(a)**). Further subdivisions occur by approximately day 29 (see **Figure 1(b)**); the prosencephalon subdivides into the telencephalon and diencephalon, while the rhombencephalon subdivides into the metencephalon and myelencephalon. This creates five subdivisions, which give rise to all parts of the brain from the cerebral cortex to the brainstem, while the rest of the neural tube becomes the spinal cord (see **Figure 1(c)** for a micrograph of a chick neural tube at this stage in development). At this point in development, the neural tube has also acquired several bends (flexures) between these distinct swellings, which leads to the distinct curvature seen from the spinal cord to the brain in the mature nervous system (see **Figure 1(d)**). By the end of proliferation, at approximately 4.5 months prenatally, the brain is more comparable in shape to the mature brain, although the gyri (folds) and sulci (grooves) present on the surface of the mature brain are not fully formed until the end of the prenatal period (see **Figure 2**).

Unlike errors in neural tube formation, which are often lethal and lead to frank anatomical defects, errors in cell proliferation result in more subtle abnormalities. These errors result in two broad categories of disorder: microencephaly, in which the brain is grossly undersized, and macroencephaly, in which the brain is grossly oversized. The term microencephaly subsumes a heterogeneous group of disorders in which the proximal cause of the significantly smaller brain is a deficit in either symmetric or asymmetric cell proliferation, engendered by either genetic or environmental factors. Often, the ultimate cause of the deficit in cell proliferation is unknown, although environmental factors such as rubella, HIV, maternal alcoholism or drug abuse, and exposure to radiation or mercury have been shown to result in microencephaly. The significantly larger brain characteristic of macroencephaly results from excessive cell proliferation, although it is unknown whether this excessive cell proliferation is due to a faster rate of proliferation, an extended period of proliferation, or decreased incidence of cell death (see later section on PCD). The ultimate cause of macroencephaly is frequently unknown, although it can be genetic in origin. Both microencephaly and macroencephaly generally result in mental retardation with accompanying seizures.

Migration

After neurons are born, they must find their way to their correct locations in the developing nervous system, in order to give rise to the intricate organization of the mature nervous system. The mature cerebral cortex consists of six horizontal layers of cells oriented parallel to the surface of the brain. Other areas of the brain, such as the hippocampus and cerebellum, contain only two layers, while still other areas, like subcortical structures such as the amygdala, are not arranged in a layered formation at all. Layer I is the outermost layer of the cortex, and layer VI is the innermost layer. Vertical columns of related cells span all six layers. The processes by which neurons find their correct home is incredibly intricate, and occurs through two distinct types of migration: (1) radial migration, and (2) tangential migration.

Radial migration occurs when cells migrate from the ventricular and subventricular zones out to the surface of

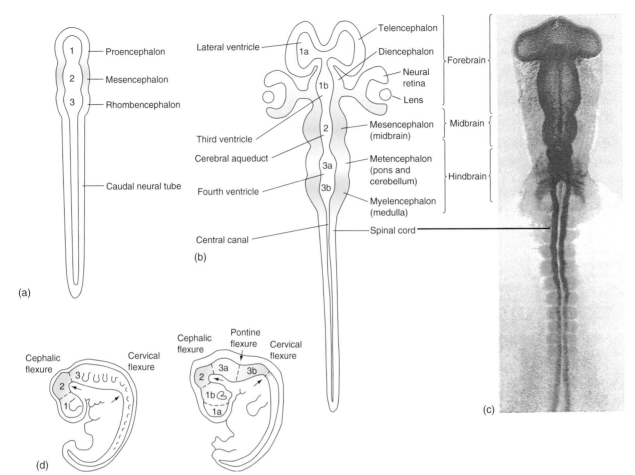

Figure 1 Stages in the development of the neural tube. (a) Three-vesicle stage of the neural tube; (b) five-vesicle stage of the neural tube; (c) micrograph of a chick neural tube at the five-vesicle stage; and (d) flexures of the neural tube. Reprinted from Kandel ER, Schwartz JH, and Jessell TM (eds.) (2000) *Principles of Neural Science*, 4th edn. New York: McGraw-Hill Companies.

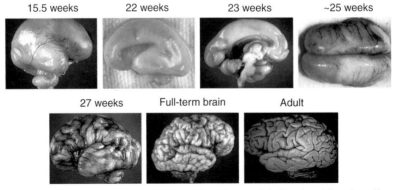

Figure 2 Overview of gross brain development from 15.5 prenatal weeks to adult. Reprinted from http://www-medlib.med.utah.edu/kw/sol/sss/subj2.html – Spencer S. Eccles Health Science Library, National Network of Libraries of Medicine, University of Utah Health Sciences Center, Salt Lake City, Utah.

the brain along perpendicular tracts. Radial migration depends upon specialized glial cells, aptly named radial glia, which are among the first cells to be produced by asymmetric division and to differentiate during proliferation. Radial glia contain projections that extend from the ventricular and subventricular zones to the outer surface of the brain. Neurons produced through asymmetric cell division form close associations with radial glial fibers and use them in order to 'crawl' to their correct locations in the cortex.

The first wave of migration out of the ventricular and subventricular zones creates the marginal zone at the surface of the brain, which contains sparsely distributed neurons and becomes layer I in the mature brain (see **Figure 3**). The intermediate zone, between the marginal and subventricular zones, contains the processes (axons and dendrites) of these newly differentiating neurons and in-growing axons from subcortical structures. After this scaffold composed of the ventricular, subventricular, and marginal zones is formed, the second wave of migration begins. The cortical plate, located between the marginal and intermediate zones, is formed by neurons migrating in this second wave (see **Figure 3**). Neurons that come to reside in the cortical plate, which later becomes layers II through VI of the cerebral cortex, migrate in an inside-out fashion. What this means is that neurons with earlier 'birthdays' settle in deeper layers of the cortex (e.g., layers VI, V, IV), whereas neurons with later 'birthdays' migrate over the earlier-born neurons to settle in more superficial layers of the cortex (e.g., layers II and III). Because widespread neurogenesis does not continue beyond a certain point in development, the ventricular and subventricular zones are not present in the mature brain. Radial glia are also not present in the mature brain, and there is some evidence that they differentiate into astrocytes (another type of glial cell) once they are no longer needed for migration. Migration in the cerebral cortex begins during the sixth prenatal week, and continues until approximately 24 weeks, although glial cells continue to migrate throughout the brain until at least the second postnatal year of life.

Although the majority of neurons migrate radially to their final destination, tangential migration also plays a role in the establishment of the mature organization of cerebral cortex. Unlike radial migration, which involves cells moving perpendicular to the surface of the brain, tangential migration involves migration parallel to the surface of the brain through the subventricular or intermediate zone. It is estimated that approximately 20–30% of cells reach their destination via tangential migration. Although it is still unclear what factors determine which populations of cells will migrate tangentially, radial and tangential migration each seem to be associated with particular types of neurons. There is also some evidence that progenitor cells engage in lateral dispersion through tangential migration.

Proliferation and migration cause the surface area of the cortex to expand rapidly. The resultant pressure exerted on the brain contributes to the formation of gyri, the folds on the surface of the brain. Thus, errors in cell migration often lead to abnormalities of the gyri. If neuronal migration to the cortical layers is aberrant in some way,

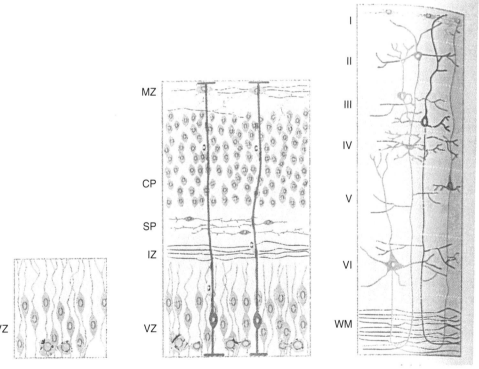

Figure 3 Migration in the developing cerebral cortex, showing the ventricular zone (VZ), intermediate zone (IZ), subplate (SP – a transient population of neurons not present in the adult), cortical plate (CP), marginal zone (MZ), white matter (WM), and layers I–VI. Adapted from Zigmond MJ, Bloom FE, Landis SC, Roberts JL, and Squire LR (eds.) (1999) *Fundamental Neuroscience*. San Diego, CA: Academic Press.

the gyri do not form correctly. In lissencephaly, all cortical layers fail to receive the appropriate number of neurons, and so the surface of the brain is completely smooth. Polymicrogyria refers to an excess of gyri, due to a much larger surface area of the outer cortical layers compared to the inner cortical layers. Defects in the corpus callosum often accompany errors in cell migration, with agenesis (failure to form) of the corpus callosum being the most severe case. These anatomical abnormalities due to errors in cell migration are usually accompanied by mental retardation, seizures, and motor problems.

Circuit Formation

Through the processes involved in neurulation, proliferation, and migration, the crude anatomical organization of the brain is laid down. However, it is not until connections between neurons (i.e., synapses) are formed that the brain begins to assume its mature function. The formation of precise connections between neurons is crucial to normative functioning. It is estimated that there are approximately 100 trillion functional synapses in the mature brain, and the processes by which the neurons of the brain form these connections are astounding in their complexity.

Much more than earlier stages of brain development, circuit formation involves progressive cycles of organization and reorganization. Initially, the connections formed in the brain are only a coarse approximation of the eventual organization of the adult brain; with each progressive cycle of reorganization, the brain becomes more finely tuned until it finally attains its mature organization. Unlike the earlier stages of neurological development (neurulation, proliferation, and migration), the formation and refinement of circuits in the brain are less tightly controlled by genetics. Rather, they are influenced by epigenetic events and external signals from the environment – indeed, external input is necessary for the proper refinement of most circuits in the human brain – although always within the constraints imposed by genetics. Circuit formation involves several steps, including the formation of specialized neural processes, the formation of synapses between neurons, and myelination. Importantly, fine-tuning is largely dependent upon regressive events, including PCD, synaptic pruning, and process retraction.

Programmed Cell Death

PCD (the term apoptosis is often used interchangeably with PCD; however, apoptosis refers to only one well-studied mechanism of PCD, characterized by segmentation of DNA into fragments of a characteristic length) is the earliest initiated of the major regressive events that

contribute to the final organization of the adult brain. Importantly, PCD is now known to be a normative part of development (i.e., its root cause is not damage to the brain, nor are the neurons and glia that undergo PCD defective). On average, somewhere between 40% and 60% of neurons produced within the brain die, although this number varies widely across brain regions – in some regions of the brain, as many as 85% of the neurons produced undergo PCD. Neurons can undergo PCD at any phase in their development, although there seem to be two major waves of cell death: an early phase that occurs during proliferation and axonal growth, and a later phase that occurs after the formation of synapses.

PCD is mediated by growth factors produced during cell–cell interactions. Growth factors, also called neurotrophins, are produced in a limited supply in the brain by both neurons and non-neuronal cells, and there is competition among neurons for access to them. Neurons that make inappropriate or nonfunctioning connections with other neurons, or make no connections at all, will not gain access to neurotrophins, and therefore will undergo PCD. Although the functional significance of PCD is not fully understood, it seems to help establish optimal connectivity in the brain by eliminating aberrant connections.

Growth of Axons and Dendrites

Axons and dendrites are the specialized processes that neurons develop as they differentiate (see **Figure 4**). They mediate communication between neurons at junctions called synapses; generally, axons are on the transmitting end and dendrites are on the receiving end of the signals passed between neurons. Astonishingly, axons can grow up to several centimeters in length, and both axons and dendrites can contain multiple branches so that one neuron can make connections with numerous others.

Growth cones, located at the end of axons, are responsible for both growth of axons and connection with their correct target neurons in the brain. Growth cones are composed of specialized structures called lamellipodia and filopodia. Lamellipodia are thin fan-shaped structures, and filopodia are spiky protrusions from lamellipodia. In order to extend its length, the growth cone attaches to an external substrate in the brain (e.g., the extracellular matrix, or axons of neighboring neurons) and modifies its internal structure – in this way it 'crawls' through the tissue of the brain to its final destination. Growth cones are also responsible for directing the axon to the correct target in the brain. This function is crucial, given the need to form precise connections among the billions of neurons in the brain. The growth cone accomplishes this through receptors that are sensitive to molecular cues in the external environment (e.g., in the extracellular matrix, or located on nearby neurons). Numerous molecules serve

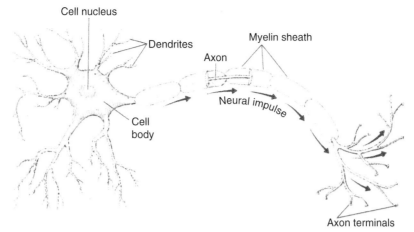

Figure 4   Schematic diagram of a neuron. Adapted from Cole M, Cole SR, and Lightfoot C (2005) *The Development of Children*, 5th edn. New York: Worth Publishers.

to attract or repulse growing axons by promoting or inhibiting growth of the growth cone, thereby directing it in one direction or another. Dendrites begin as thick protrusions from the cell body of the neuron. With the growth of incoming axons and the afferent activity that they provide, dendrites expand, form branches, and develop spines – small protrusions at which synaptic contacts generally occur.

Not surprisingly then, the timings of the development of axons and dendrites closely parallel each other. The first axons are apparent at approximately 15 weeks prenatally, although the timing of their development varies widely across brain regions. Crude dendrites also appear at approximately prenatal week 15. Dendritic spines, the sites of synaptic contact, are first apparent by the prenatal weeks 25–27. Both axon and dendrite development continues postnatally until at least the second year of life. There is an initial overproduction of both axons and dendrites, followed by a regression. This elimination is largely driven by competition, and will be discussed in more detail in the section on synaptic pruning.

The formation of axons and dendrites causes further increases in cortical surface area and density, thereby contributing to the establishment of gyri and sulci on the surface of the brain. Thus, the formation of axons and dendrites contributes to an overall increase in brain size and a more mature appearance of the brain.

Errors in axon and dendrite formation often arise as a secondary consequence of other problems in neurological development, such as problems in cell migration. Genetic and environmental factors can both play a role in aberrant axonal and dendritic development. In certain genetic syndromes, such as Down syndrome and fragile X syndrome, dendrites demonstrate reduced branching and reduced number and density of spines. Prematurity and prenatal and perinatal insults can also result in abnormalities in axon and dendrite formation. The most common phenotypic consequences of errors in the development of neuronal processes are mental retardation and seizures. In many cases of severe mental retardation with unknown etiology, postmortem analyses reveal significant abnormalities in dendritic formation, including a paucity of dendritic branches, decreased length of dendritic branches, and decreased number of dendritic spines.

Synaptogenesis

Synapses refer to the points of contact between neurons where information is passed from one neuron to the next. Synapses most often form between axons and dendrites, and consist of a presynaptic neuron, synaptic cleft, and a postsynaptic neuron. In electrochemical synapses an electrical impulse (called the action potential) travels down the length of the axon. Once it reaches the end of the axon, it causes the release of neurotransmitters into the synaptic cleft. These molecules travel across the synaptic cleft, where they interact with receptors on the postsynaptic neuron. As a result of this interaction, the postsynaptic neuron is either potentiated (i.e., more likely to fire an action potential and 'pass on' the message) or inhibited (i.e., less likely to fire an action potential). (Gap junctions are another type of synapse found in the brain. They are electrical synapses, in which the information is passed directly from one neuron to another through an electrical impulse. As less is known about their development and functional significance, they will not be discussed further.) Although it is difficult to determine when the first synapses form in the human brain, some areas of the brain may form functional synapses as early as prenatal week 15. By prenatal week 23, synapses have started to form in the cerebral cortex. Synaptogenesis continues throughout the prenatal period and peak levels of synapses are not reached until the postnatal period. This article focuses on synapse production and elimination during development. However, it is important to note that synapse formation and elimination occur throughout the lifespan, and are the mechanisms by which new learning occurs.

Peter Huttenlocher and colleagues have thoroughly described a key feature of normative synaptogenesis – specifically, that there is a massive overproduction of synapses across all regions in the human brain. Approximately 40% more synapses are produced during development than are present in the adult brain, and the quantity of this overproduction is remarkably consistent across brain regions. Topographical differences do exist, however, in the timing of synapse overproduction. For example, the rate of synaptogenesis in the visual cortex peaks between 2 and 4 months postnatally, and the peak number of synapses is reached by approximately 8 months. On the other hand, the peak number of synapses in the middle frontal gyrus does not occur until sometime between 12 and 15 months of age. There is compelling evidence that this massive overproduction of synapses seems to be largely under genetic control. For example, when a monkey's eyes are removed prior to birth so that no sensory stimulation can reach the visual cortex, the peak number of synapses in the visual cortex is not different from typical development. Thus, it does not seem as if experience is playing a role in driving the formation of synapses during this initial overproduction phase of development.

Given that the infant brain contains 40% more synapses than the adult brain, how and when is the mature number of synapses reached during development? The adult number of synapses is reached through a process called synaptic pruning, which refers to the loss of synapses in the absence of cell death.

Synaptic Pruning

Initially, the synapses that are formed in the infant brain are labile. Whether or not a synapse is stabilized or weakened and eventually pruned depends in large part on the activity of that synapse. Specifically, synaptic pruning follows the Hebbian principle of use/disuse; that is, synapses that are more active are strengthened, whereas synapses that are less active are weakened and eventually pruned. Activity at a synapse involves both the pre- and postsynaptic neuron, and both neurotransmitters and neurotrophic factors (and their receptors on the pre- and postsynaptic cells) are involved in producing the coordinated activity between neurons that is necessary for the stabilization of synaptic contacts. Thus, neurotrophic factors play a role in both neuron and synapse survival. When synapses are eliminated, this also involves the withdrawal of the axon that participated in that synapse, thereby

leading to the competitive elimination of axons that was mentioned in a previous section.

Like the timing of synapse overproduction, there are differences among brain regions in the time course of synaptic pruning, although it generally follows a much more protracted time course than synapse overproduction. As mentioned earlier, synapse production reaches its peak in the visual cortex at approximately 8 months of age. Pruning of these synapses continues until approximately 6 years of age, when the adult level of synapses is reached. On the other hand, synaptic pruning in the prefrontal cortex, where peak levels of synapses are not obtained until sometime in the first year of life, is not complete until adolescence.

Synaptic pruning, thought to be common to all neuronal systems, allows for fine-tuning of the connections in the brain based on experience. Although spontaneous, endogenous neural activity does contribute to synaptic stabilization, activity due to exogenous events impinging on neural systems (e.g., sensory stimulation) plays a crucial role in synaptic stabilization. Earlier events in the development of the brain are under tight genetic control and, although influenced by the local environment, are relatively impervious to all but the most dramatic of outside influences (e.g., teratogens). However, synaptic pruning depends largely upon the experiences that the developing child has with the world around him/her, and is the mechanism whereby the brain 'captures' experience. The incredibly precise organization of the mature brain is the instantiation of the interaction between the brain and the external environment throughout development. Thus, normative experiences during development lead to the maintenance of proper connections and the elimination of aberrant ones, whereas aberrant experiences during development will lead to a failure to maintain appropriate connections and maintenance of inappropriate connections. The last section of this article will further explore two main mechanisms by which the brain captures experience during development, although the final step in the development of mature connections within the brain is discussed first.

Myelination

Myelin is a lipid protein substance composed of glial cells that wraps around certain axons, creating an insulation effect that allows for more rapid conduction of action potentials. Thus, myelinated axons transmit information much faster than do unmyelinated axons. Myelination begins prenatally and continues, in some areas of the brain, into middle age. The time course of myelination, like synaptogenesis and pruning, varies widely across brain regions. As a general rule, myelination occurs first in neural systems that underlie behaviors that are present early in life. For example, primary sensory and motor areas are myelinated before association areas, and the neural systems involved in postural control and the vestibular sense are fully myelinated before birth. On the other hand, areas of the prefrontal cortex do not become fully myelinated until middle age.

Although not all areas of the nervous system are myelinated (e.g., the ANS is not myelinated), myelination is critical for proper behavioral functioning. Genetic and environmental factors can result in deficiencies in myelination, and myelin is also the target of certain adulthood diseases (e.g., multiple sclerosis). Demyelination results in decreased conduction velocity and increased conduction failures, leading to an overall slowing of information transmission in the brain. As one might imagine, errors in myelination often lead to mental retardation and movement disorders.

Thus, circuit formation involves PCD, the growth of specialized neural processes (axons and dendrites), synaptogenesis and synaptic pruning, and myelination. The timing of these processes during development varies across neural systems (see **Figure 5**); earlier maturing neural systems (e.g., primary visual areas) reach peak levels of synapses, undergo synaptic pruning down to adult levels, and myelinate sooner in development than later maturing systems (e.g., prefrontal cortex). Regressive events play a pivotal role in fine-tuning the connections in the brain based on experience, and it is to this topic that we turn next.

Developmental Plasticity

The early events in neurological development are under tight genetic control and therefore do not depend on the external environment for elaboration (although they are not completely impervious to experience). However, once these building blocks of the brain are in place, there is a continuous reciprocal interaction between the brain and the external environment. Through sensory input, the external environment impinges on brain circuitry, which causes progressive refinement of connections until some optimal level of organization is attained. This ability of the developing brain to adapt based on interactions with the external environment is referred to as developmental plasticity and is rooted in the regressive events (e.g., synaptic pruning) that were described previously. (The term plasticity is also used to describe the extent of recovery following brain damage (e.g., stroke) in the adult. It is important to note that the process of developmental plasticity described here is a normative part of development. The adult brain is also capable of normative plasticity, e.g., new learning causes the formation or elimination of synapses.) The extent of plasticity observed during neural development varies across brain regions. Different systems in the developing brain are more or less open to input from the environment, and are sensitive at different times across development.

William Greenough and colleagues have proposed a model of neurological development that distinguishes between two forms of plasticity: experience-expectant and experience-dependent plasticity. This model is an attempt to explain the mechanisms by which experience 'gets inside' the brain, as there is ample evidence that behavior and its underlying neural circuitry are influenced by experiences throughout life. Experience-expectant and experience-dependent plasticity differ in terms of their mechanisms (synaptic pruning vs. synaptogenesis), the characteristics of the environmental input

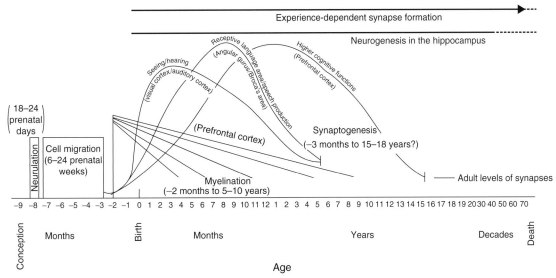

Figure 5 Developmental trajectories of mechanisms of brain development. Reprinted from Thompson RA and Nelson CA (2001) Developmental science and the media: Early brain development. *American Psychologist* 56: 5–15. American Psychological Association.

that drive these processes, and whether or not they are associated with sensitive periods. However, both types of plasticity can lead to long-lasting changes in the brain.

Experience-Expectant Plasticity

Experience-expectant plasticity occurs via the massive overproduction and the subsequent pruning back of synapses in the developing brain. Synapses that are more active are more likely to be preserved, whereas synapses that are less active are weakened and eventually eliminated; as such, the experiences that occur during developmental periods of synaptic pruning play a critical role in determining which synapses are strengthened vs. eliminated. In this way, experience-expectant plasticity can take advantage of experiences that, through evolutionary history, have become species-typical and occur at defined points in time during development (e.g., patterned visual input). Experience-expectant plasticity follows the time course of synaptic pruning, and therefore varies across different regions of the brain that have different developmental trajectories of synapse overproduction and pruning (e.g., visual cortex vs. prefrontal cortex). Because synaptogenesis and pruning occur at defined periods during development, this gives rise to a phenomenon called a sensitive period, which is a window of time during development in which specific experience(s) must occur for the normative development of the system in question. If typical experiences do not occur during that time window, or the quantities of specific experiences are not sufficient, development does not proceed in a normative fashion, even if those same experiences occur later in life.

Experience-Dependent Plasticity

Conversely, experience-dependent plasticity is a lifelong process by which the brain adapts to experiences that are unique to the individual. As in experience-expectant plasticity, experience-dependent plasticity involves synaptic changes; however, it involves the creation of new synapses and changes in the morphology of synapses, rather than the pruning of unnecessary or aberrant synapses. Synaptogenesis based on experience continues to occur throughout the lifespan, and thus, this mechanism of plasticity is responsible for learning and memory in adulthood as well as during development. As the underlying neural mechanism of this type of plasticity occurs across the lifespan, it is not associated with sensitive periods. That is, learning unique to the individual can occur at any point in time. It is important to note that human behaviors can rarely be explained entirely in terms of only one type of plasticity; most complex behaviors involve both mechanisms of plasticity.

Conclusion

In summary, neurological development follows a protracted course that involves both progressive and regressive events. These events occur in overlapping waves beginning at prenatal day 18 and continuing through adolescence, and their timing varies widely across brain regions. The brain does not develop in a vacuum; as such, it is affected by interactions with the external environment, although earlier events in the development of the brain (i.e., neural induction, proliferation, migration) are less amenable to change based on exogenous influences than are later events (i.e., axon and dendrite outgrowth, synapse formation, and retraction). Indeed, one of the hallmarks of human brain development is plasticity, or the ability of the brain to adapt in accordance with environmental influences.

See also: Brain Development; Critical Periods; Down Syndrome; Intellectual Disabilities; Nature vs. Nurture; Prenatal Development; Teratology.

Suggested Readings

Cole M, Cole SR, and Lightfoot C (2005) *The Development of Children,* 5th edn. New York: Worth Publishers.

Greenough WT, Black JE, and Wallace CS (1987) Experience and brain development. *Child Development* 58: 539–559.

Huttenlocher PR (1994) Synaptogenesis, synapse elimination, and neural plasticity in human cerebral cortex. In: Nelson CA (ed.) *Threats to Optimal Development: Integrating Biological, Psychological, and Social Risk Factors,* pp. 35–54. Hillsdale, NJ: Lawrence Erlbaum Associates, Inc.

Kandel ER, Schwartz JH, and Jessell TM (eds.) (2000) *Principles of Neural Science,* 4th edn. New York: McGraw-Hill Companies.

Monk CS, Webb SJ, and Nelson CA (2001) Prenatal neurobiological development: Molecular mechanisms and anatomical change. *Developmental Neuropsychology* 19: 211–236.

Nelson CA, de Haan M, and Thomas KM (2006) Neural bases of cognitive development. In: Damon W, Lerner R, Kuhn D, and Siegler R (eds.) *Handbook of Child Psychology: Vol. 2. Cognitive, Perception and Language,* 6th edn., pp. 33–57. Princeton, NJ: Wiley.

Rakic P, Ang ESBC, and Breunig J (2004) Setting the stage for cognition: Genesis of the primate cerebral cortex. In: Gazzaniga MS (ed.) *The Cognitive Neurosciences,* 3rd edn., pp. 33–49. Cambridge, MA: MIT Press.

Thompson RA and Nelson CA (2001) Developmental science and the media: Early brain development. *American Psychologist* 56: 5–15.

Volpe JJ (1995) *Neurology of the Newborn,* 3rd edn. Philadelphia, PA: Saunders.

Webb SJ, Monk CS, and Nelson CA (2001) Mechanisms of postnatal neurobiological development: Implications for human development. *Developmental Neuropsychology* 19: 147–171.

Zigmond MJ, Bloom FE, Landis SC, Roberts JL, and Squire LR (eds.) (1999) *Fundamental Neuroscience.* San Diego, CA: Academic Press.

Neuropsychological Assessment

J A Hofheimer, University of North Carolina at Chapel Hill, Chapel Hill, NC, USA
B M Lester, Brown University, Providence, RI, USA

Glossary

Age at assessment and adjustment for prematurity – Neuropsychological assessments take into account the chronological age (CA) of the infant in order to determine age-appropriate indicators of functioning. Adjusted gestational age (GA) is calculated by subtracting age at birth from 40 weeks and is continued up to 24 months adjusted age in order to coincide with the actual age of the brain.

Continuous scores or scales – Measures of functioning that have a standardized numerical value for assigned points and increments between points along the continuum (e.g., number of items passed).

Longitudinal or serial assessments – Assessments repeated at specified ages across time to measure developing neuropsychological functions and integrated processes (e.g., emerging expressive language reflected in cooing at 3 months, babbling at 6 months, single utterances to multiple word sentences at 12 and 24 months).

Neuropsychological assessment – Term used to describe structured tests and systematic observations that measure varied central nervous system (CNS) functions. The CNS comprises the brain, spinal cord, and the neural networks that connect brain structures and organ systems in order to function.

Normed/standardized assessments – Assessments administered to a representative sample to derive information about typical performance at specific ages. Information about these group norms is used as a reference point to compare smaller samples or individuals by ranking them in comparison to population characteristics.

Performance assessments – Performance assessments are used in naturalistic settings such as homes or child-care centers to document functioning in different areas where the child and his/her environment and caregivers can be observed in realistic and nonthreatening situations included in daily life.

Plasticity – Describes the dynamic and moldable nature of neuropsychological characteristics and the potential of the CNS to increase adaptive functioning over time, to self-correct early irregularities and problems as the infant/child matures, and to be responsive to preventive and therapeutic interventions.

Ratings/ordinal scales – Numerical scales that ascend or descend along a continuum but do not have a standardized numerical value between points on the scale (e.g., 0 = none, 1 = rarely, 2 = often, 3 = always).

Risk continuum – Infants and preschool children with documented neuropsychological problems are eligible for early intervention services based on assessment results categorized along a continuum of established or potential risk for subsequent problems.

Screening – Brief, structured assessments administered in a standardized manner for the purpose of identifying the presence of problems or documented risk factors that warrant more extensive diagnostic assessments.

Systematic observation – Observations that employ a standardized context in which to observe the individual. A prescribed set of behaviors are operationally defined to be observed and recorded during the specified conditions (e.g., mother–child interactions observed during feeding or unstructured situations).

Task specificity and continuity – This term refers to measurement of areas of functioning in a manner that is comparable across time and species. It is important because different instruments must be used at different ages, since maturation results in changes over time in the behavioral manifestation of specific functions.

Introduction

Neuropsychology, as its name implies, is the study of the neurological basis of psychological processes. It is the study of brain–behavior relations and in today's language, would be considered part of the field of neuroscience. Neuropsychologists are typically interested in connecting behavior to brain structure and function. Neuropsychological assessments, therefore, include structured tests and systematic observations that examine brain–behavior relations and measure their integrated functions. These functions reflect how the mind and body work together to process input and information internally, and then act on it. Because of the constructs included, the term 'neurobehavioral' is sometimes used interchangeably with neuropsychological.

The field of neuropsychology began with adults and was applied for diagnostic purposes. Behavioral tests were developed to include tasks associated with specific brain regions, with varying degrees of specificity. For example, an expressive language disorder could be linked to a region within Broca's area of the brain and the neural networks that connect it to other structures. Identifying tasks specific to a particular structure or pathway, and observing associated behavioral functions, enables the clinician to understand the source of the deficit and specify more effective treatment as a result.

The field of neuropsychology focuses on the underlying brain mechanisms that determine behavior, and particularly behavioral deficits, as well as their developmental trajectories across time. The successes of neuropsychology with adults led to a natural downward extension and development of neuropsychological tests for children. And, although we know less about child brain–behavior relations than we do about adult brain–behavior relations, this enterprise has also been successful. There are, in fact, elaborate neuropsychological test batteries for children and this has launched an entire industry. These tests include specific tasks to assess typical neuropsychological constructs such as attention, imitation, memory, perception, planning, problem solving, goal-directedness, receptive and expressive language abilities, sensory-processing, emotions, social and behavioral competencies, movement, and muscle tone.

Normed assessments for infants and toddlers are often used to determine the extent to which varied neuropsychological characteristics evidence performance that is optimally developing at higher than expected age levels, typically developing and within the expected age range, or performance that reflects delay or dysfunction. For example, there are a number of excellent diagnostic tests for attention deficit hyperactivity disorder (ADHD), and its inattentive and hyperactive subtypes. And despite concerns about overdiagnosis, these assessments have been successful at identifying attention deficits in even very young children, and at a time when interventions are more likely to have long-term benefits.

The further downward extension of neuropsychological assessment to infants (and even the fetus) is more difficult for several reasons. First, infant behavior is more global and diffuse than childhood behavior, and the nonverbal form of communication and limited mobility typical during infancy naturally limits functions able to be assessed. Second, we are only beginning to document the specific infant behaviors that correspond to neuropsychological test performance at later ages. Third, because the infant brain and neural networks connecting different structures are less well developed, we know less about brain–behavior relations in infants than we do with older populations.

Assessments for older children and adults cannot simply be 'scaled downward' for infants. Many infant assessments build on emerging capabilities from a 'bottom up' approach that measures domains thought to be related to neuropsychological processes that develop in later childhood. So, we are using the term 'neuropsychology' broadly here, but we do include assessments that test constructs that are thought or known to be related to neuropsychological domains in older populations and where there is an attempt to understand the underlying brain mechanisms.

In infants and young children, neuropsychological assessments are used to: (1) document where along a developmental continuum an individual is functioning at a given age, (2) describe patterns of brain development over time, (3) document the influences of biological and social risk factors as well as clinical interventions on neuropsychological outcomes, and (4) identify the precursors of risk for subsequent disorders. These tests examine both individual and integrated functions that reflect central nervous system (CNS) integrity and show the interrelationship among brain structures and cellular networks as complex functions and learning develops. During the first three years, standardized procedures are used to measure how the infant develops complex integrated behaviors, movements, and vocalizations in response to internal processes and environmental interactions. The inclusion of performance assessments in familiar contexts provides a more comprehensive view of varied functions, allows for multidisciplinary assessments in a single setting, and can be useful for identifying specific needs for and measuring the outcomes of targeted interventions.

Historical and Scientific Influences on Neuropsychological Assessment

The field of neuropsychological assessment during the prenatal to three-year period has grown in the past 10 years for several reasons. One reason is that advances in medical technology have led to increasing numbers of infants who survive, such as preterm infants born at less than 1000 grams, but are at risk for brain injury. This has resulted in the need for sensitive instruments to evaluate neuropsychological function in these infants so that appropriate intervention strategies could be developed. Second, neuroimaging techniques including magnetic resonance imaging (MRI), functional MRI (fMRI), positron emission topography (PET), near infra-red optical topography (NIROT) and spectroscopy (NIRS), evoked potentials, electroencephalograms (EEG), and brain electrical activity mapping (BEAM) have now been adapted for infants. This provides an unprecedented window into the infant's brain and an opportunity to study brain–behavior relations in infancy. Third, the application of neuropsychological assessments to at risk populations has led to studies of clinical interventions. Successful research trials have provided evidence of the beneficial effects of early preventive and therapeutic interventions. This has resulted in an increased demand for neuropsychological assessments for use in clinical trials and outcomes research. Finally, the Federal government recognized the importance of providing services for infants and preschoolers with established risk factors and special needs and resulted in mandates such as the 1987 Public Law 99–452 and the Individuals with Disabilities Education Act revised in 2004. These changes have also increased the demand for infant neuropsychological assessment tools.

Neuropsychological Domains Relevant to the Prenatal Through 3-Year Stages of Development

The assessment of neuropsychological processes includes multiple integrated areas of functioning. The chronological age at which these more global milestones are accomplished varies widely within and between domains among typically developing children, and delays are often seen in infants born to high social risk families, those born prematurely, and those who experience severe prenatal or neonatal complications resulting in lengthy illnesses and/or brain insults. Based on Aylward's Classification Schema, we provide an elaboration on those constructs and clusters for neuropsychological assessments that are relevant across the prenatal to 3-year periods.

Basic Neurological Functions

Basic neurological functions reflect the general integrity of the CNS including the presence of adaptive, healthy functioning and absence of abnormal functions.

Primitive reflexes
Primitive reflexes are automatic responses that are measured in terms of timing, strength, and symmetry and indicate how the signals are sent from the brain to the spinal cord and outward to individual muscles of the face, neck, torso, and extremities that are involved in postural control and movement. As locomotion develops, early primitive, or primary, reflexes should become extinguished and replaced by purposeful, integrated movements.

Symmetry
Symmetry refers to equal strength and coordination of movements and muscle tone on the left and right sides of the body. Problems with symmetry occur in the following conditions:

1. Left/right discrepancies are reflected in differences in the muscle tone, strength, coordination, or preference for left/right side with respect to use of extremities, trunk, head and eye movements, or auditory responses.
2. Stereotyped or lateralized postures are positions that are sustained for lengthy periods or repeated predictably and are associated with either increased or decreased muscle tone on one side, or a preference for returning to the position automatically despite assistance provided to promote symmetric positioning.

Muscle tone
Muscle tone is the extent and range of appropriately soft, moderate, or strong tone depending on state of arousal and external stimuli. Greater balance between the upper and lower body regions is expected to mature toward the point of full-term gestation at 40 weeks postconceptional age.

Motor inhibition
Motor inhibition refers to self-regulation of spontaneous and intentional movements. This includes the ability to downregulate agitated movements requiring quieting during excitation and distress to reestablish and sustain modulated movement and state of arousal.

Protective reflexes
Protective Reflexes are automatic responses to gravitational changes in position that demonstrate self-protective movements.

Visual tracking
Visual tracking includes visual fixation that is sustained and includes coordinated eye movements that are able to smoothly follow a stimulus moving in an arc from midline to left, right, vertically, and in a semicircle.

Auditory localization and orientation
Auditory localization and orientation are responses to sounds made out of eyesight, responded to by alerting, searching visually for the source of the stimuli, and resulting in visual fixation on the sound source for a sustained period.

Receptive Functions

Receptive functions indicate how sensory stimuli and perceptual information enter centrally mediated systems and become available for integrated processing. Responses to visual, auditory, tactile, olfactory, and taste stimuli are observed, and with increasing age, responses to verbal cues are included. Extreme variations in sensitivity to unimodal or multimodal sensory input, such as those that appear either blunted or overly sensitive and lead, respectively, to either a complete shutting out of stimuli or distress, are important indicators of sensory integration and its effect on self-regulatory capacities.

Visual attention

Visual attention involves the ability to orient to and sustain focus on a stimulus such as a person or inanimate object or task. Variations in sustained interest in novel stimuli, preferences for repeated stimuli, and indicators of visual recognition memory reflect more mature and complex processing of visual information.

Visual perception

Visual perception involves the input of visual information via the optic nerve and associated activation of other brain structures and circuits that produce behaviors in response to perceived images.

Auditory aspects of receptive language

Auditory aspects of receptive language include orienting and sustaining attention to sounds and words which lead to the development of spontaneous, responsive, and imitative vocalizations, pre-speech sounds and later language acquisition.

Spatial relationship processes

Spatial relationship processes involve visual stimuli and perceptions that are incorporated into purposeful operations, such as crawling around, rather than into, an obstacle, and shape identification for puzzle manipulations.

Tactile processing

Tactile processing involves responses to touch during self-initiated manipulation and exploration, as well as responses to tactile input from caregivers and environmental stimuli.

Expressive Functions

Expressive functions include observable behaviors that the child produces either spontaneously, or to stimuli presented in a standardized manner in the context of assessment. Expressive functions are complex and require the integration of sensory input, perceptions, and actions to produce intentional behaviors. Functional constructs in this cluster include:

Fine motor precision and coordination

Fine motor precision and coordination involves small muscle movements such as grasping and manipulating, that increase with an increase in purposeful movement over time.

Oral motor coordination

Oral motor coordination involves the tongue, mouth, and throat muscles and neural networks that are essential for nutritional intake (e.g., initial suck-swallow mechanisms), regulating respiration, and are also involved in the production of early vocalizations and speech sounds for verbalization.

Visual–motor integration

Visual–motor integration is reflected in movements requiring eye-hand coordination for reaching, prehension, manipulation, and later problem solving.

Fine motor-constructional movements

Fine motor–constructional movements are those involving small muscle coordination and perceptual-motor refinement to produce complex motor sequences used in such skills as block-building and shoe-lacing.

Visual–spatial orientation

Visual–spatial orientation is reflected in behaviors involved in functions that indicate how the individual orients her/himself with respect to objects in the environment (e.g., ducking the head to crawl under a table) and operates on objects and images in space for specific tasks (e.g., seeing parts of a whole, puzzle completion) using a 'mental snapshot' of the image received through the eyes.

Articulation

Articulation refers to purposeful vocalization and verbalization of thoughts and feelings leading into word production and increasing length of utterances that reflect mental representations of objects, concepts, thoughts, and emotion.

Gross motor motility

Gross motor motility involves large muscle movements involving the neck, trunk, and extremities with increasing strength and complexity necessary for progressing from self-stabilization and balance to locomotion that involves movement required for environmental exploration.

Gross motor coordination

Gross motor coordination involves increasing control and precision in the use of large muscles for intentional, goal-directed movements, as well as the progression from involuntary to voluntary functions such as those required for toilet-learning.

Processing

Processing refers to the integrated functions included in memory, learning, thinking, and reasoning. These functions are initiated with sustained attention to and processing of stored input for recall and subsequent application.

Memory involves the storage of information and learning reflects the utilization of stored information. Thinking and reasoning involve integrating concepts, ideas, and images with learned functions to produce new and more complex solutions to problems and plans of action (i.e., executive functions) or the inhibition of actions to self-regulate cognitive processing.

Temporal-sequential organization

Temporal-sequential organization is the process of ordering information in time and sequence. Concepts applicable to the first 3 years include those involving time and events (e.g., establishing a pattern of putting away toys before moving on to another task; sleep comes after a bedtime story), and order of operating on information that is processed one piece at a time, in a series or sequence (e.g., order of words in a sentence alters meaning).

Visual memory

Visual memory involves the recognition and use of stimuli previously observed to solve a problem or produce an action.

Word retrieval

Word retrieval involves recalling words that are labels for thoughts, people, objects, places, and events, and is necessary for more complex communicative, language, and cognitive functions.

Anticipatory behaviors

Anticipatory behaviors are those that reflect recall of a previously experienced sequence of occurrences or memory of events included in the sequence (e.g., a toddler getting shoes to put on before going outside).

Visual sequencing

Visual sequencing involves the ability to see and distinguish the order of symbols, words, or images, and is reflected in tasks such as putting pictures in order of occurrence in a story, or in pattern or form copying. Problems may be reflected in reversals or difficulty associated with missed steps in a sequence.

Cognitive adaptation/problem solving

Cognitive adaptation/problem solving reflects the process of reasoning to understand a concept, evaluate alternatives, and examine alternative strategies to achieve a goal.

Verbal and nonverbal abstracting

Verbal and nonverbal abstracting is the process of using words or actions to represent an idea or thought process.

Seriation and classification

Seriation and classification are aspects of concept attainment that reflect recognition of sequential properties (e.g., counting parts and placing them in sequence) and similar vs. different attributes of a concept (e.g., grouping red and blue blocks of different shapes).

Imitation

Imitation involves behaviors, gestures, or words that are repeated following observation and are indicative of a memory for and recall of those previously experienced or observed.

Judgment

Judgment is the product of evaluating and determining the importance of a concept and its characteristics.

Mental Activity

Mental activity includes attention, memory, planning, problem solving, executive functions, activity, and persistence toward achieving a goal and is the most sophisticated level of integration involving the dimensions outlined earlier. It is important to note the critical role of the infant's emerging self-regulatory capacities that influence the development of mental activity. The potential length and frequency of sustained attention episodes increases with age; however, across ages, its duration is dependent on the infant/child's perception of the stimuli. Based on varied perceptions, the quality and length of attention is sustained when stimuli are perceived as novel, interesting, and/or comfortable. In contrast, attention is limited when stimuli are overly intense, challenging, or stressful. Conscious information processing requiring focused attention is limited in the latter case by stress-buffering and coping mechanisms. These functions are automatically engaged, self-preserving strategies required to sustain physiological and psychological balance and return to a homeostatic state in situations perceived as stressful or challenging.

Attentional activities, level of consciousness, and stress-coping mechanisms

Attentional activities, level of consciousness, and stress-coping mechanisms refer to sustained attention and self-regulated functions that permit the intake of information and stimuli from the environment and subsequent internal central processing.

Perseveration

Perseveration is a process that involves lengthy sequences of integrated functions including sustained attention, information processing, and purposeful, planned activity to achieve a goal or solve a problem.

Focused attention vs. distractibility

Focused attention vs. distractibility is a dimension of functioning that is a central feature involved in effortful, sustained information processing described above. Distractibility, or a fleeting attention span, refers to lapses in the ability to concentrate on a stimulus or task and sustain the requisite degree of focused attention to persevere with information processing or task attainment. Duration of attention varies widely within and across individuals, stimuli, and situations. However, important characteristics in the assessment of infants and young children are (1) the ability to re-regulate attention and re-focus once distracted, and (2) whether regulation is a result of self- or other-initiated actions.

Behavioral states of arousal

Behavioral states of arousal are observable indicators of the level of biobehavioral activity that is required for functions that vary in requisite levels of physiological, psychological, and motor engagement. Arousal levels increase or decrease to meet demands of internal processes, as well as those in response to external demands. Lower states of quiet to active sleep serve as restorative states for internal processes. Movement from drowsy sleep-to-wakefulness transitions, to quiet, and then more active alertness provide optimal arousal levels required to sustain attention and process information in an integrated manner. Higher states include excitability, agitation, and distress. These states require effortful physiological and psychological adaptations to intense or challenging internal or external stimuli to regain balance, return to relaxed alertness, and sustain self-regulation required for higher order cortical functions.

Motor activity

Motor activity involves movement quality and quantity that both influence and are influenced by states of arousal. Imbedded in activity levels are the qualitative aspects of movement that include muscle tone, posture, coordination, symmetry, strength, purposefulness, and planning, or praxis. As such, calm smooth movements with relaxed muscle tone are associated with restorative sleep, and with quiet alertness and focused attention during awake periods. Conversely, agitated movements with tight muscle tone and rigid or restricted motion indicate elevated arousal levels requiring relaxation to regain regulated state transitions, activity levels, movement, and cognitive processing.

As noted earlier, increasing maturation and developmental complexity from the fetus, to newborn, infant, and young child have led to the development of stage-relevant assessment instruments and measurement methods. While the specific behavioral indicators of the above functions are manifested differently across time, multifactorial assessment protocols can be selected for use at individual time points and also for repeated measurement.

This insures overlapping coverage of the domains above to document status and to profile developmental patterns over time.

The Purposes, Timing, and Context of Neuropsychological Assessments

Determining the most appropriate assessment instrument and method at a given age or developmental stage, and the context in which assessments will be administered, requires attention to multiple factors. This is of particular importance during infancy and early childhood when different assessments must often be used to profile a range of varied brain functions over time. Further, the goals may differ in research about individuals or groups, descriptions of clinical populations in comparison to typically developing individuals, or clinical assessments conducted for diagnostic purposes in cases of suspected or documented problems. Another factor unique to infants and young children is that, unlike older individuals assessed independently, parents or other caregivers are often involved in the assessment process, some of which are designed for administration during home visits or in other child-care settings.

Ultimately, selection of appropriate assessment instruments and methods, as well as the timing and context in which assessments take place, depend on the questions asked and the characteristics of the child or group being assessed. Comprehensive assessments may combine (1) structured tests and systematic observations, (2) observations in more naturalistic situations and settings with individuals familiar to the infant/child (e.g., home, child-care, early intervention settings), (3) caregiver and/or teacher perceptions, and (4) observations of the home environment. Enormously diverse abilities are often reflected in behavior in response to structured tasks and toy presentations during testing, and the contrast in behavior observed with parents, professionals, and peers in less structured situations. Because of these diversities, performance assessments conducted in realistic, nonthreatening settings familiar to the infant/child (e.g., homes, child-care centers, and developmental therapy settings) have expanded options for the birth to 3 years population.

Assessments used to address questions directed toward a description of individual or group characteristics relative to population norms should be addressed using the same standardized procedures and under the same conditions in which norms were obtained. For questions involving both healthy or typically developing infants/children and those with established biomedical and/or environmental risk factors, it is important to select protocols that permit flexible administration methods and include alternative adaptations for individuals with special needs (e.g., those who are nonverbal or who have sensory or motor impairments). This is essential to insure that the results obtained are consistent and therefore can be generalized to the larger population characteristics. The generalizability of assessment findings is particularly relevant when assessment results are used to inform evidence-based practice guidelines and have wide-ranging policy implications.

Clinically indicated assessments based on established biomedical or environmental risk factors often require combinations of measurement methods relevant to the particular risk factor or documented problem. In these cases, assessment selection will depend on the nature of the insult and brain regions likely to be affected. This insures that behavioral indicators of associated functions are adequately sampled by the assessment instrument. In both typically developing and clinical populations, repeated assessments that document functioning at specific time points and permit delineation of developmental trajectories are particularly useful for understanding more vs. less plastic functions, and for identifying those that may be more amenable to preventive and therapeutic interventions.

Established risks based on early characteristics are used to determine eligibility for both assessment and intervention services. Biomedical risk includes characteristics such as extreme prematurity, prenatal substance exposure, or documented abnormal brain structure. Environmental risks include those associated with the home (e.g., lack of safety or nutritional resources), exposure to known toxins (e.g., lead paint), or family psychosocial characteristics such as economic adversity, lack of social support, or parental incarceration. The assessment process further expands the initial risk profile to enable characterization of a child along a continuum. 'Typically developing' refers to functions that are common to and clinically within normal limits for a particular age. 'Atypical' refers to unusual or idiosyncratic functioning, or that which has the potential to develop into problematic behaviors. 'Delayed' functioning is that which is more than 20% below expected age level. 'Dysfunctional' refers to behaviors that do not currently show the appropriate approximation toward adaptive functioning, or those that result in problems in other areas. Problematic or low functioning that persists over a lengthy period of time and disrupts general health and/or adaptation is referred to as an 'impairment' or 'disorder'.

To capture wide-ranging individual differences and the nonlinear and variable aspects of development within and across domains and time periods, a comprehensive assessment battery should be broad-based and incorporate an eclectic set of measures. A variety of psychometrically sound observation and caregiver report instruments are described in the sections that follow to illustrate complements to standardized, structured tasks within developmental stages.

Neuropsychological Assessments during the Prenatal Period

Factors that affect prenatal growth and maturation *in utero* also profoundly affect the fetal brain and central nervous system, and hence, influence subsequent neuropsychological development. Beginning with neural tube formation at 3–4 weeks, the brain and spinal cord become differentiated and associated nervous system components are formed. Neuronal cells proliferate, migrate to form various brain regions, and through programmed cell-death, or pruning, form the architectural foundation of the brain by around 20–24 weeks. Following at around 29 weeks and proceeding through the second and third decade, myelin tracts form beginning in the brainstem, and create an infrastructure through the white matter that interconnects brain cells and structures. The result is the formation of sensory, motor, projection, and association pathways, or neural networks, that provide the structural basis for integrated neuropsychological functions.

How these structures and pathways develop is the result of multiple factors such as genetics, exposure to teratogens, infections, maternal substance use, and the hormones involved in maternal stress responses. Indirect factors that also predispose the fetus and young child to dysfunction include prolonged exposure to maternal psychosocial stressors such as social isolation, economic and educational disadvantagement, and domestic violence.

Assessments of Fetal Neuropsychological Function and Development

During the prenatal period, genetic factors interacting with input from the intra- and extrauterine environment shape the CNS, and this interaction is the focal point of assessments during this period. Fetal activity and sensory responses to input further develop the CNS and begin to define patterns of electrical activation among developing neural networks. In addition to the now routine use of ultrasonography for obstetric assessments of anatomical development and early brain structure, CNS functions and development are assessed using measures of fetal physiology, neuromaturation, and neurobehavior.

Fetal assessments include four domains of functions using ultrasonography to record behavioral states of arousal, motor activity, and responses to stimulation, as well as concurrent fetal heart rate monitoring:

• Behavioral observations are important because all behavioral functions are dependent on the degree of arousal. State observations use ultrasound tranducers to view the eyes and body and record the amount of time the fetus spends in quiet vs. active sleep, drowsiness or quiet waking, and active waking. Temporal patterns of state transitions and their covariation with body, eye, and heart rate activity become linked as the fetus matures.

• *Movement.* Assessments of fetal movement are based on observable *in utero* activity. Doppler actigraphy can be used to detect movement velocity and duration through the use of the heart rate transducer; however, these results may differ across manufacturers and the ability to isolate fetal movements from maternal abdominal movement artifacts. Additional aspects of motor activity have been recorded using real time or videotaped two-, three-, and four-dimensional ultrasonogram recordings including (1) use of intrauterine space; (2) the amplitude, speed, symmetry, complexity, timing, force, and fluidity of movement, as well as; (3) the quantification of spontaneous movements; and (4) the inhibition of movements as gestation advances. Also of interest is the emerging development of complex movement patterns involved in thumb-sucking, swallowing, breathing, grasping, and the sequenced rotation and changes in flexion and extension involved in the fetus' transition from breech to vertex positioning.

• *Fetal responsivity.* Reactivity to external stimuli, the ability to self-regulate responses, and the return to baseline levels of regulation are central elements of sensory integration and information processing that begin during the prenatal period. To assess responsivity and regulation, ultrasound images are employed to record baseline activity and responses to a vibroacoustic stimulus (e.g., an electric toothbrush, speech sounds) activated at the level of the maternal abdomen, usually above the head of the fetus. Dimensions of responsivity observed include the magnitude of initial response, habituation or decrements in responses over repeated presentations, startles, abrupt state changes, and variations in heart and respiratory rates or rhythms.

• *Heart rate patterns.* Measures of heart rate variability rhythms and patterns of change during various states of arousal and in response to stimulation provide information about centrally mediated regulatory capacities. Self-modulation of autonomic functions, such as breathing and heart rate in the fetus, are thought to form the basis for regulating behavioral and thought processes required for higher-order cortical functions. Because changes in heart rate rhythms reflect both involuntary and voluntary processes, features measured during the last trimester include the nature and extent of changes in heart rate accelerations and decelerations, and a summary of pattern variability that is typically collected during unperturbed baseline periods, in response to stimulation, and following the response to stimulation to determine the nature and timing of changes and the return to baseline.

Multidimensional assessments of the above measures provide the opportunity to examine concurrent functions and the prenatal development of the central and peripheral nervous systems. The addition of a fetal actocardiagraph enables time-locked recording of heart rate and movement data with concurrently videotaped ultrasound images.

Assessment of Newborn Neuropsychological Function and Development (Birth to 44 Weeks Postconceptional Age)

With the newborn's availability for direct observation, interaction, and handling, assessments of neuropsychological functions expand during the first month of life. These include developmental domains relevant to the newborn's participation in interactions with the environment and other individuals. As in the case of fetal assessments, sensory, motor, state, and physiological domains are included, and increasing sophistication in these processes can be measured using a range of newborn neurological and neurobehavioral measures that have been well validated (see **Table 1**).

Newborn assessments provide information about varied domains of functioning and neurodevelopment and are used to document early competencies and problems requiring follow-up, as well as the initial influences of pre- and neonatal medical interventions. An important advantage of neurobehavioral assessments includes the information available to parents and professional caregivers about the unique capabilities and challenges of this new human being with whom they are establishing a relationship. The role of 'assessment as intervention' has been indicated in research that documented positive influences on early parent–infant relationships, behavioral regulation in the newborn, and adaptive transitions to parenthood for individual mothers, and fathers, as well as the couple's relationship.

The timing and context in which newborn assessments are conducted are similarly guided by the questions and goals. For example, assessments in the nursery during the first week of life document early postnatal function, whereas those later during the 28-day period will reflect the interactive influences of medical events and care, as well as early parent–infant and environmental interactions. Newborn assessments incorporate flexible administration requirements that are adaptable for home, hospital, and clinic visit settings. In healthy full-term infants, it is preferable to wait until the third day of life to allow the newborn to stabilize following delivery events, adjust to the initial extrauterine environment, and permit clearance of the effects of prenatal and antepartum chemical exposures (e.g., illicit and prescribed maternal medications) that influence neurological and neurobehavioral

Table 1 Exemplary neuropsychological assessments for newborns through 3-year-olds

Assessment instrument and author/s	Type[a]	Age range	Functions assessed
Newborn assessments			
Neuromaturation (Allen and Capute)	STD	27–40 wks PCA	Posture, tone, reflexes, sensory, and behavioral responses
Dubowitz Neurological Exam	STD	38–42 wks PCA	Reflexes, visual, and auditory responses, posture, movement, alertness, irritability, consolability, cry characteristics
Amiel-Tison Neurological Assessment (Amiel-Tison)	STD	32–30 wks PCA	Reflexes, active and passive tone
Prechtl General Movements	STD	∼32–56 wks PCA	Quality of movement observed: intensity, speed, fluency characteristics
NICU Network Neurobehavioral Scale (Lester and Tronick)	STD	∼33–44 wks PCA	Habituation, attention/visual and auditory orientation, range and regulation of states, motor regulation, hyper- and hypotonicity, lethargy, excitability, reflex asymmetry and abnormality, regulation, stress/abstinence behaviors, examiner facilitation
Assessment of Preterm Infant Behavior (Als *et al.*)	STD	∼33–44 wks PCA	Habituation, attention/visual and auditory orientation, range and regulation of states, physiological regulation, motor regulation, examiner facilitation, approach and avoidance behaviors, asymmetric and abnormal reflexes
Neonatal Behavioral Assessment Scale (Brazelton)	STD	37–44 wks PCA	Habituation, attention/visual and auditory orientation, range and regulation of states, motor regulation, autonomic regulation, deviant reflexes
Neurobehavioral Assessment for Preterm Infants (Korner)	STD	32–40 wks PCA	Maturity level in motor development/vigor, reflexes, alertness/orientation, irritability, % sleep, cry, state regulation, physiological regulation
Einstein Neonatal Neurobehavioral Assessment Scale	STD	37–42 wks PCA	Passive and active movements, supported positions, tone, reflexes, visual and auditory orientation, state regulation
Test of Infant Motor Performance (Campbell)	STD	32–56 wks PCA	Supported positions, tone, reflexes, visual and auditory orientation, social interaction, communication of needs
Infant/toddler assessments (1–36 + months)			
Neuromotor and sensory			
Amiel-Tison Neuromotor and Sensory Assessment (Amiel-Tison and Gosselin)	STD	Birth–72 mos	Neurosensory exam (including hearing and vision), motor milestones, tone, activity, reflexes, posture, gross motor abnormalities, head size and growth, craniofacial features
Peabody Development Motor Scales, 2nd edn. (Folio and Fewell)	STD	Birth–60 mos	Reflexes, stationary, locomotion, object manipulation, grasping, and visual–motor integration, with composite scores for Gross Motor Quotient, Fine Motor Quotient, and Total Motor Quotient
Neuromotor Behavior Inventory (Gorga *et al.*)	STD	36 mos	Gross and fine motor development, reflexes, movement quality, coordination, reactivity
Communication and language			
Preschool Language Scale (Zimmerman *et al.*)	STD	0–35 and 36–71 mos	Auditory comprehension, receptive language abilities, expressive linguistic abilities; 0–35 mos measures account for attention, interaction, vocal, and gestural behaviors
Communication and Symbolic Behavior Scales (Weatherby and Prizant)	STD and CGR	6–24 mos	Emotion, eye gaze, gestures, sounds, words, comprehension, object use; parent report includes language milestones
MacArthur Communication Development Index (Fenson *et al.*)	CGR	6–30 mos	Word and sentence use, imitating, naming, labeling, phrase, sentence, and vocabulary comprehension, sentence length and complexity
Multidimensional developmental and cognitive assessments			
Bayley Scales of Infant Development III (Psychological Corporation)	STD	1–42 mos	Language, cognitive, social, gross and fine motor, behavior regulation during tasks, perceptual motor integration, socioemotional development
Bayley Infant Neurodevelopmental Screener (Aylward)	STD	3–24 mos	Posture, tone, movement, receptive and expressive functions, cognitive processing
Mullen Scales of Early Learning (Mullen)	STD	Birth–68 mos	Differential visual and auditory learning, expressive and receptive language, visual reception
Ages and Stages Questionnaire (Bricker and Squires)	CGR	4–60 mos	Cognitive, language, motor, social skills, communication, adaptive skills

Continued

Table 1 Continued

Assessment instrument and author/s	Type[a]	Age range	Functions assessed
Kaufman Assessment Battery for Children (Kaufman and Kaufman)	STD	3–18 yrs	Sequential and simultaneous information processing, memory, learning, nonverbal abilities
NEPSY (NE for neuro and PSY for psychological; Korkman et al.)	STD	36 mos–12 yrs	Attention, executive functions, language, sensorimotor functions, visuospatial processing, and memory and learning.
Adaptive behavior measures			
Vineland Adaptive Behavior Scales (Sparrow et al.)	CGI	Birth–18 yrs 11 mos	Communication, daily life skills, socialization, motor skills
Functional Independence: Measure for Children (WeeFIM; Msall)	CGI	1–8 yrs	Self-care, mobility, understanding verbal and nonverbal communication, use of language and gestures, social interaction, play, and memory of routines
Behavioral regulation and risk detection			
Child Behavior Checklist (Achenbach and Edelbrock)	CGR	18–60 mos	Behavioral problem frequency: aggression, depression, social withdrawal, attention, emotional reactivity, somatic complaints
Brief Infant Toddler Socio-Emotional Assessment (McGowen)	CGR	12–36 mos	Social, emotional, behavioral checklist of problems and competencies
Ages and Stages Questionnaire: Socioemotional (Squires)	CGR	3–60 mos	Self-regulation, compliance, communication, adaptive functioning, autonomy, social interaction, affective expression
Autism Diagnostic Observation Schedule (Lord)	STD	14 mos–adult	Communication, play/imaginative use of objects, social interaction
Autism Diagnostic Interview (Rutter)	CGI	24 mos–adult	Communication, language, social interaction initiatives and responses, stereotypical, restricted, repetitive behaviors
Checklist of Autism in Toddlers (Baron-Cohen et al.)	STD	16–30 mos	Social behavior, communication, emotion expression, sensory reactivity
Modified Checklist of Autism in Toddlers (Robins et al.)	CGI	16–52 mos	Communication and affective behaviors, interest in children, stereotypical behaviors, joint attention, imitation
Screening Tool for Autism in Two Year Olds (Stone et al.)	STD	24–35 mos	Play, motor imitation, joint attention, responses to requests
Attention			
Auditory Continuous Performance Test for Preschoolers (Corkum et al.)	STD	36–60 mos	Go-No-Go responses to simple line drawings of familiar items presented intermittently and requiring child to push a button to indicate specified drawing; scores reflect latency and errors of omission and commission.
Reaction Time (Mahone)	STD	24–60 mos	Time from presentation of visual and auditory stimuli to response; number of trials and delay periods, omissions, and commissions measure excitatory responses and inhibition

[a]CGI, caregiver/parent interview; CGR, caregiver/parent report; mos, months; PCA, postconceptional age; STD, standardized assessment; TR, teacher report; wks, weeks; yrs, years. Adapted from Lipkin PH and Allen MC (eds.) (2005) Special issue: Neurodevelopmental assessment of the fetus and young infant. *Mental Retardation and Developmental Disabilities Research Reviews* 11(1): 171–275; Lipkin PH and Allen MC (eds.) (2005) Special issue: Neurodevelopmental assessment of the young Child. *Mental Retardation and Developmental Disabilities Research Reviews* 11(3): 1–106; Aylward GP (1997) *Infant and Early Childhood Neuropsychology*. New York: Plenum Publishing; and Hooper S, Molnar A, Beswick J, and Jacobi-Vessels J (in press) Neuropsychological assessment of the preschool child: Expansion of the field. In: Bracken BA (ed.) *Psychoeducational Assessment of the Preschool Child,* 4th edn. Boston: Allyn and Bacon.

functions. For premature and medically fragile newborns, observations without handling are useful prior to medical stabilization. Once infants are able to be handled in room air or with only the assistance of nasal cannula for oxygen supplementation, handling during assessments can be safely conducted with modifications in response to each infant's ability to regulate this input.

Assessments conducted during the immediate postnatal period provide information about initial functional integrity that is the result of maturation and intrauterine events, and over the course of the first 4 weeks, these assessments measure the newborn's development and adaptation to the extrauterine environment. In terms of developmental stage-appropriate relevance, the dimensions important to include in an assessment of newborns during the first postnatal month, or in the case of the preterm infant through 44 weeks postconceptional age, are discussed in the following behavioral terms.

- Reflexes are automatic responses to stimulation that are present at birth and diminish over time as intentional movements develop. Assessments of reflexes examine the strength, timing, duration, and symmetry of the responses of the face, mouth, trunk, and extremities. Adaptive reflexes are those elicited without delayed onset, are moderate in strength with gradual relaxation, and are equal in these features on the right and left side. Abnormally weak, strong, or asymmetric reflexes that persist, and/or those that evidence one-sided predominance may be indicative of early brain insults, injuries, or abnormalities.

- Physiological regulation is at the core of all functioning and provides a window into the central mediation of neuropsychological processes. Indicators of regulation are variable and well-paced heart and respiratory patterns, and skin color that is pink in color and reflects adequate capillary perfusion, with a return to baseline following adaptive changes in responses to handling, distress, or temperature variations. Coordination of suck–swallow–breathing mechanisms and the absence of choking or gagging when clearing respiratory secretions or following feeding is indicative of integrated gastrointestinal functions that are also centrally mediated and responsive to environmental stimuli. Twitches and jitteriness are often present in both full-term and preterm infants during the early postnatal period, and for immature preterm infants or those who appear easily overwhelmed by multisensory stimuli, tremors, startles, hiccoughs, and/or erratic eye movements may also be present, but should diminish as neonatal illnesses resolve and the infant matures. Extremely high-pitched cry sounds and aberrant patterns are also indicative of potential neurological insults.

- Habituation refers to the newborn's ability to show a strong initial response, and then to decrease responses to sensory stimuli (e.g., a light, rattle, bell, and heel touch) repeated over multiple trials.

- Attention/orientation reflects the ability to locate, fixate, and sustain focus on visual and auditory stimuli and to track animate and inanimate objects horizontally, vertically, and in a semicircular path.

- State range and regulation is assessed by observing the range of states that the infant has available, and how the infant moves through state transitions. Indicators of regulation can be seen in how smooth vs. abrupt state transitions are going from sleep, to alertness, and aroused states, and the ability to upregulate alertness as needed to focus, as well as to self-quiet from more highly aroused states such as during agitation, distress, and excitation. During distress, the ability of the infant to be consoled by the examiner is an indicator of potentially emerging functions that still require external support.

- Motor tone and movement regulation reflect initial neurological integrity with respect to muscle tone, postural preferences, and movement at rest and during spontaneous and elicited activity. Adaptation is observable in increasingly greater balance between relaxed and elevated muscle tone appropriate to the infant's state of arousal and the demands of the environment, increasing flexion, extension, and balance between muscle tone present in the upper and lower extremities, and increasing smoothness and coordination of movement. As infants gain the ability to self-regulate movement and activity levels, behavioral states are also able to become more modulated.

Neuropsychological Assessments in Early Infancy (1–18 Months)

During this period of extremely rapid growth and CNS maturation, multidimensional and multimethod developmentally oriented assessments are crucial to gaining a comprehensive view of emerging cognitive, language, social, motor, perceptual, emotional, and self-help capabilities.

Physical examinations that include head growth and vision and hearing screening may accompany neuropsychological assessments to identify possible co-varying medical problems. For premature infants, and any infants who experienced hypoxic insults or teratogenic exposures, this is of particular importance since problems with perceptual, neurological, gross motor, and quantitative capacities are more likely, as are the precursors of high-prevalence/low-severity problems of learning disabilities, attention deficits, and behavioral disorders.

During early infancy, neuropsychological constructs important to assess include those which emerge as a function of early sensory and movement experiences with the environment and individuals of importance, such as parents, siblings, extended family, and child-care providers and peers. Relevant constructs include:

- Visual and auditory acuity and memory (indicated by recognition and preferences) lead into early cognitive processes including imitation of facial expressions, gestures, vocalizations, and movements, as well as reasoning activities that involve object permanence (objects/people out of sight still exist in the infant's mental representation), concept formation, adaptive tool use, puzzle completion and block building, problem solving, and persistence with sustained attention to attain a concrete goal.

- Prelinguistic communication including spontaneous and reciprocal vocalizations and gestures, joint attention, turn-taking, increasing sound production from cooing, to vowel–consonant combinations and multisyllabic babbling.

- Exploratory behaviors involving fine and gross motor coordination for manipulation of objects, purposeful reaching, and grasping.

- Prelocomotion movements involving head, neck, and torso control; balance; and strength to support the infant's own weight in prone and pre-sit/crawl positions.

- Early locomotion in the form of crawling, pulling to stand, cruising while holding on for support, and independent walking.

- Self-regulatory capacities reflect stress-coping mechanisms and emotion modulation. During this period, these functions expand to increase self-soothing during agitation and distress, the ability to tolerate intense multisensory stimuli and novel situations, and modulate activity levels and frustration tolerance to persist toward a goal on self- or other-initiated tasks.

- Sequenced social interactions increase in the number and length of exchanges and episodes. These give-and-take exchanges involve sustained eye contact, affective warmth, seeking and sustaining physical contact, spontaneous and reciprocal vocalizations, initiatives to engage social partners, and responses to the social partner's initiatives. Over time, interactions include the integration of socially focused exchanges with those involving environmental exploration and play with objects.

Neuropsychological Assessment During the Toddler/Preschool Period (18–36 Months)

Two primary areas of developmental achievements that are typically accomplished during the second year of life are the infant's ability to (1) use gestures and vocalizations to label concepts, objects, and people; and to communicate interests, needs, emotions, and goals; and (2) become more independent and mobile in explorations of the environment. As a result, behavioral regulation may become more challenged by the toddler's own initiatives. These require persistence to master emerging competencies with autonomy, but are also limited by the very concrete nature of cognitive processes that do not yet permit the incorporation of abstract concepts into formal reasoning. During the second and third year, relationships with caregivers, siblings, and peers also become more complex as they evolve into increasingly more diverse joint attention focused on social, play, and exploratory themes; conversations; and activities. In addition, behavioral indicators of the toddler's differentiation between self and other, and the beginnings of empathetic responses begin to emerge. Adult–child and child–child exchanges provide opportunities that promote the development of prosocial and self-monitoring behaviors, and the role of adult social partners requires the provision of both scaffolding to assist in toddler-initiated activities and goal attainment, as well as limit-setting to insure safety and promote self-regulation in challenging situations. These increasingly complex interactions and integrated CNS response patterns result in higher cortical functions involved in reasoning,

planning, and problem-solving processes. Through increases in sustained attention for information processing, recall and working memory become more sophisticated and are incorporated for early executive functions.

The scope and extent of developing neuropsychological functions that are able to be assessed expands dramatically during the second and third years, and global measures of 'intelligence' that summarize verbal and performance characteristics typically begin at 36 months. However, the use of a global intelligence quotient (IQ) score or developmental quotient as an overall assessment of neuropsychological function is limited to and by the summarization process involved in scoring. As a result, a comprehensive neuropsychological assessment battery will include multiple dimensions and methods such as structured tests, maneuvers, and tasks, as well as systematic observations to assess multiple capabilities (see **Table 1** for examples). In addition, measuring early indicators of emerging executive function at this stage should include instruments that tap behaviors similar to those involved in everyday functions in the real world. Functions important to assess include:

- Posture, gait, strength, fluency, and coordination of movement, activity level, and speed during large muscle activity such as locomotion and synchrony of left- and right-sided movement.

- Prehension, hand posture, and coordination during reaching, grasping, manipulation, and holding writing instruments, including precision in the use of tools, puzzle and form board completion, and construction tasks.

- Visual–motor integration to complete puzzles and block tasks requiring matching images and shapes and to imitate structural characteristics of constructed objects, copying shapes and forms using crayons and pencils.

- Characteristics of sustained attention that indicate the ability to focus on a specific stimulus, inhibit responses to distractions from extraneous stimuli, and the development of control over excitation and inhibition required to react appropriately to a visual or auditory stimulus.

- Concept formation and task attainment that reflects (1) simultaneously processing visual and spatial information to recognize a pattern or reason through a problem's solution, and (2) sequential processing of temporal sequences of information, where each idea is related in a linear and temporal manner to the preceding one, held in memory, and used within a few seconds.

- Problem solving and planning are included in executive functions that reflect concept formation, cause and effect relationships involved in reasoning, and sustained task orientation that persists to goal attainment or mastery, and with sufficient motivation and tolerance of frustration.

- Receptive communication involves the ability to identify objects or images verbally referenced by another, and with increasing ability to relate morphological markers such as pronouns, prepositions, plurals, and tense.

- Expressive communication using words, along with gestures and facial expressions, with increases in the length of utterances, the use of morphological markers and the complexity of content included in naming and verbalizing thoughts about objects, images, people, ideas, feelings, and actions. Turn-taking during conversation and joint referencing of topical information increase as vocabulary and usage customs are used and learned.

- Social and emotional competencies include initiating independent exploration and play, as well as combining autonomy with connectedness with significant individuals (parents, siblings, playmates). Toddlers become aware of their importance and are able to articulate positive attributes, enjoying recognition of strengths, and accepting help with challenges. Playing alongside playmates leads into emerging participation in group activities. Temperament characteristics can become more moderated with support and greater regulatory control is evident as communication and socialization skills become more refined and sophisticated.

- Adaptive life skills emerge as toddlers develop the ability to integrate the above functions in their natural environment. These include (1) functional activities such as feeding, dressing, toilet learning; (2) involvement with peers in social play and learning environments, taking both leader and follower roles appropriately; and (3) beginning participation as an active contributor in the family and, where applicable, child-care context.

Future Trends: Integrating Neuroimaging and Brain Mapping of Structure and Function with Neuropsychological Assessments in the First 3 Years

Brain imaging and mapping methods to characterize brain structure and electrical, metabolic, and oxygen transport activity have recently been adapted for applications beginning in the neonatal period and are elaborated elsewhere in the encyclopedia. Pending clinical trials currently underway, diffuse optical tomography (DOT) may be added to assessments available for use in newborns. DOT is a newly developed technique using light-reflecting patches to map functional activity in the neonatal brain by measuring blood movement and its oxygen levels. DOT and near-infrared (NIR) OT have been useful for examining functioning of the primary sensory area of the cortex, and event-related OT paradigms can provide important information about brain functions underlying perceptual, motor, and cognitive development in early infancy. Advantages to optical topography are

that it permits safe assessment without the exposure to radiation, and without the need for either constraint or sedation, both of which have differential influences on consciousness and attention that limit observable functions and the information available as a result.

In older infants, toddlers, and preschoolers, the use of fMRI has been instrumental in documenting the anatomy and function of varied brain regions and their relations to behavior and cognitive processing during varied tasks. Newer adaptations of diffusion tension imaging (DTMRI) to examine fiber tracts and myelination are being developed for use in younger children and should help delineate the development of healthy and adaptive neuropsychological development, as well as illuminating the mechanisms underlying developmental disorders associated with structural and functional characteristics.

Conclusions

The developmental course and competencies within components involved in neuropsychological functions varies widely across individuals. The assessment process is essential for documenting qualitative aspects of functions within each domain at a given time point, as well as individual developmental trajectories in functioning across the first 3 years. This is important for understanding healthy neuropsychological development, as well as for identifying vulnerabilities and appropriate interventions. Examining brain–behavior relations using multidimensional and multimethod assessment protocols provides a comprehensive view of the developing child. Incorporating parent and professional caregiver reports with home environment observations, in addition to structured tasks administered in both formal and real world settings, enable the most complete measurement of neuropsychological functions. This profile can then be used to document individual characteristics and develop preventive and therapeutic interventions to address problems and facilitate adaptation most effectively.

See also: Bayley Scales of Infant Development; Cognitive Neuroscience; Developmental Disabilities: Cognitive; Neurological Development.

Suggested Readings

Aylward GP (1997) *Infant and Early Childhood Neuropsychology.* New York: Plenum Publishing Corp.
Aylward GP (2002) Cognitive and neuropsychological outcomes: More than IQ scores. *Mental Retardation and Developmental Disabilities Research Reviews* 8(4): 234–240.

Bell MA and Wolfe CD (2004) Emotion and cognition: An intricately bound developmental process. *Child Development* 75(2): 366–370.

Dedham S (2005) Assessing Social–Emotional Development in Children from a Longitudinal Perspective, National Children's Study. http://www.nationalchildrensstudy.gov/research/analytic_reports/upload/Assessing-Social-Emotional-Development-in-Children-From-a-Longitudinal-Perspective-for-the-National-Children-s-Study.pdf(accessed on 20 July 2007).

Hooper S, Molnar A, Beswick J, and Jacobi-Vessels J (in press) Neuropsychological assessment of the preschool child: Expansion of the field. In: Bracken BA (ed.) *Psychoeducational Assessment of the Preschool Child,* 4th edn. Boston: Allyn and Bacon.

Lipkin PH and Allen MC (eds.) (2005) Special issue: Neurodevelopmental assessment of the fetus and young infant. *Mental Retardation and Developmental Disabilities Research Reviews* 11(1): 171–275.

Lipkin PH and Allen MC (eds.) (2005) Special issue: Neurodevelopmental assessment of the young child. *Mental Retardation and Developmental Disabilities Research Reviews* 11(3): 1–106.

Meisels SJ and Fenichel E (eds.) (1996) *New Visions for the Developmental Assessment of Infants and Young Children.*

Washington, DC: Zero to Three: National Center for Infants, Toddlers and Families.

Patterson J, Heim S, Friedman JT, Choudhury N, and Benasich A (2006) Development of structure and function in the infant brain: Implications for cognition, language and social behaviour. *Neurosciences and Biobehavioral Reviews* 30(6): 718–729.

Public Broadcasting System (2002) 3-D brain anatomy. *The Secret Life of the Brain.* http://www.pbs.org/wnet/brain/3d/index.html (accessed on 20 July 2007).

Sudheimer K, Winn B, Kerndt G, Shoaps J, Davis K, Fobbs A, Jr., and Johnson, J. *The Human Brain Atlas,* http://www.msu.edu/~brains/brains/human/index.html (accessed on 20 July 2007).

The National Children's Study Plan (2004) http://www.nationalchildrensstudy.gov/research/study_plan/upload/NCS-Study-Plan-2004.pdf (accessed on 20 July 2007).

The National Children's Study Plan (2004) http://www.nationalchildrensstudy.gov/research/methods_studies/upload/Pilot-Study-Protocol-Application-of-Measures-of-Spontaneous-Motor-Activity-for-Behavioral-Assessment-in-Human-Infants.pdf.

Newborn Behavior

E C Goldfield, Harvard University, Boston, MA, USA

Glossary

Attractor (repeller) – A goal state of a system, recognizable in newborn infants by behaviors that tend to converge toward it (or diverge away from it). Mathematical analyses reveal a relatively small set of basic attractors, but their interactions make possible a rich set of states from which to explore the environment.

Behavioral dynamics – The underlying predispositions of humans to organize behavior around certain goals, such as visually exploring, eating, communicating, and locomoting. Each of these unique goals may be achieved by particular organizations of the multiple subsystems of the body and environment.

Perception-action (PA) cycle – A flow of information and energy between biological/psychological systems and the environment that makes it possible for systems to grow and achieve differentiated functions. The organization of newborn infant PA cycles in achieving particular goals is revealed by stable states, coordinative relationships between body segments, during goal-directed movements in the context of social and nonsocial information.

Introduction

The newborn period, extending to 12 weeks after birth, encompasses a remarkable transition from limited perceptual guidance of movement to the beginnings of well-organized perceiving and acting. Just after birth, newborns are motorically immature, but exhibit certain well-organized behaviors that may have specific functions during both the fetal period and the transition from a fluid to an air-breathing environment, as well as during later development. For example, intrinsic patterns of *in utero* bilateral kicking may orient the fetus for vertex (head down) delivery, while hand placement with thumb in the mouth, and swallowing of amniotic fluid may maintain the organ systems that will need to sustain life immediately after birth. These organized patterns are at the same time amenable to changing experiences as the muscles work against the full force of gravity, inflate the lungs for the first nascent breaths and cries, and allow rhythmical suckling at the mother's breast. A challenge for researchers has been to understand this balance between the functional preparedness of newborn behavior and its adaptability to changing environmental circumstances.

Stepping, rooting, and other early newborn behaviors are often called reflexive, but there is a reason to question what a reflex actually tells us about the underlying basis for newborn behavior. Classically, a reflex is an organized pattern of motor behavior made possible by spinal circuitry and elicited by a particular type of sensory stimulation. For example, the rooting reflex is an orientation of the head toward a source of peri-oral stimulation. However, it may not be possible to elicit rooting in certain organismic states of sleep and wakefulness, called behavioral states, and conversely, rooting may occur spontaneously, when the infant has not eaten for a while. Therefore, a broader context may help clarify the prepared behavioral patterns of newborns and their significance for development from the earliest postnatal period to around 12 weeks, when some dramatic new developmental changes occur, thus effectively ending the 'newborn' designation.

The Functional Organization of Behavior

Intrinsic Organization

Since the mid 1990s these has been a notable shift away from an approach that emphasizes the domination of reflexes in newborn behavior toward an appreciation of behavior as influenced by the growth-related changes in characteristics of component systems in the context of a changing environment. A dynamic(al) systems approach provides a new vantage point from which to understand the emerging stability of newborn behavior in the face of growth and of environmental perturbations. It asserts that behavior is not localized in any internal structure (such as the spinal cord in the case of reflexes) nor controlled by environmental contingencies. Instead, behavior emerges as an outcome of the interactions between nervous system activity, the physics of the environment, the biomechanics of the body, perceptual information about the current state of the body (e.g., due to patterns of receptor stimulation during head orientation, or provided by ongoing autonomic functions, such as breathing), and the demands of certain functional tasks. These tasks include eating, grasping hold of things, locomoting, and communicating with others. Each task changes the way that the resources of the embodied nervous system and environment are used to achieve a behavioral outcome.

Perception-Action Cycles

When the earlier example of newborn rooting is considered in the broader functional context of obtaining nutrients, such as milk during breastfeeding, it becomes apparent that rooting is just part of a pattern that initiates and maintains an organized sequence of behavior, what may be called a perception-action or PA cycle. Rooting, as part of an appetitive PA cycle, continues until the infant is either satiated or the caregiver withdraws the nipple. It serves to orient the mouth in the direction of the breast, and at the same time initiates mouthing activity that becomes useful for suckling when milk flows from the breast. It is the combination of the context of hunger, an intact nervous system capable of guiding the mouth to the breast and latching onto the nipple, the availability and perception of the breast nipple, and the flow of milk that temporarily assembles a dynamical solution for the task of eating. The set of movements that characterize an appetitive PA cycle are only apparent when all of these, and possibly other, components are coupled together into a stable ensemble. Sometimes, only partial context is available to the newborn, and this may initiate, but not maintain the appetitive cycle, as is the case in the clinical elicitation of a 'rooting reflex' by stroking the cheek. What, then, is the glue that sustains organized PA cycles of newborn behavior?

Behavioral States: A Context for the Organization of Newborn Behavior

To understand the origins of the distinctive human ways of being and acting better, developmental scientists have derived taxonomies for newborn behavior, called behavioral states. These are defined as discontinuous stable patterns of sleep and wakefulness that may emerge from spontaneous interactions among many fluctuating subsystems (see **Table 1**). Each stable behavioral state is comprised of a set of component physiological subsystems, such as breathing and heart rate. The average frequency of the rhythms generated by these subsystems fluctuates around a certain range of activity. The interactions between these rhythms determine whether observable behavior will remain in a particular stable state or make a transition to one of the other states. For example, an indication that a newborn's behavioral state is about to switch from rapid eye movement (REM) sleep to regular sleep is usually a change of breathing from fast, irregular to slower respirations followed by cessation of facial twitches and episodic limb movements, a slowing of heart rate, and a shift of electroencephalogram (EEG) activity from a low-amplitude high-frequency to a high-amplitude low-frequency pattern.

The tendency of muscle groups to function together in a task-oriented fashion varies as a function of behavioral state, and this implies that the origins of the newborn human's intentionality to do different things may emerge out of the context of behavioral state transitions. This is apparent in postural changes during the transition between behavioral states. From state 4 waking activity to state 2 (active) sleep, there is a loss of active posture: the baby's arms fall gently, with the fingers open to a semi-flexed tonic posture, and the legs are abducted. During state 1 sleep, by contrast, newborns show more symmetrical arm flexion and leg adduction. During state 2 sleep, there are fine movements of the fingers and toes as well as smiles and grimaces not present in state 1.

The functional specificity of muscle group organization, depending upon the current state of component subsystems, is also apparent in newborn head orientation.

Table 1 Newborn behavioral states and their defining component behaviors

Behavioral state	Definition
State 1 (regular, quiet, synchronous, or non-REM sleep)	The infant is at rest, and resistance of the limbs to passive movement by an examiner is low. There is little diffuse motor activity except for intermittent startles and occasional rhythmic mouthing. The eyelids are firmly closed and at rest, and eye movements are rare. The face is relaxed and symmetrical. Respirations are regular in rhythm (between 30 and 40 min^{-1}) and constant in amplitude.
State 2 (irregular sleep, paradoxical REM sleep)	The eyes are closed and may be pinched or relaxed. Intermittent horizontal and vertical eye movements can be observed through eyelids. Respirations are irregular, faster than in state 1 (average 48 min^{-1}), and the overall pattern may be interrupted by brief apneic (nonbreathing) spells. The face is relaxed, but there are intermittent grimaces that range from 'smiling' to pre-cry faces. Mouthing is not rhythmic. Resistance of the limbs to passive movements is greater than during state 1. Limb movements that involve the trunk and one or more limbs follow no obvious temporal sequence, and periods of relative inactivity vary with periods of stirring.
State 3 (alert inactivity)	The limbs and trunk are at rest except for occasional small movements. The face is relaxed. The eyes are open and have a 'bright, shiny appearance'. Respirations are constant in rate and amplitude, but more variable and faster than in state 1. While alert, the infant scans the environment, and maintains a stable posture.
State 4 (waking activity)	There are frequent bursts of generalized motor activity involving the limbs, trunk, and head. These vary in intensity and duration. The eyes are open and the infant may be silent, moaning, grunting, or whimpering, but does not cry for sustained periods. Respirations are grossly irregular. The eyes may scan intermittently, but only during periods of relative motor inactivity.
State 5 (crying)	Cry vocalizations are the essential defining criterion. They may vary in intensity from persistent whimpering to loud screaming. Vigorous crying is accompanied by diffuse motor activity, or by a rigid trunk posture. Patterns of respiration are subordinate to crying.

REM, rapid eye movement.

Back-lying newborns with the head supported gently at the body midline will turn it to the right when released, and keep it in a predominantly right-sided posture. This bias, referred to as functional lateral asymmetry, appears due to a combination of factors, including behavioral state, generalized postural asymmetry, and the biomechanical constraints of a heavy head supported by the weak muscles of the neck.

Waking States

The stabilization of recognizable sleep states during the postnatal period, as described in **Table 1**, is accompanied by differentiated waking. For example, caregivers soon distinguish when the infant is 'ready for play', 'hungry', or 'in need of a nap'. Implicit in these temporally recurring and differentiated waking states is that the newborn is becoming increasingly able to express in its behavior the goals that characterize what humans are inclined to do, or to avoid. Researchers have attempted to quantify how the infant's behavior becomes organized around these differentiated goals. Particular ensembles of waking behavior that are likely to recur with certain temporal regularity, and are organized around certain identifiable goals are referred to here as behavioral dynamics.

An example of behavioral dynamics is when the newborn's hand moves inexorably toward the face, enters the mouth, and is explored by the lips and tongue. We are more likely to see overall quieting behavior when this 'hand to mouth' behavior occurs, because peri-oral stimulation promotes non-nutritive sucking (NNS), which, in turn, has a pacifying effect on the infant's cardiac and respiratory activity. The central location of the mouth at the body midline as well as the dense innervation of the oral mucosa with many different types of receptor cells point to its fundamental unifying role in the earliest newborn behavior. When newborns bring their hands in contact with their mouths, the hand to mouth movements remain within a stable peri-oral region, suggesting that these organized movements reflect the goal-directed influences of an underlying attractor. An attractor is a concept from the mathematics of dynamical systems that expresses the tendency of movement paths that begin from many points to converge at a single endpoint. For example, during experimental tests in which a drop of sucrose solution is dispensed onto the tongue, newborns show a dramatic increase in hand movements to the mouth. Sucrose may have the effect of modifying the strength with which the underlying oral-attractor becomes the endpoint for many different points of origin of the hand.

With a change in the strength of one of the many goals underlying human behavior, we may see a change in the composition of the body's muscle groups used to enact the goal. For example, when a newborn becomes cold, there may be a transition to an attractor that marshals the organization of muscle groups in ways that increase body temperature, such as crying. Crying (discussed in greater detail below) promotes tightly shut eyes, and muscle flexion brings the limbs in close to the body, a likely means for reducing body heat loss. The flexion tendency also makes it more likely that the hand in proximity to the head will be brought to the mouth. The resulting pacification has the effect of relaxing muscle stiffness and flexion, and so dissolves the coordinative pattern of crying. The eyes open, the body quiets, and the newborn is visually alert and ready to explore the environment by means of moving the now relaxed limbs away from the body toward something being looked at.

With each transition to a different goal and a change in the underlying behavioral dynamics, the mouth becomes capable of assuming a new range of behaviors. For example, when quiet and visually engaged in looking at an adult who playfully protrudes the tongue, the infant may, in turn, extend his or her tongue. Now, the infant's hand rests at his or her side. Instead of using the mouth for NNS, or crying, the newborn now uses it as a means of exploration, social engagement, or communication. Such newborn tongue protrusion may even indicate a form of imitation (a possibility considered further below). The distinction between the infant's mouthing behavior during self-quieting, compared to tongue protrusion during visual engagement with an adult, implies that the lips, tongue, and other parts of the oral anatomy assume a different range of movement configurations depending upon the extant behavioral dynamics.

The sections that follow consider how the intrinsic organization of behavior just described is reflected in the kinds of things that newborn infants do. Newborns become able to orient to and explore sights and sounds, feed at the breast, cry vigorously when hungry, cold, or in pain, bring their hands to the mouth, kick, imitate certain observed facial gestures, and interact with other people. Although tightly organized to regulate physiological arousal, these behaviors also promote orienting to explore the physical and social world. The infant's own behaviors in a social context begin to dissolve the underlying organization of attractors so that they may become reorganized for further interactions.

The Organization of Newborn Behavior

Looking

Humans are a highly visual species. During the first few weeks after birth, newborns hungrily forage for visual information by looking at or away from specific objects and events in a manner that suggests an underlying behavioral dynamics. In behavioral experiments with newborns, it is possible to identify which of several objects an infant is looking at by determining corneal reflections of the objects with special infrared video cameras. Newborns

characteristically look at a particular object for some period of time and then look away. Computer simulations have been used to create mathematical models that behave in the same way as the visually foraging newborn, namely, by producing patterns of looking at and looking away with the same temporal organization. The simulations of transitions between looking at and looking away from objects that work best are characterized by a model that includes a certain amount of white noise, and a means for the system to make sudden transitions from one stable state to another, called hysteresis. In other words, the characteristic durations of newborn looking behavior can be captured by a means for rapid switching between two stable states (looking at or looking away) and a process that pushes the system to switch between these two stable states.

By placing visual gaze shifts in the broader context of the infant's body movements, it becomes apparent that during periods when there is little or no object movement, spontaneous fluctuations in motor activations may be responsible for 'unlocking' visual gaze from a state of 'looking at' to one of 'looking away'. For example, among 1-month-olds, during a period about 2.5 s before gaze shifts away from an object or event, amount of body movement increase and then briefly plateau. Then, about 1.5 s before, and again immediately prior to a gaze shift, body movement increases. These three successive increases in the amount of body movement prior to a shift in visual gaze away from an object or event may generate sufficient noise to drive the system from the stable 'gaze at' state to a 'gaze away' state. A source for the system noise that links general body movements to visual gaze shifts may be a brain area called the basal ganglia. Increased basal ganglia motor circuit activity appears to unlock visual gaze by suppressing inhibition of saccadic eye movements involved in visual gaze transitions. This coupling between general body movement and visual gaze highlights the embodied nature of all newborn behavior.

During periods when newborns fix their visual gaze on a changing pattern of optical stimulation, they are able to explore the information available. An example of visual information that is attractive to newborns and changes their visual behavior is a moving field of dot patterns that is made to either flow toward (loom) or away (zoom) from the head. In one experiment, 3-day-olds looked at a screen with flow patterns whose velocities ranged from 10 to 120 cm s^{-1}. Pressure-sensitive air bags placed under each infant's head measured any changes in head position and movement toward or away from the looming or zooming event. Compared to baseline trials on which the dots were motionless, mean head pressure was greater in all motion conditions, and was linearly related to the velocity of the looming patterns.

Considered together, these studies of looking behavior indicate that newborns become increasingly able to shift attention to particular targets, rather than be captured by motion, and become better able to organize body movements in the service of visual exploration, so that looking does not interfere with the performance of other behaviors. In other words, the eye–head system starts to become an integrated part of other PA cycles.

Eating

A starting point for understanding the behaviors involved in newborn breastfeeding and bottle feeding is sucking behavior. A traditional distinction is made between NNS and nutritive sucking (NS), or suckling, on the basis of the distribution of sucks over time and their relative variability. NNS consists of bursts of 5–10 sucks produced at an oscillation frequency of about 2 Hz, with sucking bursts, and pauses between bursts, of approximately equal duration. By contrast, NS is a slower, approximately 1.0–1.5 Hz rhythm that is characterized by a very long burst of suckling separated by relatively brief pauses. Even when the newborn produces well-organized suckling, NNS remains as a distinctive stable state.

Feeding behavior, like looking, appears to be governed by an underlying system that is able to rapidly switch between the NNS and suckling patterns. This switching between the NNS and suckling patterns may be made possible by the same kind of 'noise' described earlier for the visual system. For example, it is not unusual to see higher-frequency 'tremor' rhythms superimposed on sucking, and tremor may be an indication of a means by which the nervous system is able to rapidly switch between stable organizations of muscle groups.

Several studies have also examined how the intrinsic dynamics of infant sucking activities may be modulated by sensory input. One, for example, used externally applied mechanical stimulation to attempt to modify the intrinsic dynamics of the newborn's preferred sucking rhythm. For most of the newborns tested, the cycle period of sucking was lengthened to match the slower stimulation pattern, so that sucking became synchronized in a one-to-one relationship with stimulation. Another study has proposed an internal dynamic quantity, called tau guide, as a mechanism for precise control of intra-oral pressure during individual sucks. Tau guide is hypothesized to be generated within the nervous system, and changes from a rest level to a goal level. According to the hypothesis, during sucking, the infant uses perceptual information to detect the gap between the current intraoral pressure and its goal level, and regulates intraoral pressure so that it effectively closes the gap.

Other studies have shown that the ongoing activity of participating organ systems involved in feeding, including respiration and swallowing, has specific influences on the sucking pattern. It has been possible to use certain mathematical tools to reveal the ways by which newborns are able to couple the dynamics of multiple rhythmic

behaviors into a functional system for pumping milk into the mouth while maintaining breathing. For example, there are stable frequency relationships between newborn NNS and respiration, including two sucks for each breath, and three sucks for every two breaths, the patterns preferred by healthy full-term newborns during NNS.

When swallowing is considered with respect to the relation between sucking and breathing, the picture of how breastfeeding is achieved becomes remarkably complex. The human pharynx is the shared anatomical pathway for both air to the lungs and nutrients to the esophagus and gastrointestinal tract (see **Figure 1**). The variables involved include not only brain systems, but also the mechanical properties of the skeletal anatomy, valves and pumps of the oral anatomy, spring-like properties of the muscles and tendons, and information from receptor arrays lining lingual–pharyngeal tissue. For swallowing activity to be successfully integrated into the respiratory cycle during oral feeding, the pharynx must be continually reconfigured to achieve two mutually exclusive goals: swallowing and respiration. During swallowing, the airway is protected by elevation of the larynx so that it makes contact with a structure called the hyoid, and so that another structure, the epiglottis effectively seals off the airway. The reconfiguration of the pharynx from a passageway for air to the lungs to one that pushes and pulls fluids into the opening to the gastrointestinal tract must occur within fractions of a second over repeated cycles of sucking, swallowing, and breathing.

Among invertebrates, nonhuman vertebrates, and humans, rhythmic interactions between body organs tend to fall into certain types of phase relationships, where phase refers to the relative timing of a point in

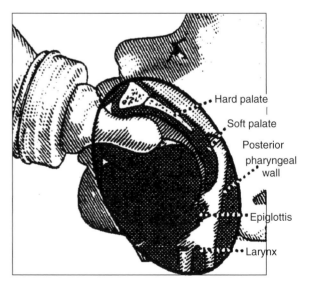

Figure 1 Oral anatomy used for suckling. A resting position of the tongue during feeding with a bottle and nipple is shown. Note that the soft palate is relaxed, and that the tongue and lips form a seal around the nipple.

one rhythm with respect to a second point on another. There is growing evidence that the behavioral dynamics of newborn breastfeeding involves a coupling of multiple systems that enter into lawful phase relationships with each other. In one study of breastfeeding by month-old infants, sucking, swallowing, and breathing were recorded. **Figure 2** illustrates the interactions between swallowing and the respiratory pattern of inspiration and expiration. It shows that swallows tend to occur in clusters of two or three in succession. When a cluster of swallows occurs, there are particular influences on the respiratory pattern. In this particular case, the respiratory inspiration is suppressed, as indicated by the reduced height of the inspiration peak. This implies that swallows do not occur at random locations within the respiratory cycle, but rather are organized around inspiration peaks. **Figure 3**, based upon a mathematical analysis of the relative phase at which swallowing occurs, shows that infants consistently swallowed at two locations within the respiratory cycle: close to 90° and 270° relative phase, respectively. Thus, the phase locations of swallowing occur just before or just after peaks of respiratory inspiration. In this way, swallows occur within 'safe regions' of the respiratory cycle, defined by their phase location.

Breastfeeding is a particularly challenging task for infants, because the flow of milk from the breast may be quite variable. For example, there are periods during which there are hormonally induced 'letdowns' of milk, responsive to the stimulation of sucking and the mother's own physiology. Nevertheless, most healthy newborns fed by breast rapidly learn to coordinate sucking, swallowing, and breathing so that the goal of ingesting milk does not compete with the goal of breathing. The finding of safe regions for swallowing within the rhythmic pattern of sucking and breathing implies that as long as swallows occur within a particular range of relative phase values around the peak of respiration, the airway is protected from milk entry. There is some evidence that perceptual information specific to the flow rate of milk may change the infant's behavior to keep swallows within this safe range. Thus, the tendency in feeding behavior is for newborns to become increasingly effective at using perceptual information to guide coordination of sucking, swallowing, and breathing behavior.

Crying

The first lusty cries of newborns not only clear the lungs of residual amniotic fluid, but also signal to caregivers 'here I am'. How is the cry signal used for communication? The production of newborn cry sounds results from a complex interplay of autonomic and central nervous activity as well as the dynamics of laryngeal vocal fold (or cord) vibration resulting from high velocity air forced from the lungs through narrow anatomical passageways. Muscle groups of the entire body seem to be coupled together to produce these forceful expulsions of air from the lungs. This is apparent from the rigid posture of the trunk and limbs during crying. After interacting with the vocal folds, the acoustic energy of the vibrating air molecules carries information that is specific to the structure of the human vocal tract, and therefore serves as one of the earliest forms of vocal communication between newborns and their caregivers.

Research on newborn cries over more than four decades has identified the frequency components of both typical and pathological cries, and it has become possible to use acoustic analysis of newborn cries for diagnosis of specific clinical problems. Acoustic analysis of the component frequencies of cry sounds is made possible by a device, called a spectrogram, that produces a picture of sounds (see **Figure 4**). Initial studies emphasized one component of cry, its fundamental frequency F_0, the lowest frequency component, generally perceived as pitch. One reason for the emphasis on fundamental frequency is that there is a well-understood relationship between physiological stress and the way that the autonomic nervous system is involved in cry production. Via the tenth cranial nerve of the parasympathetic nervous system, also called the vagus nerve, the nucleus ambiguous of the medulla provides input to various organs involved in crying. These organs include the bronchi of the lungs, esophagus, pharynx, larynx, and heart. Acute stresses precipitate a parasympathetic withdrawal of vagal output from the nucleus ambiguous, resulting in increased

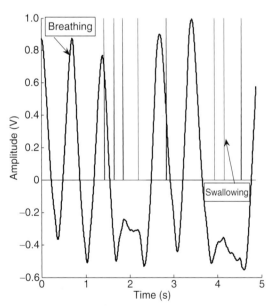

Figure 2 The location of four swallows, filtered to show where their peak amplitude occurs, is indicated by a vertical line for each. The inspiratory peaks and valleys of the respiratory cycle are marked by crosses. Swallows tend to be located within particular portions of the respiratory cycle, namely, just before or after an inspiration peak.

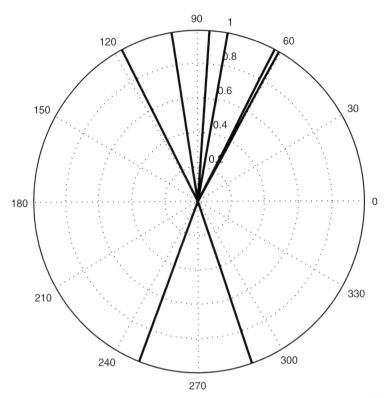

Figure 3 When each of the swallows of **Figure 1** is plotted with respect to its relative phase location within the respiratory cycle, they tend to occur within a 'safe region' for swallowing, that is, at around 90°, and 270°, relative phase.

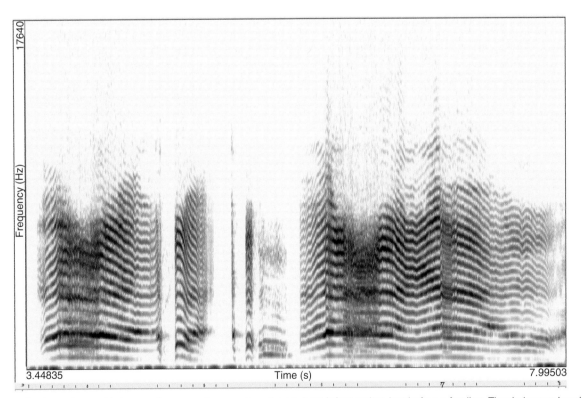

Figure 4 A spectrographic image of an acoustic recording of a newborn infant crying, just before a feeding. The dark wavy bands are frequency components created by the vibration of the vocal cords when air is vigorously expelled from the lungs.

heart rate and an increase in F_0. The cries of healthy nonstressed infants have F_0 values within the 200–600 Hz range. The average duration of a single cry is about 0.5–1.5 s, and crying usually has a melodic pattern of falling or rising/falling.

An increasingly accepted view is that crying is a graded signal. In other words, cry vocalizations vary quantitatively on some acoustic dimension, such as duration or frequency. By increasing or decreasing the values along this dimension, an acoustic signal is produced that can be distinguished categorically by human perceivers. The most common cry characteristic indicating pathology is unusually high F_0 (i.e., very high-pitched crying), often up to 3 times the normal frequency (e.g., 570–1360 for prematurely born newborns). Abnormal cries have been identified for newborns with chromosomal, endocrine, metabolic, and neurological pathology, as well as malnourishment, exposure to harmful toxins or drugs *in utero*, and prematurity. The information value of the newborn cry signal increases dramatically when other variables are considered along with F_0. For example, pathology is also associated with an acoustic variable referred to as biphonation, the simultaneous production of two fundamental frequencies that results from independent vibration of the left and right vocal folds at unrelated frequencies. Biphonation indicates that in pathological conditions, instead of the sound production mechanisms working cooperatively, the vocal folds are not well coordinated. Biphonation is rare or absent in healthy infants, but common in newborns with pathology.

On the view that newborn cries are a graded signal, excessive crying by infants under 3 months of age, sometimes called colic, may be viewed as part of a normal pattern rather than as pathological. Even though they cry excessively, the F_0 of colicky newborns is within the normal range. Moreover, an organic etiology of colic is rare, and infants with colic do not have difficult temperaments. Why, then, do some infants between birth and 3 months cry excessively? According to the transient responsivity hypothesis, infants differ in their responsivity to similar stimulation, and these differences are expressed through various amounts of crying. An opiod-dependent mechanism has been identified as a contributor to increased responsivity and the excessive crying of infants with colic. For example, infants with colic who are given sucrose, an opioid-dependent calming agent, return to crying sooner after a period of time has elapsed following sucrose administration.

To summarize, the acoustic properties of crying seem to correspond directly to the changing characteristics of the many component physiological systems of the body. The information carried by the acoustics of the cry is, in a sense, a compressed summary of information about subsystems that can be decoded by other humans. Thus, by crying, the newborn has an effective means for directly communicating the status of the many subsystems of the body with a single, information-rich acoustic signal.

Performatory Use of the Hands

Although we tend to think of reaches as being performed only by the hands, the earliest newborn reaches suggest an initial tendency for the entire body to extend toward an object in a relatively undifferentiated fashion. For example, 3-week-olds recorded by means of sophisticated motion analysis systems, reach for objects by extending not only both arms but also their legs (and sometimes their head). These early reaches have distinctive temporal and spatial characteristics. The temporal organization of the earliest reaches consists of movement units based upon velocity profiles of arm trajectories. Each unit consists of an acceleration and deceleration phase, so that the boundary between movement units is a point of no acceleration. Movement units also reveal certain spatial characteristics, including particular curvature. The most distinctive changes in movement direction occur at the transition between movement units. In other words, the preferred places for changing movement direction are speed valleys. The two arms also have a tendency to move together along the body's longitudinal axis, abduct and adduct together, and extend together in the forward direction. These results all support a class of reach trajectory models based upon control of the hands via shifting equilibrium points through modulation of certain system parameters, such as stiffness.

The role of vision in the earliest reaches has been a controversial subject. However, a series of studies show that the earliest reaches are equally proficient in the light or dark, and do not require that the infant see the arm or hand. Instead, there is now evidence that the first reaches use haptic (active touch) and proprioceptive (joint sense) input to get the hand somewhere in the vicinity of the desired object. The newborn's spontaneous movement of the arms prior to these first reaches between 12 and 22 weeks is the starting point for successful reaches. Learning consists of modulating the stiffness and energy producing components of the arms so that they get the hands to the target. Each infant approaches this task with a particular intrinsic dynamics, a style of movement. Some infants make highly energetic flapping movements with the arms, while others make small and slow movements. In the former case, infants must learn to reach against a background of rhythmic, high-velocity movements from the shoulder. They do so by means of stiffening the joints through muscle co-activation (simultaneous activation of antagonist muscles) in order to modulate speed and force production. By contrast, more quiet infants who initially keep their hands on their chest or in their mouth, a low energy background, must scale up their arm movements in order to reach. Their task is to supply additional muscle power to their current movements. In both cases a single control parameter (a nonspecific parameter that moves the system through different states), muscle stiffness, is used to modulate existing movement trajectories, either by damping out excessive energy or by allowing addition of muscularly provided energy into the system.

Recent computer simulation studies have verified that the first reaches at the end of the newborn period are modulations of the arm's intrinsic dynamics. The simulations use an artificial neural network to control a model of an infant arm (a collection of linear springs that behave like muscles moving idealized masses of a particular size and shape like body tissue) interacting with the environment. Considered together, the motion analysis and simulation studies provide a clear picture of the starting point for learning to reach at the end of the newborn period.

Locomoting

Though one may think about newborn behavior as beginning soon after birth, certain postnatal behaviors may serve earlier functions *in utero*. Between 28 and 36 weeks gestational age, the body of the fetus has grown sufficiently to fill the uterus. Contact of the legs with the uterine walls may make it possible for kicking movements to change body orientation so that close to the time of delivery the fetus is in a vertex position, with the head near the cervix. After birth, the context of these same leg movements changes dramatically, as gravity exerts its full influence on the body. It is against this background of the transition from a fluid to an air medium, and the pull of gravity on the body, that the study of neonatal kicking and stepping began to change our view of the relation between brain, body, and environment more than two decades ago.

The logic of these classic studies is as follows: Newborn infants may be observed to perform kicking movements while in a supine (on the back) posture, and to produce stepping movements when held upright. Curiously, however, while supine, newborns continue to produce kicking movements, their upright stepping movements 'disappear' during this same period. What might be the basis for the apparent disappearance of upright stepping but not supine kicking? An initial study found that supine newborns perform kicking movements that are identical to upright stepping with respect to kinematic measures, such as joint angles, and electromyographic (EMG) measures, such as relative timing of muscle activations. One possible explanation for the apparent disappearance of stepping is that the underlying central muscle activations continue, but with the rapid deposit of fat in the legs, the full effects of gravity produce a force great enough to resist the forces produced by the leg flexor muscles, and prevent them from being lifted. In other words, in an upright posture, the leg muscles are too weak to move the leg mass against gravity because the rate

of body mass increases much more rapidly than rate of increase in leg strength. By contrast, in a supine posture where gravity does not act against leg flexion, kicking is possible.

To further examine this explanation, another study examined the relationship between leg mass and rate of physical growth at 2, 4, and 6 weeks of age. Physical growth was determined by anthropometric measures of body build characteristics, including ponderal index, a measure of relative stockiness (weight/crown-heel length) and estimated by leg volume. At 4 weeks of age, newborns who most rapidly gained weight and 'chubbiness' performed the fewest number of steps. Those infants who gained most stepped less, and this implies that muscle strength may have lagged behind rate of weight gain. To further examine this possibility, an experiment was conducted that added small weights to the legs to approximate average weight gain in the legs between 4 and 6 weeks. With weights added, stepping by 4-week-olds declined significantly, and both knee and hip angles increased, indicating less strong flexion. A second experiment used a manipulation that reduced the effects of leg mass by allowing infants to perform stepping movements while their legs were immersed in a tank of water. As predicted, compared to out-of-water stepping, when the legs were submerged, there was an increased step rate and knee angles decreased (indicating stronger flexion). Considered together, these early studies of newborn stepping and kicking support the view that behavior is the outcome of a combination of influences, including central muscle activation, body growth, changes in muscle strength, gravitational context, and sensitivity to perceptual (e.g., haptic and proprioceptive) information.

Current theoretical advances in understanding interactions between neural and biomechanical systems, as well as improvements in motion analysis and computer technologies have made it possible to identify (1) the initial conditions for coordination of newborn kicking, (2) possible changes in system parameters that may be the basis for modifying intrinsic dynamics, and (3) the significance of individual differences between healthy full-term infants and preterm infants at risk for debilitating medical conditions such as cerebral palsy. There are approximately 200 joints of the human body. Uniaxial joints work like hinges, biaxial joints like a hinge mounted on a swivel, and multiaxial joints like a ball and socket. The muscles are like springs, and the motor system is designed to modulate the coupling of the jointed body segments by changing the stiffness, damping, and length properties of groups of muscles that act together.

Two- and 4-week-old newborns exhibit a tight coupling between hip, knee, and ankle joints during kicking, the apparent result of simultaneous contractions of antagonist muscles around several joints during flexion, called co-contractions. This tight, intra-limb coupling of the joints during kicking movements may allow the newborn to explore the consequences of their own actions with a reduced set of possible movement trajectories. Within a few weeks, however, there begins a change in the tight intralimb coupling of the joints and, concomitantly, in the variability of movement trajectories. By 4 months of age, with looser coupling of the limb segments at the joints, infants begin to have the opportunity to change movement trajectories in order to capitalize on the natural dynamics of the legs. Thus, from fetal leg movements through the early weeks of the postnatal period, there appears to be continuity in coordinated intralimb activity that serves an initial function to aid the birth process, and eventually becomes integrated into the locomotor function by a process of modifying intrinsic dynamics.

The major neuropathology of premature infants of very low birth weight is called white matter injury (WMI), in reference to injury to areas of the brain containing the cortico-spinal tracts, which pass near the lateral ventricles and involve motor pathways. WMI is of particular concern because it appears to be related to later movement problems, including cerebral palsy. A consistent finding of studies that have compared intralimb coordination of preterm infants with or without WMI, and with healthy term infants is a difference in the decoupling of joints at the end of the newborn period. While healthy 1-month-olds born at term exhibit a decoupling of the more distal joints (knee–ankle, hip, ankle), premature infants with a history of WMI show a persistence of tight coupling among the leg joints. This implies that damage to motor areas of the brain interferes with the normal process by which limb movements are modified in the service of exploring new patterns.

Imitating

Skepticism greeted the initial reports that newborns were able to imitate adult facial gestures, such as tongue protrusions and mouth opening, and the controversy over neonatal imitation has continued for three decades. One reason for the skepticism is that the reported ability to imitate a seen facial gesture would seem to require cognitive abilities not apparent in other aspects of newborn behavior. That is, for neonates to imitate a facial gesture requires comparing a seen gesture (e.g., the tongue of an adult) with proprioceptive information about a gesture of their own that they cannot see. Consider imitation of mouth opening and tongue protrusion. In the imitation paradigm, an adult presents each newborn with each gesture, half presented first with mouth opening, the remainder in the reverse order. During each of two 4 min periods, there are 12 intervals during which the experimenter alternately demonstrates each gesture for 20 s, and then assumes a passive face for 20 s. The infant sucks on a pacifier during the demonstration. After presenting each gesture and assuming a neutral face, the pacifier is removed and replaced for the next demonstration. Videos of the infant's face are scored to determine frequency and duration of tongue protrusions and mouth openings, without knowledge of whether the infant is looking at the adult tongue protrusion, or mouth opening, or the passive face.

The basic finding of the original studies and of the many subsequent replications is most robust for a particular gesture, tongue protrusion, compared to mouth opening. Newborns produce more tongue protrusions of longer duration in response to the adult tongue protrusion delay than to a mouth-opening display. One explanation for this finding is active intermodal mapping (AIM) hypothesis, a claim that imitation is a process of matching a gesture to a seen target. The hypothesis is based upon a presumed feedback loop between the newborn's motor performance (e.g., protruding the tongue) and a seen target (the adult's tongue). Further, the hypothesis is based upon mediation by a neural system that enables newborns to detect equivalences between their own acts and seen gestures.

Despite many replications, critics have argued that neonatal tongue movements are not based upon the capability for matching, but rather are a prepotent response to any sufficiently arousing event in any sensory modality. For example, newborns show tongue protrusions during the silence following periods of music (the Barber of Seville, no less). In this alternative explanation, tongue protrusion is a form of mouthing in response to arousal, a very early exploratory behavior. But there may be something special about specific neonatal tongue and mouth movements and hearing speech sounds, rather than music. When presented with two sounds /a/, typically produced with the mouth open, or /m/, typically produced by sealing the lips, newborns produced more mouth opening after /a/ models than after /m/ models.

A stunning recent discovery about the brains of monkeys and humans supports the idea that the early nervous system is able to respond in specific ways, or resonate to, biological actions (such as tongue protrusion), as expected for matching behavior. In the monkey, there are neurons, called 'F5 mirror neurons' that discharge both when the animal makes a specific action, and when it observes another individual making a similar action. It should be noted that neurons with these properties do not code individual muscle movements. Instead, they correlate with specific actions. Brain-imaging studies of humans show parallels in the human brain with monkey mirror neurons. When humans observe hand-grasping movements or produce these movements, there is an activation of the left inferior frontal cortex, the left superior temporal sulcus, parts of the left parietal lobe, and the rostral part of the supplementary motor area. Significantly, these areas are all lateralized to the left hemisphere of the brain, the hemisphere involved in the production of hand/arm gestures.

It is well known that the brain is organized into regions that correspond to particular parts of the body, called body maps, and that visual displays of particular organs, particularly parts of the face and hands, activate specific brain regions. This implies that activation of mirror neurons in different brain regions could map to specific parts of the body. But a complete account of neonatal imitation will have to consider not only specialized brain regions, but also the constraints imposed by the characteristics of body organs of an embodied brain. For example, while brain maps may emulate 'where' the body is, muscular and skeletal structure restrict what body parts are able to do under the constraints of gravity and other forces acting on them. Neonatal imitation may indicate the starting point from which infants must learn that tongues and mouths can be used to do some things, but not others. Both the intrinsic dynamics of the tongue and mouth, apparent in neonatal imitation, and its possibilities for exploratory activity of what it can do, will probably play a role in understanding this intriguing phenomenon.

Emerging Behavioral Dynamics at the End of the Newborn Period

New Possibilites for Exploration

While PA cycles during the first days of life are organized by goal-states, or attractors that seem to limit the possibilities for action, those at the end of the newborn period between 8 and 12 weeks seem to exhibit a dissolving of attractors so that new possibilities for action may be explored. This period has been called the 'two month revolution', and is characterized by a new selectivity in directing PA cycles to perceptual information that modulates the control of muscle settings and energy output. This revolution, then, is all about the infant gaining perceptual control of action at a time when the degrees of freedom of action are dissolving.

One illustration of this emerging capability is in the way infants learn to move an overhead mobile by producing precise leg postures or movements that have certain parameter settings, that is, a certain degree of flexion or extension. Even month-old infants are able to learn to kick in order to move a mobile, using a learning procedure called visual conjugate reinforcement. In this procedure, the mobile is tethered in some way to a leg so that kicking produces an interesting visual event, is reinforcing, and so is likely to continue. By 3 months of age, infants become able to learn a more specific motor solution that establishes perceptual control over something moving in the environment. In one study, goniometers, devices worn at the joints to identify angular rotation, were used to determine whether 3-month-old infants could produce the precise knee flexion angle specified by a contingent relation to the mobile. Whenever an infant produced the specified

angle, the mobile was made to move. Remarkably, during this period of 8–12 weeks, infants begin to use a strategy of controlling their knee flexions by producing small movement fluctuations around the joint angle specified by the experimenter as the one that activates the mobile.

A second example of infants learning to precisely modulate their behavior during perceptually guided exploratory activity comes from a study of 2-month-olds and newborns. The infants were presented with sounds related in specific ways to their sucking behavior. In an analog condition, the amount of pressure applied on the pacifier directly covaried with the pitch (fundamental frequency). In this condition, sound provided the infant with information about continuous modulation of sucking behavior. Each time that infants sucked above a minimum pressure threshold, they heard a zero delay continuous sound with frequencies that varied according to the amount of pressure produced. By contrast, in the nonanalog condition, pitch variation was random. In the analog condition, 2-month-olds, but not newborns, generated significantly more pressure just at the required threshold. As was the case for kicking, infants at the end of the newborn period are now able to precisely modulate their perceptually guided actions.

Conclusion

Beginning at around 8–12 weeks, behavioral states start to become differentiated into the more familiar waking activities of looking at and away, reaching and grasping, eating, kicking, and imitating others. The process by which this occurs is not yet completely understood. However, there seems to be a general trend toward dissolving the tight coupling of intersegmental movements in the service of activities that direct action and attention more selectively to distal social and nonsocial events. This trend illustrates that from birth onward, there is a continuing complementary relationship between acting and perceiving, and that the development of newborn action has consequences for both more mature performatory skills and more effective exploration.

Acknowledgments

The writing of this article was supported by grants R01DC007127, R43HD047128, R43HD049954 from the National Institutes of Health to the author, and by a grant from the National Institutes of Health to the Children's Hospital Boston Mental Retardation and Developmental Disabilities Research Center, PO1 HD18655.

See also: Breastfeeding; Crying; Feeding Development and Disorders; Motor and Physical Development:

Locomotion; Motor and Physical Development: Manual; Neuropsychological Assessment; Perception and Action; Reflexes; Sleep.

Suggested Readings

Goldfield E (1995) *Emergent Forms: Origins and Early Development of Human Action and Perception.* New York: Oxford.

Goldfield E (2007) A dynamical systems approach to infant oral feeding and dysphagia: From model system to therapeutic medical device. *Ecological Psychology* 19: 21–48.

Meltzoff AN and Moore MK (1997) Explaining facial imitation: A theoretical model. *Early Development and Parenting* 6: 169–192.

Thelen E and Smith LB (1994) *A Dynamic Systems Approach to the Development of Cognition and Action.* Cambridge: MIT Press.

Thelen E, Corbetta D, Kamm K, *et al.* (1993) The transition to reaching: Mapping intention and intrinsic dynamics. *Child Development* 64: 1058–1098.

Warren WH (2006) The dynamics of perception and action. *Psychological Review* 113: 358–389.

Wolff PH (1987) *The Development of Behavioral States and the Expression of Emotions in Early Infancy.* Chicago: University of Chicago Press.

Nutrition and Diet

M M Black, University of Maryland, Baltimore, MD, USA
B Lozoff, University of Michigan, Ann Arbor, MI, USA

Glossary

Body mass index (BMI) – Weight in kilograms divided by (height in meters)^2.

Cretinism – A condition of severely stunted physical and mental growth, caused by untreated congenital deficiency of thyroid hormones (hypothyroidism).

Low birth weight – Birth weight less than 2500 g.

Premature – Delivery prior to 37 weeks.

Stunted – Length-for-age (<2 years)/height-for-age (>2 years) that is less than –2 standard deviation scores based on age and gender-adjusted growth charts.

Synaptogenesis – The formation of synapses, which are the junctions that allow neurons (cells of the nervous system) to form interconnected neural circuits to signal to each other and to non-neuronal cells, such as those in muscles or glands.

Wasted – Weight-for-length (≤2 years)/BMI (>2 years) that is –2 standard deviation scores or less based on age and gender-adjusted growth charts.

birth weight are at risk for poor development, particularly if they are raised in a low-income family without access to adequate nutrients or nurturant caregiving. Epidemiological evidence suggests that the negative cycle initiated early in life is often manifested through growth, health, and academic problems in childhood and adolescence, and can continue into adulthood with increased risk for chronic illnesses and decreased economic potential. In addition, women who are undernourished are at risk for inadequate fetal nutrition during pregnancy, thereby extending the negative cycle into the next generation. Although a lifespan approach emphasizes that nutritional deficiencies at any point in the cycle can lead to subsequent problems throughout the lifespan, disruption of a negative cycle can often occur through interventions, such as adequate nutrients and a stimulating and nurturant family. This review of the evidence related to nutritional deficiencies is divided into 11 topics related to nutrition and early child development: (1) early years, (2) pregnancy, (3) breastfeeding, (4) micronutrient deficiencies, (5) infant growth, (6) premature birth and low birth weight, (7) failure to thrive (FTT), (8) overweight and rapid weight gain, (9) environmental stress, (10) feeding styles, and (11) food security.

Introduction

Nutrition is a major consideration for the healthy development of infants and young children. Undernutrition can begin prenatally and impact functioning throughout the lifespan (see **Figure 1**). Infants born early and with a low

Early Years

The early years of life (conception through the first 3 years) are often the focus of attention on nutrition because they represent a period of rapid increases in weight, height, organ growth, and developmental skills.

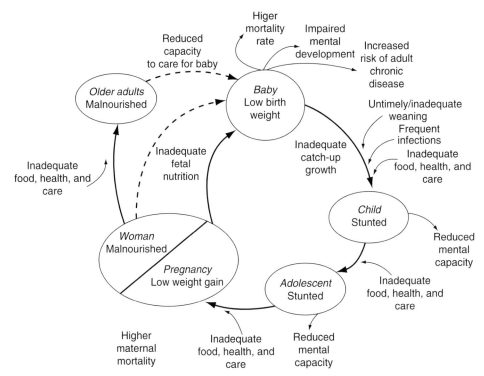

Figure 1 Conceptual model of the effects of undernutrition throughout the lifecycle. Reproduced from *Commission on the Nutrition Challenges of the 21st Century – Ending Malnutrition by 2020: An Agenda for Change in the Millennium*. Washington, DC: International Food Policy Research Institute, 2000, with permission from ACC/SCN.

Nutritional demands are high during this period and nutritional deficiencies can have long standing consequences.

Brain development begins prenatally and extends through adolescence (**Figure 2**). Cell migration and synaptogenesis (the formation of synapses, which are the junctions that allow neurons to form interconnected neural circuits to signal to each other and to non-neuronal cells, such as those in muscles or glands) begin prenatally, with newborns having many more synapses than adults. The early months and years are characterized by the formation and pruning of synapses, often in the prefrontal cortex where higher learning and regulation take place. The timing of these processes varies. For example, synaptogenesis and pruning occur in the areas of the brain governing vision and hearing prior to the areas that govern speech and language. There appear to be sensitive periods when development is especially vulnerable to nutrient deficiencies or lack of appropriate experiences. For example, children who experience chronic undernutrition early in life experience a slow down in linear growth (length) and are at risk for short stature and academic problems in childhood and reduced earning capacity in adulthood.

Pregnancy

During pregnancy, women's nutritional demands are high. Specific micronutrients are necessary for healthy

development of the fetus. For example, deficits in folic acid (vitamin B9) can lead to neural tube defects. Iodine deficiency can result in cretinism (a condition of severely stunted physical and mental growth, caused by untreated congenital deficiency of thyroid hormones) and mental retardation. Anemia attributed to iron deficiency (ID) can contribute to low iron stores in the fetus and interfere with the capacity for effective caregiving. The deficiencies may be prevented through prenatal vitamins or fortified foods that contain the necessary micronutrients, including folate, iron, and calcium. However, low-income women may have difficulty purchasing prenatal vitamins. Although fortification is present in many grains and cereals in the US, it may be inadequate to meet the needs of pregnant women.

In the US, the Special Supplemental Nutrition Program for Women, Infants, and Children (WIC) provides nutrient-rich food, educational counseling, and referrals to pregnant and nursing women, infants, and children under age 5 years who meet income and nutritional eligibility. Income eligibility is based on a household income below 185% of poverty and nutritional eligibility is based on a health professional determining that the applicant is at nutritional risk. On average, 1.95 million infants per month, or about half of all infants in the US receive WIC services.

WIC provides vouchers that may be redeemed at local grocery stores for specific foods, such as milk, eggs,

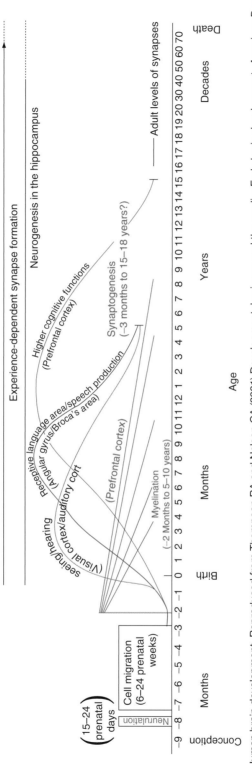

Figure 2 Human brain development. Reproduced from Thompson RA and Nelson CA (2001) Developmental science and the media: Early brain development. *American Psychologist* 56(1): 5–15.

cheese, fortified nonsweetened cereals, 100% fruit and vegetable juice, peanut butter, and infant formula and cereal. Most evaluations of WIC have focused on children's growth and have compared WIC participants with nonparticipants. However, the two groups often differ on motivational factors, making it difficult to attribute differences solely to WIC participation. Several studies that adjusted for confounding factors have found that WIC has a positive impact on infant birth weight, iron status, and early growth, with no additional risk for overweight.

Breastfeeding

Scientists hypothesize that there are at least three reasons breastfeeding may benefit cognitive development. First, the biological properties of breast milk, particularly essential fatty acids, provide the most appropriate food for the developing brain. Second, breast milk contains antibodies, growth factors, cytokines, and antimicrobial compounds that support the infant's immune system, providing protection against infectious risks and potentially promoting early cognitive development. Finally, the physical closeness of breastfeeding contributes to the mother–infant relationship and thereby enhances cognitive development.

Numerous studies have assessed the relationship between breastfeeding and mental development. However, it can be difficult to separate the motivational factors, along with the race/ethnic and socioeconomic differences associated with breastfeeding choice. Because breastfeeding cannot be randomized, scientists must rely on observational studies where the decision to breastfeed is closely linked to socioeconomic status. Mothers who breastfeed may differ in ways from mothers who choose not to breastfeed or are unable to breastfeed. Separating the effects of breastfeeding from the effects of the environment on a child's cognitive ability must be approached with care. Although most investigators adjust for mother's race/ethnicity and socioeconomic status, most have not examined factors such as maternal intelligence quotient (IQ) or motivation to breastfeed.

Most studies have reported a positive association between breastfeeding and better mental development in full-term or preterm children. Twenty-seven of 40 studies in a recent review concluded that breastfeeding provides an intellectual advantage over formula-feeding. An additional 10 studies not included in the review, all reported a positive association between breastfeeding and cognitive ability on at least one measure. A 1999 meta-analysis of breastfeeding and cognitive development reported a benefit of 3.2 points in IQ for breastfed compared with formula-fed children. This benefit was found after statistical control for covariates such as socioeconomic status and maternal education. Low birth weight infants who were breastfed were reported to have an even greater benefit

of approximately 5.2 points in IQ. However, the absence of adequate control for environmental factors, such as maternal intelligence, motivation, and quality of parenting, raises concerns regarding the conclusion that breastfeeding leads to better cognitive development. Some studies have found the relationship between breastfeeding and cognitive development reduced to nonsignificant levels after adjusting for quality of parenting and maternal intelligence.

Some studies have also reported a dose–response effect, where the greater the length of breastfeeding, the better the developmental outcome. However, three studies found the highest cognitive scores in children breastfed to either 8 or 9 months with no additional benefits of breastfeeding on intelligence scores for longer durations of breastfeeding.

The American Academy of Pediatrics (AAP) and the World Health Organization (WHO) recommend exclusive breast milk for infants during the first 6 months and continued breastfeeding for at least the first year of life. Rates of breastfeeding initiation in the US have increased over the past three decades and are approaching the 'Healthy People 2010' national goal of 75%. However, duration lags far below the goal of 50% at 6 months. Breastfeeding rates are lower among African American and socioeconomically disadvantaged women than among White and Hispanic mothers. Mothers with higher levels of education or income are more likely to initiate breastfeeding and breastfeed longer than women with lower levels of education or income. These patterns are similar to findings from a 2000 survey in England in which 62% of women initiated breastfeeding, but at 6 weeks only 43% were providing any breast milk. In developing countries, rates of breastfeeding initiation are higher than in the US or England, but duration and exclusivity remain concerns.

Multiple factors have contributed to the increase in rates of breastfeeding initiation in the US, including an increased awareness of the merits of breastfeeding, baby-friendly hospitals, and breastfeeding promotion programs through WIC and other organizations. As rates of initiation have increased, breastfeeding has become normative in some populations with opportunities for peer support. Although many of the same factors could influence breastfeeding duration, there are also environmental constraints that limit breastfeeding duration. For example, flexible work hours, paid maternity leave, on-site child care, and a supportive work environment (e.g., lactation breaks and facilities for expressing breast milk) may facilitate breastfeeding duration.

Micronutrient Deficiencies

Micronutrient deficiencies (e.g., iodine, iron, and zinc) affect millions of young children throughout the world. These micronutrients are necessary for early brain development and functioning and have been linked to child development. However, investigating the impact of micronutrient deficiencies on children's cognitive development poses serious challenges. Not only do micronutrient deficiencies frequently co-occur, but children with micronutrient deficiencies are often raised in very low-income families. Since economic hardship can limit families' ability to provide care and to foster their children's development, both nutritional and social factors may interfere with children's development. Deficiencies of iodine, iron, and zinc have been studied. Study designs typically focus on infants at risk for nutritional deficiencies and use randomized controlled trials to examine the impact of supplemented micronutrients on children's development.

Iodine Deficiency

An estimated 35% of the world's population (1.99 billion) have insufficient iodine intake, although a global program to reduce iodine deficiency through salt iodization has produced substantial progress. Iodine is a constituent of thyroid hormones, which influence central nervous system development and regulate many physiological processes. Iodine deficiency can lead to cretinism and irreversible mental retardation, making it the most common preventable cause of mental retardation.

Recent research focuses on subclinical iodine deficiency. A 1994 meta-analysis of 18 studies concluded that IQ scores averaged 13.5 points lower in children and adolescents with iodine deficiency. A 2005 meta-analysis of 37 Chinese studies concluded that IQs averaged 12.5 points lower for children growing up in iodine deficient vs. sufficient areas. IQs averaged 8.7 points higher in children who received iodine supplementation pre- and postnatally than those who did not. Although studies of varying quality were included in both meta-analyses, similar results were found. Furthermore, iodine supplementation in the first and second trimesters of pregnancy, compared to supplementation later in pregnancy or treatment after birth, decreased the prevalence of moderate and severe neurological abnormalities and increased developmental test scores through 7 years in a longitudinal study in China. Taking these numerous studies together, there is overwhelming evidence that iodine deficiency interferes with normal child development.

Iron Deficiency

ID is considered the world's most common single nutrient deficiency and may result in anemia. Although anemia has many different causes, the most common is ID due to inadequate dietary intake of bioavailable iron or blood loss. Pregnant women and young children are at high risk for ID due to increased iron needs and limited dietary sources of iron. In developing countries, an estimated 46–66% of children under 4 years of age are anemic, with half attributed to ID. Although the prevalence of iron deficiency anemia (IDA) has declined markedly in the US in the past three decades, poor, minority, and/or immigrant infants and toddlers remain at increased risk for IDA and ID without anemia.

The peak prevalence of early ID/IDA in human infants is 6–24 months. Cross-sectional studies among healthy infants (not premature, undernourished, or ill) have consistently shown that infants with ID/IDA displayed poorer mental, language, motor, and/or social/emotional functioning than infants with adequate iron status. IDA infants were observed to be more wary, hesitant, solemn, and unhappy than infants with adequate iron status and they spent more time close to their mothers and showed less social interaction with adults.

Even after 3 months or more of iron therapy in infancy, the majority of studies reported continued poor development in infants who initially had poor iron status. However, a few studies reported dramatic improvements in development. With post-treatment intervals ranging up to adolescence, nine follow-up reports of global outcomes observed poorer outcome in individuals who had anemia in infancy, compared with individuals with a history of adequate iron status. A recent meta-analysis estimated IQ to be 1.73 points lower for each 10 g l^{-1} decrease in hemoglobin. A follow-up of Costa Rican adolescents who had been born at term and were free of health problems in infancy other than ID showed persisting motor differences, more grade repetition, increased anxiety/depression, social problems and inattention rated by parents and teachers, and a widening gap in cognitive scores to 19 years, despite iron therapy that corrected IDA in infancy. In contrast to these studies of iron treatment for IDA infants, recent randomized controlled trials in developing countries of iron supplementation show improved motor and social–emotional development in infants who received iron.

Iron's role in carrying oxygen to the body via hemoglobin in red blood cells is well known. However, effects on behavior and development are attributed to iron's essential role in many other enzymes, cofactors, and cells. Iron is required for so many central nervous system processes that multiple, diffuse, and subtle effects might be expected. Animal models provide convincing evidence that early ID alters brain metabolism and neurotransmission and disrupts myelination, leading to behavioral changes.

Human studies that have examined neurophysiologic functioning have shown that infants with IDA have slower neural transmission using auditory brainstem responses and worse performance on tests that examined neurocognitive processing, spatial memory, selective attention, executive functioning, and affect (wariness, hesitance, decreased positive affect), compared to nonanemic infants. Many of these tasks involve circuits connecting cortex, striatum, and limbic structures, with dopamine as the major neurotransmitter.

In sum, the evidence is robust that the short- and long-term development of 6–24-month-old infants with IDA is compromised. Iron treatment does not consistently yield improvements, yet the results of recent supplementation trials indicate that adverse effects can be prevented and/or reversed with iron early in development or before ID becomes severe or chronic. Thus, it appears to be important to protect the developing brain from ID. It should also be noted, though, that excessive iron can be harmful, suggesting that iron supplementation programs should target children who are not iron sufficient.

Zinc Deficiency

Zinc is a trace mineral, found in animal source food, that plays fundamental roles in cell division and maturation, and in the growth and function of many organ systems, including the neurological system. Zinc supplementation trials among nutritionally deficient infants have demonstrated beneficial effects of zinc on mortality and on multiple indicators of health, including growth, diarrhea, and pneumonia morbidity.

Evidence from animal models suggests that zinc deficiency may affect emotionality and response to stress–factors that play critical roles in shaping infant responsiveness and development. Investigations of zinc supplementation on infants' development and behavior have yielded inconsistent findings. There have been at least twelve randomized controlled trials assessing the effects of zinc supplementation on children's behavior and development, three involving both zinc and iron supplementation. Although several trials have reported beneficial effects of zinc with and without iron supplementation, primarily on motor development, the effects have been small. Other trials have found no or negative effects. One trial from Jamaica showed that zinc supplementation benefited children's cognitive and motor scores, but only when it was introduced in combination with psychosocial stimulation.

Many factors could interfere with clear interpretation of the zinc supplementation trials. First, zinc deficiency is difficult to document and many scientists have enrolled low-income infants presumed to be zinc deficient. Second, micronutrient deficiencies often co-occur, thus providing zinc alone or with iron may not alleviate other nutritional problems. Third, there may be interactive effects between zinc and iron, resulting in adverse effects. Finally, the low-income context surrounding zinc deficiency may interfere with children's developmental progress, even in the context of zinc supplementation.

Other Micronutrient Deficiencies

Other micronutrient deficiencies have not been as well studied as iron, zinc, and iodine. The available research indicates that there may be developmental and behavioral effects of vitamin B12 deficiency, which may occur in breastfed infants of mothers who are vegan or strict vegetarians. The most common symptoms are increased lethargy and irritability, along with cognitive and motor delay. The developmental delays have been attributed to impaired myelination. Folate deficiency around the time of conception and the first weeks of pregnancy can lead to fetal malformations (neural tube defects). The role of vitamin A deficiency in childhood blindness is also well known. National and international programs to prevent neural tube defects and vitamin A-related blindness have had considerable impact.

Infant Growth

Growth serves as an objective measure of children's well-being during the first years of life when energy needs are high. Birth weight triples in the first year and birth length increases by 50% over the first year and doubles by age 4 years.

Growth Charts

The Centers for Disease Control and Prevention publishes growth charts that can be used to track children's growth. Most of the data used to construct the growth charts come from the National Health and Nutrition Examination Survey (NHANES), a national survey which periodically collects height, weight, and other health information on the American population. The current growth charts were originally constructed using data from 1977. The 2000 revision includes recent data to ensure that breastfed babies are included, that the analyses reflect recent statistical procedures, and that charts include body mass index (BMI).

The WHO has recently released growth charts based on data collected from Ghana, India, Norway, Oman, Brazil, and the US, as part of the WHO Multicentre Growth Reference Study. The new WHO Child Growth Standards illustrate that early growth to age 5 years is dependent on nutrition, feeding practices, environment, and access to healthcare, rather than on genetic, cultural, or ethnic differences. Under optimal conditions, across the six countries studied, there are no differences in children's height and weight. Although there are individual differences among children's growth, across large populations, the average growth of young children is similar. These findings emphasize the importance of ensuring that young children receive adequate nutrition, feeding practices, caregiving environments, and access to healthcare.

Anthropometric Indices

Weight-for-age is commonly used in pediatric clinics to track children's growth and is an excellent indicator of changes in weight over time. However, weight-for-age is difficult to interpret because it does not account for variations in height. When a child's weight-for-age is low, it is not clear whether the primary problem is low weight, short stature, or a combination of the two. Weight-for-height (weight plotted by height regardless of age) reflects body proportionality. The 2000 update of the growth charts includes BMI for children over 2 years of age (BMI = weight in kilograms/(height in meters)^2).

Low weight-for-height, or wasting, is often an early sign of malnutrition, and may reflect low caloric intake. Chronic malnutrition may result in decelerated skeletal growth, indicated by low height-for-age, or stunting. Thus, weight-for-height and height-for-age provide a nonredundant, comprehensive picture of growth. Because individual children's height also reflects genetic contributions from their parents, height-for-age should be adjusted by a formula using the mean height of their parents. Premature infants may be plotted on special charts or standard growth charts, adjusted for prematurity. Recommendations are to adjust for gestational age up to 24 months on weight, 40 months on height, and 36 months on head circumference.

Weight-for-age, weight-for-height, and height-for-age can be expressed as percentile scores, percent of median scores, or standard deviation scores. Percentile scores are commonly used clinically because they are relatively easy to interpret, but are less useful when describing variations at the extremes (e.g., <5th percentile). Percent of median scores are often used to describe change and are calculated by dividing the child's weight (or height) by the median expected weight (or height) (50th percentile) based on the child's chronological age. Standard deviation scores (Z-scores) are commonly used for analyses because they can be used to characterize extremes and to facilitate comparisons across ages.

Premature Birth and Low Birth Weight

Birth weight is associated with multiple factors, including maternal nutrition, parity, and smoking, along with access to prenatal care. Infants born prior to 37 weeks' gestation are premature or pre-term and infants whose birth weight is under 2500 g are classified as low birth weight. In middle and upper-income countries, most infants with low birth weight are also premature. Technological advances have improved survival of premature infants and recent attention has focused on the neurodevelopmental consequences of prematurity. In spite of methodological problems in long-term follow-up studies, children born prematurely often have more problems in neurologic function, visual motor performance, cognition, academic performance, language, executive functioning, attention deficit disorder, and behavioral problems than full-term children of normal birth weight.

A recent analysis examined the growth, health, and cognitive functioning at age 8 among 655 children born low birth weight (<2500 g) and premature (<37 weeks' gestation). Children were divided into growth categories by their prenatal and postnatal growth. Children who were small for gestational age (SGA weight-for-gestational age <10th percentile) with adequate postnatal growth did not differ from children with adequate prenatal and postnatal growth on any measures of growth (height, weight, BMI, or head circumference), cognition, or academic achievement at age 8 years. Children with postnatal growth problems (FTT) were smaller, and had lower scores on measures of cognition and academic achievement at age 8 years than children with adequate growth, particularly when they also had prenatal growth problems (SGA). Thus, there does not appear to be an independent effect of SGA status on 8-year cognitive status and academic achievement if postnatal growth is adequate.

In low-income countries, infants with low birth weight are often born at term and have experienced intrauterine growth retardation (IUGR). IUGR has been associated with poor postnatal growth, behavior problems, and cognitive deficits, particularly if the infant also experiences poor prenatal head growth. There are global estimates that over 30 million infants are born each year with impaired growth.

Undernutrition, Stunting, and Failure to Thrive

When children do not receive adequate calories and nutrients, their rate of weight gain slows down, often indicated by a decline on the growth charts. Although undernutrition is a serious global problem that contributes to the deaths of about 5.6 million children under five in low-income countries each year, it is less prevalent than stunting, which exceeds 50% in some low-income countries. When undernutrition is chronic early in life, linear growth can be affected and children may be stunted. Children whose length is at least two standard deviations below the norm for their age are considered to be stunted.

The negative effects of stunting extend beyond poor growth. Longitudinal data from at least seven countries provide convincing evidence that children who are stunted early in life experience learning, academic, and behavior problems that interfere with school attainment and ultimately with economic productivity.

In middle and upper-income countries, children who experience early undernutrition are often diagnosed with

FTT. There are no agreed-upon definitions of FTT. Some clinicians base their diagnosis of FTT on a single measure of weight-for-age or weight-for-height below the 5th or 3rd percentile, with little attention to the child's growth history, and others base their diagnosis on a deceleration in growth over time. Deceleration in the rate of growth is a good indicator of growth problems, but requires multiple measures over time and relatively sophisticated interpretation. With no universally agreed-upon criteria to determine when FTT has occurred or even the index that should be used to assess growth, FTT can be an imprecise diagnosis.

There is little reliable information on the long-term consequences of FTT. However, FTT is widely recognized as a serious pediatric problem. The long-term consequences of FTT are thought to include growth deficits, decreased immunologic resistance, diminished physical activity, depressed performance in assessments of cognitive development, and poor academic performance. The relationship between nutritional status and consequences is often mediated by family, environmental, and cultural variables, making the family an ideal context for prevention of the negative consequences of FTT.

Evidence from community-based studies suggests that growth improves and by 6–9 years of age, most children with FTT have experienced growth recovery. Although children with a history of FTT are often shorter and thinner than peers who did not experience FTT, their growth parameters no longer indicate wasting or stunting. Several studies have shown that children with FTT who received intervention had better growth than those who did not. In addition, several recent studies and review have found that by school-age, children with a history of FTT have IQ scores that are approximately 4 points lower than children without a history of FTT, when comparison groups are matched for socioeconomic variables.

Some caution is recommended in reading the existing literature on FTT because much of the information has been derived from hospitalized children in academic, referral centers. Because most children with FTT are treated on an outpatient basis, studies that rely on hospitalized patients are likely to represent extreme and complex cases of FTT. In addition, many studies of FTT include small samples, a lack of appropriately matched comparison groups, unstandardized assessments, evaluators who are aware of group assignment, inattention to differences in age or nutritional status, and cross-sectional, rather than longitudinal research designs.

Overweight and Rapid Weight Gain

In children over 2 years of age, overweight is defined by BMI equal to or greater than the 95th percentile, based on age and gender-adjusted growth charts. Risk of overweight is defined as BMI over the 85th percentile and under the 95th percentile. For children under age 2, weight-for-length is used rather than BMI and overweight is often considered with weight-for-length equals or exceeds the 95th percentile on age and gender-adjusted growth charts. A recent study of low-income infants and toddlers in six cities found that 9% of the infants and 14% of the toddlers were overweight, in contrast to the expected rate of 5% and in New York City, 40% of the children enrolled in WIC between the ages of 2 and 4 years had a BMI over the 85th percentile, in contrast to an expected rate of 15%. Data from the NHANES IV, a nationally representative sample of the US population collected in 2003–04 found that 17.1% of children age 2–19 years were overweight.

Pediatric overweight is a concern because overweight children are at increased risk to become obese adults, particularly if their parents are overweight. The epidemic of pediatric overweight often begins with rapid weight gain early in life. Rapid weight gain is defined as a change in weight status of 0.67–1.00 standard deviation scores. At least 22 studies have found that infants who experience rapid weight gain are at risk of overweight during childhood and adulthood. The Feeding Infants and Toddlers Study (FITS), an investigation of the dietary patterns of 3000 infants and toddlers, showed that in many cases children's mean energy intakes exceed their mean energy requirements; in other words, many children are overfed. Although the role of family environment on children's growth is well recognized, most interventions have focused on advice regarding children's diet and physical activity. Limited attention has been directed toward feeding styles and parent–child interactions in relation to diet and growth patterns.

The mechanisms driving the connection between rapid weight gain and overweight are unclear. The pattern that includes low birth weight, followed by catch-up growth or rapid weight gain, followed by overweight is associated with diseases, such as type 2 diabetes and cardiovascular diseases during adulthood.

In the Avon Longitudinal Study of Pregnancy and Childhood (ALSPAC), a large birth cohort, approximately 25% of newborns show rapid or catch-up growth and 25% show slow or catch-down growth. Postnatal growth is thought to be driven by infant regulatory processes, including satiety. Infants who show early catch-up growth during the first 2–3 years of life are more likely than those who grow according to expectations or show catch-down growth to be overweight and insulin resistant at age 8 years. This finding is consistent with the 'thrifty phenotype' hypothesis in which a fetus exposed to poor nutrition experiences, permanent changes in insulin metabolism, and body fat distribution. In the face of an obesigenic environment, these metabolic changes can increase the risk for obesity, diabetes, and cardiovascular diseases.

The pathways between low birth weight, rapid weight gain, and overweight raise concerns in low-income countries, where rates of low birth weight are high. Rapid weight gain (catch-up growth) has been seen as a health-promoting strategy to avoid the morbidity and mortality associated with low birth weight, yet it may increase vulnerability to chronic illness in adulthood. Taking a lifespan approach may be useful in deciding recommendations for infant feeding. Data from Brazil have shown that rapid weight gain in infancy, regardless of birth weight, was associated with lower risk for mortality and hospital admission than poor weight gain. Catch-up growth that follows growth restriction, such as IUGR or FTT usually includes muscle and bone growth, along with fat. In contrast, rapid weight gain that does not follow a period of growth restriction generally results in accumulation of fat without additional bone or muscle accumulation. Nutritionists and other scientists often recommend that exclusive breastfeeding be adopted for the first 6 months of life as a means of promoting optimal growth and reducing the likelihood of rapid weight gain.

Environmental Stress

In investigations of nutrition and child development, many scientists have ignored the social context, beyond controlling for maternal education and family income. Children are influenced by interactions with their family, primarily their primary caregiver. Early attachment forms the basis of healthy social relationships. In the absence of a secure attachment relationship, children may be at risk for emotional and regulatory problems that interfere with subsequent academic and social development.

Nutritional deprivation often occurs in the context of poverty, highlighting the importance of considering how contextual variables, including environmental stress and caregiving behavior, relate to brain development. Although brief periods of moderate stress allow children to develop appropriate stress responses, exposure to high levels of stress early in life during periods of rapid brain development can lead to numerous physical and developmental problems. Chronic and unpredictable stress can have lasting negative neurodevelopmental consequences that may undermine children's emotional and cognitive development, ultimately interfering with their academic achievement and social relationships.

The neurobiological mechanisms proposed to account for the cognitive deficits that occur in children with a history of malnutrition include deficits in the nutrients necessary for adequate physical growth and functioning as well as dysregulated hypothalamic–pituitary–adrenal (HPA) axis functioning. The HPA system coordinates the stress response through multiple mechanisms resulting in the eventual release of glucocorticoids (cortisol) from the adrenal cortex. Excessive cortisol can impair brain regions housing cortisol receptors. Intact HPA regulation is important for early development and ongoing maintenance of cortical systems involved with emotion, learning, memory, and attention and impulse control.

In addition to an inadequate and/or inconsistent food supply, undernourished children often experience a lack of positive interactions with their primary caregivers. Effective caregivers play a critical role in helping children to modulate their emotional and physiological response to stressful events. In the absence of positive interactions and stimulation, children may experience deficits in the development of their stress-sensitive regulatory systems. If they are also undernourished, they may be in a position of double jeopardy. An overexposure to stress in combination with disruptions in HPA-axis functioning may be harmful to children's neurodevelopment. Heavily secreted neuroendocrine agents associated with chronic stress produce neurotoxic effects that may damage the developing brain, especially in areas rich in glucocorticoids such as the hippocampus, corpus callosum, and areas of the prefrontal cortex. Elevated levels of catecholamines and cortisol can also lead to inadequate brain development through the mechanisms of accelerated loss of neurons, delays in myelination, abnormal pruning, and the inhibition of neurogenesis. Children who are repeatedly exposed to stress are at a higher risk for being chronically hyperaroused to aspects of their environment, with possible negative effects on their attention and executive cognitive processes. In summary, the combination of nutritional and caregiving risk factors early in life may place undernourished children at risk for negative cognitive outcomes, possibly mediated by poorly modulated stress reactivity.

Feeding Styles and Eating Behavior

Although the role of the family on children's early growth is well recognized, most interventions to promote healthy growth in young children have focused on advice regarding children's diet and physical activity. Almost no attention has been directed toward feeding styles.

Feeding styles refer to the interactive behavior between caregivers and children that occurs during meals. Embedded within the dimensions of nurturance and structure that form the basis for parenting styles, four feeding styles have been described: sensitive/responsive, controlling, indulgent, and uninvolved. A sensitive/responsive feeding style, high in nurturance and structure, represents caregivers who form a relationship with their child that involves clear demands and mutual signals and bids for mealtime interaction. A controlling feeding style, high in structure and low in nurturance, represents caregivers who use forceful or restrictive strategies to control mealtimes. An indulgent feeding style, high in nurturance and low in structure, occurs when caregivers allow children to make decisions around meals, such as when and what they will eat. An uninvolved feeding style, low in both nurturance and structure, represents caregivers who have limited knowledge and involvement in their child's mealtime behavior. Scientists have hypothesized that the sensitive/responsive feeding style is optimal and leads to healthy growth because it encourages caregivers to provide healthy food on a predictable schedule and to respond to children's regulatory cues regarding hunger and satiety. However, there have been few investigations of feeding styles among infants and toddlers and existing information is somewhat contradictory. The most consistent findings suggest that a restrictive feeding style is associated with children's overweight. However, because most studies are cross-sectional, it is difficult to determine whether caregivers respond to their infants' high weight status by trying to restrict their intake or whether infants respond to caregiver feeding restriction with increased consumption. More work is necessary to understand how feeding styles are related to infant consumption, growth, and early development.

Food Security

Food security is defined as having an adequate supply of safe, nutritious, and culturally appropriate food to ensure a healthy lifestyle. In contrast, food insecurity is not having adequate food to meet daily needs. In 2004, an estimated 18.5% of US households with children under the age of 6 years were food insecure. Rates of food insecurity in low-income countries vary by region, but are often very high.

School-age children raised in food insecure households are at risk for attentional problems, low physical function, poor academic performance, and poor psychosocial functioning. The impact of food insecurity on children may be through both nutritive and/or non-nutritive pathways. The nutritive pathway suggests that in the absence of adequate food supplies, families may reduce both the quantity and quality of their food intake, leading to inadequate nutrient intake. In other words, families may rely on low cost, high-energy foods that may be filling, but low in nutrients. The non-nutritive pathway suggests that parental anxiety, stress, and depression that have been associated with the inability to provide adequate food may contribute to behavioral and developmental problems among children.

Children from food insecure households are also at risk for overweight. Although it may seem counterintuitive for children to be overweight in food insecure households, there are at least two possible explanations. Not only do families often rely on high-energy dense food that is low in nutrients (e.g., noodles), but they may binge when food is available. Both strategies may lead to a positive energy balance, resulting in weight gain.

Less is known about the impact of food insecurity among children under 3 years of age. However, recent studies have shown that food insecurity is associated with caregiver reports of poor infant health, increased likelihood of hospitalization, behavioral problems, and developmental risk, in comparison with food secure households. Thus, food insecurity poses additional risks to young children beyond the challenges of poverty.

Conclusion

In summary, nutrition is an essential aspect of the growth and development of young children, particularly through the third year of life. Infants who experience nutritional deprivation during the prenatal period are at risk for a lifetime of negative consequences that may extend to the next generation, emphasizing the importance of a lifespan approach to nutrition. In addition to caloric restrictions, micronutrient deficiencies can interfere with children's growth and development, often by interfering with brain development and function. In spite of global concerns about undernutrition and stunting, the epidemic of overweight and rapid weight gain is spreading among infants and toddlers, threatening to undermine their health through childhood and adulthood. Interventions are needed not only to ensure adequate nutrition, but also to ensure that young children are exposed to feeding styles during mealtime interactions that encourage regulatory behavior and introduction to healthy food choices.

See also: Abuse, Neglect, and Maltreatment of Infants; Brain Development; Breastfeeding; Diarrhea; Endocrine System; Failure to Thrive; Feeding Development and Disorders; Mortality, Infant; Obesity; Physical Growth; Premature Babies; Prenatal Development.

Suggested Readings

Black MM (2003) Micronutrient deficiencies and cognitive functioning. *Journal of Nutrition* 133: 3927S–3931S.
Casey PH, Whiteside-Mansall L, Barratt K, Bradley RH, and Gargas R (2006) Impact of prenatal and/or postnatal growth problems in low birth weight preterm infants on school-age outcomes: An 8-year longitudinal evaluation. *Pediatrics* 118(3): 1078–1086.
Engle PL, Black MM, Behrman JR, *et al.* (2007) Strategies to avoid the loss of developmental potential among over 200 million children in the developing world. *The Lancet* 369: 230–242.

Grantham-McGregor SM and Ani CC (1999) The role of micronutrients in psychomotor and cognitive development. *British Medical Bulletin* 55: 511–527.

Grantham-McGregor S, Cheung YB, Cueto S, *et al.* (2007) Over two hundred million children fail to reach their developmental potential in the first five years in developing countries. *The Lancet* 369: 60–70.

Lozoff B and Georgieff MK (2006) Iron deficiency and brain development. *Seminars in Pediatric Neurology* 13(3): 158–165.

Ogden CL, Carroll MD, Curtin LR, McDowell MA, Tabak CJ, and Flegal KM (2006) Prevalence of overweight and obesity in the United States, 1999–2004. *Journal of the American Medical Association* 295(13): 1549–1555.

Thompson RA and Nelson CA (2001) Developmental science and the media: Early brain development. *American Psychologist* 56(1): 5–15.

Walker SP, Wachs TD, Gardner JM, *et al.* (2007) Child development: Risk factors for adverse outcomes in developing countries. *The Lancet* 369: 145–157.

Relevant Websites

http://www.cdc.gov – National Center for Health Statistics, Centers for Disease and Prevention children's growth.

http://www.who.int – World Health Organization, Multicentre Child growth standards.

Obesity

C F Bolling, Cincinnati Children's Hospital Medical Center, Cincinnati, OH, USA
S R Daniels, University of Colorado Health Sciences Center, Denver, CO, USA

Glossary

Adipocyte – Individual fat cell.
Adiposity (or body mass index, BMI) rebound – The period between 4 years and 8 years when a child's BMI is at its nadir.
At-risk for overweight (AROW) – 85th or greater and less than 95th percentile BMI for age and gender.
Body mass index (BMI) – A mathematical formula to assess relative body weight. The measure correlates highly with body fat. BMI is calculated as weight in kilograms divided by the square of the height in meters ($kg\,m^{-2}$).
Energy density – A general description of calories per volume. A high-calorie, low-volume food is generally high in fat or sugar content and is low in fiber or water content.
Ideal body weight (IBW) – A term describing the weight that people are expected to weigh based on age, sex, and height which is the weight for an individual that results in a body mass index of 20–25.
Overweight – 95th or greater percentile BMI for age and gender. For adults, this is represented by a BMI 25 or greater. In adults, obesity is defined as having a BMI 30 or greater.

Introduction

Obesity is a term generally reserved for the study of adult medicine and is defined by having a body mass index (BMI) of over 30, historically the 90th percentile for adults. In pediatric patients, weight status is generally more often described as either overweight or at-risk for overweight (AROW). Overweight is defined as being at greater than or equal to 95th percentile BMI for age and gender. AROW is defined as being greater than or equal to the 85th percentile and less than the 95th percentile BMI for age and gender.

There are experts in the field of obesity who advocate for a definition of pediatric obesity consistent with the Institute of Medicine accepted adult definitions in which overweight is defined as having a BMI greater than or equal to the 85th percentile and less than the 95th percentile and obesity is defined as greater than or equal to 95th percentile. Other experts in the field also advocate for the use of greater than or equal to the 99th percentile as being obese. Resolution of this occasionally confusing terminology is expected as the study of overweight matures as a discipline.

Further delineation occurs between morbid obesity and super-obesity. Universally accepted definitions are lacking, but general classifications are accepted. For adults, morbid obesity or extreme obesity is often defined as being over 100 lb overweight or having a BMI of 40–50 or 50–100% over ideal body weight (IBW). Super-obesity is similarly defined as being approximately greater than 200 lb overweight, having a BMI of 50–60 or being 225% over IBW. Some studies will define persons over a BMI of 60 as being super–super obese. These classifications are less widely accepted in the pediatric practice.

For reference, the BMI of a 'typical' 12 kg (26.4 lb) and 87 cm (34 in) 2-year-old boy at the 50 percentile for height and weight is 15.9. The 'normal range' for BMI for a 2-year-old is form 14.8 at the 5 percentile to 19.3 at the 95 percentile. The same 87 cm 2-year-old boy would need to weigh14.6 kg (32.1 lb) to be considered 'overweight'. Minimum BMI is typically achieved between age 5 and 6 when the 50th percentile BMI is 15.4. After this point, BMI 'rebounds'. Early BMI rebound is considered to be a risk factor for later obesity. Girls' BMI are very similar to boys with earlier achievement of final BMI reflecting faster progression through puberty.

Other definitions of overweight are currently under consideration, but are, as yet, not widely accepted. Certain researchers and clinicians advocate for measurements that more accurately measure total body fat as BMI can be elevated by increased musculature. Abdominal circumference is more difficult to measure and is less standardized in technique, body impedance analysis requires additional equipment and can be somewhat inaccurate, and dual X-ray absorptionetry (DEXA) scan exposes patients to radiation and incurs added costs. Displacement techniques of body fat analysis are under development.

Epidemiology

US

Rates of AROW and overweight are on the increase throughout all areas of the US. The commonly accepted rates of 10% between the 85th and 95th and 5% of the population were generated from longitudinal studies carried out between 1967 and 1994. Using these values, subsequent surveys of pediatric height and weight have demonstrated an approximate doubling in the prevalence of both AROW and overweight children.

Highest rates of AROW and overweight come in certain sociodemographic groups. Higher rates are associated with low socioeconomic status. Being African American, Native American, Latino, or Appalachian is also associated. The highest rates of overweight occur in the Southeastern and Midwestern areas of the country.

The prevalence of super-obesity is difficult to describe in younger age groups, but is increasing in adolescents. Approximately, 750 000 American adolescents, or approximately 2.5% of the population, have a BMI greater than 40 and well over 1 000 000 adolescents have a BMI between 35 and 40.

Other Nations

Comparing national rates of pediatric obesity is problematic for a number of reasons. Differing definitions, variations in measurement practice, varying cultural acceptance of weight status, disparities in body composition all conspire to make comparing rates between countries very difficult. In spite of these limitations in comparing country rates, longitudinally following individual country rates has demonstrated a worsening international problem.

Nations with developed economies

While the US has experienced the most profound explosion in overweight pediatric prevalence, many other nations are experiencing a similar phenomenon. The UK, Germany, France, Italy, Spain, Canada, and Australia have closely followed patterns seen in the US. Other industrialized nations in Europe have shown a similar but delayed pattern. Developed nations in Asia have seen a milder but still significant increase in prevalence in overweight.

Developing nations

One of the more concerning epidemiologic occurrences since 2000 has been the spread of pediatric overweight to nations with developing economies. Previously unreported, China, India, and Mexico have all experienced a statistically significant increase in the rates of pediatric overweight. Increasing access to food and access to technology encouraging sedentary behavior is felt to be a major contributor to this rise in these rates and, as a result of increasing economic development, is expected to worsen in these countries.

Etiology

Pediatric overweight may be described as either being endogenous, caused by innate biologic processes, or exogenous, caused by external factors. This distinction does not imply exclusion of behavioral modification for endogenous obesity nor the exclusion of pharmacologic or surgically based treatment for exogenous overweight.

Exogenous Overweight

The relatively fixed number of cases from endogenous causes of overweight implies that the greatest number of cases of overweight is due to an increase in the number of cases of exogenous overweight. Promotion of increased calorie intake and discouragement of activity have combined to create a more obesigenic environment. These factors that may be modified by behavioral and environmental determinants have upset energy balance and led to an increase in weight status.

Increased energy intake

Calorie intake in average American children had remained steady until approximately 1990. Since 1990, studies have indicated an increase of approximately 10–15% in daily caloric intake across most pediatric age groups. The source of this increase in calories is likely due to increased intake of simple sugars.

The percentage of daily calories derived from fruit juice and sweetened drinks including soft drinks and sports drinks have doubled from 1994 to 2004 in preschool groups. In other pediatric age groups, soft drink consumption has been accelerating. In recent surveys when describing generally accepted food classifications, soft drinks are the third greatest contributor of calories in 6–8-year-olds, second highest contributor in 9–11-year-olds and greatest contributor in 12–15-year-olds.

Fast food has been linked to decreased fruit and vegetable intake, decreased milk intake, increased sweetened drink consumption, increased calorie intake, increased intake of high-calorie foods, and increased intake of starchy vegetables (potatoes). These are behaviors that have been associated with excess weight gain. Approximately, 25% of children aged 4–8 years eat fast food on any given day. French fries are the most commonly eaten vegetable for children aged 15–24 months.

All groups have experienced a steady decline in the intake of foods low in energy density, namely fresh fruits and vegetables. Large nutritional studies estimate that 25–33% of American preschool children consume no fruits or vegetables. In other studies, the leading vegetable for children in all age groups is identified as deep-fat fried potato products. Other studies have demonstrated increased intake in other high-energy density foods. Various studies have demonstrated increases in snack foods, prepared baked goods, candy, pizza, hamburgers, fried chicken, and Mexican and Chinese fast food.

Portion control studies also demonstrate the increase in portion size seen in American dietary habits. Vended items, fast food promotions, and buffet-style eating habits have all been implicated in elevating calorie intake.

Decreased energy expenditure

Average energy expenditure has also been implicated as a root cause in the increased prevalence of pediatric overweight. In the US example, parental concerns over safety, the proliferation of point to point automobile transport, and limitations of public transit have reduced walking and cycling as transportation methods for children. Studies have shown a decrease in outdoor time and an overall total decrease in time spent in active play. Environmental studies have begun to make a link between green space interconnectivity/accessibility and rates of overweight. The connection between pediatric overweight and urban sprawl associated with a lack of connected and accessible parks is not completely clear.

Excess screen time is also associated with increased overweight. Children who spend more than 2 h daily in front of computer, television programming, video games, or DVD/VHS movies have been shown to have elevated rates of pediatric overweight. Educational academic mandates have also reduced time available in school days for physical education. This has presumably further reduced activity during school time.

Other considerations

Breastfeeding appears to be protective against pediatric overweight. Studies have indicated that children who bottle-feed have significantly higher concentrations of insulin than children who breastfeed. Elevated insulin promotes fat deposition and more rapid development of adipocytes in young children. Breastmilk also contains factors like epidermal growth factor and inflammatory hormones such as tumor necrosis factor-alpha (TNF-α)

that promote fat cell growth. Breastfeeding may also increase levels of leptin which suppresses appetite. It has also been demonstrated that children who breastfeed have lower overall intake of calories and protein than bottle-fed children. Other studies suggest that formula contains higher levels of protein than breast milk and that this may cause increased weight gain in infants.

Children with early adiposity rebound may be at greater risk for overweight at a later age. Adiposity rebound is the period between 4 and 8 years when a child's BMI is at its nadir. Children with an earlier nadir (between 4 and 5 years of age) tend to have a greater risk of obesity, hypertension, impaired glucose tolerance, and diabetes in adulthood. Early adiposity rebound has also been recorded in a number of childhood diseases that are characterized by adult obesity, including congenital adrenal hyperplasia, hypothyroidism, hyperphenylalaninemia, and acute lymphoblastic leukemia. Unfortunately, the mechanism of adiposity rebound leading to these conditions is not well described. These factors make addressing documented early weight gain a priority in reducing pediatric overweight.

Endogenous Obesity

Endogenous causes of obesity are much less common and are usually associated with other obvious medical syndromes. These organic causes of obesity may be mediated by specific hormone deficiencies. Leptin that is secreted by adipocytes crosses the blood brain barrier to influence energy balance and reduce adipose content by increasing heat generation and decreasing appetite. Leptin-deficiency states have been associated with obesity. Likewise, other hormonal deficiencies and hormone receptor dysfunction states have been linked with genetic causes of obesity.

Certain chromosomal anomalies are associated with obesity. The prevalence of overweight in Down syndrome is greater than that in the general population when it has been accurately assessed. Prader–Willi syndrome which is accompanied by characteristic physical features and developmental delay is caused by a chromosomal deletion of a section of chromosome 15. Obesity in Prader–Willi syndrome is likely related to over secretion of the growth-promoting hormone, ghrelin. Sim-1, a syndrome characterized by a balanced translocation between chromosomes 1 and 6, has been associated with obesity. WAGR syndrome (WAGR – Wilm's tumor, anorexia, ambiguous genitalia, and mental retardation) is associated with obesity through an apparent chromosome 11 deletion.

Other polygenic syndromes are associated with obesity. These syndromes are likely to be mediated hormonally. Patients who are carriers for the genetic enzyme deficiency, pro-opiomelanocortin (POMC) deficiency, and relatives of patients with this defect appear to have lack of neural regulation of appetite, excess eating and resulting obesity. A deficiency in certain cellular hormone receptors, melanocortin-4 receptor deficiency, is likely a cause for obesity in heterozygous family members due to hyperinsulinism. Bardet–Biedl syndrome is a polygenic, autosomal recessive condition characterized by central obesity, mental retardation, underdeveloped gonadal tissue, and kidney abnormalities. Albright's hereditary osteodystrophy is an autosomal dominant disorder in which patients demonstrate short stature, obesity, round facies, extremity abnormalities, and nonfunctional soft tissue transformation into bone. Patients with fragile X-syndrome often have obesity accompanied by mental retardation, large testes, large ears, macrocephaly, large mandibular jaws, and high-pitched speech. Borjeson–Forssman–Lehman syndrome is characterized by mental retardation, epilepsy, underdeveloped gonadal tissue, and obesity. Cohen syndrome is an autosomal recessive disorder and is characterized by obesity, mental retardation, small head size, unusual facial features and disorders of eye and neural tissue that impair vision. Alström syndrome is inherited in an autosomal recessive pattern and is characterized by high insulin and glucose as well as sensory neurologic deficits. An extremely rare syndrome associated with excess weight gain is MOMO (macrosomia, obesity, macrocephaly, ocular abnormalities) syndrome. Acromegaly and growth hormone excess may result in increased weight but is generally accompanied with increased height growth.

Obesity as a Complication of Medical or Surgical Therapy

Obesity may also present as a side effect of medical therapy. Cushing's syndrome from chronic steroid use for asthma, juvenile rheumatoid arthritis, or other disease processes may result in overweight. Central nervous system procedures may result in disturbance of the hypothalamic appetite regulation center that may prevent satiety.

Pathophysiology

While the basic pathophysiology of overweight and obesity involves a simple mismatch between energy intake and energy expenditure with resulting fat deposition, the effects on the body are far reaching and potentially devastating.

Cardiovascular Effects

Dyslipidemias
Increased intake of dietary fats contributes to elevated circulating triglycerides and cholesterol through direct absorption and can lead to overweight. However, the relation between overweight and circulating levels of agents associated with atherosclerosis is not completely understood.

Hyperlipidemias are multifactorial in origin and are regulated by genetic, exercise, and dietary factors. High-density lipoprotein (HDL) or 'good cholesterol', which increases with increasing activity, is associated with decreased atherosclerosis. HDL is involved in the clearing of agents that cause clot formation and the transport of them to the liver. Low- and very low-density lipoproteins (LDL and VLDL) or 'bad cholesterols' are elevated in part by increased lipid and cholesterol intake and are associated with an increase in these clot-forming agents. Inflammatory processes associated with elevated circulating triglycerides and lower density lipoproteins have also been implicated with atherogenesis. C-reactive protein has also implicated as mediating this clot-formation process.

Hypertension
The relationship of obesity and overweight to hypertension is well established. The prevalence of overweight in hypertensive patients combined with the response in blood pressure to weight loss speaks to a causative relationship between weight status and hypertension. Unfortunately, the pathophysiologic mechanism is still poorly defined.

Renal Effects

Renal complications of obesity include hypertension as described above and complications associated with the development of diabetes. The pathogenesis of these processes is, again, incompletely understood but likely related to inflammatory processes.

Endocrine Effects

Hyperinsulinism
Weight status has a demonstrable impact on the development of insulin resistance. In particular, adipocyte-derived hormones, TNF-α and adiponectin, are potent inducers of insulin resistance through cell membrane mechanisms. This increase in insulin resistance ultimately can lead to type II diabetes. The mechanism is unknown, but there is also an association with obesity in patients with type 1 diabetes.

Cytokines in obesity
A variety of hormones have been implicated in the development of obesity and the complications seen in it. **Table 1** summarizes the source, mechanism, and probable effect of some of the more understood hormones. It should be noted that the interaction between these hormones is unclear and the identification of other cytokines are areas of needed research.

Gastrointestinal Effects

Adipocytes, long felt to be merely storehouses of fat for use in times of limited food, have become more understood as inflammatory cells. Some of the most dramatic activity as inflammatory cells occurs in the liver. Nonalcoholic fatty liver disease and the more severe

Table 1   Hormones important in appetite and weight regulation

Agent	Source	Other	Mechanism	Effect
Insulin	Pancreas	Postprandial	Facilitates cellular uptake of glucose	Growth, energy metabolism
PYY	GI	Postprandial	Decreases release of orexigenic hypothalamic neuropeoptide Y (NPY) via arcuate nucleus	Induces satiety and decreases food intake
Ghrelin	GI	Preprandial	Increases expression of NPY	Stimulates food intake
GLP-1	GI	Postprandial	Increases postprandial insulin release	Inhibits food intake
PP	GI		?	Inhibits appetite and promotes energy expenditure
Leptin	Adipose		Inhibits NPY, melanin concentrating hormone, orexin A, agouti-related peptide, cannabinoid systems Upregulates pro-opiomelanocortin/mela-nocortin, cocaine and amphetamine regulated transcript and corticotropin-releasing hormone	Suppression of food intake
Orexin A(&B)	Hypothalamus	Affects sleep wake cycle	Integration of metabolic and circadian sleep debt influences	Promotes wakefulness and increases appetite
Adiponectin	Adipose	Inversely related to BMI; female > male	1. Bind to receptors affecting AMP kinase 2. Complementary to leptin	Promotes gluconeogenesis, glucose uptake, TG clearance, weight gain and insulin resistance
TNF-α	Adipose	Lipolysis and apoptosis (cell death)	Acute phase protein which initiates a cascade of cytokines and increases vascular permeability	Induction on insulin resistance

GI, gastrointestinal tract

nonalcoholic steatohepatitis are both felt to be mediated through the local inflammatory effects of adipocytes that secret TNF-α and other agents.

Psychological Effects

Children who are overweight perceive their different weight status usually by age 6 years. This perception of difference may interfere with assimilation and self-image. Depression and poor school performance have been linked to overweight in childhood. Degree of overweight is positively correlated with poor school performance, lessened self-esteem and depression.

As the average weight of children continues to increase, this perception of 'being different' may subside. This may reduce the stress certain children feel about being different. Unfortunately though, this increasing average population weight may reduce the recognition of abnormally high weight in other patients by making it less physically obvious.

Neurologic Effects

Idiopathic intracranial hypertension or pseudotumor cerebri is a potentially life-threatening swelling of the brain. It has symptoms that resemble the symptoms of brain tumor due to increased pressure. It has been linked in repeated studies with obesity. This condition is also increased in diseases which are characterized by coagulation disorders. The inflammation-mediated coagulation disorders seen in obese patients have led to the theory that thromboembolic events in the cerebrospinal fluid reabsorption system in the central nervous ventricular system in overweight patients is the instigating factor in pseudotumor cerebri for them.

Hematologic Effects

Venous stasis, inactivity, and microvascular injury associated with diabetes create a milieu more favorable to thromboembolism formation in overweight and obese patients.

Pulmonary Effects

A relatively common complication of obesity is hypoventilation syndrome with sleep. This process is likely related to anatomic obstruction and to altered central control of respiration. While the pathogenesis of this syndrome is not completely understood, the resulting cardiac effects are likely due to ongoing high carbon dioxide levels and low oxygen levels.

Orthopedic Effects

Overweight patients have an increased likelihood of having slipped capital femoral epiphysis (SCFE) or Blount's disease (progressive bowing of the proximal tibia). Both processes are felt to be mechanical complications of excess weight. The fact that the incidence of these disorders increases with increasing weight lends support to the acceptance of this mechanism.

Clinical Picture and Diagnostic Testing

The clinical picture of obesity and overweight can be varied. This variability stems from the multiple possible comorbidities and the unpredictable expression of those comorbidities.

Some of the more common historical presentations include behavior problems, sleep difficulties, snoring, depression, lethargy, shortness of breath on exertion, ankle sprain, asthma, sleep apnea, headache, abdominal pain, leg pain, back pain, vomiting, and diarrhea. Common physical examination findings include limited mobility, shortness of breath, flat affect, large tonsils, premature height growth, hypertension, abdominal discomfort, acanthosis nigricans (excess neck pigmentation from high circulating insulin levels), generous suprapubic fat pad and bowing of the proximal tibia.

Table 2 describes a suggested inventory of historical questions and physical examination items to document during a clinical visit.

Laboratory evaluation is not necessary in most cases. However, poor response to therapy or extreme overweight requires diligent exclusion of organic causes of overweight. The implications of certain laboratory values, such as fasting insulin and oral glucose tolerance, are not fully understood and therefore not universally recommended. Table 3 lists labs to consider in the evaluation of an overweight patient.

Treatment

A basic principle of treatment has been the use of a graduated approach guided by severity of overweight

Table 2   History and physical exam template for a visits with overweight preschoolers

History (should be complete, but the following lists all needed areas of focus)

Chief complaint	What are your feelings about your/your child's weight status?
Present illness	What is the course of your child's weight over the past 6 months?
	What are your feelings about your child losing weight?
	Have you tried to help your child lose weight before?
	If so, how did it work?
Diet	What are your child's three favorite vegetables?
	What does your child like to drink?
	What does your child eat that makes him gain weight?
	What are your and his good habits?
	What are your and his bad habits?
Exercise	Tell me about your child's activity level.
	Tell me about your feelings with exercise.
	Explain to me what it is like to bike and walk in your neighborhood.
Child-care	Where and how often?
	Does the child-care promote physical activity? Explain how or why not.
Primary doctor	Who is your family doctor or pediatrician? What has he/she told you about your weight?
Family history	Document at least the following processes in all first and second degree relatives: obesity, hypertension, cardiovascular disease, dyslipidemias, diabetes, thyroid disease.
Past medical	Medications, allergies, surgeries, hospitalizations, other chronic illnesses such as attention deficit with hyperactivity disorder.
Review of systems	Headache, hot/cold intolerance, sleep problems, joint symptoms, back pain, depression, sleep problems shortness of breath, leg pain, polyuria, polydipsia, snoring.
Social history	Living arrangement.

Physical exam (a complete examination is required, but the following lists all needed areas of focus)

Height	
Weight	
Calculated BMI	
General	Affect, general comfort level, acute distress
Head	Facies, appearance
Eyes	Optic disks
Throat	Posterior pharynx
Neck	Thyroid palpation, acanthosis
Heart	Murmur
Lungs	Rales, wheezes
Abdomen	Liver size
Genital	Tanner stage
Skin	Rash, axillary or intertrginous
Orthopedic	Proximal knee and ankle exam, scoliosis check

and age. Generally, the level of complexity of intervention increases with degree of overweight and increase in age. The continued increase in obesity prevalence across all age groups has called into question all approaches to weight management, but there is a general consensus among experts that the intensity of intervention has typically not been adequate.

Although uniformity in treatment is lacking, guidelines for targeting specific behaviors to prevent obesity do exist. In 2005, the American Heart Association recommended the following for healthy weight promotion in preschoolers (**Table 4**).

Feeding Habits for Obesity Prevention

The most appropriate approach for young children is establishment of good eating habits. Young children should be fed on demand and be allowed to self-regulate intake, particularly in the neonatal period. 'Plate clearing' should be discouraged. Meal times should be predictably and consistently scheduled. Limited options are felt to promote trying new foods since children will often eat previously untried foods if previously selected options are not available. Similarly, foods should be presented repeatedly. It is estimated that children will try a food seven times before determining if they like the taste. Meal times

should be of a finite length. Making multiple 'on demand' meals and allowing late night snacks may promote excess caloric intake and promote behavioral problems associated with food. Going to bed with an empty stomach is not contraindicated in young children. Healthy foods should be prepackaged for easy access and should be readily available on countertops and in the refrifgerator.

Behavioral Options for Overweight Children

There are many proposed and promoted behavioral options for dietary change in adults, but relatively few options for children. Even inside major medical centers, organized evidence-based and clinically effective programs for overweight children are lacking. Research in this area suggests certain approaches show more promise.

Readiness to change in parental behavior is critical. Historically, the didactic approach of most physicians to parents has been ineffective in bringing about dietary change. Practitioners have tended to address behavior change in the same way other health recommendations were made, that is, prescriptively. Behavioral studies indicate that parents are unlikely to regard even demonstrably overweight children as being overweight. This mismatch between parental perception and practitioner perception has impaired parents' willingness to implement behavior changes. A movement to address readiness, a principle long used in substance abuse work, promises to improve adherence. Behavioral techniques such as motivational interviewing, readiness based tailoring of materials, and more intensive follow-up hold promise.

Behavior modification has been the most commonly used behavioral technique in weight management and remains the central approach of most organized programs. Reward for implementation of healthy habits and redirection from unhealthy habits are common techniques. Teaching parents goal-setting techniques and using nondietary rewards has shown efficacy. Limitation to two to three goals, frequent follow-up, and inclusion of positive activity goals, as opposed to purely dietary denial goals, appears appropriate.

Table 3 Laboratory evaluation of an overweight patient

Consider often
Fasting: Glucose, total cholesterol, high-density lipoprotein cholesterol, low-density lipoprotein cholesterol, triglycerides
Not necessarily fasting: AST, ALT, γ-GT, alkaline phosphatase, total and direct bilirubin, total protein, albumin

Consider if indicated
Fasting: Insulin
Not necessarily fasting: CBC, calcium, sodium, potassium, chloride, bicarbonate, blood urea nitrogen, creatinine, free thyroid hormone, thyroid stimulating hormone, body composition analysis (body impedance analysis, DEXA scan, displacement techniques)

Table 4 American Heart Association Guidelines for healthy weight in preschoolers

Parents chose meal times, not children

Provide a wide variety of nutrient-dense foods such as fruits and vegetables instead of high-energy–density/nutrient-poor foods such as salty snacks, ice cream, fried foods, cookies and sweetened beverages
Pay attention to portion size; serve portions appropriate for the child's size and age
Use nonfat or low-fat dairy products as sources of calcium and protein
Limit snacking during sedentary behavior or in response to boredom and particularly restrict use of sweet/sweetened beverages as snacks (e.g., juice, soda, sports drinks)
Limit sedentary behaviors, with no more than 1–2 h per day of video screen/television and no television sets in children's bedrooms
Allow self-regulation of total caloric intake in the presence of normal BMI or weight for height
Have regular family meals to promote social interaction and role model food-related behavior

The setting of these programs is nearly as varied as their content. Physician offices, tertiary care centers, community health centers, and schools all deliver these and other forms of intervention. Since pediatric overweight is a heterogeneous illness in both origin and treatment, the most appropriate location for delivery is expected to vary with patients and families.

A common concern expressed by practitioners is hesitance to deliver dietary interventions to pediatric patients for fear of unmasking or promoting anorexia nervosa, bulimia or other eating disorders. This risk appears to be small particularly in younger children. In fact, allowing progression to heavier weights may be a greater risk for eating disorders. Eating disorders, in most instances, represent a different psychopathology than that seen in pediatric overweight and practitioners should not avoid discussion of weight with respect to these fears.

The treatment of the extremely overweight infant and toddler is an area of needed research. Approaches to treating extreme overweight, BMI over the 99.5 percentile for age and gender, appear to require very intensive and specialized treatment regimens to bring about normalization in BMI. Children in these categories often come from families with markedly disordered parenting skills. These families often demonstrate a dysfunctional preoccupation with food and disordered parenting and behavioral enforcement.

Successful interventions are rare. Some experts suggest handling cases of extreme overweight similarly to cases of failure to thrive due to undernutrition because of the similar risk to long-term health and the inability of the caregiver unit to provide appropriate nutrition. This approach, which is associated with significant stress for patients, families, and caregivers should be undertaken with great caution and with close involvement of a consistent social worker.

Pharmacologic Options

Pharmacologic intervention for pediatric weight management is not readily accepted nor has it been adequately studied for efficacy or safety due to concerns with side effects in young children. Certain agents have demonstrated limited efficacy in adults and may have a role in certain older pediatric patients over age 12 years with extreme overweight (BMI percentile >99th percentile). These agents include orlistat, bupropion, rimonabant, topiramate, and sibutramine.

Surgical Options

As with pharmacologic agents, surgical options such as gastric bypass and laparoscopic band placement have a therapeutic role in adolescents with comorbidities and extreme overweight but are not applicable to young children who are growing.

Prognosis

As described above, the complications of pediatric overweight are many and range across a variety of organ systems. Unfortunately, a singular effective approach to the management of pediatric overweight is not present and is unlikely due to the multifactorial etiology of pediatric overweight. There are few effective interventions at present. Consequently, the progression to adolescent and subsequent adult overweight and obesity has been unrelenting. Children who are overweight at any time in the first 5 years of life are at 5 times greater risk of being overweight in early adolescence and being overweight on early adolescence is a significant risk factor for adult obesity. Recent studies suggest that a child who is overweight or AROW (BMI percentile >85th percentile) at age 3 years is six times more likely to be overweight by age 9 years. A child who is overweight by age 9 is 11–30 times more likely to be a clinically obese young adult. While the treatment of pediatric overweight is not, as yet, uniform or effective, the urgent need for effective interventions is obvious.

See also: Breastfeeding; Demographic Factors; Endocrine System; Feeding Development and Disorders; Fragile X Syndrome; Genetics and Inheritance; Maternal Age and Pregnancy; Nutrition and Diet; Physical Growth.

Suggested Readings

Barlow S and Dietz W (2002) Management of child and adolescent obesity: Summary and recommendations based on reports from pediatricians, pediatric nurse practitioners, and registered dietitians. *Pediatrics* 110: 236–238.

Bowman SA, Gortmaker SL, Ebbeling CB, Pereira MA, and Ludwig DS (2004) Effects of fast-food consumption on energy intake and diet quality among children in a national household survey. *Pediatrics* 113: 112–118.

Farooqi S (2005) Genetic and hereditary aspects of childhood obesity. *Best Practice and Research: Clinical Endocrinology and Metabolism* 19(3): 359–374.

Gidding SS, Dennison BA, Birch LL, *et al.* (2006) Dietary recommendations for children and adolescents: A guide for practitioners. *Pediatrics* 117(2): 544–559.

Hedley AA, Ogden CL, Johnson CL, Carroll MD, Curtin LR, and Flegal KM (2004) Prevalence of overweight and obesity among US children, adolescents, and adults, 1999–2002. *JAMA* 291(23): 2847–2850.

Thompson D, Obarzanek E, Franko D, *et al.* (2007) Childhood overweight and cardiovascular disease risk factors: The national heart, lung, and blood institute growth and health study. *Journal of Pediatrics* 150(1): 18–25.

US PreventiveServices, Task Force (2005) Screening and interventions for overweight children and adolescents: Recommendation statement. *Pediatrics* 116: 205–209.

Whitlock EP, Williams SB, Gold R, Smith P, and Shipman S (2005) *Screening and Interventions for Childhood Overweight: Evidence Synthesis.* July 2005, Agency for Healthcare Research and Quality, USA.

Object Concept

S P Johnson and K C Soska, New York University, New York, NY, USA

Glossary

A-not-B error – In simple hiding games, infants will sometimes search at a location where they had previously found an object (the 'A' location), even after watching it hidden someplace else (the 'B' location).

Action systems – Locomotor, manual, and oculomotor (eye movement) behaviors that may play a central role in developing object concepts.

Allocentric reasoning – Coding of spatial location in terms of landmarks in the environment (compare egocentric reasoning).

Ecological approach to perception – A theoretical view suggesting that the way to understand human cognition is to study the moving, acting human as he or she exists (and evolved) in real-world contexts.

Egocentric reasoning – Coding of spatial location in terms of the observer's own viewpoint (compare allocentric reasoning).

Electroencephalography (EEG) – Recording of differences in small electrical currents produced by the brain and measured at the scalp; they reflect the brain's response to a specific visual or auditory stimulus.

Neural synchrony – A common firing mechanism among circuits of neurons in the brain that work together to code an event.

Object concept – The ability to represent objects in the absence of direct perceptual support, including some (internal) cortical activity that registers the presence of a hidden object or hidden object part beyond what is available via sensory input, as well as some (external) behavioral manifestation of the representation.

Objectification – Knowledge of the self and external objects as distinct entities, spatially segregated, persisting across time and space, and obeying certain commonsense causal constraints.

Prefrontal dorsolateral cortex – A part of the brain that is thought to be important in short-term memory and inhibition of habitual behaviors.

Visual preference paradigms – Methods used to probe learning, memory, representation, and discrimination in preverbal infants, based on the tendency of infants to look longer at visual stimuli that are novel, interesting, or otherwise discriminable.

Introduction

Adults experience a world composed of objects at various distances. We perceive these objects as continuous and enduring even when they are out of view, part of a mature system of object concepts. We consider theories of how object concepts develop in infancy, focusing on the seminal views of Jean Piaget, and more recent alternatives based on innate concepts. We then present evidence from a variety of paradigms designed to elucidate the precise mechanisms of object concept development. This evidence points to emerging action systems and neural development as providing crucial support for object concept development.

Object Concept

We live in an environment filled with countless objects, each of which occupies a unique spatial location. Objects in the world tend to be predictable; for example, we know that inanimate objects do not move in the absence of some outside force, objects cannot be in two places at once (nor two objects in the same place), and objects do not vanish out of existence and then reappear. But the visual environment that is seen 'directly' (i.e., the light that is reflected to the eye from visible surfaces in the environment) changes with every head and eye movement, and objects themselves may move out of sight and subsequently return to view. Nevertheless, our experience is not a world of transitory, intangible, disembodied shapes, but rather one of substance, volume, and depth.

Do infants also experience a world of solid objects? Or might they instead perceive only what is directly visible, failing to infer the permanence of objects without, say, extensive experience, a certain level of brain maturation, or both? Note the similarity of these questions to the classic 'nature–nurture' issue, the subject of long and fierce debates. The origins of object perception have interested philosophers for centuries, and discussions have often centered on the extent to which knowledge of objects is gained from visual, manual, or some other active experience, or is the product of innate (unlearned) cognitive skills. Systematic empirical approaches to these vital questions were unavailable until the early twentieth century with the publication of a succession of books by Jean Piaget. He introduced a series of tasks posed to his own young children in an attempt to chart the development of object representations – amongst other cognitive skills – across infancy. Some of these tasks are described subsequently. Also described are alternative theoretical views, followed by discussions of studies that examine carefully how object concepts might develop across the first several months after birth. These studies, by and large, are consistent with Piaget's theory, although the scope of the theory, in hindsight, appears to have been limited.

Piaget's Theory

Piaget presented a theory of object concepts that comprised development of knowledge of objects in tandem with their spatial relations, because one cannot perceive or act on objects accurately without awareness of their positions in space relative to other objects. The foremost explanandum of Piagetian theory was objectification, the knowledge of the self and external objects as distinct entities, spatially segregated, persisting across time and space, and obeying certain commonsense causal constraints. Piaget suggested that objectification is rooted in the child's recognition of her own body as an independent object and her own movements as movements of objects through space, akin to movements of other objects she sees. This constitutes a transition from egocentric to allocentric reasoning. Over time, thinking and reasoning about objects become detached from actions, and actions are placed on the ongoing, observed series of surrounding events in the construction of the reality of time and space. That is, it no longer becomes necessary for the infant to act upon on object for her to gain an understanding of its properties. The progression from egocentric to allocentric spatial reasoning and to a mature object concept was revealed to Piaget and other developmental psychologists by changes in infants' behavior in the normal, day-to-day flow of activities, and when confronted with a series of tasks that Piaget devised.

Objectification was thought to be an outcome of coordination of actions. Initially, behaviors are simply repeated, one at a time and then become organized into more complex strings of action sequences. At the same time, infants begin to explore novelty, as when trying new behaviors, or using familiar actions with no clear prediction of outcome. These behaviors are evident in everyday play activities, as when Piaget observed his daughter repeatedly hide and reveal a toy under a blanket. Piaget proposed that these simple games led the child to establish spatial relations among objects, such as above, below, and behind, largely by manual experience. For example, infants who are learning to reach (at 4–6 months) soon discover which objects are within reach and those that are not – a kind of depth perception. Therefore, both direct experience (to learn when search is successful or not) and deduction (reasoning from general principles to specific instances) contribute to the developmental process.

Development of action systems, spatial concepts, and object concepts was organized into six stages. Initially (during stages 1 and 2), infants exhibited a kind of recognition memory, for example, seeking the mother's breast after losing contact shortly after birth, and within several months, continuing to look in the direction of a person's exit from the room. These behaviors were not systematic, however, and Piaget considered them more passive than active. For Piaget, active search, initiated by the child, was a critical feature of mature object concepts.

More active search behavior emerged after 4 months, and marked the beginnings of true objectification during stage 3. Piaget outlined five examples, in roughly chronological order. The first of these was visual accommodation to rapid movements, when an infant would respond to a dropped object by looking down toward the floor, behavior that became more systematic when the infant himself dropped it. A second behavior, interrupted prehension, refers to the infant's attempts to re-acquire an object that was dropped or taken from her hand if it is out of sight momentarily and within easy reach. (The infant will not search yet, however, if the object is fully occluded.) Deferred circular reactions describes the infant's repetitive gestures when interrupted during some object-oriented play activity, resuming the game after some delay (necessitating memory of the object, the actions, and their context). Reconstruction of an invisible whole from a visible fraction was evinced, for example, by retrieval of an object from a cover when only a part of the object was visible. Finally, the infant became capable of removal of obstacles preventing perception, as when he pulls away a cover from his face during peekaboo, or withdraws a fully hidden toy from beneath a blanket. This behavior marked the transition to stage 4.

During stage 4, beginning at about 8 months, the infant will search actively for a hidden object under a variety of circumstances. Searches may be erroneous, however, when the object is hidden first at a single location followed by (successful) search, and then hidden in another location as the infant watches (see **Figure 1**). Here, the

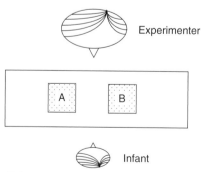

Figure 1 Schematic overhead view of an infant and experimenter participating in a hidden object search task designed to elicit the A-not-B error.

infant may remove the obstacle at the first location the object was hidden, even though she saw it hidden subsequently somewhere else. This response has come to be known as the A-not-B error. Piaget also described an intriguing incident when one of his daughters, aged 15 months, saw her father in the garden. When asked, "Where is papa?" she pointed to the window of his office in the home, as if there were two papas: "papa at his window" and "papa in the garden." These behaviors mark awareness of and search for a vanished object, but their erroneous nature, according to Piaget, indicated a fundamental limitation of the emerging object concept: There is not yet true objectification. During stage 4, the object is considered an extension of the infant's own behavior, and identity of objects is not preserved across perceptual contacts. That is, if an object appears at a particular place as a function of a child's activity, there is no concept yet of continuity across time and space.

Objectification is completed across the next two stages as the infant first solves the problem of multiple visible displacements, searching at the last location visited by the object (stage 5), and then multiple invisible displacements (stage 6). Finally, the infant searches systematically at all potential hiding locations visited by the object. For Piaget, mature search revealed detachment of the object from the action, and knowledge of the infant's body itself as one object among many, brought into an allocentric system of organized objects and events.

Evaluating Piaget's Theory

Piagetian theory has received a great deal of interest, in particular the A-not-B error, but a number of researchers have explored earlier developmental patterns as well. The theory enjoys strong support for many of the details of behavior that Piaget described, but many researchers have questioned the reasoning behind the developmental changes in these behaviors.

Consider first the A-not-B error. There have been hundreds of successful replications of the effect in 8–12-month-old infants. Nevertheless, the basis for the error, and what it reveals about object concept development, remain a matter of relentless dispute. Three examples of research paradigms that have examined Piagetian claims help to illustrate this controversy. Adele Diamond has used the A-not-B error as an index of brain development, specifically an area known as 'prefrontal dorsolateral cortex', which is thought to be important in short-term memory and inhibition of habitual behaviors (so-called 'inhibitory control'). According to Diamond, the A-not-B error occurs in infants because there is a difficulty in maintaining a short-term representation of the object and its location, plus a difficulty in inhibiting a tendency to reach at a 'primed' location. Renee Baillargeon has

suggested that the A-not-B error is a poor index of infants' object concepts, because of a general lack of coordinated manual search behavior in infants who are still learning to reach appropriately. Finally, Linda Smith and Esther Thelen have claimed that the A-not-B error tells us nothing at all about object representations or concepts, because the error arises from specific task demands, reaching history, and the experimental context. Infants even produce the error in the absence of any hidden toy!

Turning next to other evidence of early object concepts, numerous experiments have revealed that by 2–4 months of age, infants appear to maintain representations of partly and fully hidden objects across short delays. These experiments rely on 'visual preference' paradigms, using techniques developed in the 1960s and 1970s by Tom Bower and further refined by Elizabeth Spelke and others. These paradigms built on methods pioneered by Robert Fantz, who discovered that infants tend to lose interest in repetitive visual stimuli, and recover interest to novel stimuli. Some researchers, in addition, have devised a variant of the novelty-preference paradigm known as the violation-of-expectation method, which relies on the assumption that infants will look preferentially in general at odd or unusual events. A well-known example was described by Renee Baillargeon and colleagues, who showed 5-month-old infants a stimulus consisting of a rotating screen that appeared to move through the space occupied by a previously seen object. They reported that infants looked longer at the event in which the screen 'passed through' the object relative to the event in which the screen stopped at the object's location (see **Figure 2**). The first event, therefore, was claimed to violate the previously seen object's solidity, but the second event was consistent with an expectation of solidity. Violation-of-expectation methods, too, are controversial, because we can never be sure why infants look longer at violations – it has been suggested, for example, that the violation in this example is interesting because there is more motion in the event. Nevertheless, there are dozens of corroborative and related findings that young infants perceive objects as persistent and whole across short intervals of time and space. Simple reaching measures, for example, are consistent with this interpretation: young infants have been found to reach in the dark toward an object in a previously visible location. In addition, recordings of brain activity in infants, in particular electroencephalography (EEG) (differences in small electrical currents at the scalp over the brain), have revealed object representations that are maintained under occlusion. This evidence comes from coordinated bursts of neural activity that may reflect short-term memory for objects that were recently hidden.

The outcomes of these experiments are by and large consistent with Piaget's claims: evidence for the rudiments of object concepts, in place early in infancy, which are elaborated with learning and experience.

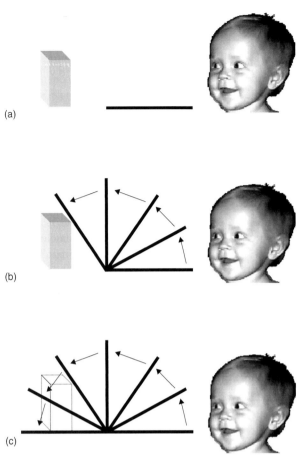

(a)

(b)

(c)

Figure 2 Schematic depiction of the events used to probe young infants' object representations across short intervals of occlusion. (a) The infant sees a box and a screen that is flat on the table. (b) The screen rotates up to the box and stops, a so-called possible event. (c) The screen appears to rotate through the space seen to have been occupied by the box, an impossible event. Reproduced with permission from the parent.

Reaching errors in the context of multiple hiding locations have been observed in many experiments but remain a source of controversy, and it is unclear what such behavior reveals. Also in question is a central tenet of Piaget's theory of object concept development: the idea that early object concepts are egocentric, not allocentric. Few active theoreticians would likely agree with this notion, and the evidence that Piaget offered in support of this proposal seems weak relative to other aspects of the theory. On the other hand, two ideas originating in Piaget's theory have been supported by more recent research: first, the possibility that newborn infants do not perceive occlusion (and therefore no functional object concept), and, second, the importance of the infant's own behavior in constructing object representations. These ideas are discussed in subsequent sections of this article.

In summary, Piaget inspired decades of fruitful research that have documented clearly the development of object concepts within several months after birth. These

concepts guide detection of anomalous visual stimuli (such as impossible events), guide reaching toward previously seen objects, and are manifest in recordings of cortical activity as infants view occlusion stimuli. Despite this progress, fundamental questions remain in the extent to which object representations develop with experience, learning, and general maturation. These questions are considered in subsequent sections of the article.

Nativist Theory

Central to nativist theory are the tandem possibilities that some kinds of knowledge form a central core upon which more diverse, mature cognitive capacities are built, and that some kinds of knowledge are unlearned. Philosophical discussions of innateness are ancient; historically, these discussions have centered around the extent to which human knowledge must necessarily be rooted in, or is independent of, postnatal experience. Plato and Descartes, for example, proposed that some ideas were universal and available innately because they were elicited in the absence of any direct tutoring or instruction, or were unobservable in the world, and thus unlearnable (e.g., concepts of geometry or God). With the advent of rigorous testing methods in the last century, the debate began to shift from the role of innate concepts to the role of innate process in shaping knowledge acquisition. Donald Hebb, for example, noted the 'intrinsic organization' that characterized the neonate's electroencephalogram, which he postulated as a contributing mechanism of subsequent perceptual development, based primarily on associative learning. Innate process was an important facet of Gestalt perceptual theory as well: dynamic forces of electrical activity in the brain were thought to guide general perceptual organization, alongside experience with specific object kinds. For researchers advocating an innate process, the innateness is not any knowledge per se, but the ability for the child's developing brain to quickly and easily pick up many types of information.

More recently, theories of innate concepts have again become more common: concepts of objects as obeying certain real-world, physical constraints, such as persistence and identity across occlusion, and solidity. Three arguments have been offered for such hypothesized innate object concepts. First, veridical object knowledge can be elicited in very young infants under some circumstances, suggesting that early concepts emerge too quickly to have been derived from postnatal learning. Second, infants' detection of apparent violations of simple physical events has been proposed to reflect weighing 'contrastive' evidence. To nativists, though, young infants would not have had sufficient opportunities to observe conditions under which an object behaves in a manner consistent or inconsistent with a particular concept. If this is a principal mechanism of development of object concepts, it follows that a concept of persistence across occlusion must be innate, because it cannot have been acquired from observing contrastive evidence in the real world. Third, there is evidence that nonhuman animals' mechanisms for tracking objects across occlusion may operate in similar ways to those of humans, suggesting that object concepts were programmed via evolutionary pressure.

The majority of evidence for early object concepts comes from experiments in which looking times are recorded relative either to a familiarization stimulus (i.e., a novelty preference) or to some aspect of object knowledge that the infant is purported to bring to the task (i.e., a violation of expectation). As noted previously, there is evidence from a variety of laboratories and experimental settings for short-term representations of objects under occlusion that are functional by 2–4 months after birth. Nevertheless, the question of developmental origins cannot be addressed merely by noting competence at a young age. Evidence for innate object concepts would come from, for example, functionality at birth, emergence in the absence of experience, or stability across development, and at present no such evidence exists. Moreover, experiments on infants' perception of partly occluded objects, reviewed next, cast doubt on the viability of nativist theory to explain early object concepts.

In the 1960s, Tom Bower devised a clever task to examine infants' discrimination of the perceptual equivalence of two visual stimuli. The stimuli were identical, except one was partially occluded (see **Figure 3**). An operant conditioning procedure was employed with 1-month-old infants, with sucking rate as the operant response (the infant was required to suck on a pacifier for the visual display to appear). The infants were first exposed to a partly occluded triangle, and reduced sucking rates were interpreted as evidence of perceptual discrimination. The infants maintained sucking rates in response to a complete (unoccluded) triangle, taken as evidence for phenomenal identity, and perception of the partly occluded triangle (the training stimulus) as having a definite form behind the occluder. Presentation of triangle parts (separated by a gap) resulted in decreased response, taken as evidence that these incomplete forms were perceived as different than the partly occluded triangle – in other words, the infants perceived the partly occluded triangle as complete. In experiments with 4-month-olds, Philip Kellman and Elizabeth Spelke were unable to replicate the finding of perceptual completion on the basis of static information; they reported that only motion was effective in specifying unity. After habituation to a partly occluded rod, the infants looked longer at two rod parts than at a complete object, but only when the rod parts moved relative to the occluder (see **Figure 4**). These experiments challenge the notion that young infants perceive object completion on the basis of Gestalt perceptual information such as good continuation, but leave open the question of development of perceptual completion in infancy.

This question was addressed by Alan Slater and colleagues, who replicated the methods of Kellman and Spelke with newborns, tested less than 3 days after birth. In contrast to 4-month-olds, newborns responded to a partly occluded object display solely on the basis of its visible parts, failing to perceive completion behind the occluder. Scott Johnson has found that under some conditions, 2-month-olds perceive object unity, as when the occluder is made narrow and the distance of perceptual interpolation is reduced, relative to a display in which older infants are able to achieve perceptual completion. Johnson and colleagues reported similar patterns of evidence in experiments examining perception of continuity of object trajectories (see **Figure 5**). Four-month-olds perceived continuity only when the object was out of sight for a very brief period of time; when out of sight for a more extended duration, the infants appeared to perceive only the visible segments of the object trajectory, failing to perceive persistence. In other words, they behaved in like manner to the newborns in the experiments described previously, responding only to what is directly visible. Six-month-olds seemed to perceive continuity even under the longer occlusion duration.

Consider these results in the light of nativist theory. All evidence to date indicates that perception of occlusion is not available to newborn infants; instead, developments in perceptual completion occur across the first several months after birth. Without perception of occlusion, of course, a functional object concept is impossible, and therefore we conclude that there is no innate object concept as such. Nevertheless, some potential mechanisms of development are consistent with, and indeed rely on, innate structure and process. These are presented in subsequent sections of the article.

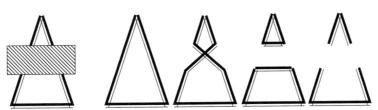

Figure 3 Training (left) and four test stimuli used in the Bower experiment on 1-month-olds' perception of a partly occluded wire triangle.

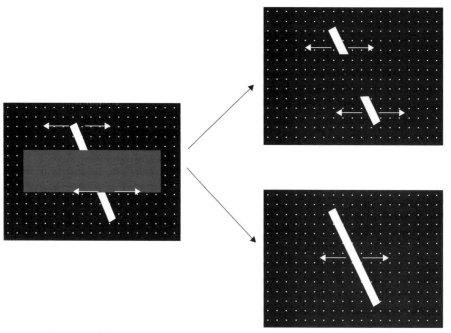

Figure 4 Events presented to young infants in investigations of perception of partial occlusion. After habituation to the partly occluded rod at left, infants view displays depicting either the rod segments that were formerly visible (top), or a complete version of the rod (bottom).

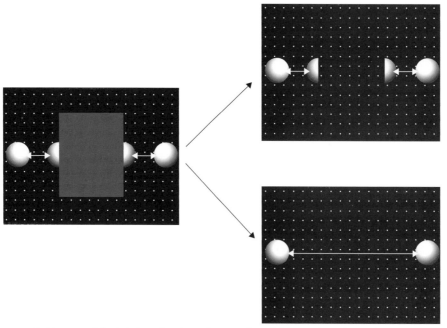

Figure 5 Events presented to young infants in investigations of perception of object trajectories under occlusion. After habituation to the partly occluded object trajectory at left, infants view displays depicting either the trajectory segments that were formerly visible, without the occluder present (top), or a continuous version of the trajectory, again with no occluder (bottom).

Evaluating Nativist Theory

As noted previously, there is evidence from a variety of laboratories and experimental settings for representations of objects as solid bodies that are spatiotemporally coherent and persistent; these representations appear to be functional by 2–4 months after birth. Obtaining such evidence for competence in these tasks at a young age is an important step in determining how object concepts develop, but the arguments discussed previously do little to shed light on this important issue. Nativist theory draws praise, however, for the cultivation of exciting, alternative perspectives on questions of cognitive development and for serving as the inspiration for the generation of an abundance of data. Development is always a matter of building new structure upon the old, whether the structures under consideration are concrete, such as arrangements of neural connections, or more abstract, such as object concepts. The ultimate value of nativist theory, instead, may be the attention it calls to the potential role of more general developmental processes that may operate outside experience, even while lacking specific proposals for how this might occur in the case of object knowledge. The infant is delivered to the world outside the uterus an active perceiver, endowed with the readiness and ability to acquire information, prepared to discover the patterns and regularities in the events she views in the surrounding environment. An understanding of the state of neonates' perceptual systems may be a more well defined question under the purview of nativism than is development of object concepts.

In summary, nativist theory has provided provocative claims for innate concepts, yet provides little insight into developmental mechanisms. One problem with nativist theory is a failure to consider evidence from experiments that investigate object perception in newborns and very young infants. In the next section, we consider alternatives that may hold more explanatory power.

Developmental Mechanisms of Object Concepts: Action Systems

In the previous sections of the article we presented and critiqued two theories, each of which captures a part of the larger picture of object concept development. From Piagetian theory comes the notion that object concepts likely take many months to mature, from an initial response to missing (occluded) object parts to the ability to solve complex hiding tasks. In addition, the possibility that the infant's own behaviors have a direct role in concept development is appealing, and Piaget described evidence from hiding tasks to support this idea. Nativist theory stresses the importance of development that occurs outside experience. This viewpoint is correct for some perceptual skills: newborn infants distinguish between separate regions of visual space that constitute visible surface fragments, they retain information for short intervals, and there are distinct visual preferences at birth (e.g., edges are preferred over homogeneous regions). Nevertheless, there is strong evidence that infants are not born with object representations or concepts. In the remainder of the article, we will address the question of how perceptual completion might develop in infancy. We will return to the issue, initially suggested by Piaget, of action systems in developing object concepts: locomotor, manual, and oculomotor

(eye movement) behaviors that appear to provide a crucial supportive – or perhaps causal – role in early object perception.

The possibility that action and motor development can promote the understanding of object properties has a long history within developmental psychology research. As noted previously, Piaget placed the actions of infants at the forefront of his theories of perceptual development. On Piaget's theory, the sensorimotor period is characterized by increasingly coordinated actions that permit infants to learn about objects in the world, and motor skills were thought to be the primary means by which object knowledge was constructed into a representational system. Piaget popularized the idea that the active child could – through exploration of objects – obtain information relevant for future understanding of several properties, including object permanence and perceptual completion.

Building upon the idea that the actions of the developing child could promote learning about the visual world, Eleanor Gibson posited several areas in which exploratory skills facilitate object knowledge. Newborns use visual scanning to obtain information about important events in the world. Over the next few months, infants become increasingly skilled at coordinating eye movements with head movements. For Gibson's approach to object perception, this nascent exploratory system allows infants to learn about the events of the visual world. Manual exploratory systems grow increasingly skilled around 4 months, giving infants even more opportunities to learn about the distinctive features of objects. As self-locomotion begins around 8 months, infants use their own actions to situate objects within the three-dimensional (3D) world and discover the layout of an environment on their own. In Gibson's 'ecological' approach to perception, infants' object knowledge is grounded within action as the two form a mutual, self-reinforcing loop. The interplay of perception and action in the infant's object concept reflects the realm in which object knowledge takes place in the mind of ecological developmentalists. The real world is where actions take place, where cognition is used, and where the infant learns and grows. Action is constant and inherently meaningful for the developing infant.

The theoretical link of perception and action within development takes on a more unidirectional role for other researchers. For instance, Joseph Campos, Bennett Bertenthal and colleagues have proposed that developments in independent locomotion likewise can ignite a host of new skills. The authors have been major proponents of the organizational nature of self-locomotion for many domains including social, spatial, and object perception, and emotional development. On their perspective, there is a hierarchal and nested relation among motor development and cognitive and perceptual skill acquisition. The onset of locomotion provides various experiences and processes that in turn stimulate a range of psychological reorganizations. For example, locomotion involves a continual updating of one's position in space, and this in turn may lead to improvements in spatial reasoning: learning to keep track of specific target locations, encoding spatial relations among targets, using landmarks for spatial coding, and so forth, leading then to more effective search strategies. Emily Bushnell and Jean-Paul Boudreau proposed that motor development may necessarily lead perceptual development within several domains. Depth perception and knowledge of 3D object structure, for example, were hypothesized to be deeply rooted in action development. On their view, coupled visual–manual exploration affords infants the most direct, well-controlled, and veridical perception of 3D forms, and kinetic cues to form can be revealed through infants' exploration. These two proposals are examined in more detail in the following sections.

Object Concepts and Search Behavior

Self-locomotion may help the infant understand spatial transformation of layouts because he or she is actively in control of the visible changes to the world. When infants are moved passively through the world, they may encode spatial relations egocentrically, in Piagetian terms, but overcome this as active locomotion changes the way the infant experiences the world. Additionally, when under active control, there are many redundancies to the information about the objects in the environment and their displacements as the infant moves, including motor commands, vestibular changes (balance and sensing body movements), and visual signals.

Karen Horobin and Linda Acredolo were the first to provide conclusive evidence that locomotor development was linked to performance on traditional Piagetian hidden object tasks. Across several different versions of an A-not-B task, infants aged 8.5–10 months who had more independent locomotor experience were consistently more successful at locating the hidden object. The authors observed that infants who had more independent locomotion experience displayed more attentiveness visually to the hiding of the objects to be searched for. Thus, simple attention to the task relevant information seems to improve with self-locomotion, in addition to search behavior. Follow-up studies by other researchers found that it was not simply hands-and-knees crawling that provided benefits to object search, but experience with independent locomotion through the use of a walker was also able to facilitate improved action-object knowledge. Additionally, unlike previous work, all of the infants in the sample were of the same age – the simplest way to control for age (or more likely maturation *per se*) as the factor at work in the progression of object search. Results like these indicate that locomotor experience, and not the age of the child alone, account for the success on object search tasks.

Martha Ann Bell and Nathan Fox continued this line of inquiry, recording electroencephalogram (EEG) and examining locomotor skills in the same infants. Frontal EEG signals have been linked to success on object permanence tasks with a delay period inserted. At the onset of crawling experience in infancy, there is also increased coherence of EEG activity over frontal cortex, which may be related to increasing organization of neural networks within the frontal lobe. The frontal lobe, as discussed previously, is of importance for inhibition and short-term memory. In these experiments, infants at 8 months with any amount of locomotor experience or a high amplitude frontal EEG signal were found to be highly successful on the search tasks. Interestingly, there was no interaction between measures of brain maturation and self-locomotion as predictors of success on the search tasks. The authors concluded that there may be multiple pathways to the same result, and that success on object permanence tasks may be driven by different means for different children – locomotor skills for some and cortical maturation for others.

A problem for those proposing that the onset of self-locomotion is crucial for object concepts are results, some of which were described earlier, that infants as young as 4 months of age seem aware of the existence of hidden objects, when tested in purely visual assessments. Bennett Bertenthal attempted to reconcile these apparently conflicting findings by appealing to a potential dissociation between registering and interpreting object events and acting upon objects. Visual processing in the cortex follows two distinct pathways, one for recognition and one for action. Bertenthal proposed that the ventral, recognition pathway may be precocious and drive looking behavior. The dorsal, action stream, on the other hand, may develop later; spurred by locomotor experience, this pathway achieves competency later. Self-locomotion clearly plays a role in aiding infants' searches for hidden objects, yet does not appear to influence looking behaviors in a violation of expectation paradigm.

Manual Learning and Experience

Amy Needham has demonstrated that manual experience with objects can aid infants in understanding their physical boundaries. In her early work, Needham showed that infants at 4.5 months of age were found to 'expect' two objects with distinct shapes, sizes, and colors to be physically separate, even if the objects were immediately adjacent (i.e., in direct contact). This finding was made by observations of infants' looking times as they watched two distinct looking objects either move together or move apart as a hand pulled on them. Infants were predicted to look longer and be more interested in the event that violated their expectation of the objects' physical properties (the violation-of-expectation paradigm discussed earlier). That is, if they assumed the two objects were physically joined, then pulling on one should move both objects together, whereas if they were disjoined, pulling on one should only move the one object.

Needham then examined how manual object exploration might be involved in the development of boundary perception. She reported that infants in a particular age group who were the most active explorers were those who consistently responded with longer looking toward the event display in which the two objects moved together. Infants of all exploratory skill levels have shown evidence of being able to assign object boundaries based on spatial information alone (an ability that may be related to perceptual completion, according to Needham). Yet, only when infants become truly proficient manual explorers do they utilize the featural information of objects to segregate them. The more active manual explorers examined (visually) the objects in a separate object exploration task for at least two-thirds of the time they spent holding it. Compared to the less active explorers, the active explorers may have had more general experience learning about objects and thus segregated the two new objects shown to them in the looking time part of the experiment while the less active explorers did not Object exploration thus appears to be linked to the ability to segregate and assess the boundaries of objects in infancy.

In experiments designed to examine the facilitation of these skills in younger infants, Needham gave 3-month-olds 2 weeks of experience using sticky mittens, small gloves covered in Velcro that stuck to small objects, also covered in Velcro. These tools allowed the infants a chance to view their own actions and the effects they had on objects at an age when their fine motor skills (notably fingering and bimanual grasping) were compromised compared to older infants. Infants given mitten experience were significantly more likely to switch between visual and oral exploration of objects without mittens compared to same-aged controls. The intervention appeared to boost attentiveness toward the visual properties of the objects and spurred infants' engagement with novel objects. There were no reported improvements in fine (motor skills, however). It seems that learning about the contingencies of actions on the physical world spawned new interest in objects and may have driven sensitivities to relevant and novel aspects of objects, learned primarily through action-based learning.

Integrating Information Over Time and Space: The Role of Eye Movements

Object manipulation is surely a vital part of the acquisition of object knowledge, but it cannot contribute in any meaningful way to the developmental origins of perceptual filling-in, because these origins appear earlier in development than does skilled manual exploration. The oculomotor system, in contrast, is largely functional at birth and matures rapidly, and even neonates scan the environment actively. There are important developments at around 2–3 months, however, in scanning 'efficiency'; young infants sometimes tend to fixate specific parts of a visual display rather than all the visible surfaces. Recent studies have found that overcoming this tendency – that is, engaging in more broad-based scanning – is associated with perceptual completion in 3-month-old infants. Infants who exhibited less efficient scan patterns, measured with an independent target search task, tended to perceive a partial occlusion display in terms of its constituent parts only (not as a whole). Infants who exhibited more efficient scan patterns provided evidence of unity perception. This implies that one way in which infants come to perceive partly occluded surfaces as coherent objects occurs via an active process of comparing the visible parts and integrating them into a whole.

Oculomotor Learning and Experience

Learning about occlusion and perceptual filling-in might be a deductive process: repeated exposure to many instances of objects becoming occluded and re-emerging, and subsequent identification of partly occluded objects as continuous, via an associative process. Occlusion and disocclusion are common occurrences in the real world: infants are exposed to multiple instances of such events routinely in the normal visual environment, and young infants are adept at rapid associative learning. Recent evidence from an anticipatory eye movement paradigm showed that when 4-month-old infants viewed a repetitive trajectory, they tended not to look ahead to where the ball was about to emerge from behind the occluder, in contrast to 6-month-olds, who showed a higher proportion of anticipations. But when 4-month-olds were first presented with a few trials with an unoccluded trajectory, followed by the occlusion stimulus, their rates of anticipation were roughly equivalent to those of the older infants. In other words, given experience, the 4-month-olds' performance was boosted to the level of the older infants. This effect fades after a short delay (30 min), however, suggesting that repeated exposures to multiple instances of hiding and revealing events, across weeks or months of developmental time, are necessary to ensure robust learning about these kinds of trajectory. Nevertheless, this research provides evidence that oculomotor development coupled with everyday visual experience may be an important mechanism behind the development of some kinds of object concept.

Developmental Mechanisms of Object Concepts: Neural Systems

For the sake of the present discussion of developmental origins of object concepts, it is worth highlighting some of what is known about cortical mechanisms of perceptual filling-in, and how such mechanisms might develop in infancy. Perception of connectedness across a spatial gap may be accomplished with relatively low- and mid-level mechanisms (i.e., cortical areas V1 through inferotemporal cortex), and development consists of at least two kinds of neural maturation. First, long-range cell-to-cell interactions in early visual areas connecting neural circuits coding for common edge orientations may reach sufficient maturity within several months after birth to support unity perception under some circumstances. Second, there are improvements in firing patterns of cell assemblies across the brain by reduction of neural 'noise'.

Perception of object persistence under occlusion may be accomplished by somewhat higher-level mechanisms (i.e., centered in inferotemporal and perirhinal cortex) that support neural activity coding for objects that have become occluded, and that guide overt behavioral responses. These behaviors include anticipatory eye movements in young infants, and reaching behaviors in older infants. This progression toward appropriate search in the context of complex hiding tasks is consistent with a view positing age-related strengthening of neural representations, such that with development, stronger representations support success at enacting appropriate behaviors across a wide range of situations involving occlusion. One candidate mechanism, mentioned previously, may promote development of many kinds of organized cortical activity: 'neural synchrony'. Processes such as binding of object features and location or coordination of object representations and object-oriented action have been hypothesized to be linked to neural synchrony. Neural circuits that participate in a common goal engage in synchronized activity, firing in brief bursts in the 40 Hz range. Evidence has emerged that there are changes in synchronized activity in infants that accompany perceptual changes, when perception of object occlusion is compared to perception of nonocclusion events.

A final piece of evidence highlighting the importance of neural developments to theories of object concepts comes from a recent experiment in which infant rhesus monkeys were tested in an object trajectory experiment similar to one described previously, with human infants. Eye movements were recorded as the monkeys viewed a target object move back and forth behind an occluder; patterns of oculomotor anticipations provided an index of object concepts. The youngest monkeys tested (5 weeks old) showed similar rates of anticipation to 4-month-old humans, and the proportions of anticipation improved with age. The rate of improvement, however, was dramatically faster in monkeys relative to humans. Other visual functions, as well, mature far more rapidly in monkeys. If simple visual experience were the sole mechanism, we would not find this great a difference in developmental timeliness between humans and monkeys. These results suggest that cortical maturation may support object concept development, rather than a specific period of experience viewing objects in the environment.

Conclusions

We discussed claims and evidence from two theories of object concept development: Piagetian theory and nativist theory, and we presented evidence from a wide range of experimental paradigms that that no single account can embrace the multitude of cortical and behavioral changes that underlie the emergence of object concepts in infancy. Significant progress, nevertheless, has been realized. We now know where to look for answers: the rudiments of veridical object concepts are evident in the first 6 months after birth. We know also the kinds of tools to use: assessments of eye movements, for example, and cortical development (e.g., recording EEGs) have revealed important hints to behavioral and physiological changes that accompany development of object concepts in young infants. The multipronged approach advocated in this article rejects polemic debates between the roles of nature or nurture, debates which, when it comes down to the details of developmental process, are ultimately meaningless. There is no pure case of development caused in the absence of either intrinsic or external influences. The question is what mechanisms are responsible for perceptual and cognitive development. There are many mechanisms, and, therefore, no one correct approach to the question of development of the object concept.

See also: Cognitive Development; Cognitive Developmental Theories; Habituation and Novelty; Neonativism; Piaget's Cognitive-Developmental Theory; Symbolic Thought.

Suggested Readings

Atkinson J (2000) *The Developing Visual Brain.* New York: Oxford University Press.

Cohen LB (1998) An information-processing approach to infant perception and cognition. In: Simion F and Butterworth G (eds.) *The Development of Sensory, Motor, and Cognitive Capacities in Early Infancy: From Perception to Cognition*, pp. 277–300. Hove, East Sussex, UK: Psychology Press.

Diamond A (1990) The development and neural basis of memory functions as indexed by the AB and delayed response tasks in human infants and adult monkeys. *Annals of the New York Academy of Sciences* 608: 267–317.

Elman JL, Bates EA, Johnson MH, Karmiloff-Smith A, Parisi D, and Plunkett K (1996) *Rethinking Innateness: A Connectionist Perspective on Development.* Cambridge, MA: MIT Press.

Gibson EJ (1988) Exploratory behavior in the development of perceiving, acting, and the acquiring of knowledge. *Annual Review of Psychology* 39: 1–41.

Johnson SP (2003) The nature of cognitive development. *Trends in Cognitive Sciences* 7: 102–104.

Piaget J (1954) *The Construction of Reality in the Child* (M. Cook, Trans.). New York: Basic Books (Original work published 1937).

Spelke ES and Newport E (1998) Nativism, empiricism, and the development of knowledge. In: Damon W and Lerner RM (eds.) *Handbook of Child Psychology, Vol. 1: Theoretical Models of Human Development*, pp. 275–340. New York: Wiley.

Parental Chronic Mental Illness

T Ostler and B Ackerson, University of Illinois at Urbana–Champaign, Urbana, IL, USA

Glossary

Alogia – A poverty of thinking inferred from observing language behavior and speech.

Anhedonia – An inability to experience pleasure.

Catatonia – A motionless, apathetic state or certain types of excessive motor activity.

Delusions – False beliefs based on incorrect inferences about external reality. The belief is sustained despite clear evidence or proof to the contrary.

Dual diagnosis – A term used to refer to an individual who has both a psychiatric disorder and a substance abuse or addiction problem.

Externalizing behaviors – A term used to refer to aggression, delinquency, and hyperactivity in children and adolescence as opposed to internalizing behaviors such as depression and anxiety.

Folie a deux – A rare psychiatric condition in which a symptom of psychosis (usually a delusional or paranoid belief) is transmitted from a parent to a child. The Diagnostic and Statistical Manual of Mental Disorders (DSM-IV) refers to this syndrome as shared psychotic disorder.

Hallucinations – Sensory perceptions that have a compelling sense of reality of true perception but that occur internally, that is, without external stimulation of a sensory organ.

Hypomania – A persistently expansive, irritable or elevated mood associated with an unequivocal change in functioning that does not cause marked impairment. It is accompanied by some of the following symptoms: grandiosity, pressure of speech, flight of ideas, inflated self-esteem, psychomotor agitation, and excessive involvement in pleasurable activities that have a high potential for painful consequences.

Kindling effect – Kindling effect refers to what happens with recurring manic episodes over time.

The individual may experience manic episodes more frequently over time due to changes in the brain caused by previous episodes. It is similar to what occurs in seizure disorders. Kindling specifically refers to the repeated triggering of certain nerve cells over time.

Mania – An abnormally and persistently expansive, irritable or elevated mood that lasts at least 1 week. It causes marked impairment in the individual and is accompanied by some of the following symptoms: grandiosity, pressure of speech, flight of ideas, inflated self-esteem psychomotor agitation, and excessive involvement in pleasurable activities that have a high potential for painful consequences.

Negative symptoms – Symptoms that involve a diminution or loss of functioning, such as blunted affect, apathy, self-neglect, loss of motivation, difficulty with abstract thinking and social withdrawal. Negative symptoms usually occur first and may be present during periods of remission (i.e., periods when there are no symptoms) as the illness progresses.

Positive symptoms – Symptoms that involve an excess or distortion of normal functions, such as hallucinatory behavior, conceptual disorganization, and delusions.

Psychotic disorders – Psychiatric disorders involving severe impairment to thought and perception. Such disorders can include positive symptoms of schizophrenia such as disorganized speech, grossly disorganized or catatonic behavior.

Stress-diathesis theory – A theory whereby a genetic predisposition or vulnerability (diathesis) interacts with stresses from life events in the environment (stressors) to trigger psychiatric disorders. The greater the underlying predisposition is, the less stress is needed to trigger the disorder. In cases where there is a smaller genetic contribution, greater levels of stress are required to produce psychiatric illness.

Wrap around services – Comprehensive mental health services designed to help individuals with severe and persistent mental illness. They are often home based and include case management, psychiatric treatment, and rehabilitation services.

Introduction

Individuals who are diagnosed with a mental disorder experience clinically significant distress or impairment in social, occupational, and other important areas of functioning. The individual also shows a pattern of symptoms that is characteristic of a specific psychiatric disorder in the Diagnostic and Statistical Manual of Mental Disorders (DSM-IV), the standard manual that is used for diagnosing disorders in the US. Mental illness symptoms vary greatly across individuals even with the same diagnosis and they may be mild or severe. Several mental illnesses have a chronic course and symptoms wax or wane over time.

About one-third of women in the US and one-fifth of men show evidence of psychiatric disorder. The majority of these individuals are parents. For these individuals parenting is a central and highly valued role. However, when an individual's illness is both chronic and severe, parenting is usually compromised to some degree. While many individuals are able to care for their children either alone or with the support of others, others struggle in the parenting role as they confront the dual challenges of dealing with a mental illness while meeting the stresses associated with raising children. In some cases, mental illness symptoms can interfere with an individual's judgment, behavior, feelings, and energy to the point that they seriously compromise the individual's ability to recognize risk or to provide for their child's basic needs and safety.

Children of parents with mental illness are also vulnerable and exposure to parental mental illness can compromise a child's development and well-being in a variety of ways. Problems are likely to be more enduring if a child is exposed to parental mental illness in the early years of life, a sensitive developmental period in which a child is highly dependent on the parent for survival. During this period, early environmental stimulation and emotional responsiveness from a caregiver are essential in influencing how well an infant or young child fares in his or her development and well-being.

This article provides an overview of the effects of mental illness on parenting and on infants and young children. Fathers with chronic mental illness can be and are primary caregivers. At the same time, women with chronic mental illness are far more likely to be involved in caring for children. For this reason, focus is given to women as parents. Focus is also given to chronic mental illnesses and to parenting in the peripartum period, a time period when women are especially prone to either develop a mental illness or to experience illness exacerbations. In the sections that follow, the article describes major types of chronic mental illness, discusses the challenges that individuals with chronic and severe mental illness face in the parenting role, and outlines how different mental illnesses symptoms can affect parenting. The article then addresses factors that can increase parenting risk in individuals with mental illness and presents a model for understanding how chronic parental mental illness can affect children's development. Literature on the outcomes of infants and young children of parents with mental illness is then synthesized followed by a description of approaches for developing effective, multi-faceted interventions that can address the needs of children and their parents.

Types, Symptoms, and Course of Chronic Mental Illnesses

Schizophrenia

Schizophrenia and other psychotic disorders are some of the most severe mental illnesses. Schizophrenia is characterized by severe disruption in cognitive functioning and perceptions. The most pronounced symptoms, sometimes referred to as positive symptoms, are hallucinations, delusions, disorganized thought process, and grossly disorganized behavior. Hallucinations are false perceptions (e.g., hearing voices) that are not based upon any external stimulus. Persons with schizophrenia do not imagine hallucinations. They actually experience the perception (hear, see, etc.), but it is caused by abnormal activity in their brain rather than an external stimulus. Delusions are false beliefs that are not consistent with a person's culture or religious beliefs and are caused by a disruption in reasoning abilities. Disordered thought content seen in delusions often accompanies impairment in thought processes. Examples of disorganized thought process are flight of ideas, loose associations, tangential thinking, disorganized speech, and incoherent speech. In addition to impairments in cognitive abilities and perceptions, individuals with schizophrenia may also experience disorganized behavior manifested as agitation, catatonia, or an inability to perform goal-directed behavior, such as caring for oneself. The extent that any of these symptoms are present varies according to the subtype of schizophrenia and the severity of the disorder in a particular individual. Any or all of the positive symptoms may be present during an acute phase of the illness.

Schizophrenia also consists of negative symptoms, which include flat affect, social withdrawal, ambivalence, alogia, and anhedonia. These symptoms may be present in the residual phase of the illness as well as in the active phase. Because the side effects of antipsychotic medication can also contribute to lethargy and withdrawal, it may be difficult to determine the extent to which these behaviors are due to medication or the negative symptoms of the illness. It is important to understand that withdrawal, ambivalence, and other negative symptoms are a function of the illness and not personal traits of the individual. Schizophrenia is best understood as a chronic psychiatric disability that impacts social functioning as well as cognitive abilities.

Bipolar Disorders

Bipolar disorders are marked by extreme mood swings, from depression on one end to mania or hypomania on the other end. Formerly called manic-depression, bipolar disorder is now categorized as having two forms. Bipolar I disorder is classic manic-depression. Individuals experience highly euphoric moods, referred to as mania, that impair their reasoning and judgment. These mood states, which may include feelings of grandiosity, flights of thought and speech, and impaired judgment, may last days, weeks, or months but eventually subside. When not in a manic state, individuals may experience normal moods for a period of time or may go directly into a major depressive episode.

In bipolar II disorder individuals more often experience a depressed mood, but they still alternate between depression and elevated moods. However, their elevated mood states never escalate past hypomania, a milder form of mania that lasts for at least 4 days, but unlike mania it is not severe enough to cause impairment in functioning. In both mania and hypomania individuals may have very little sleep, talk excessively, and engage in excessive pleasure seeking behavior. At times manic states may not be easily recognized because the individual's mood may be irritable or agitated instead of euphoric. However, they still experience a reduced need for sleep and other excessive behaviors seen in mania.

Bipolar disorder is considered a chronic mental disorder and it often results in psychiatric disability. The fluctuating nature of the disorder contributes to difficulties in social and occupational functioning. Many people with bipolar disorder are able to hold jobs, engage in social relationships, and raise families. However, their ability to function in any of these roles is compromised when they experience an episode of either major depression or mania/hypomania. Rapid cycling, or the frequent shifting from one mood episode to another, may occur in more severe cases. The longer an individual has had the illness, the greater they are at risk for developing rapid cycling, similar to the kindling effect in seizure disorders.

Major Depression

Depression is the most common mental disorder. It affects about 10% of people in the US in a year and about 17% experience it during their lifetime. Individuals with major depression, also referred to as clinical depression, are at much higher risk for having another mental disorder, such as anxiety or substance abuse.

Major depression is more than just feeling sad or 'blue'. It is defined as experiencing one or more major depressive episodes. Symptoms include feeling chronically sad or depressed, anhedonia, changes in eating or sleeping, lack of energy, feeling helpless or hopeless, having problems with memory or concentration, and being socially withdrawn. Individuals with recurring major depressive episodes have a psychiatric disability that may impair their ability to work and to function socially.

Major depression may begin at any developmental period. Depressive episodes typically last 6–9 months in children and adolescents. About half of the children who experience major depression will experience another episode within 2 years. Adolescent depression often continues into adulthood. Other individuals may not experience their first depressive episode until well into adulthood. For some, depressive episodes are episodic, with long periods of normal mood during which time they are able to fully engage in life. Other individuals experience a severe form of the disorder where depressive moods are more frequent and have a longer duration.

Fortunately, depression has proved to be a very treatable illness. A variety of antidepressant medications have been shown to be effective, all of them working in some way on the neurotransmitters serotonin and epinephrine. Several forms of psychotherapy have also been shown to be very effective, with research showing strong support for various forms of cognitive therapy (understanding how people perceive, attribute, and interpret meaning) and interpersonal therapy. The most effective treatment strategy is a combination of psychotherapy with antidepressant medication, especially if a person has had two or more major episodes of depression.

Anxiety Disorders

Anxiety, a vitally important physiological response to dangerous situations, prepares an individual to evade or confront threats. In some individuals, the mechanisms that regulate anxiety break down and the individual experiences excessive anxiety. There are several anxiety disorders, all characterized by clinical levels of excessive anxiety. An individual who is diagnosed with panic disorder has repeated panic attacks, high intensive episodes of anxiety that occur without a precipitating cause. During a panic attack, an individual may experience shortness of breath, rapid heart rate, trembling, restlessness, lightheadedness or dizziness, perspiration, as well as cold hands and feet.

An individual who is diagnosed with generalized anxiety disorder (GAD) experiences pervasive worries for at least 6 months about a variety of events or activities. It is difficult for the individual to control these worries and he or she experiences ongoing tension and restlessness. The duration, intensity, and frequency of the anxiety are out of proportion to the actual likelihood that the feared event will occur.

Obsessive-compulsive disorder (OCD) is another severe anxiety disorder characterized by recurring and intrusive thoughts or images (obsessions) and repetitive behaviors or mental acts (compulsions) that an individual feels compelled to perform in response to the obsession. Some compulsive behaviors are very obvious, such as excessive hand washing, while others are more internal and not easily observed, such as mental checking or counting. These obsessions and compulsive behaviors are very time consuming, cause great personal distress and significant functional impairment. Unlike obsessive-compulsive personality disorder, these behaviors are not merely signs of an overly perfectionistic personality. Adults with OCD are aware that their behavior is abnormal and dysfunctional, but they feel as if they have little or no control over these thoughts and behaviors. OCD has a strong biological basis. It is very persistent and requires extensive treatment involving medication and psychotherapy.

Individuals who are exposed to a life-threatening event or a threat of serious injury may develop a severe anxiety disorder in response to their trauma. There are two types of severe anxiety disorders that may occur as a result of trauma, acute stress disorder, and post-traumatic stress disorder (PTSD). Acute stress disorder occurs within the first month after experiencing trauma. PTSD is the more chronic of these disorders. Symptoms persist for more than 1 month and may last for many years.

PTSD symptoms can be grouped in three categories: re-experiencing of the event, avoidance of stimuli associated with the trauma and numbing, and increased arousal. In adults and adolescents re-experiencing may take many forms which include recurring and intrusive images and thoughts, distressing dreams or nightmares, flashbacks, and other feelings as if the trauma were recurring. Avoidance behaviors may be related to avoiding thoughts and feelings as well as avoiding places, people, and activities and a sense of detachment may also be experienced. Arousal symptoms are both physical (autonomic nervous system) and psychological (irritability, hypervigilance). Because many of these symptoms may also be seen in depression or other anxiety disorders, PTSD may be missed or confused with another mental disorder. In addition, individuals with PTSD are at risk for developing other mental disorders and substance abuse.

Personality Disorders

Personality traits are normal variations of human behavior and personal characteristics. Personality disorders reflect rigid, inflexible, and maladaptive forms of behavior that lead to personal distress or functional impairment – social and/or occupational. To be diagnosed with a personality disorder, maladaptive behavior must be seen in at least two of the following areas: cognition (how the person sees themselves and others), affect (range and intensity of moods), interpersonal functioning, and impulse control. While some inflexible traits or maladaptive behaviors may emerge during adolescence, personality disorders are not diagnosed until early adulthood.

The DSM-IV lists 10 personality disorders that are categorized into three clusters. Cluster A consists of paranoid, schizotypal, and schizoid personality disorders. These three disorders share the common trait of odd and eccentric behavior, social aloofness, and milder forms of symptoms that are associated with schizophrenia. Cluster B consists of antisocial, borderline, histrionic, and narcissistic personality disorders. These disorders are all characterized by dramatic, emotional, and erratic behavior. They also have a high comorbidity with mood disorders and substance use disorders.

Cluster C consists of avoidant, dependent, and obsessive-compulsive personality disorders. Individuals with these disorders all exhibit anxious or fearful behaviors and the disorders appear to be closely associated with anxiety disorders. In recent years there has been special attention given to borderline personality disorder, which is diagnosed more frequently in women. Once considered extremely difficult to treat, dialectical behavior therapy, a psychosocial treatment that combines behavioral theory with components of cognitive therapy, and other forms of cognitive therapy have been shown to be effective.

Mental Illness and Parenting: Dual Challenges

Mothers with severe and persistent mental illnesses (e.g., schizophrenia, bipolar disorder, depression) face a dual challenge. They have to manage a chronic illness that causes impairments in judgment and social functioning while also dealing with the stress and complex demands of parenting. However, even the severe and persistent mental disorders are typically episodic in nature. The symptoms and behaviors that pose risk for a mother's children, then, fluctuate over time and are amenable to a variety of treatment interventions.

The special challenge these mothers face is that while most of them express a strong desire to be good mothers, the stress of parenting can exacerbate their symptoms. Therefore, these mothers need help both with learning how to manage their psychiatric disability as well as with learning effective parenting techniques. They require special interventions that address the interaction between the demands and stress of being a parent and the symptoms of their particular illness.

Mothers with depression, bipolar disorder, and schizophrenia experience negative or depressed mood symptoms. In depression and bipolar disorder these occur as major depressive episodes, which may be of limited duration or may extend for months or years. In schizophrenia these negative moods are part of the negative symptoms of the disorder. These negative symptoms may exist even when other symptoms such as delusions and hallucinations are not prominent. When a parent experiences depressive moods they may be emotionally unavailable or exhibit maternal insensitivity to their children. They may also withdraw and exhibit lower levels of energy which may impair their ability to provide for their children's basic needs. Discipline of their children may also be erratic or ineffective during these periods of negative moods. It is important to note that these mood symptoms are typically episodic and are often amenable to treatment with medication. Mothers can be trained to recognize when these symptoms occur and to seek treatment and social support for their family. Services for these parents and their families should address emotional and social support needs.

Another common symptom of severe and persistent mental illnesses is lack of sustained motivation. This can result in inadequate care of children's hygiene, failure to provide appropriate clothes and adequate nutrition, and inconsistent child discipline. This apathy and amotivation may be misunderstood as a lack of desire to engage in the parenting roles.

When mothers with a chronic mental illness have been interviewed about their roles as parents, they report a strong desire to be effective parents and they derive a great deal of pride and self-esteem from being parents. Several studies have found that many of these mothers are aware of their difficulties in performing the parenting role. Therefore, it is important to distinguish between the symptoms of their illness and a lack of desire to function as parents. Similar to episodes of negative moods, they need to learn effective coping strategies for dealing with periods of lower motivation and how to appropriately seek assistance during these times.

Mothers with psychiatric disabilities may also experience cognitive deficits that impair their ability to accurately interpret or understand their children's behavior. In fact, unrealistic expectations of children's behavior along with impaired problem-solving abilities are more reliable indicators of risk for child maltreatment than psychiatric diagnosis.

Cognitive deficits are a key symptom of schizophrenia and other psychotic disorders. Severe deficits are easily recognized in the form of delusions and problems with forming coherent thoughts. Fortunately, these symptoms can be managed with appropriate medication. More subtle deficits may not be as easily recognized. In these cases the parent may misinterpret a child's behavior and overreact. Mothers with severe mood and anxiety disorders may also have unrealistic expectations of their children. This is caused both by their illness and by a tendency at times to rely on older children to help care for the house and younger siblings. For these reasons, parent skills training is an important component of treatment for many parents with chronic mental disorders. Education regarding developmentally appropriate behavior and parental expectations should be an important component of this training for these parents.

Parenting and Chronic Mental Illness in the Peripartum Period

Women are especially vulnerable to developing a psychiatric illness and to experiencing symptom exacerbations during the childbearing years, that is, in the time when they conceive, carry, and give birth to children. This section examines how parenting is affected by different chronic mental disorders and their symptoms in the period during pregnancy and after birth.

Depression

About 10% of women develop clinical depression during pregnancy. New mothers (10–20%) develop depression after giving birth to their babies. These rates double in low-income mothers and in adolescent mothers.

Although the symptoms of depression in pregnancy are the same as the symptoms that occur in depression at other phases in life, they often go unrecognized because normal pregnancy changes cause similar symptoms such as difficulties in sleeping, tiredness, changes in body weight, and strong, emotional reactions.

Clinical depression in pregnancy can pose formidable problems for the mother and baby to be. A mother who becomes depressed during pregnancy may fail to seek out prenatal care. In addition, she may not eat properly, lose weight, and increase her use of addictive substances, particularly smoking and alcohol use. If a mother develops suicidal thoughts as part of her depression, there is a risk that she may overdose on medications, posing a substantial risk for herself and her fetus.

There is growing evidence that depression in pregnancy can negatively affect fetal and infant well-being. Untreated maternal depression in pregnancy has been associated with premature labor and with low infant birth weight. Maternal smoking and substance abuse can all exert a negative effect on fetal and infant development. Pregnant mothers who are depressed also experience high levels of stress. Their babies, in turn, show high levels of activity during pregnancy and high stress hormone levels after birth.

Recognizing factors that increase the chances that a pregnant woman will develop depression can help in preventing depression in this critical phase of life. **Table 1** lists several factors that increase the risk that a pregnant mother will develop depression.

Postpartum depression is not the same as the postpartum 'blues', which is a normal experience for many women in the immediate postpartum period. Women experience the blues within the first 10 days after birth. They alternate between feeling irritable, having an elated mood, and having increased crying spells. Women who develop postpartum depression, by contrast, experience sleep and appetite disturbances, impaired concentration, feelings of inadequacy, and a sad mood. These symptoms occur within 6 months after a woman has given birth to her child.

Postpartum depression can greatly affect how a mother feels about herself as a parent and how she perceives and responds to her newborn baby. A mother who becomes clinically depressed after giving birth may develop a negative attitude toward her baby or harbor negative feelings and thoughts about her ability and desire to parent. She may be emotionally unavailable to her baby and have difficulties in responding to her baby's cues. Some mothers feel that their baby hates them. Most women with postpartum depression feel guilty about these thoughts and are anxious about their ability to parent.

The exact etiology of postpartum depression is unknown, but the lack of sleep, stress, and new responsibilities that are part of having a baby can contribute to its development. **Table 2** summarizes factors that increase the risk that a woman will develop depression in the postpartum period.

Depression in the postpartum period often remains unrecognized by mothers, family members, and mental health professionals alike. In about 50% of cases, however, episodes of postpartum depression are continuations of a depressive episode from pregnancy. Mothers may be reluctant to acknowledge that they are depressed after giving birth to their child because it may seem incongruous with the happiness they feel they should experience in the mothering role. Given the negative repercussions that it can have on parenting, recognizing symptoms of depression in the postpartum period as early as possible and helping mothers to seek treatment is essential.

There is some evidence that prolonged interventions may be needed to achieve positive outcomes for parenting. A significant proportion of women who are vulnerable to postnatal depression, however, refuse to engage in treatment. Understanding the barriers to engaging in services is therefore essential for achieving better outreach and care for these women and their babies.

Bipolar Disorder and Schizophrenia

Bipolar disorder and schizophrenia can pose risks to parenting at any time in the life span, but there are specific risks that can be recognized during the prenatal period. Impaired judgment and hypersexuality, both symptoms of mania, can contribute to high rates of unplanned pregnancies and HIV infection in women with bipolar disorder. High rates of substance use, including nicotine, that are characteristic of individuals with both bipolar disorder and schizophrenia, can increase the risk to the fetus in the first trimester of pregnancy. In addition, women with schizophrenia are more prone to have higher rates of unplanned or unwanted pregnancies and to recognize their pregnancy later than nonmentally ill mothers.

Psychotic denial of pregnancy is a complication that can co-occur with some chronic psychiatric disorders and, though rare, can lead to a high level of risk to the mother and unborn baby. A woman who psychotically denies pregnancy is unaware that she is pregnant. She may misinterpret or ignore symptoms of pregnancy. She may attribute fetal movements to gas or interpret labor as signs of menstruation. As delivery approaches, she may not seek out help or go to a hospital, placing both the women at risk for precipitous delivery of the baby, and, in some cases, for fetal abuse or neonaticide.

Psychotic denial of pregnancy is more common in women with schizophrenia than in women with bipolar disorder or severe personality disorders. Treatment involves integrating comprehensive obstetrical and psychiatric care, medication, and supportive psychotherapy with an evaluation of a mother's parenting skills.

Postpartum psychosis is a rare condition that typically starts within the first few days to 2–3 weeks postpartum. It has a rapid onset and is characterized by hallucinations and/or delusions. Having bipolar disorder or severe

Table 1   Factors that increase risk of clinical depression during pregnancy

A past history of depression or substance abuse
A family history of mental illness
Anxiety about the unborn baby
Problems with a past pregnancy or birth
Young age
Marital or financial problems
Little social support

Table 2   Factors that increase the risk for postpartum depression

A previous history of depression
A family history of mood disorder
Little social support
Anticipating a separation from the unborn baby after birth
Prior custody loss of a child

postpartum depression are major risk factors for postpartum psychosis.

If untreated, postpartum psychosis can greatly affect a mother's ability to parent her baby. Some mothers with postpartum psychosis experience a loss of love for their babies, a feeling which they often experience as painful. Others may develop bizarre beliefs about their babies, thinking, for instance, that the baby is still in the uterus, or that the baby is deformed or dead. Some mothers with postpartum psychosis try to harm their infants. The short-term prognosis for parenting is usually good if a mother responds to medication and is in treatment.

Anxiety Disorders

Little is known about how anxiety affects parenting during pregnancy. However, mothers with GAD apparently experience higher levels of distress when their young child is engaged in routine activities and in structured play tasks than nonanxious mothers. Obsessional rituals associated with OCD, another anxiety disorder, can interfere with childrearing responsibilities. A parent with OCD, for instance, may be overmeticulous and demand too much from a young child. Similarly, obsessive self-doubting can contribute to a young child doubting his or her abilities. In some cases, obsessive symptoms may lead to repetitive checking to ensure a young child is safe. Clearly, to the extent that they are communicated to a child, obsessive worries and compulsions can burden the child emotionally and increase his or her anxiety level.

There is little systematic research on the parenting capabilities of individuals with PTSD. Parental PTSD has, however, been found to be a salient risk factor for PTSD in offspring. Clinical evidence suggests that parents with PTSD may have difficulty in expressing emotions and in recognizing a young child's cues, especially if the child is distressed. There is evidence for interactive effects between child and parent. Studies, for instance, show that if a child is traumatized, the child's trauma symptoms may reactivate PTSD symptoms in a parent.

Personality Disorders

Mothers with personality disorders have serious problems in social and occupational functioning which can make it difficult for them to sustain a safe, predictable environment for their babies. Since many are victims of childhood abuse and neglect, they are often vulnerable in intimate relationships, including those with their young children. This vulnerability may make it difficult for a mother with a personality disorder to distinguish her own needs from those of her baby and for her to tolerate her baby's distress. A mother with a personality disorder may also project feelings she canot tolerate in herself onto her young child. Change can occur for individuals with this

diagnosis, but it usually takes considerable time to engage a parent in the treatment process which the parent may perceive as threatening.

Assessing Parenting Risk in Individuals with Chronic Mental Illness

Many individuals with mental illness raise their children to adulthood, either alone or with the support of others. Some protective factors that ameliorate risk and are associated with good enough parenting are listed in **Table 3**.

Risk for serious parenting problems is especially high in individuals whose illness is chronic and severe. As many as 60–80% of women with chronic and severe mental illness may relinquish or lose custody of their children at some point in their lives. There is some evidence that custody loss may occur more frequently right after birth or in the early years of parenting, probably because women are at high risk in these periods for developing a major mental illness or for experiencing illness exacerbations.

Some factors that can signal risk for serious parenting problems during pregnancy for mothers with a chronic mental illness include: a marked ambivalence about wanting a baby, delusions about the pregnancy or baby, a denial of pregnancy, significant family tension prior to delivery, refusal of prenatal care, thoughts of harming the baby to be, a suicide attempt during pregnancy, poor support, and lack of compliance with treatment.

Only two mental disorders, depression and substance abuse, have been specifically linked to child maltreatment and their overall contribution is small. Overall, illness dimensions and symptoms appear to be more important predictors of parenting risk than psychiatric diagnoses. **Table 4** provides an overview of illness dimensions and symptoms that increase parenting risk in individuals whose illness is chronic and severe.

While mental illness symptoms can increase risk, maltreatment is multiply determined. It results from a broad range of environmental and familial factors that interact with each other to compromise a parent's ability to nurture and provide adequate care and protection for a child. **Table 5** summarizes factors, beyond the parent's psychiatric symptoms, that can contribute to parenting risk.

Table 3 Protective factors for parenting in individuals with psychiatric disorders

Good coping skills
A supportive network of friends and relatives
Compliance with treatment
Responsiveness to treatment
Good insight into illness symptoms and the need for treatment
Will power and motivation to change

Table 4 Psychiatric factors that can increase parenting risk

Dual diagnosis
A comorbid substance abuse problem
Active psychotic symptoms
Aggressive or violent behavior
Poor insight into the mental illness
Including a child in delusions
Parent has command hallucinations
Lack of response to treatment
Noncompliance with treatment
Low level of adaptive functioning

Table 5 Nonpsychiatric factors that can increase parenting risk

Neglect of the baby's basic needs
Apathy or hostility toward the baby
A projection of feelings onto the baby (e.g., 'he hates me')
A refusal to hold and engage the baby
Parent has an intrusive or hostile interactive style
Parent has expectations that the child should provide the parent with comfort and support
Parent lacks basic knowledge about the child or holds unrealistic expectations about child
Parent has difficulties in meeting their own basic needs
Parent utilizes extreme disciplinary measures
Parent has a small or unviable support network
Parent has difficulties in establishing and maintaining supportive relationships
Parent denies he or she has problems
Domestic violence
Marital disharmony and conflict

How Parental Mental Illness Affects Infants and Young Children

Young children who experience parental mental illness are often characterized as a high-risk group of youngsters. Some of the risk to children is due to biological and genetic factors, but risk also results from environmental influences, including poor parenting, marital discord, socioeconomic disadvantage, and the increased stresses that result from living with a parent with mental illness. Child factors, including temperament, intelligence, and gender can also contribute to risk.

Parental mental illness may affect children's well-being and development in different ways. Risk may be transmitted genetically to a child. There can also be a direct impact on the child's development and well-being through exposure to the parent's illness. Parental mental illness can also impact a child's development indirectly via poor parenting or through its impact on the parent's interpersonal behavior. The effect on children's development may also occur through factors that are associated with chronic mental illness such as poverty, social adversity, and disadvantage. Marital discord, for instance, can result in part from living

with an individual who has a chronic mental illness and can impact children's development and well-being. Genetic factors can also interact with environmental factors to affect child outcome.

Child factors can interact with parenting in an individual with chronic mental illness, thereby affecting child outcome. In early development, for instance, perinatal and medical complications, prematurity, or a low birth weight, conditions more common in infants of mothers with chronic mental illness, may contribute to severity of postpartum depression in a mother, and thereby influence how she cares for her baby and how the baby fares developmentally.

A young child's temperament is another factor that can contribute to parenting, thereby affecting a child's developmental pathway. A baby with a difficult temperament, for instance, may elicit different responses from a parent with a chronic mental illness than a baby with an easy temperament, thereby contributing to a more difficult parenting pathway and to a less favorable outcome for the child. Having a child with disabilities or a chronic illness can also contribute to the overall stress that a parent experiences in the caregiving role. Supporting the view that child factors interact with parenting to influence child outcome is the finding that children with is behavioral disorders or disabilities are more likely than other children to experience maltreatment by a caregiver.

The stress-diathesis theory helps to explain how risk develops. In this theory, child vulnerability due to genetic or to early environmental stresses interacts with later stresses to precipitate risk or the onset of illness symptoms in the child. For instance, if the child's parent has a heritable psychiatric disorder, the child may have an elevated genetic vulnerability for developing a disorder under adverse environmental conditions. This child may be particularly susceptible to poor parenting. Under adverse conditions, including stress and poor parenting, the child's disorder may be expressed. Whether risk in a vulnerable child is actualized, however, will turn on the degree to which the child is vulnerable biologically to begin with, how the mother fared during pregnancy, how the child has been parented and cared for after birth, and by the larger environment in which he or she lives including the stresses the child experiences.

Effects on Children's Development and Well-Being

Studies have documented that parental mental illness can affect various aspects of young children's well-being and development. Studies show increased rates of externalizing problems, delays in cognitive development, particularly in boys, and interpersonal difficulties, including attachment insecurity and feelings of guilt.

Children of parents with mental illness are also at increased risk for developing a psychiatric disorder over the course of their life. By age 10 years, over 20% of children born to a mother who has major depression are likely to develop a major episode of depression or dysthymia, a low-grade form of chronic depression, twice the amount of children born to mothers who had never been depressed. A child with a parent with major depression has a 40% chance of developing an episode of depression by age 20 years. This rate increases to 60% by age 25 years. If a parent has a dual diagnosis, risk is increased further. Problems are more enduring if the child is exposed to parental mental illness in the early years of development, a period when vulnerability emerges and is maintained.

The next section reviews recent findings on the outcomes of infants and young children of parents with mental illness. Since much research attention has been given to major depression in mothers, this work is emphasized. However, when available, findings on the effects of other disorders are discussed. Emphasis is also given to identifying areas and sources of strength in children, an area that has, until recently, been neglected.

Infancy

Maternal depression in the postpartum period affects mothers' ability to respond in a sensitive and contingent manner to a baby's cues and to show delight in the baby's presence. Their babies in turn show limited engagement, poor eye contact, and muted affective expressions. They are also more prone than babies whose mothers are not depressed to develop insecure attachment patterns to their mothers as assessed in the Ainsworth Strange Situation procedure, a standard observation that is used to classify mother–infant attachment quality when the baby is 12 months of age.

Babies of mothers with postpartum depression are most prone to develop an insecure-disorganized attachment pattern, a pattern which has been linked to frightened or frightening maternal behavior. This pattern is viewed as an at-risk pattern and is associated with high levels of insecurity in the mother–child relationship.

Several studies show effects of postpartum depression on early cognitive development. Infants of mothers who have postpartum depression, for instance, have been found to be significantly delayed in their language development and on the development of object permanence, a key measure of early representational capacities in infants when compared to infants of nondepressed mothers. Object permanence is constructed over the first 18 months of life and involves the child coming to grasp that what is out of sight is not out of mind.

Infants of mothers who develop depression in the postpartum period are also disadvantaged in their behavior and in their social and emotional development. They show more negative responses with other adults, less

sharing, and less concentration than infants whose mothers are not depressed in the postpartum period. They are also more prone to act out in order to obtain a response from an adult, and have more eating and sleeping problems, more temper tantrums and more difficulties with separations.

Studies on the attachment quality and cognitive development in infants of mothers who are depressed in the postpartum period have found that development is more compromised when the mother has a severe rather than mild episode of depression and if her illness is chronic and occurs in the context of other adversities. Poor outcomes in behavior and cognitive development may persist even after the mother's depression has abated. In the early years of life, the mother is the baby's primary environment. Small wonder, then, that the adverse effects of maternal depression on infant development are mediated through the quality of the mother–child attachment bond.

Young boys of mothers with postpartum depression may be at particular high risk for adverse effects in attachment, behavior, and cognitive functioning. One explanation for this difference is that girls appear to hold a maturational advance which may protect them more than boys from the experience of postpartum depression. Another explanation is that mothers who are depressed may treat their sons and daughters differently.

Less is known about the effects of chronic psychotic disorders in a parent on infant well-being and development. Interactions between mothers with psychosis and their babies have been found to be more deviant and negative than those of mothers and infants in a control group. Mothers with schizophrenia show greater deficits while interacting with their babies than mothers with mood disorders. They are more insensitive to their babies' cues, more remote, intrusive, and self-absorbed. Their babies in turn are more avoidant and have poorer interaction quality than babies of mothers with mood disorders. Babies of mothers with psychotic disorders lag in their cognitive functioning, including the development of object permanence and show more anxiety in exploring objects. One study found that at age 12 months, babies of mothers with postpartum psychoses showed no fear of strangers, a development which appears on the average at about age 8 months and is observable in almost all infants by age 12 months. The findings suggested aberrance or delays in the infants' social development.

Early childhood

Maternal depression can exert a strong negative effect on the self-system of young children and on their social and emotional development during toddlerhood and the preschool years. For instance, young children of depressed mothers are more prone than children of nondepressed mothers to express negative views about their own worth and performance.

According to John Bowlby, the father of attachment theory, young children construct so-called 'internal working models' of self and other based on their day-to-day experiences with their primary caregiver. These internal or representational working models include children's notions of self and others – how worthy and able the self is and how caregivers are likely to respond if the child is in need. With increasing development, children's internal working models are generalized to other important relationships.

If the primary caregiver is experiencing chronic severe depression, she may not focus on the child's needs, grow irritated at the child's bids for attention, or tell the child her behavior is 'too much' or is making the parent 'ill'. A young child may conclude from these experiences that she is not lovable and that she is responsible for the parent's illness. The child may also have a working model that expects others to respond to the child's needs with irritation or lack of concentration.

Postpartum depression is linked to behavior problems in toddlers and to distractibility and antisocial behavior in the preschool years. The risk of a child developing behavior problems is increased if there is marital conflict and if the family is economically disadvantaged. Choice of play can also be affected, with children of depressed mothers being more prone to avoid more personally challenging creative play and to engage in simple physical play than children of mothers who are not depressed.

A substantial number of young children with depressed caregivers do not evidence dysfunction. Such findings point to the need to look at protective factors in the broader social context in which young children develop and are raised. If a mother is not experiencing current difficulties or conflict with the child's father, for instance, the child may fare better in his development.

Separation and custody loss

Between 60% and 80% of mothers with chronic mental illness may lose temporary or permanent custody of their children at some point in their lives. Some studies suggest that custody loss may occur early on, either at birth or in the first years of life. If a parent with a chronic mental illness is hospitalized, the child may stay with the nonmentally ill parent, or with relatives or friends until she stabilizes and recovers. Others may be placed in foster care.

Infants and young children who experience a separation are at higher risk in all areas of development as they experience not only the loss of a healthy mother and loss of a normal family life, but a loss of stability and confidence that the mother is available. How well they fare will turn not only on their own vulnerabilities and constitution, but on the care they receive from their mother and from alternate caregivers. If a child has already established an attachment bond to the biological mother who is mentally ill, he or she may experience profound changes in their feelings toward the mother during and after the separation.

Long-term effects

The impact of chronic parental mental illness on family members is referred to as a 'burden'. Children are confronted not only with the objective burden of coping with the parent's symptoms, the stigma of the illness, and with additional caregiving responsibilities, they may also grieve for a lost childhood, or for a parent they knew and loved before the illness set in. This burden is stressful and contributes to the sense of isolation and loneliness that many of the children experience.

Several long-term patterns can be identified in children who grow up with a parent with a chronic mental illness. Many children, for instance, experience difficulties in deciphering which of their family experiences are normal and which are not. Some children may feel guilty that they are healthy or feel embarrassed at the odd behaviors their parent may engage in. Many do not have someone with whom to talk to about what they are going through. Children who experience these feelings need advice and help from adults so that they can come to terms with the illness, and understand and acknowledge how the illness affects themselves and their family.

Role reversal and intensified self-sufficiency are other patterns that may be evidenced in children of parents with chronic mental illness as they grow older. Children who evidence these patterns have adapted their behavior to make things work within a family which is under considerable strain. Even very young children may show these patterns. Role reversal and intensified self-sufficiency often build on a child's need to control situations to obtain some outward security about what she can expect. While sometimes viewed as mature, if extreme, these patterns can come at a high emotional cost to a child. Children who are parentified or highly self-sufficient, for instance, have great difficulties in relying on others for help or support. In addition, they may miss out on being a child and their own capacity to feel and to learn may be constricted.

Family members may fail to acknowledge a mental illness or minimize or distort its effects on the individual and family. As a result, children may learn to keep the illness secret as they grow older. Secretive and distorted communication patterns in turn can contribute to a child feeling a need to hide her own feelings and needs from others. In extreme cases, children who hide their own feelings and thoughts develop a false sense of self. Such children try to do or be what they think is right for others in the family. Underlying this outward appearance of perfection, however, is a fundamental fear that the child is not good enough.

If a child lives alone with a parent who has a chronic mental illness, the child may become enmeshed in the

Table 6   Heritability of major mental illnesses: Child's lifetime risk of becoming ill

	General population rates if neither parent is ill (%)	Risk if one parent is ill (%)	Risk if two parents are ill (%)	Risk for other monozygotic twin if one twin is ill (%)	Risk for dizygotic twin if one twin is ill (%)
Schizophrenia	1.5	10	40	18–60	15
Major depression	10	20–25	30–50	50–60	20
Bipolar disorder	1	5–10		40–70	10–20

Reproduced from Brunette M and Jacobsen T (2006) Children of parents with mental illness. In: Hendrick V (ed.) *Psychiatric Disorders in Pregnancy and the Postpartum: Principles and Treatment*, p. 200. Totowa, NJ: Humana Press, with permission from Humana Press.

parent's symptoms. Children in this situation may become the parent's confidant and be burdened with too much information to the detriment of their own development. Children in this circumstance often experience high levels of anxiety and keep their worries to themselves. Some children enter their parent's psychotic world and accept their beliefs as their own so as to feel close to a parent who is hard to reach, a condition that is called a '*folie a deux*'.

Risk for psychiatric disorders

While environmental context is important in the etiology of mental illness in a child, genetic factors also contribute to risk and interact with environmental factors in the expression of vulnerability. The genetic risks for children of parents with schizophrenia, major depression, and bipolar disorder are summarized in **Table 6**.

Recent work on anxiety disorders also shows both genetic and environmental contributions. There are higher rates of anxiety disorders among children of anxious parents, but only when the child's mother has the disorder. A maternal history of anxiety disorder doubles the risk that a child will develop an anxiety disorder. If a mother has both an anxiety and a depressive disorder, the risk that her child will develop an anxiety disorder is tripled. This high risk of transmission is thought to be linked to genetic factors, but also to the higher levels of general pathology that mothers with dual diagnoses are likely to exhibit. Studies on transmission from fathers to children need further study. Fathers may be less likely than mothers to report symptoms of anxiety.

Factors that ameliorate risk

Risk to children is cumulative. The more risk factors present, the greater the likelihood that the child will fare poorly in his or her development, especially if the risks occur in the early years of development. Some important protective factors that can ameliorate risk and influence young children's outcomes favorably include help and understanding from family members and relatives, a stable living environment, feeling loved by parents, including the parent who has a mental illness, and psychotherapy, either individual or within the family. Understanding that they

have not caused the illness and that they are not to blame for the parents' symptoms is also essential.

Conclusions

Parents with mental illness face the dual and challenging demands of managing their disability while meeting the many stresses associated with raising children. When the illness is chronic and severe, parenting is usually compromised to some degree. How well an individual fares as a parent, however, will turn on many factors, including the parent's responsiveness and compliance with treatment and the social support he or she receives in the parenting role. To ensure positive outcomes, parents with chronic mental illness need a comprehensive range of multifaceted interventions. In designing such interventions, individual strengths should be considered as well as the needs of the children. Interventions should be closely informed by an assessment of parenting and children's needs. They may include medication management, pregnancy decision making, trauma and abuse therapy, substance abuse treatment, marital and family counseling, comprehensive case management, self-help, parenting mentoring, assistance with housing, and independent living. Assessment of the home environment and the parent's social support system is crucial. Building support networks for the parenting role and meeting the needs of affected children are other essential aspects of such interventions. Community mental health services targeted specifically for parents with chronic mental disorders and their families may include: intensive case management, psychiatric rehabilitation day programs that include parent skills training and day care for preschool children, psychoeducation classes that include information about child development and parenting skills along with information about mental disorders and symptom management, and crisis nurseries and other types of respite care for young children when the mother's symptoms become acute. Because children of mothers with chronic mental disorders are at risk, they need interventions that provide wrap-around services and linkage with schools and healthcare providers. These children may also benefit from education about their parent's mental illness along with community support services.

See also: Abuse, Neglect, and Maltreatment of Infants; Attachment; Depression; Emotion Regulation; Mental Health, Infant; Mental Health, Intervention and Prevention; Postpartum Depression, Effects on Infant; Risk and Resilience; Separation and Stranger Anxiety.

Suggested Readings

Ackerson B (2003) Coping with the dual demands of severe mental illness and parenting: The parents' perspective. *Families in Society* 84: 109–118.

Ackerson BJ (2003) Parents with serious and persistent mental illness: Issues in assessment and services. *Social Work* 48: 187–194.

American Psychiatric Association (2000) *Diagnostic and Statistical Manual of Mental Disorders DSM-IV-TR Fourth Edition* (Text Revision). Washington, DC: Author.

Brunette M and Jacobsen T (2006) Children of parents with mental illness: Outcomes and interventions. In: Hendrick V (ed.) *Treatment of Psychiatric Disorders in Pregnancy and the Postpartum*, pp. 197–227. Totowa, NJ: Humana Press.

Cleaver H, Unell I, and Aldgate J (1999) *Children's Needs – Parenting Capacity. The Impact of Parental Mental Illness, Problem Alcohol and Drug Use, and Domestic Violence on Children's Development.* London: TSO.

Göpfert M, Webster J, and Seeman MV (eds.) (2004) *Parental Psychiatric Disorder: Distressed Parents and their Families,* 2nd edn. Cambridge: Cambridge University Press.

Holley TE and Holley J (1997) *My Mother's Keeper: A Daughter's Memoir of Growing Up in the Shadow of Schizophrenia.* New York: Morrow.

Murray L and Cooper PJ (eds.) (1997) *Postpartum Depression and Child Development.* New York: The Guilford Press.

Nicholson J, Biebel K, Hinden B, Henry A, and Stier L (2001) *Critical Issues for Parents with Mental Illness and Their Families* (KEN01–0109). Rockville, MD: Center for Mental Health Services, Substance Abuse and Mental Health Services Administration.

Ostler T (2007) *Assessing Parenting Competency in Individuals with Mental Illness.* Baltimore, MD: Paul H. Brookes Publishing Co.

Relevant Websites

http://www.aacap.org – American Academy of Child Adolescent Psychiatry.

http://www.nmha.org – Mental Health America.

http://www.nami.org – National Alliance on Mental Illness.

http://www.niaaa.nih.gov – National Institute on Alcohol Abuse and Alcoholism, National Institutes of Health.

http://mentalhealth.samhsa.gov – National Mental Health Information Center, Center for mental health services.

http://www.nida.nih.gov – The National Institute on Drug Abuse, National Institutes of Health.

http://www.lookingglass.org – Through the Looking Glass.

Parental Leave

J S Hyde and J L Petersen, University of Wisconsin, Madison, WI, USA

Glossary

Buffer effect – A protective factor that reduces the risk of a potentially harmful situation.

California Paid Family Leave Act – The first paid parental leave legislation in the US that allows both men and women in the state of California 6 weeks of leave at 55% pay to care for a newborn or ill family member.

Family and Medical Leave Act (FMLA) – Federal legislation for family leave that requires employers with more than 50 employees to provide a minimum of 12 weeks unpaid, job-guaranteed leave for parents to take care of an infant or for an elderly or sick family member

Family leave – Leave from work for purposes of caring for an infant or for an elderly or sick family member.

Family salience – The importance of family.

Maternity leave – A women's leave from work at the time of a birth to recover from childbirth and care for a newborn.

Parental leave – A mother's or father's leave from work at the time of birth or adoption of a child.

Work salience – The importance of work.

Introduction

Although the transition to parenthood is an exciting and joyous time for many parents, the addition of a newborn or adopted child may also add stress to an already hectic lifestyle. Particularly in a dual-earner household, parents may worry about finances and job security in addition to caring for a new life. As more women enter the labor force and more households become dual earners, a need for a paid parental leave policy becomes ever more apparent. 'Parental leave' refers to a mother's or father's leave from work at the time of birth or adoption of a child. 'Maternity leave' is a more specific concept referring to a mother's (not a father's) leave from work at the time of a birth to recover from childbirth and care for a newborn. 'Family leave' is a more general term encompassing both parental and maternity leave and refers to leave from work for purposes of caring for an infant or for an elderly or sick family member. This article will focus primarily on parental leave during the transition to parenthood.

Policy Review

Before 1993 the US was the only industrialized nation without a federal parental leave policy. Even with the inception of the Family and Medical Leave Act (FMLA) in February 1993 the US still lags behind many European nations in the generosity of federal parental leave policy. The FMLA requires that employers with more than 50 employees provide a minimum of 12 weeks unpaid, job-guaranteed leave. Both mothers and fathers are covered equally under the FMLA and they may accumulate paid vacation or personal days to use for parental leave. Employers must continue to provide health benefits but are not required to extend other benefits during parental leave.

Despite the benefits of the FMLA, parental leave policy in the US can still be improved. Women work disproportionately for small businesses with fewer than 50 employees, leaving a large number of women uncovered by the legislation. For those women who are covered by their employers, a leave of 12 weeks is often too short, leading to physical and mental health implications for the mother as well as reduced marital satisfaction and less time to develop a secure relationship with the infant. Finally, an unpaid leave gives many parents no option but to cut their leaves short due to financial concerns. Taking 3 months off work without pay can be detrimental to many people's finances but especially for parents with the financial burden of caring for a new life.

In 2004, California became the first state in the US to enact a paid parental leave policy. The California Paid Family Leave Act allows both men and women 6 weeks of leave at 55% pay to care for a newborn or ill family member. During its first year, over 150 000 parents took advantage of the paid parental leave program. Since then, 28 other states including Massachusetts, New York, and New Jersey have introduced paid parental leave bills into their legislature. This is a promising avenue of policy reform as states take responsibility for providing a paid parental leave policy.

It may be helpful to put US parental leave policy in the context of other nations' policies. Many countries including Sweden, Italy, and China offer a paid parental leave policy. Sweden in particular is known for the most generous parental leave policy. In an effort to restore population following a severe loss in World War II as well as an effort to increase gender equality, Sweden offers 15 months of paid, job-guaranteed leave for both mothers and fathers. For the first 12 months pay is approximately 90% of the normal wages; for the last 3 months it is reduced further. Mothers also have a right to work at 75% time until the child is 8 years of age. Italy offers a maternity leave of 2 months paid leave prior to the birth of a child and 3 months after birth with a pay of 70% of normal wages. Italian mothers also have the option of an additional 6 months leave at 30% pay. In China mothers are offered 3 months paid leave and fathers are provided with 15 days. Opportunities are also made available for mothers to nurse while they are at work. These cases illustrate how culture affects parental leave policy and the generosity of paid leave policies in other nations.

Wisconsin Maternity Leave and Health Project

Before reviewing the data on the effects of parental leave we will briefly describe the Wisconsin Maternity Leave and Health (WMLH) project, the source of many of the results discussed below. The WMLH project is a longitudinal study of over 500 women, their partners, and their infants in the Wisconsin area. Women were interviewed in their homes during (1) the first trimester of pregnancy (2) 1 month postpartum, (3) 4 months postpartum, and (4) 12 months after birth. Almost 82% of the women were employed when the study began. This project was the first large-scale study of psychological aspects of parental leave and continues to be one of the best sources of data on the topic. The participants in this study are representative of the US population in household income and education; therefore, this study may be generalized to other men and women in the US.

Parental Leave and Health

Mental Health

There is evidence to suggest that overall, women's employment is associated with improved mental health. These conclusions are based, however, on studies of women at various times in the life span, and may include single and married women, and women with or without children. The year after child birth may be a time of particular stress including physical recovery from childbirth, postpartum depression, caring for an infant with around-the-clock needs, and associated sleep deprivation for the mother.

Depression
Rates of depression in women after childbirth (8–20% of postpartum women) are higher than rates in the general population of women (3–4% of women). Levels of depression following childbirth are dependent upon a number of

factors including employment status following the birth of a child. According to data from the WMLH project, length of parental leave interacts with several variables to affect levels of depression. Marital concern is one such factor that interacts with length of maternity leave to predict rates of depression. Women who took a short parental leave (6 weeks or less) and who were high in marital concern showed elevated risks of depression compared to women who took longer leaves (12 weeks or more) and women who took a short leave but were not high on marital concern. It seems that concern for the marriage adds an addition stress, that when combined with a short maternity leave, increases maternal depression.

Length of leave also interacts with work vs. family salience in predicting depression. Women who were higher on work salience than family salience and took a long leave were more likely to show increased levels of depression than women high on work salience who took a shorter leave. Many women are highly involved with their work prior to pregnancy and may find staying at home with an infant to be a difficult transition. They may be eager to return to work and resent the time that they feel they must spend at home to care for an infant. A long leave may not always be beneficial, especially when the mother is eager to return to work. Therefore, the effects of varying lengths of leave on depression are dependent upon individual characteristics of the woman. Policy should reflect these individual needs by allowing women the opportunity to take long leaves but recognizing that long leave is not beneficial to all women.

Women who were high on family salience relative to work salience were low in depression regardless of when they returned to work. These women may feel that they are providing for their families regardless of their length of leave. Working mothers are providing for their children financially whereas mothers at home are providing care for their infant. Because these women are more concerned about family life than work, they are less affected by taking time off work and concerns with their job.

The association of length of maternity leave with depression is dependent upon a number of factors including work rewards and marital concern. Women play multiple roles as wife, mother, and employee. These roles logically interact to provide a complex influence on maternal mental health. Length of maternity leave may provide a buffer effect from this role conflict by allowing women an opportunity to provide care for an infant while having a sense of job security.

It is well known that maternal depression has consequences for infant development. Mothers with depression are less responsive to their infant and are at greater risk of developing an insecure maternal attachment. Clearly, it is in the best interest of the families and society as a whole to promote mothers' mental health in the postpartum period.

Anxiety

Although anxiety may not be related to length of maternity leave *per se*, it is associated with hours worked per week and full-time employment during the first year after birth. The WMLH project found that higher levels of anxiety were reported for women working full time 4 months postpartum compared to women working part time or as homemakers. These women who work full time may feel overloaded with the stress of both work and caring for an infant who, at 4 months, may not yet sleep through the night.

Difficult infant temperament and work concerns also predicted maternal anxiety. A difficult infant temperament may exacerbate the stress of working long hours and caring for an infant. Difficulty at work may also increase anxiety as it adds another role-related concern of being a good employee as well as a good mother.

Physical Health

Maternal recovery

Time off work may be essential for women to recover from the physical labor of pregnancy and the rapid physiological changes following pregnancy. Childbirth is a physically taxing experience that reduces energy and vitality and creates health problems for some women. Women need time to physically recover from the process of giving birth. Postpartum physical symptoms include breast tenderness, constipation, uterine cramps, and respiratory symptoms. Women reported worse health at 1 and 4 months postpartum than either during pregnancy or at 12 months postpartum. Typically, recovery from childbirth has been said to take an average of 6 weeks, but this actually refers to the time it takes for the uterus to return to its size before pregnancy. Recent studies find that complete recovery may take up to 6 months for women to return to their typical level of health and activity. Recovery from childbirth usually takes longer with Cesarean delivery than vaginal birth. This form of delivery is more common in the US than in many other countries. Therefore, recovery for American women is expected to be longer on average than that of women in other nations.

In a 1997 study, Patricia McGovern and colleagues found that length of maternity leave contributed to women's physical health although the direction was not linear. Women who took leaves between 3 and 5 months long reported more vitality and fewer limitations to their daily role than women who took leaves shorter than 3 months or longer than 5 months. This suggests that a leave of 3–5 months is optimal for recovery from childbirth and better maternal health. Women who take a short leave may not have recovered fully from pregnancy and childbirth, whereas women who take a long leave may be more susceptible to infection from their infant.

Reduced sleep in association with caring for a newborn is a likely contributor to poor postpartum health. Data from the WMLH project show that the greatest loss of sleep occurs 1 month postpartum, but even after 4 months women are still getting less sleep, on average, than before pregnancy. Reduced sleep may aggravate already existing health problems and weaken the immune system allowing other health problems to be introduced. Women who work throughout the day do not have an opportunity to catch up on sleep lost the night before. Working long hours and being concerned about that work is likely to affect nightly sleep as well.

Unfortunately, women's parental length of leave is rarely determined by their physical health. A number of factors, most commonly economic concerns, may reduce the length of maternity leave regardless of physical health, forcing a woman with poor physical health to return to work. Providing a longer paid maternity leave is arguably a cost-effective strategy for employers to minimize employees' sick leave.

Infant health

Mothers who took a leave longer than 3 months also reported better health of their infants. This may be because working women whose children are in childcare have an increased risk of infection from other children in the care facility. Women taking parental leave also have more time to attend to their infant's needs and devote more attention to their child who is vulnerable to infection. This higher level of care is likely to ward off infection by providing a healthy immune system. For example, mothers who were not employed during the first 12 weeks of their infant's life were more likely to have their infant immunized than mothers who worked.

In 2000 Christopher Ruhm found that European countries with a generous paid parental leave policy had a lower infant mortality rate than countries with unpaid leave. A 1-year parental leave was associated with a decrease in infant mortality of about 20%. This is a staggering finding suggesting the importance of paid parental leave on infant mortality. Paid parental leave allows more parents, especially fathers, to take time off work to care for an infant. This individualized care reduces infant disease and infection and has a significant effect on infant mortality.

In addition, infant health was associated with more maternal vitality. Infant health may be related to parental health as infectious diseases spread throughout the family. Waking in the middle of the night to care for an ill infant likely drains a mother's energy and leads to increased sleep deprivation. In light of this evidence, longer parental leave may be a cost-effective means of reducing health problems in both the mother and the infant.

Breastfeeding

A number of studies suggest that there are many benefits to breastfeeding including increased health of the infant and enhanced cognitive development. Infants who are breastfed develop a temporary immunity to some diseases and have a reduced risk of obesity in childhood. The World Health Organization recommends at least 6 months of exclusive breastfeeding for improved infant health. Breastfeeding is very time-intensive, requiring the mother to devote several hours a day to feeding her infant. A short maternity leave (less than 6 months) does not allow women to devote the time necessary to feeding their infant exclusively on breast milk. Length of maternity leave is associated with increased frequency of breastfeeding. At 6 months postpartum only 10% of women employed full-time breastfed their infant in comparison to 24% of women who were not employed. Frequency of breastfeeding is also related to milk production. If a woman is unable to breastfeed or pump regularly, her milk supply will diminish. Private places to breastfeed or pump at places of employment are rarely available in the US. In China women are provided with breaks for nursing and pumping in private locations on the jobsite. This allows women to return to work while continuing to provide the nutrition needed for their child's health.

Fathers' Parental Leave

Paternal leave may have beneficial effects for both the father–infant and marital relationship. Fathers who take at least some leave are more likely to have a secure relationship to their child and be more involved with their child later in life. The father–infant bonding early in the child's life seems to affect the relationship later in life. Parental leave provides fathers the opportunity to grow close and remain close with their children. Fathers who took a longer leave were more likely to be high in both family salience and gender equality suggesting that fathers who are eager to be involved with their children and share in the responsibility of caring for them take longer parental leaves.

Parental leave also provides increased support for the mother. By sharing household and childcare responsibility, the father is able to relieve the mother's stress and enhance the marital relationship. Fathers may wish to take parental leave at the same time as the mother in order to take responsibility for childcare while the mother recovers from birth, or they may opt to take leave at different times so that both parents may return to work quickly while knowing their infant is being cared for by a parent.

Despite the positive effects of paternal leave, few fathers take an extended leave to care for an infant. Although about 90% of fathers in the WMLH project took some time off work following the birth of their child, the average leave was only 5 days in comparison to 9 weeks for mothers. A short leave may be due to a number of factors including negative attitudes from coworkers and supervisors and, more commonly, financial considerations. Many fathers consider themselves to be the breadwinner and may take a shorter leave not because they are unsupportive, but rather because they are expected to provide financially for their new family. In the WMLH project fathers were more likely to take paid vacation or sick leave off work than unpaid parental leave following the birth of a child. Therefore, although the FMLA provides equal job protection for mothers and fathers, fathers are much less likely to make use of the legislation as long as the leave is unpaid. Data from the Families and Work Institute support this assertion citing that 70% of fathers took leave before legislation and only 75% took leave after the FMLA was passed. In Sweden, where fathers are provided with 12 months of parental leave at 90% pay, the average paternal leave is 53 days. Of American fathers 92% said they would drop to at least part time work for a year to care for a newborn if they were guaranteed 100% pay. This suggests that fathers are willing to take parental leave to care for an infant or mother but are less likely to take leave if the leave is paid.

Father's parental leave also has implications for gender equality. Discrimination against women in the work force is commonly excused with the assumption that women take longer parental leave than men or quit their jobs after birth and are therefore temporary employees. If men took longer parental leaves, this assumption would be called into question. In addition, fathers who take equal responsibility for infant and childcare allow mothers to return to work sooner providing more gender equity in both the home and the work force.

Parental Leave and Relationship Quality

Marital Relationship

Researchers generally agree that marital quality typically declines after the birth of a child. This is especially true for women and may last for 18 months or more following a birth. Many factors may contribute to this decline including reduction in time spent together as a couple, the husband's worry about supporting a family, the wife's worry about returning to work, and the quality of the sexual relationship. The hectic time of caring for a newborn and worrying about job security adds additional stress to a marriage that may lead to decreased satisfaction.

According to data from the WMLH project, length of leave and number of hours worked interacts with a number of variables to predict marital satisfaction for the wife. In regard to length of leave, women who took shorter leaves and were dissatisfied with their childcare had the greatest marital incompatibility. Women who take a short leave may

not have the financial resources to place their children in adequate childcare and their worry over childcare may spill over to the marital relationship. In regard to work hours there were two profiles of women with high levels of marital dissatisfaction: (1) women who worked long hours and were satisfied with their work status and (2) women who worked shorter hours and were dissatisfied with their work status. Those in the first group are likely to be women who are very involved in their work and have less time to cultivate, or perhaps are not interested in, a close marriage. The second group is comprised mainly of women who work part time but would prefer to be home full time. Financial necessity is the driving force behind their employment, and they may resent their husbands for not being better providers, creating a sense of marital incompatibility.

Parental leave provides both parents with the opportunity to spend more time caring for the marital relationship rather than worrying about balancing work and family demands. In particular, a paid parental leave would allow new parents to spend time with the newborn without resenting their partner for neglecting financial responsibilities.

Father–Infant Relationship

Not only does parental leave permit the formation of a strong father–infant relationship, but according to the WMLH project maternal employment during the child's first year of life may also affect the father–infant relationship. When mothers either did not work or worked part time during the child's infancy, fathers were more involved in care giving and were more sensitive and responsive to the infant than when wives worked full time. When fathers were satisfied with their marital quality and their wives did not work outside the home they were more positive in their interactions with the infant, whereas when wives work full and part time, the relationship between father's marital satisfaction and infant interactions was negative. Fathers may feel forced to care for their child when the mother is working and thus resent the time they spend with their infant. In contrast, fathers whose wives are not working may be more willing to voluntarily interact with their infant and therefore enjoy the relationship they share with their children more. This suggests that maternal employment during the first year of an infant's life may indirectly affect the father–infant relationship.

Mother–Infant Relationship

Another benefit of parental leave is increased opportunity to bond with the infant and develop a secure attachment. A number of studies have examined the effect of maternal employment on mother–infant attachment. Researchers such as John Bowlby and Mary Ainsworth suggest that maternal interaction with an infant is correlated with a more secure relationship. They suggest that the first year of life is a particularly sensitive time for mother–infant bonding. Quality of maternal interaction may also be more important that quantity of time spent together. Therefore, working mothers who value the time spent with their infant outside of work may have rewarding mother–infant relationships.

The WMLH project found results consistent with attachment theory. Results indicate that shorter leaves were associated with more negative maternal affect and behavior toward the infant. Length of leave also interacted with other risk factors such as maternal depression, mother's health symptoms, and infant's temperament to predict the quality of the mother–infant relationship. Among mothers experiencing depressive symptoms, poor physical health, or those dealing with an infant with difficult temperament, a longer leave provided a buffer effect for a more rewarding mother–infant relationship.

Quality of the mother–infant relationship is likely due to a number of factors in addition to maternal employment. Recent research suggests that parent–child bonding is a lifelong process rather than a 'sensitive period' during the first year of life. Warmth and responsiveness from both parents is an evolving process present throughout the child rearing process.

Parental Leave and Infant Development

The National Institute of Child Health and Human Development (NICHD) study of Early Child Care and Youth Development is the largest study of early child care to date. They found that amount of time spent in childcare was a significant predictor of behavioral problems and cognitive deficiencies in children in grade school. Children who spent more time in childcare, rather than being cared for by their parents, were more likely to have more behavioral problems and less cognitive ability. In addition, those children were more likely to have poor work habits and more mother–child conflict through third grade. However, a stronger predictor of cognitive ability and academic skill was quality of childcare. Children who experienced higher-quality childcare performed better on tests of cognition, language, and other academic skills such as math and reading, than children in poor-quality day care.

Maternal employment during the first year of life has negative effects on infant development when childcare is poor. Women who take a short parental leave because of financial concerns may not be able to afford good-quality childcare. A paid parental leave would provide low-income parents with an opportunity to care for their child themselves without worrying about poor childcare. A paid leave may also allow parents to save money for good childcare when they return to work.

Employer Benefits

Although the most vocal argument against paid parental leave is the burden on the employer, many employers are beginning to see paid parental leave as a benefit to their business. With the growing research documenting the health and psychological effects of maternal employment soon after giving birth, businesses are becoming concerned about issues of work productivity. Workers who take a short parental leave are likely to be absent from work more often due to health problems of the worker and infant. In addition, employees with an infant at home may be more distracted at work. They are likely to be sleep deprived, worry about the well-being of their infant, and stressed about balancing work with family. All of these are likely contributors to reduced work productivity.

More employers are also becoming concerned about the message that they send to their employees. Employers have a duty beyond profit that includes worker care. By providing a paid parental leave, businesses send a message to their employees that they are concerned and supportive of family life. Employees who work for a company that is supportive of their personal decisions are likely to be more diligent workers because they are motivated to support a company that is supportive of them. In contrast, workers who resent their employer for their parental leave policy are less likely to give back to their company in terms of productivity. In addition, businesses with generous benefits such as paid parental leave attract more workers providing competitive applicants for employment. Overall, paid parental leave helps most employers by providing diligent workers and cost-effective benefits.

Conclusion

The available evidence suggests that the US is in need of a paid parental leave policy providing adequate time to care for a newborn infant. Short parental leave adversely affects mental health, physical health, and relationship quality of both parents and the infant. However, negative effects such as depression are also reported for long leave when the parent is eager to return to work. Parental leave should reflect the individual considerations of the parents and infant allowing parents the opportunity to take efficient time off work to provide for their infant.

Countries such as Sweden have provided an example of a superior parental leave policy providing parents with adequate payment and time to make the transition into parenthood smoothly. This Swedish legislation has increased quality of work as well as quality of family life for those who take advantage of it. In addition, egalitarian gender roles in the work place are becoming more accepted as fathers increasingly take advantage of parental leave and responsibility for childcare.

Although a short maternity leave may have negative effects during the infant's first year of life, maternal employment after the infant's first year may have many beneficial effects. Women who work provide an extra income to alleviate the family's financial concerns. They are also a positive role model for their children, especially daughters, by showing that women are as smart and capable as men in the work force. Working mothers may add goals and aspirations increasing their quality of life, and as the number of women in the work force increases gender equality is becoming more of a reality. Parental leave provides women with the opportunity to spend time with their infants and maintain the job security that produces these benefits for them and for society.

Women should not have to choose between caring for their infant and job security. The job security provided by parental leave policies is crucial for women to avoid this dilemma and gain equality in the work force. A paid policy would provide the financial support for mothers and fathers to enjoy the pleasure and excitement of welcoming a new life into a growing family without the burden of worrying about job security and financial concerns.

See also: Attachment; Child and Day Care, Effects of; Family Support, International Trends; Marital Relationship; Maternal and Paternal Employment, Effects of; Postpartum Depression, Effects on Infant.

Suggested Readings

Galtry J and Callister P (2005) Assessing the optimal length of parental leave for child and parental well-being: How can research inform policy. *Journal of Family Issues* 26: 219–246.

Haas L (1992) *Equal Parenthood and Social Policy: A Study of Parental Leave in Sweden.* Albany: State University of New York Press.

Hyde JS, Essex MJ, Clark R, and Klein MH (2001) Maternity leave, women's employment and marital incompatibility. *Journal of Family Psychology* 15: 476–491.

Hyde JS, Essex MJ, Clark R, Klein MH, and Byrd JE (1996) Parental leave: Policy and research. *Journal of Social Issues* 52: 91–109.

Klein MH, Hyde JS, Essex MJ, and Clark R (1998) Maternity leave, role quality, work involvement, and mental health one year after delivery. *Psychology of Women Quarterly* 22: 239–256.

McGovern P, Dowd B, Gjerdingen D, Moscovice I, Kochevar L, and Lohman W (1997) Time off work and the postpartum health of employed women. *Medical Care* 35: 507–521.

NICHD Early Child Care Research Network (2005) Early child care and children's development in primary grades: Follow-up results from the NICHD study of early child care. *American Educational Research Journal* 42: 537–570.

Ruhm C (2000) Parental leave and child health. *Journal of Health Economics* 19: 931–960.

Waldfogel J (2001) International policies toward parental leave and child care. *The Future of Children* 11: 99–111.

Relevant Websites

http://www.paidfamilyleave.org – California Paid Family Leave.

http://www.dol.gov – Family and Medical Leave Act.

http://www.ilo.org – International Labor Organization.

http://www.sweden.gov.se/sb/d/2025/a/19953 – Sweden's Parental Leave Act.

http://www.dol.gov – U.S. Department of Labor: Women's Bureau.

Parenting Styles and their Effects

M H Bornstein and D Zlotnik, National Institutes of Health, Bethesda, MD, USA

Glossary

Authoritarian parents – Parents who use punitive, absolute, and forceful disciplinary tactics and who place a high level of importance on obedience and conformity.

Authoritative parents – Parents who expect their child to comply to a reasonable set of rules and are responsive to the child's needs and are respectful and supportive of the child's autonomy and individuality.

Avoidant attachment – An infant–caregiver relationship characterized by indifference on the part of the infant toward the caregiver.

Cronbach's coefficient alpha – A statistical measure used to assess internal consistency reliability of items in a scale. If there is little correlation and items are independent, the Cronbach coefficient alpha will be low and close to zero; however, if items are well correlated the Cronbach coefficient alpha will be higher and approximate one.

Demandingness – One of two important dimensions of parenting; referring to the degree to which the parent expects and demands maturity and responsibility from the child.

Externalizing behaviors – Psychosocial problems that are manifested in turning symptoms outward such as aggression or delinquency.

Familismo – A Latino concept for thinking of the family as an extension of the self in addition to feelings of loyalty, reciprocity, and family cohesion.

Indifferent parents – Parents who are not dedicated to their parenting roles and are uninvolved in helping foster the optimal development for their child.

Internalizing behaviors – Psychosocial problems that are manifested in turning symptoms inward, for example, depression or anxiety.

Marlowe–Crowne social desirability scale – A measure to assess social desirability bias.

Parental Authority Questionnaire (PAQ) – A parenting styles assessment instrument consisting of three 10-item scales that correspond with Baumrind's authoritative, authoritarian, and permissive parenting styles.

Parenting practice – Specific parental behaviors, such as spanking, making sure children are doing their homework, and demonstrating an interest in children's activities.

Parenting style – Several elements that combine to create the emotional climate in which parents communicate their attitudes about their child. Style is conveyed through body language, temper, tone of voice, emotional displays, and quality of attention.

Permissive parents – Parents who are highly responsive to their child's needs but exert little control over the child's behavior, allowing the child the freedom to act and choose activities as he or she pleases.

Resistant attachment – An infant–caregiver relationship characterized by ambivalence toward the caregiver.

Respeto – A unique quality of Latino families that emphasizes the importance of being respectful and obedient.

Responsiveness – One of two important dimensions of parenting referring to the degree to which the parent responds to the child's needs in an accepting and supportive manner.

Secure attachment – An infant–caregiver relationship characterized by trust.

Temperament – Constitutionally based individual differences in behavioral characteristics that are relatively consistent across situations and over time.

Introduction

The type of parenting style a parent exhibits greatly affects child development. Diana Baumrind, Eleanor Maccoby, and John Martin were integral in identifying four main types of parenting styles: authoritative, authoritarian, permissive, and indifferent. We explain how parenting style is manifested in infancy through early childhood. Additionally, we examine the characteristics of each parenting style and how each style affects children's temperament, attachment relationships, academic success, and psychological development. The effects of parenting styles are embedded in class, cultural, and historical contexts. The typical definitions used for each parenting style may not accurately represent all cultures; therefore, we examine the effects of parenting styles for European, Asian, African, and Latin American cultures. Furthermore, we explain how various factors such as family socioeconomic status (SES), maternal employment status, parental education level, parental stress, marital problems, and parental depression affect the parenting style a parent is likely to exhibit.

Parenting Styles

A parenting style consists of several elements that combine to create the emotional climate in which parents communicate their attitudes and practices about childrearing with their child. Within the context of their style, parents express their attitudes toward children's responsibilities and engage in a variety of specific parenting practices such as spanking, ensuring children are doing their homework, and involvement in children's activities. Parenting styles convey parents' overall feelings about the child through body language, tone of voice, emotional displays, and quality of attention. Parenting styles are often considered as traits due to their consistency across time and context, this consistancy in interaction patterns are apparent as early as the first year of a child's life. Virtually all aspects of parenting are informed by culture, and each culture prescribes unique socialization patterns and traditions to achieve its childrearing goals. Therefore, it is important to be aware that there is no optimal parenting style for all cultures and the implications of one parenting style may vary for children from different cultural and socioeconomic contexts.

Research generally takes a typological approach to parenting styles. The most prominent contributor to parenting style research is Diana Baumrind, who conducted innovative research with predominantly well-educated, middle-SES, North American families. Baumrind's typologies are compilations of ranges of parenting behaviors that reflect the level of control, clarity of communication, maturity demands, and nurturance exhibited by parents. Baumrind combined these dimensions to define three distinct styles of parenting: authoritative, authoritarian, and permissive.

Each parenting style has a unique set of behaviors and characteristics associated with it. The first parenting style is authoritative. Authoritative parenting is characterized by a parent who demands that the child comply with a reasonable set of rules and is simultaneously responsive to the child's needs and respectful and supportive of the child's autonomy and individuality. The second style, authoritarian, characterizes a parent who is controlling and thus discouraging of the child's autonomy, values obedience and limits the child's emotional expression. The third style, permissive, characterizes a parent who fails to set restraints on the child and does not believe in punishment regardless of the child's actions. These typologies are further elaborated below.

Building on Baumrind's typologies, Eleanor Maccoby in collaboration with John Martin tested the generalizability of Baumrind's typologies on more diverse sets of populations. They conceptualized parenting styles as being assessable along two separate dimensions, responsiveness and demandingness. These dimensions combined to produce four parenting styles similar to Baumrind's typology: authoritative, authoritarian, permissive, and (a newly added type) indifferent. The first dimension, demandingness, refers to parental control and the degree to which the parent expects the child to exhibit maturity and responsibility. For example, demandingness is expressed in terms of parental supervision, disciplinary efforts, and willingness to respond to the child if he or she disobeys. The second dimension, responsiveness, refers to how child-centered and warm the parent is. Responsiveness promotes the child's individuality and is exhibited in behaviors that are receptive, supportive, and compliant to the child's individual needs and demands. Having analyzed parents along these dimensions, Maccoby and Martin found that authoritative parents score high in demandingness and responsiveness, authoritarian parents are high in demandingness but low in responsiveness, permissive parents score high in responsiveness but low in demandingness, and indifferent parents score low in responsiveness and demandingness (see **Figure 1**).

Responsiveness	Demandingness		
		High	Low
	High	Authoritative	Permissive
	Low	Authoritarian	Indifferent

Figure 1   A scheme for classifying parenting styles based on dimensions of demandingness and responsiveness.

Parenting Style Typology

Different parenting styles construct different emotional climates in the home. We now explore the type of emotional climate each of Baumrind's parenting styles creates, the styles of behaviors and characteristics parents exhibit, and the outcomes each parenting style likely facilitates.

The Authoritative Parenting Style

An authoritative parent exerts firm control over the child, expects maturity, and establishes reasonable guidelines for the child to abide. Simultaneously, authoritative parents make disciplinary decisions by integrating the point of view of the child as long as the parent perceives it to be reasonable. Authoritative parents utilize reason and control when disciplining the child. Authoritative parents, however, are careful not to use harsh forms of punishment or restrict their child's autonomy. Authoritative parents also show warmth, love, and acceptance for their child, encouraging the child to be independent, autonomous, and assert individuality. Another important characteristic of authoritative parenting is parent–child verbal give-and-take which helps facilitate open communication between children and their parents. This reciprocal dialogue consists of parents being open to the opinions of the child but at the same time not failing to express their own perspectives. Authoritative parenting is like a democracy in which the feelings and ideas of both the parents and the children are recognized and supported.

The Authoritarian Parenting Style

An authoritarian parent stresses the importance of compliance, conformity, parental control, respect for authority, and maintaining order. Such parents exercise high degrees of control on and maturity demands from their children; however, this is coupled with low amounts of nurturance and clarity of communication. Complete obedience is expected from children, and authoritarian parents will put a stop to any action the child takes to defy them. When children deviate from the strict standards set for them, the authoritarian parent favors the use of harsher forms of punishment than are used by authoritative parents. The authoritarian parent often discourages the child's autonomy and instead attempts to shape the child to exhibit behaviors and attitudes the parent deems to be desirable. This strategy could hinder the child's maturation by not allowing the child adequate experience making decisions and taking responsibility for his or her own actions. Unlike authoritative parenting, where open discussion is encouraged, in authoritarian parenting, reciprocal dialog and verbal give-and-take between parent and child is discouraged. Authoritarian parents do not discuss thought processes behind their absolute childrearing rules. Instead, the authoritarian parent holds the belief that the parent's word is considered final.

The Permissive Parenting Style

A permissive parent is described as having a high level of nurturance and clarity of communication, paired with low levels of control or maturity demands. They have little expectation of mature behavior from the child, allowing the child the freedom to act and choose activities as he or she pleases. Furthermore, the permissive parent rarely governs the child's time schedule and allows children to determine their own bedtime, mealtime, and time spent watching television. The permissive parent makes few demands of the child and rarely requires the child to do chores around the house or use appropriate manners. Additionally, the permissive parent tends to be extremely accepting and supportive of all the child's behavior and actions including sexual and aggressive impulses.

The permissive parent also often holds the belief that restricting the child's actions in any way might infringe on the child's autonomy, in turn hindering normative child development. As a result of this philosophy, the permissive parent rarely implements rules or guidelines for the child's behavior. Furthermore, the permissive parent often sees her or himself as a resource for the child only if the child decides to utilize the parents as such. Additionally, the permissive parent may care more about being the child's friend than an authority figure. The permissive parent tends to refrain from sharing true sentiments with the child, while allowing the child to freely express negative feelings and behaviors. Permissive parents take a passive approach to disciplining children. They avoid using punishment, asserting authority, or imposing restrictions on the child, whenever possible. The only disciplinary tactic used is reasoning, and parents look to the child for his or her opinion when deciding to implement any type of structure or rule.

The Indifferent Parenting Style

An indifferent parent is characterized as being neither demanding nor responsive to the child. The indifferent parent is not dedicated to parenting roles and is disinterested in helping foster optimal development of the child. The indifferent parent limits time and energy dedicated to the child. Moreover, the indifferent parent is characterized by having little knowledge or involvement in the child's personal life, seldom shows concern for what goes on at school or with the child's friends, and rarely factors the child's opinion in decision making processes.

Additionally, indifferent parents fail to implement guidelines or rules to control the child. Indifferent parents have a parent-centered lifestyle and put their personal needs and interests first rather than concerning themselves with what is best for the child. Indifferent parenting differs from the other three types of parents who all rear their children according to a set of beliefs about what is optimal for the child's development. Indifferent parents fail to set regulations for their children, not because they have the philosophy that it will hinder the child's development, but instead because they are too preoccupied with their own life to concern themselves with implementing rules for their children. In extreme cases, indifferent parents could be considered negligent.

Measurement of Parenting Styles

Parenting styles have been measured using direct observational techniques, but more commonly data are obtained through interviews and questionnaires of parents and children. However, the accuracy of reports is debatable because parent and child responses tend to differ. Some researchers suggest that reports from children may be more accurate because children are less influenced by social desirability biases (the desire on the part of the person answering to 'look good' to the interviewer). Moreover, parenting style in the eyes of children may have more significance. Additionally, SES may affect the accuracy of parenting style reports because some argue that parents of different SES tend to be more or less prone to social desirability biases which could undermine the validity of these assessments.

The Parental Authority Questionnaire (PAQ) developed by John Buri is a commonly used instrument to categorize parenting styles. The PAQ is a 30-item assessment consisting of three 10-item scales that correspond with authoritative, authoritarian, and permissive parenting style. The PAQ assesses children' perceptions of their parent's parenting style and is completed by children about each parent independently. On the questionnaire, the children indicate how well each statement describes a parent based on a 5-point scale, 1 indicating "I strongly disagree that this statement relates to my mother or father" and 5 indicating "I strongly agree that this statement applies to my mother or father." An example of an item that corresponds with authoritative parenting is: "As I was growing up, once family policy had been established my mother discussed the reasoning behind the policy with the children in the family." An example of a statement corresponding with authoritarian parenting is: "Whenever my mother told me to do something as I was growing up, she expected me to do it immediately without asking questions." An example of a statement corresponding with permissive parenting is: "My mother has always felt that what children need is to be free to make up their own minds and to do what they want to do, even if this does not agree with what their parents might want."

The PAQ has proved to be a reliable and valid measure of Baumrind's parenting style typologies. In a test–retest reliability study in which participants completed the PAQ twice over a 2-week period, high reliabilities were found for mother's authoritativeness, authoritarianism, permissiveness, and father's authoritativeness, authoritarianism, and permissiveness. Cronbach coefficient alphas were used to calculate internal consistency reliability for the measure, and high values were obtained for each of the PAQ scales. A third study that measured the discriminant validity of the PAQ indicated that mother's authoritarianism was inversely related to mother's permissiveness and authoritativeness, and father's authoritarianism was inversely related to father's permissiveness, and authoritativeness. Also, mother's permissiveness was not related to mother's authoritativeness. A fourth study assessed criterion validity to examine whether parental nurturance is correlated with authoritative, authoritarian, and permissive parenting styles. Authoritative parents (mother and father) were found to be highest in parental nurturance; authoritarian parenting was inversely related to nurturance for both mothers and fathers; and parental permissiveness was unrelated to nurturance for both mothers and fathers. A final study examined if the PAQ is influenced by social desirability biases by looking at correlations with the Marlowe–Crowne Social Desirability Scale. For example, it would be problematic if people agreed with more authoritative and with fewer authoritarian statements because they wished to appear more socially desirable. PAQ scores did not correlate with the Marlowe–Crowne Social Desirability Scale; therefore, the PAQ does not appear to be vulnerable to social desirability response biases. These studies show that the PAQ is a reliable and valid measure for categorizing parenting styles according to Baumrind's typologies.

Approaches to Parenting Infants and Young Children

Infants

Although the majority of parenting styles research has focused on developmental outcomes in adolescence, parenting styles influence the child's development during the infancy and toddler periods as well. Parenting styles and behaviors must appropriately coincide with the differential tasks and demands of the infancy and toddler periods. Parents play an extremely influential role in early development, and parents are unambiguously responsible for their child's initial adaptation to the world. Parents influence their infants directly by means of their genes, beliefs, styles, and behaviors as well as indirectly by means of their influences on one another and the multiple contexts in which they live. During infancy, the majority of babies' experiences stem from interactions they have within the family. However, postinfancy, their social context expands as children are old enough to enter other social situations, like play groups and school.

Researchers have established a taxonomy identifying four categories of parental caregiving during infancy; these include: nurturant, social, didactic, and material. Together, these modes are perhaps universal, even if their emphasis, frequencies, and durations vary across cultures. Nurturant caregiving meets the physical needs of the infant. Infant mortality is a perpetual parenting concern, and from the moment of conception parents are predominantly responsible for promoting infants' wellness and preventing their illness. Parents nurture offspring by providing sustenance, protection, supervision, and grooming to their infants, in addition to shielding infants from risks and stressors. Social caregiving includes various visual, verbal, affective, and physical behaviors parents use in engaging infants in interpersonal exchanges (kissing, tactile comforting, smiling, socializing, and playful face-to-face contact). Parental displays of warmth and physical expressions of affection toward their offspring peak during infancy. Furthermore, social caregiving influences the regulation of infant affect as well as managing infant social relationships with others, including relatives, nonfamilial caregivers, and peers. Didactic caregiving consists of parental efforts used to stimulate infant's engagement and understanding of the environment outside the dyad. Didactics include focusing the baby's attention on properties, objects, or events in the baby's surrounding; introducing, mediating, and interpreting the external world; describing and demonstrating; as well as provoking or providing opportunities to observe, to imitate, and to learn. Normally, didactics increase over the course of infancy. Material caregiving includes the ways in which parents provision and organize their infant's physical world. Adults are responsible for the number and variety of inanimate objects (toys, books) available to the infant, the level of stimulation, the limits on physical freedom, and the overall physical dimension of babies' experiences. An indifferent parent would fail to provide adequately for these parenting tasks for their infants, which could lead to developmental problems in their child.

Adults differ considerably in their caregiving behaviors and styles, even when they come from the same culture and from similar socioeconomic backgrounds. However, individual parents do not vary much in their activities from day to day even if parenting activities change over longer periods and in response to children's development. Authoritative parents are likely to be sensitive to their infants' developmental progress and tailor their caregiving to match their infants' developmental needs. For example, as infants age, parents provide more didactic experiences for their child. Additionally, responsiveness is a major component of parenting infants. Authoritarian parents differ from authoritative parents in their level of responsiveness with their infant. For example, authoritarian parents tend to be less responsive to their child's crying to try to keep the child under control. Parents who respond promptly, reliably, and appropriately to their babies' signals give infants a good message from the start. For example, when a baby cries and a mother comes, the baby already feels she or he has an effect on the world. An infant whose parents are indifferent or permissive, may be frequently angry because they may find their parent's inaccessibility and unresponsiveness painful and frustrating. Furthermore, babies uncertain about the parent's responsiveness may grow apprehensive and become easily upset by stressful situations.

It is commonly assumed that the overall level of parental involvement or stimulation affects the infant's overall level of development. However, increasing evidence shows that characteristics of individuals shape their experiences and reciprocally those experiences shape the characteristics of individuals through time. Therefore, through infants' interactions with their parents they actively contribute toward their own development by virtue of their unique characteristics, expressivity, and temperament. Thus, infant temperament and maternal sensitivity operate in tandem to affect child development and the parent–child relationship. Additionally, parents' attitudes about their infants and the activities they engage them in are each meaningful to the development of infants.

Parental personality affects a person's abilities as a parent. Features of a personality favorable to good parenting might include empathic awareness, predictability, nonintrusiveness, and emotional availability. Additionally, adult adaptability can be critical in the first few months when infants are less 'readable', for example, their activities are more erratic and disorganized, and their cues less distinct and well differentiated. Being a self-centered parent can cause difficulties when parents put their own needs first and are not sensitive toward their infants' needs.

Toddlers

Parenting styles, parental support, guidance, and structure play a pivotal role in navigating the toddler period. During this period, parents are vital in mediating toddlers' entry into a wider social realm and influencing the affective responses, communicative styles, and social repertories that their children bring to forming meaningful and sustainable relationships and associations.

During the toddler period the quality of responsiveness in parent–child relationships is established. Children prone to engage in power struggles with caregivers elicit more negative perceptions. Similarly, mothers of toddlers rated high in 'negative reactivity' tend to have more authoritarian characteristics, for example, they are often more controlling and less guiding in style, and their children are less compliant. Children who are unruly

despite their parents' attempts at guidance contribute to a potentially devastating 'cycle of coercion' in parent–child relationships. Researchers indicate that to establish a toddler's willing compliance it may be necessary to have well-coordinated interaction behaviors with the child, in the sense that parents' behaviors scaffold the child's effort and parents set the stage for what the child might do next.

An additional developmental challenge of toddlers is for them to develop empathy and organize their emotional sensitivity. It is important for toddlers to learn this through maternal modeling, as maternal sensitivity and reasoning have been found to relate positively to empathic, prosocial response during the child's second year of life. As children age parenting strategies may involve different disciplinary practices than those of earlier childhood, more extensive shared regulation of children's behavior, and altered patterns for effective control.

Child Temperament

Beginning shortly after birth, a child's individuality is manifested primarily in temperament, constitutionally based individual differences in behavioral characteristics that are relatively consistent across situations and over time. That is, individual differences in temperamental characteristics are somewhat stable; however, temperamental characteristics are not expected to be rigidly stable as a child develops. Child temperament can greatly affect the type of parenting style a parent exhibits. Researchers agree that parenting styles are evident during infancy; however, the particular style a parent exhibits is subject to change as a consequence of a changing child temperament. A child's dominant mood, adaptability, activity level, persistence, threshold for distress (or happiness), and other characteristics are important because of the influence they have on others, and because they constitute the foundations of personality. For example, parents who start out with an authoritative style, being warm, affectionate, and sensitive when the child is an infant could alter their parenting style as the child ages and becomes more of a challenge for the parents as a result of an increasing behavioral repertoire or striving for autonomy.

Children's individual temperaments may require differing parental behaviors and styles to lead to optimal developmental paths. For example, some children are receptive to a parent's disproval, and an authoritative approach to socialization is effective. However, this type of parental behavior may not be effective with an imperturbable child, and as a result a more effortful method of discipline may be necessary, and parents may take a more authoritarian approach to disciplining their children. As a result of having a more problematic child, parents may find it necessary to escalate to using greater amounts of anger and harsher disciplinary measures to control their child. Parents who respond to a problematic child with high levels of punitive behavior sets into motion a negative cycle of coercive behavior that could result in the development of a child who is aggressive and difficult to control.

Parent–Child Attachment

Child attachment is an issue that also interacts with parenting styles in affecting child development. Child attachment to their mother is assessed using the Strange Situation paradigm and children are divided into four categories: avoidant, resistant, secure, or disorganized attachment. Secure attachment between infant and caregiver is characterized by trust; avoidant attachment is characterized by indifference on the part of the infant toward the caregiver; resistant attachment is characterized by ambivalence toward the caregiver; and disorganized attachment is characterized by inconsistency in attachment toward the caregiver. The secure behavior pattern has been seen as an indicator of healthy mother–infant interaction and emotional growth. Intrusive, overstimulating, and rejecting parenting is associated with insecure-avoidant attachment in infants, whereas insecure-resistant attachments are linked to inconsistent, unresponsive parenting, very characteristic of the indifferent parenting style. Secure attachment has additionally been shown to lead to the development of psychologically and socially skilled children. It has been proposed that mothers of future avoidant babies express anger and rejection of their babies, mothers of groups of resistant babies are insensitive and inept, and mothers of secure babies are more affectionate and effective in soothing their babies.

Variation in Approaches to Parenting

Cultural Effects

Parenting styles and practices are not universal and are often moderated by social and cultural contexts. Virtually all aspects of parenting are informed by culture. Culture influences parenting behaviors and child development from early in infancy through such factors as when and how parents care for infants, the extent to which parents permit infants freedom to explore, how nurturant or restrictive parents are, which behaviors parents emphasize, and so forth. It is important to be aware that each culture has unique socialization patterns and traditions to achieve the childrearing goals of that society. For example, some cultures uphold the use of physical punishment whereas other cultures morally object to that practice.

Generally, authoritative parenting seems to contribute to the most positive outcomes for all youth regardless of SES, ethnicity, or culture. However, authoritative parenting is less common among African American, Asian American, or Latin American families than European American ones. Instead, among ethnic minority families, the authoritarian parenting style is more prevalent than it is among European American families.

What makes authoritarian parenting more prevalent in certain cultures than others? Perhaps one reason is that authoritarian parenting does not always have the same adverse effects on children of ethnic minority backgrounds, particularly in the case of low-income families. The more restrictive parental practices associated with authoritarian parenting are often considered overly controlling or harsh in middle-class European American communities. However, in neighborhoods that are less safe, have higher levels of poverty, and more frequent levels of antisocial activities, more restrictive parenting may serve an adaptive strategy by providing a high level of supervision and support.

Another consideration is that the discrepancies between authoritative and authoritarian parenting for European Americans may not be relevant in other cultural contexts. The same definitions for authoritative parenting may not make sense when applied to other cultures. For example, in many ethnic minority families a high level of control may be combined with warmth. This does not fit the European American definition of authoritarian or authoritative parenting. If researchers look solely at the parent's use of control, families of different cultures may be mislabeled as authoritarian when in fact they do not possess other negative aspects of authoritarian parenting besides high levels of control. We now turn to explore in more depth how parenting styles appear in Asian, African, and Latin American cultures.

Cultural effects: Asian. Parenting styles may have different effects in Asian families because of their differing values, attitudes, and traditions from those of Western families. For example, equality, self-determination, individualism, and competition are ideals associated with Western culture. This differs dramatically from Eastern ideals of collectivism, harmony, and purity. These disparities lead to different approaches to parenting that each culture considers appropriate and desirable. Although one cannot generalize how all Asians parent, some particular themes unite them. For example, research shows that Asian families stress the importance of parental control and restrictiveness. In turn, Asian parents are less likely to express affection or show reciprocity, and parent–child relationships are less close compared to Western families. Additionally, Asian parents are often more concerned with their child's academic success than are European American parents. Many Asian parenting beliefs stem from traditional Confucian and Buddhist thought that stresses the importance of respect for authority.

It is common for Asian parents to change their parenting style as their child ages. For example, Asian parents generally have few expectations and indulge every need of their child in the first few years of life. However, when the child reaches 'the age of understanding' (around age 6), parents shift to harsher and stricter styles of parenting. At this age children learn discipline and obedience and the importance of respecting authority and promoting family coherence. With modernization, this pattern of lax parenting style at younger ages is beginning to change as parents realize children are capable of understanding earlier in life.

Some researchers argue that Baumrind's parenting style typology is not culturally relevant for Asian families because of the different meanings Asians place on responsiveness and parental control. Generally, researchers assess parental responsiveness from parents' emotional and physical expressions and affections toward their children. However, most Asian parents exhibit responsiveness in a manner different from most European Americans. For example, in Asian cultures responsiveness is expressed in a parent's involvement, support, and prioritizing the caregiving and education of their children rather than emotional and physical demonstrativeness. Therefore, responsiveness cannot be measured accurately given the strict European American definition. Additionally, parental control also holds different meanings for Asian vs. European American cultures. For Asian families, strict control over the child generally occurs in conjunction with positive characteristics such as parental care, concern, and involvement. Asian children perceive this control as a reflection of their parent's dedication and concern for them as long as the control is not excessively domineering or harsh. Furthermore, parental control is linked to traditionally desirable traits for children in Asian cultures – for instance, self-control, tolerance of frustration, diligence, self-confidence, positive attitudes toward others – and it can be beneficial to gaining high levels of achievement. Parents who fail to exhibit characteristics of control and restrictiveness are often seen as negligent and uncaring by others within Asian culture. However, from the viewpoint of someone from another culture, these restrictive and controlling parental practices may appear authoritarian and be considered undesirable. Therefore, research categorizing Asian parents based strictly on Baumrind's typology may be problematic because it may not accurately represent the manner that responsiveness, control, and warmth are expressed and interpreted by Asian families.

Studies of Asian families in both the US and Hong Kong demonstrate that authoritative parenting does not always lead to the same beneficial outcomes for Asian children as it does for children of European decent. Authoritative parenting style is correlated with higher academic achievement and better grades for Americans and Australians of European decent, but this does not hold

true for children in Hong Kong of Chinese decent. In turn, studies of Hong Kong Chinese indicate that, instead, authoritarian parenting styles actually benefit children's academic performance and leads to higher grades among Chinese children.

Not only do parenting styles have different effects on European Americans vs. Asians, but the effects also differ within Asian populations based on generation level of immigration. Research shows that authoritative parenting is predictive of academic outcomes for European Americans, but this does not hold true for either first- or second-generation Chinese. This pattern of findings shows that first-generation Chinese do not benefit from authoritative parenting styles. The effects of parenting style on second-generation Chinese show somewhat inconsistent effects on children lying somewhere in between how parenting styles affect European Americans and how they affect first-generation immigrants. This suggests that some effects of authoritative parenting are beneficial to second-generation Chinese but others are not. Second-generation Chinese are more similar to European Americans than first-generation, but there are still many cultural differences. First-generation immigrants are more familiar with traditional Chinese society and culture, unlike second-generation immigrants who were born in the US and tend to be more assimilated to American culture and tradition.

Cultural effects: African American. Cultural differences also account for the differing effects of parenting styles in African Americans families. Research indicates that having authoritarian parents may not adversely affect African American children as is thought to be true for European American children. Conversely, the benefits of authoritative parenting as seen with European American populations may not have the same positive effects on African American children. Authoritative parenting is not predictive of success for African American children; instead, authoritarian parenting actually leads to greater academic success and higher intelligence quotient (IQ) scores for African American children, especially in the case of high-risk families. Researchers speculate that for children growing up in low-income and unsafe neighborhoods, authoritarian parenting could actually play an adaptive and protective role.

Different cultures attribute disparate meaning to the same parenting behavior. For example, strict parental control and discipline have different meanings for African American compared to European American children. In African American families, firm control and discipline are not perceived negatively, but instead as signs of love, concern, and affection from the parents. Additionally, African American communities often endorse parental practices that may not be upheld in European American culture. One example is the use of physical punishment. Middle- and low-income African Americans tend to use physical punishment without reservation more often than European Americans. Research indicates that around 66% of middle-income and lower-income African American mothers endorse spanking as a form of punishment compared to just 25% of middle-income European American mothers. This does not indicate that African Americans are more likely to endorse child abuse and maltreatment. Punitive punishment is correlated with children exhibiting more externalizing behaviors for European Americans, but this does not hold true for African Americans. The effects of harsh disciplinary practices vary depending on how a particular community perceives those practices. For example, if parents in a community have normative views and feel justified using a practice such as spanking, then children will react normally and will not be adversely affected by the practice. The context surrounding a parent's action is important in determining how it will affect the child.

In African American communities, a unique kind of parenting exists called, 'no nonsense' parenting. This type of parenting is characterized by high levels of control and physical restraint, in the context of maternal warmth. This type of parenting appears to combine authoritarian and authoritative parenting styles. 'No nonsense' parenting has been shown to result in greater cognitive and social competencies and fewer internalizing behaviors in African American children.

Cultural effects: Latinos. For Latino communities, there has been less research indicating differences in the effects of parenting styles compared to African American and Asian families. However, there are some unique characteristics to take note of for Latino families. One distinctive characteristic of Latino families is the concept of 'respeto' which means proper demeanor. Latino families emphasize the importance of being respectful and obedient and exercise greater levels of control over children's' behavior than European American families.

Another consistent theme in Latino communities is that they are generally more family oriented than European Americans. The term familismo refers to thinking of the family as an extension of the self in addition to feelings of loyalty, reciprocity, and family cohesion. Research indicates that Latino youth tend to seek advice from family members, have positive attitudes toward parents, feel more satisfied by family life, and feel more obligated to respect and help their parents than European American children. Research indicates that 'familismo' leads to positive effects for Latino youth such as high-quality parenting and favorable academic and social outcomes. Furthermore, in times of trouble or transition, Latino families tend to rely on their extended family and to utilize family resources to resolve the problem at hand and cope with stress. However, there is also within group variation. For example, first-generation Latin Americans

tend to have more positive attitudes toward their parents in comparison to children of later-generations. Perhaps, this finding reflects assimilation to the culture of the US.

Latinos have an increased likelihood to drop out of high school. Therefore, researchers debate whether Latino families place less emphasis on educational achievement. One study showed that Latina mothers are very willing to assist with their child's school work, however, Latina mothers often hold the belief that their assistance has little effect on the child's academic success. In general, researchers feel that issues confronting Latin Americans academically are not related to culture or parental socialization, but instead have to do with the poverty, segregation, and discrimination that are negative consequences of immigration, resettlement, and resulting minority status.

Socioeconomic Status and Maternal Employment

Biology, personality, and perceptions of role responsibilities constitute factors that influence parenting from the start. However, societal factors condition and channel beliefs and behaviors of parents as well. Family situation, social status, and culture for example encourage diverse patterns of parenting perceptions, styles, and practices. Parenting is influenced by family configuration, level of parental stress, marital relationships, and parents' social networks, among other social-situational factors.

SES affects many aspects of parenting styles and behavior. Mothers in different SES groups behave similarly in certain ways; however, there is considerable evidence to support the claim that parenting styles vary with SES. Parent–child relationships in middle-class families are characterized as being child centered, accepting, and egalitarian. Higher-SES mothers tend to exhibit warmth, are more involved in their child's life, and value the child's self-direction. Lower-SES families tend to be parent centered and focus on maintaining control, order, and obedience from children.

Why does economic status have an effect on parenting styles? One prominent explanation is that low-income families, which lack economic resources, limit the quality and quantity of goods the family can provide their children. For example, low-income families have less money to buy cognitively stimulating educational toys and books that are beneficial to a child's cognitive development. Moreover, poverty and economic insecurity negatively affect a parent's mental health which may relate to unsupportive parenting sometimes exhibited by low-income parents.

Having low SES is considered a risk factor in children's development also on account of its detrimental effects on the quality of mother–infant interaction. Low-SES adversely affects mothers' psychological functioning and promotes harsh or inconsistent disciplinary practices. Research shows that low-income parents are more likely to adhere to authoritarian and punitive parenting styles compared to middle-class parents. Additionally, as previously mentioned low-income parents are less likely to provide their children with cognitively stimulating educational activities at home. Lower-SES mothers often think that it is a bad idea to spoil children and consequently are less warm and supportive toward them. Furthermore, low-income parents tend to be less receptive to their child's needs and less likely to reward their child's positive behavior. In extreme cases the lack of child-centered behavior could develop into child abuse or neglect, phenomena that are more prevalent in low-income families.

A related issue of interest is the effect a parent's employment status has on parenting styles. Studies indicate a link between a mother's employment status, the type of parenting style exhibited, and the child's developmental outcomes. For example, having a mother with a job outside of the home is linked to a more authoritative style parenting. Furthermore, maternal mood has been found to be correlated with maternal employment status. Studies show that working mothers are less likely to suffer depression. In turn, this results in more successful academic and social outcomes for children, especially in the case of low-SES families.

Parental Education

Another external factor that seems to affect parenting style is parental education level. Families with higher levels of parental education tend to be more authoritative and lower in authoritarian and permissive parenting. This finding is further supported in a study of exclusively African Americans that indicated that maternal education is correlated with child-centered parenting. Studies conducted in both Egypt and China replicated the finding that mothers with less education were less likely to exhibit authoritative parenting than mothers with more education. Additionally, mothers with low levels of education are more likely to use physical punishment to discipline their children, and they place more emphasis on conformity. However, mothers with higher levels of education have been linked to more supportive, child-centered parenting.

Parental Stress, Marital Problems, and Divorce

Parental stress can have potentially damaging effects on parents' attitudes and behaviors toward children. Parental stress can come in many forms such as financial troubles, lack of social support, or it can stem from problems within the marriage. Stressors adversely affect the general well-being and health of parents and demand attention and emotional energy from them. Parental stress can reduce parental participation, attentiveness, patience, and tolerance toward children and increase the use of punitive practices. This disruption in family functioning can negatively impact children's social competence. Social support can improve parenting satisfaction, affecting the availability of mothers to their infants as well as the quality of mother–infant interactions. Well-supported mothers are less restrictive and punitive with their infants than are less well-supported mothers, and frequency of contacts with significant others improves the quality of parent–infant relationships as well as parents' sense of their own effectance and competence.

Marital problems affect more than just the individual's own relationship; they can also compromise a person's ability to be a good parent. For example, parents in unhappy marriages can become preoccupied with their marital problems leading them to detach emotionally from their children and become less engaged in their upbringing. Due to this preoccupation, parents may act overly lax and permissive, engendering a sense of rejection in children. Mothers and fathers who are dissatisfied with their marriages are more likely to exhibit authoritarian parenting styles. Also, parents who are depressed are more prone to have marital problems, and as a result, are less likely to be authoritative. The negative consequences of parental stress influence a parents' well-being in addition to the well-being of a marriage and the parent–child relationship.

Divorce changes a family dynamic in many ways including effects on parenting styles. Studies show that divorced parents are similar in parenting style based on their SES and level of education. For example, a divorced mother or father is more likely to be authoritative if she or he has higher levels of education and is middle-class. In many families of divorce, a child usually resides with only one parent. Having a noncustodial father can be difficult for children. However, research shows that the amount of time noncustodial fathers spend with their children is generally unrelated to child adjustment. Instead, the important factor is the quality of the father–child relationship. Having a close relationship with an authoritative nonresident father leads to better outcomes for the child than having a distant relationship with a nonauthoritative nonresident father. For example, children who have a close relationship with a nonresidential authoritative father have greater academic success and exhibit fewer externalizing and internalizing behaviors. However, having a father who is intermittently involved or infrequently visits the child can lead to a different type of father–child relationship. These fathers are often more permissive and take on a role as a recreational companion instead of that of teacher or disciplinarian.

Parental Depression

Parental depression not only has detrimental effects on the parent's own mental health but often negatively affects parenting as well. Depressed mothers demonstrate a style of interaction marked by intrusiveness, anger, irritation, and rough handling of their infants. Infants tend to respond to this style of parenting with gaze aversion and avoidance. Such feelings surely diminish responsiveness or discoordinate interactions, and so depressed parenting may have short- as well as long-term consequences for infants.

Mothers with depression are more likely to exhibit authoritarian or indifferent parenting styles. Depressed mothers display limited amounts of nurturing and are less responsive to their child's needs. Instead, depressed mothers tend to exhibit anger, retaliation, and ineffectively deal with problems. Often, parenting of depressed mothers is characterized by high levels of control, hostility, and punishment. Depressed parents often alternate coercive parenting tactics with lax attitudes sometimes to the point of indifference, anxiety, and guilt-induction. This inconsistent array of parenting behaviors can be confusing and difficult for a child to process.

Depression is often characterized by increased negative social cognitions and negative attributions. For example, depressed mothers tend to say critical and unsupportive things to their children, and are more likely to admit to feeling disappointed in them. Research indicates that mothers with depression have an increased likelihood to label their preschool aged children's problem behavior as internal and stable characteristics particular to the child instead of normative developmental issues for children of a given age. Depressed mothers are likely to endorse statements such as: "It's my fault; I am responsible for all bad things that happen, it will always be that way." Some research suggests that depressed parents' negative attributions about their children's behavior are associated with harsh parenting practices which potentially result in the development of psychological problems for the children.

Through various socialization mechanisms, children's mental health can be compromised by exposure to a depressed parent's negative behavior and cognitions. Over the course of time, symptoms of depression, such as negative affect, self-criticism, and negative attributional style may develop in the child. Having a depressed parent can lead to problems in children's cognitive, social, and emotional development. One possible reason for the child's developmental problems is that depressed parents inadequately model social skills and productive coping strategies.

Effects of Parenting Styles/Behaviors on Infants and Children

Each parenting style has a more or less unique set of effects on a child's development. Research indicates, however, that the effects of parenting styles on child outcomes are not always consistent. The effect of parents on children cannot be examined in isolation; instead, it is important to recognize the influences of factors such as culture, neighborhood, and SES have on parenting behaviors and childrearing. One issue that has become a major focus of parenting styles research is whether the positive effects of authoritative parenting are universal and transcend the boundaries of ethnicity, SES, and household composition. With some exceptions, the majority of research indicates that authoritative parenting leads to favorable child outcomes. This strong connection has been replicated in numerous studies taking into consideration factors such as geographical location, social stratum, and family structure. However, as previously discussed, more recent culturally sensitive research has shown that parenting styles may have different meanings in different cultures and the same definitions of parenting styles may not hold true in different cultures. We now turn to elaborate on the typical child outcomes associated with each parenting style.

Effects of Authoritative Parenting Style

Experts contend that rearing a child in an authoritative home leads to favorable outcomes for European American children. Authoritative parents tend to rear children who are socially responsible, competent, self-assured, adaptive, creative, curious, independent, assertive, successful in school, friendly, cooperative with peers and parents, and generally happy. Furthermore, the authoritative parenting style leads to the development of mature moral reasoning, prosocial behavior, and high self-esteem. Children of authoritative parents exhibit low amounts of internalizing behaviors such as depression and anxiety and externalizing behaviors such as antisocial behavior and substance use. Another positive aspect of authoritative parenting is that over time these positive effects on adjustment continue to build.

What about authoritative parenting leads to such positive outcomes for children? First, authoritative parents help the child to develop self-reliance by providing necessary controls that a developing child needs while still granting the child appropriate amounts of autonomy. Children of authoritative parents are better equipped to cope with life stresses and less likely to succumb to peer pressure, due to the competencies authoritative parents have instilled. Second, the reciprocal give-and-take dialog between authoritative parents and their children helps to promote intellectual development which is integral to the child gaining competence. In addition, reciprocal dialog fosters the development of social and cognitive skills that help children function successfully in environments outside the home. Another important aspect of authoritative families is that they incorporate the opinions of both children and parents during family discussions. Authoritative parents explain decisions, rules, or expectations they have to the child, enhancing the child's understanding of social systems and social relationships. Furthermore, this knowledge facilitates development of the child's reasoning skills, moral judgment, and empathy. Also, the warmth, nurturance, and parental involvement authoritative parents provide create an environment in which a child identifies with and even admires the parents. This strong bond can render children more open to parental influence because they look up to the parents and respect their opinions. Additionally, as a result of sharing a warm and close mutually respectful relationship with their family, children tend to endorse similar attitudes and values to their parents. This has positive effects on socialization and friendship formation for the child. For example, children of authoritative parents tend to form bonds with others who have attitudes and values similar to those endorsed by their parents. Therefore, children of authoritative parents are more likely to have friends their parents approve of and are less likely to be involved in antisocial behavior compared to children reared in nonauthoritative homes.

Authoritative parenting has proved to be the most advantageous for European American children's academic achievement. More specifically, European American children reared in authoritative homes perform better in school, attend classes more regularly, are more engaged in the classroom, have higher expectations, and profess more positive academic self-concepts. Authoritative parents are successful at helping to improve their children's academic performance even if children initially struggle academically.

One reason authoritative parenting benefits academic achievement is that authoritative parents emphasize a healthy achievement orientation and intrinsic motivation toward learning. Children who learn because of intrinsic motivation gain pleasure from learning and mastering new material and concepts rather than being motivated by external rewards or punishment. Moreover, authoritative parents promote the development of the child's work ethic by being less controlling and having more positive thoughts regarding the child's academic achievement. Authoritative parents are often more engaged in their child's other activities and have a better grasp of what goes on in their child's life outside the family. Additionally, some common traits of authoritative parents also may affect a child's achievement. For example, authoritative parents tend to be of higher SES, which alone correlates with higher achievement. Furthermore, they are likely to promote educational activities in the home environment, have higher academic achievement themselves, and tend to be brought up in families where their parents had higher levels of income and education than nonauthoritative parents.

One can easily understand too why the reciprocal relations characteristic of authoritative parenting is ideal for a child's transition across life's stages. Gradual changes in family structure that are appropriate to the child's developmental transitions give youngsters more age-appropriate independence and autonomy. Furthermore, later adjustments are smoother for an authoritative family because change is gradual and adapted to the child's developmental needs throughout the child's life.

Additionally, the child's own behavior may be a factor in fostering authoritative parenting styles. Children who exhibit favorable characteristics such as being responsible, confident, independent, curious, and open to sharing details of their life with parents will in turn draw out favorable responses from parents such as warm and authoritative parenting. For their part, children who exhibit less favorable characteristics such as aggression, dependence, or immaturity will tend to elicit more negative responses from their parents such as harsh or indifferent treatment. A reciprocal cycle is in motion in which an agreeable and mature child naturally elicits more authoritative parenting which results in the development of greater maturity and other positive qualities in the child.

Effects of the Authoritarian Parenting Style

The effects of authoritarian parenting are less positive than an authoritative upbringing for European American youth. Children reared by authoritarian families tend to depend on their parents (especially girls), be more submissive, less socially adept, less confident, less intellectually curious, and less committed to achievement in comparison with children reared in authoritative homes. Furthermore, children reared by authoritarian parents often exhibit hostility and shyness toward peers and show higher levels of aggression. One positive effect of authoritarian parenting is that children often score reasonably well on school achievement and low on deviance measures.

Later life transitions are often more difficult for children from authoritarian families whose parents interpret their child's growing need for independence and autonomy as disobedient and disrespectful. As a result of having punitive and cold parents, children may rebel against their parents' standards explicitly trying to exert greater autonomy and individuality. This rebellion does not indicate genuine emotional autonomy but instead attempts to express aggravation with authoritarian parents' strictness, control, and lack of understanding.

Additionally, it is important to note that there can be advantages of authoritarian parenting styles in some cultural and socioeconomic contexts. For example, authoritarian parenting can play an adaptive and protective role for children growing up in low-income and unsafe neighborhoods, as more restrictive parenting can keep children safe and away from harm. Also, in African American families, authoritarian parenting characteristics such as firm control and discipline (so called 'no nonsense parenting') are not perceived negatively, instead they are seen as signs of love, concern, and affection from caregivers. Advantages to authoritarian parenting are also seen in Asian American families. For example, strict control is thought of as a reflection of a parent's dedication and concern for children and leads to traditionally desirable traits for children such as self-control, diligence, and self-confidence.

Effects of the Permissive Parenting Style

The developmental outcomes for children reared in permissive homes are also more negative compared to those reared in authoritative homes for European American youth. These effects are somewhat universal and similarly affect children from various socioeconomic backgrounds and cultures. Children of permissive parents generally experience less academic success and have higher levels of drug and alcohol use. Children of permissive parents display a number of similar traits to children reared by authoritarian parents, for example, lack of assertiveness, greater dependency on parents, and lower levels of self-control. Despite the appearance that permissive and authoritarian parenting styles are opposites to each other, in actuality they share the common bond of minimizing opportunities for children to learn to cope with stress effectively. Authoritarian parents accomplish this by limiting autonomous decisions made by their child. Permissive parents do this by failing to implement standards for appropriate behavior, thereby granting their

children freedom to behave in any manner they please. Consequently, children of permissive parents tend to be limited in their capacity to deal with difficult circumstances and may be unprepared to cope successfully with problems that arise normally in life.

Additionally, children reared in permissive families are often immature, fail to control their impulses, and lack self-reliance. Studies show that parental permissiveness, indulgence, and lax supervision are associated with aggression in children. Such permissive behavior and attitudes on the part of parents could in fact legitimize the child's aggressive behavior. As a result, aggressive children may continue to act out if their behavior seems to be accepted by their parents. Furthermore, high levels of parental punitiveness can further exacerbate externalizing problems and render a child more prone to aggression.

A child from a permissive home reared in an environment lacking rules and guidelines may consequently find it difficult to adjust to societal rules during adulthood. With the lack of guidance from parents, children reared in permissive homes tend to rely on their peers (instead of parents) for guidance and emotional support. This is potentially problematic because the people they are turning to for advice and support are usually just as naive as the child seeking the advice. Without adequate guidance, children from permissive homes often become distanced from parents, and in turn become emotionally and psychologically dependent on peers. Children from permissive families are increasingly likely to be influenced by peer pressure. Additionally, children reared in permissive homes are more likely to bully classmates. This phenomenon is most likely due to the fact that permissive parents fail to discourage their children from expressing negative and disrespectful behavior.

The effects of permissive parenting tend to be stronger for boys than for girls. Some think that the increased impact on sons is due to society's tendency to place fewer limits on boys' behavior. Furthermore, boys who are highly impulsive and aggressive may wear out their parents and make their parents' disciplinary efforts seem futile leading them to take a more lax and permissive approach to parenting.

Effects of the Indifferent Parenting Style

A consistent finding is that indifferent parenting has the most detrimental long-term outcomes on children especially in the case of neglect and abuse. Research shows that by the age of 2 years, children of indifferent mothers already show clear signs of problematic attachment relationships and overall deficiencies in psychological, cognitive, and social development. Children reared by indifferent parents tend to be immature, irresponsible, impulsive, ineffective leaders, and also susceptible to peer pressure. Furthermore, they are more prone to exhibit internalizing and externalizing problems, and additionally may have sex and use alcohol and drugs at younger ages. Additionally, these children have difficulty achieving academically and fail to demonstrate social responsibility and social assertiveness. Indifferent parents do not provide children with adequate guidance; consequently, children fail to acquire knowledge about appropriate ways to behave. The detrimental effects of indifferent parenting continue to accumulate throughout life and are evident all the way through young adulthood. For example, young adults from indifferent families are more likely to be hedonistic, lack tolerance to frustration, and poorly control their emotions. Additionally, these young adults lack long-term goals, drink excessively, and are more likely to have criminal records. Other factors that could lead to indifferent parenting include poverty, mental illness, unemployment, marital distress, or other such factors causing parents to be too overwhelmed to be invested in parenting.

Parents in the Same Family Who Differ in Parenting Style

In some families, the two parents may differ in their approach and attitudes toward parenting. What effect do two differing parenting styles have on the child's development? Having parents with the same parenting style matters only in the case that the type of parenting exhibited is authoritative. If parents agree on the same style but are authoritarian, permissive, or indifferent, the child's developmental outcomes tend to be less positive than they would be if at least one parent favors an authoritative style. Part of the problem of having parents differ in parenting style is that it leads to difficulty in coordination and cooperation in the childrearing process. For example, one parent could actively undermine and disparage the other parent. Also, one parent could become overly involved in the child's life causing the other parent to withdraw and feel disconnected from the child. All of these conditions can engender disharmony and stress in a child's life potentially leading to developmental problems. In contrast, if both parents display authoritative parenting styles, cooperation, and warmth, child outcomes are generally more positive and children show more prosocial behavior and peer competence.

Summary

Authoritative, authoritarian, permissive, and indifferent parenting styles have varying effects on child development. The majority of research indicates that authoritative parenting leads to the most beneficial child outcomes for European Americans. In addition, an abundance of culturally sensitive research shows that parenting practices and behaviors carry different meanings in different cultures. Therefore, care must be exercised in drawing implications of different parenting styles based on narrow typological definitions. Parenting style research continues to expand as researchers study more in depth parenting styles, differing effects on gender, and different cultural, economical, and geographical contexts.

Acknowledgments

Preparation for this article was supported by the Intramural Research Program of the NIH, NICHD.

See also: Attachment; Discipline and Compliance; Family Influences; Marital Relationship; Postpartum Depression, Effects on Infant; Routines; Safety and Childproofing; Social Interaction; Temperament.

Suggested Readings

Baumrind D (1978) Parental disciplinary patterns and social competence in children. *Youth and Society* 9: 239–276.
Baumrind D (1991) The influence of parenting style on adolescent competence and substance use. *Journal of Early Adolescence* 11(1): 56–95.
Bornstein MH (2002) *Handbook of Parenting,* 2nd edn., vol. 1–5. Mahwah, NJ: Lawrence Erlbaum Associates, Inc.
Darling N and Steinberg L (1993) Parenting style as context: An integrative model. *Psychological Bulletin* 113(3): 487–496.
Maccoby EE and Martin JA (1983) Socialization in the context of the family: Parent–child interaction. In: Mussen PH (ed.) and Hetherington EM (vol. ed.) *Handbook of Child Psychology: Vol. 4. Socialization, Personality, and Social Development,* 4th edn., pp. 1–101. New York: Wiley.

Relevant Websites

http://www.cfr.nichd.nih.gov – Child and Family Research.
http://www.parentingscienceandpractice.com – Parenting: Science and Practice.

Perception and Action

B I Bertenthal, Indiana University, Bloomington, IN, USA

Glossary

Action system – Functionally organized action requiring continuous and dynamic perceptual modulation of the many factors (i.e., inertia of limbs, posture, direction, and distance of target) necessary for executing a response.

Affordance – Perceptual information about an object or surface specifying a possibility for action. This information is only perceived if the action is within the motor repertoire of the actor.

Coordination and control – Coordination involves organizing the multiple parts of a goal-directed action into proper relation with one another. For humans, coordination is a formidable task that involves almost 800 muscles that act to generate and dissipate energy at approximately 100 joints. Control involves tuning the specific parameters of a movement (e.g., displacement, amplitude, and speed of limb movements) to the local conditions in order to optimize coordination.

Embodied knowledge – Pragmatic or sensory–motor knowledge about the physical or social world that enables a spatially coordinated action even when the goal is not conscious or continuously visible. This knowledge can be contrasted with symbolic knowledge that involves a representation of the world that can be mentally transformed and linguistically coded.

Haptic perception – An active tactile process (pertaining to touch) that involves both sensory and motor systems to identify an object. In the human hand, tactile information is provided by the receptors in the skin, the muscles, and the joints. For example, if we hold a cube, we perceive it through the skin of our fingers and the position of our fingers.

Mirror neurons – These neurons are located in the ventral premotor cortex of the monkey's brain and discharge when the monkey performs a goal-directed action, as well as when the monkey observes a conspecific or human experimenter perform the same action.

Perceptuomotor scaling – The timing and force of motor responses are modulated by the relevant perceptual information. Each response is different (e.g., crawling vs. walking) and necessitates a different scaling between the perceptual information and the response synergies (i.e., interactions between the components of the response, such as muscles, limbs, joints, etc.).

Predictive tracking and reaching – Pursuing a moving target that disappears behind another object or surface and anticipating its reappearance based on the spatiotemporal information specifying the movement of the target prior to its disappearance.

Proprioception – The sense of position and movement of the limbs that is derived from sensory receptors in the joints, tendons, and muscles. This information is used to specify the orientation of the body in space and the direction, extent, and rate of movement of the limbs.

Simulation – Representing an observed action performed by someone else by covertly activating the same action in one's motor system.

Introduction

Traditional research on motor development focused primarily on how movements were generated by 'motor programs' in the central nervous system. The Russian physiologist, Nikolai Aleksandroich Bernstein (1896–1966) was one of the first to recognize that spatially coordinated behaviors involved more than simply programming muscular responses, because other factors such as inertia of the limbs, reactive forces from the support surface, and initial postural conditions always combine with active muscle forces in producing complex chains of multisegment movements. All of these factors, or degrees of freedom, necessitate that active muscle forces are modulated by a combination of different sources of perceptual information specifying the self and the environment to ensure a functionally organized and goal-directed response.

As actions continue to change over time so will the modulation of the perceptual information. In essence, perception and action form a continuous loop in which, according to James Gibson (1904–79), "we must perceive in order to move, but we must also move in order to perceive." All spatially and temporally coordinated behaviors require the coupling of perception and action. For example, reaching for an object is guided by perceptual information specifying the relation between the self and the environment which changes as the reach progresses.

These perceptual changes produce adjustments to hand and arm movements to insure that a reach is successful, which, in turn, modify the perceived relation between the reach and the target. Similarly, perceptual information is necessary to maintain a balanced posture during the reach, but again the perceptual information changes as the posture is adjusted to that information.

This cycle of perceptual changes and motor responses is dynamic and continuous. Neither perception nor action alone is sufficient to simultaneously maintain postural stability and perform goal-directed actions. Moreover, each time the same action is performed (e.g., reaching for a glass), the initial conditions between the actor and the goal (e.g., distance and size of the glass, posture, inertia of the limbs) will differ requiring variations in the movements and the response.

In view of these many factors that must simultaneously contribute to the execution of a goal-directed action, it would be misleading to conceptualize perception and action as independent processes. Instead, it is much more parsimonious to view these processes as opposite poles of a functional unit or action system. The earliest developing action systems will be those related to supporting biologically adaptive functions, such as orientation, exploration, locomotion, manipulation, and communication.

Origins of Perception–Action Coupling

When are perception and action first coupled? Until recently, the answer to this question was dominated by Jean Piaget's (1896–1980) view of sensorimotor development. He proposed that perceptions and actions are initially independent but become gradually coordinated with experience. The implication is that the behavior of the neonate is essentially reactive and not sensitive to contextual information. More recent findings from studying infants reveal a very different picture of the early behavioral organization of the young infant.

Perceptuomotor Behavior of Neonates

Newborn infants are capable of performing a number of actions that are regulated by perceptual information. For example, they turn their eyes in the direction of a sound, visually scan differently in the light and the dark and concentrate their fixations near high contrast edges, visually track moving targets, increase the frequency of hand-to-mouth contact following oral delivery of a sucrose solution, and show hand extensions toward a visible target. Until the availability of more sensitive instruments for measuring neonatal responses, these behaviors were often overlooked because they are quite fragile and inconsistent. For example, one reason that neonates show difficulty in tracking moving targets is that their heads are not yet independent of their trunks which are quite unstable and subject to intermittent movements.

It thus appears that newborns enter the world prepared to perceptually control some actions, especially those that are essential to their survival and adaptation. This preparation is a function of both the intrinsic organization of the brain, as well as behaviors that are practiced in the uterus. For example, the proprioceptive guidance of the hand to the mouth is established in utero by the beginning of the second trimester of pregnancy, and is readily observed in neonates. Furthermore, the mouth is more likely to remain open during arm movements when the hand goes directly to the mouth than when it first touches other portions of the face. The opportunity to practice this behavior in the uterus no doubt contributes to the degree of specificity that is present in its control at birth.

Some behaviors may not be practiced *in utero*, but nevertheless show a rudimentary perceptuomotor coupling from birth that is necessary for their functioning. Indeed, newborns are intrinsically biased to move their arms in such a way that their hands remain in the field of view. While lying supine with arms pulled down by small weights, newborns will resist this force on the side of the body to which their head is turned (see **Figure 1**). Interestingly, the resulting posture is consistent with a neonatal reflex, known as the tonic neck reflex, and is similar to the posture assumed by a person fencing. This behavior is not, however, simply a function of a reflex, because infants viewing a video monitor localized on one side but displaying the opposite hand, resist the weight with the hand opposite to the direction in which they are looking. Moreover, newborns viewing their hand in a dark room keep it positioned within a narrow beam of light and move their hand when the beam moves. This behavior is extremely adaptive because it biases infants to visually explore information that can be gathered by one of the principal information acquisition devices available from birth – the hands. In sum, infants are born prepared to coordinate their movements with perceptual information, especially when the coupling will benefit their acquisition of new information about themselves and their environment.

Even though some actions are spatially coordinated from birth, this coordinative pattern represents only a skeletal structure that will continue to develop for a long time to come. The development of perception–action systems involves a confluence of factors that include neural and biomechanical changes, as well as task and environmental factors. As infants continue to practice performing these actions, they will develop improved coordination and control. In the case of sucking, these changes take place very quickly. Within a few days after birth, the sucking system functions with considerable precision to optimize the intake of nutrients. Neonates learn very quickly to

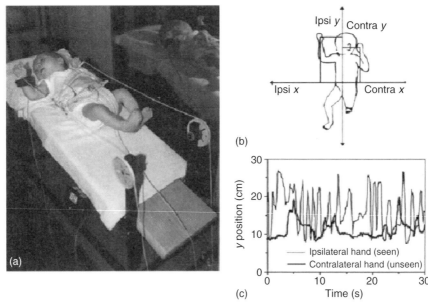

Figure 1   (a) An 18-day-old baby participating in the experiment. (b) Schematic representation of how the hands were measured in terms of x and y coordinates. (c) A typical time series showing the changing y-axis location of both arms waving without weights attached. Reprinted with permission from van der Meer ALH, van der Weel FR, and Lee DN (1995) The functional significance of arm movements in neonates. *Science* 267: 693–695. Copyright (1995) AAAS.

adjust the change in sucking pressure to the flow of milk that changes from suck to suck. They can also learn to modify their sucking in an experimental situation that provides them with access to their mother's voice. By 5 weeks of age, infants can use sucking as a means to bring a picture into focus. These latter two examples show that even early action systems are not limited to specific biological functions and that they can be used as a means to an arbitrary goal, such as listening to the mother's voice, as well as serving to fulfill an intrinsic goal, such as gaining nutrients.

Adaptation to Changes in Brain and Body

Although practice and experience are certainly necessary for the development of these action systems, they are not sufficient because the developing infant is also changing in body size and strength and the brain is developing as well. For example, the optical components of the eye are still growing at birth, the photoreceptors will continue to mature and migrate toward the center of the retina (i.e., fovea) during the first few months, and the synaptic connections between neurons of the central visual pathways in the brain will continue to develop for some time. These changes will improve the resolution of the visual image, which will contribute to improvements in the accommodation and convergence of the eye, as well as greater acuity for perceiving visual patterns. Likewise, the perception of relative depths and distances in the spatial layout will become more precise with the neural development of the visual system.

A more specific example of how the incompletely developed visual system constrains the functioning of an action system involves the saccadic localization of visual targets. When young infants detect a visual target flashing or moving in the peripheral portion of their visual field, they will move their eyes to center their gaze on the target. This movement involves a direct mapping between the retinal location of the target and the neuromuscular stimulation of the appropriate eye muscles, which changes as a function of the distance of the eyes from the visual stimulation. This mapping is present from birth, yet the localization process is imprecise and involves multiple saccades (rapid eye movements that jump from one location to another) before the target is foveated. It is not until 4 months of age that localization is accomplished with a single saccade. One factor contributing to this development is learning the precise relation between the neural pulse duration innervating eye muscles and the saccade magnitude necessary for rotating the eye to the correct position. Nevertheless, it is surprising that the calibration process takes over 4 months to complete, especially since it is estimated that infants make between 3 and 6 million eye movements by 3.5 months of age. It has been hypothesized that the reason for this lengthy process is that the mapping of retinal locus onto an oculomotor command is constrained by the changing distribution of photoreceptors on the retina. This situation makes it necessary for the infant to adapt continually to this changing sensorimotor relation during early development.

Although some action systems are present at birth, it is clear that many others will develop in the months and years to come, and all of them will become better tuned and coordinated as a function of both neural development and experience. In the remainder of this article, we will discuss some of the organizing principles by which this development occurs with illustrative examples from the different action systems that play a pivotal role in early development.

Principles of Perception and Action

Reciprocity between Perception and Action

Sensitivity to surfaces and objects

Perceptual control of behavior depends on the detection of the relevant perceptual information, as well as the coordination of responses necessary for the action system. As simple actions, such as pursuit tracking of moving targets, saccadic localization, or hand–mouth coordination are practiced and repeated, they become better controlled and coordinated, which demands that the necessary perceptual information is detected with increasing specificity. An excellent example of this mutual reciprocity between perception and action is revealed by research on the minimum audible angle necessary for detection of a change in sound-source location. In this task infants are expected to turn their heads to the right or left of midline if they are capable of localizing the sound. The minimum detectable difference decreases rapidly between 8 and 24 weeks of age and then continues to decrease more gradually through 80 weeks of age. It is noteworthy that the most rapid improvement occurs during and just following the time that infants are developing independent control of their heads and torso. Until they develop enough control to stabilize their heads, it is not possible for them to localize a sound source with sufficient resolution to differentiate sounds that are close together.

Another compelling example of the reciprocity between perception and the improved coordination of actions involves haptic perception. Adults detect many different properties of objects, such as size, texture, weight, hardness, and temperature, from haptic explorations. In the case of a blind individual, touch would serve as the principal means for learning about the material properties of objects. Some of these properties, such as size and temperature, demand minimal control of the hand and fingers, whereas other properties, such as weight and shape, require much greater control. Intriguingly, the ages at which infants first discriminate different object properties correspond to the developmental changes in the control of the hand and fingers. For example, infants discriminate size within the first few months, but texture, temperature, and hardness which involve tactile exploration are not detected until around 6 months of age, and weight and shape which involve grasping and lifting are not detected until even later.

In the preceding two examples, motor development facilitated the perceptual sensitivity of infants to the properties of surfaces and objects over time. There are two other sources of perceptual information that are involved in the development of actions. One source is proprioceptive and it involves the positions, orientations, and movements of body segments relative to each other. The final source is the perceived relation between self and environment and it involves the position, orientation, and movement of the whole or a part of the body relative to the environment. Let's consider how motor experience contributes to these two latter sources of perceptual information.

Sensitivity to movements of the body

The development of self-produced locomotion on hands-and-knees involves a rather protracted period of development. Most infants begin to crawl with their abdomens on the ground by around 7 months of age. During this initial period of crawling, infants show considerable variability in their locomotor strategies and explore many different patterns of interlimb coordination, including pulling themselves with only their hands, or lurching forward by pushing up with their legs, or moving one limb at a time, or even moving all four limbs at the same time. The support of their abdomens on the ground enables infants to engage in any interlimb pattern of movement without risk of losing balance or falling. During this period of development, they are able to explore a wide variety of different interlimb patterns for locomoting.

Once infants develop sufficient strength to support themselves on hands-and-knees, they quickly converge on an interlimb pattern of moving diagonally opposite limbs (e.g., left arm and right leg) simultaneously and 180° out of phase with the other pair of limbs. The selection of this specific pattern is a function of perceiving the optimal coordinative structure to ensure balance while minimizing the expenditure of energy. These are intrinsic goals that drive the infant to select the optimal locomotor gait pattern from among the many variations that were previously explored. This process by which behaviors go through a period of considerable variation before a stable new organization develops is repeated often in development, and is especially common in the development of motor skills, such as stepping, sitting, and standing.

Sensitivity to the relation between self and environment

The last source of perceptual information is concerned with the relation between the body and the environment. Does the development of self-produced locomotion contribute to infants' sensitivity to this source of information? This question has been addressed by investigating whether prelocomotor and locomotor infants are differentially sensitive to whether a surface is traversible. Although some surfaces are more easily traversed than others, for example, a roadway vs. a narrow footpath along a mountainside, most afford some form of locomotion. One dramatic exception is a surface that ends abruptly at a precipice or cliff.

This type of surface has been simulated in the lab with a 'visual cliff', which consists of a large sheet of plexiglass suspended 4 ft above the floor (see **Figure 2**). A narrow board is placed across the middle, dividing the plexiglass into two sides. On one side (referred to as the shallow side), a textured checkerboard pattern is placed directly under the glass, so that it appears as a rigid and supportable surface. On the other side (referred to as the deep side), the checkerboard pattern is placed 4 ft below the glass, so that this side simulates an apparent drop-off. In most studies, infants are placed on the centerboard and encouraged to cross to the mother who alternates standing across from the deep and shallow sides of the cliff. The question of interest is whether infants will be less likely to crawl across the deep side than the shallow side of this apparatus.

The visual cliff was designed originally to test depth perception, but more recent research suggests that infants are sensitive to depth information prior to the age when they begin crawling. If avoidance of the deep side of the cliff was specifically a function of depth perception, then all infants should avoid the deep side from the earliest age at which they could be tested. This is not what is observed, however. Infants' avoidance of the deep side is related to their crawling experience – infants who have been crawling for 6 weeks are much more likely to avoid the deep side of the visual cliff than infants who have been crawling for only 2 weeks. Converging evidence come from studies measuring infants' heart rate as they are lowered toward the deep or shallow sides of the visual cliff. Prelocomotor infants show heart rate deceleration (indexing interest and attention) to the depth information as they are lowered onto the deep side of the cliff. By contrast, locomotor infants with a few weeks of crawling experience show heart rate acceleration (indexing wariness or fear).

Why is perceptual information about the traversibility of surfaces interpreted differently by locomotor and prelocomotor infants? The answer is that the information specifying the apparent drop-off is only perceived as something to avoid when it is relevant to controlling the action of locomotion. If infants are not yet able to locomote, then this perceptual information can still be perceived, but it will not be perceived as a danger because this appraisal is specifically related to locomoting beyond the apparent drop-off. In essence, the visual cliff surface represents an 'affordance', or a possibility for action. This affordance is only perceived if the action is available to the infant. Thus, the perception of affordances and the motor status of the infant are intimately related.

Infants learn to perceive affordances for locomotion from their everyday crawling and walking experience. As infants acquire more experience with crawling, they become more accurate in perceiving whether or not these surfaces afford traversibility. For example, infants become more accurate with experience in choosing which sloping surfaces can or cannot be descended. Moreover, their perception of the traversibility of surfaces changes when the possibility for locomotion is manipulated by loading them with weights or extending their leg length with platform shoes. Similarly, varying the slant, friction, or rigidity of the support surface, etc., also alters the perceived possibilities for locomotion.

The preceding perceptual judgments are all scaled to the motor capabilities of infants. This is an important point to emphasize because it implies that the learning of specific perceptuomotor skills cannot be generalized. The perceptual learning that accrues during the period of crawling is not transferred to upright locomotion. At the onset of walking, infants who avoid steep slopes when crawling show no hesitation in attempting to walk down these same slopes. Perceptual learning of affordances is highly specific and the mapping between vision and posture that emerges with the development of crawling will require a new mapping with the development of walking. This lack of transfer is not surprising given that each new form of locomotion involves a different set of response

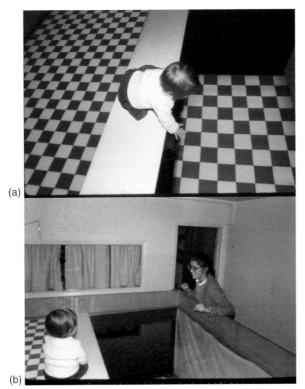

Figure 2 A photograph of the visual cliff with the baby sitting on the centerboard. (a) Baby is looking down at the edge of the apparent drop off; (b) baby is looking across the deep side of the cliff at the mother.

synergies that need to be coordinated and controlled by the perceptual information.

In sum, the development of perception and action is reciprocal. Improvements in the tuning of perceptual sensitivities enable finer control of motor responses. Likewise, changes in body size and shape, strength, postural control, and coordination of multiple body parts enable perceptual experiences that were heretofore unnecessary or unavailable. These changes in perception and action are cyclic and repetitive, and enable infants to continually improve their fit between their own action capabilities and the perception of their bodies and the affordances in the environment.

Planning and Prospective Control

Significance of future-directed information

Our actions, like those of all animals, must be coordinated with the physical and social environment, and this coordination demands perceptual guidance and control. In walking along an unpaved, narrow path, for example, we select which surfaces to contact and which to avoid. Likewise, when reaching for a fork, we guide our hand to select this utensil and simultaneously avoid or inhibit our hand from reaching for the spoon or knife. These actions are accomplished in real time and their control requires more than feedback following their execution. It is only possible to modify a movement that has not yet been executed, which is why it is necessary to predict what will happen next and prospectively control the action. Information needed for the specification of upcoming events is available from the spatial and temporal changes in the optic and acoustic arrays. As adults, we readily appreciate the spatial and temporal components in the control of actions. For example, we know that it is necessary to be in the right place at the right time to catch a ball, meet a person, or give a lecture. Likewise, infants show considerable sensitivity to the spatiotemporal coordination necessary for the control of actions.

Unlike neonatal reflexes that are automatically triggered by specific stimuli (e.g., Moro reflex – extensions of arms and legs with loss of support), actions are goal directed and they often involve multiple body parts that are hierarchically organized into a single system. For example, the eyes, head, and trunk must be coordinated when tracking a moving target that continues beyond the immediate field of view. Thus, actions must be scaled to the spatial and temporal changes in our body, as well as in the external world. Even a simple reach for an object requires the ability to predict what will happen next to the moving limb, as well as to the object that is to be grasped. Prospective control involves implicit knowledge of the body schema, as well as knowledge of the spatiotemporal regularities that govern physical and social events in the external world.

Smooth visual pursuit tracking

What sorts of prospective information are available to infants and how is this information used for controlling their behavior? One of the earliest examples of prospective behavior involves the smooth visual pursuit of moving targets. In order to track an object smoothly it is necessary to anticipate its future position from its past history of movement, because the motor commands for moving the eyes in response to the movements of the target are not instantaneous but delayed by the inertia of the eye, as well as the rate of neural transmission. Smooth pursuit is present from birth, but it is intermittent and limited to large targets. As the eyes begin to trail the target, infants' eye movements become jerky because they are forced to execute corrective saccades (rapid eye movements from one fixation to the next). Beginning around 6 weeks of age, smooth pursuit improves rapidly and attains adult levels by 14 weeks of age for targets that move smoothly and gradually slow down before reversing directions. By 20 weeks of age, infants successfully track targets that cycle back and forth and abruptly change direction.

This evidence for early pursuit tracking is even more remarkable when one considers that it often requires the coordination between head movements and eye movements. Some head movements are unrelated to fixation, and both visual and vestibular mechanisms are involved in compensating for these movements to some extent from birth. Between 3 and 5 months of age, head movements increase in response to a moving target, but for quite some time lag behind the target because of the greater inertia associated with the head. In order to stabilize gaze on the target, the eyes must lead the target to counteract the delayed head tracking. Thus, smooth pursuit involves the coordination of eye tracking and head tracking which continues to improve as infants develop better control of their heads and greater sensitivity to target velocity.

Reaching for stationary and moving objects

A similar pattern of jerky and inconsistent movements accompanies the initial development of reaching which begins sometime between 12 and 18 weeks of age. When adults reach for a stationary object, they execute a single movement unit characterized by the arm initially speeding up and then slowing down as it approaches the target. The trajectory of the arm movement is smooth and precise requiring only a slight adjustment at the end to grasp the object. By contrast, infants initially execute multiple movement units as their reaching arm gradually approaches the object; each movement unit brings the hand closer to the object, but the reach takes longer and is more circuitous. Over the next few months, the reach becomes better scaled to the distance and location of the object reflecting the development of an ensemble of factors including neuromuscular mechanisms, the control of posture, improved distance perception, and a more precise mapping between perceptual information and the motor responses necessary for executing the reach.

At approximately the same age that infants begin reaching for stationary objects, they begin catching objects attached to a moving rod. By 4.5 months of age, infants can catch an object moving at $30\,\mathrm{cm\,s^{-1}}$, and by 8 months infants can catch objects moving at $125\,\mathrm{cm\,s^{-1}}$. Successful catching requires that the infant predict the future location of a moving object and program arm and hand movements to arrive at that location just prior to the arrival by the object. Infants typically reach for a stationary object with their ipsilateral hand (corresponding to the same side of the body midline as the object), but they will often switch to their contralateral hand when catching an object oscillating back and forth in front of them. The choice of the contralateral hand insures more time to execute the arm and hand movement before the arrival of the object, and thus represents additional evidence of prospective control by infants.

Predictive tracking of briefly occluded moving objects

One of the critical skills necessary for predictive tracking and reaching is the prediction of the future location of a moving target. If a moving target is briefly occluded, it is necessary for the observer to represent the object's trajectory in order for the eyes to anticipate where the target will reappear. Tracking is predictive if, after following a moving target before occlusion, infants shift their gaze to the far side of the occluding surface before it reappears. This visuomotor behavior begins to emerge between 3 and 5 months of age depending on the width of the occluder, the duration of occlusion, and the velocity of the target.

Jean Piaget suggested that predictive tracking is an epiphenomenon of motor persistence – the prediction of the reappearance of the target is a function of failing to stop tracking when the target disappears rather than a function of representing the continuity of the target's trajectory. Recent evidence reveals, however, that motor persistence cannot account for such predictive tracking, as infants rarely track smoothly and continuously once the target disappears. Instead, they tend to stop and fixate on the occluding edge for a brief period of time, and then make one or two saccades to the other side of the occluder. In addition, infants predictively track along circular trajectories by 6 months of age, but this is also inconsistent with a motor persistence explanation which suggests that tracking should follow only a straight line trajectory.

Another possibility is that prediction develops from some form of contingency learning. Infants as young as 2–3 months of age learn to predict sequential alternations of targets appearing in two locations. This same type of learning is probably not sufficient, however, for explaining infants' predictive tracking of a moving target, because the likelihood of this response increases following 2 min of visual experience with an unoccluded object. During this familiarization period, the moving object is always visible so there is no opportunity for learning the contingency that a target disappearing in one location would reappear some time later in another location. Instead, it appears that infants extrapolate from the preceding spatiotemporal information to predict the reappearance of the target. In other words, infants represent the trajectory of the moving target to predict its future location.

One of the most important spatiotemporal properties of objects concerns the way they appear and disappear behind nearer objects. Consider, for example, a typical street scene where pedestrians and vehicles are continuously appearing and disappearing from view as they move, or you, the observer, moves. Adults interpret moving objects that disappear gradually behind an occluding surface as continuing to follow the same trajectory; moving objects that disappear abruptly or implode (shrink rapidly in size) are interpreted as following a discontinuous path. In a recent experiment, 5–9-month-old infants were observed tracking these different events (see **Figure 3**). The results revealed that they were more likely to predictively track a moving object that disappeared naturally (via occlusion) than unnaturally (via abrupt disappearance or implosion) (see **Figure 4**). These results are significant because they show that infants predict the

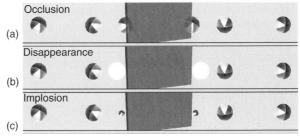

Figure 3 The three horizontal panels depict the location and appearance of the rolling ball at different times during the stimulus event. (a) Occlusion. The ball gradually disappears behind the right side of the occluding surface (located in the center of the display), and then after 2 s reappears from behind the left side of the occluding surface. Note that the shaded portion of the ball is meant to depict its nonvisible portion behind the occluding surface. (b) Instantaneous disappearance. The ball abruptly disappears when it reaches the location of the white circle and abruptly reappears 2 s later at the location of the second white circle on the other side of the occluding surface. (c) Implosion. The rolling ball rapidly decreases in size as it approaches the occluding surface and rapidly increases in size as it reappears 2 s later on the other side of the occluding surface. Note that the ball completes disappearing or begins reappearing at the same exact time that the ball abruptly disappears or reappears in the instantaneous disappearance event. Reproduced from Bertenthal BI, Longo MR, and Kenny S (2007) Phenomenal permanence and the development of predictive tracking. *Child Development* 78: 350–363, with permission from Blackwell Publishing.

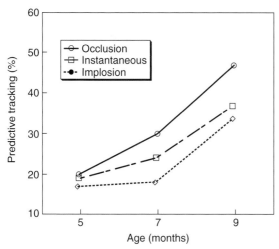

Figure 4 Mean percent tracking as a function of age and stimulus condition (occlusion, instantaneous disappearance, implosion). Reproduced from Bertenthal BI, Longo MR, and Kenny S (2007) Phenomenal permanence and the development of predictive tracking. *Child Development* 78: 350–363, with permission from Blackwell Publishing.

reappearance of objects based not only on their trajectories and the location of the occluding surfaces, but also based on the spatiotemporal changes associated with their disappearance.

Embodied knowledge

Infants do not necessarily represent the identities and spatial locations of moving objects at the same age they represent the trajectories. Even 9-month-old infants sometimes fail to notice a change in the identity (e.g., shape, color) of a moving object following a brief occlusion. (Interestingly, this finding is as true for adults as it is for infants because the same spatiotemporal information specifying the continuity of an object can sometimes obscure a change in its featural identity – a phenomenon known as change blindness.) Likewise, infants around the same age sometimes fail to represent the spatial location of a moving object during a brief occlusion. For example, 9-month-old infants can predictively reach for a briefly occluded moving object. If, however, the object does not reappear, infants search in a variety of locations but do not search behind the occluding screen, suggesting that they do not represent the spatial location of the hidden object at the same time that they represent its trajectory. In sum, infants developing representations of objects emerge piecemeal rather than all at once.

In this section, we have emphasized prospective control of smooth pursuit and visually directed reaching, but there are many other examples of prospective control that develop within the first year. For example, infants learn to posturally compensate for a loss of balance, lean toward objects that are out of reach, anticipate the size, shape, and orientation of objects that they are attempting to grasp, and guide their locomotion around obstacles. It is often suggested that infants become successful across all these tasks as they develop the capacity to represent future events. This interpretation is partially correct, but it is not the whole story.

Knowledge of the future is embodied in the specific actions performed by infants. Prospective control depends upon the developing coordination and control of multiple body parts that are continuing to change in size, shape, flexibility, and strength in conjunction with the perceptual and cognitive information necessary to forecast future events and plan adaptive actions. Thus, future-oriented behaviors emerge piecemeal from specific experiences that infants encounter through their actions. It is the dynamic interplay between actions and goals in specific contexts and tasks that fosters the development of prospective control.

Perception and Action are Context Specific

As previously discussed, actions are a product of a multiplicity of factors including physical, physiological, and energetic components. Different tasks and contexts make different demands on these components, and thus the same action will not necessarily be observed in different contexts. For example, some neurologists report that pre-reaching movements by neonates are much better coordinated when the head is stabilized than when it is unsupported. This finding is especially important because it illustrates how passive support from the environment can interact with the active control and coordination of body movements.

Coordination of leg movements

One of the best examples of context specificity in the control and coordination of actions involves the alternating step-like movements of neonates when held upright with the balls of their feet touching a flat surface. Within a few months, these movements disappear when infants are held upright, but not when infants are lying on their backs or stomachs. These differences can be explained by a simple biomechanical calculation showing that more energy is needed to lift a leg to full flexion while upright than while supine. Although gravity is a constant force in the environment, it only becomes a constraint after the newborn period when infants begin experiencing rapid weight gains that decrease the ratio of muscle to subcutaneous fat in the legs. Experimental manipulations that change the weight of the legs or the resistance of the leg to flexion (e.g., submerging infants in torso-deep water) show that the presence or absence of stepping is systematically related to the interaction between physical strength and leg resistance. These experimental manipulations highlight the importance of context in determining whether or not a specific action will be observed at a particular age.

The development of reaching in different postures is another example of the context specificity of motor control. Coordinated reaching is only possible in the context of a stable body posture that also enables stabilizing the visual target. When infants incapable of sitting without support (22–26 weeks of age) are placed in a fully supported posture (e.g., supine or reclined), they tend to reach for objects with both hands. By contrast, infants capable of sitting without support (28–38 weeks of age) reach with one hand, regardless of body posture. The younger infants reach with only one hand when placed in an unsupported seated position, because they must compensate for a loss of balance by recruiting the other hand to help stabilize their body in this position. In this context, infants shift to a different response because the demands on balance are different, not because they have undergone a change in neural or muscular control.

Scaling perceptual information to motor responses

Another reason for the importance of context specificity is that successful performance requires scaling the changing perceptual information to a specific motor response. The scaling learned in one context does not automatically generalize to new motor responses in the same or different contexts. This lack of generalizability explains why crawling infants who have learned whether or not it is safe to traverse surfaces that are sloped at different angles are unable to transfer this learning a few months later to walking down these same surfaces. As a consequence, infants must relearn whether or not it is safe to traverse these surfaces when walking as opposed to crawling.

This same lack of generalizability is observed with regard to using visual information to control posture. In adults, posture is specified by proprioceptive, vestibular, and visual flow information. It is a goal-directed behavior, even though it is typically not consciously controlled. The goal is to maintain a stable body posture relative to some frame of reference usually specified by gravity and the surface of support. When a perturbation of this position is sensed, a postural compensation is initiated. This perturbation can be specified by one or more sensory inputs, such as visual motion, which is sufficient to induce a postural compensation. When an observer sways forward, visual information radially expands in the optic array, and this expansion typically leads to an automatic postural compensation in the opposite direction. Likewise, swaying backward results in visual information radially contracting and inducing a compensation in the opposite direction.

Some postural compensations are even elicited by neonates. When reclined newborn infants are stimulated by radially expanding patterns of visual information observed on video monitors, they show sensitivity to this information by pushing back with their heads. These compensations are detected by a pressure transducer and are scaled to the speed and direction of the visual motion. In other words, infants apply more backward force to their heads as the visual motion information is perceived as moving faster. Although this finding suggests that infants are already sensitive to optical flow information for controlling posture at birth, it is still necessary for them to learn how to compensate to visual motion information for controlling other postures, such as sitting and standing.

A good deal of the research on the development of postural control has involved a 'moving room' (see **Figure 5**). In this paradigm, the infant sits or stands on a stationary floor while the walls and ceiling move forward and backward. This movement produces visual flow information congruent with the head and body moving in the

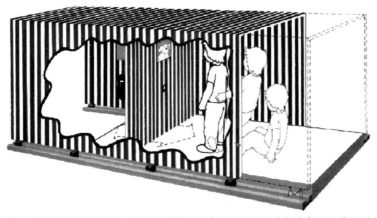

Figure 5 Schematic drawing of the moving room apparatus. As the walls move toward the infant, self-motion in the opposite direction is perceived inducing a postural compensation in the same direction as the walls are moving. As the walls move away from the infant, the opposite response is induced. Reproduced from Bertenthal BI, Rose JL, and Bai DL (1997) Perception-action coupling in the development of visual control of posture. *Journal of Experimental Psychology: Human Perception and Performance* 23(6): 1631–1643.

opposite direction, and induces a compensation of the infant's posture. Sitting infants begin to show compensations at 7–9 months of age, a period that straddles the development of this posture. During this period infants show improvements in the speed and consistency of these compensations suggesting that some period of time is necessary to learn to regulate the amount of force necessary to compensate for the perceived displacement. Similarly, infants begin to show compensations while standing between 12 and 15 months of age, but these compensations are not present immediately with the development of independent stance. Some period of learning to scale the new response synergies to the optical flow information is required before infants show the ability to maintain their balance when perturbed by the moving room. In sum, infants must learn to modulate or control each new motor response *de novo*, even if the perceptual information (e.g., optical flow for specifying postural sway) is readily detected and processed.

Development of reaching in the light and dark

Before concluding this section, there is one important caveat that should be discussed. Context specificity is important only if the changes contribute to the assembly of the action. At face value, this point is obvious, but there are many nonobvious examples in development. Consider, for example, young infants reaching for objects in the light or the dark. Historically, the prevailing view has been that reaching is initially visually guided, but more recent studies show that infants reach as accurately in the dark for sounding or glowing objects as they reach in the light for the same objects.

In one longitudinal study testing infants between 6 and 25 weeks of age, infants first contacted the object in both conditions at comparable ages (light – 12.3 weeks; dark – 11.9 weeks), and they first grasped the object in the light at 16.0 weeks and in the dark at 14.7 weeks. Infants could not see their hands or arms in the dark suggesting that proprioceptive information was sufficient to guide reaching. Additional studies reveal that there are no differences in the reaching of young infants even when more precise kinematic measures (speed, number of movement units, straightness, etc.) are used.

By contrast, adults and even 15-month-old infants show significant differences when reaching in the light and dark. These differences are most likely attributable to the specificity of the reaches. Whereas adults and 15-month-old infants scale their reaching and grasping to the size and shape of the object, infants, just beginning to reach, apply the same undifferentiated response to all objects. Thus, contextual differences relating to the ability to see the arm and hand do not affect the reaching behavior of young infants because scaling the reach and grasp to match the size and orientation of the object is not yet integrated into the organization of this behavior.

Action Understanding

Common coding of the observation and execution of actions

Recent neurophysiological, neuroimaging, and behavioral evidence suggest that perception and action share a common representation or code for the observation and execution of actions. This common code implies that visual percepts of observed actions are mapped directly onto our motor representation of the same action. As a consequence, an action is understood when its observation leads to simulation (i.e., representing the responses of others by covertly generating similar responses in oneself) by the motor system. Thus, when we observe a hand grasping a glass, the same neural circuit that plans or executes this goal-directed action becomes active in the observer's motor areas. It is the motor knowledge by the observer that is used to understand the observed goal-directed action via covert imitation.

Although this theory for explaining how we understand actions dates back to the 1890s and the ideomotor theory of William James (1842–1910), direct evidence supporting this view emerged only recently with the discovery of mirror neurons in the ventral premotor cortex of the monkey's brain. These neurons discharge when the monkey performs a goal-directed action, as well as when the monkey observes a human or conspecific perform the same or a similar action. Thus, these neurons provide a common internal representation for executing and observing goal-directed action. Human neuroimaging and transcranial magnetic stimulation studies have shown activation of a homologous frontoparietal circuit during both the observation, as well as the imitation of actions.

This neurological evidence is complemented by recent behavioral evidence showing that the observation of actions facilitates or primes responding to similar actions. For example, people automatically and unconsciously mimic each others' gestures when they are casually talking to each other. Also, people tend to respond more quickly to a stimulus when the response involves imitation as opposed to some arbitrary action. The availability of specialized processes in the brain for mapping perceived actions onto the motor system suggests that infants should be intrinsically prepared for directly matching the observation and execution of actions.

Simulation and understanding of actions

Some of the best evidence for this matching system in infants comes from observing their perseverative search errors. In the classic, Piagetian A-not-B error, 8–12-month-old infants first search correctly for an object they see hidden in one location on one or more trials, but then continue to search at that same location after seeing the object hidden in a new location. Recent accounts of this error emphasize the role of repeated reaching to the initial location. If an observation–execution matching system is functional in young infants, then simply observing someone else reach repeatedly to the same location should be sufficient for eliciting this error. This prediction was confirmed when 9-month-old infants observed a human agent hiding and finding the object, but not when they observed two mechanical claws performing the same actions. It thus appears that this matching system is limited to actions performed by human agents. Moreover, this error was restricted to observing the experimenter hiding and finding the toy with her ipsilateral hand. At this age, infants are biased to use their ipsilateral hand when reaching for objects, and thus their motor experience with their contralateral hand is less developed. A consistent finding with adults is that covert simulation of observed actions is limited to those actions that are within the motor repertoire of the observer, and the same qualification appears to apply to infants as well.

Direct matching between the observation and execution of actions enables not only covert simulation but prediction of the outcome or effects of the action. When adults perform a goal-directed action their eyes precede their hands in moving toward the goal. Likewise, when observing someone else perform a goal-directed action, the eyes move to the goal before the agent completes the action. Twelve-month-old infants show similar anticipatory eye movements when observing goal-directed actions (i.e., placing objects in a container) performed by a human agent, but not when observing a 'mechanical motion' event in which the objects move without the intervention of a human agent. These differences between the observation of human actions and mechanical events suggest that the observation–execution matching system is specific to the perception of human actions.

An important principle of the direct matching theory is that actions are understood in terms of their goals and not their movements. For example, human infants understand that the goal structure of an action is based primarily on the object toward which it is directed. By contrast, the way in which the action is accomplished is less important. For example, infants differentiate between a human agent reaching and grasping for two different objects, but do not differentiate between reaching and grasping for the same object even when it involves a new path or a new location. Six-month-old infants are sensitive to this difference, but 3-month-old infants are not. If, however, the younger infants are given a few minutes experience reaching with 'sticky mittens' (allowing them to artificially grasp small objects), then they, too, discriminate between a change in the goal of the action and a change in the movement of the action. It thus appears that even minimal experience with a goal-directed action is sufficient for infants to map their observation of the action onto some preliminary motor representation of the action.

Currently, it is unclear whether this preliminary motor representation is transient or persists for some extended period of time and could be reinstated with additional motor experiences.

Developmental origins of common coding

It is very likely that some version of the direct matching system is functional from birth. Newborn infants imitate oro-facial gestures (mouth opening and tongue protrusion), even though they've never seen their own face. The origins and developmental trajectory of this behavior are consistent with an observation–execution matching system.

It is well established that fetuses perform mouth opening and closing and tongue protrusion while *in utero*. Thus, these gestures are already part of the neonate's behavioral repertoire at birth. The evidence also suggests that neonates are more likely to match the modeled gesture after it has been presented for some period of time ($\sim$40 s), rather than immediately. This finding is consistent with a motor simulation explanation in which activation would be expected to build up gradually as the gesture is observed, as opposed to an explanation predicting an immediate response because of the availability of higher-level processes from birth. Finally, the empirical evidence suggests that the likelihood of automatic imitation increases until around 2 months of age, and then declines and virtually disappears by 5 months of age. It is during this same window of time that neonatal reflexes are gradually inhibited, suggesting that similar cortical inhibitory processes may serve to suppress neonatal imitation.

As the spontaneous elicitation of these overt facial gestures becomes gradually inhibited with age, they do not disappear entirely. Instead they become subject to volitional control such that the infant determines when and how they are elicited – imitation is no longer automatic, and the observation of a facial gesture will not necessarily lead to its execution by the infant. Thus, rather than reflecting a precocial social ability of the infant as suggested by some theorists, neonatal imitation may reflect a striking inability of the infant to inhibit activation of the motor system by direct matching mechanisms. Similar compulsive imitation is observed in adults after lesions of areas of the frontal lobe involved in inhibitory control, and even in healthy adults when attention is diverted.

Although overt imitation of facial gestures ceases with the development of inhibition, covert imitation continues and provides specific knowledge about these gestures when observed in others. Very recent evidence suggests that this same developmental process is played out at different ages for many other important behaviors (e.g., gaze direction, visually directed reaching and grasping, vocalizations of sounds). As these behaviors are practiced, the infant develops greater control of their execution, as well as knowledge of their effects or outcomes. The development of these motor schemas enables infants to covertly simulate and predict the effects of similar actions performed by others. This reliance on the developing control of self-produced actions explains why action understanding continues to develop with motor experience.

Change Mechanisms

Recent research on the development of perception and action offers new insights into how behavior changes with age and experience. In contrast to conventional views of behavioral development which emphasize stable patterns of performance that are interrupted by temporary and abrupt changes, new findings emphasize that variability is often present in the performance of infants and contributes to both further development and greater flexibility in different situations. Although we typically associate variability with the outcome of an action (e.g., location of a thrown dart relative to the bull's eye), it is also related to the execution of an action (e.g., relative coordination of eye, hand, and feet in throwing the dart). Both sources of variability are relevant to the development and improvement of new behaviors.

Variation and Selection

Variability in behavior is always present, but its function changes with age and experience. Consider, for example, visual control of posture while sitting in a moving room. When 5-month-old infants are tested they show large and random amplitudes of postural sway, but this variability declines significantly by 7 months of age. Surprisingly, this variability increases again at 9 months of age. The reason for this flip-flop is that 5-month-old infants cannot control their balance while sitting, whereas most 7-month-olds are learning to sit without support. During the learning of a new skill, infants, as well as adults reduce degrees of freedom by stiffening some joints to minimize unsafe and poorly controlled limb movements. By 9 months of age, infants are more secure with their new sitting posture and they reduce muscle stiffness, which results in greater amplitudes of postural sway. In this example, the variability in maintaining a balanced posture is first attributable to poor control of the necessary response synergies, but later variability is attributable to the need for greater flexibility to compensate for postural perturbations. Additional examples of increased variability in movement patterns accompanying the development of new levels of behavioral organization include toddlers learning to descend slopes and infants stepping on motorized treadmills.

One question unanswered by the above examples is how infants learn new perception–action couplings. The traditional view is that infants are prescribed by some genetic plan or abstract cognitive structures to follow a fixed and sequential progression of stages in the development of new behaviors. A radically different proposal is that learning follows a stochastic process (i.e., probabilistic as opposed to deterministic outcome) in which a multiplicity of developmental factors (e.g., neurological, physical, cognitive, social) induce new forms of behavior. As infants explore new behaviors that emerge with organismic (e.g., increases in muscle strength or improvements in distance perception) or environmental changes (e.g., maintaining balance against gravity in more challenging postures or responding to new task demands by parents), a distribution of implicit (e.g., minimization of energy) and explicit (e.g., intentions) goals motivate the infant to store and repeat those actions that are optimally successful.

An excellent illustration of this process is observed in infants' learning to reach. Initially, reaching for an object involves a number of discrete movement units that decrease over time. Infants initially show considerable variability in the direction and amplitude of each movement unit, but this variability decreases as they learn to select those movement units that optimize performance. It thus appears that the development of smoother and more accurate reaching is consistent with a self-organizing system in which specific visuomotor mappings are selected from a much larger distribution in order to optimize the goal of contacting the object.

Summary

Infants engage in goal-directed and exploratory behaviors from birth, and their actions become better coordinated as the perceptual information becomes more differentiated and mapped to more specific response synergies. In turn, the development of new and more complex responses requires greater perceptual specificity and greater prospective control. This mutuality and reciprocity between perception and action demands that the development of new behaviors is dynamic and multidetermined. In contrast to earlier views of behavioral development reflecting patterns of stability interrupted briefly by transitions to new behaviors, the development of perception and action show significant periods of variability in real and developmental time. This variability introduces new movement patterns or actions for achieving specific goals and also offers greater flexibility in adapting actions to task demands.

See also: Auditory Perception; Brain Development; Cognitive Developmental Theories; Future Orientation; Imitation and Modeling; Motor and Physical Development: Locomotion; Motor and Physical Development: Manual; Perceptual Development; Visual Perception.

Suggested Readings

Adolph KE and Berger SE (2006) Motor development. In: Kuhn D and Siegler RS (eds.) *Handbook of Child Psychology, Vol. 2: Cognition, Perception, and Language,* 6th edn., pp. 161–213. New York: Wiley.

Bertenthal BI and Longo MR (in press) Motor knowledge and action understanding: A developmental perspective. In Klatzky R, Mac-Whinney B, and Behrman M (eds.) *The Carnegie Symposium on Cognition, Vol. 34. Embodiment, Ego Space, and Action.* Mahwah, NJ: Erlbaum.

Bertenthal BI, Longo MR, and Kenny S (2007) Phenomenal permanence and the development of predictive tracking. *Child Development* 78: 350–363.

Bertenthal BI, Rose JL, and Bai DL (1997) Perception-action coupling in the development of visual control of posture. *Journal of Experimental Psychology: Human Perception and Performance* 23(6): 1631–1643.

Clifton RK, Rochat P, Robin DJ, and Berthier NE (1994) Multimodal perception in human infants. *Journal of Experimental Psychology: Human Perception and Performance* 20: 876–886.

Thelen E (1995) Motor development: A new synthesis. *American Psychologist* 50: 79–95.

van der Meer ALH, van der Weel FR, and Lee DN (1995) The functional significance of arm movements in neonates. *Science* 267: 693–695.

von Hofsten C (2003) On the development of perception and action. In: Valsiner J and Connolly KJ (eds.) *Handbook of Developmental Psychology,* pp. 114–171. London: Sage Publications.

Relevant Website

http://www.sidgrid.ci.uchicago.edu – Social Informatics Data Grid.

Perceptual Development

M E Arterberry, Colby College, Waterville, ME, USA

Glossary

Accretion and deletion of texture – The covering and uncovering of surface texture by one surface that is closer than the other.

Binocular disparity – A binocular depth cue that utilizes differences in the retinal image projected to each eye.

Binocular information – Perceptual information based on two eyes.

Convergence – The amount of rotation of the eyes in order to fixate a distant object.

Externality effect – Infants' propensity to attend to external contours of a compound figure.

Gestalt principles of perceptual organization – A number of principles described by Gestalt psychologists to account for the perception of spatial configuration.

Habituation – Method used to test infants' perception that relies on declining levels of attention with repetition and infants' responsiveness to novelty.

Kinematic information – Perceptual information based on motion, either of objects or observers.

Motion parallax – A depth cue based on the fact that closer objects move faster across the retina than farther ones.

Optical expansion – The change in size of surface texture that results when an object moves closer.

Other-race effect – The ability to recognize faces more easily if they are of the same race as the perceiver.

Perception – The use of the senses to acquire information or knowledge about the external world.

Person constancy – Recognition of the same person across changes in location, viewpoint, and the like.

Sensation – The registration of stimulation of a sense organ such as the eye.

Static-monocular information – Information based on a stationary viewing of distant scenes or close scenes with one eye. Also called pictorial depth cues.

Strabismus – Misalignment of the eyes.

Introduction

Perception is the use of the senses to acquire information or knowledge about the external world. Questions of perception can be asked at a basic level, such as how the five senses respond to external stimulation, or at a higher level, such as how do we determine depth or object shape. Questions of development focus on what capabilities humans have at the beginning of life and how the growing child comes to achieve adult levels.

Much of the research on perceptual development has focused on the first year or so of life, in part to answer intriguing questions about the roles of biological mechanisms and experience in directing development. Historically, the debate has centered on whether an ability is inborn (innate) or whether it emerges after birth as the result of specific experiences. This debate has been termed the nature–nurture controversy, and it has pervaded how we attempt to understand the mechanisms underlying perceptual development.

Two general views of perceptual development provide examples of the nature–nurture controversy. One view – termed constructivism – emphasizes the construction of perception through learning. For the constructivist view, the starting point is trying to make sense of sensations. In every day experience, our senses are bombarded with stimulation, and the perceiver's task is to make meaning of this stimulation. Over time, the young or naïve perceiver begins to bring order to this barrage of information. A prediction for development based on this view is that development of perception is protracted and likely to be reliant on specific experiences. A second view – termed ecological – starts at a very different point. The basic premise is that the perceiver is awash in information, not meaningless stimulation, and humans evolved (even the youngest perceivers) to pick up this information. Predictions for development based on this view are that some abilities may be present at birth and those that emerge later are based on a fine-tuning of perceptual processes rather than the emergence of those processes. One limiting factor that is not directly addressed by these views is biological maturation. Some abilities are not present at birth due to physical maturation of perceptual systems, such as vision. Thus, a complete story of perceptual development takes into account, physical maturation, the role of experience, and a developing sensitivity to information.

Topics related to perceptual development, such as visual development, auditory development, development of touch, and intermodal perception, are found elsewhere in this volume. Here we will focus on the perception of objects – physical and social objects. First we will cover how we know where objects are (depth perception) and then we will discuss various aspects of objects, including their three-dimensional (3D) shape, events between objects, and aspects of social objects, specifically faces.

Depth Perception

Our understanding of depth perception in infancy began with the first study conducted in the late 1950s by Eleanor J. Gibson and Richard D. Walk. They used an apparatus called the visual cliff. The visual cliff is a glass table with a board bisecting it. Under half of the table a checkered cloth is right against the surface. Under the other half of the table, the cloth is on the floor. When lit properly, the glass surface cannot be seen; thus, from the center board, there appears to be a shallow side and a deep side. Gibson and Walk placed infants between the ages of 6 and 14 months on the center board and looked at whether they would crawl over the shallow and deep sides. Avoiding the deep side was taken as a sign of depth perception. Of the 36 infants tested, 27 crawled over the shallow side. Of the 27, 24 did not crawl over the deep side. Later, using heart rate as a measure researchers found that infants as young as 1 month of age perceive a difference between the deep and shallow side of the visual cliff. As infants were lowered down to the glass surface of the deep and shallow sides, their heart rate changed in different directions – it increased over the shallow side and it decreased over the deep side.

These initial visual cliff studies documented depth perception in the first year of life. Later studies addressed what information infants may use for perceiving depth. Adult perceivers have access to three different types of information for depth perception – kinematic information (or motion-carried information), binocular information, and static-monocular information (or pictorial depth cues).

The study of the development of depth perception in infancy has relied heavily on spatially appropriate behaviors, of which one example is avoiding the deep side of the visual cliff. Another spatially appropriate behavior is reaching. Infants, when they detect a depth difference, reach for the closer of two objects, even when the difference is only a few centimeters. In a number of experiments, infants' reaching has been used as a measure of their perception of depth. Often, when infants do not show sensitivity, the first question asked is whether the apparent lack of sensitivity is due to the method used to assess it. It is possible that the infants' motoric abilities are not developed enough for infants to demonstrate their existing perceptual abilities. Consequently, additional studies relying on methods other than reaching, such as habituation paradigms, have provided converging evidence for the developmental time table presented below.

Kinematic Information

Kinematic information is available when either the perceiver or object(s) are moving. One example is accretion and deletion of texture. All objects and surfaces have texture (see **Figure 1(a)** for examples of different textures). When one object moves in front of another, the texture on the farther object is covered up. This appearance (accretion) and disappearance (deletion) of texture provides adults with the ordering of surfaces in depth, and

Figure 1 Several examples of static-monocular depth information. (a) Most surfaces have texture (compare the bench with the grass and the gravel). We assume that texture on the same surface is equal in size; thus, parts of surfaces with larger texture elements are perceived as being closer than parts of surfaces with smaller texture elements. (b) The parallel sides of the path appear to converge in the distance, illustrating the depth cue of linear perspective. (c) Patterns of light and shade provide delineation of the tree bark, and the hole is specified by areas of darkness. (d) The cylindrical cement benches decrease in size with distance, providing the depth cue of relative size. For people who regularly walk this river path, the cement benches and their size is familiar, thus providing access to the depth cue of familiar size. The depth cue of interposition is illustrated by the bridge (it overlaps part of the building behind it signaling that it is closer) and the trees (they overlap part of the wall). (b) Photographs courtesy of M. K. Arterberry.

infants too are able to use this information at least by 5 months of age.

Another kinematic depth cue is the expansion and contraction of texture elements (optical expansion). When a surface or object approaches a perceiver, the texture elements expand and when a surface or object moves away from a perceiver, the texture elements contract (optical contraction). The direction of expansion and the rate of expansion provide information about whether the surface is approaching or receding and how fast. Infants as young as 4 weeks react defensively to approaching surfaces suggesting early sensitivity to distance information provided by optical expansion.

A third kinematic cue to depth is motion parallax. Motion parallax pertains to the differences in motion across the retina exhibited by objects located at different distances. For example, when driving in a car through a rural area, the rails of a nearby fence pass by much more quickly than the distant hills. Little is known about when

infants are sensitive to motion parallax information, but it is predicted to be within the first 5 months of life given infants' early sensitivity to other types of kinematic depth information.

Binocular Information

Binocular depth perception relies on the fact that we have two eyes. When we look at an object with two eyes, we adjust our eyes to place the image of the object on our fovea, the region where acuity is best. The amount we have to move our eyes together, or converge them, is information for distance. Infants as young as 3 months appear to use convergence for perceiving depth.

A second binocular depth cue is called binocular disparity. This cue uses information available at the retinal level. Because our eyes are separated, the images of objects fall at different locations on the retinas of the left and right eyes. The visual system is able to fuse these two views and use the difference or disparity between them to determine the object's location in depth. Infants become sensitive to binocular disparity starting around 16 weeks of age on an average, and they quickly are able to detect very small amounts of disparity.

Visual experience appears to be necessary for sensitivity to binocular disparity to develop. Misalignment of the eyes, a condition called strabismus commonly referred to as cross-eyed, results in inadequate overlap of the two retinal images, and many with this condition do not develop binocular sensitivity. Corrections can be made to such misalignments (usually as early as 6 months of age), and the earlier they are done, the better the resulting sensitivity to binocular disparity.

Static-Monocular Information

Although binocular depth cues provide very accurate depth information, they are only functional within a viewing distance of 3 m. Also, about 10% of the population does not have access to binocular disparity due to misalignment of the eyes or other problems with the visual system. Luckily, there are multiple sources of depth information, and we have already discussed one class of information that does not rely on two eyes – kinematic cues. A second class of information is called static-monocular depth information because these cues are available under static conditions, and they do not require both eyes or for the observer/objects to be at close distances. This information is also referred to as pictorial depth cues because many of them were described by Leonardo Da Vinci for portraying depth in a painting. These cues include shading, interposition, familiar size, relative size, texture gradients, and linear perspective (see **Figure 1** for naturally occurring examples and further explanation of each cue).

Numerous studies conducted by Albert Yonas and his colleagues have investigated the onset of sensitivity to static-monocular depth information by isolating these depth cues from other sources of information. For example, in a study on shading, infants were shown a photograph of a bump and a dent. When 7-month-olds viewed this photograph with one eye (the other was covered with an eye patch), they reach significantly more to the bump. When infants viewed the photograph with two eyes, they reached equally to both the bump and the dent, a finding that was not surprising because binocular information overrides static-monocular information. Five-month-old infants did not reach more to the bump than the dent when viewing the displays with one eye. These findings suggest that 7-month-olds were sensitive to the depth cue of shading for perceiving the layout, but 5-month-olds were not. This same pattern – 7-month-olds but not 5-month-olds showing sensitivity – was found for a number of static-monocular depth cues.

Developmental Trajectories

The foregoing discussion of depth perception suggests a progression in the emergence of depth sensitivity – earliest sensitivity to kinematic information, next to binocular information, and finally to static-monocular depth information. Recent work, however, has provided two challenges to this lock-step story. The first is several studies with 3-month-olds. Using a preferential looking procedure, infants have shown sensitivity to several static-monocular depth cues (such as shading and line junctions) that specify depth to adults. These studies in themselves do not demonstrate depth perception in young infants, but they open the possibility that use of static-monocular depth information may be available to infants younger than 7 months of age. A second challenge is the nature of development. Most of the work on depth perception has been done using cross-sectional designs. The few short-term longitudinal studies that have been conducted (both with binocular depth information and static-monocular depth information) suggest that the emergence of sensitivity shows strong individual differences. For example, some infants show sensitivity to static-monocular depth information as early as 22 weeks of age, whereas others do not show it until much closer to 32 weeks of age.

Object Perception

Perception of objects can take place at several levels. For example, we may perceive two-dimensional (2D) features of objects (called 'pattern perception'), such as their surface characteristics (e.g., the stripes on a zebra) or spatial relations among objects (e.g., a zebra is to the left or right of a horse). We may also perceive objects' three-dimensional (3D) structure (e.g., the girth of a zebra's body). Pattern perception and 3D object perception are independent, yet complementary processes, and together they help us perceive objects, their surfaces, and the spaces between them.

Pattern Perception

Infants show preferences for certain types of patterns. For example, a bull's eye will be attended to more than horizontal or vertical stripes. In addition, infants show a processing advantage for vertically symmetrical patterns compared to horizontally or obliquely symmetrical patterns, and they are able to process patterns both at the local level (the individual elements that make up the pattern) and global level (the overall pattern). In addition, young infant's attention is directed to edges and contours. For example, if 1-month-olds are shown a compound figure, such as a square inside a triangle, they will not notice if the square is changed to a circle. They will, however, notice a change in the triangle. This finding, called the externality effect, disappears by 4 months of age, and it was originally explained by infants' preference for external features of forms, namely the edges. Being biased toward edges is a good strategy for parsing the visual world into units because edge information informs us about boundaries between objects and surfaces. One finding, though, suggests that infants' attention is not always captured by external features. If the interior shape moves, 1-month-old infants will notice the change in shape. Apparently motion trumps edges and directs young infants' attention to the interior of a compound figure.

Infants at an early age also appear to be sensitive to the configuration of patterns, such as diamond being above or below a horizontal line. Infants (3–4-month-olds) show sensitivity to above and below and left and right as long as the targets (e.g., diamonds) do not change across trials. By 6–7 months, infants generalize the spatial relations of above and below, and left and right across targets, but not the spatial relation of between. By 9–10 months, infants appear to have an understanding of between across target variation. These findings suggest a developmental trend in infants' perception of configuration. Early infants perceive configural relations among objects but do not generalize the configurations to other objects. With age, the ability to generalize emerges as does the complexity of the relations they are able to perceive.

Three-Dimensional Object Perception

Information available for depth perception is also available for perceiving 3D objects. We can perceive an object's structure by using binocular information, we can see the contours of an object by attending to shading information, we can determine which object is in front of another one by using interposition information or accretion and deletion of texture under conditions of motion, and we can determine the shape of an object from motion. A popular method for studying infants' 3D object perception is the habituation paradigm. In a typical experiment, an infant is shown repeated presentations of an object. Once attention decreases, the infant views the same object in a novel orientation and a new object. If the infant recognizes the new object as new, he/she should look at it longer than to the new orientation of the old object. Several studies have assessed infants' sensitivity to different types of information for perceiving 3D shape. For example, 2- and 4-month-old infants are able to recognize the shape of rotating or oscillating objects when they view solid 3D objects, when they view wire figures, and when they view random dot displays. A solid 3D object is the most like infants' everyday experience with objects. As the object rotates, infants would have available a number of cues for shape, including the kinetic transformations at the edges, changes in shading, and the availability of key parts, such as

a corner that come available as the object fully rotates. Infants also perceive the 3D shape of a moving wire figure, a finding that suggests that the transformation of the contours in the absence of surface information is sufficient for 3D shape perception. Finally, the fact infants perceive 3D shape in kinetic random dot displays demonstrates that infants can create the edges and surfaces of a 3D object from the relative motion of surface texture. Infants' perception of shape based on binocular information is likely to appear with the development of stereopsis, around 4 months of age. In addition, infants are able to transfer information about object shape across sources of information. Four-month-olds habituated to a dynamic image of a 3D object can recognize the object when its shape is specified by binocular information.

Partly Occluded Objects

An important task for perceivers is to perceive the 3D structure of objects, even if they are not fully visible (in other words, partly occluded). The environment is cluttered, and more often than not we perceive partly occluded objects (see **Figure 2(a)**) yet we experience them as if we perceived them fully. One task for infants is to figure out which parts of the partly occluded objects go together. A simplified version of this task is a straight rod behind a block (see **Figure 2(b)**). Gestalt psychologists provided a good starting point for potential principles for solving this task. These principles of organization include common fate (things are grouped together if they move together), good continuation (straight or smoothly changing contours comprise the same unit), good form (interpretation of input is biased to see symmetrical, simple forms), similarity (parts that look the same are grouped together), and proximity (nearby things are grouped together). When viewing the rod and block in **Figure 2(b)**, we can see several principles in operation. The two ends of the rod are the same color and shape (similarity), the visible ends of the rod can be interpolated across the block to create a straight line (good continuation) and parsing the image into a rod and block, rather than a single object with strange projectiles, creates two simple forms (good form). If the visible ends of the rod moved in a rigid fashion, we would have the additional principle of common fate.

Studies of infants' perception of partly occluded objects often have used displays like the rod and block depicted in **Figure 2(b)**. In a typical experiment, infants are habituated to a rod occluded by a block. Following habituation, the block is removed and infants view a complete rod and a broken rod. If infants perceived the rod as complete in the habituation phase, they should look longer at the broken rod in the test phase. When the rod translates behind the block, in the x-, y-, or z-axis, 4-month-old infants look longer at the broken rod at test, suggesting that they perceived the partly occluded rod as

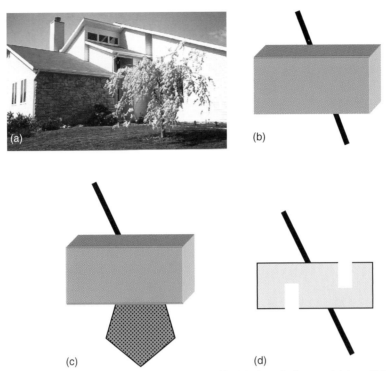

Figure 2 Examples of: (a) a naturally occurring, partly occluded object: (b) a block occluding a rod; (c) a rod block occluding a rod-blob; and (d) a 2D display of a rod covered by a block. As the rod moves behind the block, parts of the rod are visible in the gaps.

complete behind the block. This is the case even when some of the Gestalt principles are clearly violated, as in **Figure 2(c)**. When the rod and block are not moving, infants provide no evidence that they can tell that the rod is a complete object behind the block; following habituation to a stationary rod, infants look equally to the broken and complete rod. Similar results are found when the block moves and the rod remains stationary. Thus, motion of the occluded object appears to be a key variable for perception of object unity, and motion overrides other static cues.

Further work has demonstrated that infants as young as 2 months also perceive the rod as a single unit under conditions of rod motion and when (1) the block is narrower than the size tested with 4-month-olds or (2) there are gaps in the block showing more of the rod as it moves behind the block (see **Figure 2(d)**). A curious finding is that newborns appear to perceive a moving occluded rod as broken. Following habituation to a rod moving behind a block, they look longer at the 'complete' rod, suggesting that newborns perceived the rod as broken during the habituation phase. This finding is striking because it implies that babies begin life perceiving their world inaccurately, and the very young infant's first introduction to the world is fragmented. A world based on solely visible surfaces and objects would be a multicolored and multitextured mosaic from which relations among objects may be difficult to discern.

Shape and Size Constancy

Another task in object perception is recognizing an object's shape or size despite changes in orientation or location. Objects move and we move around objects. At any one time the projection of the object on the retina will be different from any other time if the observer or object is moving. The ability to perceive shape across orientations is called shape constancy, and the ability to perceive size across changes in distance is called size constancy.

Achieving size constancy requires relation information about the size of the retinal image and the distance of the object. Consider the example illustrated in **Figure 3**. The same-sized object located at different distances from the perceiver will project different sized retinal images, and different sized objects located the same distance from the perceiver will project different sized retinal images. The task for the perceiver is to differentiate these two conditions, and he or she uses distance information and the size of the retinal image to determine the real size of the object. Shape constancy works the same way, only different orientations of the object result in differently shaped retinal images (e.g., a square tilted forward projects a trapezoidal retinal image). Relying on distance information to determine the object's orientation, the perceiver determines whether he or she is seeing different objects or the same object from different perspectives.

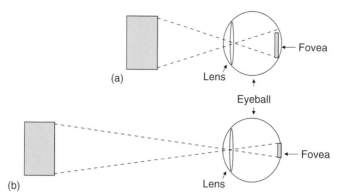

Figure 3 Schematic diagram of the relation between size and distance of an object and its retinal image. In (a) and (b), the image of the object is focused by the lens on the back of the eyeball (over the fovea). The image in (a) is larger than in (b) because the object is physically closer.

Size and shape constancy have been documented in newborn infants. For example, in one study, infants were habituated to a small cube positioned at various distances across six trials. Following habituation, infants viewed a large and small cube, positioned so they both had the same retinal size. Infants in this condition looked more to the large cube (the novel sized object) than the small cube, suggesting that they recognized the size of the small cube as being the same across all presentations and the large cube as one they had not seen before. A similar procedure was used to test shape constancy. The findings of both lines of research suggest that infants within several hours of birth have size and shape constancy.

Event Perception

Perceivers are rarely inactive. Even looking around the room while sitting on a couch is 'action'. Normal perception is bound up with ongoing action – action of the perceiver and the objects around him or her. Many of these actions and interactions can be described as events. Here we consider two events – biomechanical motion and causality.

Objects and perceivers move and the resulting patterns of motion provide information about the object. We have already seen several examples in our earlier discussions of perception of 3D object shape and partly occluded objects. People are also important moving objects, and they create distinctive patterns of motion because they are nonrigid (often called biomechanical motion). Nonrigid objects have points whose separation in 3D space changes over time. Consider the movement of a human hand. As the fingers close and open, the distance between the fingertips and the palm changes. One way to assess sensitivity to biomechanical motion is with the use of point-light displays. With point-light displays, a person or any other moving object is filmed in the dark with spots of light at key joints or intersections. These point-light displays are perceived as a coherent motion pattern, which adults readily identify as a human walking (or dancing, doing pushups, and the like). Infants as young as 5 months of age provide some evidence of perceiving a human form in point-light displays, suggesting sensitivity to biomechanical motion.

Perhaps one of the simplest events among objects is when one object moves toward a second object, contacts it, and the second object is physically displaced. Infants' perception of this type of launching event has been studied by several researchers in order to assess infants' appreciation of causality. There are two important components to a successful launching event. The objects need to touch (a spatial component), and the object needs to start moving within a reasonable time after contact (a temporal component). Typical experiments manipulate one or both of these variables to assess infants' sensitivity to these features. For example, infants may be shown a delayed-launch event in which the second object starts to move but only after a delay after contact. Infants also may be shown a noncausal event in which the first object stops short of contacting the second object, but the second object starts to move after the first one stopped. Finally, some researchers have manipulated variables that are not crucial for the perception of causality (such as changing the objects across events) to assess infants' generalization of the events.

The results show a developmental progression in infants' perception of causality. When shown simple events, namely events in which the objects roll and do not change across repeated presentations, 6.5-month-olds are sensitive to causality in launching events. By at least 10 months, infants attribute specific agents to the causal event. In other words, they attend to the object that caused the launching, and they dishabituate if the object is changed during the test phase. In more complex events, such as when balls bounce instead of roll, 10-month-old infants do not attend to the causality of the event. Thus, infants' perception of causality is present within the first year of life, and it matures across this time period.

Face Perception

Perhaps the most important class of objects in the infants' world is people. It is not surprising, then, that face perception is one of the oldest topics in infant perception, beginning with the writings of Charles Darwin in 1872 on facial expressions, and it continues to be one of the most researched topics today. No fewer than 92 papers were published between 2000 and 2006! Key questions pertain to how early in life infants perceive faces and the information infants obtain from faces.

Preferences for Faces

Early research in infants' face perception was concerned with the question of when infants perceive faces; and, in particular, when they know that faces have a particular set of features arranged in a particular way. One of the earliest studies in infant perception showed that they prefer face-like displays (see **Figure 4(a)**) over other patterned stimuli, such as a checker board (**Figure 4(b)**), and often infants will show a preference for a face with the features arranged correctly over a scrambled face (**Figure 4(c)** and **4(d)**, respectively). Perceiving a face, particularly perceiving the internal details to recognize a face or to discriminate a scrambled face from a schematic face, requires a certain level of visual resolution on the part of the perceiver. There are several findings that suggest that newborn infants have the requisite visual resolution: Infants just a few hours old are able to recognize their mothers from unfamiliar females as long as her hairline is visible, and they show a preference for faces that adults rated as attractive over faces rated as unattractive. Recently, researchers have documented the other-race effect in infants. The other-race effect was first identified in adults and it refers to the difficulty in recognizing faces of people who are not of the same race as the perceiver. The other-race effect has been documented in infants as young as 3 months of age in two ways: (1) infants show a spontaneous preference for faces of the same race and when (2) habituated to a single face, infants have difficulty recognizing the face at test if the face is of another race. Newborns, on the other hand, do not show the other-race effect. Together, these findings document impressive early sensitivity to faces.

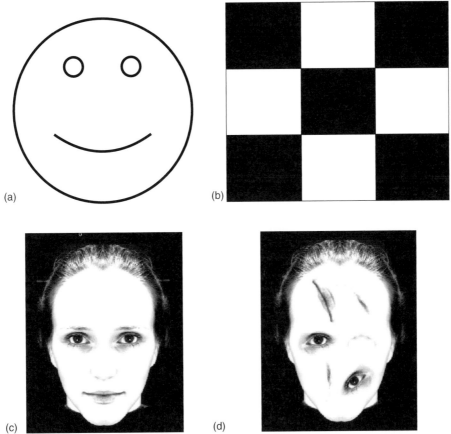

Figure 4 Examples of stimuli that could be used to test infants' preferences for faces: (a) a schematic face; (b) a checkerboard; (c) a face with the features in the correct place and (d) a scrambled face. (c, d) Photographs are courtesy of S. M. Jones.

Perceiving Specific People, Gender, and Facial Expressions

Beyond the newborn period, infants are sensitive to facial information that may be useful for recognizing specific people, perceiving characteristics of people, and for nonverbal communication. The ability to recognize a person across different views, or person constancy, is an important skill because faces (and people in general) are dynamic objects. Faces exhibit differing expressions, and infants have the opportunity to view faces from different perspectives. In order to recognize key people in their environment, it is necessary for infants to be able to perceive the constancy of a person despite such differences. One-month-old infants recognize familiar faces (their mother but not a stranger) in different views, such as frontal and three-fourths views but not in profile, and infants recognize faces across differing intensities of an emotional expression at least by 5 months of age. By 7 months, infants' face processing appears to be disrupted if the face is upside down, suggesting that with experience, infants come to process faces as whole units (called configural processing) rather than based on the individual features (called featural processing). Inverting a face disrupts adults' ability to process faces as a configuration with inter-related elements, and the same may be true for infants by 7 months. The timing of this inversion effect is consistent with infants' motor development. Most children can sit independently by 7 months, and it is possible that their experience with faces becomes more limited to upright views than at earlier ages.

In addition to recognizing particular faces, infants may use information contained in faces to categorize people into groups, such as male and female. Perception of gender by adults can be based on superficial cues, such as hair length, facial hair, and/or make-up or on structural cues, such as the distance between the eye and brow. Infants' perception of gender has been assessed in the context of categorization tasks. Infants are shown either male or female faces and are tested with a novel face of the same gender and a novel face of the opposite gender. Infants categorize gender by 9 months of age with the aid of superficial features (stereotyped hair length and clothing); however, they only seem to do it in one direction. That is, when habituated to male faces, infants looked significantly longer to the female face in the test phase but infants habituated to female faces did not look longer to the male face, as would be predicted if they had categorized the gender of the faces. This finding is consistent with other face processing or categorization studies, and the evidence is mounting that when it comes to face perception, infants develop an expertise for female faces before male faces. This may be due to the nature of infants' early experience with people. Infants who have female primary caregivers show preferences for female faces. The more rare infants who have male primary caregivers show preferences for male faces.

Faces also convey information about emotional states via facial expressions. Facial expressions may play an important role in communication for the nonverbal infant, and infants have the opportunity to experience a variety of facial expressions. Moreover, similar expressions appear in child–adult interactions across cultures. Consequently, perception and discrimination of emotional expressions becomes crucial in order for infants to be engaged social partners. Infants between 5 and 7 months of age show evidence of discrimination of the facial expressions of happiness, anger, fear, and surprise. Moreover, they are able to categorize one or more of these expressions across different people. For example, 5-month-olds who are habituated to different intensities of smiling, from a slight upturning of the mouth to a full toothy grin, modeled by four different females, will look significantly longer to a fearful expression modeled by a fifth female rather than a new intensity of smiling modeled by a sixth person. This suggests that they categorized the facial expression of smiling and treated the new smiling exemplar as fitting within that category.

Mechanisms for Face Perception

Infant face perception provides a nice example of the intersection between biological predisposition (or innate ability) and experience. Researchers have made considerable progress chronicling what infants perceive when viewing a face or a set of faces; however, less clear is the mechanism(s) underlying these abilities. There is strong evidence that infants come predisposed to attend to faces. Some claim this predisposition could be the result of an innate representation for faces, whereas others claim it could be the result of a quick learning process. Recent advances in neuroimaging and electrophysiological techniques have provided researchers with the opportunity to identify areas of the nervous system that are involved with face perception. Key areas that have been identified are the middle fusiform gyrus in the right hemisphere for perception of upright faces and the amygdala for perceiving facial expressions. Work with nonhuman primates have identified face-responsive cells in the inferior temporal cortex. Explanations for the development of face perception abilities in infants have, to greater and lesser degrees, been linked to these physiological findings.

Several proposals have been put forth. One is that face processing in infants shows a right hemispheric advantage with implication of the fusiform gyrus. These areas develop more quickly in the right hemisphere than in the left, and experience with faces contributes to the specialization of this area for face perception. A second explanation is that there are two processes, Conspec and Conlern, each subserved by different mechanisms. Specifically, Conspec is a subcortical process involving the superior colliculus and that Conlern is a cortical process involving the primary visual cortex. The later emergence of Conlern is due to maturational constraints of these areas.

The third possibility relies on speech perception as a model. In this proposal, face perception abilities initially are responsive to a wide variety of face-like stimuli, including faces from other species, and these abilities are tuned with age as a result of specific experiences. As reviewed elsewhere, the development of speech perception begins with some specific skills – infants recognize their mother's voice, and they discriminate a range of speech sounds. More impressive is the fact that young infants are able to discriminate speech sounds that adults in their environment cannot. The ability to discriminate non-native speech contrasts diminishes with exposure to language, and infants' speech perception abilities are generally tuned to their linguistic environment by 10–12 months of age. In other words, there is a perceptual window that narrows throughout the first year of life depending on experience. This third possibility suggests a similar fine-tuning of face perception abilities. For example, young infants are better than adults in recognizing faces of monkeys, and this advantage decreased across the first year of life. Moreover, infants do not initially show an other-race effect nor an inversion effect and this may be due to the need for specific experiences to fine-tune the system. Further support for this idea comes from studies of children and adults who were born with cataracts: Visual deprivation during the first 7 weeks of life due to congenital cataracts resulted in significant and apparently permanent impairment in face processing later in life.

Clearly, more work is needed to flesh out the underlying mechanisms of face perception. One commonality among all the explanations is a role for experience and its timing.

Conclusion

Infants are surprisingly competent in their perception of the world around them. Their perceptual abilities are not at the same level of adults, not at birth nor by the end of the first year of life. It might be best to characterize them perceptually as a stripped down adult. They have basic capacities that allow them to perceive things that are important to them, such as where objects are and what the objects look like.

Much of the work in infant perception is inferential in nature. From measuring attention levels or watching where infants reach, researchers draw inferences about the information infants are using and/or the nature of their perceptual experience. A limitation of this methodology is the interpretation of null findings. While it is tempting to conclude that infants lack the ability under study or that they are limited in some way in their perception, researchers can never really know. Because most methods are inferential and because they require some type of response from the infant (e.g., attention or reaching), it is possible that researchers have not found the appropriate task to document the presence of the ability rather than the ability being absent. Thus, conclusions based on the lack of a difference always have to be made cautiously. As new methodologies are developed, it would not be surprising if earlier competencies are revealed.

See also: Attention; Auditory Perception; Habituation and Novelty; Nature vs. Nurture; Perception and Action; Speech Perception; Taste and Smell; Touch and Pain; Visual Perception.

Suggested Readings

Bornstein MH, Arterberry ME, and Mash C (2005) Perceptual development. In: Bornstein MH and Lamb ME (eds.) *Developmental Psychology: An Advanced Textbook,* 5th edn., pp. 283–325. Mahwah, NJ: Lawrence Erlbaum Associates.

Darwin C (1872) *The Expression of Emotions in Man and Animals.* Chicago: University of Chicago Press (reprinted 1965).

Gibson EJ and Pick AD (1999) *An Ecological Approach to Perceptual Learning and Development.* Oxford: Oxford University Press.

Gibson EJ and Walk RD (1960) The visual cliff. *Scientific American* 202: 64–71.

Kellman PJ and Arterberry ME (2000, 1998) *The Cradle of Knowledge: The Development of Perception in Infancy.* Cambridge, MA: MIT Press.

Kellman PJ and Arterberry ME (2006) Perceptual development. In: Damon W, Kuhn D, and Siegler R (eds.) *The Handbook of Child Psychology: Cognition, Perception, and Language,* 6th edn., pp. 109–160. New York: Wiley.

Pascalis O and Slater A (eds.) (2003) *The Development of Face Processing in Infancy and Early Childhood: Current Perspectives.* Hauppauge, NY: Nova Science Publishers.

Relevant Websites

http://www.cdc.gov – Centers for Disease Control and Prevention – Child Development.
http://www.cfw.tufts.edu – Child and Family Web Guide.
http://www.zerotothree.org – Zero to Three.

Physical Growth

M Lampl, Emory University, Atlanta, GA, USA

Glossary

Anthropometry – Study of human body measurements.
Auxology – Discriptive study of growth in individuals.
Saltation – A growth spurt or measurable acceleration in growth.

Introduction

Physical growth during infancy is the remarkable process by which the average healthy human infant triples its birth weight during the first postnatal year building bones, muscles, organs, and neural tissue as the helpless newborn becomes a mobile toddler. By 2 years of age, a complete set of primary dentition has emerged and the head circumference, 50% of adult size at birth, has expanded to about 80% of final size. Length at 1 year is 150% of that at birth and nearly half of adult height is attained by the age of 2 years. Growing is a major biological event during infancy: more than a decade is required to match this short period in terms of the changes that determine the average adult's final size. Moreover, physical growth in infancy not only sets a trajectory for adult size but establishes the biological architecture for adult health as the profound effects that nutrition, illness, ecology, and social environment have on early development predict childhood, adolescent, and adult health sequelae.

How We See Growth: Measurements, Charts, and Curves

Among the first reports of infant physical growth commonly noted were newborn weights published in the mid-eighteenth century by a German obstetrician. At the same time, interest in the infant body by artists led to measurements documenting the now often cited observation that the human infant is not merely a miniature adult, but is characterized by unique proportionality, with a head that is about one-fourth of body length at birth (in contrast to the adult ratio of approximately 1–7.5). Nearly 100 years passed until systematic studies were undertaken, when pediatricians promoted the importance of serial weights as a guide to infant well-being. This observation has become a

dictum and the growth of infants is now used not only as a reflection of the health of the individual, but as a marker of the well-being of communities.

The descriptive study of growing individuals is known today as auxology (*auxein*, Greek, to grow or increase) with practitioners that include pediatricians, endocrinologists, epidemiologists, and human biologists from disciplines as diverse as medicine, public health, and anthropology. A number of national and local level studies have been undertaken over the past century with the goal of describing infant physical growth. Some of these initiatives were cross-sectional in design, measuring groups of infants and assessing their relative size by age categories. These data are useful to assess the general health of infants and children for survey purposes and are common for national level evaluations, nutritional intervention programs, international health teams, and others interested in a rapid assessment protocol.

Among the earliest longitudinal studies conducted with the goal of following individuals as they grow from infancy to childhood and adolescence, was the Iowa Child Welfare study in the US. This was followed by several initiatives that have further provided the basic information on how normal infant physical growth unfolds to date, with one of them, the Fels study, ongoing through the lifespan and across generations to this time (now in the third generation). A number of studies have provided excellent resource data for our understanding of infant physical growth among diverse populations in Europe (e.g., including but not limited to studies from the Czech Republic, Hungary, Italy, the Netherlands, Norway, Sweden, the UK, including the ongoing Avon Longitudinal Study of Parents and Children, or ALSPAC), Guatemala, Japan, the Philippines, and South Africa. Moreover, numerous studies aiming to describe the growth of infants have been undertaken to document specific effects, for example, of feeding styles or specific nutritional supplements. These studies form the corpus of our information regarding how physical growth during infancy occurs.

Measuring Physical Growth

The predominant measurement methods are used to describe infant growth based on noninvasive anthropometry, with the goal of acquiring quantitative metric assessments of size and shape. Individual body segments as well as total body size and composition are measured with equipment that varies in accuracy and precision according to measurement goals and the realities of study environment. While earlier studies employed radiographs to record individual skeletal components and dental development, more recent studies rely on noninvasive anthropometric tools to assess the size and shape of the living infant. These range from a common measuring tape and balance scale to specially designed calipers and digitized equipment requiring careful maintenance.

Parameters and equipment. The most common dimensions measured to document human infant physical growth are weight, total body, lower leg, and foot length, head, torso, and limb circumferences, and skinfold thicknesses of the torso and limbs. The validity and reproducibility of any measurement depends on the accuracy of the measurement instrument, the skill of the measurer, the cooperation of the infant, and contributions from infant state.

A nonstretchable measurement tape is the method of choice for body circumferences (head, limbs, and torso). Repeatability and reproducibility are related to the user's tension on the tape and anatomical aspects of measurement position (e.g., occipital frontal landmarks for head circumference; distance from bony landmarks for limb measures; umbilical and pelvic markers for waist and hips), mechanical factors that contribute to soft tissue or organ distensibility (e.g., respiratory phase for chest circumference; food consumption; and time since intake for waist circumference) and physiology (e.g., hydrative status for circumferences and skinfolds). Research studies identify high reproducibility for head circumference within and between observers (0.1 cm), while chest circumference is much more difficult to repeatedly measure with high reliability.

A variety of calipers are available to assess anterior–posterior and biparietal head dimensions, body widths/breadths (e.g., shoulders, hips, joints), limb lengths, and subcutaneous skinfolds. Correct anatomical positioning and technique is central to measurement reproducibility for these measurements. For body widths/breadths, spreading and/or sliding calipers are applied to bony landmarks. Issues of instrument accuracy and precision vs. measurement dependability are highlighted in assessing these measures. For example, digital equipment designed to measure limb segments (e.g, the knemometer) has instrument precision at the micrometer level. However, the accuracy of the measurement as taken from the top of the knee to the bottom of the foot is affected by contributions from compression/relaxation effects across joints and soft tissue that include circadian and diurnal physiology as well as hydration.

Subcutaneous skinfold measurements aim to provide estimates of regional body composition, as skinfold thicknesses are closely related to subcutaneous adipose tissue at the individual sites, and correlated to total body fat and percent body fat relative to weight during infancy. Measurements are assessed as double folds of skin and subcutaneous adipose tissue are raised away from the body by the examiner. This adipose-bearing 'skinfold' is measured with jaw calipers designed with a pressure spring calibrated at $10 \, \mathrm{g \, mm^{-2}}$ over an operating range that varies according to manufacturer as does the accuracy, ranging from 0.2 to 1.0 mm. A reliable measurement of subcutaneous fat depends on correct anatomical acquisition of the tissue to be measured and positioning of the calipers, skill on the part of the researcher (acquiring only fat tissue, free of underlying muscle) and status of the infant (young infants do not necessarily have well-defined body tissue compartments).

The subcutaneous sites measured in infants include limb measurements (the mid-upper arm over the triceps and/or biceps; the anterior aspect of the mid-thigh and the posterior calf) and body measurements (on the torso under the scapula and/or midaxillary region; at the level of the umbilicus and/or over the suprailiac bone at the hip to estimate abdominal fat). Interobserver differences are reported in the range of 1.2 mm for skinfold measurements. In combination with circumferential measurements, cross-sectional areas of fat and nonfat tissues can be calculated from mathematical formulas. As a single site, the circumference of the mid-upper arm together with the associated triceps skinfold provide a robust assessment of infant body composition and nutritional status. Ratios between trunk and limb skinfolds are used as indices of central adiposity, useful for assessing patterns of metabolic utilization of fat resources. Overall, fat deposition during infancy is predominantly subcutaneous; thus, anthropometrically assessed skinfold measurements provide a simple and noninvasive method for assessing infant fat acquisition and, together with circumferences, provide insight into body composition. Overall body composition studies using dual energy X-ray absortiometry (DEXA) have identified that skinfold measurements on the limbs together with total body length predict approximately 94% of the variance in total body fat mass during infancy.

Total body length is often measured in delivery rooms, clinics, and survey circumstances by stretching a measurement tape close to the infant's body. While providing a reasonable estimate of length, for more accurate assessment two observers and a recumbent infant length measuring board are needed. This instrument consists of a horizontal board with a firmly placed vertical headboard and a movable footboard; the infant is placed in the recumbent position on the horizontal base with one observer holding the infant's head in contact with the headboard in the Frankfort plane (head at a 90° angle to the horizontal). The second observer steadies the infant's body and applies gentle pressure to extend the legs into a fully stretched position. The footboard is then moved into contact with the heels and the full body length measurement is taken either by reference to a metric on the board itself or from a digitized readout built into the platform measuring from headboard to footboard.

Reproducibility reflects measurement technique, infant positioning and infant state in terms of both cooperation and physiology. Observer errors in placement of the head and inappropriately elongating the infant at an angle will result in an overestimation of body length while infant body tension, inappropriate head position, back arching, knee flexure and time since recumbency (including sitting) will underestimate the length of the infant (the latter due to compressive forces can reduce length up to 2 cm). Reproducibility within and between well trained individual observers is less than 0.2 cm, compared to a range of 2 cm with a single observer and a tape measure. A segmental length, crown-rump length, is sometimes taken during infancy, employing the same technique but flexing the thighs to obtain a measurement with the footboard pressed against the buttocks. Inter-observer differences average 0.5 cm in these measurements. Total body length is typically reported for infants up to the age of 2–3 years, when standing height measurements are initiated. The systematic differences between recumbent and standing measurements range between 0.4 and 0.8 cm.

Infant weights are often measured by simple devices under field conditions, including slings and simple bathroom-type scales on which mothers hold their infants and then weigh themselves alone, while high sensitivity digital scales are used for weighing infants in a research environment, recorded to the nearest 10 g. Quality control issues concern maintenance of the scale itself, particularly portable devices, infant clothing, and infant state (including diurnal/circadian effects), time since last ingestion and excretion. The importance of these factors is sometimes overlooked, but is a significant contributor to variance. For example, a measurement taken immediately after an infant has consumed 250 ml of liquids would not be an accurate reflection of the infant's body tissue weight alone.

These individual metrics are also employed as ratios with the aim of providing a perspective on body proportions. Weight for length is an index often used to consider relative thinness/fatness of an infant, and can provide some basis for assessing under and/or overnutrition of the infant. It is somewhat independent of age in later infancy and can provide significant information regarding the relative health of infants who lack birth records. Alternative ratios are used that aim to capture the proportionality of the infant: Rohrer's Index, or weight (g)/length^3 (cm^3), ponderal index, or length/weight$^{1/3}$, and body mass index (BMI), or weight/length^2.

What does weight really reflect? Research designed to differentiate fat and lean tissues, as well as specify bone mineral content has identified the broad outlines of infant physical growth as it unfolds not only in terms of increasing size, but in changing body composition. On average, the neonate's birth weight is composed of about 14% fat, which increases to 25–30% of weight by 4–6 months of age with gender, feeding and age effects. Boys tend to have greater fat-free mass from 2 weeks to 18 months of age, and girls, greater fat mass. As body tissues are

characterized by metabolic differences, these gender and age patterns may contribute to individual variability in energy utilization and individual variability in growth patterns. The use of air displacement plethysmographic techniques (e.g., the *Peapod*) may fill in further details relevant to issues of how metabolic processes broker the effects of nutrition on physical growth. At this time, little is known about normal infant growth physiology as blood and other cellular biomarkers are rarely investigated due to the invasive nature of the sampling. With the continued development of noninvasive approaches to permit the identification of biomarkers in saliva, urine, and fecal excretions, understanding of these specifics may unfold.

The physical growth patterns that we know much less about are those related to specific organs. While infant weight gain certainly reflects the proliferation of organ-specific tissues, large-scale studies documenting this by ultrasound, magnetic resonance imaging, and other imaging procedures *in vivo* are lacking.

In summary, infant physical growth is assessed primarily by measurements taken from external features of the body that serve to estimate its three-dimensional size and shape from circumferences and two-dimensional distances between anatomical landmarks. While some attempts have been made to develop three-dimensional imaging techniques of the external body, these are not validated at this time and the gold standard remains anthropometry for most dimensions. The sources of error in growth metrics include those from the equipment, the researcher and the infant, with both systematic and stochastic components. These are not insignificant in terms of repeated measures studies and may contribute to data interpretation. It is important that studies of infant physical growth report methods for assessing error components, including estimates of instrument accuracy and the validity, reliability and repeatability involved in data collection, as well as considerations of measurement error in data analyses.

How Measurements Have Meaning: Reference Charts

Knowing the size of an infant is not particularly informative in itself as significant individual variability in infant physical size is the norm. Consider two healthy infants of exactly the same size, 74 cm in total body length, weighing 8100 g. The female, however, is 1 year of age while the male is 6 months of age. These infants illustrate the effects of both gender and genetics on physical growth, and support the general rule that boys tend to be larger than girls and tall parents tend to have larger babies. While many people believe that whether an infant is 'skinny' or 'plump' is obvious to the eye, not all people agree about the desirability of these extremes, or what is 'normal'. Cultural beliefs range from valuing a 'fat baby' as a 'healthy baby' to disparaging a 'fat baby' as the precursor to an overweight adult. Both of these observations are based on experiential reality; the first is inductive common sense in a world without medicine where baby fat is protective, enabling infants to survive the weight loss of intermittent acute infections as the naive immune system meets the microbial environment. The latter is an increasingly salient observation in the modern world facing an epidemic of obesity.

How we know who is 'short' or 'tall' is less clear and intuitively observers react to expectations of size for age. In this way, tall for age toddlers are often faced with the expectation that they 'should be' further along in their developmental behavior, and short for age infants are often perceived as precocious. To provide an objective frame of reference for these assessments, large samples of infants have been measured to provide data for perspective on what the size of any single individual means; these data are the basis for normative concepts of infant physical growth.

Both cross-sectional (one time only) and longitudinal (repeated measures on the same individuals) protocols have been used for data collection. Some of these studies have had a regional collection strategy but were combined to provide population level perspective and others have aimed to obtain nationally representative samples with complex sampling strategies and careful analyses to provide information applicable for an entire population. Descriptive statistics of individuals' measurements by age provide mean (average), median (50th percentile), and percentile distributions that serve as reference ranges within which to compare the size of individuals of the same population.

The frame of reference is an important metric, as research has documented significant effects on infant size for age due to factors ranging from genetic predisposition to biological age (gestational age in young infants), feeding style, illness and altitude, for example, as well as lifestyle variables such as socioeconomic level and maternal education, as these mediate availability to the infant of resources ranging from nutrition to healthcare. Specific references are available for assessing the physical growth of preterm, low birth weight (1500–2500 g) and very low birth weight (≤1500 g) infants and those with clinical conditions. Local references have been developed for international and community use to assess the relative size of specific samples. Using these site- and clinical condition-specific reference sample data, infants who are 'small for age', 'large for age' and 'appropriate for age' can be identified to guide intervention decisions in specific contexts.

Mathematically derived curves then summarize these statistical distributions across age and generate the convex-shaped percentile lines characteristic of growth charts typically used in clinics and pediatric offices as references for the interpretation of 'normal infant growth'. These reference charts are tools providing a common basis for comparison so that parents, clinicians, and health workers can identify how an infant is 'doing'. The typical growth chart is constructed to present the 5th–95th

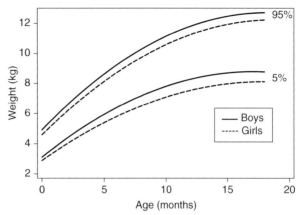

Figure 1 Weight-age charts for boys and girls (WHO, 2006).

percentile distributions, with each percentile defined as the percent of the population that has a smaller value. As gender effects are significant, separate charts and curves have been developed for boys and girls (**Figure 1**).

The utility of growth chart references is exemplified by the infants in **Figure 1**. By reference to the year 2000 national reference for US infants, the female's length is at the 50th percentile for 1-year-old girls, representing the height at which half of the girls of her age are taller and half are shorter. The male is relatively tall for his age, with a size that falls at the 95th percentile: only 5% of boys of his age are taller, while 95% are shorter. With respect to weight, he is at the 15th percentile for 6-month-old boys. The female is at the 15th percentile for girls, or 85% of 1-year-old girls weigh more than she does. By observation, the infants are neither 'chubby' nor 'skinny', both appearing relatively lean. This relationship is expressed by the index 'weight for length'. Compared to their reference groups, the infant boy is at the 25th percentile (75% of boys his age weigh more for their length) and the girl, like her weight, is at the 15th percentile.

The comparisons just described answer the question of 'what size is an infant, relative to his/her peers?' The year 2000 US National Center for Health Statistics (NCHS)/ Center for Disease Control and Prevention (CDC) reference standards chosen for this illustration are based on data collected from infants weighing more than 1500 g across states, socioeconomic levels, and ethnicity with breastfeeding percentages matching those of the US during this time.

Reference charts are important as summaries of real differences among infants in size for age, with increasing magnitudes separating the percentile ranges with age. For example, a 6 cm difference in body length separates the 5th and 95th percentiles at birth, increasing to 8 cm at 1 year, and 10 cm between 18 and 24 months. In terms of weight, 95% of healthy infants in optimal environments are between 2.5 and 4 kg at birth, 6 and 9 kgs at 6 months, 7 and 11 kg at 1 year, and 9.4 and 14.2 kg at 2 years. In the case of healthy infants in optimal environments, these ranges reflect individual differences in the rate of growth (how fast size is attained), which results from both genetic patterns and limits. A range of environmental factors (from prenatal influences to postnatal nutrition, illness, and altitude) can act to modify these genetic determinants both pre- and postnatally.

The statistical distribution is an important fundamental reality that reflects phenotypic diversity. Clinicians have a practice of assessing individual infants' growth progress by reference to the age at which their size is the average. Thus, for the exemplar infants above, at age 1 year the girl is the average length of a 1-year-old, but the average weight of a 9-month-old. This presents the image of an infant who is delayed for their age rather than an infant who is part of a normal phenotypic range. This approach has no evidence-based meaning and can lead to an erroneous understanding of infant well-being.

Reference charts provide the statistical distribution of infant size for age. The most commonly employed indicator of how an infant is doing relative to their peers is through their 'z-score' or 'standard score', a statistical short hand for how an individual compares to the median in terms of standard deviations (calculated by subtracting a median reference value from an observed value and dividing the difference by the reference standard deviation). Thus, an individual infant who is −2 z-scores in weight for age would be smaller than nearly 98% of his peers. While about 2% of healthy individuals are this small and smaller, the −2 z-score measurement is often employed as a 'cutoff' value in screening studies to identify infants at risk of underweight, stunting or wasting (the result, e.g., of severe malnutrition).

In summary, growth references are designed to assess single growth measurements relative to a group of the infant's peers. The statistical distributions summarized in these references are reflections of real morphologic differences and document individual differences in incremental growth during similar timeframes, or variability in individual's growth rate. In practice, these reference graphs/tables are often used to monitor individual's growth by observing changes in percentile status over time. This may lead to their adoption as tools to aid in predicting health, well-being, and infant survival as well as guiding interventions to maintain nutrition. The most commonly used anthropometrics for assessing infant well-being are weight-for-age, height-for-age, weight-for-height, and mid-upper-arm circumference (for more specific information about nutritional status).

How We 'See' Growth: Growth Curves

While overall growth progress is captured by a single measurement point, and a reference sample can put this into some perspective relative to other infants, the size attained at a single age does not provide much insight into growth itself. For example, weight can change rapidly with acute illness and may say more about instantaneous physiology than it does about the overall 'physical growth' of an infant. Body length, by contrast, does not typically shrink substantially, and is a good indicator of overall growth to age. Thus, anthropometric measurements provide a marker for both ongoing dynamic physiology and achieved status. But growth itself is a process of change as the infant's physical body increases in size and shape through time and repeated assessments are needed to document this process.

According to statistics collected by both the World Health Organization (WHO) and the US NCHS during the first year, the 15th percentile healthy infant increases in total body length by about 25 cm, gaining about 6 kg and 10 cm in head circumference. Typical pediatric growth 'monitoring' of this progress includes measuring infants at well child visits at approximately 1, 2, 4, 6, 9, 12,15, 18, and 24 months of age (optimal schedule according to the American Academy of Pediatrics) and at each visit, the infant's size is plotted on a growth chart. Common practice describes these serial measurement entries on growth chart references as 'growth patterns'. The assumption is that healthy infants 'track' along the percentile curves and 'crossing of centile lines' raises concerns about infants' growth progress. In the early months of life, shifting positions on the percentile charts is viewed as the normal process of 'regression to the mean', as infants at the extremes of birth size adjust their growth trajectories to the postnatal environment. With the removal of prenatal constraints to growth, some small babies (e.g., those experiencing *in utero* growth restriction) tend to 'catch up' in weight, exhibiting 'upward centile crossing' and some large babies (e.g., infants of diabetic mothers) tend to 'catch down' in weight, reflected in 'downward centile crossing'.

Physical 'growth patterns' on the growth charts are used as a key indicator of infant well-being and extended shifts in centiles often raise concerns. This can be beneficial in detecting serious medical conditions that may first manifest themselves in infant growth patterns (e.g., congenital cardiac anomalies, endocrine imbalance, metabolic disturbances). Exactly when slow growth progress becomes a significant clinical condition in itself is not a prescriptive diagnosis. In the extreme, sequential downward centile crossing or continued size for age below the 3rd or 5th percentiles may be an indicator of 'growth faltering' or raise concern that an infant may be experiencing 'failure to thrive'. Persistent slow weight gain during infancy raises concerns that some organic or nonorganic factors are interfering with the infant's growth and development. The latter may be associated with factors ranging from a poor socioemotional environment, impaired parental–infant interactions, economic barriers to adequate nutritional resources, and parental health beliefs regarding feeding. These can lead to unusual growth patterns as weight for age and weight-for-length decline to below the 3rd or 5th

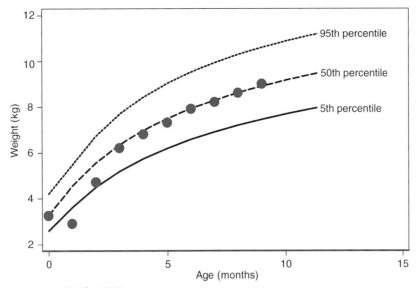

Figure 2 Weight for age in boys (WHO, 2006).

percentiles. Under extreme circumstances of social and emotional neglect, physical growth can be arrested altogether. Rene Spitz termed this response 'hospitalism' for infants maintained under stark conditions of overcrowded infant hospital/orphanages.

In practice, the most common interpretation of downward centile progress in an individual is insufficient nutrition and health personnel use these observations to guide feeding recommendations (**Figure 2**). For example, breastfeeding mothers who cannot see what their infants are actually eating often have concerns regarding whether their infants are 'getting enough' and rely on advice derived from weight gain/loss patterns to help them in determining when to provide additional nutrition. The appropriateness of using growth chart derived growth patterns as a nutritional guide, however, assumes that the charts were (1) devised with an understanding of how nutritional intake effects infant physical growth, (2) constructed from data controlling for feeding patterns of the sample reference infants, and (3) checked to see that the descriptive statistics of the pooled sample data accurately reflect the progress of individual infants. This is not necessarily the case.

The importance of reference sample characteristics for interpreting growth patterns was documented in the 1980s and 1990s by studies of breastfed vs. formula fed infants. Compared to formula fed infants, the breastfed infants' weight-for-age exhibited downward progression across percentiles from 3 months of age on the growth reference charts commonly in use at that time. This pattern might have suggested that breast milk was an insufficient source of nutrition to maintain growth and should be replaced and/or augmented with additional food sources. However, the researchers noted that the infants themselves were, in fact, thriving and concluded

that the slower weight gain of breastfed infants after the first few months was normal.

These observations focused attention on the construction of infant growth charts. The gold standard reference at the time, published in 1977 by the US NCHS and adopted by WHO for international use in 1978, was based on a limited sample of several hundred infants from the Fels longitudinal study in Ohio, who were predominantly formula fed. The importance of feeding patterns for infant physical growth were clarified by these studies and the observations are the basis for the consensus that in optimal environments, breastfed babies initially gain weight more rapidly, and then more slowly, than formula fed babies. A misunderstanding of the physical growth pattern difference between breastfed babies and those receiving alternative food sources has profound consequences for infant morbidity and mortality. As a pattern of perceived growth faltering among breastfed infants compared to nonbreastfed cohorts suggests that breast milk is insufficient to maintain growth, decisions may be made that put infants in a biological dilemma: the transition from breast milk to alternative food sources is one of the most predictive factors leading to growth failure due to pathogen exposure and consequent illness in the context of the naïve infant immune system.

The WHO responded to these observations by initiating an infant growth study with the goal of providing a reference standard based on the breastfed infant as the normative pattern. Data were collected from approximately 8500 infants from different ethnic and cultural settings (Brazil, Ghana, India, Norway, Oman, and the US); all were from healthy pregnancies among affluent, nonsmoking families and were breastfed for at least 4–6 months of age. Known as the Multicentre Growth Reference Study (MGRS), these data were found to show no significant differences between populations in infant length for age and have been used to construct growth curves, published in 2006, aiming to provide a single international standard for how infants and young children are expected to grow under optimal conditions. Thus, while the earlier reference charts were summaries of how children did grow, the WHO contends that their curves represent standards of how healthy, uncompromised infants should grow.

Upward centile crossing, particularly for infants' weight for age and weight for length measurements, is also a concern due to the changing demographics of infant size that have been documented worldwide and the concomitant long term health consequences of being overweight. For example, in the US, a secular trend of increasing weight among American infants paralleled rising obesity rates among adults over the decades between 1970 and 2000. It was found that by the year 2000 an increasing number of infants weighed more at earlier ages, shifting the statistical distribution of infant weight for age to the right compared to earlier studies. Infant obesity, defined as greater than the 95th percentile of weight for height, rose among 6–24-month-olds to 12% in 2000 relative to the 1977 statistics.

Additionally, upward centile crossing may reflect 'catch-up growth' as an infant who has experienced a serious illness or a growth insult undergoes rapid acceleration in size during recovery. This is most commonly observed for weight (**Figure 2**), but may occur in other aspects of the body. Whether or not growth that has been compromised can be regained depends on the body parameter (weight, length, head circumference, organ, and tissue), the timing of the insult, the cause, and the length of exposure. Infants are both vulnerable and flexible with high recuperative potential due to the high growth rates during this developmental period. Complete catch-up growth is defined as a return of an individual to the growth percentile level achieved prior to the insult and consequent deficit. Strictly speaking, the precise size of an individual prior to an insult is not always a factor that can be clearly identified. Numerous studies document rapid growth during infancy following either intrauterine growth retardation (IUGR; identified among infants <3% in weight-for-age at birth, for example), or nutritional/illness insults, and point to the importance of the first 6 months of life as a recuperative window for both head circumference and length deficits resulting from prenatal growth limitations. Nonetheless, the timing of the insult relative to the period of most rapid growth is critical and size alone may not be an adequate marker of physical growth adequacy. Some insults have functionally specific effects as, for example, late onset IUGR on specific aspects of the frontal lobe neural network.

In summary, serial growth measurements plotted on reference graphs commonly known as infant growth charts are often used to assess the progress of individual infants and guide decision making regarding infant health and well being. It is, however, important to recognize that these charts are designed to describe the size of infants relative to a reference sample. The growth chart percentile curve lines are statistical constructions presenting data in an easy-to-use approach for monitoring infants across ages. The graphs are not intended to provide accurate models for the paths by which individual infants grow. This is a matter answered by longitudinally collected and presented data at the level of the individual. If the curves on the charts were growth channels, individuals would grow both continuously and quite similarly, if along different trajectories. Neither of these are the case. Studies have shown that in reality, the highly variable growth rates of individual infants result in approximately one-third of infants crossing two percentile lines in the first 6 months of life for length and weight, and as many as one in five infants between 6 months and 2 years. In terms of weight for height, more than 60% of infants cross two percentile lines in the first 6 months and one in three do so between 6 months and 2 years. As part of preventive medicine, it is not uncommon for infants who fall below the 3rd or 5th percentile on sequential visits (and whose parents are not equally short), as well as those who are above the 95th and 97th percentile in weight-for-age or weight-for-height, to receive additional consideration. However, making too many assumptions regarding individual growth patterns from growth chart patterns may not be the best practice approach for identifying how well individual infants are progressing.

Growth: Change through Time Within an Individual

Growth patterns that emerge by viewing consecutive size by age in reference to a sample of infant measurements organized by percentiles, as on a growth chart, are not equivalent to a representation of how individual infants actually grow. By definition, growth is a process of change through time. The more precise question many parents are asking when they are concerned about their infants is 'how much do infants normally grow?' in some interval, be it monthly, weekly, or daily. The practical questions of 'what is not enough growth?' or 'how much is too much growth?' are not answerable by reference to patterns on size-for-age charts. The data required for these concerns are repeated measures on individual infants to assess changes in size through time as increments or decrements, as in weight gain or loss, for example.

In assessing change between consecutive measurements, technique is critical as the derivation of a change between two data points doubles the contribution of technical errors (errors at each measurement assessment). In practical terms, an overestimated measurement followed by an underestimated measurement could appear as 'no growth' during an interval and potentially cause concern regarding growth arrest. Likewise, an underestimated measurement followed by an overestimated measurement could lead to an apparent 'overgrowth' alert when none may be indicated.

But careful measurements can provide insight into growth problems much more rapidly than assessment of serial growth status points on the percentile distribution growth charts. For example, understanding how much a normal infant's head grows in circumference on a daily or weekly basis can assist in the diagnosis of clinical conditions, such as hydrocephalus (the excessive accumulation of cerebrospinal fluid surrounding the brain). While it is 'normal' for an infant to increase head circumference as much as 2 cm per month during the first half year, it would not be the 'norm' for this growth to occur in the span of one week and would be an indication for clinical follow-up.

How much head circumference, length, or weight individual infants actually gain or lose across days, weeks, and months is an individual-specific indicator of personal health status. Percentile distributions of growth rates for length, head circumference, weight, and mid-upper arm circumference (most commonly) have been generated with the aim of providing an aide for clinical screening and early detection of overweight and/or failure to thrive. Reference charts for actual incremental growth are less common than those for size achieved. Two-, three-, and six-monthly increments expressed as monthly growth rates are available from the Euro-Growth Study of more than 2200 infants collected at 22 sites in 12 European countries. Monthly growth rates for 95% of the European infants ranged between 2 and 5 cm in length during the first month, 1–3 cm at 6 months, less than 2 cm at 12 months and less than 1.5 cm in years 2 and 3, while gaining between 300 and 1400 g in the first month, 200–900 g by 6 months, 100–500 g at 1 year and steadying at less than 100 g to as much as 400 g per month in the second and third years.

In addition, growth velocities have been derived for shorter intervals than actual measurement assessments from mathematical models fitted to serial data. For example, for measurements taken at 1–3 month intervals, the actual measurements at each age are graphically connected to interpolate the size at the times in between measurements. The growth velocity is then estimated either by taking a mathematical derivative of this continuous function, or by differencing the measurements and dividing by the timeframe of interest. According to these approaches, on average, infants are expected to grow a little more than 1 mm per day in length at 3 months of age and less than 0.5 mm from 6 to 24 months, while gaining about 30, 20, and 10 g per day at 3, 6, and 12–18 months, respectively. These estimates are based on assumptions of infant growth that do not accurately reflect growth biology.

From all of these estimates it appears that physical growth declines in the rate at which it accrues as age from birth increases. These generalizations imply that growth is a

declining drain on energy resources for the individual as the first year proceeds. Estimates of the energy required to support growth are based on these assumptions and have provided the foundation on which best practices regarding nutritional supplementation for infant growth are calculated. From this point of view, the energy required for growth is small after the first half year, declining from 22% of total daily energy requirements at 3 months of age to 6% by 6 months and only 2–3% by the end of the first year.

In summary, population level data indicate an overall negative trend in the velocity of infant physical growth in length, weight, and head circumference that is rapid in the first 4 months, and decelerates over the first 2–3 years of life. In terms of general trends, both subcutaneous skinfold thickness values and the index variables, weight for length and BMI, peak during the first 4–6 months of life and tend to level off or decrease over the next 2 years. Concomitantly, as a percentage of body weight, fat-free mass decreases during the first 6 months and then increases across the first 3 years. In general, males tend to be larger than females in weight, length, and head circumference across the first year, but females have a greater percentage of their weight composed of fat. These summaries capture the general trends in infant growth and provide useful information for screening large groups of infants. They do not, however, accurately describe how individual infants grow.

How Infants Grow: Saltation and Stasis

Individual infants' physical growth biology is not documented by the smooth curves found on growth charts and is not correctly reflected in mathematically derived estimates of growth velocity. As an incremental process through time, physical growth itself is only revealed by repeated measurements of physical parameters from individual infants. When measured by trained personnel under research conditions, repeated measurements identify that infants increase the measurable dimensions of their weight, length, and head circumference discontinuously, in episodic growth spurts. In contrast to the image of slow and continuous size acquisition implied by the lines drawn on the graphical charts, the biology of infant physical growth is like many other physiological processes and proceeds in saltatory bursts of episodically timed growth events. In fact, the incremental growth evident at traditional monthly or bimonthly measurement intervals is accrued during discrete growth events, or saltations, that occur in a timeframe of hours and physical growth proceeds by a series of saltations that are separated by intervals of no measurable growth (stasis intervals).

For example, the female infant shown in **Figure 1** grew 15 cm in length over the first 6 months of life, 9 cm in the second 6 months and 6 cm between 1 year and 18 months of age. In terms of the US or WHO growth charts, she maintained an approximate 50th percentile ranking in size across these ages when her length data are plotted from monthly measurements (**Figure 3**), maintaining a healthy size by comparison with her peers of similar age across the first year. But how, exactly, was her size at each monthly measurement achieved? Was it little by little every day, as the growth chart implies, or was it by some other, less regular pathway? In the absence of more data, this would not be knowable. If one were to estimate the process between each monthly size assessment by inter-polating a daily growth rate (dividing the incremental growth by the number of days), the mathematically-derived estimate of her daily growth as approximately 0.8 mm per day in length (150 mm divided by 180 days), dropping to 0.5 mm per day during the second 6 months and 0.3 mm per day after 1 year.

This is not, however, how she actually grew; instead she grew by saltations and stasis. This infant was measured daily and her anthropometric measurements identified that her total body length grew only about 10% of the time in her first year, during the intervals between her daily measurements (thus within 1 day) at episodic (not periodically predictable) intervals. In summary, during her first 6 months, she accrued the 15 cm of growth in body length in 26 discrete saltatory growth spurt events. That is, each incremental growth saltation occurred in the interval between regularly scheduled daily measure-ments. A subsequent 26 saltations added another 15 cm in body length between 6 and 18 months of age. Each of the growth saltations averaged 0.6 cm in amplitude, and these were separated by durations of no measurable growth ranging from 1 to 42 days (**Figure 4**). In this example, the trends for growth rate decline from birth across the first year and a half resulted from a decreasing frequency of quantitatively similar growth events. Knowing the details of the day-to-day events permits an appreciation for the specific pattern by which her size for age was achieved. This permits the investigation and understand-ing of exactly what it means to grow, and thereby, what it takes to help infants grow.

These results explain the mechanistic basis of pheno-typic variability: as size is increased by discrete growth accretions, individual differences in the timing of these growth events, as well as the amount of growth at each saltation, underlie variability in attained length for age among infants as well as growth rate variance. Infants of similar initial size can achieve different sizes through time by varying the timing and/or amount of growth saltations, and infants of different initial sizes can end up at the same size through time by alternative pathways (**Figure 5**).

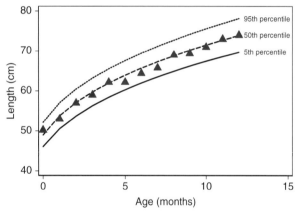

Figure 3   Length for age in girls (WHO, 2006).

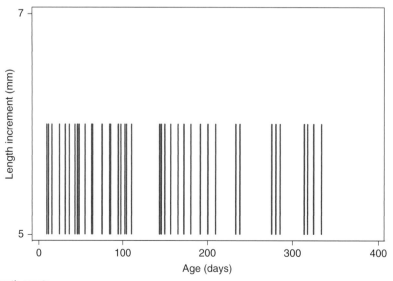

Figure 4   Saltatory growth spurts.

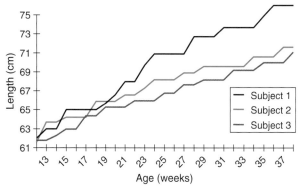

Figure 5 Individual differences in length growth patterns from 3–9 months of age. Thus infants of relatively similar body length at 3 months follow distinctly different patterns in timing and amount of growth saltations to achieve both similar and different size by 9 months of age.

Thus, being relatively short or long at any age is achieved through more or less frequent growth saltations of greater and lesser amounts. Like the pulsatile hormonal systems that underlie physical growth mechanistically, tissue accretion occurs through a modifiable process of variable amplitude and frequency.

Serial measurements of the lower leg among infants likewise identify growth in fits and starts, proceding by what has been called 'mini growth spurts', named as a diminuitive version of the larger and longer adolescent growth spurt that propels the child's body toward final adult size. Head circumference growth follows a similar episodic saltatory pattern, with a timing that suggests an integrated control of whole body growth: head growth spurts precede total body length growth saltations, as well as between length saltations, concomitant with behavioral developmental shifts during infancy. A general trend of physical growth alternating with behavioral development characterizes the early years.

Animal studies have documented saltatory growth spurts in both membranous bone across species, and lamb lower limb bones, specifically, with incremental growth across the long bone growth plates, the cellular site of bone elongation, observed to occur during recumbency. These observations focus attention on cell level activities as sites that integrate information on when growth is to take place and how much incremental growth can occur.

Changes in both weight and subcutaneous skinfold measures accompany head and length growth saltations, signaling that discrete growth saltations are metabolically active events and call for time-constrained resources. Based on corresponding weight gain and loss patterns with discrete increments in body length saltations, the equivalent of a day and a half's total caloric requirements may be required to fuel growing. Appetites increase around growth events to include a doubling of eating frequency among breastfeeding infants, signaled by fussiness, crying, and agitation. The sleep and activity patterns

of infants likewise change, with a decrease in sleeping concomitant with increased bouts of eating, followed by an increase in total hours slept and/or an increase in napping: Infants tend to sleep more when they are growing. Infant physical growth, then, is a process characterized by episodic events that take place at the level of cells, organs and tissues, reflected in biobehavioral changes at the level of the individual that may span 3–4 days. During this interval, disruptions in infant physiology and state lead to alterations in activity and affect. An appreciation that physical growth is a lived event for infants, a biologically experienced transition with effects on behavior that influence infant/caregiver interaction patterns, helps parents meet the challenges of these episodic outbursts and comfort their infants who must negotiate their body's physical changes.

The specific mechanisms of a saltatory growth program are only beginning to be understood and the specific details of organismic saltatory growth biology, in terms of how genetically determined temporal programs interact with environmental signals to permit human physical development to proceed, are the subject of investigation. The timing of growth saltations follows principles of dynamical systems, with a tempo that is episodic and not strictly periodic, and likely determined by genetics, as identical twins grow at similar times. This suggests that there is a genetic clock driving cell division and differentiation that is itself modestly modifiable, as both genetic and epigenetic effects are integrated through cross talk between a cascade of local factors that influence transcription and receptor-mediated effectors.

The biobehavioral patterns of saltatory growth biology permit hypothesis generation regarding potential paths by which a biological clock works together with energetically mediated down stream effects of gene expression, using chemical signals to direct differentiation. Cross-talking pathways permit multiple avenues for information about the environment to have an impact on the amount and timing of growth events. With sufficient negative feedback, a growth event will theoretically be suppressed, thus altering the timing of growth saltations. Thus, as a dynamic system, the pulsatility characteristics of growth events provide flexibility in the growth process. Information is integrated at multinodal points and a gene/environment negotiation occurs to alter the timing and amount of growth as hormonal signals and body composition translate the metabolic environment.

An understanding of the proximal pathways by which growth at the whole body is integrated from the level of the cell, to an organized growth of 'the brain' or 'total body length' has yet to be written. Some researchers have suggested that infant physical growth may be under different hormonal mechanisms from later growth; others disagree. It is difficult to resolve this debate definitively as extensive data on hormonal patterns during infancy have been lacking due to the invasive nature of serum sampling.

The development of noninvasive techniques (for example, salivary and urinary assays) holds the promise of filling in some of the details that are presently missing. It is clear that metabolic signals and cellular control mechanisms are integrated by protein and steroid hormones, for example, to influence physical growth as pathways involving cortisol, thyroid and growth hormone influence insulin growth factors and cross talk with leptin and ghrelin, for example. No doubt, the more proximal levels of cellular metabolism may be instrumental as primary signals from oxygen pathways integrate nutritional information more directly with broad ranging downstream effects from, for example, the hypoxia inducible factor cascade.

The variability in size and growth rates observed for infants under diverse ecological circumstances testify to the importance of these influences: for example, infants from high altitudes exemplify ecology writ at the level of body morphology, with effects ranging from decreased weight alone, or no weight effects, but short legs. Infants from an environment characterized by generally poor nutrition have been described as phenotypically 'short but plump', and 'fat but thin'. The former refers to inhibition of growth in body length that is greater than that for weight; the latter goes further and identifies individuals whose body composition is being laid down preferentially in terms of fat, rather than lean body mass. Fetal growth studies have documented selective inhibition of lean body mass growth under conditions of maternal smoking, and taken together, these observations identify distinctive growth patterns of body compartments that respond to basic physiological signals that integrate oxygen and nutrition signals through cellular metabolism, determining growth in body size and compartments.

High rates of morbidity and mortality during infancy worldwide identify the selective pressure on survival during infancy. As a result, growth patterns best suited for survival in various environments become the local growth pattern, and are the genotypic sources underlying phenotypic diversity in growth rate and size. As a genetically-based individual process, growth by alternating intervals of saltation and stasis permits each growth events to be molded by the environment. In turn, this episodic biology forms the basis for adaptability as a diversity in growth patterns is available for an infant to negotiate the path to reproductive maturity.

It is notable that the rapid growth rates of infancy are only matched during adolescence. It may be that infant physical growth biology is an entrainment for the realities that the body will face during reproductive maturity and the high selection rates on early growth patterns via infant mortality serve to match biological readiness through selection on growth patterns: thus, growth events may be more than growing. For example, common mesenchymal cells become, alternatively, muscle bone or fat under the influence of local metabolically based signals. With their fate in the hands of a time-constrained

environmental read-out, cells differentiate down alternative pathways. Growth saltations are moments of energetic negotiations determining tissue structure and function, and the cascade of biological events at these junctures may inform lifelong patterns through body composition, size and metabolic pathways inherent to cell lines.

In this way, individuals surviving to give birth to the next generation of infants pass on the means with which to negotiate the specific exigencies of local environments. That there is flexibility in these patterns is documented by intergenerational studies; not only is there heritability in birth size, but the specific effects of maternal nutritional status have been identified as secular trends in infant growth patterns among the next generation: the infants of mothers who were themselves supplemented as infants grow more rapidly and attain larger size for age. Studies identify that maternal stature and prenatal factors explain a significant proportion of variation in infant growth.

Infant Physical Growth Occurs as Integrated Events Through Growth Biology: Process and Implications

Physical growth during infancy is both an outcome and a predictor. Size at birth is the outcome of facultative fetal growth; and, in turn, size at birth predicts aspects of infant growth and these growth patterns have some predictability for future health risks. To put this into perspective, consider that infant physical growth is a continuation of developmental events set in motion at the first cell division: the average newborn is 5000 times larger than its first cell (average birth length of 50 cm, and average ovum, 50 μm). Prenatal development takes the average 8 cm embryo and culminates in a physical size at birth that reflects influences from both parents in terms of height and weight (with different genetically based mechanisms contributing to skeletal size and fat/metabolic pathways) as well as a wide array of *in utero* environmental effects.

Size at birth has significant effects on postnatal physical growth, particularly in the context of size for gestational age, with differences expressed in neonatal mortality, postnatal growth rates, and body composition. Small for gestational age infants (defined variously as those with birth weights $<10\%$ or -2 z-scores for gestational age), including some with IUGR ($<3\%$), may grow faster to decrease deficits in the early months. Some of these infants remain small in terms of weight and head circumference up to 36 months of age, while others experience catch-up in head circumference by 2 years of age. Individual variability in levels of specific growth-related factors (e.g., insulin growth factor-1, IGF-1) positively predicts catch-up growth. Large for gestational age infants (those with birth weights >4500 g or $>+2$ z-scores) are often associated with maternal diabetes during pregnancy (reflecting development in an environment of hyperglycemia). These infants often 'slow down' in early infancy.

Prematurity brings with it gestational age effects reflecting a fetus interrupted in the process of developing the body under *in utero* conditions, confronting continued physical growth in the face of functional immaturity. While a number of organ systems are activated *in utero*, others undergo shifts as the internal milieu is replaced: Lungs open for the first time and replace the placenta as oxygen exchange organs; the gastrointestinal tract, with experience limited to *in utero* fluids, makes the transition to extrauterine life through breastmilk, continuing a maternal interface with the environment for nutrients, growth factors, and, importantly, immune protection and training. The massive reorganization of the oxygen status of the organism combined with the challenge of acquiring nutritional sufficiency while metabolic pathways are established and gut absorption is developing are formidable challenges for the maintenance of postnatal physical growth. All infants lose weight immediately after birth, and may require several weeks to adjust and regain their birth status.

In sum, birth weight is highly influenced by maternal height, weight, weight gain, and *in utero* environment; but it is also a heritable trait that may reflect genetically based metabolic pathways, for example. Studies identify hereditary contributions to birth weight and length, growth in length during the first 2 years and infant head circumference of varying proportions, and have suggested persistent developmental effects of size at birth, with differences between large for gestational age and small for gestational age infants in weight and stature of about 0.5 to 1 z-score persisting to 17 years. Whether this reflects the effects of large babies becoming large adults (and vice versa) due to genetic and epigenetic effects, or something more specific is not clear. There is controversy regarding what, exactly, is the critical period for determining subsequent stature, with observations ranging from permanent fetal effects, to flexibility within the first 3 years of life, or, perhaps, beyond. Long-term consequences of birth size and infant growth rates have included size at later ages and maturational timing/aging effects: for example, population studies have linked size at birth and rapid growth rates during the first 2 years of life to early puberty; others report that tall adolescents gained more weight in infancy and had higher IGF1, while infants with lower IGF1 levels grow slowly. Taken together with studies of aging, infant growth may well be a reflection of aging more generally.

Finally, a number of epidemiologically oriented studies find predictability between infant size and growth patterns and adult health risks for degenerative diseases broadly, and metabolic diseases more specifically. The mechanisms that relate these developmental processes and final functional outcomes are not yet clear. It is likely, however, that growth biology, as a cascade of pathways acting in the essential role of bartering metabolic information, are central determinants as the architecture of the body is constructed through physical growth in infancy.

See also: Endocrine System; Failure to Thrive; Feeding Development and Disorders; Milestones: Physical; Nutrition and Diet; Obesity.

Suggested Readings

Hall J, Allanson JE, Gripp K, and Slavotinek A (2006) *Handbook of Physical Measurements.* New York: Oxford University Press.

Hall JG, Froster-Iskenius UG, and Allanson JE (1990) *Handbook of Normal Physical Measurements.* New York: Oxford University Press.

Jürimäe T and Jürimäe J (2000) *Growth, Physical Activity and Motor Development in Prepubertal Children.* Boca Raton: CRC Press.

Mandleco BL (2004) *Growth and Development Handbook: Newborn Through Adolescence.* Clifton Park, NY: Delmar.

Piaget's Cognitive-Developmental Theory

J P Byrnes, Temple University, Philadelphia, PA, USA

Glossary

Accommodation – Changing a mental structure in order to assimilate a new idea.

Assimilation – The mind's ability to incorporate an experience or new information into an existing mental structure.

Concrete operational thought – A representational form of thought characterized by reversibility, the ability to consider two dimensions, hierarchical categorization, and seriation; focused on concrete reality rather than hypothetical possibilities.

Conservation – A belief that the amount of something stays the same despite superficial transformations in the appearance of an object or array of objects.

Constructivism – The belief that concepts are neither inborn nor immediately learned through exposure to the world; rather, knowledge is build up, step by step.

Empiricism – The belief that knowledge can be acquired through the senses.

Equilibration – Restoring the balance between assimilation and accommodation.

Formal operational thought – A representational, reversible, multidimensional, and abstract form of thought; focused on both concrete reality and hypothetical possibilities.

Functionalism – A belief in the goal-directed and adaptive nature of thought.

Nativism – The belief that concepts are inborn.

Object permanence – Understanding that an object continues to exist even when it is out of view.

Preoperational thought – A nonreversible form of representational thought that is unidimensional and grounded in perceptual similarity.

Reflective abstraction – Contrasts with simple abstraction in which the properties of objects (e.g., its redness) are merely 'read off of' the objects. As children coordinate actions to achieve certain ends, the mind discovers commonalities across these coordinations, reorganizes and reconstructs them, and projects this construction onto a higher plane of thought.

Reversibility – A quality of thinking in which an observed transformation can be mentally 'undone'.

Schemes – Goal-directed behaviors that are repeatedly utilized in situations to discover the properties of objects.

Sensorimotor thinking – Objects are understood with respect to what actions can be performed on them; limited to the here and now.

Structuralism – A belief in the importance of discovering the inherent organization and the form and content of thought.

Introduction

It is sometimes said that one of the hallmarks of genius is the ability to recognize the deep significance of seemingly ordinary phenomena that are 'right under everyone's noses'. Many of the phenomena that Jean Piaget examined have been well known to parents and early childhood

educators for hundreds of years. For example, most parents have probably hidden a toy under a pillow to see if their toddlers will search for it, or heard their child say "I think the moon is following us" as they travel at night in a car or train. Piaget's unusual insight was these phenomena were manifestations of characteristic kinds of thinking in children; in other words, children's behaviors had a lot to say about the kinds of knowledge structures that they held in their minds. In addition, however, Piaget moved well beyond these naturally occurring behaviors by probing children's minds using a variety of novel experimental tasks. His explanations of children's spontaneous and elicited behaviors resonated with some scholars, but evoked strong criticism from many others. Regardless of whether scholars were trying to support or disconfirm his account, Piaget's work influenced several generations of researchers by identifying the kinds of competencies that should be investigated at specific ages. For example, few developmental psychologists examined phenomena such as object permanence or conservation of mass before Piaget brought these competences to the attention of developmental psychologists. Moreover, criticism of his methodologies likewise prompted many to devise extremely clever procedures to reveal competences at ages earlier than he found. Piaget's theory was particularly revolutionary to scholars of the infancy period in that it was one of the first to provide a detailed account of infant cognition and tried to show the continuities between infant and later cognition. Even 26 years after his death, Piaget's works are still cited over 2000 times per year.

Although it is not feasible to provide a comprehensive summary of Piaget's work in a brief encyclopedia entry, it is possible to present some of the main themes of his work and the controversies that these themes evoked.

Major Themes

The following four themes capture the essence of Piaget's perspective. (1) Of the three possible epistemological stances regarding the origin of knowledge (i.e., nativism, empiricism, and constructivism), constructivism is the most viable and compelling alternative. (2) The development of children's thinking can be described as a progression through four levels or stages of thought. (3) Of the various epistemological stances regarding the nature of knowledge (e.g., structuralism, functionalism, behaviorism, and connectionism), structuralism and functionalism are the most viable and compelling alternatives. (4) Of the four factors that explain the changes in thought that occur over time (i.e., biological maturation, physical experience, social exchange, and equilibration), equilibration is the most significant. In what follows, these themes are discussed in turn.

Constructivism. When Piaget first began his career in the 1920s, he had recently finished his graduate studies in the area of philosophy. His interest in philosophy affected all aspects of his subsequent empirical work in the area of cognitive development in the sense that he collected data to largely show that the two primary philosophical perspectives on the origins of knowledge, that is, empiricism and nativism, were incorrect. Empiricists such as philosopher John Locke and psychologist Edward Thorndike believed that people's minds are 'blank slates' when they are born, though the mind has an inherent ability to form associations between events that co-occur in the environment and can be perceived through their senses. For example, if a father nearly always wears his favorite hat when he goes out, the sight of his hat hanging on a hook may cause his children or spouse to think of him. Empiricists believe that events in the world have a natural regularity to them that is registered in the mind (e.g., the cycle of day followed by night). Thus, empiricists would argue that people could develop a concept of time by merely observing the cycles of days, months, seasons, and so forth.

Nativism is the polar opposite of empiricism. Nativists such as the philosopher Immanuel Kant and linguist Noam Chomsky believe that the world is neither regular nor organized. In addition, they argue that conceptual relations (e.g., causality and time) could not be sensed in the same way that colors or temperature could be sensed. Together, these two beliefs imply that concepts could not be acquired through simple exposure to the world. If the latter proposition is true, then it follows that the vast majority of important concepts must be inborn. As such, these concepts should be evident in a newborn or emerge in an all-or-none fashion at a particular point in time as a child's brain matures. Nativists suggest that people are born with concepts of causality, time, space, and so on in order to make sense of stimulation that makes no inherent sense.

After much reflection and experience testing children, Piaget found problems with both empiricism and nativism. As a result, he created a third alternative: constructivism. He agreed with the nativist view that people have concepts that they impose on the world to make sense of it but disagreed with the claim that these ideas were inborn. He agreed with the empiricist view that the world has a certain regularity and structure to it that children come to know through experience but disagreed with the idea that concepts are learned immediately through exposure to the world. His middle-ground stance was that exposure to the world and children's activities cause them to create mental precursors to more fully developed ideas. He felt that children's minds take these precursor components and continually build more sophisticated ideas out of them.

For example, when children are born, they lack voluntary control over their arm and hand movements. Everything is reflexive. Soon, however, they gain some voluntary control and begin creating 'grasping' and 'pushing' schemes out of reflexes (hence, reflexes serve as precursors to the schemes). Schemes are goal-directed behaviors that are repeatedly utilized in situations to discover the properties of objects. Early on, the grasping and pushing schemes are not interconnected. By around 8–12 months, however, a child who wants an attractive toy hidden behind a barrier can combine the grasping and pushing scheme together in order to retrieve the toy. Children are not born with this knowledge of how to put the two schemes together, nor can they be taught this earlier in the first year even though they have the two schemes. Children themselves think of putting the two schemes together to attain a goal (i.e., get the toy). Later on, the act of counting objects will serve as a precursor to the mathematical idea of sets, and grouping actions will serve as a precursor to mental addition and subtraction. Still later, children will combine addition and subtraction together with the insight that subtraction is the opposite of addition. In effect, actions have a certain logical structure to them that serve as a template for conceptual relations.

As a second example, consider Piaget's meticulous characterization of the slow, progressive acquisition of the concept of object permanence in infants. Infants who understand object permanence recognize that an object continues to exist even when it is out of view. Object permanence is not something that could be sensed, so it poses immediate problems for empiricists. However, if it could be shown that infants are not born with this idea either, or that it does not emerge in an all-or-none manner, such findings would be a serious blow to Kant's nativism as well. Kant used the example of the concept of space as a prototype for the claim that people are born with mental structures that help them organize their sensory experiences. One cannot have a concept of space unless one has a concept of objects and the space between these objects. If Piaget could show that children are not born with a concept of permanent objects, he would show that Kant was wrong about children being born with a concept of space.

Piaget documented six substages in the acquisition of object permanence that occur between the ages of birth and approximately 18 months. Each successive substage represented a small but significant advance on earlier understandings. These findings suggest that (1) object permanence is not present from the start (as nativists would predict), (2) it does not appear to be learned immediately (as empiricists would predict), and (3) it does not emerge in an all-or-none fashion at one point in time (as maturational empiricists would predict). Instead it truly develops, in Piaget's view.

In the first two substages, the infants confronted with hidden objects either seem oblivious to their disappearance or simply continue to stare at the location where an object was last seen before it disappeared. In the third substage, the infant may now look for an object that has, for example, fallen off her highchair instead of merely staring at the location where it fell off. However, the child may give up if the object is not immediately found and will not attempt to retrieve a desired object that is placed under a blanket in full view. In the fourth stage, the child will finally search for the hidden object placed under a blanket but makes an interesting error when the object is placed successively under two blankets in turn: instead of looking under the second of the two blankets, the child looks under the first (the so-called A-not-B error). In the fifth substage, the child no longer makes the A not-B error, but will not engage in search behaviors when the movement of the object to specific locations is not observed. For example, imagine a setup in which a child watches as an adult places a small desired toy inside a cup. The adult next moves the cup behind a small screen and surreptitiously dumps the toy out of the cup behind the screen. When the adult's hand re-emerges at the other side of the screen and the child looks inside the now empty cup, she does not immediately look behind the screen. By the sixth substage, however, infants finally do engage in search behaviors even when invisible displacements are used (as in the cup example).

In Piaget's view, all of the major concepts that he investigated are built up or constructed in this step-by-step manner. Eventually, children acquire the kinds of conceptualizations that are evident in adults. He documented the various substages in all of his books on the development of specific concepts. Note that Piaget did not deny the existence of inborn capacities (e.g., he recognizes that reflexes are inborn) or the capacity of the mind to acquire rote associations (as he pointed out in his book on memory). His point was that the full-blown, adult versions of concepts such as object permanence, causality, class inclusion, conservation, number, space, and time were neither inborn nor learned through associative mechanisms involving the senses.

Four levels of thought. Having identified the small steps that occur in the development of major concepts between birth and adulthood, Piaget then grouped chronologically arranged sets of these achievements into four levels of thought: sensorimotor, preoperational, concrete operational, and formal operational. For some concepts, for example, the first six substages that emerge between birth and 18 months might be called sensorimotor thinking, the next six that emerge between 18 months and 5 years of age might be called preoperational thinking, and so on. Each level is characterized by how children view the world.

When the world is viewed from the standpoint of sensorimotor thinking (birth to about 18 months of age), objects are understood with respect to what actions can be performed on them. For example, a bottle, a toy, and a finger are all the same because they are 'suckables'. In addition, sensorimotor thinking is limited to the here-and-now. Children who can only reason at the sensorimotor level (e.g., infants or severely retarded older students)

cannot think about the past or things that might happen in the future, according to Piaget. They simply perceive objects in current view and try to use a motoric scheme to interact with these objects.

After motoric schemes have been repeated many times to attain goals, children's minds form abstract, mental versions of these schemes. As a result, children can imagine themselves doing something before they do it. Once children can think in this representational way, they have moved into the preoperations level (begins around 18–24 months of age). In addition to being able to imagine future events, children can also think about things that happened to them in the past. Thus, preoperational children are freed from the here-and-now. Piaget called this kind of thought representational in the sense that children can re-present absent objects to their consciousness for consideration. Children who look for the hidden toy in the cup example described earlier do so because they imagined the dumping action of the adult. Thus, the sixth substage for object permanence is actually preoperational thought. Although preoperational thinking is more advanced and more adaptive than sensorimotor thought, it is limited in four ways. First, it has overly strong ties to perception, perceptual similarity, and spatial relations. For example, some 3-year-olds believe that a family exists only when the family members hug. When they are spatially separated, the family no longer exists. Similarly, many preschoolers think that an arrangement of five pennies spread out in a row contains more pennies than a pile of five pennies.

When preschoolers mentally group things, they rely heavily on perceptual similarity. For example, they think that 'dogs' and 'horses' are both 'doggies' and that 'goldfish' and 'whales' are both 'fishies'. Grouping things by perceptual similarity, of course, is not a good idea because few categories are defined this way. For example, categories such as 'doctor', 'country', 'dictator', 'polynomial', and 'acid' are not defined by the visual appearance of members of these categories. Most categories in fields such as science, mathematics, and social studies are defined in a nonperceptual, abstract way. As a result, a Piagetian perspective predicts that the real definitions of these categories would be difficult for preschoolers to grasp.

The second limitation of preoperational thinking, according to Piaget, is that it is unidimensional; that is, children can think about only one aspect of something at a time. For example, when they are asked to sort objects into categories, they use just one dimension (e.g., size) rather than multiple dimensions (e.g., size and color). In addition to studies of categorization, Piaget revealed unidimensionality in his many studies of conservation. Conservation is the belief that the amount of something stays the same despite superficial changes in appearance. In his classic 'beaker' task, for example, children are shown two short, wide glasses that have the same amount of juice. When the juice of one is poured into a taller thinner glass, the level of the juice is higher than in the remaining short glass. Preschoolers only attend to the height of the glasses and not the width in judging which of two glasses has more juice in it. After pouring, they think the tall glass has more juice even though they just said the two short glasses had the same amount. Beyond these conservation examples, it is easy to show how many concepts that are presented in school are multidimensional (e.g., the definition of a 'square' or a 'republic'), so this second limitation would cause problems for students if it persisted after preschool. The tendency to focus on just one dimension or view things only from one's own perspective has been called centration.

The third limitation of preoperational thought, according to Piaget, is that it is irreversible; that is, preschoolers often cannot mentally imagine something that has just be done (e.g., a ball of clay being rolled into a sausage) being 'undone' (e.g., the sausage being rolled back into a ball). Piaget likened this limitation to a movie projector that cannot play movies in reverse. Again, most subjects in school contain ideas that involve reversibility. In math, for example, addition is the opposite of subtraction and '-5' is the opposite of '5'. In history classes, it is common to speculate whether some trend could ever be reversed (e.g., Russian citizens going back to repressive communism after tasting freedom and capitalism). Hence, preoperational children tend to think of things in terms of their static configuration instead of thinking of them in terms of a dynamic, reversible transformation.

The fourth limitation of preoperational thinking, according to some early works of Piaget, is that children have difficulty distinguishing between reality and fantasy. For example, they sometimes have difficulty telling the difference between real people and television characters, and also are bothered by nightmares that seem awfully real.

For Piaget, these four limitations of preoperational thinking are overcome when children develop the concrete operational mode of thought around age 5 or 6. In particular, concrete operational children are no longer limited to using perceptual similarity when they group things. However, although children can understand somewhat more abstract properties, these properties still must be something one can point to or concretely describe (e.g., 'warm-blooded' for 'mammals'). In addition to going beyond mere perceptual similarity, concrete operational children also do not confuse spatial arrangements with actual quantities. For example, they know that rolling a round clay ball into a sausage shape has no effect on the amount of clay present. In addition, children can think about two dimensions at once and can also mentally 'undo' a real event that has happened. Hence, concrete operational thought is marked by its reversibility. Finally,

concrete operational children do not confuse reality with fantasy and are more concerned with playing games by the rules than with assimilating the world to their own fanciful desires. In fact, they seem to be overly concerned with 'the way things are'.

In some cultures, thinking that is (1) freed from perceptual relations, (2) reversible, (3) two dimensional and (4) realistic would be sufficient for full adaptation to that culture. In most industrialized cultures, however, people apparently need more than that if Piaget is correct in his assertion that minds adapt to the demands placed on them. For example, many things in school require comprehension of more than two dimensions and the ability to go beyond reality to think about hypothetical possibilities (e.g., give a reasoned answer to questions such as, would the Vietnam war have ended earlier if President Kennedy had not been assassinated?). Moreover, some ideas cannot be defined by pointing to something or using concrete descriptions (e.g., the fourth dimension; conservatism; the 'limit' of a function). Students who can think about multiple dimensions, hypothetical possibilities, and abstract properties are capable of the formal operations level of thinking (begins usually around age 10 or 11 years).

One further way to characterize the differences in thinking that occur with age is to consider two overarching assumptions of Piaget's theory: (1) thinking becomes increasingly abstract with development and (2) thinking becomes increasingly logical with development. By abstract, Piaget meant, removed from immediate perception and action. Thinking that is closely tied to perception or action is lower-order thinking (e.g., sensorimotor or preoperational thought). Thinking that is less tied to perception and action is higher-order thinking (e.g., concrete and formal operational thought). Moreover, as a child moves between one level of thought and the next, his or her thinking becomes more abstract because each stage transition produces thinking that is one step further removed from immediate perception and action. Thus, preoperational thought is more abstract than sensorimotor thought because the former is one step removed from immediate perception. Similarly, concrete operational thinking is more abstract than preoperational thinking because it is two steps removed from immediate perception, and formal operational thought is more abstract than concrete operational thought because it is three steps removed.

When children reach the concrete operations level for some content area, they are capable of reasoning with symbols that do not resemble their real-world referents. For example, the symbol '3' does not resemble a collection of three objects and the word 'animal' does not look like any particular animal (unlike mental images that may actually resemble their referents). In freeing the mind from particular concrete referents, children can think about the symbols themselves. Thus, although the symbol

'3' can refer to a set of three apples or three trucks, one can ignore which objects it refers to in, say, judging that when one takes away one object from any set of three objects, one is always left with two objects (no matter what those objects are). Then, when children reach the formal operations level, symbols can stand for sets of symbols. For example, 'X' can stand for '3', '4', or any other number.

In order to be ultimately capable of abstract reasoning, Piaget argued that children need to interact with objects or actual content. For example, preoperational children need to count actual sets of objects and form many sets of three things in order for their mind to create structures that help them comprehend symbols such as '3'. In particular, through the process of reflective abstraction (see glossary for definition), children's minds abstract across sets of object-oriented actions to form schematic representations of set size. Similarly, they need to work on many sets of arithmetic problems (e.g., $3 + 4 = 7$) before their mind will abstract a schema that would promote an understanding of algebraic formulas (e.g., $x + y = z$). In essence, experiences with objects, arithmetic sentences, and so forth are the 'grist' for the schema-abstraction 'mill'. Thus, Piaget would argue against the idea that nothing should be done to promote abstract thinking until children reach a certain age. Rather, he would argue that children should be given experiences that help them construct precursory ideas to later ideas. Abstract thinking will not emerge on its own without ample experiences.

As for the second assumption that thinking becomes more logical with age, Piaget meant that thinking literally conforms to the canons of logic. Long before Piaget did his experiments, philosophers devised laws and theorems that were argued to be universal truths. One such theorem was the assertion that 'If $A > B$ and $B > C$, then $A > C$.' Piaget was well versed in logic and was quite surprised to see that 7-year-olds could make such transitive inferences long before students are exposed to the idea of transitivity in logic or math courses. In a typical task, a child might be shown an array of three sticks that increase in size. The apparatus is such that the relative sizes of sticks can only be seen two at a time. First, stick A and stick B are uncovered to reveal that stick A is larger than stick B; Then, stick A is covered again while stick B and stick C are now exposed, revealing that stick B is larger than stick C. Whereas a preoperational child would have to examine each item mentioned in a transitive statement in order to reach the correct conclusion (e.g., look at all three sticks simultaneously to know that the first stick is larger than the third), concrete operational children would know the answer without actually comparing the first and third item (e.g., the first and third stick).

In addition to transitive inferences, concrete operational thought conforms to logical analyses in two other ways. First, philosophers have claimed that logical thinking requires that things be classified in such a way that valid inductive and deductive inferences can be drawn. To insure the validity of categorical inferences, it is important to have correct definitions of categories such as 'squares' or 'mammals'. The definition of 'squares' is correct if it properly includes all of the things that are squares and properly excludes all of the things that are not squares. According to a classical perspective in philosophy, the best way to create correct definitions is to use lists of necessary and sufficient attributes. For squares, for example, the necessary and sufficient attributes are that the object has to have (1) four sides, (2) equal sides, and (3) 90° angles. Anything that has all three attributes is a square and anything that lacks one or more of these attributes is not a square. Piaget argued that whereas preoperational children categorize things together if they merely look similar (e.g., a trout and a whale are both fish), concrete operational children categorize things using necessary and sufficient criteria. Thus, once again concrete operational thought is more logical than preoperational thought.

The third way that concrete operational thought is more logical pertains to the notions of negation and reversibility. Concrete operational children connect categories and operations to their opposites. For example, all of the things that are 'dogs' are grouped together with all other animals that are not dogs through the superordinate category of 'animals'. This hierarchical grouping allows a child to fully comprehend class-inclusion relations (e.g., that dogs and cats are both animals). In addition, each mental operation is linked to an opposite operation that 'undoes' the former. For example, addition is linked to its opposite, subtraction. By linking things to their opposites, children gain a sense of logical necessity. That is, they feel that their deductions must be true. Thus, when asked, "If all of the dogs in the world were to die, would there be any animals left?", concrete operational children would say, "Of course! Dogs are not the only kind of animals!"

Formal operational thinking extends the logical aspects of concrete operational thinking in new ways. In the first place, inductive, deductive, and transitive inferences can now be applied to both real things and hypothetical ideas. In addition, children become capable of performing valid experiments because formal operational students examine combinations of variables and use the isolation of variables (IOV) technique to test their hypotheses. The IOV technique involves varying only one factor while holding all other constant. Moreover, the abstract quality of formal operational thought helps children to step back from a chain of inferences and judge the validity of these inferences, regardless of the content. For example, consider the syllogism, 'All frogs are mammals. Mammals are warm-blooded. Therefore, frogs are warm-blooded.' Even though the content of this syllogism is factually incorrect (frogs are not mammals), formal operational thought helps an adolescent or adult ignore this fact and recognize that the conclusion follows if we temporarily assume the truth of the prior premises.

Structuralism and functionalism. Historical analyses of Piaget's 60-year career suggest that there were periods of time in which he alternated between his structuralist and functionalist tendencies. Whereas nativism, constructivism, and empiricism have to do with the origin of knowledge, structuralism, and functionalism have more to do with the nature of knowledge. For Piaget, a structuralist is someone who examines multiple instances of some phenomenon, identifies the inherent organization of parts within this phenomenon, and uses formalisms to describe this organization. For example, linguist Noam Chomsky examined large numbers of declarative sentences (e.g., 'Bill eats red apples' and 'The burly man hit the small dog') and noted that they all had the same basic structure: a sentence (S) can be decomposed into a noun phrase (NP) and a verb phrase (VP). In formulaic terms, this abstraction could be written as $S \rightarrow NP + VP$. The formula represents the form of the structure and the specific words (e.g., 'Bill') represent the content that fills in the placeholders or variables in the formula (e.g., NP). Piaget argued that all mental structures have both form and content. The form stays the same but the content varies.

For his part, Piaget identified the form and content of mental structures at each level of thought. For example, the form of sensorimotor structures is the scheme and the content is the objects that are acted upon by the scheme. At the preoperations level, Piaget proposed the existence of 'one way mappings' or representations that link beginning states to end states of some event in a unidirectional way. Later writings suggested that these mappings were not unlike mathematical functions such as $y = f(x)$. If an initial state of some apparatus were to be substituted for the 'y', an outcome state 'x' is the output of the function. Relying on such structures, children can be quite skilled at predicting outcomes after observing events for some time. However, these mental functions lack the ability to reverse (e.g., given the output, what was the input?). At the concrete operations level, Piaget emphasized form and content related to hierarchical categories and ordered series. For example, many categories can be expressed in the formalism, $A + A' = B$, in which A stands for a category (e.g., dogs), A' stands for its complement class (e.g., nondogs) and B stands for the superordinate category (e.g., mammals). In the case of ordered series, various objects can be arranged in terms of increasing magnitudes based on specific characteristics (e.g., height, weight, color, and loudness). These series can be represented using formalisms such as $A > B > C$, etc. At the formal operations level, Piaget emphasized logical relationships such as implication. Propositions such as 'If today is Tuesday,

I have math class' and 'If an animal barks, it is a dog' can be represented using formalisms such as $P \rightarrow Q$ (i.e., P implies Q).

During his structuralist period, Piaget endeavored to characterize the mental structures of children and his books are full of formalisms to represent these structures. His major foray into functionalism came about shortly after his children were born and he searched the scholarly literature for plausible accounts of infant development. He discovered the work of American scholar James Mark Baldwin who was a key figure in the functionalist school of thought during the late 1800s and early 1900s. Piaget incorporated many of Baldwin's insights and constructs into his own theory (e.g., Baldwin coined the terms primary, secondary, and tertiary circular reactions). Functionalists differ from structuralists in their emphasis on the goal-directed and adaptive nature of thought. The functionalist perspective emerged on the heels of Darwinian theory in the late 1800s that emphasized the idea of adaptation to the environment. It also was created as a counterpoint to the structuralist perspective of the mid-1800s that seemed to ignore the usefulness of knowledge for solving real problems. Piaget's functionalist tendencies were evident in his books on infancy in two ways. First, he argued that intelligence is first manifested in development when infants combine schemes together to achieve goals at around 8–12 months of age. Second, he claimed that intelligence consists in transforming or adapting mental structures to make them more in line with reality.

What was unique about Piaget's perspective was that he attempted to integrate the structuralist and functionalist perspectives into a single account. That is, he tried to show that when certain structures emerge in development, children use these structures to attain goals and solve problems. Moreover, when children attempt to apply structures to a particular problem and discover the inadequacy of their solutions and ideas, this experience helps promote changes in these structures. In the next section, the latter notion is developed more fully.

Four factors of development. Developmental psychologists make a distinction between developmental states and developmental mechanisms. Developmental states are like snapshots that describe the current complement of skills possessed by an individual at a particular point in time. In Piaget's theory, the four levels of thought described above are examples of successive developmental states that children pass through. In addition to describing the succession of states, however, theories also posit developmental mechanisms that explain why it is that children progress from one state to the next (e.g., why children move from the sensory-motor level of thought to the preoperations level). Piaget's developmental mechanisms included four factors: biological maturation, physical experience, social exchange, and equilibration.

With respect to biological maturation, it is important to avoid common misconceptions about Piaget's stance toward this factor. The fact that children in developed countries demonstrate the four levels of thought at similar ages has led some to conclude that Piaget was a maturational nativist. In reality, Piaget did acknowledge the similarity of age changes as possibility having a maturational component but he also expected that all children would go through his four stages at roughly the same ages mainly because he assumed that the physical structure of the world was pretty much the same for all children. Hence, children's mental structures would tend to run up against the same reality regardless of whether they lived in Switzerland, the US, or Africa. As he argued in his 1983 chapter in the *Handbook of Child Psychology*,

> It is clear that maturation must have a part in the development of intelligence, although we know very little about the relations between the intellectual operations and the brain. In particular, the sequential character of the stages is an important clue to their partly biological nature and thus argues in favor of the constant role of the genotype and epigenesis. But this does not mean that we can assume there exists a hereditary program underlying human intelligence: there are not 'innate ideas' (in spite of what Lorenz maintained about the a priori nature of human thought). Even logic is not innate and only gives rise to progressive epigenetic construction. Thus, the effects of maturation consist essentially of opening new possibilities for development; that is, giving access to structures that could not be evolved before these possibilities were offered. But between possibility and actualization, there must intervene a set of other factors such as exercise, experience, and social interaction.

Thus, if children do not interact with the physical and social world, they will not develop the structures associated with Piaget's four stages by the time they reach physical maturity in adolescence. Thus, brain maturation is a necessary but not sufficient condition for the development of knowledge. However, as the preceding quote illustrates, experience interacting with objects is not sufficient either. He acknowledged that social exchanges between children and their parents, teachers, and peers often precipitated intellectual advances through the medium of language, but also pointed out that such exchanges could not account for the progressive changes that occur during the sensorimotor period or the shift between sensorimotor and preoperational thinking. In both cases, children are preverbal and unlikely to understand what other social agents are saying. It is for this reason and the insufficiency of the other three factors that he appealed to one further factor: the construct of equilibration.

'Equilibration' pertains to restoring the balance between two competing tendencies in the mind: assimilation and accommodation. Piaget used the notion of 'assimilation' to describe the process of incorporating experiences and information into existing knowledge structures in the mind. Metaphorically, children find a 'home' for this information in their existing knowledge structures. To say that a child has assimilated an idea or experience is to say that he or she understood the idea or experience. Piaget thought that mental assimilation was analogous to the biological assimilation that takes place when the human body extracts what it needs from food and incorporates the extracted nutrients into existing organs and tissues.

Sometimes an idea is so discrepant from what a child believes or knows that it cannot be assimilated. Piaget used the notion of 'accommodation' to describe the process of changing the existing configuration of knowledge in the mind in order that the troublesome idea can be assimilated. In most cases, assimilation is always partial in the sense that children only assimilate that portion of an experience that is consistent with their current understanding. Unless an experience or idea is identical to previous ones, every act of assimilation usually precipitates accommodation of knowledge as well. For example, when a child encounters a new species of dog for the first time and is told that it is a dog, this information finds a home in the existing network of ideas (i.e., it is assimilated), but the network is also changed as the child's mind creates a new representation corresponding to the new subtype of dog (i.e., there is accommodation).

In his book, *Play, Dreams, and Imitation*, Piaget argued that "...imitation is a continuation of accommodation, play is a continuation of assimilation, and intelligence is a harmonious combination of the two." This quote suggests that when one assimilates, one inserts one's own ideas into reality; when one accommodates, one's schemes and ideas come into closer conformity with reality and tend to be fairly direct copies of it. Play and fantasy, moreover, are examples of overassimilation (i.e., putting too much of one's ideas into reality). In contrast, children engage in overaccommodation when they try to directly copy the actions of someone (without putting their own 'spin' on the actions).

To illustrate assimilation and accommodation further, consider the following example. Young preschoolers who are passengers in their parents' cars often think that the moon is following them when they drive at night. The physics of the explanation of what is actually happening is too abstract for young children to comprehend, so they could not assimilate even this explanation if it were provided. Ultimately, however, their knowledge of the physical world will change enough that they may eventually understand the explanation as young adults.

Piaget argued that confronting discrepant ideas is absolutely essential for knowledge growth. If children never had experiences or heard information that contradicted the erroneous ideas that they construct by themselves, they would never develop the correct conceptions. Thus, the 'readiness' idea of waiting until a child's mind matures enough to teach a topic to them is actually an implication of nativism, not Piaget's constructivism. Piaget did not believe that ideas were inborn as nativists do; rather, he believed that children build up their ideas step by step.

Moreover, Piaget argued that assimilation and accommodation work in opposition to each other. The central tendency for assimilation is to keep the existing knowledge structure the same and find a place for new information in this structure. The central tendency for accommodation, in contrast, is to change the existing knowledge structure. It is not possible to keep things the same and change them at the same time. Thus, only one of assimilation or accommodation 'wins out' in a given situation. This 'battle' between these processes means that change in children's misconceptions can be frustratingly slow for teachers. That is, even when a misconception is repeatedly pointed out and explained to children, they may cling to the erroneous idea for some time. Perhaps this implies that assimilation normally takes precedence over accommodation. When the battle is resolved over some idea and a balance is restored between assimilation and accommodation (i.e., equilibration has occurred), children's understanding usually moves to a higher plane and often becomes more abstract as well. For example, in order for a child to come to understand that dogs and people are both animals, they have to change their concept of 'animal' in such a way that it is more abstract (e.g., 'a living thing that can move itself' from 'furry four-legged things').

Piaget argued that equilibration was particularly adaptive because the changes that are incorporated into mental structures are such that the mental system of ideas becomes capable of anticipating future problems that might arise. That is, the change not only allows a child to assimilate a particular idea that once was difficult to grasp, it also helps the child grasp related ideas that he or she has not yet encountered. In this way, equilibration works in a manner analogous to how the immune system creates structures (i.e., antibodies) that can deal with problems that arise in the future (i.e., re-occurrence of a virus that was encountered before).

Criticisms of the Theory

Although Piaget's account has enjoyed a certain degree of acceptance in fields such as developmental psychology and education (especially the latter), many psychologists began to challenge his claims and findings soon after his account was first introduced to American audiences in the early 1960s. At a general level, the majority of critics felt that the tasks used by Piaget to reveal various levels of competence were too difficult and underestimated what children knew. For example, some argued that infants who did not search under blankets in object permanent tasks might still understand that objects exist when not in view. Searching was an undue, extra burden on young infants, they argued. To reveal object permanence in nonsearching infants, critics created several clever apparatuses. In one, 3–5-month-old infants watched as a solid screen repeatedly rotated up and away from them through a 180° arc, in the manner of a drawbridge. The screen appeared to start by laying flat on a table with one side down. It rose up and completed its arc by resting again on the table with the opposite side now facing up (in the manner of a card being turned over in solitaire). After observing the screen make a complete arc a certain number of times, test trials began. Here, a box was placed in a position behind the screen that would normally interfere with the screen's movement such that it would rest and stop on the box, rather than complete its arc and rest on the table. Half of the trials were 'possible' events in which the screen did stop and rest on the box. The other half, however, were impossible trials that used a rigged box that could collapse into a flat surface. Here, the screen completed its 180° arc and rested on the table. To an observer, the box seemed to vanish. Infants were attributed an understanding of object permanence if they showed surprise expressions and looked longer at the impossible trials than the possible trials.

In studies of older children, some critics argued that Piaget's various conservation tasks were very misleading and tricked young children through perceptual illusions. They argued that tasks should be modified to be less misleading. For example, instead of showing children the level of liquid rising in a tall, thin beaker as the liquid is poured from a short, wide beaker, the tall beaker should be hidden from view as the liquid was poured. Other critics felt that Piaget used too strict of a criterion in many of his tasks by not only requiring a right answer, but also requiring appropriate explanations and the ability to resist being persuaded by arguments to the contrary. Thus, they often created nonverbal versions of his tasks in which children could merely point to the correct answer.

A third way to counteract Piaget's suggestion that a child of a certain age could not understand a particular concept was to conduct training studies in which correct answers and verbal feedback were provided on repeated trials. For example, a child who initially failed to realize that the amount of clay in a clay ball is not increased when it is rolled into a sausage shape, might be asked to repeatedly weight the clay before and after the transformation, or be given a verbal rule of some sort (e.g., 'Even though it looks like it has more, it really doesn't').

In the 1960s, 1970s, and 1980s, training studies and studies using modified Piagetian tasks routinely revealed apparent competences in age groups younger than Piaget found. For example, whereas Piaget suggested that object permanence did not typically emerge until around 8 to 12 months of age, researchers using modified versions of object permanence tasks (e.g., the screen task described above) revealed an apparent understanding in 5- and 6-month-olds. Similarly, whereas Piaget revealed concrete operational skills in 5- to 8-year-olds using his original tasks, researchers using training tasks and modified versions of Piaget's tasks (e.g., nonverbal tasks) revealed apparent competence in 4- to 7-year-olds. As more and more of such findings emerged in the literature, the standing of Piaget's theory in the field of psychology began to diminish.

Other problems for the theory grew out of findings that suggested that:

1. Children who succeed on one measure of concrete (or formal) operations do not always succeed on other measures of concrete (or formal) operations; if competence is task-specific rather than domain-general, the notion of children being in a 'stage' of thought loses its credibility and meaning.
2. Only about 40% of adolescents and adults pass Piaget's original formal operations tasks; if passage through the four stages is a universal consequence of interacting with the physical and social world, all adolescents and adults should attain the level of formal thought.
3. Children and adults do not seem to base their mental categories on necessary and sufficient criteria; rather, categorization is based on the formation of prototypes for each category (e.g., robin in the case of bird) and the presence of characteristic features that most but not all members of the category have.
4. Young preschool children have less trouble differentiating fantasy and reality than Piaget suggested.

To all of the aforementioned empirical problems for the theory, influential philosophers and linguists have also argued against the theory on logical grounds. In most cases, these critics have had strong nativistic orientations that led them to take issue with Piaget's constructivism. For example, philosopher Jerry Fodor argued that constructivism is logically impossible. His thesis centered on Piaget's suggestion that children eventually acquire mental systems that have a logico-mathematical character to them. Fodor made the interesting observation that Piaget seemed to be saying that children acquire increasingly powerful mental 'logics' in which each successive logic was able to account for more truths about reality. But just as Gödel's famous mathematical proof showed that it is impossible to derive a more powerful logical system out of a less powerful logical system (e.g., model logic out of truth functional logic), it is impossible to derive formal operations out of concrete operations. Anything that is new about formal operations could not be present in concrete operations. If anything new does emerge, then, it must have been 'known' all along. Hence, Fodor argued that the only viable way to explain the emergence of formal operational thought is some form of maturational nativism.

Collectively, the empirical and philosophical problems identified by critics of the theory led to its ultimate demise in the field of psychology. As noted earlier, though, this does not mean that the theory no longer has influence. On the contrary, many scholars still look to the theory as a starting point for their own investigations to familiarize themselves with the various phenomena that Piaget examined. Few doubt the reality of the phenomena that Piaget observed; controversies arose over Piaget's explanation of these phenomena. In addition, many contemporary scholars appear to be amenable to the idea of constructivism and seem to prefer it to more extreme forms of nativism. Relatedly, many of the newer theoretical proposals that have been advanced in recent years have a constructivist flavor to them, but tend to emphasize domain-specific competencies (e.g., within-topic qualitative changes in insight) rather than domain-general competencies and stages. Finally, of all the cognitive-developmental theories that have been proposed to date, Piaget's theory is one of the few that is capable of predicting slow, conservative changes in conceptualizations and young children's difficulty in understanding abstract ideas.

See also: Cognitive Development; Cognitive Developmental Theories; Milestones: Cognitive; Neonativism; Object Concept; Reasoning in Early Development.

Suggested Readings

Bereiter C (1985) Toward a solution of the learning paradox. *Review of Educational Research* 55: 201–226.
Brainerd CJ (1978) The stage question in cognitive-developmental theory. *Behavioral and Brain Sciences* 1: 173–213.
Chapman M (1988) *Constructive Evolution. Origins and Development of Piaget's Thought.* Cambridge: Cambridge University Press.
Gruber HE and Vonèche J (1995) *The Essential Piaget.* Northvale, NJ: Aronson.
Piaget J (1952) *The Origins of Intelligence in Children.* New York: International Universities Press.
Piaget J (1983) Piaget's theory. In: Mussen P and Lerner R (eds.) *Handbook of Child Psychology,* 4th edn., vol. 1, p. 117. New York: Wiley.
Piaget J and Inhelder B (1969) *The Psychology of the Child.* New York: Basic Books.

Play

M Sumaroka and M H Bornstein, National Institutes of Health, Bethesda, MD, USA

Glossary

Exploratory play – Play that is directed toward the tangible properties and functions of objects.

Imaginary companion – Invisible vividly imagined characters that children play and talk with, while recognizing their unreality.

Individual differences – Variability in development and behavior as the result of different biological, cognitive, social, and environmental factors.

Interpersonal play – Direct, interactive social involvement with other participants in play with the purpose of entertainment.

Object play – Play that focuses on objects and events.

Primary circular reactions – Activities repeated for their own sake.

Security of attachment – A relationship between caregiver and child characterized by mutual trust.

Symbolic (pretend) play – Make-believe activities, in which children create symbolic uses of objects, pretend roles, and scenes.

Introduction

Play is important to children's lives and stimulates their development in many ways.

There are two main categories of play: interpersonal and object play. Interpersonal play implies participation in social interactions, such as face-to-face routines, social games, and physical play. Object play involves exploration and concentration on a toy, its functions and properties. Each kind of play contributes to psychological growth (e.g., children learn to control and express emotions); cognitive maturation (e.g., they develop creative abilities); mastery (e.g., they learn to concentrate and elongate attention span); social (e.g., they understand behaviors and feelings of others), communicative (e.g., they acquire social skills), and cultural (e.g., they rehearse traditional roles and behaviors) development. Particular types of play depend on many factors, among which are developmental capabilities of the child, play partners, and context.

Children's abilities change through the course of development, allowing parents to initiate more complex games. For example, 2–3-month-old infants are mostly

entertained by repeating simple body activities, such as repeatedly kicking their legs. By 4 months of age, infants are capable of manipulating and exploring objects. When infants reach 1 year, they become interested in physical characteristics of objects (e.g., color, texture, and shape). In the second year of life, children develop symbolism and pretense in play. They start to substitute objects for one another and imitate actions and situations, at first centering pretense on themselves and, later, involving others and objects. Children's evolving sophistication of play reflects their progression in cognitive functions, such as representation, perception, language, and attention.

Many psychologists and philosophers have studied play and its influence on the development of children. Among the main theories of play are: surplus energy theory, relaxation and recreation theory, practice theory, and recapitulation theory. Psychologist have also suggested that play helps children to rehearse certain survival skills, has anxiety-relieving qualities, and fosters psychosexual development. Researchers have related play to social, cognitive, therapeutic, and emotional functions in the child.

Development of play is often stimulated by parents and other partners who initiate and participate in child play. Play partners differ in many aspects. For example, mothers usually focus on object play, developing children's visual, language, and representational abilities, whereas fathers are prone to initiate physical play, stimulating motor and communication skills; peers and siblings tend to involve children in pretend play and stimulate social competence.

Along with play partners, children's gender also influences their types and kinds of play. From birth, children are traditionally offered different toys, infants' rooms are often decorated in 'gender appropriate' colors, and parents are more permissive during play with boys and more directive in playing with girls. Around 4–5 years of age children start to choose certain gender-segregated types of play and toys and prefer playmates of their own gender, which can be explained by biological, cognitive, and social-learning theories.

Societies around the world have different understandings of the role of play and play partners. Many cultures regard play as an exclusively children's activity and parents do not participate in play. In other cultures parents may by the first and main play partners for their infants and, usually, initiate play and direct it as participants. Through play, cultures rehearse social role behaviors, introducing expected duties and responsibilities.

Types and Functions of Play

Play is practically synonymous with childhood. Play seems to be children's primary and most enjoyable activity, and it is a prevalent form of children's interactions with parents, siblings, and peers. It is usually associated with joyful and fun pastimes for children of all ages, yet play is also a very important force in child development, because it incorporates cognitive, social, emotional, and motivational skills. Therefore, play is a broadly beneficial activity that transcends simple enjoyment. There are no specific activities ascribed to play because it can take numerous forms, and any activity might be identified as 'play' when it meets the criteria of certain types and functions. Play is acknowledged to be complex and resists definition by any single characteristic or set of actions.

Types of Play

There are two main types of play that are evident from infancy: interpersonal (dyadic) forms of play and object-focused (extradyadic) engagements. These types of play are distinguished according to identifiable characteristics. Each type of play demonstrates patterned developmental change, serves unique functions, and is meaningful in child development. Throughout development, many changes occur in types of play as well as in their frequency of occurrence.

Interpersonal play

Interpersonal play is a social activity that appears to be prevalent during the first few years of life and has the goal of having fun. It requires direct interaction of the participants and is normally characterized by high degrees of pleasure derived by both parties. Interpersonal play involves various dyadic exchanges, such as face-to-face interactions, social games or routines, and physical play.

Face-to-face interactions balance repetitive bouts and creative variations of shared affect; they are framed as playful through specific vocalizations or gestures within the stream of ongoing parent–child communication. This type of play has mainly affective characteristics, and parents seem to engage in it with the goal of teaching infants to enjoy interpersonal interactions. Imitation is a typical component of face-to-face play interactions. Face-to-face play often occurs at home during other task-oriented activities (e.g., mothers engage into face-to-face interactions while feeding or changing the baby). Face-to-face play is typical of early infancy and decreases in frequency and duration as infants reach their first birthday.

Although face-to-face play is common in early infancy, interpersonal play is not confined to this period. When face-to face interactions decrease in occurrence, parents and children begin to get involved in social games and routines, such as peek-a-boo and pat-a-cake. The unstated goal of these social routines is to teach the child set formats of social exchange and their variations, as well as to try on different roles and take progressively greater responsibility. The role of parents is usually to facilitate the game, and the child's role often involves motor behaviors that are meaningful within the context of a particular game.

Physical play is another prevalent form of interpersonal play which occurs most frequently between 1 and 4 years of age. Research distinguishes among three types of physical play: rhythmic stereotypies, exercise, and rough-and-tumble play. Rhythmic stereotypies are usually a solitary form of play that emerges during the first year of life and includes gross motor movements. Onset of exercise play starts at the end of the first year and includes motor behaviors in the context of play. Exercise play can be solitary or interpersonal. Rough-and-tumble play peaks in the preschool years. It includes kicking, wrestling, and pushing in the friendly context of play. Rough-and-tumble play can escalate in levels of aggression; thus, parents must teach children the acceptable limits of rough-and-tumble physical play and explain how to maintain friendly interactions to control their behaviors.

Object play

At the age when children begin to notice objects, mothers adjust their playful interactions from interpersonal to extradyadic, focusing attention outwards from the dyad toward objects in the environment. Thus, strictly interpersonal interactions moderate in complexity to match newly developing skills in the child.

Parental direct involvement in child object play is usually less active, and characterized by less mutual engagement than interpersonal play, because the child is often preoccupied with toys. At the time children begin to focus on objects, parents actively promote and encourage such attention by showing new objects and demonstrating the functions and properties of objects, thus encouraging children to explore and learn about their surroundings.

Functions of Play

Play serves various adaptive functions. It also contributes to several different developmental areas: psychological, cognitive, mastery, social, communication, and cultural.

Through the psychological functions of play, children learn to control their state of arousal, develop self-regulation capacities, resolve conflicts, and address traumas.

Appropriate stimulation also helps children to develop self-regulation capacities. Play enables children to experience a broad range of feelings and emotions, from fun and enjoyment to anger and sadness. Parents are the best play partners for children in terms of intensifying and prolonging their pleasure in the first few months of life. From the beginning of life, parents support babies' experience of joy by playing with facial expressions, vocalizations, and touch, and evoking gaze, smiles, and laughter from their infants. During the course of typical face-to-face interaction games, mothers build and repeat predictable sequences of actions and vary them based on their infant's response. The infant's growing awareness of contingency in these interactions adds to feelings of mastery, in addition to enabling greater tolerance for higher arousal states. Parental selective imitation of infant behavior also enables infants to mark important acts as meaningful, thereby reinforcing certain behaviors to and facilitating mutual understanding.

Object play gives parents and children an opportunity to share their joys and frustrations while exploring objects, and struggling to accomplish goal-directed activities. During object play, parents devote much more time to talking about children's inner states and emotional expressions. These activities later help children verbally label their emotions as well as correctly link their inner states to emotional expressions.

Children experience and express a wide range of emotions such as joy and sadness, fear and excitement, or pleasure and anger. Play can be a unique platform for experiencing certain emotions, for example, aggression and anger that are caused by behaviors that might not be safe or appropriate to display otherwise. During interpersonal play, children also have an opportunity to 'practice' particular life events in a playful nonthreatening manner. A well-known example is the peek-a-boo game that gives the infant a chance to experience and control emotions related to separation and reunion. By representing traumas and conflicts symbolically through play, children can release forbidden impulses and also test alternative outcomes and solutions in conflict resolution.

The cognitive functions of play are to receive and exchange information, develop skills and representational abilities, and engage in creative and divergent thinking. In infancy, caregivers use play to foster speech-like sounds and babbling, thus stimulating child language development. Joint play advances communication between child and caregiver, and parent–child object play adds opportunities for children to expand their lexicon, learning new names for objects, their qualities, and effects they can produce.

Language use in child–parent play depends on the toys presented and settings of play, however; parents' speech toward children varies if they are playing with dolls, vehicles, or shape-sorters. When playing with dolls, parents tend to talk more and use a greater variety of words, ask questions, and name and label objects and contexts. By contrast, when play involves shape-sorters, parents tend to give directions and use attention-stimulating techniques. Play with vehicles produces the least amount of parent–child communication; parental vocalizations involve mostly pretend noises and imaginative sounds. Different play contexts also provide children with different opportunities for language acquisition. Caregivers direct children's attention to objects in the environment, encouraging them to explore, and later practice new skills. Both exploratory and pretend types of play promote flexibility, creativity, and divergent thinking in children.

New behaviors and skills help children to combine actions and objects in novel ways, promoting mental flexibility. For example, imaginary play is linked to creative performance and problem solving. It stimulates the development of representational thinking by allowing children to reflect on the past and anticipate the future using language and gestures. Joint play with caregivers brings the quality of children's play to a new level. During play with a caregiver, children are expected to (and often do) exhibit higher levels of play (more sophisticated pretense and symbolism) than when playing alone. Empirical evidence shows that children's play with parents is more sophisticated, complex, diverse, frequent, and sustained than is their solitary play. Higher complexity of parent–child play is believed to advance children's abilities.

The functions of play that enhance mastery cultivate a sense of self-efficacy, motivation, and persistence toward goal achievement. Over the course of the first 2 years of life, children practice new skills and engage in multipart tasks in playing with objects. During this time parents offer essential support – first, by focusing children's attention; next, by sustaining children's attention; and finally, by fostering mastery motivation on structured tasks. Mothers who encourage their 2-month-olds to orient and explore objects in the environment have infants who explore objects more at 5 months. Additionally, parents' stimulation and responsiveness to infants at 6 months is associated with infant persistence on problem-solving tasks at 13 months.

Parents' achievements in supporting persistence and efficacy in children's goal-directed behaviors are attributable to their responsiveness to children's initiatives, accuracy in assessing children's need for help, and effectiveness in assistance. Mothers who encourage and physically aid or coach their 18-month-olds when playing, have children who persist on structured tasks.

Through joint play, parents can help children find different, innovative uses of objects thus helping children to think 'outside the box' and develop their imagination. For example, while engaged in symbolic play, parents often make objects and toys perform different roles, shifting among different imagined or real scenarios and situations. When parents give children opportunities to play freely with materials, they enhance innovative uses of objects, flexible approaches to problem-solving tasks, and more divergent thinking on tasks. Development of attachment between children and parents also affects children's mastery capacities. Research links security of attachment to exploration. Security allows children to explore more, while in turn, exploration promotes competence. Play sophistication is associated with a longer attention span and greater persistence in problem-solving.

Curiosity motivates children to explore the world, and pretend play enables them to master novel and complex environments in small scale.

The social functions of play create a base for future successful interactions and relationships by fostering children's understanding of others' feelings, intentions, and perspectives. During play, children practice reciprocal patterns of communication. Positive emotional exchanges in game rituals with parents, and later, with siblings and peers, allow children to achieve greater levels of joy than they might on their own. Role-playing, in particular, is associated with the ability to accept multiple points of view. Shifting between pretense and reality enhances children's ability to compare and contrast various perspectives, which is positively associated with social competence. In the social domain, play supports the development of mutual accordance and adjustment, or attunement, and it provides a foundation for more advanced forms of social understanding. Parent–child object play has been linked to the later quality of childrens' relationships with peers. For example, mothers' involvement in symbolic play with children between 2 and 4 years predicts their peer competence at 5 years. Children's play with their parents serves as a foundation for enhanced competence with peers, once peer interactions become prevalent in children's lives. Some forms of interpersonal play serve as a medium through which children learn norms, rules, and limits that are acceptable in society. Through games and rituals, children learn the limitations and boundaries of their behavior, first, within the family and, later, with peers. Games like peek-a-boo and pat-a-cake translate culturally appropriate elements of social interaction and set the stage for learning rule-bound conventional behaviors.

Play helps children to develop their communication skills. Through playful interactions, children learn key elements of social exchange, such as engaging a partner's attention, turn-taking, terminating social encounters, and role-reciprocity. Through face-to-face play, children learn to frame certain social exchanges as playful as well as to discern meaningful acts, and read certain expectations within a particular social interaction. Sometimes face-to-face interactions do not go smoothly; sometimes a mother may vary her vocalizations or movements too quickly and thus lose the child's attention. It is important that both partners remain attuned to each other. Through mutual involvement, face-to-face play allows parents and children to establish, maintain, and construct their relationship on the basis of common expectations, and vocalizations in play allow creative variation in interpersonal exchanges.

Play serves a variety of cultural functions, by embodying accepted social roles and values. Through culture-appropriate play, children learn local norms of behavior and are exposed to cultural traditions. Expectations about the roles of different individuals within a society start with the notion of who is an appropriate play partner.

In some cultures, it is considered inappropriate for parents to play with children. Thus, Mexican, Guatemalan, and Indonesian parents typically avoid participating in play with their children. In other cultures, such as Turkish and American, parents think of themselves as good play partners for their children. The cultural functions of play begin early in life. For example, when playing with their infants, Japanese mothers more often direct attention to themselves, whereas American mothers encourage attention to objects in the environment. When the child gets older, Japanese mothers more often involve their toddlers in 'other-directed' interpersonal pretense play, whereas American mothers more often encourage their toddlers to engage in independent object play. In this way, Japanese mothers foster generally allocentric collectivist values in play which are typical of their culture, whereas American mothers foster generally idiocentric individualist values which are typical of theirs.

Toys are cultural objects that children learn to play with in particular and culturally appropriate ways. Through participating in complex play, caregivers demonstrate traditional ways of object use. For example, when a mother models a telephone conversation during pretend play, she first dials the number, waits for a response, and only then begins to talk. If, while imitating the telephone conversation, the child forgets to dial the number, or mistakes the order of action, the mother may adjust child's actions, thus teaching the correct way of play. Parent–child object play is also a medium through which children practice real-life scenarios (e.g., doctor–patient, mother–baby). Children's knowledge of cultural activities also contributes to the structure of parent–child play. When children play with familiar toys, they are more likely to facilitate pretend play, while parents serve as an audience. In contrast, when novel toys are used in the course of parent–child play, parents are more likely to start and organize the pretense.

The Developmental Progression of Play

Play develops with the child. It begins as inspection and manipulation and moves gradually to symbolism and pretense.

For the first 2–3 months of the child's life, objects in the environment are not very important for play purposes. According to Jean Piaget, during this time infants engage in 'primary circular reactions' – activities repeated for their own sake. For example, infants may coo repeatedly or open and close their fingers repetitively, suck their thumbs, or blow bubbles; while lying awake, they may arch their backs and drop their bodies onto the mattress over and over again.

Around 4 months of age, infants develop skills to manipulate objects, but even then, they are more interested in the actions they can perform than in any object characteristics. Thus, babies may look at a toy in their field of vision, but when holding an object in their hands they bring it to their mouth rather than visually study it. Even when two objects appear related to one another – a cup and a spoon, for instance – the infant often still focuses on actions, banging the spoon in the cup rather than on the objects. Remove the spoon, and the infant is likely to continue the action.

A major change in complexity and quality of play occurs when infants approach the end of the first year. At about this time, infants engage in three different types of exploratory play: functional, relational, and functional–relational. When infants are involved in functional play, they play with toys in the way the toys were designed to be played with, like rolling a car on its wheels. In the course of relational play, infants bring together two unrelated toys (e.g., a car and a cup) with no signs of pretense. In functional–relational play, children bring two objects together and use them in the meaningful way (e.g., load a container with blocks).

Thus, first-year play is predominantly characterized by sensorimotor manipulation. In their play infants explore the environment around them, deriving information about objects: their properties, physical characteristics, functions, and effects. Because children's activities are tied to the physical properties of objects, rather than being representational, this type of play is called exploratory or nonsymbolic. In the course of development of exploratory play, infants first direct their actions and attention toward a single object and later incorporate several objects in their play. Initially these objects may be treated inappropriately with respect to function, and only later children learn to treat them appropriately. For example, during the first months children may mouth a cup, but when they get a little older they may bang a spoon and a cup. Only later with age does the child use a cup and spoon appropriately, by stirring the spoon inside the cup.

Until the second year of life there are few signs of pretense or symbolism in children's play. Pretense requires representational skills. Because representational skills only slowly emerge, pretend play does likewise. Additionally, object substitution emerges as a clear indicator of more advanced symbolic play. When the young child builds a tower out of blocks, the tower now means more to the child than the characteristics of the blocks themselves. This suggests that there are two distinct kinds of representations reflected in object substitutions: primary representations and metarepresentations. Primary representations reflect tangible properties of objects (their shape, color, substance). Thus, objects can be used for different purposes. Younger children tend to restrict object substitutions according to perceptual features, such as shape and color. The child can talk on the toy telephone, utilize a cloth as a toy blanket, or pretend a red ball is an apple. Older children are able to use metarepresentations – representations of objects in unusual ways, independent of their physical characteristics. Thus a banana can be a telephone, and blocks can be served as pastries.

When pretend play first emerges, children tend to engage into self-directed pretense, centering pretense on their own bodies and actions. Children may pretend to be asleep, to eat from toy tableware, to read a book, or to talk on a toy telephone. Older children 'decenter' pretense by involving not only themselves but surrounding objects in pretend actions. They can make a doll read a book or make a set of buttons to go for a walk as if they were people. Even after the advent of decentration, play becomes more elaborate, when children combine sequences of pretend actions into a coherent scenario and make pretend plans for the future, such as hosting tea parties, cooking dinners, taking dolls to school, and going to work.

Thus, in the second year, children's play actions take on more of a nonliteral quality. The goal of play now appears to be symbolic or representational. Play becomes increasingly generative, as children enact activities performed by self, others, and objects in simple pretense scenarios, pretending to drive toy cars, eat from empty plates, or talk on toy telephones. Symbolic or pretend play also follows a sequence in development. At first symbolic play is self-directed, later it begins to include pretense schemes that apply to others. In the same way, single-scheme pretense appears before multischeme pretense. Finally, pretense with substitution objects develops.

This developmental progression of play is a generalized version of the sequential changes in representation that take place in early childhood. The majority of children follow this developmental pattern, although there are also wide individual differences in the rates of children achieving each level of development and in the quality of each level of achievement.

Play and Other Related Functions

Engaging in play requires the activation of different cognitive factors such as attention focus and mental representation. Thus, play, especially solitary play with objects, often serves as a mirror of cognition. Infants' perceptual exploration of objects facilitates the development of representation. While playing with an object, rotating, banging, mouthing, or squeezing it, a child receives different perceptual experiences that relate to the same object. As the central nervous system develops, cognitive processing grows, and children are exposed to novel situations that allow them to experience the presence and absence of objects. Children express their interest in the temporary absence and presence of objects or others by engaging in peek-a-boo games or intentionally dropping objects. These experiences extend perceptions in the developing child gradually promoting the distinction between perceptual experiences that rely on focal sensorimotor attention and representational experiences that transcend the here and now. Children's representational play is a platform for this distinction.

In parallel with their growing play sophistication, infants exhibit tremendous development in related areas of cognition. Thus, the growth of language and engaging in pretend-play scenarios during the second year of life, both reflect the development and increasing sophistication of children's representational capacities. In the domain of language, for example, children begin to understand and produce sound sequences that function as true naming as they shift away from the context – 'restricted' use of words and phrases to more 'flexible' uses across contexts. At the same time, their attention span becomes longer and more controlled. Children can coordinate and focus their attention, disregarding extraneous distractions.

Pretense play appears to have least two independent components – play that is associated with language as well as play that is associated with attention. The two reflect different underlying mental capacities. Advances in play and language go together. Children who perform well in one domain of development usually do well in the other. Apparently, language and pretense play share a representational nature. In language, as in pretend play, objects, people, and actions are represented symbolically. In contrast to this association between language and play, children's play competence is separately associated with their attention span. The mastery motivation side of play provides an explanation of the association between play and attention. Motivation to master the environment often results in sustained periods of object exploration, or attention focus, and thereby increased competence. Some theories suggest that ability to stay on task is necessary to bring play to higher levels of sophistication. Over the first 2 years, children regulate their visual attention and gradually move from nonsymbolic to symbolic play.

A Short History of Research on Play

Play is a part of the child's daily life in every society. Many philosophers and psychologists have been interested in child play, tried to define it, explain the reasons that motivate children to engage in play, and discuss the benefits and outcomes of play for children.

Early theories of play tended to divide into four groupings based on function:

1. *Surplus energy theory.* Charles D. Spencer argued that there is a universal need for people to engage in mental and physical activities. Because young children do not have responsibilities, they expend their surplus energy through play.

2. *Relaxation and recreation theory.* Moritz Lazarus suggested that work exhausts people mentally and physically, and sleep and rest are insufficient to recover. To achieve full recreation ('re-creation'), people need to engage in actions unrelated to real life and released from the constraints of work.

3. *Practice theory.* Karl Groos opined that a period of immaturity is specifically designed for complex organisms to practice skills that are necessary for survival during adulthood.

4. *Recapitulation theory.* Luther Gulick and Granville Stanley Hall considered play to be a cathartic factor in child development. Play constitutes an outlet for certain instincts and, by weakening them, enables children to acquire more complex behaviors of adults in society.

Many theorists have addressed other specific aspects of the development of play. For example, William Stern suggested that gender-specific games, such as girls playing with dolls and boys play-fighting, foster maternal instincts in women and aggressive instincts in men, respectively. Lili Peller linked the evolution of child play to progression in psychosexual development. Sigmund Freud suggested that the purpose of play is wish-fulfillment released from the constraints of reality. Karl A. Menninger emphasized the anxiety-reducing benefits of play.

Among the most influential child psychologists of play are Erik Erikson, Lev Vygotsky, and Jean Piaget. Erikson thought of play as a way children work through tensions; he advanced the use of play for therapeutic purposes. Piaget viewed play as a tool for cognitive assimilation. Vygotsky argued that caregivers serve as important play partners who help to shape child play in its social context.

Contemporary theorists consider play to have more than instinctual and psychoanalytic functions, but also include normative emotional, cognitive, communicative, social, and cultural functions.

Play in Relation to Play Partners, Gender, and Culture

Children's growth and development are shaped by various biological, cognitive, and social factors. Play, among other developmental processes, is strongly influenced by these aspects. It varies across families, genders, and cultures. To understand child play, it is often crucial to determine the child's playmates, the gender of the child, and where the play occurs.

Play and Play Partners

Early theorists tended to focus on children's solitary play. Vygotsky changed the way the child's playmates were viewed, by introducing the notion that child play is shaped by the context of social interactions. Although play emerges from the child, adults provide the play environment and objects used in play, inducing and stimulating play. Children often initiate pretend play, but they also complete play scenarios begun by others as well as imitate the play they see. Collaborative play interactions are believed to advance play sophistication in children, bringing the child to higher levels of development.

Various play partners stimulate the development of play, and they do so in different ways. It is difficult to underestimate parental contributions to children's cognitive development through play.

At all ages, mothers are more effective than other play partners in controlling and regulating emotional arousal in play and by providing appropriate stimulation. Mothers who are more knowledgeable about play are likely to prompt their children to play at more sophisticated levels than mothers who are less knowledgeable. Generally, mothers are more likely to initiate symbolic play than nonsymbolic play with their toddlers and remain involved until the pretend scenario is completed. Depending on their children's capabilities and age, mothers take different roles in pretend scenes, sometimes facilitating the game and sometimes participating as audience. Children actively seek maternal involvement in pretend play, thus indicating their understanding of symbolic play as a joint activity. In addition, maternal initiation of symbolic play predicts the quantity of children's engagement in symbolic play and maternal responsiveness to child play predicts the quality of later child play. Child's gender influences the style of maternal play. Thus, mothers of girls tend to direct their daughters' behavior during the course of play, more than do mothers of boys, who direct them less and let them explore more. As play partners, mothers and children seem to adjust to one another, each bringing the play level of one close to the play level of the other.

Multiple studies have shown the importance of father's involvement as a playmate in infancy and childhood. While in general, fathers participate in caregiving less than mothers do, fathers tend to spend more of 'together time' playing with their infant. The ways in which fathers play with their children during the course of development differ consistently from the ways that mothers do. Different styles of play encourage development of various skills and abilities in infants and children. For example, fathers usually engage in physical games, such as lifting and bouncing, while mothers prefer educational, visual games, most of the time involving toys. During object play, mothers follow infants' gaze, notice changes of attention from one object to another, and let infants explore and choose objects of interest; fathers, in contrast, change infants' attention by initiating physical play.

Fathers' engagement in physical play is most frequent in toddlerhood and gradually declines after that. Even with the decreased engagement in physical play, father's participation is significantly higher than mother's participation in physical games. Through late childhood fathers remain frequent partners in outdoor activities, trips, and the like.

Both mothers and fathers respond appropriately to the changes in their children's abilities, by switching to more complex play patterns. Parental knowledge about play development is an important factor in fostering interactions with children.

Aside from parents, siblings and peers are also effective play partners for children and impact social and gender-typed roles of the society by engaging in culturally appropriate, and eschewing inappropriate, play behaviors. After the first year, play interactions with siblings and peers increase in prevalence and may be more intense than those with parents. Parents and siblings stimulate cognitive skills differently through play, often with different outcomes. Parents use play as a tool for learning and communicating knowledge about the real world, whereas siblings and peers often 'play for play's sake'. Like adults, older siblings have more competence and are capable of bringing child play to more sophisticated levels. Peers share similar developmental achievements; therefore, they relate to each other more as equals, without necessarily creating an intellectual hierarchy.

Aside from peers and siblings, older children often have imaginary companions – invisible individuals that are invented and vividly imagined. Even though children pretend to talk or play with imaginary companions, they usually acknowledge that imaginary companions are not real. More girls than boys are known to have experiences with imaginary companions. In the beginning of the last century, these experiences were thought to indicate mental and developmental deviations and were strongly discouraged. In the middle and at the end of the last century, scientists assumed that children with experiences of imaginary companions grow to be more creative than children without such experiences. Recent findings disprove that notion, suggesting that there is no difference in creativity in children who have an imaginary companion compared to those who do not have such experiences.

Gender Segregation of Play

Around their fourth or fifth birthday, children's play becomes remarkably gender-segregated in terms of preferred toys, playmates, and play styles. Girls prefer to play with girls; they are less interested in rough, outdoor play, but are more interested in playing with dolls. Boys play with other boys, prefer cars and constructors, and enjoy rough, outdoor games. If one looks at toys that boys and girls choose and ask to buy, children tend to ask for more gender-stereotyped toys than their parents tend to choose. While they both may request clothing, sports equipment, and educational toys, boys usually desire action figures and toy vehicles, and girls ask for dolls and toy household items.

Biological, cognitive, and social-learning theories have been marshaled to explain this phenomenon. The biological perspective includes hormonal theories. It holds that sex-typed behaviors develop due to the influence of hormones (especially androgens), during critical stages of development. Because of hormonal changes in the brain, sex-typed behaviors are altered. Differences in levels of prenatal androgens contribute to observed sex-typed behaviors such as toy choices. For example, androgenized girls (girls exposed to high prenatal levels of male hormones) prefer typical boys' toys over girls' toys.

The cognitive perspective invokes gender constancy and the gender schema concept to explain gender-specific play. Gender constancy refers to children's understanding of belonging to a certain gender identity group and this identity does not change with time, social settings, or appearance. When children achieve gender constancy, they develop skills to categorize behaviors in terms of being male or female (gender schema). These schemas influence subsequent sex-typed behaviors. For example, when a girl categorizes cooking as an example of female behavior, she will more likely play with kitchen-sets than with a tool kit.

According to the social-learning perspective, children's gender play behaviors develop as a result of social–environmental influences. Traditional views on childrearing cause different treatment of children based on their gender, thus different sex-typed behaviors are reinforced. Adults fill infants' cribs with toys that are considered to be gender-appropriate to the child. Older children imitate sex-typed behaviors of caregivers and other adults; appropriate sex-type behaviors are later encouraged by parents and peers through positive and negative responses. Same-sex play is supported by peers who see it as appropriate, while crossgender play does not usually elicit positive responses. Observational learning contributes the development of gender-segregated play as well. While playing 'house', for example, girls pretend to do dishes imitating mothers, and boys emulate fathers by pretending to fix appliances.

When they play with different toys, children acquire different play experiences and thereby develop different skills and abilities. Traditional boys' toys, such as constructors and action figures, stimulate sustained attention, creative thinking, and fantasy play that is centered on constructiveness, social pretense, and competitiveness. Because many of boys' toys, such as electric trains and radio-controlled cars, can move on their own, they may stimulate visual tracking and spatial skills. Girls' toys, such as dolls, dolls' accessory packs, and tea sets, stimulate nurturance and fantasy play that centers on domestic life. Girls' toys are usually more colorful and appealing than boys' toys, but often are less mobile. In general,

instructions and accessories for dolls point to what can be done to the doll (e.g., groom it, put on make-up, dress up), whereas directions and accessories for action figures advise what can be done with the toy (e.g., fight with weapon).

Certain categories of toys are played with equally by both boys and girls. Gender-neutral toys, such as play-doh, slinkies, and doctor kits, promote artistic and creative abilities. Gender-neutral toys change across time and culture. Contemporary girls play with sports equipment as much as boys do, but several decades ago most sports toys were considered to be boy toys only. In the countries of the former USSR, most physicians were women; thus, doctor kits were considered a strongly feminine toy, whereas in the US they are seen as masculine or gender-neutral.

When toys are rated from strongly gender-stereotyped to gender-neutral, violence emerges as a feature associated with masculine toys (e.g., weapons, toy soldiers, and certain video games); use of such toys is also associated with aggressiveness in pretense play. Toys and accessories, such as perfumes and make-up, are believed to focus girls on the value of physical attractiveness.

Moderately gender-stereotyped and gender-neutral toys (e.g., books, puzzles) tend to have higher educational value and to stimulate development of cognitive skills.

Play and Culture

The vast majority of research on developmental milestones, individual variation, and parent–child interactions in play has been conducted by Western researchers among families in the West. This monocultural tradition imposes limitations on the findings and extant theories of play. Characteristics of growth and development that appear universal can turn out to be culturally specific and vice versa.

Even though virtually all children around the world may engage in prevalent types of play, parental involvement in play differs across cultures. In some cultures, especially in hunting-and-gathering and agricultural village ones, play is regarded as mainly an amusing child activity. Children tend to find play partners among their peers rather than among adult caregivers (e.g., Mayan and the native peoples of the Americas). Parents do not practice direct teaching through play, rather they assist and direct children in group play with their siblings or peers. In contrast, other cultures view parental participation in play as an important developmental activity. In these cultures (e.g., North America), parents are the first and main play partners of children during the first years of life. This is often due to the widespread belief that children learn through play, and that play helps to develop cognitive, social, motor, and affective skills.

Parents in different countries hold different attitudes toward stimulating children's play. European and North American cultures traditionally encourage independence and autonomy, whereas Asian, South American, and African societies tend to emphasize interdependence and obedience to elders. For example, during mother–child pretend object play, US American children engage in more complex play, when mothers encourage their children's independent activity and praise them. By contrast, Japanese children respond with more complex pretend play when their mothers lead and direct joint activities.

In many cultures, interpersonal play is viewed as an activity through which parents and children strengthen their attachment and learn to exchange emotions in shared experiences. In these cultures, interpersonal play is a usual daily interaction. Interpersonal play can be also affected by child-care arrangements and everyday cultural practices. For example, in many traditional cultures, mothers use devices such as slings to carry infants and free their hands for work; this practice eventuates in less opportunity for face-to-face interpersonal play. Rather than engaging in face-to-face play interactions, these mothers structure interpersonal games that involve a third person; their own role is to direct the infant's gaze toward others.

These examples show that even though interpersonal games between parents and children are rare in some cultures, infants still engage in games with partners other than parents. Those interactions enable children to master modes of communication appropriate to their culture.

For example, the Gusii of southwestern Kenya avoid eye-to-eye contact during social interactions. This behavior derives from cultural superstitions about the possible dangers of visual contact. Even though mothers provide children with sufficient physical contact, they tend to restrain playful interactions and avoid eye-to-eye gaze. Gusii infants are viewed as incapable of interpersonal interactions; although mothers respond to infants' needs and demands, they do not engage them in play nor do they facilitate interactions. However, when specifically asked to perform face-to-face interactions, Gusii mothers and infants resemble Western dyads in many ways. Nonetheless, the dynamics of their interactions differ. Their duration of playful interchanges is shorter, and their interactions do not revolve around peaks of stimulation and affect arousal. This dynamic might be the result of different cultural beliefs. Gusii parents might view their role as protecting the child from overexcitement and distress rather than as being a source or partner of playful stimulation.

In play, cultural settings cannot be underestimated: they constitute means of play forms and organize children's experiences, provide rules and information to construct knowledge about the society, and teach appropriate roles and behaviors.

Summary

Play is a complex activity that is described best according to its types and functions. Different types of play, such as interpersonal play and object play, contribute to psychological, cognitive, and mastery in addition to social, communication, and cultural development. Types of play develop gradually with the growth of child. The infant first engages in exploratory play and progresses to symbolic play. This progression serves as an indicator of cognitive development of the child: advances in play are correlated with progress in mental representations, attention, and language acquisition. Play develops in the context of gender and culture. Toy preferences of boys and girls differ due to biological, cognitive, and social factors; play partners vary by culture due to different cultural attitudes toward play and appropriate play partners.

Acknowledgment

Preparation of this article was supported by the Intramural Research Program of the NIH, NICHD.

See also: Attachment; Cognitive Development; Cognitive Developmental Theories; Exploration and Curiosity; Friends and Peers; Gender: Awareness, Identity, and Stereotyping; Imagination and Fantasy; Imitation and Modeling; Language Development: Overview; Piaget's Cognitive-Developmental Theory; Social and Emotional Development Theories; Social Interaction; Symbolic Thought; Taste and Smell; Vygotsky's Sociocultural Theory.

Suggested Readings

Blakemore Owen JE and Centers RE (2005) Characteristics of boys' and girls' toys. *Sex Roles* 53: 619–633.

Bornstein MH (2007) On the significance of social relationships in the development of children's earliest symbolic play: An ecological perspective. In: Göncü A and Gaskins S (eds.) *Play and Development: Evolutionary, Sociocultural, and Functional Perspectives*, pp. 101–129. Mahwah, NJ: Lawrence Erlbaum Associates.

Bornstein MH and O'Reilly AW (eds.) (1993) *The Role of Play in the Development of Thought.* San Francisco: Jossey-Bass.

Pasterski VL, Geffner ME, Brain C, Hindmarsh P, Brook C, and Hines M (2005) Prenatal hormones and postnatal socialization by parents as determinants of male-typical toy play in girls with congenital adrenal hyperplasia. *Child Development* 76: 265–278.

Pellegrini AD and Smith PK (1998) Physical activity play: The nature and function of a neglected aspect of playing. *Child Development* 69: 577–598.

Piaget J (1983) Piaget's Theory. In: Kessen W and Mussen PH (eds.) *Handbook of Child Psychology: Vol. 1. History, Theory, and Methods,* 4th edn., vol. 1, pp. 103–128. New York: Wiley.

Rubin KH, Fein GG, and Vandenberg B (1983) Play. In: Mussen PH and Hetherington EM (eds.) *Handbook of Child Psychology: Vol. 1. Socialization, Personality, and Social Development,* 4th edn., vol. 1, pp. 752–833. New York: Wiley.

Tamis-LeMonda CS, Užgiris IČ, and Bornstein MH (2002) Play in parent–child interactions. In: Bornstein MH (ed.) *Handbook of Parenting,* 2nd edn., vol. 5, pp. 221–241. Mahwah, NJ: Lawrence Erlbaum Associates.

Postpartum Depression, Effects on Infant

D M Teti and N Towe-Goodman, The Pennsylvania State
University, University Park, PA, USA

Glossary

Comorbid – Term used by diagnosticians to describe an illness or condition that coexists with another illness or condition (e.g., depression is frequently comorbid with anxiety).

Depressogenic – A term describing an event or process that may be causal in the development of depression.

Goodness-of-fit – The quality of the 'match' or 'fit' between the characteristics of an individual and the environment. This term is frequently used to describe the quality of fit between infant characteristics (e.g., temperament, gender) and personality attributes of a parent. Theoretically, the better the fit, the better the adaptation of the parent and infant to each other and, in turn, the child's adaptation to the wider world.

Infant–mother attachment classifications – Infant–parent attachments are based on a scoring system developed by Mary Ainsworth and Mary Main for infants between 12 and 18 months, with particular attention to infant behavior during infant–mother reunions in the Strange Situation. Secure infants typically greet the parent, approach the parent to achieve contact, soothe quickly after contact is achieved, and are eventually able to resume toy play. Insecure-avoidant infants do not greet and conspicuously avoid the parent following reunion and appear to prefer toy play to achieving contact with or interacting with the parent. Insecure ambivalent/resistant infants overtly express anger toward the parent during reunions and have great difficulty soothing and returning to toy play. Insecure-disorganized infants appear to lack a coherent strategy in gaining access to the parent and show fear and/or confusion in response to the parent's during reunions.

Major depressive disorder (MDD) – As defined by the American Psychiatric Association's Diagnostic and Statistical Manual – 4th edition (DSM-IV), a diagnosis given for a single major depressive episode (nonrecurrent), or for multiple episodes (recurrent). MDD should be distinguished from other mood disorders that have depressive features but whose cause can be traced to a medical condition, substance use, dementia, or psychosocial stressor, or whose patterning of depressive symptoms cannot be clearly linked to the postpartum period (e.g., bipolar disorder or dysthymia).

Major depressive episode – A period of at least two consecutive weeks of depressed mood or loss of interest or enjoyment in most activities, accompanied by at least four of the following symptoms lasting 2 weeks or longer: loss of energy; difficulties in concentrating, thinking, or making decisions; a change in weight, appetite, psychomotor activity, or sleep; feelings of worthlessness or guilt; and recurrent thoughts of death or suicide, or suicide plans or attempts.

Maternal self-efficacy – Mother's beliefs or judgments about their competency in the parental role. Depressed mothers commonly report feeling less efficacious in the parenting role than do nondepressed mothers.

Negative affective bias – The tendency of depressed individuals to view oneself, others, or events in a negative or pessimistic light. Depressed women tend to hold negative cognitions about their children and themselves, which may impact their behavior in the parenting role.

Postpartum – Of, or pertaining to, the period of time, typically the first year, following an infant's birth.

Still face paradigm – An observational procedure composed of three 2 min phases: (1) free play phase – the caregiver engages the child in face-to-face play, talking and engaging the infant in a playful manner; (2) still face phase – the caregiver is instructed to maintain a flat or emotionally neutral facial expression (a 'still face') and does not respond to the infant in any way; (3) free play 'reunion' phase – the caregiver re-engages the infant in face-to-face play.

Strange situation procedure – A 21 min procedure, conducted in a laboratory playroom with toys, developed by Mary Ainsworth to assess quality of infant–parent attachment. The procedure enables one to observe infant behavior in the presence of the parent and a (typically) female stranger during a series of separations from and reunions with each. The pattern of infant behavior is then classified into one of four attachment categories (see above).

Transactional perspective – A conceptualization of development in which individual development is viewed as a dynamic process in which individual and environment mutually and reciprocally influence each other over time.

Introduction

Depression is particularly common among women of childbearing age, and approximately 13% of women can be expected to experience at least one bout of significant depression during the early postpartum period. Postpartum depression is similar in symptom profile to depressions that occur at other points in life. It is characterized by sadness or an inability to experience pleasure, accompanied by several additional symptoms, including negative cognitions (poor self-worth, perceptions of failure, guilt, and/or suicidal thoughts), somatic dysfunction (loss of appetite, sleep disturbance, fatigue), and impairment in daily functioning (e.g., inability to make decisions and to work effectively). The American Psychiatric Association's Diagnostic and Statistical Manual – 4th edition (DSM-IV) identifies a major depressive episode in terms of the symptom profile outlined above, which persists for at least a 2-week period. A DSM-IV diagnosis of major depressive disorder (MDD) may be given for a single major depressive episode, or for multiple, recurring episodes, and should not be confused with other mood disorders that have depressive features but whose etiology can be traced to a medical condition, substance use, dementia, or psychosocial stressor, or whose patterning of depressive symptoms cannot be clearly linked to the postpartum period (e.g., bipolar disorder or dysthymia). Postpartum depression is also not to be confused with the 'postpartum blues', a mild depressive condition that occurs early in the postpartum period, is not associated with significant impairment, and resolves quickly. Some postpartum depressions can also be accompanied by psychotic symptoms, such as hallucinations, delusions, and excessive psychomotor disturbances. Psychotic postpartum depressions are rare, however, and most discussions of postpartum depression are with reference to nonpsychotic depression.

Postpartum depression can have insidious effects on the mother and her family. Because of its high prevalence rate, it has become a major public health concern. Prevalence estimates vary as a function of the nature of the assessment and the window of time during which assessment takes place. Depressive symptoms can be assessed either through self-report questionnaire assessments, or by more formal clinical interviews. Self-report assessments include such well-known measures as the Beck Depression Inventory, the Center for Epidemiological Studies – Depression Scale, and the Hamilton Rating Scale for Depression, each of which taps the frequency and severity of such symptoms and provides overall score cut points that, when exceeded, identify individuals with clinical levels of symptom severity. Clinical interviews, by contrast, use a more comprehensive interview format to inquire about current and past symptoms of depression that can be used to diagnose a depressive disorder, past or present. Not surprisingly, prevalence rates of postpartum depression are somewhat lower when comprehensive clinical interview assessments are used than when mothers are asked to complete self-report questionnaires.

The effects of postpartum depression are broad-based, with consequences not only for individual functioning but also for the quality of the mother's relationships with other family members. Marital discord in families with depressed mothers is common, as are troubled relationships between the depressed mother and her children. Indeed, children of depressed mothers are at significant risk for maladjustment and cognitive delays. Infants of depressed mothers are more likely than are infants of nondepressed mothers to be fussy, irritable, or withdrawn, to deploy attention ineffectively and manifest developmental delays in significant cognitive milestones such as object permanence, and are at risk to become insecurely attached to their mothers. Among older children of depressed mothers, rates of psychiatric disorder are as much as four to five times those among their same-aged counterparts of nondepressed mothers. Although maternal depression appears to predispose children to become depressed, these children are also at elevated risk for the full spectrum of externalizing disorders, including oppositional-defiant disorder and conduct disorder. Not surprisingly, these children are also at risk for poor academic performance, and for difficulties in interpersonal relationships, depressive and anxiety disorders, substance abuse, and delinquency over the long term.

Mechanisms for the transmission of psychopathology from depressed parent to child are poorly understood. Depression appears to be at least partially heritable, which may account in part for the elevated psychiatric risk status among children of depressed women. Other biologically based influences may also be at work. Recurrent bouts of significant depression among women are common. It is not unusual that women suffering from postpartum depression have experienced depressive episodes during pregnancy and pre-pregnancy. Interestingly, infants born to mothers suffering prepartum depression manifest a biochemical profile (i.e., levels of cortisol, catecholamines, and serotonin) that is similar to that of their mothers, but different from infants born to nondepressed mothers. The potential impact of genetically and biologically based factors on the psychiatric risk status of children of depressed women has been given relatively short shrift among researchers who study parental depression and its effects. We will return to this point later.

Most research examining mechanisms of transmission of psychopathology from depressed parent to child has focused on the kinds of environments depressed parents create for their children, and the impact such environments have on the developing child's interpersonal, cognitive, and emotional life. Depressed mothers indeed create pathogenic child-rearing environments to which even very young (3–4 months old) infants are reactive. Importantly, the degree to which maternal depression singly influences child outcomes, however, depends on the chronicity and severity of the mothers' illness. A single, isolated, nonrecurrent bout of major depression, albeit debilitating to the mother while it occurs, is much less likely to affect children's adjustment over the long term than is chronic, severe depression, involving multiple, recurrent bouts of depression during the early postpartum period and beyond. Unfortunately, a woman who experiences postpartum depression is likely to experience at least one additional depressive episode sometime during her child's first 5 years of life.

Also important to note is that depression is more likely to occur under adverse environmental circumstances, such as poverty and single parenthood, and it may also be but one feature of a broader spectrum of psychiatric symptoms. It is common to find, for example, that depression is comorbid with anxiety, and that depression, broadly speaking, is a salient feature of a variety of other psychiatric disorders. Interestingly, recent research suggests that depression that is chronic and severe may be comorbid with some personality disorders, as outlined in DSM-IV, axis II diagnoses. Indeed, some have proposed that chronic, severe depression is almost always comorbid with personality disorder, and that the depression is a by-product of the significantly impaired interpersonal relationships, problems in living, and emotional volatility that characterize personality disorders. This has raised significant concerns about whether chronic, severe depression without features of personality disorder can be distinguished from the effects of personality disorder alone. The ability to address these concerns rests on whether mothers with recurrent MDD that is not comorbid with an axis II disorder can be identified and compared, in terms of features of the mother–child relationship and child developmental outcomes, with mothers whose recurrent depression is paired with personality disorder. Most research to date has not systematically addressed the effects of maternal depression with vs. without comorbidity with other psychiatric problems.

Depressed Women as Parents

Depressed Mothers' Cognitions

Because cognitive distortions feature so saliently in depression, we begin a discussion of depressed mothering with a focus on what is known about depressed mothers' thoughts about themselves as parents and their thoughts about their children. Put simply, depressed women hold decidedly negative cognitions about their children and themselves. Depressed mothers are more likely than are nondepressed mothers to perceive themselves as inadequate parents, and to enjoy parenting less. Depressed mothers are also more likely to view their children negatively, in terms of their overall social competence and adjustment. Because children of depressed mothers are indeed at risk for maladjustment, it is unclear if depressed mothers' negative views of their children are accurate, or if they represent depression-induced cognitive distortions. Some studies suggest that the difference between depressed and nondepressed mothers' perceptions of their children is not based on the negative affective bias associated with depression, but on the tendency of nondepressed mothers to be more positive about their children than is actually warranted (i.e., a 'positive affective bias'). Indeed, when depressed and nondepressed women's perceptions of their children were compared with perceptions obtained from nonfamilial sources such as teachers, there is some evidence of greater concordance between depressed mothers' perceptions and teacher perceptions of the same children than between nondepressed mothers' and teachers' perceptions. However, because of depressed women's tendency to dwell on and exaggerate problems of all types, it is likely that depressed mothers' negative perceptions of their children are in part driven by a negative affective bias, the strength of which is probably directly proportional to the severity of their depressive symptoms.

It is reasonable to expect that a depressed mother's tendency to dwell on the negative, or to perceive a perfectly normal, developmentally appropriate behavior or accomplishment as problematic, may have its own impact on a developing child's emotional well-being. A child whose mother repeatedly labels her/him in negative terms is likely, at the least, to be at risk for low self-esteem, and possibly for a host of internalizing and externalizing problems. The negative affect and negative cognitions that define depression, however, are intimately tied to action tendencies. It is thus not surprising that depression takes a toll on the quality of mother–child interactions. The symptoms associated with depression challenge the ability of mothers to interact with their children in a developmentally supportive manner, and many studies now available describe depressed mothering as noncontingent and unresponsive, irritable and intrusive, insensitive, asynchronous, and incompetent. Difficulties observed in depressed mothering may stem from deficiencies in the depressed mother's awareness and interpretation of her child's behavior (i.e., a 'signal detection' deficiency). For example, a depressed mother's rumination and self-absorption can influence her attention to and awareness of her children's needs and social signals, and can also interfere with her ability to process social information efficiently and accurately. Her negative affective bias may create tendencies to misinterpret child behavior, and depressed mothers may be inclined to attribute negative intentions and motives to their children's behavior. Further, a depressed mothers' own need for support and comfort may lead her to expect more support and comfort from her child than the child is able to provide. Parenting difficulties among depressed mothers may also stem from the general slowing effect depressed affect has upon one's capability and motivation to act. Lack of energy and indecisiveness are hallmark features of depression, which in turn would be expected to influence a mother's motivation to respond promptly and contingently to child signals that she does comprehend. Thus, the problems observed in depressed parenting may arise from the debilitating effect depression has on mothers' capacities for processing social information (awareness and interpretation of child cues), and from the dampening effect of depression on a mother's capacity and motivation to respond contingently.

Depressed Mother–Infant Interactions

In infancy, the emotional climate of parent–child interactions may be particularly important for the development of self-regulation, secure attachments, and the promotion of other social and emotional competencies. Unfortunately, the disturbances associated with depression have a clear impact on the emotional quality of early mother–child interactions. Depressed mothers interact less with their infants, are less aware of their infants' signals, and are less contingently responsive to their infants' bids for attention. The joint attention, shared positive affect, and appropriate scaffolding that characterizes warm, nurturant parent–child relationships are often missing in depressed mother–infant dyads. Further, depressed mothers show less emotional availability and affection toward their infants, display less pleasure and positive emotion during interactions, and express more negative affect overall. Some depressed mothers may alternate between being disengaged and then overly stimulating, the latter of which can be so intrusive that they appear disorganizing to the infant. In turn, their infants' behavior is conspicuously devoid of positive affect, and is also characteristically high in distress or protest, unresponsiveness to maternal bids, avoidance, and withdrawal, and this behavior sometimes generalizes to other, nondepressed adults. The infant's distress and unresponsiveness in turn may increase the mother's feelings of inadequacy or rejection, thus creating a vicious cycle of negative, dysregulated affect in the mother–infant relationship.

Experimental evidence underscores the premise that depressed mothers' emotional unavailability and lack of responsiveness is emotionally dysregulating to infants. In 1978, Edward Tronick and colleagues developed the still face paradigm, a procedure that requires mothers to mimic the flat affect and unresponsive behavior commonly seen in depressed mothers. The procedure is composed of three very brief episodes: In the first episode, the mother engages the child in face-to-face play, talking and engaging the infant in a playful manner; in the second episode, the mother is instructed to maintain a flat or emotionally neutral facial expression (a 'still face') and does not respond to the infant in any way; and in the final 'reunion' episode, the mother re-engages the infant in face-to-face play. Infants of nondepressed mothers are typically very positive and engaged during the face-to-face play, but show a heightened level of arousal and distress to their mothers' sudden emotional unavailability and unresponsiveness during the still face. Typical reactions on the part of the child include attempts to re-engage the mother through smiling, vocalizations, or fussing, and distressed facial expressions such as frowns or grimaces. Infants may use a variety of methods to try to regulate their discomfort during the still face, such as turning their head away from the mother and averting their gaze, or engaging in self-soothing behaviors such as sucking on their thumb. The effects of the still face often linger even when the mother re-engages the infant, with infants often continuing to show distress afterwards. Research with the still face paradigm demonstrates that even very young infants (i.e., as young as 3 months of age) are emotionally attuned to maternal affect and can become emotionally dysregulated when mothers' normally positive affect is withdrawn.

Interestingly, when the still face procedure is conducted with depressed mothers and their infants, clear differences emerge between these dyads and nondepressed mother–infant dyads. First, when the mother is depressed, there is less distinction in the behavior of both the child and the mother across the three episodes. There are often less shared positive emotions during face-to-face play, with more neutral affect and withdrawn behavior in both the mother and infant. Second, during the still face phase, infants of depressed mothers show less active attempts at regaining their mothers' attention than do infants of nondepressed mothers. Instead, infants of depressed mothers become more quiet and withdrawn, and devote more energy toward self-comforting or distraction. Such behavior has led some to suggest that the still face episode is similar to the normative behavior of the depressed mother, and that infants of depressed mothers are more likely to make attempts at managing their distress without maternal assistance. The inability of infants to gain comfort and support from their mothers when distressed may have serious consequences for the formation of secure attachments, as well as in the development of healthy strategies for regulating emotions.

Tronick's work with the still face paradigm prompted the development of his 'mutual regulation model' as an integrative framework for understanding how mother and infant affective states become mutually and reciprocally regulatory. Among typical, nondepressed mothers with very young infants, mothers' use of contingently responsive, positive affect during interactions with their infants significantly exceeds their use of negative affect. Maternal positive affect in turn elicits similarly positive affective responses (smiles, coos, laughs) from the infant, and both mothers and infants find each others' positive affective signals to be mutually rewarding and reinforcing. Over time, mutually reciprocal positive affect predominates in interactions between nondepressed mothers, which carries developmental benefits for the infant's socio-emotional development over the long term. By contrast, mutually reciprocal, negative affect predominates in interactions between depressed mothers and their infants. Depressed mothers may be unresponsive to or critical of their infants' behavior and social cues, leading their infants in turn to withdraw and become distressed. Depressed mothers' lack of sufficient use of contingently responsive positive affect may render them less capable than nondepressed mothers to soothe their infants when distressed (indeed, depressed mothers' negative affect may be, in many instances, the cause of their infants' distress). The infants in turn may become dysphoric and overly reliant on self-soothing and self-stimulatory behaviors to regulate their negative emotions, placing them at risk for psychopathology.

Depressed Mothering and Infant–Mother Attachments

Attachment theory would predict that depressed mothers' interactional difficulties with their infants, if prolonged, will predispose infants to become insecurely attached. Indeed, maternal sensitivity during infancy, which can be defined as an empathic awareness of and appropriate responsiveness to infant needs and social cues, is taken by attachment theory as the single most important predictor of attachment security in infancy. Research that has examined linkages between maternal depression and infant–mother attachment security typically employs the Ainsworth Strange Situation procedure, a brief, 21–24 min seven-episode procedure used for infants between 12 and 18 months of age. The procedure, which almost always takes place in a small room that is novel to the infant, puts the infant through a series of 3 min episodes of separations

and reunions with the mother, a (typically) female stranger, and one episode in which the infant is alone.

Specific attention is given to the infant's behavior during the two Strange Situation reunion episodes with the mother. Secure infants typically greet the mother during infant–mother reunions, approach the mother and seek her out for comfort (if the infant experiences separation distress), and are ultimately able to return to toy play and exploring their environment in the mothers' presence. Sensitive mothering during the infant's first year would be expected to promote secure infant–mother attachments, which, as many studies now attest, predicts healthy adjustment in the preschool years and beyond in terms of empathic awareness, child compliance, and peer relations. Insecure-avoidant infants, by contrast, typically do not greet the mother during reunions. They do not approach the mother except in the context of toy play, and it is not uncommon for insecure-avoidant infants to prefer to play with toys rather than interact with their mothers. Maternal insensitivity characterized by intrusiveness and rejection would be expected to predict insecure-avoidant infant–mother attachments, which some attachment theorists propose is developed as a defense against maternal rejection. Insecure-ambivalent/resistant infants direct overt expressions of anger toward their mothers during reunions and typically do not soothe in response to maternal attempts to do so. Mothering characterized by unresponsiveness and/or inconsistency in responsiveness would be expected to predict insecure-ambivalent (resistant) infant–mother attachments. Both insecure-avoidant and insecure-ambivalent/resistant attachments, albeit not adaptive to the infant over the long term, are viewed as 'strategies' the child has developed to maintain access to the attachment figure (the mother) in times of stress. Insecure-avoidant infants learn not to seek out their mothers because doing so in the past has led to rejection. Thus, they employ a 'close, but not too close' strategy to maintain some degree of proximity to the mother. Insecure-ambivalent/resistant infants have learned that overt expressions of anger and prolonged distress is 'what works' to keep their mothers focused on them. This strategy, although maladaptive to their development over the long run, is functional in the short term to maintain access to their mothers. Both insecure-avoidance and insecure-resistant/ambivalent infants are at risk for difficulties in later mother–child relationships and peer relationships, compared to secure infants.

Elevations in insecure infant–mother attachments (i.e., insecure-avoidant and insecure-ambivalent resistant attachments) have been reported in several studies of depressed mother–infant dyads. Further, when mothers' depression is chronic and severe over the infant's first year, infants are at risk for developing insecure-disorganized attachment to their mothers, which some attachment theorists cite as the most insecure of all of the insecure attachment classifications. Unlike the insecure-avoidant and insecure ambivalent attachment patterns, which appear to be governed by clear-cut strategies (albeit not ideal) for accessing the attachment figure, insecure-disorganized attachment is identified by conspicuous absence of a clear-cut strategy. Disorganized attachment is instead hallmarked by fear and confusion about how to access the attachment figure (the mother) at times when it is in the infant's best interests to do so. In the Strange Situation, insecure-disorganized infants are identified by any of a variety of behavior patterns signifying fear and/or confusion during the infant–mother reunion episodes. For example, disorganization is identified when the infant manifests clear-cut expressions of fear (e.g., infant brings hand to mouth and has a fearful expression) of the mother when she enters the room to begin the reunion episode. It is also identified when the infant freezes or stills in the mother's presence for a substantial period of time, or when the infant, upon approaching the mother, repeatedly veers away from her. These are but a few of a variety of indicators of disorganized attachment, all of which reflect a state of fear or confusion about how to access the attachment figure in times of stress. Rates of disorganized infant–mother attachment are found to be elevated among infants of alcoholic parents, substance abusing parents, and parents with significant psychopathology. Of the three insecure infant–parent attachment classifications, children identified as insecure-disorganized are at highest risk for the development of behavior problems in the preschool years.

Attachment theory proposes that, over time, children develop working models of relationships that spawn from their early attachments with their caregivers, models that are carried forward and applied in subsequent relationships. Such models can be thought of as a set of affectively laden cognitions or expectations about relationships that develop as a result of repeated interactions with attachment figures and that guide behavior and the processing of social information. Attachment theory predicts that children with secure working models develop expectations that their caregivers will be appropriately responsive to them when needed, and such children in turn come to believe that they are worthy of love and support. Such expectations are consistent with a history of sensitive, responsive caregiving. Children who develop insecure working models, by contrast, do not expect their caregivers to be appropriately responsive, and insecure working models may serve as a foundation for low self-worth. Importantly, attachment theory also proposes that children internalize not just the child's role in their early attachment relationships, but the role of the parent as well, and that they are likely to carry forward and enact the parent's side in subsequent relationships with others. Indeed, it is the development of these working models that provides the theoretical link between the insecure

attachment patterns infants develop to their depressed mothers and the adjustment problems these children present later in development.

It is important to emphasize, however, that the link between maternal depression and insecure infant–mother attachment is most clear when mothers' depression during the infants' first year is prolonged. A single maternal depressive episode during the postpartum period that resolves and does not recur is unlikely to have long-term negative effects on security of infant–mother attachment, nor on other aspects of infant and preschool-child functioning.

Depressed Mother–Toddler Relationships

Emergent social, emotional, and cognitive capabilities in the toddler years create new opportunities for change and growth, but may also place new demands on the depressed mother. Although the affective connection between the toddler and mother is clearly still important, the inability to appropriately structure and build upon the child's activities may be especially damaging during this developmental period. Depressed mothers are less able to follow the child's interests or facilitate joint attention, making mutual engagement in activities challenging. Further, depressed mothers' lack of verbal communication and reduced responsiveness in interactions with their toddlers may impact the acquisition of linguistic and cognitive skills, important developmental tasks during this time. Similar to the difficulties seen in infancy, depressed mothers often display sad, anxious, or irritable affect with their toddlers, and their interactions lack the shared positive affect and coordination of their nondepressed counterparts. In turn, their children appear to have difficulty regulating negative emotions, showing less positive emotions and more frequent depressed, anxious, or angry behavior.

Toddlers' growing desire to assert their independence often increases parent–child conflict during this period, and depressed mothers may be less able to provide the gentle guidance and limit setting necessary to successfully negotiate these conflicts. Some mothers experiencing depression are more likely to avoid confrontation with their toddlers, expressing fears over their child's willful behavior and their inability to assert appropriate authority. Conversely, some mothers experiencing depression resort to harsh discipline, showing greater hostility toward their children and utilizing more physical punishment than their nondepressed counterparts. Maternal feelings of helplessness and lack of control over their children's behavior increases the likelihood that they will employ coercive or punitive tactics in disciplinary encounters. In fact, maternal depression may be considered a risk factor for physical abuse and maltreatment of young children. In either case, these ineffective socialization techniques employed by depressed mothers are often met with dysfunctional behavior on the part of the toddler. In some cases, children of depressed mothers show more frequent defiance, hostility, aggression, and externalizing behavior. Alternatively, the toddlers of depressed mothers may show more depressed affect and withdrawal themselves, as well as helplessness in the face of challenges. Notably, the behavior of these toddlers often matches that of their mother, such that the affect and symptoms of the mother are mirrored in her child's actions.

Interestingly, disorganized attachment in infancy is predictive of two rather sophisticated yet very maladaptive preschool behavior patterns directed toward the mother, and both of these patterns have been linked to chronic maternal depression. One of these patterns is characterized by the child's repeated attempts to take care of and nurture the mother (i.e., a role-reversing 'caregiving' pattern). Such a pattern, on the surface, does not present with any outward signs of trouble or hostility between the child and mother. However, a role-reversed caregiving pattern that develops in a child at such an early developmental stage has been identified by some as representing attempts on the part of the child to repair a damaged relationship, with consequences for the child's emotional well-being. Insecure-disorganized infant–mother attachment is also associated with a second maladaptive preschool behavior pattern, characterized by repeated, overt attempts by the child to embarrass and punish the mother. These 'coercive' child behavior patterns are thought to develop in response to a caregiving history characterized by unresponsiveness and inconsistency, perhaps particularly in the area of appropriate limit-setting. The coercive and caregiving preschool patterns may be different manifestations of an overarching 'controlling' strategy of accessing mothers in times of stress. Not surprisingly, these caregiving and coercive patterns have straightforward links to child behavior problems.

Maternal Depression and Child Outcomes in Middle Childhood and Adolescence

There tend to be fewer studies of the effects of maternal depression on developmental outcomes of school-aged children and adolescents, but the data that are available indicate that such children are at high risk for depression, anxiety disorder, conduct disorder, delinquency, attention deficits, and academic failure. Similar to younger children with depressed mothers, interactional difficulties are common between children of depressed mothers and their parents, with withdrawal, poor limit setting, and criticism being central features of depressed mothering for children in this age range. School-aged children and adolescents develop stable representations of themselves

in relation to others, and they are more likely than are children of nondepressed mothers to develop negative attributional styles and low self-worth. Peer relations may also suffer, with children of depressed mothers being more likely to suffer peer isolation, loneliness, and rejection. It is not uncommon for teachers of children of depressed mothers to rate them as being more aggressive and disruptive, in comparison to children of nondepressed mothers.

Individual Differences in Depressed Mother–Child Relationships and Child Outcomes

Despite the well-documented associations between postpartum depression and difficulties within the mother–child relationship, it is important to emphasize that problematic interactions are not seen in all cases in which the mother is experiencing depression. Further, the association between maternal depression and relationship disturbances is less clear in samples that are not also considered 'at risk' due to factors such as poverty or high interparental conflict. Some mothers experiencing depression appear quite normative in their interactions with their infants, and environmental sources of stress or support may play a large role in altering the effects of depression on the mother–child relationship. Although postpartum depression is clearly a risk factor, the numerous individual differences in the way postpartum depression may impact parent–child interactions should not be overlooked.

The Role of Maternal Self-Efficacy

One important source of individual differences in depressed mothering may be variations encountered in maternal self-efficacy, or a mother's beliefs in her own competencies as a parent. Maternal self-efficacy is a construct that has grown out of Albert Bandura's social-cognitive theory. Bandura defines self-efficacy as a set of beliefs or judgments about one's competency at a particular task or setting. Self-efficacy beliefs are viewed as the final common pathway in predicting the degree of effort one expends to succeed at a particular task. Self-efficacious individuals are strongly motivated to marshal whatever resources (personal, social, economic, etc.) that are available to them to succeed at a given task. Self-inefficacious individuals, by contrast, are likely to give up prematurely, despite the fact that success may be within reach. Whereas the strongest predictor of self-efficacy is the degree of prior success at that task, self-efficacy beliefs are also sensitive to social persuasion, vicarious experiences (e.g., modeling), and affective state.

Given the link between self-efficacy and affect, it is not surprising that depressed mothers feel less efficacious in the parenting role than do nondepressed mothers. At the same time, social-cognitive theory would predict that maternal self-efficacy should also be sensitive to support for their mothering provided by intimate support figures (social persuasion), by previous learning experiences about mothering by watching other competent mothers (modeling), and by mothers' perceptions of how 'easy' or 'difficult' their infants are to care for (perceptions of infant temperament, which should be linked with mothers' histories of prior successes and failures with the infant). Thus, variation in maternal self-efficacy is not a simple, direct function of variations in maternal depression, but also of variations in other social influences in the environment. Self-efficacy theory would also predict, however, that any influences of mothers' affective state, social persuasion, or prior experiences with their infants on parenting should be mediated by maternal self-efficacy, which is the final common pathway in the prediction of behavioral competence.

Douglas Teti and Donna Gelfand tested this hypothesis in 1991 in a study of 86 mothers (48 with clinical depression, and 38 nondepressed) of first-year infants. Maternal self-efficacy was assessed with a scale developed by the authors that tapped mothers' self-efficacy beliefs in nine parental domains relevant to mothering an infant in the first year of life (e.g., soothing, maintaining infant attention, diapering, feeding, changing), with a tenth item asking mothers to report on their overall feelings of competence in the mothering role. Ratings of mothers' behavioral competence (e.g., sensitivity, warmth, disengagement) with their infants were conducted from observations of feeding and free play by 'blind', highly reliable observers. Standard, well-established measures were used to assess severity of maternal depressive symptoms, social marital supports, and infant temperament.

As predicted, mothers' parenting efficacy beliefs were negatively associated with maternal depressive symptoms and perceptions of infant temperament, such that mothers felt less efficacious in the maternal role when they were more depressed and when they perceived their infants as more difficult. Mothers' self-efficacy beliefs, by contrast, were positively associated with perceived quality of social-marital supports and with observer judgments of maternal behavioral competence with their infants. In addition, as expected, mothers' behavioral competence was significantly related to perceptions of infant temperamental difficulty (negatively) and with social–marital supports (positively). Importantly, maternal self-efficacy beliefs continued to predict maternal behavioral competence even after maternal depressive symptoms, social–marital supports, and infant temperamental difficulty were statistically controlled. Further, when maternal self-efficacy was statistically controlled, the linkages between maternal behavioral competence and maternal depression, infant temperament, and social–marital supports were substantially reduced in

magnitude. Taken together, these findings identified maternal self-efficacy beliefs as a central mediator of relations between mothers' behavioral competence with their infants and the severity of maternal depressive symptoms, perceptions of infant temperamental difficulty, and social–marital supports.

These findings indicate that depression is more likely to debilitate parenting quality when maternal self-efficacy is also compromised. This is likely to be the case in many depressed mothers because of the strong linkage between affective state and self-efficacy beliefs. However, maternal self-efficacy is also sensitive to infant temperament and social–marital supports, and thus it is possible for depressed mothers to have more positive self-efficacy beliefs about parenting, and in turn to parent more effectively, when their infants are temperamentally easy and when they receive consistent encouragement from intimate support figures. Conversely, the combination of significant depression and difficult infant temperament and/ or inadequate social–marital supports may be particularly devastating in their joint effects on maternal self-efficacy beliefs. In their 1991 study, Teti and Gelfand found this to be the case when examining the single vs. joint impact of maternal depression and infant temperamental difficulty on mothers' parenting efficacy beliefs. Maternal self-efficacy was much more compromised among mothers who had high levels of depressive symptoms and who also perceived their infants to be difficult. Further, the joint 'impact' of severe maternal depression and infant temperamental difficulty on maternal self-efficacy was significantly greater than what would have been expected from an additive model of effects.

Maternal Depression in Transactional Perspective

Interestingly, studies that examine the impact of maternal depression in the context of other risk and resilience factors are not common. The dearth of such research is surprising, given that developmental scientists now embrace the spirit of the Transactional Model of development, articulated by Arnold Sameroff over 30 years ago. This model posits that development is a complex function of ongoing, mutually occurring influences between the child and the environment, such that, at any given point in time, one must take into account the impact of the environment on the child as well as the impact of the child on the environment in order to understand individual differences in developmental trajectories. The Transactional Model is a vast conceptual improvement over the more static 'main effects' models, which purport to predict development on the basis of knowledge of a single environmental event or child characteristic measured at a specific point in time, and over 'interactional models', which improves upon main effects models by taking into joint consideration single environmental events and single child characteristics, again measured from a single time point. Although we feel that a fair test of the Transactional Model, in terms of predicting development across several years, may not be possible, it should govern our thinking about how individual differences in depressed mother–child relationships and in child outcomes can be explained by examining how maternal depression's effects are moderated by specific child characteristics and by features of the maternal environment. We believe such an emphasis is long overdue, because the links between maternal depression, parenting, and child outcomes are far from uniform.

Such a perspective was represented in some ongoing work by the first author, who examined predictive relations between postpartum maternal depression and maternal sensitivity during interactions with infants, maternal self-efficacy, and infant behavior problems, assessed at different points during the infants' first year in a sample of approximately 120 African American, premature infants (56% female) and their mothers. Interestingly, maternal depressive symptoms, assessed prior to infant hospital discharge, did not predict maternal sensitivity toward the infant in the home when infants were 4 months and 12 months of age (corrected for prematurity), nor were they predictive of maternal self-efficacy at 4 months infant corrected age. They were, however, predictive of mother reports of infant behavior problems at 12 months, but only modestly.

When specific child characteristics, assessed either prior to infant discharge or at 4 months of infant corrected age, were taken into account, more specific linkages between early postpartum depression and later mother–infant outcomes emerged. For example, depressed mothers who perceived their infants to have unsettled, irregular states of arousal prior to discharge were observed, by raters who were blind to all other data, to be less sensitive during interactions with their infants at 4 and 12 months of infant corrected age than were mothers without postpartum depression but who also saw their infants as unsettled and irregular. No link between postpartum depression and maternal sensitivity at either age point was observed among mothers who did not perceive their infants as having problems in state regulation. In a separate analysis examining the role of infant gender in linkages between maternal postpartum depression and mother-reported child behavior problems at 12 months, significant longitudinal linkages were only observed for male infants, but not female infants. Thus, the main effect of maternal postpartum depression on 12 month infant behavior problems, reported above, appeared to be accounted for in mother–male infant dyads, but not mother–female infant dyads. This finding is consistent with a large literature documenting that male children tend to be more vulnerable to environmental stressors, including parental psychopathology, than are female children. Very few of these studies, however, document such vulnerability in male children during the first year of life.

What this work emphasizes is that the impact of maternal depression on child outcomes is at least in part dependent on the quality of fit between the mother's illness and characteristics of the children themselves. Goodness-of-fit, of course, is a construct that is well-understood among child temperament theorists, who argue that fit between parental and child characteristics, and not each individual's characteristics alone, is ultimately the driving force that underlies the quality of the relationship that develops between parent and child and, in turn, individual differences in children's outcome. We do not mean to imply that there are certain circumstances under which the effects of maternal depression on child development are nonexistent or not worth pursuing. Indeed, even in cases of a better fit between a depressed mother and a specific child, the mother's depression may be influencing the child in ways that may not be evident at a particular time or in terms of the measures used to assess such effects. The construct of fit, however, has not been systematically employed to understand individual differences in depressed mother–child relationships and maternal depression's effects on child outcomes. We believe such an emphasis is long overdue.

The role of partner involvement in families with depressed mothers, both in terms of the quality of support provided to mothers, and as a potential buffering or exacerbating influence on child development, is also poorly understood. What little work that has been done examining fathers in depressed mother households suggests that these fathers are also likely to be distressed, although it is unclear to what degree such distress is a product of coping with a spouse with an affective illness. Of course, children growing up in households with two parents with affective disorders would likely be at even greater risk for maladjustment than would children with only one affectively disturbed parent, but there is little prior work that documents how much greater this risk might be.

It does appear, however, that the quality of support fathers provide to depressed mothers may be an important buffering influence on the effects of maternal depression. It is quite common for mothers to report high levels of marital distress. Marital distress, in turn, has well-known deleterious effects on child adjustment, and some have speculated that the marital distress that is so common in depressed mother households may actually mediate the effects of maternal depression on child development. Indeed, Robert Emery and colleagues, in a paper published in 1982, found that the degree to which fathers adjusted to their depressed wives disorder was a significant predictor of children's rates of psychiatric symptoms.

Specifically, Emery found that the negative effects of mothers' depression on children's adjustment were practically negligible after controlling for marital distress, suggesting that maternal depression's effects may operate via its impact on the larger family system. Low levels of marital distress in depressed mother households is rare; however, when fathers have some insight into their partners' illness, they may be better able to provide appropriate emotional support, which in turn may help mothers parent more effectively and, in turn, the quality of children's attachments to their mothers. In addition, fathers who adapt better to their wives' depression are likely to be better, more engaged parents with their children, which may buffer any direct negative effects of mothers' depression on children. We believe that an important goal in intervening in families with depressed mothers is not simply to work to alleviate mothers' depression and (if needed) promote competent parenting skills, but also to help other family members cope with the mother's illness more effectively by promoting a better understand and appreciation of the nature of the mothers' illness. Indeed, research on the impact of maternal depressed on children as filtered through the larger family system is sorely needed and may foster a better understanding of why some children, in the face of maternal depression, fare better than others.

Conclusions

Maternal depression can have serious consequences for children in social, emotional, and cognitive developmental domains, and children of depressed parents are four to five times as likely as children of nondepressed mothers to be at risk for behavior problems. Children's risk for behavioral disturbances appears to be directly proportional to the chronicity and severity of mothers' depression. Even very short bouts of maternal depression appear to have an emotionally dysregulating effect on infants as young as three months of age, and postpartum depression that is recurrent places infants at risk for insecure attachment. Children who grow up in depressed mother households are at risk for elevated psychiatric symptoms, both internalizing and externalizing, and to develop psychiatric disorders along a broad spectrum, including depressive and anxiety disorders, oppositional defiant disorder, and conduct disorder. Mechanisms of parent-to-child transmission have focused primarily on the impact of depressogenic mothering, although there is also evidence that depression is partially heritable. Importantly, depression's effects on mothering, and on children's development, are heterogeneous and may be buffered or exacerbated by a variety of additional parent, child, and environmental influences. Understanding the effects of maternal depression in the context of other risk and protective factors is a worthy goal for the field.

Fortunately, depression ranks as one of the more treatable psychiatric disorders. Women who suffer from postpartum depression can avail themselves of a variety of treatment approaches, including pharmacological, psychotherapeutic (e.g., cognitive-behavioral, psychodynamic, and support-based 'talking' therapies), or some combination. In addition, approaches that target mother–child interactions have also been successful, in particular when maternal depression co-occurs with skill deficits in mothering. All of these treatment approaches have been effective, to varying degrees, in reducing symptom severity and improving quality of mothering. Pediatricians are likely to be the first health professionals to identify postpartum depression. It is thus important to equip pediatricians with the training and assessment tools to screen for postpartum depression, and to refer mothers to the appropriate mental health facilities for further evaluation and treatment.

Mothers who suffer from depression clearly need help, not just for themselves but for their children. Continued research is needed to understand more clearly the heterogeneous nature of maternal depression and its effects, what role maternal, child, spousal, and family characteristics play in this regard, and to develop effective interventions. Efforts to increase public awareness of postpartum depression and its effects on children are also critically important, if only because such awareness could lead to more mothers seeking treatment.

See also: Attachment; Depression; Emotion Regulation; Marital Relationship; Maternal Age and Pregnancy; Mental Health, Infant; Mental Health, Intervention and Prevention; Parental Chronic Mental Illnesses; Parental Leave; Parenting Styles and their Effects; Risk and Resilience; Screening, Newborn and Maternal Wellbeing; Social and Emotional Development Theories; Socialization in Infancy and Childhood; Temperament.

Suggested Readings

Elgar FJ, McGrath PJ, Waschbusch DA, Stewart SH, and Curtis LJ (2004) Mutual influences on maternal depression and child adjustment problems. *Clinical Psychology Review* 24: 441–459.

Embry L and Dawson G (2002) Disruptions in parenting behavior related to maternal depression: Influences on children's behavioral and psychobiological development. In: Borkowski JG Ramey SL,, and Bristol-Power M (eds.) *Parenting and the Child's World: Influences on Academic, Intellectual, and Social–Emotional Development. Monographs in Parenting*, pp. 203–213. Mahwah, NJ: Erlbaum.

Gelfand DM and Teti DM (1990) The effects of maternal depression on children. *Clinical Psychology Review* 10: 329–353.

Goodman SH and Gotlib IH (1999) Risk for psychopathology in the children of depressed mothers: A developmental model for understanding mechanisms of transmission. *Psychological Review* 106: 458–490.

Nylen KJ, Moran TE, Franklin CL, and O'Hara MW (2006) Maternal depression: A review of relevant treatment approaches for mothers and infants. *Infant Mental Health Journal* 27: 327–343.

O'Hara MW (1997) The nature of postpartum depressive disorders. In: Murray L and Cooper PJ (eds.) *Postpartum Depression and Child Development*, pp. 3–31. New York: Guilford.

Radke-Yarrow M (1998) *Children of Depressed Mothers: From Early Childhood to Maturity.* Cambridge, UK: Cambridge University Press.

Speranza AM, Ammaniti M, and Trentini C (2006) An Overview of maternal depression, infant reactions, and intervention programs. Clinical Neuropsychiatry: Journal of Treatment Evaluation 3(1): 57–68.

Teti DM and Gelfand DM (1991) Behavioral competence among mothers of infants in the first year: The mediational role of maternal self-efficacy. *Child Development* 62: 918–929.

Relevant Websites

http://www.aafp.org – American Academy of Family Physicians.

http://healthyminds.org – Healthy Minds. Healthy Lives.

http://www.nimh.nih.gov – National Institute of Mental Health, National Institutes of Health.

http://www.4woman.gov – National Women's Health Information Center.

http://www.nlm.nih.gov – United States National Library of Medicine, National Institutes of Health.

Pragmatic Development

N Akhtar and K Herold, University of California, Santa Cruz, Santa Cruz, CA, USA

Glossary

Communication – The exchange of ideas and/or feelings, often via speech, but also via gestures, eye contact, etc.

Comprehension – Understanding of words, gestures, etc.

Conventional symbols – Usually words, but also sometimes arbitrary gestures, that are understood by the community to have a particular meaning.

Deictic gestures – Gestures such as pointing that refer to something in the nonlinguistic context.

Ellipsis – The omission of certain words or phrases from a sentence, especially when that information can be retrieved from the preceding linguistic context.

Joint attention – A state achieved when two (or more) individuals attend to the same thing at the same time and are mutually aware of the other's focus of attention.

Morphology – The branch of linguistics concerned with word structure.

Narratives – Telling of a sequence of events in a particular order.

Pragmatic bootstrapping – Using one's understanding of communicative intentions to learn language.

Pragmatics – The branch of linguistics concerned with the uses of language for the purpose of communication.

Production – Expression or use of words, gestures, etc.

Proto-words – Phonetic forms used by very young children with a consistent meaning, but that are not considered conventional words in the adult language.

Scaffolding – The graduated assistance provided by adults to infants and young children to aid them in their cognitive or linguistic development.

Social referencing – Checking in (usually via gaze) with a social partner to judge his/her reaction to something.

Still-face paradigm – A method used in infant social development research whereby a parent interacting with his/her infant is asked to stop interacting verbally and to provide no facial expressions.

Symbolic gestures – Gestures (e.g., a thumbs-up) that stand for or represent something else.

Syntax – The branch of linguistics concerned with sentence structure.

Introduction

Pragmatics is the branch of linguistics concerned with the use of language for the purpose of communication; it is concerned with the use of language in context. Pragmatic approaches to language acquisition focus on the fact that children's primary motivation in acquiring language is to communicate with others, and they learn language in the context of conversational interactions (i.e., in communicative contexts). Since the emphasis is on communication, pragmatic development begins in the prelinguistic period, as infants begin to communicate before they start using any linguistic forms.

Babies can be said to communicate from birth in that their reflexive cries tell their caregivers that they need food or comfort. Researchers make an important distinction, however, between unintended acts that communicate information (e.g., shivering communicates that an individual is probably feeling cold) and acts that are intended to communicate. In a classic paper published in 1975, Elizabeth Bates and her colleagues distinguished between the perlocutionary (pre-intentional) stage in which babies behave in ways that have communicative effects and may be interpreted by adults as communicative (e.g., crying, smiling, vocalizing) and the illocutionary (intentional) stage in which infants demonstrate increasing control over their (nonverbal) communicative behaviors, and can establish and maintain attention on a shared 'topic'.

Most researchers agree that intentional communication begins in earnest around 9–10 months. This is widely recognized as the period in which both the ability to produce intentionally communicative acts and the ability to comprehend the communicative intentions of others really takes off. In this article, we provide a description of the most notable developments in infants' and children's communicative abilities, beginning with a brief description of some of the pre-intentional behaviors in early infancy that are interpreted as communicative by infants' caregivers. We then describe some of the intentionally communicative acts of late infancy, focusing on gestures. Finally, we examine toddlers' learning and use of conventional symbols (words), their subsequent production of phrases and sentences, and the development of the ability to engage in extended discourse in the preschool years. In each section, we describe the major communicative milestones of the period and discuss the abilities that are hypothesized to underlie attainment of these milestones.

In particular, it is infants' ability to read the intentions of others that is considered to play a very important role in their communicative development. Quite contrary to the Piagetian view of the egocentric child, the emphasis now is on infants' and toddlers' skills of perspective-taking. With new methods of assessing infants' comprehension, huge strides have been made recently in establishing that infants are sensitive to the goal-directedness (intentionality) of others' behavior from a relatively early age. Indeed, it is around the same age (9–10 months) as they themselves begin to engage in intentional behavior that they also show evidence of understanding the intentions of others. Initially, however, babies do not communicate intentionally. Their behavior communicates information to their caregivers, but they lack the motor, cognitive, and social skills necessary to engage in intentional acts of communication.

Early to Mid-Infancy

Newborns cannot behave intentionally, but they are born with certain visual and auditory preferences that enable them to enter into social interactions. For example, they prefer human voices to other types of sounds, and will sometimes even stop crying in order to attend to someone talking softly to them. On the basis of prenatal auditory experience, they also prefer to listen to their own mother's voice rather than another woman's voice. These preferences for speech ensure that babies will get plenty of exposure to the language they are going to be learning. In terms of visual preferences, newborns like to explore complex stimuli – stimuli with lots of contrast and contours; in particular, they like to look at human faces. A preference for faces means babies will spend a great deal of time looking at the faces of their caregivers, and often caregivers will interpret the resulting eye contact as an intention to interact. Among adults, mutual gaze generally signals an intention to communicate. Even if a baby doesn't have this intention when it gazes at its caregiver's face, the caregiver (at least in Western middle-class cultures) will tend to interpret the baby's behavior as intentionally communicative. Caregivers sometimes interpret clearly noncommunicative sounds (like burps) as communicative signals by acknowledging them and responding to them in some way. This contingent responsiveness of caregivers may play an important role in showing infants that their behaviors have a predictable impact on people. Then, eventually, when they are cognitively mature enough, infants will start to intentionally act to get reactions from their caregivers.

Early on, however, it is the caregiver who takes most of the responsibility for social interactions. In some sense, caregivers create the illusion of a communicative interaction with a newborn. In early infancy, babies are not themselves very good at turn-taking. What looks like turn-taking behavior seems more a function of what the caregiver is doing than what the infant might be doing. For example, during nursing, infants produce sucking bursts and they pause in between them. Often the mother will do or say something during these pauses. Initially newborn babies do not really initiate or maintain turn-taking interactions but their pauses give mothers the opportunity to turn feeding sessions into social interactions. The same is probably true of what are known as 'proto-conversations'. In these face-to-face interactions the caregiver and infant seem to be engaging in a conversation in that the caregiver says or does something, the infant appears to respond by smiling or vocalizing, and they go back and forth in this manner. It may be that early on what looks like turn-taking is actually the caregiver skillfully inserting behaviors into pauses in the baby's ongoing behavior. Gradually, however, as infants get older and enter the mid-infancy period, they start to take a more active role in these kinds of interactions.

In the mid-infancy period, infants start to show more awareness of social interactions. The evidence for increased awareness comes from studies of infants' participation in routine games and from what is known as the 'still-face procedure'. Games such as peek-a-boo have a predictable sequence and over time infants develop an anticipation of 'what happens next' (also known as script knowledge or event knowledge). Thus, when parents or researchers interrupt the regular sequence by not doing what they normally do, the infants respond by trying to get the adult to continue, sometimes even taking the adult's turn in the game themselves. Similarly, in the still-face paradigm, researchers ask parents to engage their infant in a face-to-face interaction and then at a signal from the experimenter, they are asked to adopt a still face and stop interacting with their infant. What usually happens is that the infant will first attempt to re-engage the parent and when those attempts fail, become distressed. Both sets of results are interpreted as the baby being sensitive to the normal structure of a social interaction. It is interesting that allowing the parent to continue to touch the baby during the still-face can attenuate the effect, indicating that a sense we often neglect in the realm of communication – touch – also serves to communicate to young infants.

Around 4–6 months there is a noticeable change in social interactions as infants start to become more interested in objects out in the environment. Their interactions with their caregivers start to be centered on objects and they don't spend as much time in face-to-face interactions. Adults tend to follow the infant's interests and talk about what the infant is looking at or playing with, leading to episodes of what is known as joint attention. These episodes – when adult and infant are focused on same thing – set the stage for more complex social and linguistic achievements, but at this early stage they are achieved mainly through the adult's efforts to follow what the infant seems to be interested in.

Over this period of time, babies also gain control over their muscles and therefore develop control over a wider range of behaviors – including communicative behaviors such as smiling, gazing, and vocalizing. Developing motor skills thus plays a role in how well and quickly infants can respond to their social partner's communicative behaviors, and probably also in the next big step in the infant's communicative repertoire: the production of gestures. Gestures play a very important role in early communication and they provide one way of assessing whether a given child is on track in terms of early language development. One of the difficulties in assessing language delays or problems in young children is that there is such a wide range of what is normal in terms of when a child utters their first word, so it is difficult to know whether a given child is simply a late bloomer or truly delayed. Researchers have found that these two groups of children can be differentiated by their comprehension of words and their use of gestures; those with poor comprehension of words and low use of gestures are the ones who continue to show signs of delay 1 year later. The infants with high comprehension of words and use of gestures tend to catch up to their age level 1 year later. Early use of gestures is therefore an important predictor of subsequent language development.

Summary

In early infancy babies engage in several social behaviors that enable them to interact with others and have communicative effects. Adults are primarily responsible for initiating and maintaining these early interactions. In mid-infancy, infants' interests shift to objects; caregivers tend to follow their infants' interests and initiate and maintain episodes of joint attention with them. It is not until the last part of the first year that infants begin to clearly initiate episodes of joint attention themselves by, as we discuss in the next section, pointing to something and then checking to see if the caregiver has followed the point.

Late Infancy

Around 9–12 months, infants begin to take a more active role in establishing periods of joint attention. For example, they will follow an adult's gaze to determine what the adult is looking at, and they start using points to actively manipulate their caregiver's focus of attention. It seems that at this age they are starting to understand that another's focus of attention can be different from their own, and that one needs to ensure that one's social partner is focused on the same thing to communicate about that thing. This is also the age at which social referencing first appears. Social referencing involves infants checking their caregiver's expression when they're in an uncertain situation – essentially trying to get information from their caregiver about a new situation or object. So, it is around the end of the first year, when babies start to use communicative gestures, that there is strong evidence for truly intentional communication.

Initially, infants primarily use deictic gestures (sometimes accompanied by vocalizations) such as pointing, showing, and giving. A variety of behaviors have been used to establish the intentional nature of infants' early gestures. First, babies tend to use them only or primarily when they have an attentive audience. Second, they tend to alternate gaze between their addressee and the event or object of interest, suggesting they are checking to see if their message has been received. And third, they make attempts to repair failed messages by repeating and/or elaborating the message when there are signs that their social partner has not attended to the message or has misunderstood it.

Repairing failed messages is a particularly good indication that preverbal infants can communicate intentionally as it shows that babies recognize when their communicative goals have not been achieved, and they are able to (and motivated to) adjust their behavior to achieve their goals.

For example, when parents misunderstand or ignore their 1-year-old infant's communicative signals, the infant is likely to repeat the original signal, to augment it in some way (with additional vocal emphasis or the addition of a gesture, for example), or to substitute another signal for the original one. Infants will produce repairs of failed messages when they have failed to achieve some desired object (e.g., a special toy), but will also do so when their goal is simply to share their interest in something. Some experimental studies show that somewhat older toddlers will repair failed messages even when they have achieved their instrumental goal, suggesting even more strongly that the ultimate goal is to communicate, not just to get what they want. This and other findings like it have been used to argue that, in addition to using language as an instrument to get things done, infants and toddlers are also motivated from very early on to acquire language to express themselves and share their interests.

Pointing

Language is used, by children and adults, for both instrumental and sharing functions, and so are early gestures. Perhaps the most studied deictic gesture is the point – the extension of the index finger to an object or event. Early studies described two distinct functions of 1-year-old infants' points: imperative (instrumental pointing to request the object pointed at) and declarative (pointing to share interest in the object or event pointed to). Subsequent studies have confirmed this distinction that imperative points involve using a person as means to obtain an object (the goal), whereas declarative points involve using an object as a means to obtain adult attention. Declarative pointing is therefore seen as involving a deeper understanding of others as having attentional states that can be manipulated. Indeed, the claim is that the use of declarative pointing implies an attribution of an internal psychological state (as opposed to mere agency) to the addressee. While some studies have shown a nearly simultaneous emergence of the two types of points, others suggest that declarative points may develop a few months later than imperative points. Later emergence of the declarative point and the fact that use of it (and not of the imperative point) correlates with an independent measure of intention understanding, supports the view that declarative points rely on a more complex social–cognitive understanding.

Michael Tomasello has argued quite strongly that the infant's use of declarative points means that she has in some sense an understanding of others as intentional agents with mental states such as attention. The claim is that when babies use imperative points they may simply be using their social partner as a tool; that is, imperative points may rely on understanding of adults as causal agents but not necessarily as mental agents. Declarative points, on the other hand, are not used to obtain material

goals, but simply to direct attention and to share an experience; thus, they appear to be more purely communicative, as they do not involve any instrumental goals.

While some researchers argue for attributing less sophistication to 1-year-old infants, and intentional understanding certainly develops in complexity over the first few years of life, there is considerable evidence to support the view that intentional understanding is present in nascent form at the end of the first year. In this regard, it is interesting that autistic children show a dissociation between the two types of points – they have difficulty with declarative pointing (both comprehension and production) but not with imperative pointing. The same dissociation is seen in human-reared apes. This dissociation provides additional support for the conclusion that declarative points may index a deeper understanding of others' minds than imperative points. While this is one possible interpretation, it is also possible that the dissociation is due to motivational differences rather than an inability to detect others' mental states; that is, not using declarative points may be related to less interest in sharing sights and sounds with others. We know of no studies that have attempted to tease apart the motivational versus sociocognitive explanations, but recent studies may lead in that direction.

These studies describe a third function of prelinguistic pointing: to provide information. In these studies, 12- and 18-month-olds spontaneously pointed to an object they inferred the experimenter needed to complete a task. This type of point is particularly interesting because it appears to involve both the cognitive ability to understand the experimenter's need for information and the motivation to cooperate with and help the experimenter. It would be interesting to conduct a similar study with autistic children to see if they are motivated to engage in this type of pointing. Finding that these children do not point to inform would not be very instructive on its own. However, if they, for example, looked to the object the experimenter needed but did not point to it, that might provide evidence that they possess the sociocognitive capacity to determine what the experimenter needs, but lack the motivation to provide that information. For present purposes, however, it is sufficient to note that all three types of pointing that toddlers engage in – imperative, declarative, and informative– are examples of intentional communication that involve directing the attention and/or behavior of others.

It is widely agreed that 1-year-old infants use intentional vocalizations and gestures to communicate, but there is less consensus on the number and variety of specific meanings or communicative intentions their vocalizations and gestures express. As discussed previously, pointing is used for imperative (instrumental) as well as declarative (sharing, commenting) and informative purposes, but prelinguistic infants also make use of varied intonation patterns to produce requests for actions, to greet their social partners, to protest or reject the actions of others, and so on. Eventually they begin to use words for these and other communicative functions.

Symbolic Gestures

Before they start using words, however, many infants and toddlers produce symbolic gestures in interactions with their caregivers; for example, sniffing to label a flower. These gestures appear to be used for the same communicative functions as early words; that is, to request, comment on, and label objects, and to describe children's experiences. Some of these gestures are learned within interactive routines, but some seem to be spontaneously generated by children themselves. Regardless of how they originate, these gestures seem to be generalized and used in a contextually flexible way (i.e., in different contexts for different communicative functions), much as early words are, and so their acquisition probably relies on the same social and cognitive skills that word learning does (see the next section). The production of symbolic gestures emerges earlier than word production probably because infants and toddlers have better control over the large muscles used in forming a gesture than they do over the many tiny muscles used to articulate words. One interesting finding is that children who are trained to use multiple symbolic gestures may have an advantage (compared to children with no training) in subsequent verbal comprehension and production. With or without training, it is possible that children's early use of symbolic gestures can facilitate or bootstrap their subsequent communicative development in several ways.

One possibility is that once babies start producing some symbolic gestures, adults around them start to treat them differently – they may talk to them more because there is more to communicate about. So, infants who produce more symbolic gestures may receive more verbal input overall than, for example, a baby who only points. A related possibility is that once babies start producing gestures, it is easier to read their minds and figure out what they are focused on – so that makes it easier to establish joint attention with them and determine their specific communicative intentions. If the baby makes the sign for 'Hungry', for example, the parent might respond with "Oh, you're hungry," thereby providing a verbal label for what the child is feeling at the time. In this way the children might receive more relevant verbal input. Finally, another possibility is that by using symbolic gestures and being understood children might become even more motivated to talk and be even better understood. These are all hypotheses at this point and remain to be tested systematically.

It is important to note that almost all of the developments in preverbal intentional communication we have described have also been demonstrated by captive apes: for example, pointing, gaze following, gaze alternation, and even communicative repairs. There are a few important differences, however. One is that the apes tend to use their communicative gestures for imperative purposes only. Second, to our knowledge, they do not invent novel symbolic gestures as young human infants do. Finally, the apes in these studies do not appear to use their human-like communicative behaviors in communication with conspecifics, suggesting that these are behaviors that they learn only through training and that the learning does not transfer to their interactions with one another. These differences between apes and children suggest that apes' understanding of communicative signals may be qualitatively different from the understanding of human toddlers; that is, the apes may only appreciate the impact of their gestures on the overt behaviors of the humans who interact with them, and not any impact on their mental states. An alternative hypothesis is that human-reared apes may have the same cognitive level of understanding of internal states as young children but they may, in sharp contrast to human infants, lack the motivation to share these states with others.

Summary

Near the end of the first year of life, a variety of preverbal behaviors (gaze following, gaze alternation, communicative repairs, pointing, vocalizations, and symbolic gestures) demonstrate not only that infants have the ability to communicate intentionally, but also that they have come to understand others as intentional beings like them. Although nonhuman primates in captivity also engage in some of these behaviors, they seem to do so in qualitatively different ways from human infants, for example, using pointing only for instrumental purposes, and not using it to communicate with other apes.

Early Word Learning and Use

Before beginning to use conventional symbols (words), some children produce transitional communicative forms known as phonetically consistent forms or proto-words. These forms function as words in that they are used intentionally for consistent communicative functions but are unlike words in that they are not fully conventional symbols in the adult linguistic system, for example, saying "baba" to request one's bottle. Use of proto-words is a significant development because it indicates very clearly that toddlers understand that specific sound patterns can be used for specific communicative intentions, a necessary precursor for word-learning.

On average, infants demonstrate the first signs of word comprehension at approximately 9 months of age, but don't start to spontaneously produce words until around 12 months. While there are huge individual differences in the age of onset of word comprehension and production, the lag between comprehension and production is a very robust finding. This lag is probably due, in large part, to the difficulties associated with coordinating the many nerves and muscles involved in speech production. Indeed, early difficulties with articulation may also explain why toddlers' first words tend to include the same phonemes they used most frequently in earlier babbling. Toddlers' earliest words also tend to be used for similar communicative intentions as their preverbal gestures, but as children acquire more words, they learn to use those words in new ways; that is, the variety of communicative intents expressed increases, as does the intelligibility of children's productions. Children also gradually develop the capacity to take into account multiple aspects of the interaction context in producing different speech acts. Finally, as in the prelinguistic stage, they continue to negotiate communicative breakdowns with their caregivers but they are more adept at tailoring the reformulations of their initial utterances to the type of feedback provided by their social partner. For example, they respond differently to specific versus general queries of their utterances ("What does he need?" vs. "What?") and they are able to monitor their own speech for errors and respond appropriately when queried.

Many researchers now view children's ability to discern others' communicative intentions as playing a critical role in early word-learning. In brief, the view is that words are used primarily to direct the attentional states of addressees, and that children match the sound patterns they hear to their interpretations of what the speaker is trying to get them to attend to. If words are used by speakers to direct the attentional states of their listeners, then the child listener's goal in communicative contexts is to try to understand what a speaker is directing their attention to with a given word. Indeed, Bruner has argued that an act of reference is actually an intention to invite the listener to engage in joint attention.

Many experimental studies have shown that 18- and 24-month-old toddlers can use a variety of pragmatic cues to establish joint focus with their interlocutors, and thereby determine their communicative intentions. These include gaze direction, facial expressions, event or script knowledge as well as sensitivity to the prior discourse topic. Children's use of these cues enables them to attend to the appropriate referents and learn the words their caregivers use, but it also indexes a motivation to establish joint attention with others. In all of these studies, the onus is on the child participant to establish joint attention with the adult in order to learn the word the adult used. Clearly, young children are very motivated to do so.

It is also important to note, however, that in all of these studies the children were engaged in a dyadic interaction with the experimenter. One interesting question is whether toddlers are also able to determine the communicative intentions of a person who is not interacting with them. This is an important question because anthropologists suggest that in many communities, young children do not experience as many one-on-one interactions with adults as

the children we typically study, yet they do not appear to be greatly delayed in language-learning. Children growing up in these contexts seem to be quite good at monitoring others' interactions, which leads to the hypothesis that they may learn a great deal of language by listening in on the conversations of others. Indeed, children in all cultural contexts probably learn a great deal of language in this way. For this reason, researchers have begun to examine young children's ability to learn new words through overhearing – that is, through monitoring third-party interactions.

The main findings so far are that 2-year-old children are equally good at learning a new object label through overhearing as when they are directly addressed. Older 2-year-olds are able to learn a verb through overhearing as well. Eighteen-month-old infants are also able to learn a new object label through overhearing but it is not as easy for them as it is for 2-year-olds. Another recent study has shown that 18-month-old children can monitor and comprehend communicative gestures that are not directed to them.

These are interesting findings, but it is not clear to what extent the experimental contexts used in these studies are similar to the everyday contexts in which children overhear new words. In these studies, the children in the overhearing condition were seated as onlookers to the adults' interaction but there was nothing to really distract them from that interaction. There was nothing else that was particularly interesting going on; certainly, the most interesting thing in the room was the interaction between the two adults who were playing with fun toys. But in real life, children don't just sit down and pay attention to others' conversations. There are generally other things going on that compete for their attention. If children are truly motivated to attend to others' communicative intentions, they should do so even when they are engaged in an interesting activity themselves. More recent studies have shown that 2-year-olds can also learn new words through overhearing when they are engaged in another distracting activity. These experimental studies of word-learning through overhearing along with naturalistic observations of children's attention to third-party conversations demonstrate that toddlers are motivated to monitor the communicative intentions of people who are not even interacting with them, giving them multiple sources from whom to learn words.

It is probably true that many (if not most) children spend a significant amount of time in multispeaker environments in which they are not always directly addressed; therefore, overhearing contexts may represent a vital part of young children's early language learning experiences. The vast majority of studies of early language learning focus on dyadic contexts; only a few relatively recent studies have systematically examined children's word-learning through overhearing. Future studies will need to explore the cognitive skills that underlie children's ability to learn through overhearing, and whether children who grow up in societies where they are expected to learn through observation are actually better at learning through overhearing than children growing up in communities that emphasize direct teaching.

Summary

Children first use nonconventional forms (proto-words) to communicate, and at around 12 months begin producing more traditional words, with varying success. While their intent is quite often to highlight their own wants and needs, they also use words to communicate their perspectives in attempts to share those perspectives with others. They repair misunderstood utterances, and use words to direct the attention of the person they are communicating with. Young children are quite skilled at learning new words, even when those words are not being directed to them. These findings indicate that children can monitor others' interactions, and can learn words from overheard conversations as well as from conversations in which they are directly involved.

Multiword Speech

Before toddlers begin to combine words, they first combine gestures with words, for example, pointing to a book and saying "mommy" to indicate something like "That book belongs to my mom". These gesture-plus-word combinations are said to 'pave the way' for two-word combinations as children who are first to produce gesture-plus-word combinations are also first to produce word–word combinations. One way in which gesture–word combinations may facilitate the production of word–word combinations is that they may lead parents to 'translate' the communicative intents children express with gesture–word combinations into word–word combinations, providing an appropriate models for children on how to verbally express their communicative intents.

Early word combinations allow the child to begin to rely somewhat less on the nonlinguistic context to get their communicative intentions across. In the one-word stage, their holophrastic (one-word) utterances can only be interpreted with heavy reliance on context and even then the child's intent may be ambiguous. Although two-word utterances can also be ambiguous, they provide a bit more information about what the child has in mind. Across the languages that have been studied in detail, children's early word combinations tend to be used for a similar range of communicative functions. For instance, toddlers make requests, reject and negate others' assertions, describe and comment on actions and locations, talk

about possessions, etc. They also ask questions, often yes/no questions that are marked with rising intonation, but 'where' questions are also frequent. In their two-word utterances. toddlers tend to mark new information with stress, suggesting that they take the context (and perhaps the listener's perspective) into account when formulating their early multiword utterances.

There is not as much known about the communicative intentions of children in the later stages of linguistic development when they start producing full-length sentences. This is likely because the emphasis (of most researchers) appears to shift to matters of form (morphology and syntax) rather than function (pragmatics) when children start speaking in longer sentences. Formalists define language as a system of abstract rules for combining various parts of speech, independent of the contexts of use of those rules. Functionalists, on the other hand, define language as the use of symbols and rules for combining those symbols for the purpose of communication. While the differences between formal and functional approaches to language may appear to be merely differences in emphasis – after all, both form (structural rules) and function (communication) are crucial aspects of human language – because of their focus on communication, functionalist approaches tend to be more developmentally friendly. However, most of the research on children's developing syntactic abilities is not framed in terms of communicative intentions because grammar has been considered by many theorists and researchers to be a completely autonomous linguistic module. More recent functional approaches to grammatical development are promising, but it remains true that most of the research on the early development of syntax and morphology does not explicitly examine the communicative functions of the various constructions children are learning to comprehend and produce.

It is noteworthy, however, that some longitudinal studies have found positive correlations between measures of pragmatic development and grammatical development, and some researchers believe that joint attention may play an important role in grammatical development. This is consonant with Tomasello's view that "learning words and learning grammatical constructions are both part of the same overall process," the process being reading the communicative intentions of the people speaking those words and constructions. The process is slightly different in the case of grammatical constructions because the child has to pay attention to (and abstract) a pattern of symbols and link that pattern to the speaker's communicative intent. In this view, sentence-level constructions are, like words, essentially pairings of form and function (communicative intent). It is certainly the case that different syntactic constructions can provide different perspectives on the same scene or event (e.g., the passive vs. active transitive construction in English), and children and adults do use different syntactic constructions to convey different communicative intentions. We know of no empirical research, however, that has directly addressed the question of whether children learn syntactic constructions in the same way as they learn words; that is, through "pragmatic bootstrapping" or attention to speakers' intentions. The fact that autistic children sometimes show a dissociation between pragmatic and syntactic abilities – producing grammatically correct utterances that are often pragmatically odd – suggests that pragmatic development alone cannot account for the development of syntax.

Ochs and Schieffelin's description of the language socialization of Kaluli children, however, provides illustrations of the role of pragmatics in some aspects of grammatical development. They found that there are several grammatical forms that are frequent in input to Kaluli children but the children themselves do not use them because it is not culturally appropriate for them to do so, for example, command forms of a verb that the society's rules dictate can only be used by adults to children and not vice versa. The children show comprehension of these verb forms at a young age (by 19 months) but they do not use them themselves. Similarly, there are grammatical forms that are relatively infrequent in the input that the children do pick up and use. The main point is that children do not just learn the words and constructions that they hear frequently – they are paying attention to the pragmatic contexts in which those words and constructions are used, and they use the ones that best fit their communicative goals within the constraints of the cultural context. Indeed, Ochs and Schieffelin conclude that "children's use of particular grammatical forms at particular moments of their language development is profoundly linked to social and cultural norms, expectations, and preferences which may not be explicit and are not easily counted or detected."

Summary

Children's early ability to combine gestures with words facilitates their ability to combine words with each other. As children move from two-word combinations to multiword utterances, they rely somewhat less on the extralinguistic context and more on linguistic means for expressing their communicative intentions, although context remains vital to communication throughout development. The new linguistic skills that allow children to produce complex constructions also allow young toddlers to engage in extended discourse, the topic of our final section.

Extended Discourse

In the preschool years, children begin to engage in extended discourse on various topics; that is, they become better conversationalists and tell better stories. To do these things effectively, they need to adapt to their audience and use linguistic devices such as ellipsis pronouns, and various causal connectives to maintain coherence and cohesion across utterances. They have to monitor their listener's comprehension and, in general, they need to use social perspective-taking and their developing linguistic skills to ensure this comprehension. In addition, children learn to use mental state terms such as 'think', 'want', and 'believe' to convey their own feelings and perspectives as well as those of story protagonists. Although conversations often contain narrative sequences, we discuss these two types of extended discourse – conversational development and narrative development – separately.

Conversational Development

Becoming a skilled conversationalist is important because it plays a role in peer relationships; children who are good at conversation are more effective at interacting with their peers and better liked by them. But becoming an effective conversationalist is a difficult task because it involves coordinating many different skills, both linguistic and nonlinguistic. For example, one has to plan what one is going to say, monitor and comprehend one's partner's responses, time one's turns appropriately, maintain relevance to the topic at hand, maintain an appropriate distance, use eye contact appropriately, and so on. There are also a number of conversational rules (some of which vary by culture and subculture) that children must learn, including of course the famous Gricean maxims of Quantity (say enough, not too much or too little), Quality (be sincere or truthful), Relation (be relevant), and Manner (be clear).

As young preschoolers are generally more egocentric than older children their contributions to conversations are not always relevant, and may not provide enough information in a clear manner to their conversational partners. Young children sometimes appear to assume that their listeners have access to the same information as they do. Motivation seems to play an important role in conversational competence, however; when engaged in referential communication tasks in a laboratory, preschoolers appear less competent than when engaged in more meaningful situations in which they are highly motivated to get their message across. In real-life situations, children will try various ways of repairing or reformulating their initial utterance when it is clear that their partner has misunderstood them. Some studies have shown that children will adjust the type of repair they use in different communicative situations. For example, toddlers are more likely to simply repeat their initial utterance (or say it louder) when queried by their mother and more likely to reformulate it when queried by an adult stranger, suggesting that they may be sensitive to the fact that strangers are less likely to understand them whereas their mother may not have heard what they said. Similarly, toddlers also respond differently to different types of requests for clarification. They tend to repeat all of what they had said when asked "What?" but they give only the requested information when asked a more specific question ("You want what?"). In general, these studies of communicative breakdowns show that even young children have some rudimentary knowledge of appropriate conversational behavior: they recognize when communication fails and have a variety of means for repairing breakdowns. They are also clearly motivated to achieve communicative success, as they engage in repairs even when they get what they want but their conversational partner has indicated a misunderstanding verbally.

There are individual differences in how successful young children are at turn-taking; some do not wait for their partner to stop speaking (although it must be noted that in some communities, this type of overlapping speech is the norm), while others wait too long before taking their turn. In general though, young children appear to be relatively good at conversational turn-taking. Other aspects of conversational exchange, however, seem to undergo more protracted development. These include the abilities to smoothly initiate, maintain, and end conversations. Young children are generally not very skilled at initiating conversations, but they are more likely to do so with family members than strangers. When interacting with peers, young children are less likely to maintain a topic over several conversational turns than they are when interacting with adults. This is most likely due to the responsive scaffolding of the adults children typically interact with.

Through their interactions with parents, siblings, peers, and teachers, children learn that they should speak differently (use different speech registers) in different social settings. For example, in school they typically speak differently to teachers than to their peers, and are more likely to use politeness markers such as 'please' and 'thank you' with adults than with other children. Language socialization studies have shown that in many cultures parents actively teach children when to say what; however, politeness consists of far more than simply knowing when to use the appropriate words. It also involves understanding various social roles and how they relate to the use of different linguistic forms. In some communities, children are required to use different lexical and grammatical forms with different individuals. Children in these communities attend to how males and females speak differently, and to the various relationships among individuals, and who speaks how to whom, in order to learn with whom to use different grammatical forms. They are generally not directly instructed in these understandings but come to them through keen observation of others' interactions. As with all pragmatic developments, the development of politeness relies heavily on children's social understanding.

Narrative Development

Narratives are similar to conversations in that both involve perspective-taking and a certain degree of linguistic skill. In both it is important to provide relevant information in a clear and unambiguous way. But conversations and narratives differ in one significant way. Whereas conversations are dialogues between two or more participants who essentially build on and provide a context for each other's contributions, narratives involve, for the most part, decontextualized monologues. There is in some sense necessarily less scaffolding because a narrative usually involves a longer stretch of speaking, and children therefore have to rely more on their linguistic skills in getting the message across. This may explain why narrative skill has been linked to literacy development. Children who are good at producing coherent narratives appear to have an advantage in learning to read, perhaps because experience with decontextualized language plays an important role in literacy.

Children's earliest narratives occur in the context of conversations so they have lots of responsive support initially, but as they get older they depend less on adults' scaffolding, and their contributions become longer, more coherent, and more complex. They often begin by recounting stories with adult encouragement, and typically construct their stories in response to prompts or other adult scaffolding behaviors. Very young children also learn to tell stories by narrating ongoing events. This is especially prevalent in pretend play, when children will often narrate their constructed imaginary situations to one another. By 4–5 years of age, children have typically learned a 'story grammar', or a set of rules that provide the structure for a good story. These rules vary by culture, and children tend to adopt the storytelling structures of their parents, and others in their community.

A 'good' narrative often has a specific organizational pattern. The speaker presents an explicit topic, and discusses it in a way that clearly states the relations among a sequence of events. For many narratives the grammar consists of an introduction that orients the listener followed by an organized sequence of events that leads to some type of conclusion. The setting or introduction includes the place and the characters involved. This is generally followed by a sequence of events or episodes and then some kind of ending or resolution. Older children's narratives are more sophisticated in several ways – they include mention of the characters' motivations and internal states, they describe multiple events and, in general, there are more explicit connections made between the events so that the story actually 'flows'. Good narratives make use of various linguistic devices to achieve coherence and cohesion. These include conjunctions (and, but, or), causal connectives (because, so), temporal connectives (then), the appropriate use of pronouns, definite and indefinite articles, etc. These devices bridge different parts of the narrative in appropriate ways and, in some cases, are essential to maintain coherence of the narrative as a whole.

Summary

In early childhood, children begin to engage in extended discourse. They learn culturally specific rules of conversation and politeness, and become sensitive to the need to use different speech registers in different settings. Their emerging linguistic skills as well as their increasing ability to take others' perspectives enable them to produce more coherent and cohesive narratives. Early interactions within the family set the stage for these developments and while some parents actively socialize these skills, children also learn a great deal through observation of 'how things are done' in their communities.

Concluding Remarks

Intentional communication begins with infants' use of gestures to request and comment on objects and events. Toddlers progress to using words for these and other communicative functions, then combine gestures with words, and then combine words with words. There appears to be some continuity between these stages of communicative development in that infants' use of symbolic gestures predicts their use of words and their use of gesture–word combinations predicts their use of word–word combinations. The ability to produce effective narrative sequences is positively correlated with subsequent literacy skills, but there is little evidence on the relations between earlier communicative developments and the ability to engage in extended discourse.

We have noted throughout our review that social–cognitive abilities (e.g., understanding of others as intentional/mental agents, perspective-taking) provide the foundation for pragmatic development. Pragmatic development is also inextricably linked to children's motivation – evident at a very early age – to communicate with others and to interpret others' communicative intentions. While intention-reading skills have been demonstrated in some nonhuman primates, the motivation to connect with others and share experiences is postulated to be unique to humans. It is perhaps this distinctive combination of social–cognitive skills and motivation to communicate that sets human children apart and enables them to progress as rapidly as they do through the various stages of pragmatic development.

See also: Autism Spectrum Disorders; Grammar; Literacy; Preverbal Development and Speech Perception; Semantic Development; Social Interaction; Theory of Mind.

Suggested Readings

Adamson LB (1996) *Communication Development During Infancy.* Boulder, CO: Westview Press.

Akhtar N and Tomasello M (2000) The social nature of words and word learning. In: Golinkoff RM and Hirsh-Pasek K (eds.) *Becoming a Word Learner: A Debate on Lexical Acquisition*, pp. 114–135. Oxford: Oxford University Press.

Baldwin DA (2000) Interpersonal understanding fuels knowledge acquisition. *Current Directions in Psychological Science* 9: 40–45.

Bloom L (1998) Language acquisition in its developmental context. In: Kuhn D and Siegler RS (eds.) *Handbook of Child Psychology, Volume 2: Cognition, Perception, and Language*, pp. 309–370. New York: Wiley.

Bruner JS (1983) *Child's Talk: Learning to use Language.* New York: Norton.

Ninio A and Snow CE (1996) *Pragmatic Development.* Boulder, CO: Westview Press.

Tomasello M (2003) *Constructing a Language: A Usage-Based Theory of Language Acquisition.* Cambridge, MA: Harvard University Press.

Premature Babies

K Minde, Montreal Children's Hospital, Montreal, QC, Canada
P Zelkowitz, McGill University, Montreal, QC, Canada

Glossary

Corrected age – The age of the infant from birth, minus the number of weeks of prematurity. For example, if an infant is 10 weeks old according to the date of birth, but was born 8 weeks premature, the infant's corrected age is 2 weeks. Corrected age is used to chart the infant's development until at least 2 years of age.

Extremely low birth weight (ELBW) – It is defined as infant weight under 1000 g at the time of delivery.

Gestational age – The number of weeks of age of the fetus or newborn infant, based on the time from the mother's last menstrual period until the present date.

Intrauterine growth restriction (IUGR) – A term used to describe infants who are not growing at the normal rate during pregnancy. These infants are smaller in size than they should be based on their gestational age.

Low birth weight (LBW) – It is defined as infant weight under 2500 g at the time of delivery.

Neonatal intensive care unit (NICU) – A hospital nursery that provides specialized care for sick babies, including those born prematurely. The NICU is staffed by highly trained specialists, and has advanced equipment for the treatment of complications of premature delivery.

Prematurity – Refers to birth occuring before the 37th week of pregnancy. A full-term pregnancy is considered to be 40 weeks.

Very low birth weight (VLBW) – It is defined as infant weight below 1500 g at the time of delivery.

Introduction

Infants born prematurely, that is, after less than 37 weeks' gestation, or weighing less than 2500 g at birth, have long provided an opportunity to assess the potential role of biological adversity and the changes it may induce in parenting behaviors and in the development of children. Developmental outcomes in premature and low birth weight (LBW) infants are a product of multiple complex variables. To take LBW as an example, we know that despite the objective medical criteria defining this condition, LBW is often associated with other moderating factors such as multiple births, low socioeconomic status, or particular emotional responses by the parents of LBW infants. At the same time, the experience of the premature infant and his or her family in the hospital, as well as the medical and developmental outcome of this infant, will vary with the degree and type of complications he or she experiences as well as the technology available in different settings. Similarly, medical problems during the neonatal period may be associated with more or less frequent hospitalizations later on and can be precursors of a lifelong handicap or a treatable abnormality. Different combinations of all these factors can influence the future physical, emotional, and cognitive development of the affected children as well as the well-being of their families.

In this article, we first delineate the scope of the problem, that is, define the current understanding of the difference between LBW and prematurity and examine the number of children affected by these conditions. We will then summarize data on the consequences for these children, including the biological and emotional risks they face in later life. We will then outline current thinking about the etiology of prematurity and LBW, and examine the factors that might mediate developmental outcome in these children. Finally, we will discuss the practical implications of these data for various health professionals and mental health practitioners and outline intervention strategies and programs that have demonstrated practical value for the support and development of these vulnerable infants and their families.

Defining Prematurity

LBW has long been a popular focus for studies of pregnancy outcome because it is strongly associated with infant mortality and both short- and long-term morbidity. LBW refers to infants born weighing 1500–2500 g, very low birth weight (VLBW) to those weighing 1000–1499 g and extremely low birth weight (ELBW) to those less than 1000 g. However, birth weight is determined by both the rate of fetal growth and duration of gestation. LBW can therefore occur because an infant is born too early (pre-term birth) or is small for his or her gestational age (SGA), often also used as a proxy for intrauterine growth restriction or intrauterine growth restriction (IUGR). It is also now recognized that the determinants of gestational duration, that is, pre-term birth, are quite different from those of inadequate fetal growth, and the associated IUGR. Each of these conditions, in turn, has different health consequences. For example, pre-term birth leads to high rates of mortality, as well as medical, neurocognitive and behavioral problems while IUGR in its severe form is associated with metabolic derangements and in less extreme cases with long-term deficits in growth, learning problems and even with chronic adult diseases such as hypertension, type 2 diabetes, and coronary heart disease. It is therefore preferable to discuss separately pre-term birth and IUGR when considering the relationship of specific risk factors to pregnancy outcome and later developmental challenges.

The rate of LBW infants varies across countries and ethnic groups. Prevalence rates are from 5% to 7% in developed countries and up to 20% in developing countries. Lower rates are generally attributed to better prenatal care. However, it has been shown that the difference among the developed and developing nations is more attributable to higher prevalence of IUGR rates than pre-term births in the latter nations (6.6 vs. 2.0 times, respectively). Moreover, even in the developed world one finds a significantly different incidence of low birth weight rates among populations of varying social class. For example, in a Canadian study, pre-term rates among women of varying income quintiles ranged from

5.7% to 7.4% while the incidence of IUGR varied from 8.0% to 12.1%. Overall rates of low birth weight children have also increased in the developed world during the past 20 years (up from 7.2% to 7.9% in the US, according to one group of investigators) because of the increase of births following fertility treatment with its associated greater number of multiple births as well as the older age of childbearing women.

Outcome of Low Birth Weight Children

The outcomes of children with LBW have been of interest to investigators for five decades. Studies can be divided into those considering the physical well-being, learning, and behavior of these children. Some authors have also calculated the additional costs associated with raising LBW children.

Children born early and with LBW share a number of consequences, ranging from increased mortality to more neurodevelopmental disabilities, behavior problems, and financial costs for the affected families. In addition, the families of such children are frequently exposed to the highly technological environment of an intensive care nursery and the unknown potential complications of their children. This, together with their concerns about the medical status of the infant, can cause severe stress and anxiety.

Before we discuss these issues in more detail, some cautionary notes are indicated. The changes in neonatal intensive care in the developed world have been very dramatic, especially during the past 20 years. This means that follow-up studies reporting on the behavioral or cognitive outcome of specific samples of LBW infants describe children who were treated a number of years previously and may not reflect the outcome the same children would have experienced had they been born today. Furthermore, most outcome studies report on the treatment results of a specific institution, often a well-known university center, that may not be representative of all institutions in that country, that is, these are not population based studies, and they do not compare different areas of the world. There has, in fact, been only one study, by Saroj Saigal and colleagues, in four international population based cohorts of LBW survivors (the Netherlands, Bavaria, New Jersey, and southern Ontario in Canada) who were followed longitudinally in a comparative fashion, documenting significant differences in outcome.

Moreover, a higher incidence of disabilities is reported in studies following such children over longer periods further putting into question their value for the present day outcome of such infants. This is due to the fact that long-term follow-up studies tend to have higher dropout rates among the comparison groups, and here again especially among the less educated members.

Taking these points into consideration, we will discuss the challenges that these children present along their various developmental pathways, and reflect on the most informative population based short, medium, and long-term outcome studies. Both cognitive and behavioral consequences will be described. Finally, we will examine the mediating psychosocial factors that affect the development of premature and LBW children.

Early Consequences

The LBW newborn infant faces a number of formidable immediate tasks after birth. An important one, shared by all newborns, is the mastery of state regulation that allows the baby to establish regular, survival-facilitating, behavioral adaptations. This task is made far more difficult for an LBW infant, with his/her immature neurological system, to adapt in an neonatal intensive care unit (NICU) than it would be in the finely tuned intrauterine environment. To compensate for this biological handicap these infants demand more external caretaker support than do full term infants. However, as Heidelise Als and others have shown, the NICU technology may interfere with sensitive care and the intrusive interventions these infants often receive may lead to negative consequences for the later behavioral organization of these infants. Specifically, these infants have been described to have poor autonomic and motoric functioning and state organization during their early months. This, in turn, makes them less responsive to social stimulation and gives their caretakers fewer cues as to how to handle them appropriately. VLBW children do not initiate social interactions as often as full-term infants, and their rates of social initiation increase more slowly than those of full-term children over the first 3 years of life. Moreover, VLBW infants have difficulty with tasks of joint attention, where they must attend simultaneously to a person and a shared object; because the ability to maintain joint attention is related to language and cognitive development, deficits in this domain are associated with poorer developmental outcomes in VLBW children.

Later Consequences

There exists a large literature reporting on the survival rates as well as on the cognitive and behavioral well-being of children and adults with different birth weights. In this chapter we will primarily discuss a selection of papers published during the last decade describing the outcome of VLBW and ELBW infants. Inclusion criteria required the authors to use a case-control design, report objective cognitive and/or behavioral data, and have an attrition rate of less than 30%. Studies assessing outcomes at school age, adolescence, and adulthood will be included.

Neurodevelopmental Handicaps

In general, it is fair to say that complications of prematurity increase with decreasing gestation. These include an increase in mortality, health resource use and long-term neurodevelopmental disability rates. However, more than 50% of admissions to NICUs have a gestational age of 35 weeks or more and only 1% of infants are born at less than 32 weeks' gestational age and 0.3% are born before 28 weeks of gestation. The latter group has a mortality of about 50% and of the survivors, 10–20% have major sensory, motor, or cognitive impairments, resulting in severe disability. A far larger number (40–60%) have a combination of vulnerabilities, characterized by: a high prevalence of borderline intelligence; learning disorders, often related to nonverbal intelligence and arithmetic; poor fine and gross motor coordination; difficulties with sustained attention, working memory and executive functions; and social and emotional immaturity. While they do experience significant catch-up growth between age 8 and 16 years, the boys are still about 9 kg and the girls are 5 kg lighter than full-term children at age 17 years. They are also on average 10 and 8 cm, respectively, smaller than their peers at that age. It is of interest that term infants weighing between 1500 and 2500 g at birth, that is, having experienced IUGR, have a mortality rate 5–30 times greater than infants with birth weights between the 10th and 50th percentile. They also show a somewhat lower IQ at adolescence (3.5 points) and may have impaired language development.

Mental Health

Concerning their mental health, there is a real difference between how these youngsters are perceived by their parents and how they perceive themselves. While ELBW adolescent survivors rate themselves similarly to full-term children in their self-esteem, behavioral characteristics, and overall mental health, their parents give them high scores for depression and attention deficit hyperactivity disorder (ADHD). In fact, they rated 30% of these youngsters above the clinical cut-off point on internalizing symptoms, four times higher than did the parents of control children. While having high ratings on a symptom checklist does not automatically imply the presence of a psychiatric disorder, there are few good data on the direct psychiatric morbidity of LBW children. Klaus Minde and colleagues found that 12% of 69 VLBW children who were prospectively followed had a psychiatric diagnosis at age 4 years, most of them showing symptoms of ADHD. In fact, meta-analyses that combine data from numerous studies confirm that children born premature are more than 2.5 times as likely as full-term children to develop ADHD. Marit Indredavik and colleagues assessed 56 VLBW, 60 SGA, and 83 control teenagers, comparing their psychiatric symptomatology based on well-validated questionnaires and a semi-structured psychiatric interview. The indepth interview revealed that 25% of the VLBW children had a psychiatric disorder versus 10% of SGA and 13% of the control children. While self-ratings did not differentiate among the three groups, parental ratings indicated significantly higher number of anxious and depressed symptoms in the VLBW group and higher attention and delinquent symptoms in both the VLBW and SGA group than in the control group.

It is of interest that the ADHD in these youngsters only very rarely presents with other externalizing co-morbidities such as oppositional defiant disorder (ODD) or conduct disorder (CD). This may be indicative of the primarily neurobiological etiology of this disorder and the families from these children come. This is confirmed by a study by Maureen Hack that provides data on the behavioral outcomes of 241 survivors among VLBW infants at age 20 years and 232 matched controls. Self-reports did not differentiate between VLBW and full-term youth, and parental ratings of the women survivors were higher on only one of 11 behaviors (internalizing problems). However, parents rated both their young adult boys and girls as primarily having attentional difficulties and 'thought problems' while the girls were also said to have significantly more anxious and depressive symptoms. This suggests that long time VLBW survivors of the 1970s continue to improve over time and that their early cognitive and behavioral challenges do not lead to disabilities that severely compromise the quality of their adult lives.

Mediating Factors

Pre-term Birth as a Crisis

Developmental outcome in VLBW infants is best understood as an interaction between biological vulnerability and environmental factors, such as parental attitudes and behavior. A substantial percentage (up to 50%) of mothers who give birth to an LBW infant have experienced one or more previous spontaneous abortions. Hence, many of them are anxious during the LBW pregnancy and work hard to prevent losing yet another baby. This often takes the form of weeks or even months of bed rest with all its associated challenges. In addition, the baby, especially when very premature, will be born after a very abbreviated period of preparation for the mother. For example, many mothers have no chance to attend a childbirth preparation class. Mothers also experience a much shorter period of feeling the movements of their babies. All this affects the mother's inner and external readiness for the birth of her child. In addition, the actual birth is often unexpected and becomes a crisis rather the culmination of an organic and 'normal' process that all of us expect and for which we are biologically wired. This sense of crisis is highlighted by the often medically precarious state of the infant, the high technology NICU, and the perceived preoccupation of the medical staff with technology rather than psychological care and sensitive support. In fact, Klaus Minde and colleagues have documented the effect this crisis, combined with specific background factors of the mother (e.g., her relationship with her own mother and spouse), have on parental visiting practices at the NICU and have also shown that the frequency of visits to the nursery predicts the sensitivity of later caretaking practices. Moreover, the administrative organization of most NICUs requires nurses to work 12 h shifts on 3 days per week, resulting in frequent changes of key nursing staff caring for an individual infant. This means that parents face and deal with a significant number of nursing staff, making it less likely for them to talk about their fears or general concerns. Mothers also may have to deal with their families who sometimes question their alleged ability to produce a healthy full-term infant, leading to additional guilt that, in turn, can affect childcare practices.

Psychological Distress and Parental Behavior

There is considerable evidence to suggest that psychological distress can affect the ability of parents to interact sensitively and responsively with their VLBW infants, and that this may in turn have a negative impact on infant development. Observing the behavior of parents while feeding their infants in the NICU, Phyllis Zelkowitz and colleagues found that medical risk factors such as birth weight, gestational age, and severity of neonatal illness were not related to parental behavior. However, parental anxiety did have an effect on parent–infant interaction: more anxious mothers and fathers touched and spoke less to their infants, and were less aware of and responsive to their infant's needs. Parental anxiety continued to exert an effect on parental warmth and contingent responsivity when the infant was 3, 9, and 24 months of age (corrected for prematurity), with more anxious parents exhibiting less sensitive and more intrusive parenting behavior at all these points in time. Moreover, parental anxiety was associated with more internalizing behavior problems and poorer cognitive development in the infants at 24 months of age.

Other studies have shown that mothers who report high levels of distress are less likely to engage in cognitive growth fostering behavior such as providing stimulation at a level that is appropriate to the VLBW infant's stage of development. There are also implications for the social and behavioral development of VLBW infants. For example, emotional distress can diminish a mother's capacity to behave in a warm and flexible manner with her VLBW infant; by age 4 years, children who had experienced less warm responsiveness from their mothers tend to initiate fewer social interactions. Early maternal distress is also related to reports of internalizing and externalizing symptoms in VLBW children in early and middle childhood. The experience of pre-term birth may also give rise to post-traumatic stress symptoms in mothers; such symptoms have been found to be associated not only with less sensitive and more controlling maternal behavior, up to 18 months following the birth of the VLBW infant, but also predict disturbances in infant sleep and feeding behavior.

Parental Representations

There are other issues that can lead to a cascade of developmental and behavioral challenges. All parents bring their personal internal representations to a pregnancy and the newborn infant. This means that they imagine their baby to have certain characteristics that may be triggered by the way the infant looks or behaves early on or by past experiences a parent had with his/her own family. While this phenomenon is seen in parents of both full-term and pre-term babies, there is persuasive evidence that these early perceptions continue to influence parental interactions with their children for many years. For example, when faced with premature twins, most parents prefer one of the twins and show this both by interacting in a more sensitive and supportive fashion toward this child for at least the first 4 years of their twins' lives.

Finally, there is evidence that mothers of VLBW infants diagnosed with significant neurodevelopmental delays at 18 months of life respond differently to them as early as 1 month after birth, compared to a matched group of mothers whose children were equally ill at this time but tested within a normal range of intelligence at 18 months. This occurred although only 30% of physicians of the handicapped group mentioned the possibility of a delay to the mothers at the 6 months follow-up meeting with a further 50% doing so at 9 months. Specifically, the mothers with the delayed children at 1 and 3 months of age talked to, smiled, and instrumentally touched their children much more than did the mothers of nondelayed peers. At 6 and 9 months, the mothers of the handicapped group had changed and now smiled, talked, and touched their infants significantly less than did the mothers of the normally developing children. This occurred without the mothers' conscious awareness of their children's later intellectual challenges and documents the amazing interactional sensitivities human beings can develop.

Etiology of Low Birth Weight

The etiology of LBW is complex and multi-determined. Historically, mortality, and LBW are closely related, because mortality among LBW infants is high. While infant death rates 24 days after birth in the developed world are now generally less than 7 per 1000, the World Health Organization in its Global Strategy for Health for All by the year 2000 hoped to bring most countries of the world below 50/1000, a goal England and Wales had already reached in the mid-1940s. This documents the very significant differences in the incidence of pre-term birth and IUGR in different countries but shows that within each country there are also profound variations among low and high social class families, ranging from 1.1 to 1.6:1. Thus, despite the recent overall decline in LBW and early deaths among LBW children worldwide, both statistics are still class related. Nevertheless, even here one cannot generalize as there are socioeconomically disadvantaged minority groups who show fetal growth rates that actually exceed those in the social class of the general majority population. Examples here are Chinese immigrants in Canada, North African immigrants in Israel, and Mexican immigrants in the US. While the reason for this phenomenon is not known, it has been explained by the tendency of recent migrants to retain favorable nutritional and behavioral characteristics of the country they came from; for example, fewer of these mothers smoke during their pregnancy. The same applies to racial/ethnic differences where black and white populations in the US show substantial differences in the risk of pre-term births, while black immigrant groups from Africa and the Caribbean seem to be partly protected from the increased risk. The same applies to infants born in the US to foreign-born mothers who have a significantly lower rate of LBW (4.5%), prematurity (9.2%), SGA (8.4%), and infant mortality (4.6%) than infants born to US born mothers.

The question remains, of course, how socioeconomic disadvantage leads to increased risk of adverse pregnancy outcome. The literature here is rich and a full discussion would be beyond the space of this review. We will therefore confine ourselves to briefly summarizing well-established associations between socioeconomic disadvantage and pregnancy outcome but review in more detail data linking psycho-neuro-endocrine processes with fetal as well as later development.

Biological Determinants

Michael Kramer and colleagues, in their 2000 paper, provide a pie diagram where the size of the pie slice corresponds to each etiological causal determinant of IUGR and pre-term birth in the US (see **Figures 1** and **2**). As can be seen in **Figure 1,** cigarette smoking and low weight gain of the mother make up almost 40% of the etiological fraction of IUGR births. It is important to recognize that these contributing conditions reflect the North American reality and would look quite different in a developing country where cigarette smoking would be a less significant etiological component while low stature or low weight gain would be more important. The pie

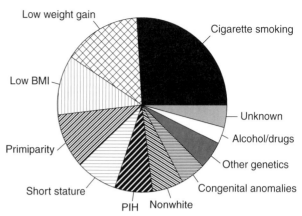

Figure 1   Etiological determinants of intrauterine growth restriction in a developed country in which 25% of the women smoke during pregnancy and a substantial minority are nonwhite. BMI, body mass index; PIH, pregnancy-induced hypertension. Reproduced from Kramer MS, Seguin L, Lydon J, and Goulet L (2000) Socio-economic disparities in pregnancy outcome: Why do the poor fare so poorly? *Paediatric and Perinatal Epidemiology* 14: 194–210. With permission from Blackwell Publishing.

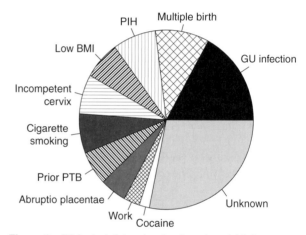

Figure 2   Etiological determinants of pre-term birth in a developed country in which 25% of the women smoke during pregnancy and a substantial minority are nonwhite. BMI, body mass index; Gu infection, upper genital tract infection; PIH, pregnancy-induced hypertension; prior PTB, prior pre-term birth. Reproduced from Kramer MS, Seguin L, Lydon J, and Goulet L (2000) Socio-economic disparities in pregnancy outcome: Why do the poor fare so poorly? *Paediatric and Perinatal Epidemiology* 14: 194–210. With permission from Blackwell Publishing.

chart for determinants of pre-term births (**Figure 2**) contains, among others, multiple births, genitourinary infections, and an incompetent cervix which explain some 40% of this condition. The pie also shows a big slice (about 30%) that is labeled 'unknown'. This indicates that more cases of pre-term births occur without any known cause compared to IUGR cases where the 'unknown' slice is about 4%.

It is of interest that the quality of prenatal care, when tested in randomized trials, even when women at high risk for pre-term delivery are included, does not seem to have a relationship with LBW or pre-term delivery. The reason may be that the activities associated with a good prenatal visit (taking mothers' blood pressure, urine analysis, weighing, abdominal palpitation) have no known benefit to prevent pre-term delivery or IUGR. Furthermore, there is no evidence that advice to reduce smoking is affecting pregnancy outcome because it is very rarely accepted. This suggests that women who initiate prenatal care early in their pregnancy have a different psychological profile from those who do not and that one has to examine these psychological factors to develop effective preventive measures.

Psychosocial Determinants

Stress and social support are not consistently associated with premature birth. One reason for this may have to do with issues of measurement. For example, stress can be measured by the number of negative life events a mother has encountered, by the daily hassles she faces, her degree of anxiety and depression, or by her 'perceived' amount of stress. Confounding variables here are that certain potentially stressful life events such as changes in residence or employment may be more common during pregnancy but have a less distressing connotation. It is currently therefore seen as more appropriate to ask women what they perceive as stressful rather than just counting the number of past adversities. In addition, it is important to assess stress prospectively as women seeking meaning for an experienced pre-term birth may be more likely to recall stressful events to 'make sense of it'. Finally, stress is more strongly associated with birth before 35 weeks' gestation while later pre-term birth is more likely related to placental and circulatory problems.

Some prospective studies that used large samples and good assessment strategies have shown a more direct association between life events with a high negative impact on the mother and maternal anxiety during pregnancy and pre-term birth. Stressful life events have been found to be associated with twice the risk of pre-term delivery, and anxiety during pregnancy confers a threefold risk. Low body mass index, in association with depression during pregnancy, has also been found to be associated with premature labor. This suggests that specific combinations of biological and psychological risk factors may be required to develop prenatal complications.

Thus, by the year 2000 there was a general consensus that the prevalence of stress, depressive symptoms and distress are increased during pregnancy, especially in vulnerable populations, such as black and Hispanic women, inner-city women and those of low socioeconomic status. It had also been established that anxiety, depression, and stress can cause negative pregnancy outcomes and is associated with both pre-term birth and IUGR. As these factors have an even more profound impact on pregnant women in developing countries it seems likely that we are dealing with a psychological as well as a physiological phenomenon. However, there is no validated theoretical model that could explain why only a minority of all poor or stressed mothers has problematic pregnancies. Investigators have therefore more recently looked at the role played by individual differences in psycho-neuro-biological processes and their evolution during pregnancy in determining outcomes related to fetal/infant health and well-being. This line of research is based on the developmental trajectory model, which states that the effects of genes on fetal development and birth outcomes are conditioned by the environment within the fetus and uterus. This means that even genes that carry a potentially negative behavioral characteristic can be modified by positive environments, especially during fetal life. Adopting this model, Pathik Wadhwa has shown in a number of studies that the effects of psychosocial stress are mediated, in part, via maternal–placental–fetal neuroendocrine mechanisms, with corticotropin releasing hormone (CRH) playing an essential role. Specifically, Wadhwa and colleagues documented that independently of obstetrical risk, each unit increase of prenatal life stress was associated with a 55 g decrease in birth weight and a 32% increase in the relative risk of LBW. His group also found that women with greater perceived available support had bigger babies, implying that support can modify the stress-related CRH changes. These clinical findings were supported by increased maternal adrenocorticotropic hormone (ACTH) and cortisol levels in the stressed group whereas social support was negatively associated with those hormone concentrations. Women with high anxiety and high CRH tend to deliver earlier than those with anxiety but low CRH, suggesting that maternal stress hormones play an important role in pre-term delivery through their interaction with placental hormone production. This would also provide a possible explanation for the inconsistent association between observed psychosocial stressors and pre-term birth since changes in psycho-neuro-endocrine processes are required to translate them into negative developmental events while experiences that can modify these processes can lead to good developmental outcomes. On the other hand, chronic exposure to poverty, racism, or other unmodified adversities may also be associated with continuing physiological changes in later life, the pre-term birth, affecting behavioral, immune, and vascular mechanisms and leading to diabetes and cardiovascular diseases in late adulthood.

Costs of Premature Birth

The final aspect of pre-term birth we want to highlight briefly is the cost of the associated neurodevelopmental sequelae to their families or government agencies. The average lifetime costs per person with mental retardation has been estimated to be $1 040 000 while the cost for each individual with cerebral palsy is $921 000 in 2003. In addition, the average cost of hospital services for infants born at less than 28 weeks between 1970 and 1993 was $22 798 measured in 1998, increasing by 75% if the birth weight of the infant was less than 1000 g. By 1998, the cost of treatment in an NICU for each surviving baby born at less than 1000 g in the UK came to between $160 000 and $340 000. This explains the interest society has had in developing ways to provide better and less costly survival of these infants. Antenatal steroids, indomethacin, and surfactant given to mothers at risk have all provided significant reductions in cost as well as in neonatal respiratory distress syndrome (RDS) and intraventricular hemorrhages (IVH), increasing survival rates and decreasing long-term disability. However, we must recognize that these forms of treatment can be associated with an increased risk of severe disability in infants of 24 weeks' gestation and younger.

In summary, LBW children and their families experience a great number of possible consequences, from compromised cognitive functions and behavior of the children to the difficult day to day lives of their families. Effective management of these challenges can only be achieved with the help of multiprofessional teams whose members work closely with the affected families.

Interventions with Very Low Birth Weight Infants

Because children born pre-term are at risk for intellectual deficits and behavior problems, interventions have been designed to improve developmental outcomes in these children. These interventions have ranged from those targeting specific aspects of infant care, such as the need for supplementary sensory stimulation, to those offering a comprehensive package of services including medical follow-up, parent support, and educational daycare for the infants. The challenge has been to humanize the care, promote parental involvement in this care, and to optimize the development of these fragile, high-risk infants.

Supplemental Stimulation

Pre-term infants are thrust from the protected environment of the womb into the high-tech environment of the NICU. There is a mismatch between their stage of development and the sensory input to which they are exposed. On the one hand, pre-term infants are subject to loud noise, bright lights, and painful procedures that their central nervous systems are ill-equipped to handle. In contrast, because of their medical fragility and

prolonged placement in an isolette, they do not receive the tactile and kinesthetic stimulation that full-term infants would experience naturally during the course of routine infant care by their parents. Approaches to intervention have been developed to address both over- and under-stimulation of pre-term infants: developmental care counteracts the former condition, while programs such as infant massage and kangaroo care provide supplementary stimulation.

The benefits of infant massage, in terms of both weight gain and infant alertness, have been demonstrated; there is a lack of follow-up data to indicate the longer-term impact of massage on infant development. Parents can be trained to massage their infants, thereby supporting their role as caregivers in the NICU. Infant massage is generally offered only to medically stable infants, suggesting that heavier pre-term infants are most likely to benefit from this intervention during the very early stages of their hospitalization.

Skin-to-skin, or kangaroo care, is another treatment modality offering both tactile and vestibular stimulation to pre-term infants. The method was pioneered in Colombia, to address concerns about hypothermia and infection due to a lack of incubators; kangaroo care has subsequently gained widespread acceptance in South America and in other developing countries around the world. This technique involves the placement of the infant in direct skin contact with the parent for extended periods of time. Kangaroo care is associated with improved temperature regulation and respiration, and promotes breastfeeding. Moreover, there have been demonstrated benefits in terms of state regulation, including longer periods of quiet sleep and alert wakefulness. Few studies have examined the long-term effects of kangaroo care on infant development and the parent–infant relationship. Ruth Feldman and colleagues, following a sample of pre-term infants to 6 months of age who had been randomized to either kangaroo or traditional care while in the NICU, found that those who had received kangaroo care exhibited better cognitive and motor development than those receiving traditional care. In addition, parents who had offered kangaroo care were more sensitive in interaction with their infants, and provided a more stimulating home environment. Longer-term follow-up is required in order to determine whether these benefits are maintained.

Developmental Care

In contrast to interventions that provide supplemental stimulation, developmental care is an intervention strategy based on the premise that fragile premature neonates are exposed to overwhelming and inappropriate stimulation in the NICU environment. Careful observation of the infant, and adaptation of the caregiving environment to meet the individual needs of each infant, is required in order to reduce stress and promote growth and development. The Newborn Individualized Developmental Care and Assessment Program (NIDCAP) developed by Heidelise Als and colleagues, employs specially trained professionals to observe the infant's neurobehavioral functioning, and to consult with parents and NICU staff to develop approaches to care that meet the particular needs of the infant. Adaptations include support for feeding, positioning, skin-to-skin contact, and the provision of a quiet environment with adjustable lighting. Evaluation of the NIDCAP intervention indicates benefits to the infant in terms of weight gain, fewer days of assisted ventilation, shorter NICU stays, and better autonomic regulation. The fact that professionals involved in treatment decisions such as duration of ventilation and timing of discharge may not be blind to group assignment raises some questions about the assessment of these variables in the evaluation of the program. As with sensory stimulation programs, the longer-term impact of developmental care on infant development and parent–infant relationships remains to be demonstrated. The need for highly trained observers to work in close collaboration with other NICU personnel to put the developmental care program into practice has posed limits on its implementation, requiring allocation of significant resources that may not always be available.

Psychosocial Interventions

Parent education programs have also been utilized to promote a positive parent–infant relationship in the NICU and after discharge. Such programs provide information about infant care and the particular needs of the premature infant, through one-to-one discussions with an intervener or demonstrations of the infant's behavior and self-regulatory capacities while parents observe an infant assessment of the infant's sensory and regulatory capacities via the Neonatal Behavioral Assessment Scale (NBAS). Participation in such programs has been shown to reduce parental distress and promote parenting competence. However, many of the studies involved small numbers of families, and samples of convenience; long-term benefits of these experimental education programs have not been demonstrated. The strength of such programs may be in their individualized approach, as well as their emphasis on intervening with the parents in order to optimize parent–infant interaction.

Comprehensive intervention programs such as the Infant Health and Development Program (IHDP) were based on the early childhood intervention literature, that advocates for the provision of a variety of services in the preschool period to promote good cognitive development in disadvantaged and at risk populations. The experimental intervention that lasted 3 years and was tested at eight sites in the US by the IHDP had three components: home visits, center-based developmental education, and parent support groups. While immediate postintervention results indicated that heavier LBW infants (i.e., those weighing 2001–2500 g at birth) showed better cognitive development than those in the comparison group, there were no such effects in the lighter birth weight group. These differences had largely disappeared by age 5 years, as did differences between intervention and comparison group children in extent of behavior problems.

One significant limitation of broad, comprehensive intervention programs, such as the IHDP, is that they are of long duration, costly and time-consuming for both service providers and families. This raises questions about the economic feasibility and practical utility of transferring broad-based, multicomponent interventions into clinical practice. Moreover, these programs do not always target the infants and families at greatest risk, but instead offer services to families of infants born at weights up to 2500 g. Certainly, with respect to the IHDP, benefits for the lower birth weight infants have not been demonstrated, while the long-term benefits for the heavier infants have been modest, at best.

While parental distress is often assessed as an intervention outcome, it is seldom the focus of the intervention itself. Because such distress may interfere with the parent's ability to provide sensitive and responsive care, the need to intervene with parents directly, rather than with the infant alone, has become increasingly evident. One very recent approach, developed by Melnyk and colleagues, to reducing parental distress was to teach parents of infants born at weights under 2500 g how to cope with stressful aspects of the NICU experience. Through a series of audiotapes and brochures parents learned about specific stressors in the NICU environment and about strategies to cope with them, as well as ways to be involved in their infant's care. Intervention group mothers reported fewer stressors in the NICU, and less state anxiety and depression when the infants had reached 2 months corrected age, but they were not more sensitive or responsive in their interactive behavior than control group mothers. The children in the intervention group spent an average of 3.9 fewer days in hospital, amounting to a savings of nearly $5000 per infant. Another intervention that targeted stress reduction offered mothers brief videotaped instruction in the use of problem-focused and emotion-focused coping strategies. Mothers of infants born at weights under 2500 g were randomly assigned to one of these two treatments, and a control group of mothers watched an informational video about the NICU. Both treatment groups were significantly less anxious than controls, and mothers who received the emotion-focused treatment exhibited lower levels of depression as well. Telephone support from an experienced mother of a VLBW infant has also been shown to reduce levels of stress, depression, and anxiety.

There have been recent therapeutic interventions directly aimed at reducing psychological distress among mothers of VLBW infants. One such program involved several sessions of cognitive-behavioral group therapy, in order to prevent the development of postpartum depression in mothers of VLBW infants. At follow-up, there were no differences between the intervention group and the control group in terms of diagnosed cases of depression via clinical interview. This intervention did not prove to be effective in reducing rates of depression, which were high (26–29%) in both groups. The fact that the intervention was not delivered on an individual basis may have affected the outcome. In contrast, a crisis intervention program that offered individual counseling focusing on symptoms of trauma reduced symptoms of post-traumatic stress in mothers of VLBW infants. However, it should be noted that this intervention was not evaluated in a randomized controlled trial.

Intervention programs aimed at reducing distress among mothers of pre-term infants have used a wide variety of modalities of intervention, including cognitive-behavioral group therapy, individual counseling, videotaped instruction, and support from peers. Moreover, the outcome measures of interest are quite disparate, ranging from clinical diagnosis to self-report measures of symptoms, to more general measures of stress. The diversity of approaches and outcome measures makes it difficult to compare these programs, and to draw general conclusions about the elements that are likely to be effective in this population. The timing of follow-up is also an important consideration. Most programs evaluated outcomes immediately following the intervention; there is a need to determine whether there are longer-term benefits as well. Some studies did not employ random assignment of participants to treatments, rendering their findings inconclusive. A further difficulty in assessing the efficacy of the intervention programs involves the comparison groups, who were generally said to have received standard care. In fact, the nature of such care was quite variable, and could include pastoral services, social work contact, parent education group sessions, and a developmental physiotherapy playgroup. It should also be noted that sample sizes in these intervention studies tend to be quite small, and several of the studies included mothers of infants at weights from 1500 to 2500 g, so that the results cannot necessarily be generalized to the families of higher-risk VLBW infants. Finally, none of these programs were offered to fathers, who also experience distress, and who might also benefit from intervention. Nonetheless, these intervention programs confirm the high levels of distress among parents of pre-term infants, and suggest that brief interventions can be effective in reducing distress, at least in the short term. It seems likely that an individualized approach, targeting the specific feelings and concerns of parents, can be beneficial. However, it is essential to evaluate these approaches in randomized controlled trials and to assess longer-term outcomes, in terms of parental distress, parental interactive behavior, and infant development. In addition, programs designed to meet the needs of distressed fathers of VLBW infants need to be developed and evaluated. This is of particular importance since there is evidence that anxiety affects paternal interactive behavior, which in turn is associated with less satisfactory cognitive and behavioral outcomes in VLBW infants.

Conclusion

Despite the enormous technological advances of the past several decades, the premature birth of an infant remains a medical, psychological, and social crisis. Pre-term and LBW infants are medically fragile, experiencing complications of the respiratory and cardiovascular systems, and are at risk for brain hemorrhage and lesions; they may require neonatal intensive care for extended periods of up to 3 months. While the majority of prematurely born infants do not have major neurodevelopmental handicaps and develop well, a significant proportion will exhibit learning difficulties, attention deficits, and emotional problems. There are high costs both to the individual family and to the society at large for acute neonatal care and subsequent medical, educational, and social service follow-up. Although the causes of prematurity have not been fully explained, there is strong evidence implicating maternal prenatal anxiety and stress, with their attendant effects on maternal neuroendocrine function. These neuroendocrine changes may not only precipitate premature labor, but may also affect infant development *in utero* and after delivery. The type of stress experienced by the mothers can be either intrapsychic or social in nature, and will determine potential foci for preventive intervention. Following pre-term birth, it is essential to adopt a family focus from the earliest days of treatment in the NICU. Health professionals and parents alike must be attuned to the special needs of the high-risk premature infant; moreover, NICU staff must support parents in their efforts to cope with the intense emotions that follow pre-term birth. Early intervention strategies should incorporate programs that help parents to manage their distress and provide sensitive care to their infants, in order to ensure optimal developmental outcomes for these high-risk children.

See also: Birth Complications and Outcomes; Mortality, Infant; Newborn Behavior; Prenatal Care; Prenatal Development; Screening, Newborn and Maternal Well-being; Screening, Prenatal; Touch and Pain.

Suggested Readings

Als H and Gibes R (1990) *Newborn Individualized Developmental Care and Assessment Program (NIDCAP) Training Guide.* Boston, MA: Children's Hospital.

Bhutta AT, Cleves MA, Casey PH, Cradock MM, and Anand KJS (2002) Cognitive and behavioral outcomes of school-aged children who were born preterm: A meta-analysis. *Journal of the American Medical Association* 288: 728–737.

Hack M, Youngstrom EA, Cartar L, *et al.* (2004) Behavioral outcomes and evidence of psychopathology among very low birth weight infants at age 20 years. *Pediatrics* 114: 932–940.

Hess CR (2005) NICU-based interventions for high-risk infants. In: Teti DM (ed.) *Handbook of Research Methods in Developmental Science*, pp. 295–315. Malden, MA: Blackwell.

Indredavik MS, Vik T, Heyerdahl S, Kulseng S, and Brubakk A-M (2005) Psychiatric symptoms in low birth weight adolescents, assessed by screening questionnaires. *European Child and Adolescent Psychiatry* 14: 226–236.

Kramer MS, Olivier M, McLean FH, Dougherty GE, Willis DM, and Usher RH (1990) Determinants of fetal growth and body proportionality. *Pediatrics* 86: 18–26.

Kramer MS, Seguin L, Lydon J, and Goulet L (2000) Socio-economic disparities in pregnancy outcome: Why do the poor fare so poorly? *Paediatric and Perinatal Epidemiology* 14: 194–210.

Melnyk MM, Feinstein NF, Alpert-Gills L, *et al.* (2006) Reducing premature infants' length of stay and improving parents' mental health outcomes with the Creating Opportunities for Parent Empowerment (COPE) neonatal intensive care unit program: A randomized, controlled trial. *Pediatrics* 118: e1414–1427.

Minde K, Corter C, Goldberg S, and Jeffers D (1990) Maternal preference between premature twins up to age 4. *Journal of the American Academy of Child and Adolescent Psychiatry* 29: 367–374.

Saigal S, den Ouden L, Wolke D, *et al.* (2003) School-age outcomes in children who were extremely low birth weight from four international population-based cohorts. *Pediatrics* 112: 943–950.

Wadhwa PD (2005) Psychoneuroendocrine processes in human pregnancy influence fetal development and health. *Psychoneuroendocrinology* 30: 724–743.

Zelkowitz P, Bardin C, and Papageorgiou A (2003) Maternal anxiety and behavior in NICU and impact on development in infants born <1500 g (VLBW). *Pediatric Research* 53(4): 317A.

Relevant Websites

http://www.marchofdimes.com – March of Dimes website on Prematurity: The Answers Can't Come Soon Enough.

http://www.pediatrics.wisc.edu – University of Wisconsin Department of Pediatrics: For Parents of Preemies.

http://www.nichd.nih.gov – National Institute of Child Health and Human Development: Research on Pre-term Labor and Premature Birth.

http://www.excellence-earlychildhood.ca Centre of Excellence for Early Childhood Development.

Prenatal Care

M C Lu and J S Lu, David Geffen School of Medicine at UCLA, Los Angeles, CA, USA

Glossary

Allostasis – The body's ability to achieve stability through change. Through allostasis, the autonomic nervous system, the hypothalamic–pituitary–adrenal (HPA) axis, and the cardiovascular, metabolic, and immune systems protect the body by responding to internal and external stress.

Amniocentesis – A procedure in which a small sample of amniotic fluid is drawn out of the uterus through a needle inserted in the abdomen to screen the fetus for genetic defects.

Antepartum – Occurring or existing before birth; often used interchangeably with prenatal and antenatal.

Chorionic villus sampling (CVS) – A procedure in which a small sample of the placenta (chorionic villi) is removed through a needle inserted in the abdomen or through the cervix to screen the fetus for genetic defects.

Developmental programming – The process whereby a stimulus or insult, at a sensitive or critical period of development, permanently alters the structure or function of an organ or system, with lasting impact on health and development. Also referred to as fetal programming or fetal origins of health and disease.

Organogenesis – The process by which organs are formed during embryonic development.

Reproductive life plan – A set of personal goals about having or not having children based on personal values and resources, and a plan to achieve those goals.

Teratogen – Any agent that can disturb the development of an embryo or fetus, which can result in pregnancy loss or birth defect.

Introduction

Prenatal care is healthcare provided to a woman during pregnancy. Ideally, prenatal care should begin before and continue after pregnancy, as part of a continuum of women's healthcare. The goal of prenatal care is to promote the health and well-being of the mother, fetus, and family. The growing body of evidence on fetal origins of health and disease further elevates the importance of prenatal care in promoting not only the immediate outcome of pregnancy, but also health and function of the child over the life course.

History of Prenatal Care

The idea of prenatal care is often attributed to John W. Ballantyne around the turn of the twentieth century. Ballantyne proposed that to prevent fetal abnormalities and reduce maternal, fetal, and neonatal deaths, medical supervision of pregnant women should be provided throughout pregnancy rather than only in labor. In 1901, Ballantyne succeeded in getting one bed reserved for expectant mothers in Edinburgh's Royal Maternity Hospital; over the next two decades this single bed evolved into a 23-bed ward. By 1927, England had 600 prenatal clinics.

In America prenatal care originated in Boston. In 1901, Mrs. William Lowell Putnam began a program of nurse home visits to pregnant women enrolled in the home delivery service of the Boston Lying-in Hospital. The program was so successful that an outpatient clinic was established at the hospital in 1911, to which all patients were urged to report as early as possible in pregnancy. The prenatal visits consisted of history and physical examination, blood pressure measurement, and urinalysis. Concerns about toxemia (preeclampsia), diagnosed by high blood pressure and excess protein in the urine, shaped the content of prenatal care from the start and played an important role in establishing the timing and frequency of prenatal visits.

One of the strongest early proponents of prenatal care in America was J. Whitridge Williams at Johns Hopkins Hospital. In his presidential address before the American Association for the Study and Prevention of Infant Mortality in 1914, Williams proposed that fetal mortality could be reduced by 40% by good prenatal care, primarily from early detection and prompt treatment of syphilis and toxemia. Deaths from dystocia (difficult birth) could be reduced with competent obstetrical examination to detect pelvic abnormalities before the onset of labor, and deaths from premature births could be reduced if the patients were instructed in personal hygiene, rest, and diet. In 1954, Nicholas J. Eastman attributed organized prenatal care with having 'done more to save mothers' lives in our time than any other single factor.' He also noted a marked reduction in low birth weight (LBW) births among women who received adequate prenatal care.

Federal and state governments also played an important role in promoting prenatal care in America, particularly for the poor. The Children's Bureau was created by President Taft in 1912; one of its first tasks was to investigate the high infant mortality (124 deaths per 1000 live births) in the US. Its report on infant mortality gave official recognition, for the first time, to the importance of prenatal care. Between 1921 and 1929, nearly 3000 prenatal care centers were established in the US, under the auspice of the Sheppard-Towner Act. The Social Security Act of 1935 renewed and expanded federal activity in maternity care, which was broadened in 1963 to include a full spectrum of diagnostic and consultative services, hospitalization during pregnancy for high-risk patients, and nursing, dental, social, nutritional, and transportation services.

Several studies published in the 1970s found a significant association between no prenatal care and the incidence of LBW. In 1973, Kessner and colleagues proposed an index of adequate prenatal care utilization, which takes into account the month of pregnancy in which prenatal care begins and the number of visits adjusted for the gestational age at delivery. The Kessner Index, as it has come to be known, was among the first measures to demonstrate a systematic relationship between adequacy of prenatal care utilization and LBW. Gortmaker reanalyzed the same data in 1979 using a modified Kessner Index, and found that the percentage of LBW births decreases with increasing adequacy of prenatal care use, and that the relationship between prenatal care and infant mortality was restricted to the impact of prenatal care on LBW. Citing these and several other studies, a 1985 Institute of Medicine (IOM) report concluded that the 'overwhelming weight of the evidence is that prenatal care reduces low birth weight'.

The enrollment of all pregnant women in prenatal care was promoted by the 1985 IOM report as a national policy to reduce the risk of LBW. Soon thereafter, in the mid- and late 1980s, the US Congress enacted a series of legislative initiatives that incrementally expanded Medicaid eligibility to low-income pregnant women and children independent of their welfare status. Many states followed with further expansion of Medicaid eligibility and streamlining of the process of enrollment into prenatal care. Arguments for expansion of access to prenatal care were buttressed by cost-effectiveness analyses which suggested that savings could be achieved by reducing LBW. In 1986, the US Public Health Service assembled an expert panel to assess the content of prenatal care. In its 1989 report, the expert panel identified the three basic components of prenatal care as (1) early and continuing risk assessment, (2) health promotion, and (3) medical and psychosocial interventions and follow-up. Following the report, several states expended considerable effort to enhance the content of prenatal care, motivated in part by the expectation that increases in early initiation and adequate utilization of high-quality prenatal care would lower the risk of LBW and, as a result, reduce infant mortality rates.

In large part as a result of these federal and state efforts, the use of early and adequate prenatal care increased substantially over the last two decades of the twentieth century. By 2004, of the more than 4.1 million births in the US, 83.9% of women began prenatal care in the first trimester, and only 3.6% had late (care beginning in the last trimester of pregnancy) or no prenatal care. Approximately 50 million prenatal visits were made in the US in 2001. In a century since its introduction, prenatal care has become one of the most widely used preventive healthcare services in the US and in most parts of the developed world.

Preconception Care

Ideally, prenatal care should begin before pregnancy. Organogenesis begins early in pregnancy; the heart begins to beat at 22 days postconception, and neural tube closure is complete by 28 days postconception. Placental development begins even earlier, starting with implantation at 7 days postconception. Poor placental development has been linked to such pregnancy complications as pre-eclampsia and preterm birth, and may play a role in fetal programming of chronic diseases in later life. By the time most pregnant women have their first prenatal visit, it is often too late to prevent some birth defects or defective placental development.

More importantly, early prenatal care is often too late to restore allostasis. Allostasis refers to the body's ability to maintain stability through change. Examples include feedback inhibition on the hypothalamic–pituitary–adrenal (HPA) axis to keep the body's stress response in check, or modulation of the body's inflammatory response by the HPA axis. In the face of chronic and repeated stress (psychological or biological), however, these systems can get worn out. If a woman enters pregnancy with worn-out allostatic systems (e.g., dysregulated stress or inflammatory response), she may be more vulnerable to a number of pregnancy complications including preterm birth.

The growing recognition of the limits of prenatal care and the importance of women's health before pregnancy has drawn increasing attention to preconception care. As defined by the US Centers for Disease Control and Prevention (CDC), preconception care is a set of interventions that aim to identify and modify biomedical, behavioral, and social risks to a woman's health or pregnancy outcome through prevention and management. The American College of Obstetricians and Gynecologists (ACOG) recommends that a routine visit by any woman who may, at some time, become pregnant presents an opportunity to promote preconceptional health, whether or not she is planning on getting pregnant. Men should also get preconception care, though the content of preconception care for men is less well defined.

Several models of preconception care have been developed. Major components of preconception care include risk assessment, health promotion, and medical and psychosocial interventions and follow-up, as summarized in **Table 1**.

There is currently no consensus on the timing of preconception care, probably because there are different ideas about what preconception care should be or do. For some, preconception care means a single pre-pregnancy check-up a few months before couples attempt to conceive. A single visit, however, may be too little too late to address some problems (e.g., promoting smoking cessation or healthy weight), and will miss those pregnancies that are unintended at the time of conception (approximately half of all pregnancies in the US). For others, preconception care means all well-woman care, from pre-pubescence to menopause. In practice, however, asking providers to squeeze more into an already hurried routine visit may not be feasible, and some components (e.g., genetic screening or laboratory testing) may not be indicated for every woman at every visit.

Preconception care is probably more than a single pre-pregnancy visit and less than all well-woman care. A good place to start is to ask every woman at every visit about her reproductive life plan. A reproductive life plan is a set of personal goals about having or not having children based on personal values and resources, and a plan to achieve those goals. The provider should ask the woman if she plans to have any (more) children, and how long she plans to wait until she (next) becomes pregnant. If it is within the next year or two, the provider should bring her and her partner back for a full assessment and counseling. The schedule of follow-up visits should be individualized according to identified risks. If she does not plan on becoming pregnant in the next 1–2 years or ever, the provider should continue to provide well-woman care but make sure she has effective contraception if needed and update her reproductive life plan at every routine visit.

Preconception care is an integral part of women's healthcare. However, in the absence of universal healthcare as in all other developed nations, many low-income women in the US have no or limited access to preventive or primary health services when they are not pregnant. Physicians and other healthcare providers in the US also face many barriers in providing preconception care, including inadequate reimbursement, time, training and support. In 2005, the CDC issued a useful set of recommendations for promoting preconceptional care in the US, which are summarized in **Table 2**.

Prenatal Care

Prenatal care consists of a series of clinical visits and ancillary services designed to promote the health and well-being of the mother, fetus, and family. The American

Table 1   Major components of preconception care

Risk assessment

- *Reproductive life plan.* Ask your patient if she plans to have any (more) children, and how long she plans to wait until she (next) becomes pregnant. Help her develop a plan to achieve those goals.
- *Past reproductive history.* Review prior adverse pregnancy outcomes, such as fetal loss, birth defects, low birth weight, and preterm birth, and assess ongoing biobehavioral risks that could lead to recurrence in a subsequent pregnancy.
- *Past medical history.* Ask about past medical history such as rheumatic heart disease, thromboembolism, or autoimmune diseases that could affect future pregnancy. Screen for ongoing chronic conditions such as hypertension and diabetes.
- *Medications.* Review current medication use. Avoid category X drugs and most category D drugs unless potential maternal benefits outweigh fetal risks (see **Table 3**). Review use of over-the-counter medications, herbs and supplements.
- *Infections and immunizations.* Screen for periodontal, urogenital, and sexually transmitted infections as indicated. Discuss TORCH (toxoplasmosis, other, rubella, cytomegalovirus, and herpes) infections and update immunization for hepatitis B, rubella, varicella, Tdap (combined tetanus, diphtheria and pertussis), human papilloma virus and influenza vaccines as needed.
- *Genetic screening and family history.* Assess risk of chromosomal or genetic disorders based on family history, ethnic background, and age. Offer cystic fibrosis screen. Discuss management of known genetic disorders (e.g., phenylketonuria, thrombophilia) before and during pregnancy.
- *Nutritional assessment.* Assess anthropometric (body mass index), biochemical (e.g., anemia), clinical, and dietary risks
- *Substance abuse.* Ask about smoking, alcohol, drug use. Use T-ACE (tolerance, annoyed, cut down, eye opener) or CAGE (cut-down, annoyed, guilty, eye-opener) questions to screen for alcohol and substance abuse.
- *Toxins and teratogens.* Review exposures at home, neighborhood and work. Review Material Safety Data Sheet and consult local Teratogen Information Service as needed.
- *Psychosocial concerns.* Screen for depression, anxiety, intimate-partner violence, and major psychosocial stressors.
- *Physical examination.* Focus on periodontal, thyroid, heart, breasts, and pelvic exams.
- *Laboratory tests.* Check complete blood count, urinalysis, type and screen, rubella, syphilis, hepatitis B, HIV, cervical cytology; Screen for gonorrhea, chlamydia, and diabetes in selected populations. Consider thyroid-stimulating hormone.

Health promotion

- *Family planning.* Promote family planning based on a woman's reproductive life plan. For women who are not planning on getting pregnant, promote effective contraceptive use and discuss emergency contraception.
- *Healthy weight and nutrition.* Promote healthy prepregnancy weight through exercise and nutrition. Discuss macro- and micronutrients including 5-a-day and daily intake of multivitamin containing folic acid.
- *Health behaviors.* Promote such health behaviors as nutrition, exercise, safe sex, effective use of contraception, dental flossing, and use of preventive health services. Discourage risk behaviors such as douching, nonseatbelt use, smoking, alcohol and substance abuse.
- *Stress resilience.* Promote healthy nutrition, exercise, sleep, and relaxation techniques; address ongoing stressors such as intimate-partner violence; identify resources to help your patient develop problem-solving and conflict resolution skills, positive mental health, and relational resilience.
- *Healthy environments.* Discuss household, neighborhood, and occupational exposures to metals, organic solvents, pesticides, endocrine disruptors, and allergens. Give practical tips such as how to reduce exposures during commuting or picking-up dry cleaning.
- *Interconception care.* Promote breastfeeding, back-to-sleep, positive parenting behaviors and reduce ongoing biobehavioral risks.

Medical and psychosocial interventions for identified risks

Academy of Pediatrics (APA) and ACOG in 2002 have defined prenatal care as a "comprehensive antepartum care program that involves a coordinated approach to medical care and psychosocial support that optimally begins before conception and extends throughout the antepartum period". As defined by the Expert Panel on the Content of Prenatal Care, the three major components of prenatal care are (1) early and continuing risk assessment, (2) health promotion, and (3) medical and psychosocial interventions and follow-up.

Early and Continuing Risk Assessment

Confirmation of pregnancy and determination of viability

Prenatal care begins with confirmation of pregnancy. Most women present after missed menses; given wide availability of home pregnancy tests many women present after a positive home pregnancy test. About 30–40% of all pregnant women will have some bleeding during early pregnancy, which may be mistaken for a period. Therefore, a pregnancy test should be routinely performed in women of reproductive ages presenting with abnormal vaginal bleeding.

The pregnancy test detects β-subunit of human chorionic gonadotropin (hCG) in maternal serum or the urine. β-hCG is produced by the placenta. With a sensitive test, the hormone can be detected in maternal plasma or urine by 8–9 days after ovulation. A negative pregnancy test should be viewed as an opportunity to provide preconception care and promote family planning.

It is important to differentiate normal pregnancy from a nonviable or ectopic pregnancy. In the first 30 days of a normal gestation, the doubling time of plasma β-hCG concentration is 1.4–2.0 days. That is, the plasma β-hCG level is expected to double every 48 h in early normal pregnancy.

Table 2 Summary of the CDC/ATSDR Select Panel's recommendations to improve preconception health and healthcare in the US

Recommendation 1. Individual responsibility across the life span. Each woman, man and couple should be encouraged to have a reproductive life plan.

Recommendation 2. Consumer awareness. Increase public awareness of the importance of preconception health behaviors and preconception care services by using information and tools appropriate across various ages; literacy, including health literacy; and cultural/linguistic contexts.

Recommendation 3. Preventive visits. As a part of primary care visits, provide risk assessment and educational and health promotion counseling to all women of childbearing age to reduce reproductive risks and improve pregnancy outcomes.

Recommendation 4. Interventions for identified risks. Increase the proportion of women who receive interventions as follow-up to preconception risk screening, focusing on high priority interventions (i.e. those with evidence of effectiveness and greatest potential impact).

Recommendation 5. Interconception care. Use the interconception period to provide additional intensive interventions to women who have had a previous pregnancy that ended in an adverse outcome (i.e., infant death, fetal loss, birth defects, low birth weight, or preterm birth).

Recommendation 6. Prepregnancy checkup. Offer, as a component of maternity care, one prepregnancy visit for couples and persons planning pregnancy.

Recommendation 7. Health insurance coverage for women with low incomes. Increase public and private health insurance coverage for women with low incomes to improve access to preventive women's health and preconception and interconception care.

Recommendation 8. Public health programs and strategies. Integrate components of preconception health into existing local public health and related programs, including emphasis on interconception interventions for women with previous adverse outcomes.

Recommendation 9. Research. Increase the evidence base and promote the use of the evidence to improve preconception health.

Recommendation 10. Monitoring improvements. Maximize public health surveillance and related research mechanisms to monitor preconception health.

Source: Johnson K, Posner SF, Biermann J, *et al.* (2006) CDC/ATSDR Preconception Care Work Group; Select Panel on Preconception Care. Recommendations to improve preconception health and health care – United States. A report of the CDC/ATSDR Preconception Care Work Group and the Select Panel on Preconception Care. *Recommendations and Reports*. 55(RR-6): 1–23.

In patients whose pregnancies are destined to abort, the level of β-hCG rises more slowly, plateaus or declines. Serial β-hCG levels, often in combination with transvaginal ultrasound, can be used to determine the viability of early pregnancy.

Estimating gestational age and date of delivery

Gestational age should be determined during the first prenatal visit. Accurate determination of gestational age may become important later in pregnancy for the management of obstetrical conditions such as preterm labor, intrauterine growth restriction, and postdate pregnancy. Clinical assessment to determine gestational age is usually appropriate for the woman with regular menstrual cycles and known last menstrual period (LMP) that was confirmed by an early examination. Ultrasonography may be used to estimate gestational age. For determining gestational age in the first trimester, the crown-rump length is most accurate. If carefully performed, it has a variation of only 3–5 days.

The mean duration of pregnancy, calculated from the first day of the LMP, is approximately 280 days. The estimated date of delivery (also called estimated date of confinement, or due date) may be estimated from a known LMP by subtracting 3 months and adding 7 days to the LMP (Naegele's rule). For example, if the LMP began on 6 December, the expected date of delivery would be 13 September. This presupposes a 28-day menstrual cycle and may be subject to error, especially in those with longer or shorter menstrual cycles. Where recall of LMP is uncertain, the due date can also be estimated using ultrasonography.

Reproductive history

History repeats itself, and as George Santayana warns, "those who fail to learn the lessons of history are doomed to repeat them." Several pregnancy complications, including preeclampsia, preterm delivery, and thromboembolism, carry high recurrence risks in a subsequent pregnancy. In the case of postpartum cardiomyopathy, recurrence carries high mortality risks. Thus, prenatal risk assessment should include a careful review of the woman's and couple's reproductive history, including previous pregnancy complications, and identification of ongoing biobehaviral risks that might predispose recurrence in the current pregnancy.

Medical assessment

Prenatal risk assessment should include an evaluation for significant medical problems, past or present. Patients with chronic hypertension are at increased risk for preeclampsia, preterm delivery, fetal growth restriction, placental abruption, and stillbirth. Patients with pregestational diabetes have elevated risks for stillbirth, birth defects, fetal macrosomia, and delivery complications. Recent data suggest that their children may be at increased risk for diabetes and obesity if their blood sugar is poorly controlled during pregnancy. Children born to women who were hypothyroid in early pregnancy are at increased risk for developmental delay because maternal thyroid hormones play a critical role in neuron migration during early fetal brain development. Pregnancy may exacerbate certain maternal medical conditions, most notably pre-existing cardiac diseases. Pregnancy increases the heart's workload (cardiac output is increased by nearly 50% during pregnancy, and nearly doubles in the immediate postpartum period) which may be too much for a diseased heart to handle; case fatality for certain cardiac diseases during pregnancy approaches 25–50%. Because some patients may be asymptomatic and unaware of their cardiac diseases before pregnancy (e.g., rheumatic heart disease from childhood rheumatic fever), prenatal assessment should include a complete physical examination (including listening to the heart) and appropriate workup as indicated for any cardiovascular symptom.

Some infections could pose a serious threat to the pregnancy. Periodontal, sexually transmitted, and some urogenital tract infections (bacterial vaginosis and asymptomatic bacteriuria) have been associated with greater risk for preterm delivery. Prenatal risk assessment should also investigate the risks of TORCH infections (toxoplasmosis, rubella, cytomegalovirus, herpes, and other infections such as syphilis, hepatitis B, and HIV). Voluntary and confidential HIV antibody testing, with appropriate counseling and consent, should be offered to all pregnant women. Serological screening for syphilis, rubella antibodies, and hepatitis B virus surface antigen is also recommended for all pregnant women. Patients at risk for exposure to cytomegalovirus (people who work in neonatal intensive care units, childcare facilities, or dialysis units) or toxoplasmosis (cat owners and people who eat or handle raw meat) can be offered blood tests to determine their immunity to these infections; those who are nonimmune should be counseled regarding avoidance of exposure during pregnancy. Of the six recommended adult immunizations, three are contraindicated during pregnancy (rubella, varicella, and HPV), two are recommended for pregnant women at risk for exposure (Tdap and Hepatitis B), and the influenza vaccine is recommended for all pregnant women during the flu season (between December and March in the US).

Medications

Some medications can cause birth defects when taken during pregnancy. For example, the anticoagulant coumarin and its derivatives have been associated with birth defects. Because heparin is not teratogenic, women requiring anticoagulation should be switched to heparin therapy. Angiotensin-converting enzyme inhibitors (ACE inhibitors), a class of medications used to treat high blood pressure, can cause birth defects when taken in the first trimester, and kidney damage and even fetal death when taken in the second and third trimesters. Patient on ACE inhibitors should be switched to a safer antihypertensive for their pregnancy, preferably before pregnancy.

Medication use during pregnancy should always be based on a careful risk-benefit calculus. As a general rule, the fewest number of medications at the smallest effective dose for the shortest duration should be used. The US Food and Drug Administration (FDA) categorizes medications into categories A, B, C, D, and X, based on known teratogenicity (**Table 3**). Generally speaking, category X medications (e.g., isotretinoin) should never be used just before or during pregnancy, and category D medications (e.g., phenytoin) should be used only if potential maternal benefits outweigh known fetal risks and there are no safer alternatives. Category A (e.g., folic acid) and B medications (e.g., acetaminophen) are probably safe to take. For category C (e.g., fluoxetine), potential benefits should be weighed against known fetal risks.

Family history and genetic risks

Prenatal risk assessment should include a careful evaluation of personal and family history of genetic disorders. Certain genetic disorders such as sickle cell disease may put the pregnancy at greater risk. Patients with phenylketonuria (PKU) cannot metabolize the amnio acid phenylalanine which is present in nearly all foods, diet soft drinks, and certain artificial sweeteners. During pregnancy, high blood levels of phenylalanine in the mother are devastating to the fetus. In up to 90% of such cases, the babies will have mental retardation and/or a small

Table 3 Current Food and Drug Administration categories for drug use in pregnancy

Category A	Adequate and well-controlled studies have failed to demonstrate a risk to the fetus in the first trimester of pregnancy (and there is no evidence of risk in later trimesters).
Category B	Animal reproduction studies have failed to demonstrate a risk to the fetus and there are no adequate and well-controlled studies in pregnant women OR Animal studies have shown an adverse effect, but adequate and well-controlled studies in pregnant women have failed to demonstrate a risk to the fetus in any trimester.
Category C	Animal reproduction studies have shown an adverse effect on the fetus and there are no adequate and well-controlled studies in humans, but potential benefits may warrant use of the drug in pregnant women despite potential risks.
Category D	There is positive evidence of human fetal risk based on adverse reaction data from investigational or marketing experience or studies in humans, but potential benefits may warrant use of the drug in pregnant women despite potential risks.
Category X	Studies in animals or humans have demonstrated fetal abnormalities and/or there is positive evidence of human fetal risk based on adverse reaction data from investigational or marketing experience, and the risks involved in use of the drug in pregnant women clearly outweigh potential benefits.

head size (microcephaly). Many also will have heart defects, LBW and characteristic craniofacial features. Patients with known PKU should be placed on a special PKU diet at least 3 months prior to pregnancy and continue the diet throughout pregnancy. Weekly blood tests to monitor phenylalanine levels should be performed during pregnancy.

Family history of single gene disorders such as muscular dystrophy, cystic fibrosis, sickle cell disease, and fragile X syndrome, chromosomal abnormalities such as Down syndrome, unexplained mental retardation, recurrent fetal losses, and major congenital anomalies should be reviewed. Couples with such family history should be offered genetic counseling.

Some genetic diseases are more common in certain ethnic groups. For example, many obstetricians nowadays routinely screen couples of Ashkenazi Jewish ancestry for 10 genetic disorders that are more common in this population: Bloom syndrome, Canavan disease, cystic fibrosis, familial dysautonomia, Fanconi anemia group C, Gaucher disease, glycogen storage disease type I, Mucolipidosis type IV, Niemann-Pick disease types A and B, and Tay-Sachs disease. For couples of African ancestry, genetic screening for sickle cell disease or trait should be offered. Couples of Mediterranean, as well as Middle Eastern, African, Southeast Asian and Southern Chinese ancestry, should be screened for thalassemia. ACOG recommends that all couples who are pregnant or contemplating pregnancy be offered cystic fibrosis screening, regardless of their ethnic background. Since all of these disorders are autosomal recessive, both parents must be carriers for the couple to have an affected child. If one partner tests positive to be a carrier, then the other partner should be screened as well. Of course, for a couple with different heritages, genetic screening should begin with the partner at genetic risk based on ethnic background.

Down syndrome is the most common chromosomal abnormalities among liveborn infants characterized by congenital heart defects and mental retardation. The risk of Down syndrome is age dependent; maternal ages of 25, 35, and 45 years carry 1/1205, 1/365, and 1/32 chance of Down syndrome, respectively. ACOG recommends that all pregnant women, regardless of their age, should be offered screening for Down syndrome. Several screening tests are available. In the first trimester, nuchal translucency, an ultrasound exam that measures the thickness at the back of the neck of the fetus, as well as two maternal serum markers (free β-hCG, pregnancy-associated plasma protein-A (PAPP-A)) can be used to detect Down syndrome. In the second trimester, three maternal serum markers (hCG, AFP, and estriol; so-called triple markers) are commonly used to detect Down syndrome; inhibin-A can be added to improve sensitivity of screening (so-called quadruple screening). Women found

to be at increased risk of having a baby with Down syndrome with these screening tests should be offered genetic counseling and the option of chorionic villus sampling (CVS) or mid-trimester amniocentesis.

Some women may elect to undergo CVS or amniocentesis without first going through these screening tests, based on their reproductive or family history or age-related risks. Because the risk of pregnancy loss from an amniocentesis (generally quoted at 1/200) is outweighted by the risk of any chromosomal abnormalities, including Down syndrome, at age 35 years (1/178), some obstetricians routinely offer amniocentesis to women ages 35 years and older for prenatal diagnosis of Down syndrome based on age-related risks alone. The husband's age does not appear to increase the baby's risk for chromosomal abnormalities such as Down syndrome, though there is a small increase in the risk of several autosomal dominant conditions such as achondroplasia, Apert syndrome, and Marfan syndrome.

Psychological and social assessment

Prenatal risk assessment should also include a thorough psychological and social assessment. The three most important areas for psychological and social assessment are family violence, depression, and stress.

The experience of family violence is quite common among pregnant women in the US. Most studies of the prevalence of physical abuse during pregnancy report estimates in the range of 4–8%, though higher estimates (around 20%) have been reported in some populations. Family violence puts maternal health and child development at great risk. The literature contains solid links between intimate-partner violence and child abuse. Thus prenatal risk assessment should include routine screening for family violence. The screening should be prefaced with a statement to establish that screening is universal, such as, 'I would like to ask you a few questions about physical, sexual, and emotional trauma because we know that these are common and affect women's health'. Direct questioning using behaviorally specific phrasing should follow, such as:

Has anyone close to you ever threatened to hurt you?
Has anyone ever hit, kicked, choked, or hurt you physically?
Has anyone, including your partner, ever forced you to have sex?
Are you ever afraid of your partner?

Disclosure rates will be higher when the questions are asked face-to-face by the healthcare provider rather than through a questionnaire, and when behaviorally specific descriptions rather than the terms 'abuse', 'domestic violence', or 'rape' are used. Abuse victims are often accompanied to healthcare appointments by the perpetrator, who may appear overprotective or overbearing, and may answer questions directed toward the woman. It is important to ask the patient questions in private, apart from the male partner. It is also important to ask the patient questions apart from children, family, or friends, and to avoid using them as interpreters when asking questions about violence.

Maternal depression affects a large number of women and their children. Reported prevalence of major and minor depression ranged from 8.5% to 11% during pregnancy, and 6.5 to nearly 13% during the first-year postpartum. Maternal depression can have negative long-term impact on both maternal health and child development. Thus, prenatal risk assessment should include routine screening for maternal depression and other affective disorders (e.g., anxiety). Fairly accurate and feasible screening measures are available, including the Postpartum Depression Screening Scale (PDSS), Edinburgh Postnatal Depression Scale (EPDS), Beck Depression Inventory (BDI), and the Center for Epidemiologic Studies Depression scale (CES-D), and Diagnostic criteria have been established through the Diagnostic and Statistic Manual (DSM) of mental disorders. The evidence available, albeit limited, suggests that providing some form of psychosocial support to pregnant and postpartum women at risk of having a depressive illness may decrease depressive symptoms.

Maternal stress is perhaps the hardest to screen; clinicians are often at a loss as to how to screen or what to do with a positive screen. Yet chronic stress can pose significant risks to maternal health and child development. For the mother, chronic stress can cause wear and tear to her body's adaptive systems, which could lead to more rapid deterioration in her health and function over time. For the fetus, maternal stress could result in the re-programming of the child's brain and other vital organs, leading to increased vulnerability to disease and dysfunction later in life. Several studies have linked maternal anxiety and stress during pregnancy to developmental programming of neuropsychiatric disorders in the offspring, including attention deficit hyperactivity disorder, autism, epilepsy, and schizophrenia. There is an important need for the development of a multidimensional screening tool for stress that can be feasibly implemented in a clinical setting. For now, clinicians need to ask about major stressors in women's lives (e.g., homelessness, unemployment, family violence, social isolation) at every prenatal visit, and find resources and supports to help the family deal with these stressors.

Nutritional and behavioral assessment

Nutrition can play an important role in promoting maternal health and child development. The growing body of research on fetal programming further elevates the clinical and public health significance of maternal nutrition before and during pregnancy. However, prenatal care providers often overlook women's nutritional needs. Nutritional screening should address the ABCDs of

nutritional risks: anthropometric (e.g., low or high body mass index (BMI)), biochemical (e.g., for anemia or folate deficiency in some populations), clinical (e.g., eating disorder), and dietary (e.g., content, pattern, food insecurity). An abbreviated six-item version of the Household Food Security Scale can be used to screen for food insecurity. Inquiry should also be made about folate or multivitamin supplementation use before and during pregnancy.

A number of maternal risk behaviors can put the pregnancy at risk, including cigarette smoking, alcohol, and drug use. Cigarette smoking poses a significant threat to the health of the mother, her infant, and her subsequent pregnancy. Approximately one in eight (11.2%) American women who gave birth in 2002 reported smoking cigarettes during pregnancy. Effective models of clinical intervention for smoking cessation and relapse prevention have been developed and should be incorporated into prenatal care. Prenatal exposure to alcohol and other substances like cocaine and amphetamines have been associated with birth defects as well as adverse pregnancy and neurodevelopmental outcomes. According to the Behavioral Risk Factor Surveillance System, in 1999 the prevalence of any alcohol use and binge drinking among pregnant women in the US was 12.8% and 2.7%, respectively. Several screening questionnaires have been developed to detect problem drinking which may also prove helpful in detecting substance abuse, including T-ACE (tolerance, annoyed, cut down, eye opener) questions and the CAGE (cut-down, annoyed, guilty, eye-opener) questionnaire. All women should be screened at the time of their first prenatal visit and re-screened throughout pregnancy, and referral for evaluation and treatment should be offered to those who screen positive.

Laboratory evaluation

Prenatal risk assessment should also include laboratory evaluation. **Table 4** lists the laboratory tests that are recommended by ACOG, APA, and other national organizations for prenatal care.

Health Promotion

One of the most important functions of prenatal care is to provide information and support to the woman for self-care. A comprehensive review of health promotion activities during prenatal care is beyond the scope of this article. Here we will spotlight several important areas for patient education and health promotion.

Alleviating unpleasant symptoms during pregnancy

Nausea and vomiting is a common complaint during pregnancy, complicating up to 70% of pregnancies. Eating small, frequent meals, avoiding greasy or spicy foods, having protein snacks at night, saltine crackers at

Table 4 Routine prenatal laboratory screening

Tests	Timing	Clinical significance
Hematocrit or hemoglobin	1st visit	Screen for maternal anemia, which can cause low birth weight, fetal growth restriction, and anemia in infants
Urine testing	1st visit	Screen for bacteria in urine (bacteriuria). Untreated asymptomatic bacteriuria is associated with increased risk of pyelonephritis and preterm birth
Determination of blood type and antibody screen	1st visit	Screen for maternal ABO blood type, Rh factor, and antibodies against Rh and other proteins that can attack the fetus' red blood cells and cause erythroblastosis fetalis
Determination of immunity to rubella virus	1st visit	Screen for IgG antibodies against rubella. Rubella infection in nonimmune pregnant women can cause congenital deafness, cataracts, heart defects, mental retardation, liver and spleen damage, and schizophrenia
Syphilis screen	1st visit	Screen for syphilis, which can cause stillbirth, hydrops, preterm labor, birth defects, and congenital syphilis
Hepatitis B virus surface antigen	1st visit	Screen for chronic persistent hepatitis B infection, which can be vertically transmitted if newborn does not receive both hepatitis B vaccine and HBIG with 12 h of birth
HIV screen	1st visit	Screen for HIV infection. Mother-to-child transmission can be minimized with combination antiretroviral therapy during pregnancy, labor, and neonatal period
First trimester screen (Nuchal translucency, free β-hCG, PAPP-A)	11–13 weeks	Screen for Down syndrome and trisomy 18, 85% detection rate at 5% false positive rate
Second trimester screen (hCG, AFP, estriol)	15–20 weeks	Screen for Down syndrome and trisomy 18; 69% detection rate at 5% false positive rate; inhibin-A added to improve accuracy; AFP also detects neural tube defects
Glucose tolerance screening	24–28 weeks	Screen for glucose intolerance which, if confirmed, suggests gestational diabetes; choice of universal screening vs. risk-based approach
Group B streptococcus screening	35–37 weeks	Screen for GBS colonization, which is a leading cause of neonatal pneumonitis and sepsis

AFP, alpha fetal protein; GBS, group B streptococcus; HBIG, hepatitis B immunoglobulin; hCG, human chorionic gonadotropin; HIV, human immunodeficiency virus; PAPP-A, pregnancy-associated plasma protein A; Rh, rhesus.

the bedside, and room-temperature sodas are nonpharmacological approaches that may provide some alleviation. Antihistamines, vitamin B$_6$, and accupressure ('sea sickness arm bands') may also be used. Patients with dehydration and electrolyte abnormalities from severe vomiting (called hyperemesis gravidarum) should be evaluated for possible secondary causes, and hospitalized for rehydration and antiemetic therapy.

Heartburn affects about two-thirds of women at some stage of pregnancy, resulting from progesterone-induced relaxation of the esophageal sphincter. Avoiding lying down immediately after meals and spicy or greasy food, and elevating the head of the bed may help reduce heartburn. Antacids calcium carbonate, alumina and magnesia, or an H2 blocker such as ranitidine may also be used.

Constipation is a troublesome problem for many women in pregnancy, secondary to decreased colonic motility. Dietary modification, including increased fiber and water intake, can help lessen this problem. Stool softeners may be used in combination with bulking agents. Irritant laxatives should be reserved for short-term use in refractory cases.

Hemorrhoids are caused by increased venous pressure in the rectum. In the absence of any sound research about the best means of preventing or treating this condition, advice similar to that given to nonpregnant sufferers may be appropriate, such as rest, elevation of the legs, and, most importantly, avoiding constipation.

Leg cramps are experienced by almost half of all pregnant women, particularly at night and in the later months of pregnancy. The cause is unclear. Massage and stretching may afford some relief during an attack. Both calcium and sodium chloride appear to help reduce leg cramps in pregnancy.

Backaches are common during pregnancy, and are lessened by avoiding excessive weight gain. Additionally, exercise, posture, sensible shoes, and specially shaped pillows can offer relief. In cases of muscle spasm or strain, analgesics (such as acetaminophen), rest, and heat may lessen the symptoms.

Headaches and migraines are also more common during pregnancy, possibly related to hormonal changes in the first trimester, and posture and tension from carrying extra weight in the third trimester. Applying warm and cold compresses, reducing stress, getting rest and exercise, eating well-balanced meals, maintaining good posture, getting a massage, and avoiding headache triggers such as chocolate, aged cheese, peanuts, and preserved meats can offer relief. Acetaminophen may help reduce the symptoms. Avoid using aspirin or nonsteroidal anti-inflammatory drugs,in the third trimester because of potential fetal harms.

Providing lifestyle advice

During the first trimester, increased fatigue is reported. Women should be advised to rest when tired, and reassured that the fatigue usually abates by the fourth month of pregnancy. Normal prepregnancy activity levels are usually acceptable. The APA and ACOG have concluded that women with uncomplicated pregnancies usually can continue to work until the onset of labor. General advice on work is clearly inappropriate; such advice should be individualized to the nature of the work, the health status of the woman, and the condition of the pregnancy. Work that requires prolonged standing, shift or night work, and high cumulative occupational fatigue has been associated with increased risk for LBW and prematurity. Where working conditions involve occupational fatigue or stress, request for a change in work during pregnancy should be supported by the prenatal care provider.

Women should be advised to continue to exercise during pregnancy, unless it is complicated by pregnancy-induced hypertension, preterm labor or rupture of membranes, intrauterine growth retardation, incompetent cervix, persistent second- or third-trimester bleeding, or medical conditions that severely restrict physiologic adaptations to exercise during pregnancy. They should avoid exercise in the supine position after the first trimester, and should be encouraged to modify the intensity of their exercise according to maternal symptoms. Any type of exercise involving the potential for loss of balance or even mild abdominal trauma should be avoided. ACOG advises a thorough clinical evaluation be conducted before recommending an exercise program. In the absence of aforementioned contraindications, pregnant women should be encouraged to engage in regular, moderate-intensity physical activity for 30 min or more a day.

Travel is acceptable under most circumstances. Prolonged sitting increases the risk of thromboembolism; pregnant women should be encouraged to ambulate periodically when taking a long flight or car ride. Support stockings may help reduce lower extremity edema and varicose veins. International travel that places the patient at a high risk of infectious disease (such as travel to areas with a high rate of transmission of malaria or typhoid fever) should be avoided, whenever possible. When such travel cannot be avoided, appropriate vaccinations should be administered. Live attenuated virus vaccinations are generally contraindicated in pregnancy, but inactivated virus vaccines may be acceptable.

Women should be reassured that increased, unchanged, and decreased levels of sexual activity can all be normal during pregnancy. Available evidence does not support any prohibition of sexual activity during normal pregnancy. Abstinence may be advisable in cases of preterm labor, repeated pregnancy loss or persistent second- or third-trimester bleeding.

Promoting healthy nutrition

While the nutritional care plan should be individualized, every woman can benefit from nutritional education that includes counseling on weight gain, dietary guidelines, physical activity, avoidance of harmful substances and unsafe foods, and breastfeeding. **Table 5** summarizes the recommended ideal weight gain for pregnant women, by prepregnancy BMI. Inadequate weight gain has been associated with preterm birth and fetal growth restriction, whereas excessive weight gain has been associated with fetal macrosomia and postpartum weight retention.

Weight gain is of secondary importance to nutrition; the clinician should emphasize the right amount of nutrition over the right amount of weight gain. The estimated energy requirement increases by a negligible amount in the first trimester, 350 kcal in the second trimester, and 500 kcal in the third trimester. Based on these numbers, the energy requirement for an active pregnant woman of average height (162 cm) ranged from 1950 to 2100 kcal d^{-1} (depending on her prepregnancy BMI) in the first trimester, 2300 to 2450 kcal d^{-1} in the second trimester, and 2450 to 2600 kcal d^{-1} in the third trimester.

Pregnant women should be encouraged to eat a balanced diet consisting of three meals and two snacks a day, and avoid skipping meals and prolonged fasting. The diet should be comprised of high-quality protein, complex carbohydrates made up primarily of whole grains, smart fats (e.g., omega-3 fatty acids), and fruits and vegetables of rainbow colors rich in micronutrients. Certain foods should be minimized, including saturated fatty acids, trans-fats, partially hydrogenated oils, refined flours, and added sugars. Still other foods should be avoided altogether during pregnancy, including swordfish, shark, king mackerel and tilefish (to reduce fetal exposure to methylmercury), soft cheeses and unpasteurized milk, hot dogs, luncheon meats, deli meats, raw or smoked seafood (Listeria), raw or undercooked meat (toxoplasmosis), unwashed vegetables, raw vegetable sprouts, and unpasteurized juices (toxoplasmosis, *Escherichia coli*, and other infections), liver (vitamin A toxicosis and other toxins), and herbal preparations. Prenatal vitamins are often prescribed during the first prenatal visit, but their benefits (other than reducing the risk of neural tube defect

Table 5 Recommended ideal weight gain for pregnant women, by prepregnancy BMI

Weight	Prepregnancy BMI	Total weight gain (lb)
Underweight	<19.8	28–40
Normal weight	19.8–26.0	25–35
Overweight	26.1–29.0	15–25
Obese	>29	At least 15

Institute of Medicine Committee on Nutritional Status during Pregnancy and Lactation, Food and Nutrition Board (1990) *Nutrition during Pregnancy Part I: Weight Gain. Washington, DC: National Academics Press.*

with periconceptional supplementation) have not been conclusively established. A comprehensive review of nutrition during pregnancy is beyond the scope of this article; prenatal care providers should become knowledgeable with guidelines for nutritional assessment and competent in providing nutritional counseling during pregnancy.

Reducing environmental exposures

A large number of environmental exposures during pregnancy can affect maternal health and fetal development. Common household exposures include lead, drinking water, air pollution, household products, and molds, dust mites, and allergens. Lead is a potent developmental neurotoxicant and immunotoxicant, and household exposures can come from old paint, leaching from plumbing, and consumer products such as lipsticks, hair dyes, and lead-glazed houseware, plates and potteries. Drinking water may contain organic solvents, pesticide residues, and trace amounts of chloroform and other chlorinated and brominated organic compounds that are known reproductive toxicants. A large number of indoor air pollutants can also affect fetal growth and development, including tobacco smoke, carbon monoxide, nitrogen dioxide, and particles from stoves, heaters, fireplace, and chimney, perchloroethylene and other chemicals from dry cleaning, and possibly radon and asbestos. Some common household products contain reproductive toxicants, such as bathroom deodorant products (e.g., toilet bowl deodorizers, air fresheners, surface disinfectants, and some cleaning products which may contain organic solvents, endocrine-disrupting chemicals such as alkylphenols, and sometimes pesticides), cosmetics (which may contain formaldehyde or glycol ethers), some mouthwashes and medicated skin products (which can contain phenols) and food-related packaging and plastic wrap (which can contain phthlates and bisphenol-A). In utero exposure to molds, dust mites, and allergens in susceptible individuals may increase the risk for preterm birth, and possibly increased risk for allergies, atopy, and asthma in childhood due to fetal programming of the immune response. Prenatal care providers should advise their patients on how to avoid common household exposures that may affect fetal growth and development.

Foods may be a source of environmental exposures. Animal fats may contain dioxins, which can cross the placenta easily and are found to be potent neurotoxicants and immunotoxicants to the developing fetus. Reducing intake of animal fats by pregnant women, or women who are planning to get pregnant (since dioxins are stored in body fat with a long half-life), can help reduce fetal exposure to dioxins. Fish and seafood may contain methylmercury, polychlorinated biphenyls (PCBs), and other pollutants, which are also known fetal neurotoxicants. **Table 6** summarizes the 2004 Environmental Protection Agency and Food and Drug Administration joint advisory related to consumption of fish and shellfish.

Residence near a toxic waste dump, dry cleaners, gas stations and auto-repair shops, agricultural operations, or even parks, playgrounds and golf courses (which are routinely sprayed with pesticides) may expose the mother and fetus to potential reproductive toxicants. Exposure to high levels of carbon monoxide, ozone, and particulate matters from residence near or commuting on major freeways or streets may place the fetus at greater risk of fetal cardiac defects and preterm birth. For many pregnant women, the workplace poses the single greatest environmental threat. Women who work in manufacturing may be exposed to organic solvents such as glycol ethers or heavy metals like cadmium. Women who work in agriculture may be exposed to pesticides and herbicides. Prenatal care providers should advise their patients that under OSHA's Hazard Communication Standard, all employers are required to label containers with chemical name or hazard warning, provide Material Safety Data Sheet for every chemical handled at the facility, and provide training on the health and safety hazards of toxic substances to which workers are exposed. Patients can also be referred to Teratogen Information Specialists for more information.

Table 6 2004 US Environmental Protection Agency/Food and Drug Administration Fish Advisory

What you need to know about mercury in fish and shellfish
2004 EPA/FDA Fish Advisory for
- Women who might become pregnant
- Women who are pregnant
- Nursing mothers
- Young children

Do not eat shark, swordfish, king mackerel, or tilefish because they contain high levels of mercury.
Eat up to 12 oz (2 average meals) a week of a variety of fish and shellfish that are lower in mercury.
- Five of the most commonly eaten fish that are low in mercury are shrimp, canned light tuna, salmon, pollock, and catfish.
- Another commonly eaten fish, albacore ('white') tuna has more mercury than canned light tuna. So, when choosing your two meals of fish and shellfish, you may eat up to 6 oz (one average meal) of albacore tuna per week.

Check local advisories about the safety of fish caught by family and friends in your local lakes, rivers, and coastal areas. If no advice is available, eat up to 6 oz (one average meal) per week of fish you catch from local waters, but don't consume any other fish during that week.

Promoting family planning

Family planning is vital to the health and well-being of women and their families. Unintended pregnancy and short interpregnancy intervals are associated with increased risk for adverse birth outcomes in a subsequent pregnancy; family planning can reduce the risk by promoting effective contraceptive use and optimal birth spacing. An unintended pregnancy also puts future maternal health and social well-being at risk; family planning can protect maternal health and choice. Discussion of family planning should begin during prenatal care.

Promoting breastfeeding

Breastfeeding has been shown to significantly reduce morbidity and improve cognitive development during infancy and childhood. Encouragement by prenatal care providers has been shown to significantly increase breast-feeding initiation among American women of all social and ethnic backgrounds. Providers should initiate discussion with the pregnant woman and her family regarding breastfeeding during the first visit, including possible barriers to breastfeeding, such as prior poor experiences, misinformation, or nonsupportive work environment. Partners, peers, and other family members or friends may also exert important influence on women's decision to breastfeed. Referrals to childbirth preparation classes or lactation consultations may provide additional encouragement to breastfeed.

Medical and Psychosocial Interventions

Medical and psychosocial interventions should address identified risks. For many pregnant women, no medical interventions other than routine prenatal care are needed to support a normal pregnancy. Some prenatal interventions have been proved to be effective in preventing pregnancy complications and improving birth outcomes. Examples include provision of prenatal, intrapartum, and neonatal antiretroviral therapy to prevent vertical (mother-to-child) transmission of HIV and the administration of progesterone to reduce the recurrence risk of preterm delivery. A comprehensive review of prenatal medical interventions is beyond the scope of this article; systematic reviews of many prenatal interventions are available through the Cochrane database.

Given the important impact of maternal stress on birth outcomes and fetal programming, several models of pre-natal psychosocial support have been developed. One of the most widely used models in public health programs is the nurse home visitation program developed by Dr. David Olds and colleagues. The program provides nurse home visitation during pregnancy and the first 2 years postpartum. Evaluation of the Memphis/Shelby County program found that while there were no statistically significant program effects on LBW or stillbirth, women who received home visits by nurses had fewer closely spaced subsequent pregnancies, longer inter-pregnancy intervals, and several long-term benefits to children's health and family well-being have also been demonstrated. Other innovative programs that provide psychosocial support to pregnant women, such as group prenatal care (e.g., centering pregnancy), await further evaluation.

Follow-Up Visits

Following the initial visit, additional prenatal visits are routinely scheduled every 4 weeks until 28 weeks' gestation, then every 2 weeks until 36 weeks' gestation, and then weekly until delivery. The schedule of these follow-up visits, however, should be tailored to the needs of individual patients. The regularity of scheduled prenatal visits should be sufficient to allow the clinician to monitor the progression of the pregnancy, provide education and recommended screening and interventions, assess the well-being of the fetus and mother, as well as to reassure the mother, and detect and treat medical and psychosocial complications.

During each regularly scheduled visit, the clinician should evaluate patient weight gain, blood pressure, urine protein and glucose, uterine size for progressive fetal growth, and fetal heart rate. After the woman reports quickening (first sensation of fetal movement, typically around 20 weeks' gestation for first pregnancy and earlier for subsequent pregnancies) and at each subsequent visit, she should be asked about fetal movement. She should also be instructed to perform routine fetal movement counting.

Between 24 and 34 weeks, women should be taught warning symptoms of preterm labor, which include uterine contractions ('abdomen tightens like a fist' every 10 min or more frequently), leakage of fluid, vaginal bleeding, low, dull back pain or pelvic pressure (feeling that the baby is pushing down), cramps (feel like a period, or abdominal cramps with or without diarrhea). Beginning late second trimester, women should also be taught to recognize the four cardinal symptoms of pre-eclampsia, which are headache (typically frontal, severe, and persistent), visual changes, hand or facial swelling, or epigastric or right upper quadrant pain. Near term, they should be instructed on the symptoms of labor.

Fundal height has long been used to assess fetal growth. The distance between the top of the pubic symphysis and the top of the uterus (fundus) in centimeters should equal the gestational age in weeks; this correlation holds best between 18 and 32 weeks. However, considerable intra- and interobserver variations (by as much as 4 cm) have been demonstrated, and detection rate for intrauterine growth restriction of less than 30% has been reported in several large studies. Beginning at 28 weeks, systematic examination of the abdomen is carried out at each prenatal visit to identify the lie (e.g., longitudinal, transverse, oblique), presentation (e.g., vertex, breech, shoulder), or position (e.g., flexion, extension or rotation of the occiput) of the fetus. If the abdominal examination suggests nonvertex presentation (e.g., breech), confirmation is usually obtained with an ultrasound. Patients with frank breech presentation may be offered a vaginal breech delivery if other conditions are met; patients with other nonvertex presentations should be offered external cephalic version (whereby the fetus is turned to a vertex position by external manipulation) at 37 weeks, or a scheduled Cesarean delivery.

In addition to the initial laboratory tests, additional laboratory tests may be recommended during prenatal care. First trimester screen is typically performed between 11 and 13 weeks, and include β-hCG and PAPP-A along with sonographic nuchal translucency to screen for Down syndrome and other chromosomal anomalies. Second trimester screen consists of serum unconjugated estriol, alpha-fetal protein (AFP), and β-hCG, and are ideally performed between 16 and 18 weeks' gestation. Inhibin-A may be added to improve sensitivity of the screen; AFP can also be used to screen for neural tube defects. Between 24 and 28 weeks, screening for gestational diabetes is typically performed using a 1-h glucose challenge test. This can be done on all patients, or selectively based on risk factors such as family history of diabetes, previous birth of a macrosomic, malformed or stillborn baby, hypertension, glycosuria, maternal age of 30 years or older, or previous gestational diabetes. The cost–benefit of diabetic screening during pregnancy remains highly controversial, though recent evidence on prenatal programming of childhood obesity and insulin resistance might suggest a more favorable cost-benefit calculus for universal screening. Repeat measurements of hemoglobin or hematocrit levels early in the third trimester have been recommended. Tests for sexually transmitted infections (e.g., syphilis) may also be repeated at 32–36 weeks of gestation if the woman has specific risk factors for these diseases. CDC recommend universal screening for maternal colonization of group B Streptococcus (GBS) at 35–37 weeks of gestation (see **Table 4**).

The value of selective ultrasound for specific indications has been clearly established; that of routine ultrasound in low-risk pregnancies remains undetermined. At present, there is no evidence that ultrasound examination during pregnancy is harmful. Controlled trials have failed to demonstrate that routine ultrasound examinations for dating in early pregnancy, anatomical survey in midpregnancy, or anthropometry in late pregnancy improve perinatal outcomes. Varying levels of expertise make this a particularly difficult issue about which to make a general statement.

Postpartum and Internatal Care

Women should be advised to receive a check-up 4–6 weeks after childbirth, and sooner after a Cesarean delivery or a complicated gestation. This postpartum visit is believed to offer an important opportunity to assess the physical and psychosocial well-being of the mother, counsel her about breastfeeding and family planning, initiate preconception care for the next pregnancy, and address nascent problems within the family. Analogous to a postoperative visit, the postpartum visit may also provide an opportunity for the obstetrician to evaluate a woman's postpartum recovery from the delivery, such as assessing for involution of the uterus or intactness of the perineal wound repair. The optimal timing and content of the postpartum visit remains to be determined.

Internatal care (also referred to as interconception or interpregnancy care) refers to a package of healthcare and ancillary services provided to a woman and her family from the birth of one child to the birth of her next child. For healthy mothers, internatal care offers an opportunity for wellness promotion between pregnancies. For high-risk mothers, internatal care provides strategies for risk reduction 'before' their next pregnancy. The extent to which internatal care is provided to women between pregnancies in the US is not known, and issues around financing, delivery, and content of internatal care remain unresolved.

Rethinking Prenatal Care

Increasingly, the effectiveness of prenatal care for improving pregnancy outcomes is being challenged. That prenatal care has contributed to the making of healthier mothers and babies is incontrovertible. Prevention of Rh isoimmunization is one of many examples. However, contrary to the IOM reports claim that the 'overwhelming weight of the evidence is that prenatal care reduces low birth weight', the evidence of effectiveness of prenatal care for preventing LBW and its twin constituents, preterm birth and fetal growth restriction, remains inconclusive. Furthermore, the growing body of evidence on fetal origins of health and disease calls for some rethinking about the content, timing, and delivery of prenatal care in order to optimize fetal programming. The ultimate success of prenatal care in improving pregnancy outcomes and optimizing fetal programming may hinge on the development of a much broader conception of prenatal care than currently prevails – a reconceptualization of prenatal care as part of a longitudinally and contextually integrated strategy to promote optimal development of women's reproductive health not only during pregnancy, but over their entire life course.

See also: AIDS and HIV; Birth Complications and Outcomes; Breastfeeding; Endocrine System; Prenatal Development; Screening, Prenatal; Teratology.

Suggested Readings

Alexander GR and Kotelchuck M (2001) Assessing the role and effectiveness of prenatal care: History, challenges, and directions for future research. *Public Health Reports* 116: 306–316.

American Academy of Pediatrics and American College of Obstetrics and Gynecology (2000) *Guidelines for Perinatal Care,* 5th edn. Elk Grove Village, IL: American College of Obstetrics and Gynecology.

American College of Obstetricians and Gynecologists (1995) ACOG technical bulletin. Preconceptional care. *International Journal of Gynaecology and Obstetrics* 50: 201–207.

Expert Panel on the Content of Prenatal Care (1989) *Caring for Our Future: The Content of Prenatal Care.* Washington, DC: Public Health Service.

Harold S (1980) *Obstetrics and Gynecology in America: A History,* pp. 142–145. Chicago, IL: The American College of Obstetricians and Gynecologists.

Institute of Medicine (1985) *Committee to Study the Prevention of Low Birth Weight. Preventing Low Birth Weight.* Washington, DC: National Academy Press.

Institute of Medicine Committee on Nutritional Status During Pregnancy and Lactation, Food and Nutrition Board (1990) *Nutrition During Pregnancy Part I: Weight Gain.* Washington, DC: National Academics Press.

Johnson K, Posner SF, Biermann J, *et al.* (2006) CDC/ATSDR Preconception Care Work Group; Select Panel on Preconception Care. Recommendations to improve preconception health and healthcare – United States. A report of the CDC/ATSDR Preconception Care Work Group and the Select Panel on Preconception Care. *MMWR Recommendation and Reports.* 55(RR-6): 1–23.

Lu MC, Kotelchuck M, Culhane JF, Hobel CJ, Klerman LV, and Thorp JM, Jr. (2006) Preconception care between pregnancies: The content of internatal care. *Maternal and Child Health Journal* 10(7): 107–122.

Lu MC, Tache V, Alexander G, Kotelchuck M, and Halfon N (2003) Preventing LBW: Is prenatal care the answer? *Journal of Maternal-Fetal Neonatal Medicine* 13: 362–380.

Relevant Websites

http://www.aap.org – American Academy of Pediatrics, Dedicated to the Health of Children.

http://www.acog.org – American College of Obstetricians and Gynecologists, Women's Health Care Physicians.

http://www.marchofdimes.com – March of Dimes, Saving babies, together.

http://www.otispregnancy.org – Organization of Teratology Information Specialists.

http://www.cdc.gov – US Department of Health and Human Services. Centers for Disease Control and Prevention, Division of Reproductive Health: Home.

http://mchb.hrsa.gov – US Department of Health and Human Services Health Resources and Services Administration, Maternal and Child Health Bureau.

Prenatal Development

J A DiPietro, Johns Hopkins University, Baltimore, MD, USA

Glossary

Age of viability – The lowest gestational age at which survival following delivery is possible, typically with significant technological support. The most commonly accepted current gestational age of viability is 23 weeks' gestation.

Anteflexion and retroflexion – Forward and backward bending of the body or body part.

Circadian rhythms – A daily cycle of behavioral or biological patterns.

Gestation – The period of time from fertilization to birth. In humans, this encompasses 266 days or approximately 38 weeks.

Habituation and dishabituation – Habituation is response decrement to repeated presentations of an unchanging stimulus. Dishabituation refers to resumption of response following presentation of a different stimulus than that used to evoke habituation.

Neurobehavior – Measurable features of developmental functioning that are maturational in nature and are presumed to reflect the underlying neural substrate.

Neuroendocrines – Hormones that mediate interactions between the nervous system and the endocrine (hormonal) system Neuroendocrines are released into the blood in response to nervous system stimulation.

Ontogeny – The origin and development of an individual from embryonic period to adulthood.

Post-term birth – Delivery following 42 weeks' gestation.

Pre-term birth – Delivery prior to 37 weeks' gestation.

Introduction

A single, fertilized cell develops into the complex organism that is a human newborn infant in just 266 days. The explosive rate of growth and development during this period is unparalleled at any other point in the lifespan. A resurgence of interest in the prenatal period as a staging period for well-being and disease in later life has been fostered by the enormous attention devoted to the hypothesis of 'fetal programming' advanced by D. J. Barker and colleagues. This rapidly emerging field of study focuses on the role of maternal and fetal factors in adult organ function, including the brain and nervous system. That earlier circumstances, including those during the prenatal period, might affect later development is hardly newsworthy to developmentalists. In 1929, the foundation of the Fels Research Institute in Yellow Springs, Ohio, was based on a longitudinal study of child growth and development that commenced with intensive investigation of the fetal period. Although investigators had limited access to the fetus due to the primitive research tools available to them, their research questions and orientation were truly prescient and the results they generated were surprisingly consistent with more recent findings using more sophisticated technologies.

Human gestation encompasses the period of time from conception to birth. By convention an additional 2 weeks is added to account for the average period of time between the last menstrual period and ovulation so that the average term gestation is 40 weeks long or 280 days. However, normal full-term birth spans the gestational period from 37 to 41 weeks. Pregnancies that end before 37 weeks are referred to as pre-term; those at and beyond 42 weeks are post-term. Survival of preterm infants has improved dramatically during the last several decades as a result of improvements in neonatal intensive care. However, the age of viability, or the earliest gestational age at which some babies can survive with aggressive technological support, is currently 23 weeks' gestation. Prior to this time, development of the respiratory and other organ systems is insufficient to sustaining extrauterine life. At the other end of the spectrum, pregnancies that last too long are also hazardous. However, current obstetric practices have drastically reduced post-term gestations through the use of induced or surgical deliveries.

The fertilized ovum enters the uterine cavity shortly after conception. Mitotic division generates the blastocyst, a hollow ball of cells that becomes implanted in the wall of the uterus within the first 2 weeks. Weeks 2–8 comprise the embryonic period, during which time differentiation of organs and structures proceeds rapidly. By the ninth week after conception, approximately 95% of all structures within the body are developed although the embryo weighs less than 10 g and is only 50 mm long. This week also marks the transition from the embryonic to fetal period, although there is no clear physical demarcation. The embryo and fetus develop in the intrauterine cavity within an amniotic sac, which is filled with amniotic fluid. During the embryonic period, the structures necessary to support development originate and progress through a series of stages, ultimately resulting in the umbilical cord and placenta. The placenta provides nutrients, exchanges gases, and manufactures hormones vital to maintenance of the pregnancy. A mature placenta is intended to function for a full-term pregnancy; thus, post-term risks to the fetus are often due to the deterioration of the placenta's ability to optimally support the fetus. The circumstances that stimulate labor and delivery are not well understood, although there is significant evidence that signals from the fetus itself serve as impetus.

The fetal period proceeds until birth and is marked by final development of organ morphology and function, including prolonged development of the brain and nervous system. The 'hardware' of the brain – neural tube closing, neuronal and glial cell proliferation and migration – commences early in gestation, while the 'software' elements of synapatogenesis, process elimination, and myelination continue through term and after birth. Organs are most vulnerable to insult when they are developing most intensively. Thus, exposure to potentially harmful substances during pregnancy has consequences for structural malformations of most organ systems only during the embryonic period or shortly thereafter. However, the potential for harmful effects of functional brain development, with implications for cognitive and behavioral development after birth, persist throughout pregnancy. **Figure 1** provides a schematic description of the shifting vulnerabilities during gestation.

The terms growth and development are often used interchangeably but they refer to distinct processes. Growth is typically defined as an increase in cell size or number; development implies differentiation of function or complexity. The remainder of this article focuses on fetal neurobehavioral development, a set of features of prenatal functional development that are measurable and observable functional indicators that are presumed to reflect development of the nervous system. The study of fetal neurobehavioral development reflects a backward or downward extension of principles and theories that have been applied since the early 1970s to characterize infant behavior. In fact, developmentalists who study the fetus commonly assert that "nothing neurologically interesting happens at birth." While it is obvious that birth presents transitional challenges for a number of organ systems, such as the circulatory and respiratory systems, it is not well recognized that by the end of gestation the fetus demonstrates virtually the same behavioral repertoire as a newborn infant. Put another way, all behaviors exhibited by neonates have been observed at some point during the fetal period.

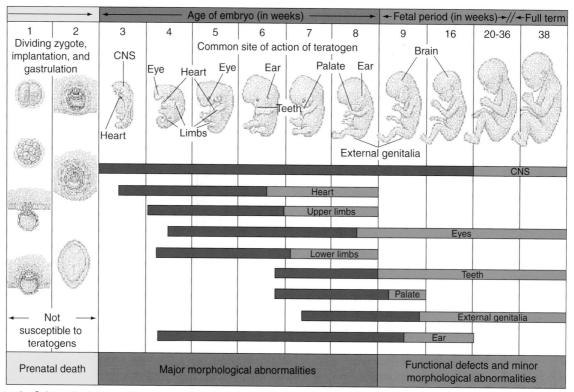

Figure 1   Schematic representation of growth and development during gestation. Reproduced from Moore KL and Persaud TV (1993) *The Developing Human: Clinically Oriented Embryology*, 5th edn. Philadelphia: W.B. Saunders Company, with permission from Elsevier. CNS, Central Nervous Systems.

Development during the prenatal period proceeds along a continuum, with behaviors becoming incrementally more complex and varied as gestation proceeds. Like all other developmental periods, the fetal period is not monolithic; behavior in the early fetal period is largely reflexive and involves the entire body while behavior near term is far more fluid, integrated, and distinct. Although no other developmental period yields the same potential to reveal the complexities of human ontogeny, no other period of developmental inquiry is so heavily dependent on technology to answer even the most basic of questions. Before proceeding to detailing current understanding about prenatal developmental ontogeny, a brief review regarding technologies necessary to view and monitor the fetus is provided.

Fetal Monitoring Techniques

Although speculation about the nature of fetal behavior has existed since antiquity, the advent of real-time ultrasound in the early 1970s enabled modern scientific investigation of prenatal development. Visualization can reveal specific behaviors (e.g., thumb-sucking), qualitative aspects of movement (e.g., fluidity of flexion and extension), structural features of the fetus (e.g., size), and characteristics of the uterine milieu (e.g., volume of amniotic fluid). In addition, refinement of techniques to monitor fetal heart rate and its

patterning, using Doppler ultrasound, has provided another important source of information regarding prenatal neural development. Doppler has also generated techniques to detect fetal motor activity without ultrasound visualization and makes it possible to measure the amount of blood flow and resistance in maternal and fetal vessels, including umbilical, cerebral, and uterine arteries. The most recent technological advance is the development of three-dimensional (3D) and so-called four-dimensional ultrasound (i.e., 3D image plus addition of a fourth dimension of real time motion) that allows visualization of details, such as fetal facial expressions and hand movements, which were not previously possible. **Figure 2** presents examples of traditional two-dimensional (2D) and 3D images.

Although 3D technology holds great potential for future studies, it is yet to be implemented broadly. Almost all knowledge about human prenatal development has been generated by information from a mixture of existing ultrasound methods, including 2D ultrasound and fetal heart rate monitoring. Regardless of how sophisticated ultrasound may become in the future, the human fetus will always remain slightly beyond our actual reach.

Fetal Neurobehavioral Development

Theoretical orientations regarding neurobehavioral development early in the postnatal period generally focus on

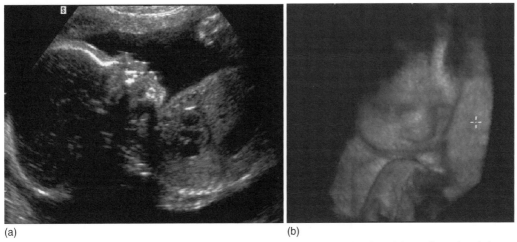

(a)   (b)

Figure 2 Sample images (a) traditional two-dimensional ultrasound and (b) recently developed three-dimensional ultrasound.

four domains of functioning: autonomic, motor, state, and responsive/interactive capacities. These domains are hierarchical in nature such that sufficient maturation of function of each precedes emergence of the next. That is, in order to sustain interaction with the environment, one needs to be able to maintain a certain degree of state control; in order to maintain state control, one needs to inhibit unnecessary motor activity, and so on. Information about prenatal development can also be organized in this manner as their ontogenic origins are rooted firmly in the fetal period. In the fetus, the specific aspects of functioning within each domain include (1) fetal heart rate and its patterning, (2) quantitative and qualitative aspects of motor activity, (3) the emergence and consolidation of behavioral states, and (4) interaction with the intrauterine and external environments.

Fetal Heart Rate

In infants and children, patterns inherent in continuously monitored heart rate are frequently used indicators of the autonomic nervous system. In particular, features of variability in heart rate are considered to reflect the development of parasympathetic processes related to the vagus nerve (i.e., vagal tone) and have been linked to aspects of infant and child behavior and development. More information exists about the development of fetal heart rate than any other domain. Noninvasive methods to measure fetal heart rate by placing a simple Doppler transducer on the maternal abdomen have been commonly used in clinical obstetric practice and research for decades and a great deal is known about development of components of the fetal heart rate. A fetal heart beat is detectable near the sixth gestational week. As the cardiac system rapidly develops, heart rate increases over the next 4 weeks to a baseline rate of approximately 160 beats per min (bpm). Heart rate declines to approximately 135–140 bpm by term, although normal limits span a wide range.

Patterns in fetal heart rate during the prenatal period and labor are more revealing about nervous system development than is heart rate. In fact, the principal means available to determine general fetal well-being or distress relies on the direction and magnitude of periodic fluctuations in heart rate. Fetal heart rate that is characterized by variability over time and includes transient, acceleratory excursions of heart rate well above baseline is interpreted as a reassuring sign of fetal health. In contrast, lack of variability and deceleratory episodes (i.e., significant slowing of heart rate well below baseline levels) can be indicative of neural compromise or distress. The heart rate decline observed during gestation is accompanied by an increase in the number and size of accelerations, a reduction in deceleratory periods, and an increase in beat to beat and longer-term components of heart rate variability. Both have been attributed to changing cardiovascular needs and cardiac functioning in the developing fetus that have both non-neural and neural influences. Maturational changes in the innervation of sympathetic and parasympathetic autonomic processes and progressive assumption of higher levels of central mediation are among the neural components of these gestational changes.

Fetal Motor Activity

During gestation, fetal movement progresses from uncoordinated movements that involve the entire body to more integrated, narrow, behavior patterns. Spontaneously generated motor activity is present during the embryonic and early fetal periods. **Figure 3** shows the gestational age at emergence of 15 types of motor behaviors studied in a sample of 11 fetuses observed on ultrasound at weekly intervals early in gestation.

There is progression in the emergence of each behavior, from the least to the most differentiated. In addition, there is greater individual discrepancy in the emergence of more complex patterns, suggesting that these may be

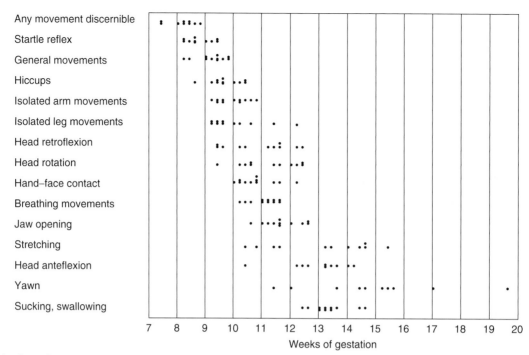

Figure 3 Gestational age of emergence of specific fetal motor behaviors in a sample of 11 fetuses viewed serially with ultrasound. Adapted from de Vries J, Visser G.H, and Prechtl HF (1982) The emergence of fetal behaviour. I. Qualitative aspects. *Early Human Development* 7: 301–322.

more reflective of the development of higher-order brain processes. Note that this figure shows only the first observed incidence for each; once a behavior is expressed, it continues to persist throughout gestation.

Specific movements are believed to serve preparatory or functional roles that increase survivability at birth. For example, fetal breathing motions begin early in gestation and become more common over time, so that by term the fetus exhibits fetal breathing movements approximately a third of the time. Although air is not a component of the intrauterine environment and these movements serve no role in oxygen regulation, they probably reflect rehearsal of behavior patterns of the diaphragm and other muscles that are central to respiration. Fetal hiccupping and yawning are commonplace although neither has clear functional significance. However, fetal sucking movements in general and thumb-sucking in particular are also common activities that may strengthen neural connections necessary for the successful transition to postnatal feeding. It also suggests that non-nutritive sucking (i.e., sucking that is not associated with nutrition) may serve a self soothing or regulatory role both before and after birth. Other behaviors play clear roles in optimizing the intrauterine environment. For example, fetal swallowing assists in regulation of the amount of amniotic fluid present. Development begins with the fetus in a breech, or head up position; fetal motor behaviors consistent with stepping along the intrauterine wall have been observed as the fetus makes the transition from a breech to vertex position

(i.e., head down) position midway through gestation. This has raised speculation that some fetuses that remain breech by the time of delivery differ in their motor development from those who successfully assume the vertex presentation.

Animal models have provided developmental psychobiologists with an important source of information to study the adaptive significance of specific behaviors prior to birth because they may be studied either with special preparation of eggs, for precocial avian species, or with preparations that make viewing the developing fetus more accessible in mammalian species. For example, newborn rat pups display a specific type of locomotion that is necessary to early survival but disappears soon after birth; this coordinated behavior originates during the prenatal period. Experimental manipulations in animal models have also served to identify basic mechanisms and progressions of behavioral expression in the developing embryo of fetus as well as the contributions of both intersensory experience and the intrauterine environment in shaping ontogeny.

Fetal movements are normally not felt by pregnant women until the 16th to 18th week of pregnancy. After this time, women perceive most large amplitude, prolonged movements but are poor detectors of other spontaneous or evoked fetal movements, detecting as few as 16% of movements at term. This makes reliance on maternal report an unsuitable source of data in studies of fetal motor activity; instead investigators rely on ultrasound-visualized or

Doppler-detected measurement of fetal motor behavior. Most longitudinal studies report that the fetus becomes less active as gestation advances although movement amplitude or intensity increases as the fetus becomes larger. Inhibition of behavior is considered a hallmark of early child development in the postnatal period; thus, this pattern appears prenatally. In the latter half of gestation, fetuses move approximately once per minute, and are active between 10% and 30% of the time. Such estimates vary, in part, because of differences in how the end of one movement and beginning of the next are defined. Fetal activity patterns exhibit rhythmic periodicities during relatively short cycles during the day as well as circadian rhythms, with fetal motility peaking late in the evening. Although sex differences in motor activity are commonly observed in studies of infants and young children, sex differences in fetal motor activity are not apparent.

Fetal Behavioral State

During the second half of gestation, fetal heart rate and movement patterns become integrated such that fetal heart rate increases and becomes more variable when the fetus is moving and is lower and less variable when the fetus is still. This coupling develops in a predictable fashion and has been most often attributed to centrally mediated co-activation of cardiac and somatomotor processes; thus, it provides information regarding the integration of neural processes. Near 32 weeks' gestation, coupling of these two aspects of development is joined by synchronous activity of other kinds, particularly fetal eye and breathing movements. In the late 1970s, investigators determined that periods in which there were predictable co-occurrence of specific patterns in three parameters – heart rate, motor activity, and eye movements – represented behavioral states that correspond to the sleep–wake states observed in the newborn. Four fetal behavioral states were discerned, labeled 1F, 2F, 3F, and 4F, in concert with state scoring methods developed for neonates. These fetal states approximate quiet sleep (1F), rapid eye movement (REM) sleep (2F), quiet waking (3F), and active waking (4F). Investigations conducted since that time tend to confirm the relative comparability of these states to those of newborn infants. In the postnatal period, behavioral state provides the context for evaluating and interpreting all other behaviors. As the fetus matures, state parameters gradually develop linkage between two parameters and ultimate coincidence accompanied by predictable state transitions during which near-simultaneous changes occur in all parameters. Mature states do not emerge until near 36 weeks; prior to that time, fetuses are most often observed in either indeterminate states or those that are best characterized simply as general periods of quiescence or activity, and the transitions between them are indistinct. **Figure 4** presents characteristic recordings of 8 min each of a fetus in quiescence and

activity. Understanding of the central mechanisms underlying maturation of state in the fetus are not yet well elucidated although patterning in temporal activation linked to the reticular formation has been implicated.

Once states coalesce, fetuses spend most of the time in either quiet or active sleep. Periods that seem consistent with wakefulness are less common, and in particular, episodes in which the fetus seems to be both quiet and awake are rarely observed, leading some to speculate that such a period either does not exist, or that perhaps investigators do not know how to recognize it. The newborn infant also expresses a fifth behavioral state encompassing fussiness and crying, but such activity is not included in the traditional definitions of fetal states. However, if developmentalists are to stand behind their observation that the newborn behaves in the same way as a near term fetus does, prenatal crying should exist. Because the larynx must be surrounded by air to produce an audible cry, but this is not the case in the fetus, other indicators of crying would need to be detectable. Anecdotal evidence of fetal crying has existed for a number of years, and recently ultrasound has identified inspiratory and expiratory diaphragmatic patterns that appear to be a fetal analog to an infant crying in response to a loud sound. It is important to note, however, that if this fifth state is confirmed, it, like other states, appears only near the end of gestation.

Fetal Responsivity

Human fetal sensory systems develop in an analogous order to those of nonprimate species: cutaneous, vestibular, auditory, and lastly, visual. It is fairly well accepted that the fetus has the capacity to feel pain and other sensations, but again, this would be expected from a neurological basis only near the end of term. The fetus exhibits behaviors that seem to generate information about the intrauterine environment – grasping the umbilical cord, licking the placenta, pushing off the uterine wall with hands and feet. Interest in demonstrating fetal responsivity to stimuli originating outside the uterus dates to the 1930s Fels Study; preferred stimuli at that time included door buzzers and warning horns. Women often report feeling fetal motor activity in response to loud sounds. More recently, fetal responses ranging from heart rate surges, abrupt changes to an active behavioral state, and startles to more subtle responses, including bladder emptying and reduction in fetal breathing movements, have been generated using a variety of vibroacoustic devices. Vibroacoustic stimulation refers to auditory and/or vibratory stimuli activated on or near the maternal abdomen, usually above the fetal head. Because fetal hearing matures relatively early, and sound is efficiently conducted in a dense medium (e.g., amniotic fluid), the use of loud or intense stimuli has generated a number of

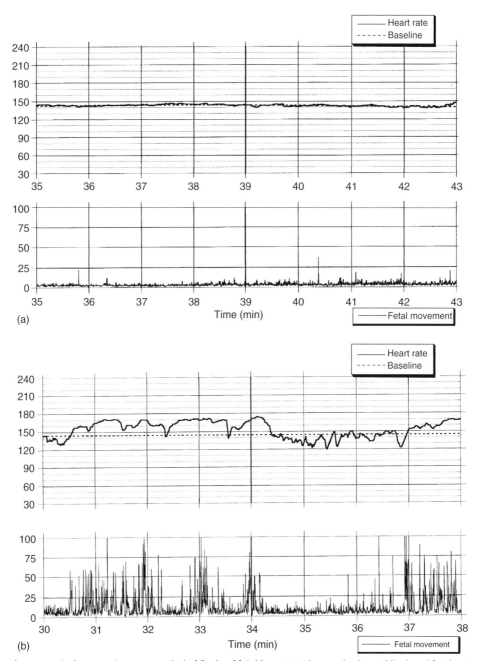

Figure 4 Doppler-generated segments over a period of 8 min of fetal heart rate (upper, horizontal line) and fetal motor activity (lower, vertical lines) in a fetus at 36 weeks' gestational age (a) reflecting periods of quiescence (1F) and (b) active waking (4F).

concerns about safety and the potential for causing fetal discomfort. Nonetheless, it is clear that from at least midway through gestation, the fetus can respond to stimuli that originate outside of the uterus.

The question of whether the fetus responds to more nuanced stimuli in a manner indicative of higher cognitive or information processing is extraordinarily difficult to answer conclusively. Consider for a moment the challenges of assessing memory in infants. Babies cannot directly communicate what they know; they fall asleep unpredictably, have little motor control, and in general

behave in ways that limit our ability to test them. Add to these challenges the additional feature of not being able to actually see the subject of testing and you begin to approach the difficulties of this type of fetal research. Nonetheless, the fetus seems capable of habituation, a primitive form of sensory learning requiring response decrement to repeated presentations of invariant stimuli. Habituation, as measured by successive reductions in motor and heart rate responses to vibroacoustic stimuli, has been observed late in pregnancy. Such observations suggest that the mature fetus has rudimentary learning capacities. However, because fetal research is technically difficult to implement and often not conducted with the same experimental rigor as studies with infants, dishabituation is often not assessed. This makes it difficult to determine whether studies have shown true habituation in the fetus rather than simple response fatigue.

Given the difficulties in measuring subtle fetal responses, most studies on fetal learning capabilities expose fetuses to stimuli during gestation but test on recognition after birth. Virtually all of these focus on fetal ability to learn features of auditory stimuli. Although the intrauterine environment conducts external vibroacoustic stimuli well, this is not the only source of auditory stimulation. The background noise level within the uterus, based on animal and human models, has been estimated to be about 30 decibels, roughly consistent with the noise level in an average residence without a stereo on. Sounds are generated by maternal physiological processes (e.g., cardiac, digestive sounds, and placental sounds) and partially absorbed exterior noises. External sounds of high frequency generate greater intrauterine attenuation than low-frequency sounds. Prominent above this background is the partially altered, but distinguishable, maternal voice, which is conveyed both through internally conducted vibrations of the vocal chords as well as externally through the uterine wall. Fetal responses to auditory stimuli can be elicited as early as 24 weeks' gestation, suggesting that the fetus has a history of exposure to the maternal voice that is at least 4 months long.

Seminal work by DeCasper, Fifer, and colleagues provides the most convincing evidence for prenatal learning by examining whether newborn infants appear to recognize their own mother's voice. Although these studies are based on relatively small samples, and involve complicated methods to assess voice recognition in newborns, such studies indicate that fetuses do learn to discriminate their own mother's voice from that of another woman and prefer listening to their mother's voice. In addition, newborns prefer voices that are altered to reflect the acoustical properties as experienced *in utero* and voices that speak in their own language. Newborn infants can detect other maternal features, such as odor, suggesting that multidimensional maternal recognition that originates prior to birth may be adaptive for survival after birth. There is much less research on explicit efforts to expose fetuses to non-naturally occurring sounds in an effort to evaluate associative learning. There is evidence that fetuses can discern rhythmic variations in speech and musical stimuli detected by alterations in fetal behavior during stimulus onset. However, research on the ability of fetuses to learn specific musical segments as manifest by neonatal recognition is both preliminary and inconclusive.

The idea that exposing fetuses to auditory stimuli for the purpose of enhancing prenatal brain development or providing direct tuition in, for example, classical music or other patterned stimuli, is absolutely unsubstantiated by existing research. Although a number of commercial products for fetal stimulation are available for purchase, these are of dubious safety. In terms of efficacy, there is no credible scientific evidence that providing extra external stimulation to fetuses is beneficial, and a great deal of sentiment that it may in fact be harmful. Because fetal hearing is relatively mature, and the basal uterine environment relatively quiet, deliberate exposure to loud sounds may, at best, interfere with normal sleep–wake cycles and, at worst, may harm fetal hearing. The intrauterine environment is exquisitely tuned to maximizing development of the fetal brain and nervous system and there is no compelling reason to expect that disturbing normal ontogeny would provide benefit to it. In fact, evidence from animal models suggests that providing prenatal sensory stimulation beyond what is typically encountered for a species can result in interference with normal development.

Factors That Influence Fetal Development

Developmental Discontinuity

Although there are progressive linear changes in heart rate, motor activity, state development, and sensory/interactive capacities over the course of gestation, the trajectory of these changes shifts at a specific gestational period. Such shifts, or periods of discontinuity, are common during infant and child development and connote a period in which there is a qualitative shift in one or more domains. The first commonly recognized discontinuity occurs in the third month after birth, at which time infants become more interactive and progress beyond newborn behavior patterns. With respect to the development of fetal behaviors, the period between 28 and 32 weeks' gestation has emerged as a transitional period for maturation prior to birth. The discontinuity can be generalized as follows: prior to 28–32 weeks, the fetus displays immature neurobehavioral patterns with a relatively steep developmental slope; after 32 weeks, the trajectory of development becomes significantly less steep. In some ways, a fetus that has passed this transition is more similar to a newborn than to an immature fetus. These observations encompass most fetal parameters that change over gestation, including heart rate patterns, motor activity, fetal movement–heart rate coupling, fetal breathing motions, and responsivity to stimuli. The onset of these trends coincides with a period of rapid increase in neural development and myelination. This suggests that prenatal brain development toward the end of pregnancy is somewhat overdetermined and may serve as a protective mechanism for early birth. Support for this position is provided by the ultimate developmental and cognitive success of pre-term infants who are born after this gestational period, despite immaturity in other organ systems. This is not to imply that development ceases after this period, or that certain aspects of fetal neurobehavior do not continue to develop in a linear fashion. For example, there is a linear increase in periods of wakefulness for fetuses that are post-term. However, at the very least, decelerative trajectories indicate that the rate of fetal maturation peaks early in the third trimester and begins to taper off well before term.

Fetal Congenital Anomalies and Pregnancy Risk Factors

If fetal neurobehaviors reflect the developing nervous system, it would be expected that factors with known neurotoxicity or that jeopardize normal pregnancies would also affect expression of fetal neurobehavior. Indeed, fetuses afflicted with a variety of chromosomal anomalies or malformations, including Down syndrome and neural tube defects, show variation in normal fetal development. This includes fetuses whose physical growth is proceeding below normal limits (i.e., intrauterine growth restriction). Exposure to a variety of potential teratogens (including alcohol, nicotine, methadone, and cocaine) has also been shown to affect various aspects of normal behavioral development. Fetuses of women with conditions that threaten pregnancy and change fetal growth, such as diabetes, exhibit differences in development, in this case presumably due to alterations in glucose metabolism and availability. However, despite the potential for detection of fetal compromise, the field is not sufficiently advanced to be able to predict poor developmental outcomes after birth based solely on detection of atypical patterns of fetal neurobehavior.

The Maternal Context

The psychological bond between mother and child has been extolled throughout history and literature but there is relatively scant scientific information on the inception of this relationship prior to birth. Whereas the knowledge base concerning neurobehavioral development is quite broad because it has been a subject of investigation for over 25 years, information on the maternal–fetal interface is quite new and much of it requires additional replication and scientific investigation. There are no direct neural connections between the mother and the fetus. Thus, to affect the fetus, maternal psychological functioning must be translated into physiological effects. This translation may occur through a number of processes, including direct transmission of neuroendocrines to the fetus through the placenta, alterations in maternal blood flow that affect levels of oxygen and nutrients available to the fetus, or changes in the intrauterine milieu that the fetus may detect through sensory channels.

Fetal behavior exhibits circadian rhythms. For example, fetal heart rate is lowest in the early morning hours and fetal motor activity peaks in the evening. However, during daytime hours, there are no consistent peaks or valleys of fetal activity or inactivity. It is unclear how or whether maternal diurnal patterns contribute to the observed fetal variations. Most information on whether maternal states influence the fetus has been generated by studies that monitor the fetus during periods of maternal arousal, induced through either physical exertion, including exercise, or mild psychological stress. Both have been associated with subtle alterations in fetal neurobehavioral functioning during the period of exposure.

There are a few studies that attempt to correlate maternal psychological attributes or experiences, including anxiety and stress perception, with fetal neurobehavior and longer-term outcomes in children. This interest has been sparked by evidence from animal models suggesting that chronic stress during pregnancy interferes with prenatal brain development in a manner that generates persistent and deleterious effects on postnatal development. However, to extrapolate these findings to assume that there must be similar effects on human fetuses may not be wise given the nature of how stress is conceptualized and measured.

In animal models, subjects are exposed to a series of experimental procedures that are controlled in terms of duration, frequency, and intensity. In contrast, human studies necessarily rely on measuring the elusive construct of psychological stress during pregnancy and then observing whether there are associations with child development years later. Maternal psychological distress before and after pregnancy are related, and there are well-known environmental influences of maternal distress on child rearing. Because what is measured in virtually all human studies of 'stress' during pregnancy is maternal affect and emotional responses to daily circumstances in women's lives, it makes it difficult to know with certainty that there is a causal association and that other factors, including genetic mechanisms, are not involved. Moreover, the handful of studies that have detected deleterious effects of maternal pregnancy distress on developmental outcomes have yielded inconsistent and unreplicated results, including evidence of a paradoxical response of 'accelerated' postnatal development in children whose mothers reported moderately high levels of anxiety and stress.

When child development research was in its infancy, the common perception was that actions of parents in general, and mothers in particular, influenced the child. An influential paper by Bell in the 1960s introduced the construct of an opposite direction of effects: that parental behavior is directly influenced by characteristics and behavior of the child. Similarly, prenatal studies of development have focused on how pregnant women affect the fetus. Recent evidence indicates that the maternal–fetal link is also bidirectional. Specifically, fetal motor activity in the second half of pregnancy stimulates episodic sympathetic surges in the maternal autonomic nervous system, even when women are unaware that the fetus has moved. Such maternal sympathetic activation by the fetus may serve as a signal function to the pregnant woman in preparation for the consuming demands of early child rearing. At the same time, pregnancy appears to result in maternal hyporesponsivity to environmental challenges; taken together these phenomena may serve to direct maternal resources away from less relevant environmental demands. As with postnatal maternal–child interaction, the best model for maternal–fetal interaction may be a transactional one, in which each influences the other in a dynamic cycle of reciprocity, but there is much to be learned in this regard.

Continuities from Fetus to Child

Investigation of normative development during gestation has been the focus of most of the research to date. The study of individual differences in fetal functioning and implications for predicting to postnatal development has been largely relegated to clinical applications. The progression from an age-based focus to interest in individual differences among fetuses parallels that observed in infant research. Do individual differences begin before birth? The presumption is that because there is wide variability in neurobehavioral development at birth, this range of individuality must begin prior to birth. There is good evidence that fetal neurobehaviors are relatively stable within individuals over time during gestation, thereby satisfying a primary requirement in their establishment as an individual difference. Unfortunately, there are not enough scientific investigations in which fetal neurobehavioral measures are examined in relation to child developmental or temperamental outcomes to be utterly conclusive. It is difficult to design such studies because the nature of the measures of specific domains of function as well as the methods needed to measure them are quite different in fetuses and children. However, those that have been undertaken reveal that there are basic continuities between fetus and child. These studies fall into two categories: those that attempt to document within-domain consistency between similar aspects of function, and those that investigate cross-domain predictiveness. The latter category presupposes that there is conservation of rank ordering across individuals from the fetal to infant periods on specific dimensions. Some degree of within-domain individual consistency spanning from the fetus to young child has been found for heart rate and variability, motor activity, and state control. This means that fetuses with faster heart rates have faster heart rates in childhood; more active fetuses tend to be more active toddlers; and fetuses

that spend more time in quiet sleep tend to spend more time in this state in infancy. Cross-domain predictions are based on the consideration that some fetal measures are markers for general nervous system development, and as such, should have predictive validity to later aspects of functioning that have similar neural underpinnings. These studies have focused on the associations between fetal neurobehavior and either subsequent infant temperament or developmental proficiency. There is some evidence that fetuses with greater heart rate variability and coupling between movements and heart rate show more mature developmental outcomes in the first few years of life, and there is a suggestion that fetal heart rate and motor activity predict infant irritability and attentional performance. The current state of knowledge regarding the genesis and measurability of stable individual differences during the prenatal period is based on modest, single study findings that await replication and extension. Nonetheless, there is both strong theoretical support as well as modest empirical support that the fetus is indeed the precursor to the child.

Conclusions

The origins of development begin during the fetal period. Recent technological advancements have opened a window to this period of ontogeny that has resulted in an expanding field of inquiry. Substantial information exists to support the developmental progression of a range of fetal neurobehaviors over the course of gestation. Less is known about the manner in which individual differences arise and are conserved after birth, and the ways in which characteristics of the maternal and intrauterine environments affect the fetus, and how the fetus may, in turn, affect these contributors to its own development. However, there is little doubt that the period before birth sets the stage for the entirety of human development.

See also: Auditory Development and Hearing Disorders; Birth Complications and Outcomes; Critical Periods; Habituation and Novelty; Newborn Behavior; Physical Growth; Premature Babies; Prenatal Care; Screening, Prenatal; Teratology.

Suggested Readings

Barker DJ (1998) *Mothers, Babies, and Health in Later Life.* New York, NY: Churchill Livingstone.
de Vries JI, Visser GHA, and Prechtl HFR (1982) The emergence of fetal behavior. I. Qualitative aspects. *Early Human Development* 7: 301–322.
DiPietro JA (2004) The role of prenatal maternal stress in child development. *Current Directions in Psychological Science* 13: 71–74.

DiPietro JA (2005) Neurobehavioral assessment before birth. *Mental Retardation and Developmental Disabilities Research Reviews* 11: 4–13.

Lecanuet JP and Schaal B (1996) Fetal sensory competencies. *European Journal of Obstetrics & Gynecology and Reproductive Biology* 68: 1–23.

Lecanuet JP, Fifer WP, Krasnegor NA, and Smotherman WP (eds.) (1995) *Fetal Development, a Psychobiological Perspective.* New Jersey: Lawrence Erlbaum Associates.

Moon CM and Fifer WP (2000) Evidence of transnatal auditory learning. *Journal of Perinatalogy* 20: S36–S43.

Moore KL and Persaud TV (1993) *The Developing Human: Clinically Oriented Embryology,* 5th edn. Philadelphia: W.B. Saunders Company.

Nijhuis JG, Prechtl HFR, Martin CB, and Bots RS (1982) Are there behavioural states in the human fetus? *Early Human Development* 6: 47–65.

Smotherman WP and Robinson SR The development of behavior before birth. *Developmental Psychology* 32: 425–434.

Sontag LW and Richards TW (1938) Studies in fetal behavior: I. Fetal heart rate as a behavioral indicator. *Monographs of the Society for Research in Child Development* 3(4 (Serial No. 17)): 1–67.

Preschool and Nursery School

H H Raikes, C Edwards and J Jones-Branch, University of Nebraska–Lincoln, Lincoln, NE, USA

Glossary

Asili nido – 'Safe nests', the Italian term for infant–toddler centers.

Barnehage – 'Children's gardens', care and education programs for children aged 0–3 years, in Norway.

Early childhood programs for children of age 3 years and under – Federal and state-supported center-based programs, private nursery schools, home visiting programs with a child development emphasis, out-of home-enrichment programs for children, and 0–3 programs that originated in countries other than the US.

Early Head Start – A variation of the federal Head Start program for children in poverty under the age 3 in over 700 US communities.

Ecole Maternelle Française (EMF) – Publicly supported French nursery schools serving about a third of French 2-year-olds.

Educare – High-quality 0–3 programs for children in poverty that blend funding from Head Start and other federal sources, states, localities and philanthropy, coordinated by the Bounce Learning Network.

Even Start – Parent–child literacy program.

Home visiting programs – Regular home visitor services offered in children's homes to parents and children for purposes of enhancing children's development. Examples of four programs are provided in this section.

Out-of-home enrichment programs – Educational programs for children under age 3 years that may also include instruction for parents. Several examples are included here.

Part C of the Individuals with Disabilities Education Act – A program that provides services for children under age 3 years with identified disabilities.

Introduction

This article provides descriptions of nursery education for children under the age of 3 years, including an overview of quality features for such programs, and descriptions of center-based, home visiting, out-of-home enrichment programs, programs for 0–3 year olds that are identified with other countries. It concludes with an overview of extant research on the effects of early childhood programs for 0–3 year olds.

Overview of Early Childhood Programs

Early Childhood Education (ECE) programs are highly prevalent in the US and in European countries, and are growing in emphasis in other parts of the world today. Children under age 3 years participate in group or formal educational experiences for a variety of reasons: (1) social and cognitive preparedness for preschool or formal schooling or enrichment; (2) remediation or intervention; (3) to learn specific skills deemed important by parents; or (4) for childcare in order for parents to work or pursue training. ECE for children age 3 years and under (sometimes referred to as nursery, crèche, or infant–toddler programs) is somewhat challenging to define as can be

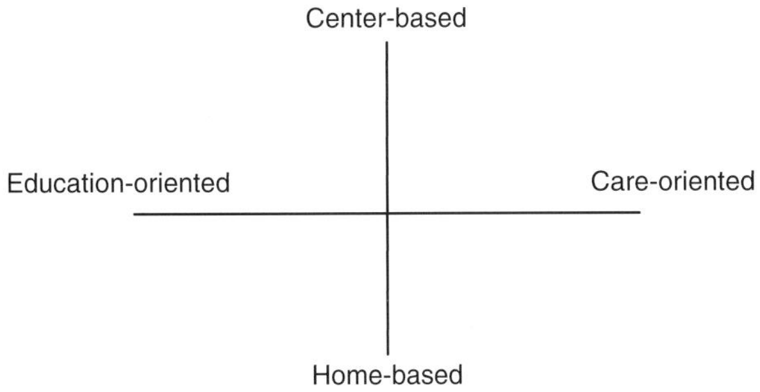

Center-based

|

Education-oriented ———————————— Care-oriented

|

Home-based

Figure 1 Care and education for children aged 0–3 years in the US – education and care, center-based and home-based.

seen in **Figure 1**. Programs appear to array along a horizontal continuum with those more focused on education at one end and those more focused on care on the other. Many European countries provide systems of publicly supported services for children under three explicitly integrate functions of support for working families and childhood education and socialization, for example, the *barnehage* ('children's gardens') of Norway and *asili nido* ('safe nests') of Italy.

In the US, increasingly, education and care functions are becoming blurred. This blurring seems to be occurring for a number of reasons. First, many mothers of infants and toddlers from all educational and income groups are now in the US labor force (US Department of Labor reported that 61% of mothers with children under age 3 years were in the labor force in 2000). Closely related, states are responding to the need for full-day childcare and market demands with efforts to promote higher standards in caregiving settings for all children. Second, there is increasing recognition of the importance of infant development, particularly infant brain development. The widespread awareness of the importance of stimulation, nutrition, and emotional footings during the age 0–3 years time period has led to increasingly more intentional approaches to care and education, particularly on the part of parents purchasing care and education for their infants, as well as to a renewed dedication to intensity and quality in early intervention settings for infants and toddlers, among policy and programmatic leaders. Thus, along a vertical axis, programs with the child's education as target (as opposed to those explicitly aiming at parents or parental self-sufficiency) range from those providing part or full-time (20–40 h per week) center-based services to children (on top) to those providing out-of-home shorter-term education-oriented programs (middle) to those providing in-home, child-oriented education. In this article we address the full range of both axes but minimize the caregiving functions of childcare that are addressed elsewhere in this encyclopedia. It is important to consider this full range of educational opportunities for children under age 3 years in the US, organized as it is to a large extent by the developmental needs of

very young children; for children over 3 years of age, formal educational opportunities are more consistently concentrated in center-based settings and are also more consistently accessible to children. We also include information about the most formal educational settings in several European countries.

This article is intended for early childhood professionals and potential infant–toddler professionals in the US as information that will help them examine and understand the various professional niches for working with this important age group. It is also intended to be useful to parents of infants seeking a statement about the state of the art in the US and in European countries of programs for infants and toddlers; it also outlines availability of educational programs for parents and children. In some states most of these programs are for infants whose parental circumstances put them at risk, but in other states, many educational programs are offered to all children, either for free or for a fee.

The article begins with an overview of characteristics associated with quality in early childhood programs for children under 3 years of age. We then turn to a review of center-based ECE programs that have an educational or intervention emphasis. These may include center-based Early Head Start programs, State Pre-Kindergarten programs that may include infants and toddlers, other intervention programs for disadvantaged children under age 3 years, Part C programs for 0–3-year-olds, and private nursery schools. Next, we reference out-of-home educational programs for infants and toddlers that are briefer in nature and, then, home visiting programs that are designed to provide educational opportunities for the child. Finally, we include reference to center-based programs in a number of European countries for children aged 0–3 years. For the most part, we do not include discussion of childcare, as that is the topic of another article in this series, and we do not reference home visiting programs that focus more explicitly on the parent or on self-sufficiency, more completely discussed elsewhere in this encyclopedia. We conclude with a section reporting research on programs for at-risk children aged 0–3 years.

Participation in Early Childhood 0–3 Programs in the US

It is difficult to know how many children under the age of 3 years participate in the types of nursery education programs we have identified, given the wide-ranging types of programs that have been included. Some 61% of mothers of infants and toddlers are in the labor force in the US and a majority of their children are cared for in out-of-home settings. The focus of this article is on educational settings for infants and toddlers, some of which overlap with child care. There were 63 000 children attending Early Head Start in 2004; 200 000 children under age 3 years enrolled in Part C programs in 2004; and an estimated 400 000 participate in home visiting programs annually. The number of children in enrichment nursery education and special programs is not known. Certainly, substantial numbers of infants and toddlers in the US are involved in formal educational settings, although more 3- and 4-year-olds are in such settings, as reported in the National Household Survey.

Features of Quality Early Childhood Programs for Children 0–3

A number of features have been identified as important within infant–toddler early education settings because they associate with positive outcomes for children: responsive relationships; low group sizes and ratios; emphasis on health, safety, and hygiene; developmental appropriateness of the educational program; and physical environment. These criteria apply to center-based settings but they are useful guides in other settings as well. We address each in turn.

The 'quality of interaction and relationship' between teachers/caregivers and children is critically important in ECE settings for children under age 3 years. Very young children are comforted and learn in the context of sensitive interaction and secure relationships; therefore, it is critical that teachers of infants and toddlers are sensitively and contingently responsive to children in group care. When an infant cries, a teacher should be there to meet the need; infants in a group setting should be rocked and held and responded to when they coo, babble, and say their first words. Many programs for infants and toddlers are organized so that children always have the same primary caregiver and, in some cases, so children keep the same teacher over the infant–toddler years. These practices enable the child to feel secure while away from home and to use the teacher as secure base for exploration and comfort while in the out-of-home setting. Studies have demonstrated that children under age 3 years form relationships with teachers/caregivers that are regarded as attachment relationships, that these relationships manifest in ways parallel to attachment relationships with parents – some secure and some avoidant or anxious – and that secure relationships with teachers and caregivers are associated with favorable social–emotional outcomes for children in the early childhood setting.

Small group sizes and low teacher–child ratios are important given the importance of responsive caregiving. Small groups – no more than six or eight children – enable the child to relate to a primary caregiver. Similarly, small groups of children per teacher (1:3 or 1:4) enable primary caregiving and intimate, responsive relations to form between teachers and children. Small, stable groups

of children also promote children's early peer friendships and their learning prosocial behaviors in ways that can be positively guided. Group sizes and ratios in center-based care and education programs and in licensed family child care are typically regulated.

Emphasis on health, hygiene, and safety is an important value in settings for infants and toddlers, and observers should note the presence of critical hygienic practices around diapering, feeding, napping, and illness. Teachers should follow strict cleaning and hand washing for themselves and children after diapering, before eating, and when using tissues. Rules for responses to illness within the program should be carefully proscribed and dutifully followed in order to minimize the transmission of illnesses in a group setting, a situation for which infants and toddlers are vulnerable, as they still may lack natural immunities to many diseases. Infants and toddlers in group settings have been found to have more upper respiratory infections than children cared for in home settings so health and hygiene practices are important for minimizing illness. Additionally, small group sizes, low ratios, and consistent teachers who have relationships with infants and toddlers contribute to safety practices that must be monitored carefully in settings with children so young. Studies of quality in group settings for infants and toddlers in the US frequently report that health, hygiene, and safety practices are suboptimal, so it is of great importance that these practices are monitored.

Using developmentally appropriate practices that stimulate children's learning in appropriate ways is also critical in group settings for children under age 3 years. Infants and toddlers learn in ways that are different from how older preschool age children learn. For example, for children under 12 months of age, learning is frequently in the sensory and motor mode and occurs in small 'bites' and at 'teachable moments' in the course of caregiving and play routines. For toddlers who are beginning to incorporate representation through language and play into their learning, it is important that environments be rich in language and opportunities for symbolic play. Studies of quality in group settings frequently find lower scores observed for the quality of the learning environment than for more interactive aspects of group settings (the teacher–child relationship), so it is important that the learning environment be given attention. Several curricula for organizing learning experiences for infants and toddlers in group settings have been developed, which we describe in the section on 'Private or specialized nursery schools for children aged 0–3 years'.

Finally, the physical environment for group settings for infants and toddlers is important. In order to facilitate developmentally appropriate exploration for children in this age range, the environment must be completely child proof (safe to an exploring infant or toddler in all aspects), incorporating features that both protect and stimulate children (e.g., low sectionals that partition older and younger children from one another, as appropriate, yet allow teachers to see all the children; ramps and high/low spaces for children to explore; low sinks, toilets, tables, and other surfaces accessible to small children; shelves that enable teachers to make available but also control use of materials and manipulatives; and opportunities for inside and outside play with an abundance of opportunities to explore natural materials such as sand and water). Furthermore, young children need extensive time in the out of doors to develop a love of nature, habits of vigorous activity, and the self-regulation that are promoted by outdoor play. In the US, Louis Torrelli, James Greenman, and Deb Curtis and Margie Carter offer expertise in designing spaces for groups of very young children.

A very good measure of the quality of infant–toddler center-based settings is the Infant Toddler Environment Rating Scale-Revised, developed at the well-known Frank Porter Graham Child Development Institute at the University of North Carolina – Chapel Hill. This measure assesses most of the items listed above and other features. A score of 5 or above on this measure is a good indicator that an environment is good quality; increasingly infant–toddler center-based programs participate in state Quality Rating Systems that give star or levels of ratings of program quality, often publicly available to consumers via state department web sites.

Center-Based Programs Providing Early Childhood Education to Children under 3 Years of Age

We focus here on the nursery/ECE settings of a more formal nature where some children are cared for or whose parents chose them for enrichment or remediation. These categories include (1) federal Early Head Start and federal/state Even Start programs; (2) state-sponsored Pre-Kindergarten programs; (3) Part C of the Individuals with Disabilities Education Act programs; (4) programs that blend Head Start, state and local funds such as Educare programs; and (5) private nursery schools for children aged 0–3 years in the US. Again, we do not discuss child care here; nor do we discuss a myriad of programs for 'parents' of children under age 3 years, such as teen parent programs, as our focus is on programs that directly target infants and toddlers, although many of the programs we reference here have substantial parenting components. Thus, this section does not include the numerous parent education programs and family support programs.

Early Head Start

Early Head Start programs offer federal Head Start services to children under age 3 years and their families. Head Start was authorized in 1965 but Early Head Start

came into being through the 1994 authorization of the Head Start Act. The blueprint for Early Head Start was created by the national Advisory Committee on Services to Families with Infants and Toddlers as national experts sought to infuse Early Head Start with best practices in prenatal to age 3 years services. Early Head Start programs are two-generation in nature (have services for both children and parents); 90% of all participations have incomes at the poverty level or lower. Services begin for the mother prenatally in order to promote health and psychological outcomes for the child. As noted, programs in the US today served about 63 000 low-income children ages 0–3 years in 2005 in over 700 US communities. The program is estimated to serve about 3% of the children who would be eligible for services. Early Head Start programs are organized around the Head Start Performance Standards and studies have documented that infant–toddler group programs are typically of high quality.

Early Head Start programs may be center based (offering part-day or, more typically, full-day center services for children with a minimum of two home visits a year for parents), home based (weekly home visits and monthly group socializations with groups of children) or a mixture (children receive a combination of center- and home-based services and/or children and parents may receive home visiting for a period of time, often the first year of life, and the children attend centers while parents continue to receive home visits).

The child development component in home visiting programs is emphasized; children as well as parents are expected to benefit from the services when they are delivered in the homes. Home visitors typically set goals with parents focused on children's development; toys and materials may be left for the child to use during the ensuing week, and child as well as parent service needs are discussed and planned for.

Each Early Head Start program serves about 75 children on average. The majority of programs are affiliated with three to five Head Start programs that typically serve much larger numbers of children. These programs are in urban as well as in rural areas, with rural areas somewhat more likely to deliver services through home visiting and urban areas through center-based services. In 2004, the race/ethnicity of children in the Early Head Start program was slightly under a third African American, under a third Hispanic, about a quarter white, with smaller proportions from other minority groups. Some Early Head Start programs are also offered on Native American reservations and in migrant communities.

Even Start

Federal Even Start Family Literacy was authorized in 1988 as the Improving America's Schools Act. Since 1992 it has been administered at the state level with authority to award subgrants delegated to states. The program's purposes as defined in the Improving America's Schools Act are "to help break the cycle of poverty and illiteracy by improving the educational opportunities of the nation's low-income families with children 0–7 by integrating early childhood education, adult illiteracy or adult basic education, and parenting education into a unified family literacy program." These programs may supplement or stand alone with other 0–3 programs serving low-income families.

State Sponsored Pre-Kindergarten Programs

While most state-sponsored pre-kindergarten programs serve children 3 years of age and even more typically 4-year-olds, a few offer center-based services to children aged 0–3 years (e.g., Nebraska). These programs typically supplement Early Head Start services by serving more children or by adding hours or days. Nebraska is one state that includes services for infants and toddlers among its pre-kindergarten, state-funded programs. About 18% of Nebraska children attending state-supported pre-kindergarten programs in 2004 were under age 3 years. In this state, priorities are given to children of teen parents, those of low birth weight, those in low-income families, and those not speaking English. Some of the infants and toddlers are served in center-based and some in home-based programs. Illinois sets aside 11% of its state pre-kindergarten funds for serving infants and toddlers.

Part C Programs

Families of young children with disabilities are eligible for early intervention services as mandated by Part C of the Individuals with Disabilities Education Act. As reported in a nationally representative sample commissioned by the US Department of Education, conducted by SRI, International of Menlo Park, CA, and referred to as the NEILS study, about 200 000 children (or 1.8% of all children aged 0–3 years) were enrolled in Part C programs. Higher percentages of children at later ages have identified disabilities. These children have individualized family service plans (IFSPs). Some are enrolled in center-based services, others receive home-based services and others, individualized referrals. In all cases, the service plan is designed to address the educational and other needs of the young child and his/her family.

The NEILS study, commissioned by the US Department of Education, reported that the average age at which families reported a concern about their child was 7.4 months. A diagnosis was made, on average, 1.4 months later, and the child was referred for early intervention an average of 5.2 months after the diagnosis, with the IFSP being developed 1.7 months later or at an average age of 15.7 months. This study reported that most families were very positive about their entry into early intervention programs. They reported discussing their concerns with a medical professional and finding that person helpful. Families reported relative ease in accessing services, felt that services were related to their perceived needs, rated positively the professionals working in early intervention, and felt that they had a role in making key decisions about child and family goals. A small percentage of families experienced significant delays in getting services, wanted more involvement in service planning, or felt that services were inadequate. Minority families, families with limited income, and families with less-educated mothers were more likely to report negative experiences.

Educare Programs, Bounce Learning Network

Educare programs blend Head Start, other federal, state, local and private philanthropy funds to offer center-based services that begin before children's first birthday (in some sites, doula services begin before birth). These programs offer highest-quality 0–5 services for children to families at greatest risk. The Bounce Learning Network, operated by the Ounce of Prevention of Chicago, IL, is the organizational framework for Educare programs for underserved, low-income infants and toddlers in a number of cities; including Omaha, NE, Milwaukee, WI, Chicago, IL, Tulsa, OK, Kansas City, KS, and Denver, CO. New programs are being added to this network. The programs offer intensive high, quality full-day, full-year, center-based programs in outstanding facilities designed to optimize environmental opportunities. The Educare high bar for quality is maintained by emphasizing core features – employing teachers with bachelor's degrees, employing master teachers, emphasizing children's literacy, social–emotional development and opportunities for expression through the arts, and using evidence-based practices. Facilities are linked to public schools in each community.

Private or Specialized Nursery Schools for Children aged 0–3 years, Including Montessori

A number of private schools offer education experiences for children under age 3 years, usually a somewhat small group and often in connection with a larger program offered for older children. These may or may not be indistinguishable from childcare programs; many are full-day programs. These may include private church-related programs, privately or collectively owned programs, laboratory schools on university campuses, and specialized programs such as Montessori schools. Many offer services for children aged 0–3 years but may also include a 3–5 (or beyond) emphasis.

Montessori schools, following the philosophy of the Italian educator, Dr. Maria Montessori, typically include older children but may begin serving children below a year of age. Some begin when children are able to walk, around 15 months; when children are 18 months of age or at age 2 or 2.5 years. These programs share their founder's view of children as competent beings and emphasize the importance of observation of the child interacting with his environment as the basis for ongoing curriculum development, highlight sensitive periods of development during which a child's mind is particularly open to learning specific skills or knowledge, and a belief in the 'absorbent mind', the limitless motivation of the young child to achieve competence over his or her environment and to perfect his or her skills and understandings as they occur within each sensitive period, and self-correcting 'auto-didactic' materials. Parents may notice that the environments and materials in an infant/toddler Montessori program differ from what they see in other center-based programs for infants and toddlers. For example, children may sleep on futons vs. cribs, and engage in practical life and sensory experiences, and the environment is organized to be organizing and supportive of autonomy, yet calm and not overstimulating. Many are surprised at the purposeful and independent work that even very young children are able to accomplish in Montessori settings.

Curricula and Specialized Programs that Can be Embedded into Child Care, Nursery Programs or in the Home

A number of specialized approaches and curricula exist that may be imbedded within nursery, childcare, or intervention programs. Some of these curricula may be purchased or subscribed to by parents as well. While the total number of infant curricula is truly extensive and covers a wide range of quality and developmental appropriateness, we present several here that may be useful for professionals and, in some cases, parents to access. While the curricula and approaches represent some of the most frequently used by programs and parents, others are available.

The 'Active Learning' Series from the Frank Porter Graham Child Development Institute, published by the Pearson Learning Group, devotes a volume to each specific age group – infants, ones, twos, threes (and older). Each volume contains over 300 clearly formatted activities intended for use in home visiting programs or center-based early care and education programs.

'Beautiful Beginnings' offers a curriculum of developmental experiences for children ages 0 through 36 months of age. This easy to use curriculum, built around children's strengths in multiple areas of development, is used in centers, family childcare, home visiting programs, and by parents.

'The Creative Curriculum' series, developed by Teaching Strategies, Inc., includes specific resources for curriculum development for infants and toddlers (as well

as for preschool-age children, school-age children, and children in family childcare). This curriculum focuses on how children learn, what children learn, the parent's role, the teacher's or provider's role, and the physical environment.

'Hawaii Early Learning Profile HELP' (0–3 year olds) is a center-based curriculum for children from birth through age 3. It is a curriculum-based assessment that provides play-based activities and intervention strategies for skills in six developmental domains. It can be used by physical, speech, and occupational therapists; early childhood educators; infant specialists; psychologists; social workers; and nurses.

'High/Scope'–the High/Scope educational approach is a set of guiding principles and practices that adults follow as they work with and care for infants/toddlers (as well as for preschoolers, and elementary, and adolescent students). Children in High/Scope settings are engaged in a consistent routine that includes time for children to plan, carry out, and reflect on their own learning activities as well as time to engage in small- and large-group activities.

'Transdisciplinary play-based assessment and transdisciplinary play-based intervention' was designed by Toni Linder offers a practical way to assess children's learning styles, interaction patterns in four areas of development. This system for children infancy through age 6 years is particularly helpful for developing intervention plans in a parent and teacher team.

Home Visiting Programs

Home visiting programs predominantly serve families with children aged 0–3 years, with some beginning during pregnancy and a few continuing services until children are age 5 years. According to Deanna Gomby, who has written periodic reviews of home visiting in the US, approximately 400 000 families with young children participate in the six largest home visiting programs in the US. These programs share the intention of maximizing outcomes for young children, although the role of the home visitor may vary. For example, the home visitor may focus more on the parent in some programs, on the parent–child relationship in others or work directly with the child in still others. Home visiting programs vary also by the qualifications of the home visitor; some employ professional nurses while others build the program around paraprofessionals, frequently from the neighborhoods of families being visited. Four of the five largest home visiting programs in the US that include services to parents with infants and toddlers are briefly described. (The fifth of these largest programs is Early Head Start which was described above.) (1) Healthy Families America; (2) The Nurse–Family Partnership; (3) Parents as Teachers, and (4) The Parent–Child Home Program. Other home visiting programs with a child development emphasis may be sponsored specifically by local communities, states, or organizations.

Healthy Families America

Healthy Families America home visiting programs exist in 430 communities within the US with the specific purpose to promote positive parenting and prevent child abuse among families at risk who have children under the age of 5. Families receive weekly home visits initially, diminishing to once a quarter for older children. Home visitors include both paraprofessionals and those with bachelors' degrees.

Nurse–Family Partnership

The Nurse–Family Partnership serves 250 communities nationally. Public health nurse visitations begin before birth and continue through the child's second birthday, initially weekly and fading to monthly. This program serves low-income, first time mothers and seeks to enhance child development by improving pregnancy outcomes, health and economic self-sufficiency.

Parents as Teachers

Parents as Teachers is the largest home visiting program serving 3000 sites nationally as well as providing services in at least six other countries. Parents as Teachers visits begin before birth and continue through the child's third birthday, but some may continue longer. This program seeks to give children a firm foundation for school success by empowering parents, increasing parent competence and confidence, and by developing home–school community partnerships. Parents as Teachers programs may be targeted for children at risk, but in some communities it is universally available to all parents (http://www.parentsasteachers.org).

Parent–Child Home

Parent–Child Home programs serves 137 sites nationally as well as in the Netherlands and Bermuda, with two visits a week beginning when children are 2 years of age and continuing until they are 4 years old. Families targeted are low-income, as well as parents of low education, teen parents, homeless parents, and parents who do not speak the native language. This program emphasizes the development of language and literacy skills and parents' ability to promote these. Books and materials are provided for the parents to use with their children (http://www.parent-child.org).

Out-Of-Home Enrichment Programs

There are many out-of-home enrichment experiences available for young children and their families. An out-of-home enrichment experience will refer to any experience that occurs outside of the home setting and is targeted for children ages 0–3. Formal experiences refer to any program that has an organized curriculum and is being offered outside of the child's home environment by a professional trained in the content area. A fee may be required along with parent participation for the age category of 0–3. Informal experiences refer to opportunities available to children and families who do not have a curriculum, but still offer benefits to the child's development. There may be fees associated with some of these experiences (**Table 1**).

Center-Based Programs for Children 0–3 in European Countries

We now leave the US and consider formal care and education available in selected European countries. Here we focus on full-time and part-time education and care. The early education picture for children under 3 looks very different in Europe vs. the US, for two key reasons. First, in the European nations – indeed in most industrial nations other than the US – new mothers (and sometimes even new fathers) are entitled to paid parental leave for at least several months and sometimes up to a full year or more. In the Organization for Economic Cooperation and Development (OECD), for example, the average period of paid parental leave for the 30 members (excluding the US) is 10 months, with the pay ranging from a basic daily stipend to 90% of regular salary. Thus, infants with working parents in Western Europe tend to be cared for at home by a parent for the first year of life. During the second year, however, many of the infants are placed in care as the mothers go back to work. Second, in Europe, many nations (often the very same ones with the most generous parental leaves) provide a government-subsidized system of education and care for children under 3. In some cases, these infant–toddler services are separated off into a more care-oriented stratum of services running parallel to a more educationally oriented system for children aged 3–5. Yet, across Europe, trends are seen toward expanding the supply and quality of infant–toddler services as part of an integration of care and education under education auspice. These trends are especially strong in France, Italy, and the Scandinavian countries. According to Michael Lamb and colleagues, in France, for example, about 20% of children aged 0–2 years old attend publicly supported centers, and this percentage rises to 100% for children aged 3. By age 3, almost 100% children not only in France but also in Italy and Belgium

Table 1 Examples of out-of-home enrichment experiences for infants and toddles

Formal experiences	Program	Offerings	Website
Music	**Kindermusik** Begin in the 1970s in the US from Germany. It is international, with over 5000 licensed educators. The curriculum is research based.	Through shared experiences, parents learn more about music and their children's abilities as the children learn how to integrate fun with musical play.	http://www.kindermusik.com
	Gymboree Began in 1976. Currently the program has over 500 franchises in 26 countries. The curriculum is research based.	Play-based developmentally appropriate learning experiences for parents and children.	http://www.gymboreeclasses.com
Swimming*	*YMCA/YWCA American Red Cross*	Swimming lessons from birth with certified educators.	http://ymca.com http://ywca.com http://www.redcross.org
	Club Swim Private schools that specialize in infant/toddler swimming lessons	Comprehensive website for aquatic enthusiasts.	http://www.clubswim.com

Informal experiences	Offerings		Where to find local information
Play dates/groups	Children and parents who gather on a regular basis. Parents either take-turns leading the play session or the group of parents will hire a person to provide activities. A main goal of these gatherings is for children and parents to socialize with one another.		Local Chamber of Commerce
Storytelling/reading	Children and parents meet with a storyteller or reader on a regular basis. The stories told and books read are developmentally targeted for children within the age range to which they are offered.		Local libraries or bookstores such as: Borders (www.borders.com) or Barnes and Noble (www.barnesandnoble.com)
Children's museums	Displays are interactive and are designed to provoke and stimulate children's development in the areas of social, physical, language, and cognitive development.		Local Chamber of Commerce
Parks	Parks offer children the opportunity to play with peers similar in age while challenging them with their cognitive and physical abilities through problem-solving and climbing or walking on structures.		Local Chamber of Commerce or The City Parks and Recreation Department

A cautionary note: The American Academy of Pediatrics (http://aap.org) recommends that children not be expected to have formalized swimming training before the age of 4 years, stating that developmentally children are not ready to swim alone before this time and should always have a parent within 'touch' length (http://aappolicy.aappublications.org/cgi/content/full/pediatrics;105/4/868). Any training prior to age of 4 years should be thought of as water safety and not as swimming readiness courses. The leading cause of death in children ages 1–2 years is accidental drowning.

participate in educationally oriented center-based programs (both public and private), as do at least two-thirds of 0–2-year-olds in Iceland, Spain, Denmark, Norway, Hungary, and Sweden.

A sketch of the educational policies and national guidelines of the European countries with the highest percentages of 0–2s in publicly supported care suggests that a strong educational mission is coming to prevail. For example, parents in France have a range of different kinds of programs for their children under 6, with the most educationally oriented being the *Ecole Maternelle Francaise* (EMF) (French nursery school system). The EMF is a publicly supported system that in 1995 served about 34% of 2-year-olds and 100% of children aged 3–5, with the goals of compensating for cultural disadvantages, preventing developmental delays, preventing later school failure, and equalizing educational opportunities. The children,

aged 2–6, are typically grouped by age in classes that are somewhat large by American standards but with consistent quality supported by trained professional teachers who have the same status, salary, duties, and training as primary school teachers. The French terms for child care outside the home are *programmes d'accueil* ('programs of welcoming') and *programmes d'eveil* ('programs of awakening'). Thus, the mission of the public system is to invite children into French society and arouse their capacities for learning and development. A Child Care Study Panel of the French American Foundation suggested that seven principles animate the French childcare system. Most of the principles (e.g., integrated focus on care and education, skilled staff, preventive healthcare, quality incentives, maternity leave, and parental choice) overlap with American values and approaches, but one (beauty) seems quite distinctive from the perspective of the US, where esthetics are less emphasized. As authors Richardson and Marx, from the French-American connection have noted, "The resources and beauty invested in buildings and equipment for children celebrate and express children's value to society. Well-designed space and furnishings are integral to program quality."

In Italy, likewise, certain regions and localities have become recognized worldwide for their high-quality public early childhood systems serving children under age 3 years and their families, including children with disabilities. The *asili nido* ('safe nests', the Italian term for infant–toddler centers) developed as a result of a national law passed in 1971 and are intended to set up a system for children under 3 years of age parallel in some ways to the Italian publicly-supported *scuole del infanzia* for children aged 3–6 years. The *asili nido* are full-day programs that are open 10–11 months a year, usually serving 30–60 children divided into three age groups with two or more teachers for each age group. Their mission blends family service and education, resulting in a strong trend away from a custodial approach to infant–toddler care to a developmental orientation, and this has created a rising trend in Italian parents across all social classes to appreciate the programs as a developmental benefit and source of pleasure for children, not primarily as a convenience or service for working parents. Certain cities, particularly in Northern and Central Italy, such as Reggio Emilia, Pistoia, Milan, and San Miniato, have become known for their leadership in innovating and implementing strategies that lead to excellent education. All of these strategies place a focus on process rather than products or outcomes.

- System-wide and center-wide goals are decided upon through discussion and dialog among stakeholder groups of parents, teachers, and administrators.
- Professional development and teacher education are based on activities of ongoing observation and reflection.
- Families are brought in and involved in multiple ways that are particular to each city and region. Families are regarded as partners rather than consumers.
- Sense of group belonging life is the focus of the infant–toddler center experience for children and parents and the impetus for learning, well-being, and lasting relationships.
- Continuity and closeness of social relationships is promoted by strategies such as the *inserimento* (delicate process of transition into the center), *diario* (memory book given at the end), pedagogical documentation; teacher–child continuity over several years; and welcoming, soft, and beautiful physical environments.

Each of the Scandinavian countries, finally, has its own unique array of programs – public and private, part-day and full-day, home and center based – serving its children under age 3 years, yet certain generalizations seem to hold true across this whole region which shares the Nordic history, culture, and languages. The Scandinavian nations in general feature generous social welfare provisions that support and promote women's political and economic labor force participation. Programs serving infants and toddlers usually favor a mixed-age or 'family' grouping in order to promote the child's emotional security and continuity with the same adults and peers over time. Furthermore, education and care are part of an integrated philosophy that traces back to the progressive philosophies of Froebel, Pestalozzi, and Montessori but that has been adapted to the Nordic emphasis on free play, homelike environments, and active daily engagement with nature and the outdoors. Self-initiated free play is considered essential for children's development and vital for the child's well-being and development. Children are dressed in warm snuggly clothes and sent outside to play avidly for hours in challenging, exciting playgrounds or to enjoy regular excursions to forests and parks. Children's rights are anchored in legislation to a greater extent in the Scandinavian countries than in many other places; for example, corporal punishment (even by parents) is prohibited in Sweden and Norway, and children of divorce must be allowed access to both parents in Finland.

Findings from Research: Intervention Program Effects on Disadvantaged Infants and Toddlers

Societies differ somewhat in their reasons for supporting infant–toddler nursery education. As noted above, many European countries may offer 0–3 programs for both care and educational purposes. In the US, as **Figure 1** shows, programs may be more educational or more care oriented in their purpose. As noted, in the US, a number of programs are designed to create opportunities for children at risk. These programs often have the explicit purpose to improve developmental outcomes and some have conducted rigorous research, comparing children who received the 0–3 service with eligible children who did not receive the service. In the next section, we provide findings from some of the best known of these studies to illustrate the positive advantage that has been attributed to educational opportunities for infants and toddlers among children at risk. There are three types of programs providing evidence about program practices and infants and toddlers: (1) Evidence of positive program effects from programs that are no longer in service; for example, demonstration programs designed to determine if positive outcomes were possible or likely under specific intervention conditions. (2) Other programs contributing to the evidence base (such as Nurse Family Partnerships, Early Head Start that have already been described) that are in operation today. (3) Finally, newer programs (e.g., national home visiting programs, Educare programs) are incorporating data into their regular practices using findings for continuous program improvement. Findings from the first two groups are presented; the work represented by the third group is more recent, typically generated for internal and local use and thus is not widely available.

The Carolina Abecedarian Program

Among the demonstration center-based programs for infants and toddlers, the best known is the Abecedarian project, which was carried out in North Carolina beginning in the early 1970s. The first-born children of African American single teen mothers were randomly assigned to receive the experimental Abecedarian full-day, full-year, high-quality center-based services from before they were a year old until they entered kindergarten. A group of 111 children were enrolled into the study. Children in the control group who did not receive the educational Abecedarian program did receive health, nutrition and supportive social services that Abecedarian children received. When children were 3 years of age, program children had intelligence quotient (IQ) scores a full standard deviation larger than those of the control group (101 vs. 84 for the control group). Abecedarian children were followed into adulthood and at each assessment point, they were developing significantly better than the control group. Although Abecedarian was an expensive program to implement (5 years of full-time care and education), cost–benefit analyses show $4 returned for every dollar invested because Abecedarian children were less likely to need special education, were more likely to graduate from high school and to have greater adult earnings.

Infant Health and Development Program

Another well-known study assessing intervention effects and beginning in infancywas the Infant Health and Development project (known as IHDP), carried out in eight communities. It was designed to test whether an Abededarian-like Program could be effective for children at risk due to low birth weight. This program featured home visits to mothers and children until children were 12 months of age and then full-time center-based care until children were 36 months of age.

Like Abecedarian, IHDP showed positive impacts on program children when children were still toddlers that were apparent in subsequent follow-up periods. The children were followed up at age 18 and among the heaviest low-birth weight group, positive program effects were still detectable.

Early Head Start Research and Evaluation Project

The Early Head Start Research and Evaluation project (the Early Head Start program was described earlier) randomly assigned 3001 children and families to program and control group within 17 of the program communities around the country. When the program ended, program children had significantly better cognitive, language, and social emotional development than control group children. Effect sizes were particularly large for African American children and children who had enrolled during pregnancy, those in families at a medium level of demographic risk, and those enrolled in mixed approach programs featuring center-based and home visiting services.

Children were followed up at age 5 years and a number of the positive effects were sustained particularly social emotional and approaches toward learning outcomes, as well as outcomes showing that parents were offering children more stimulation for learning and demonstrated fewer depressive symptoms.

Nurse Home Visiting

Multiple studies (carried out in Elmira, NY, Memphis, TN, and Denver, CO) have found that children and parents who participated in Nurse Home Visiting programs (Nurse Home Visiting serves families beginning before birth and continuing until 2 years of age) demonstrated positive outcomes attributed to the program. In this program a public health nurse visits enrolled monthly during the prenatal period and continues to meet with them until children are age 2 years. During this period the nurses provide health, development and parenting information and support for the parents. Across most programs, parents had fewer child abuse infractions (Elmira) and children had fewer childhood injuries (Elmira, Memphis) and other positive outcomes. Today, several states in the US have adopted the Nurse Home Visiting model.

Summary

These studies taken together illustrate that intensive programs for infants and toddlers who are at risk due to poverty and for other reasons are beneficial to the children, with benefits lasting into school and beyond.

Conclusions

In all, many children in the US (and in European countries as well) under the age of 3 years are enrolled in early nursery education. These programs array along continua from center-based to home-based and whether primarily for purposes of care or for purposes of enrichment. Programs may be primarily full-time, around 40 h a week or only be for an hour or so a week (e.g., enrichment programs and home visiting programs with a child emphasis). In the US, many of these programs target children in low-income households because intervention is believed to be of compensatory value for the ill effects of poverty and other risk factors, although only a small percentage of children who qualify for such programs are actually served. In all, many children at all income levels are likely to encounter 0–3 programs. Despite model programs, rates of participation are much lower than for children at age 3 and 4 years because of substantially lower investments in 0–3 programs by state and federal government.

See also: Child and Day Care, Effects of; Family Support, International Trends; Head Start; Friends and Peers; Literacy; Maternal and Paternal Employment, Effects of; School Readiness; Special Education.

Suggested Readings

Bailey DB, Hebbeler K, Scarborough A, and Spiker D (2004) First experiences with early intervention: A national perspective. *Pediatrics* 113–114: 882–896.
Cochran M (1993) *International Handbook of Child Care Policies and Programs.* Westport, CT: Greenwood Press.
Committee on Sports Medicine and Fitness and Committee on Injury and Poison Prevention (2000) Swimming Programs for Infants and Toddlers. *Pediatrics* 105(4): 868–870.
Edwards CP and Raikes H (2002) Extending the dance: Relationship-based approaches to infant–toddler care and education. *Young Children* 57(4): 10–17.
Gandini L and Edwards CP (2001) *Bambini: The Italian Approach to Infant/Toddler Care.* New York: Teachers College Press.
Kamerman, SB (2001) Early childhood education and care: International perspectives. Testimony prepared for the United States Senate Committee on Health, Labor, and Pensions, March 27, 2001.
Lamb ME and Ahnert L (2006) Nonparental child care: Context, concepts, correlates, and consequences. In: Renninger KA and Lerner RM (eds.) *Handbook of Child Psychology, Vol. 4: Child Psychology in Practice*, pp. 950–1016. New York: Wiley.
Richardson G and Marx E (1989) *A Welcome for Every Children: How France Achieves Quality in Child Care: Practical Ideas for the United States.* New York: French-American Foundation.
Watt N, Ayoub C, Bradley RH, Puma JE, and LeBoeuf WA (2006) *The Crisis in Youth Mental Health: Early Intervention Programs and Policies.* Westport, CN: Praeger.

Relevant Websites

http://www.fpg.unc.edu – Active Learning Series, FPG Child Development Institute, The University of North Carolina at Chapel Hill.
http://www2.acf.dhhs.gov – Administration for Children and Families, Department of Health and Human Services.
http://aap.org – American Academy of Pediatrics.
http://www.amshq.org – American Montessori Society.
http://www.redcross.org – American Red Cross.
http://www.brookespublishing.com – Brookes Publishing, Co.
http://www.clubswim.com – Club Swim, Inc.
http://www.gymboreeclasses.com – Gymboree, Gym-Mark, Inc.
http://www.healthyfamiliesamerica.org – Healthy Families America, PCA America.
http://www.highscope.org – High/Scope Educational Research Foundation.
http://www.kindermusik.com – Kindermusik International, Inc.
http://www.nextdoormil.org – Next Door Foundation.
http://www.nursefamilypartnership.org – Nurse-Family Partnership Program.
http://www.ounceofprevention.org – Ounce of Prevention Fund.
http://www.parentsasteachers.org – Parents as Teachers National Center, Inc.
http://www.teachingstrategies.com – Teaching Strategies, Inc.
http://www.educareomaha.com – The Educare Center of Omaha.
http://www.parent-child.org – The Parent-Child Home Program, Inc.
http://www.vort.com – VORT Corporation.
http://ymca.com – YMCA, Young Men's Christian Association.
http://ywca.com – YWCA, Young Women's Christian Association.

Preverbal Development and Speech Perception

R Panneton, Virginia Tech, Blacksburg, VA, USA
M McIlreavy, University of Georgia, Athens, GA, USA
N Bhullar, Widener University, Chester, PA, USA

Glossary

Bootstrapping – The ability of infants and children to use their conceptual knowledge in one domain (e.g., syntax) to create new understanding in a second domain (e.g., word meaning).
Categorical perception – The ability to detect a change in a given speech sound along a continuum; not gradual changes but in instances of discrete categories.

Iambic pattern – A weak–strong pattern for multisyllabic words in which primary linguistic stress does not occur on the first syllable (e.g., in English, sa-lute).
Perceptual attunement – The process by which infants initially show broader, less-constrained acuity in discriminating between various elements, but with more experience, maintain discrimination of some contrasts but not others.

Phoneme – A basic sound unit of a spoken language. Each unit consists of a distinctive sound that comprises a given language.

Phonology – The branch of linguistics that focuses on the sound systems of different languages.

Prosody – The intonation, rhythm, and stress in speech. Also known as suprasegmental because these features are not limited to single sounds but extend over syllables, words, or phrases.

Statistical learning – An approach to understanding language in terms of identifying speech sounds that have high probabilities of occurring together.

Stress timed language – A language class in which there are stressed syllables appearing at a roughly constant rate and where nonstressed syllables are shortened.

Trochaic pattern – A strong-weak pattern for multisyllabic words in which primary linguistic stress occurs on the first syllable (e.g., in English, sís-ter).

Voice-onset-time (VOT) – Refers to the length of time that passes between the beginning of vibrations of the vocal cord and the release of a consonant.

Introduction

During the first year after birth, most humans are continuously embedded in a social milieu within which they acquire information about people and objects, emotions and expectations, causes and consequences. Along with growing social awareness and knowledge, infants begin to understand and produce gestures in their native language system (vocal and manual) that convey their perceptions, feelings, and intentions, as well as those of their social partners. Often, when we think about language acquisition, we focus primarily on word learning. For hearing infants, it involves much more than this, including the perception and production of individual sounds, combinations of sounds, intonations, stress patterns, orderings of units (words, phrases, sentences), and accents. Language also involves movement in the face (e.g., lips and mouths), body posture, and interpersonal routines.

As complicated as this may seem, most toddlers are making requests, naming objects, identifying people, and beckoning attention by the age of 18 months. Without a doubt, infants listen to and learn from the communication that is directed to them. According to an influential model by developmentalist Anne Fernald, vocal communication

between caregivers and infants serves development in the preverbal period in three ways: (1) speech captures and maintains infants' attention to others; (2) speech conveys emotion to the infant, not only about the speaker's feelings, but also about the speaker's interpretations of the infant's feelings, helping to regulate emotional experiences; and (3) speech provides lexical/linguistic information necessary for native language learning. Importantly, all of these functions continuously influence infants and children, although certain milestones within each function may be age-related (e.g., infants may be more sensitive to some aspects of vocal emotion during early as opposed to later infancy).

The aim of this article is to characterize the functions listed above via the existing literature on language-related accomplishments that take place for many infants in their first postnatal year, with an eye on the processes that nurture and shape language development. To do so, we will first briefly consider how developmental psychologists are able to ascertain infants' understanding of language when they are not yet producing it, and when infants appear to be sensitive to language-relevant information. Next, we will discuss language learning during infancy from two perspectives: from a social/emotional view that describes the richness of the interactive framework within which almost all early language learning takes place; from a perceptual/biological view that describes the various components of language which infants can and do perceive in the course of learning how to communicate, and how the biology of infants is becoming organized and specialized in ways that promote language processing. Both of these perspectives have generated a considerable amount of research, and contribute in important ways to the ultimate organization and structure of children's emerging communicative competencies. We will also consider aspects of preverbal development that highlight the importance of ecology in considering just how infants learn language in their everyday environments (outside of ideal laboratory settings) but are not yet well understood, and in need of future research attention.

How Do We Study Language Perception in a Nonverbal Infant?

It is easy to understand why the topic of language learning in infants has garnered so much attention and inquiry from developmentalists. Almost all infants learn language and are trying to actively communicate with others by the end of the first postnatal year (**Figure 1**).

But ironically, it is difficult to go about studying language learning when our primary subjects do not yet use it! Developmental researchers have dealt with this by devising interesting techniques that capitalize on several aspects of infants' rapidly improving perceptuomotor skills. For example, as infants get older (usually by 4 months of age), they become proficient at controlling their own head movement, and can independently (**Figure 2**) turn to the left and to the right. One popular task used

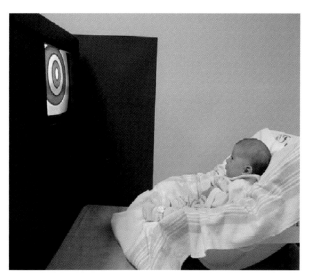

Figure 1 Photograph of a 1-month-old infant in a speech preference procedure. Whenever the infant looks at the colored target, a speech sample begins to play, for the duration of the look that initiated that particular trial. From the Infant Perception Laboratory, Department of Psychology, Virginia Tech.

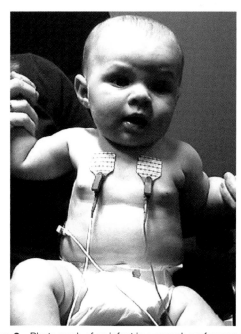

Figure 2 Photograph of an infant in a speech preference study who has been readied for the recording of heart rate (HR) activity. Two pediatric electrodes are attached to the infant's chest (above the breast bone) and a third is attached to the infant's lower right side (this electrode acts as a reference). The infant's HR activity is then recorded online during the procedure, and is event-marked so that it is possible to examine changes in HR activity during each experimental trial. From the Infant Perception Laboratory, Department of Psychology, Virginia Tech.

in language perception research takes advantage of this skill by allowing infants to hear certain words when they turn to their right (e.g., native language words) compared to other kinds of words on their left (e.g., foreign language words). In this particular task, we would conclude that infants recognize and prefer their native language if they turned their heads more often to the right (we would also test more infants with these words on their left to make sure there was no turning bias). There are quite a few different kinds of behavioral techniques that are used to ask questions about infant language processing, and capitalize on (**Figure 3**) different behavioral competencies. However, a full presentation of these methods is beyond the scope of this article. Thus, we summarize the most commonly used behavioral tasks for studying language perception during infancy in **Table 1**.

In addition to the clever behavioral methods that researchers have developed for the purpose of understanding preverbal development, this field of study has also greatly benefited from advances in a variety of psychophysiological techniques. Efforts to adapt brain-relevant recording procedures for use with infants and young children, such as scalp electroencephalography (EEG), magnetic resonance imaging (MRI), and optical topography (OT), have led to a greater understanding of neural structure and function (**Figure 4**) underlying language development. A sample of such neuropsychological methods are summarized in **Table 2**, and we will integrate findings from this literature with those from behavioral studies as we present some of the major findings from research on preverbal development. In doing so, it is important to acknowledge that the infant brain is not simply a smaller version of that found in the adult. Studies on the organization of adults' nervous systems clearly show that certain areas of the brain tend to be specialized for language (e.g., left temporal

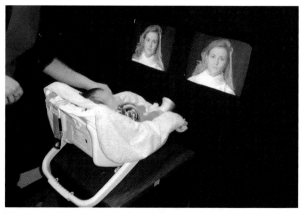

Figure 3 Picture of an infant in the two-choice preference procedure. When the infant looks at the monitor on the right, one speech stream will play. When the infant looks to the left, a different speech stream will play. Preferences can be discerned by calculating the magnitude of looking in each direction. Reprinted with permission from Dr. Janet Werker's website: http://infantstudies.psych.ubc.ca/meth_two.html.

Table 1 Current behavioral methodologies for studying infants' language perception

Testing method	Examples of primary tasks	Dependent measure
Habituation	Infant is presented with a sound (e.g., the phoneme /ba/) repeatedly and then is tested with the familiar sound and a novel sound (e.g., /pa/)	If infant attends more to novel than to familiar sound.
Preference	Infant is presented with a visual display accompanied by one sound (e.g., native language) then by the same display accompanied by a second sound (e.g., foreign language); sounds stay on as long as infant looks at the display	If infant looks longer at the visual display when one of the two sounds is available.
Conditioned head turn	Infant is presented with a continuously repeating background sound (/ba/) which occasionally switches to a novel sound (/pa/); when infant looks in the direction of the sound that changes, reinforcement is delivered	If infant turns head to the side whenever sound changes compared to when there is no change.
Recognition/ matching	Infant is presented with two side x side visual displays of a speaking head and hears a centrally located sound-track that corresponds to one of the displays	If infant looks longer to the side that corresponds to the sound-track.
Segmentation	Infant is presented with a stream of acoustic input (e.g., phonemes, words, sentences) and then tested in a head-turn task with two different sound types (familiar on one side; novel on the other).	If the infants looks more the side that produces the familiar (or sometimes novel) stream of sounds.
Word/object pairing	Infant is repeatedly shown object A paired with word A, and a object B paired with word B. During test the infants sees+hears object A + word A, but also sees+hears a recombination (object A + word B).	If the infant attends longer on the 'switch' trial (object A + word B) than on the familiar trial.

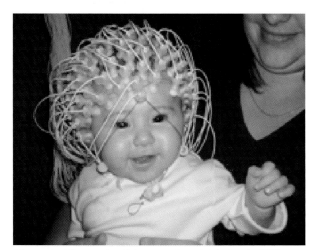

Figure 4 Picture of an infant wearing a high-density EEG cap for scalp recordings of brain activation patterns. Reprinted with permission from Dr. Laurel Trainor's website: http://www. psychology.mcmaster.ca/ljt/.

cortex), and that when such areas are compromised through disease or injury, language impairments are highly likely. Infants' brains are quite different in both structure and function, and we should exercise appropriate caution in drawing parallels between findings with infants and adults. In spite of this caveat, it is important to explore evidence for similar and different neurological/neurophysiological mechanisms that appear to be related to various aspects of early language learning, for our understanding of both typical as well as atypical infant development.

The Beginnings of Human Speech Perception

Late in prenatal development (at the start of the third trimester), human fetuses can hear (i.e., detect and/or react to sound). Fetuses are exposed to a variety of acoustic information, much of which consists of maternal speech sounds. Prenatally occurring maternal speech can be considered vibroacoustic because it resonates through the mothers' skeleton; maternal speech also occurs in a higher frequency band than most other *in utero* sounds, and it is louder at the fetal ear than typical airborne voices as it gets amplified by the bone structure of the female body. Prenatal work has shown that fetuses respond to their mothers' voices with greater heart rate changes (more heart rate decelerations, indicative of increased attention). After birth, newborns prefer their mothers' voice compared to an unknown female's voice, perhaps due to their exposure to the maternal voice *in utero*. Interestingly, newborns do not prefer the voices of their fathers, suggesting that male voices are not as readily available for fetal perception.

A more direct demonstration of fetal learning comes from a study with pregnant women in Paris, who read a nursery rhyme aloud three times a day for 4 weeks toward the end of their pregnancies. Prior to delivery, two nursery rhymes were presented via loudspeakers to the fetuses; the one the mothers had been reciting and a novel rhyme. The fetuses showed significant changes in heart rate to the familiar rhyme but no change in heart

Table 2   Current psychophysiological methodologies for studying infants' language perception

OT (optical topography)	The recording of changes in vascular blood flow from the scalp by measuring the absorption of infrared light in the brain (2–3 cm from the surface); cerebral blood flow increases in areas that are more active depending on the task. Optical fibers are placed on the scalp to both emit and detect changes in blood flow. Can be administered during sleep.
EEG (electroen-cephalogram)	The recording of electrical activity from the scalp, which reflects patterns of cortical activation/deactivation caused by synchronous firing of neuron assemblies. Although the temporal resolution of EEG activity is poor, it is a useful measure of the relationship between patterns of brain activity in relation to perceptual/cognitive function. Must be administered while awake.
ERP (event-related potential)	The recording of electrical activity from the scalp, similar to EEG except that the change in cortical activation/deactivation is time-locked to the onset of a discrete event. Of primary interest is the latency to significant changes in the amplitude of activation patterns (i.e., waveforms) that reflect brain activity during event processing. Can be administered during sleep.
MMN (mismatch negativity)	An ERP waveform component that is generated by an unexpected change in some repetitive string of events (e.g., a sudden change in the pitch of successive tones). MMN is evoked in response to changes in the physical features of a sound stimulus such as frequency, location, intensity and duration and also changes in patterns of sound. Can be administered during sleep.
fMRI (functional MRI)	The recording of changes in cerebral metabolic activity (blood volume shifts and blood oxygenation) in specific areas of cortex as a function of task parameters. The spatial resolution of fMRI (localization of cortical sources) is superior to EEG, but temporal resolution is similar to ERP. Can be administered during sleep.
Heart rate change	The recording of average length of interbeat intervals (heart period) during event processing. Increases in heart period reflect heart rate deceleration (associated with attention) whereas decreases in heart period reflect heart rate acceleration (associated with alerting or attention termination). Administered while awake.

rate to the unfamiliar rhyme. Other evidence of prenatal language learning has shown that when pregnant women recite a passage regularly, 2–3-day-old newborns modify their sucking patterns in ways that allow them to hear the familiar passage. Newborns prefer recordings of their mothers' voices filtered in ways that mimic how such voices sound *in utero* over unfiltered versions that newborns experience after birth. Also, newborns prefer recordings of their native language (even when spoken by unfamiliar females).

Although it is unclear which aspects of maternal language are perceived prenatally, it appears that some information specific to the mother (her vocal signature) and her native tongue (language rhythm) are evident in the prenatal environment, and that this experience biases the newborn toward certain language sounds after birth. In contrast, one recent study with newborns suggests that not all early biasing comes from prenatal experience with mothers' voices. In this study, newborns showed a preference (**Figure 5**) for nonsense words (e.g., 'neem') over nonspeech sounds that shared every acoustic dimension with the nonsense words, except the spectral properties that allowed the words to sound 'speech-like'. Similar findings have come from our laboratory with 1-month-olds in which they showed a preference for normal speech over speech that was filtered to preserve its pitch patterning, but obscured the words (this is in contrast to the study mentioned above in which newborns preferred to hear a filtered version of their mother). From these results, it appears that infants are more likely to pay attention to speech sounds than nonspeech sounds (when the voice is someone other than their own mother), even

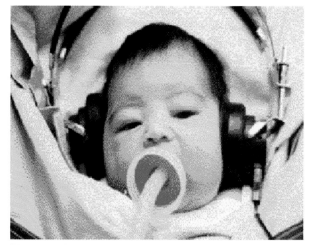

Figure 5   Picture of a 2-day-old newborn wearing headphones and sucking on a non-nutritive nipple that allows her to hear certain speech recordings, depending on when and how she sucks. Reprinted from Dr. Willam Fifer.

from the earliest days after birth, and may reflect a strong perceptual bias toward language.

Such behavioral findings are supported by recent neurophysiological studies on whether there is an early developmental sensitivity to language-specific information in newborns. For example, using both OT and functional MRI (fMRI), researchers have found greater activation (e.g., increased blood flow) in language-specific brain regions in both Italian and French newborns to forward speech, compared to the same speech played backwards or to silence. Interestingly, other studies have found that newborns are more responsive to displays of the human face than to almost any other visual scene, suggesting that from birth, the human infant is highly attuned to visual and auditory concomitants of language. This face + voice sensitivity may be advantageous for infants' perceptual, emotional, and cognitive development during the numerous interpersonal interactions they are about to experience.

The Social and Emotional Ecology of Infant Language Learning

Language learning after birth takes place in a rich, interactive context in which caregivers, siblings, and others communicate with infants in order to regulate their attention, modulate their emotions and arousal levels, and teach them about themselves and the world around them. Moreover, infants are also surrounded by ongoing communication events between other partners and have numerous opportunities to observe dynamic properties of these exchanges. Thus, the consideration of early language learning is best served by a full description of this social milieu, especially with regard to the emergent communication patterns between infants and others.

Across many of the worlds' cultures, adults interact vocally with infants via speech and song. Infant-directed speech (IDS) often sounds considerably different from the speech that adults use when interacting with other adults, that is, adult-directed speech (ADS). When comparing the two, IDS is characterized by higher pitch, greater pitch variability, fewer words per utterance, longer pauses between utterances, slower rate, more repetition, and greater hyperarticulation (speech that is clearly enunciated). Generally, these are referred to as 'prosodic modifications' in that they primarily influence the way that speech 'sounds' to the listener. Adults often modify speech prosody to convey emotion, increase emphasis, and highlight intention, particularly in their speech to infants and children. When addressing infants, such modifications occur in the speech of mothers, fathers, other adults, and even children, and occur within a wide variety of language cultures (French, Italian, German, Japanese, Mandarin, Spanish, Australian, British English, American English, Japanese Sign Language, American Sign Language).

Several studies have shown that infants (especially when young) prefer IDS over ADS, although this depends on certain aspects of the testing context. For example, 1-month-olds show no preference for IDS over ADS when both are spoken by their own mother. However, they do prefer IDS when both are spoken by an unknown female. This further suggests the potency of the maternal voice for infant attention, possibly due to prenatal experience with the mother's voice, as young infants' preference for the maternal voice can override their preference for IDS. In contrast, 4-month-olds prefer IDS over ADS even when both are spoken by their mothers, showing their

emerging interest in this enhanced speaking style and perhaps the diminished potency of the maternal voice as infants age. When paired with a smiling female face, female IDS effectively increases infants' attention, but female ADS does not. As infants get older, IDS has been found to increase attention, aid in emotion regulation, highlight linguistic information, and enable infants to better discriminate speaker gender, speech content, and temporal synchrony of facial information (coordination of lips, voice, and face movements).

Recently, it has been argued that infants' attention to IDS is primarily due to their perception of its emotional valence, especially for positive vocal emotion or 'happy talk'. Typically, IDS is emotionally rich, which may help to highlight the communicative intent (**Figure 6**) of the speaker. In fact, adults more accurately classify speaker intent when listening to IDS compared to ADS utterances. Interestingly, when IDS and ADS are equated for emotion valence (both speech types are rated by adults as 'happy'), infants show no preference for IDS over ADS. Likewise, when pitch characteristics are held constant, but one group of IDS utterances are judged as 'happy' and another judged as 'sad', infants prefer the happy speech. Therefore, it may be more accurate to say that infants are particularly drawn to speech that conveys a high degree of positive emotion, and that IDS is more likely to do so (at least in some cultures) than ADS. This being said, it is

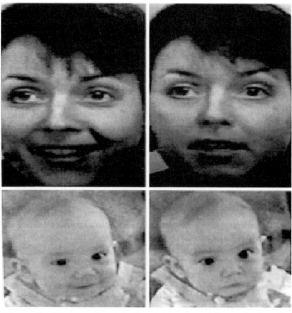

Figure 6 Picture of an infant watching two videos of a female speaker. On the left, she is presenting IDS, and on the right she is presenting ADS. Note the differences in emotional expression on the infant's face to these two interactive styles. Reprinted from Werker JF and McLeod PJ (1989) Infant preference for both male and female infant-directed talk: A developmental study of attentional and affective responsiveness. *Canadian Journal of Psychology* 43: 230–246.

not the case that happy speech is the only speech to which infants respond, as IDS is often employed and effective when calming distressed infants or prohibiting activity in older infants. The vocal components of soothing and prohibitive speech are not the same as those in happy speech, yet infants readily respond to both.

The manner in which adults convey their emotions in speech to infants changes developmentally across the first postnatal year. It has been found that mother's adapt their patterns of interaction (including their voices but also facial and body gestures) according to the age of their infants. More specifically, mothers modify their voices primarily to calm and soothe a newborn and gently introduce them into social interactions. There is also an important social dynamic that is evident in these early communicative patterns not only for the infant but for adults as well. Studies that have compared caregivers' speaking and singing styles both in the presence and absence of their infants have found that mothers exaggerate their prosody more when interacting with their infants. That is, they sing and speak in a higher pitched voice, with a slower tempo, place more pauses between phrases, and have a more loving tone but only when their infant is actually present. Comparatively, the extent of these prosodic modulations declines when mothers sing as if their infant was present.

Although infants and caregivers contribute uniquely to the social situation, most often the caregiver is the more responsible agent for the coordination of the social interaction. Over time, these interactions lay the foundation for infants' understanding of their own emotions as well as the emotional messages being expressed to them. From 3 to 9 months, mothers typically alter their different intonation patterns that help optimize interactions (elicit attention and encourage participation), particularly as this is a time in which infants are able to initiate and contribute as an active partner in the social interchange. Infants appear to differentiate these interactive patterns, even by their vocal characteristics alone. When familiarized with different female voices, all conveying the same intention (e.g., eliciting activity), infants do not increase their attention to a new voice with the same intention, but do increase their attention to a new voice from a different intention category (e.g., calming). Additionally, 5-month-olds have shown differences in facial affect when presented with approval and prohibitive IDS (more smiling to approvals, more negative emotion to prohibitives). Interestingly, infants did not show any affective differences in response to approval and prohibitive ADS. These results suggest that infants can discriminate affective vocal expressions occurring in IDS and that it is more effective than ADS in eliciting infant emotion.

By 9 months, mothers actually attenuate some of the vocal exaggerations associated with positive emotion, replacing them with an increase in their use of directive utterances ("Don't put that in your mouth, sweetie."). As we will see in the next section, it is during this time that infants are becoming more aware of and tuned into the linguistic structure of their language, and thus may not rely as much on exaggerated vocal emotion to maintain their attention to speech. In fact, recent evidence from our laboratory suggests that the preference for IDS over ADS seen in younger infants is somewhat weaker in 8-month-olds. One interesting question that arises from studies investigating infants' speech preferences is whether the vocal emotion in IDS differentially affects infant learning at various ages. In her recent dissertation project, N. Bhullar found that 11–13-month-old infants discriminated a change in a target word carried in a set of IDS sentences (that remained constant) when they were presented by a dynamic female speaker who was portraying a happy expression. In contrast, another group of same-aged infants did not discriminate the word change under similar conditions except that the female speaker was portraying a sad expression.

In one of the few psychophysiological studies to focus on the perception of emotional prosody in speech, 7-month-old infants' event-related potentials (ERPs) were compared to happy, neutral, and angry speech. The amplitude of the first negative ERP wave was greatest for angry speech over frontal areas of the infants' brains (indicating more emotional attention to this event) and the amplitude of the first slow, positive ERP was greatest for happy and angry speech over temporal areas, but not so for neutral speech. This ERP pattern suggests enhanced sensory processing of emotionally loaded linguistic events (happy and angry speech). These psychophysiological data support the hypothesis that infants are primarily responsive to the emotional valence of speech, but they do not address the issue of whether infants prefer one emotional valence to another (e.g., happy over angry speech).

To this point, it is clear that the language ecology of the infant is replete with speech that appears tailored to their interests and needs, even if the primary motivation of adults who talk to infants is to convey their feelings of warmth and nurturance. From this input, infants construct their initial understanding of their native language, so we now turn to those processes that allow infants to decipher the information they will need to become competent communicators with those around them.

Infants' Perception of the Speech Stream

As is clear from the section above, the input to the infant is a critical aspect of language development. Given the complexities of language, however, it is not immediately obvious how any given language learner, but especially an infant, manages to listen to, comprehend, and then produce meaningful speech. As it turns out, infants can (and do) attend to many different aspects of language, and this perceptual multiplicity is highly adaptive because perception at one level almost always informs the perceiver about language at other levels (in the developmental literature, this is called 'bootstrapping').

By way of illustrating this point, we will discuss infants' perception of prosody (the intonation and rhythm patterns of language) and phonology (the individual speech sounds of language) as each pertains to the acquisition of language-relevant information. Although prosody and phonology continuously interact in natural speech (see **Figure 7**), it has been fruitful to consider them as separate sources of information for infants' language learning. Recall that prosody can reside above the level of individual speech sounds (e.g., the emotional tone of utterances), but it can also be linguistically relevant. Prosodic features provide important cues for phrase, clause, and word segmentation, and contribute to languages' stereotypical sounds.

Phonology often refers to individual speech sounds, such as consonants, vowels, clicks, and tone changes (e.g., in Thai) that are linguistically significant. The world's languages vary greatly in phonotactic structure, with some languages allowing certain combinations of speech sounds while excluding others (e.g., th- but not dp- at the start of an English word). Phonology also involves the combinations of phonemes into higher-order elements that are lexically meaningful (morphemes, syllables, words). Clearly, infants learning a language must perceive and produce its phonotactic elements, so a considerable amount of research has concentrated on this developmental process.

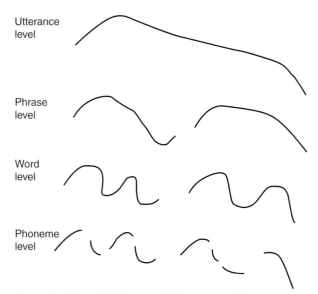

Figure 7 Hierarchical levels of pitch contours in human speech, starting with phonemes (lower portion) and ending with utterance level intonation contours (upper portion). Reprinted from Sagisaga Y (1990) Speech synthesis from text. *IEEE Communications Magazine* 28: 35-41.

Utterance level

Phrase level

Word level

Phoneme level

Perception of Prosody

Because the prosody of IDS is highly exaggerated and infants' attend more to IDS than to other speaking styles, IDS is likely to be advantageous for its language-promoting properties. One such prosodic source is linguistic rhythm, which varies across the world's languages. Some languages are stress-timed (their rhythm is determined by differential vocal emphasis on certain syllables) whereas others are syllable-timed (their rhythm is fairly constant because all syllables receive similar emphasis, but some syllables may receive stress primarily through consonant/vowel lengthening) or mora-timed (their rhythm is influenced more by voicing durations, in that some syllables contain vowels that are longer than others). Within stress-timed languages (such as English and Dutch), some are dominated by a strong–weak trochaic pattern (as in English words such as 'féline' and 'pérson') compared to a weak–strong iambic pattern (such as the English words 'sustáin' and 'decidé'). Other kinds of prosodic features include intonation contours as they relate to communicative intent (e.g., rising pitch movement toward the end of a sentence to convey a question), lengthening of vowels in final syllables to indicate that a sentence is coming to an end, and periods of silence that indicate separation between successive utterances/words.

As early as 4 days old, newborns discriminate their native from a non-native language, even if the speech is acoustically filtered but leaving the prosodic contours intact. However, no discrimination is seen if newborns hear these filtered contours played in reverse, suggesting that the dynamics of forward pitch movement in speech is one early source of familiarity for infants. Newborns can distinguish between two languages with different stress/rhythm patterns (e.g., Dutch and Japanese) but have considerable difficulty discriminating two languages within the same stress category (e.g., Dutch and English). With more experience and better perceptual skills, 4-month-olds (and older infants) begin to show discrimination between languages within the same rhythm class, such as Spanish and Catalan, and even between two accented versions of the same language (American English and British English). In general, it appears that language stress or rhythm is one of the first ways in which infants begin to categorize languages, with broad rhythmic classes acting as perceptual 'anchors' from which they refine their perception of differences across and within their own and other languages.

Several neuropsychological studies have found support for infants' perception of linguistic prosody, one of the major cues for speech segmentation (e.g., stress patterns, phrases, clauses, words). Five-month-old, but not 4-month-old, German infants showed significant mismatched-negativity (MMN) effects in brain activity while hearing strings of bisyllabic words with their native stress pattern (e.g., trochaic) punctuated by an occasional word with a different stress pattern (e.g., iambic). Although these results show infants' attunement to the prevalent stress pattern in their native language, the results are slightly different from those found with behavioral studies. As mentioned above, infants show preferences for their native stress patterns in individual words at around 7 months of age, but not earlier. Thus, the discrepancy is in the finding that 5-month-olds discriminated a change in syllable-level stress whereas no preference for dominant native stress pattern has been seen until about 7.5 months of age. This most likely reflects younger infants' sensitivities to cues that do differentiate words before they are able to perceive that one such pattern predominates in their own native system. This is similar to the finding that younger infants discriminate both native and non-native phoneme contrasts, before they become attuned to those that are present in their own language. However, it would be interesting to couple the use of ERP and behavioral protocols in the same sample of infants to verify that discrimination using one technique does not necessarily predict discrimination in the other, contingent on infant age.

With age and experience, infants' perception of prosodic stress/rhythm continues to improve, helping infants with a particularly difficult task: segmenting ongoing speech into syllables and words, particularly in the second half of the first postnatal year. Studies have shown that by 6 months, American infants prefer native over non-native words (e.g., English vs. Norwegian), and by 9 months, infants prefer bisyllabic words with the predominate stress patterns of their native language (e.g., trochaic or iambic), even if the words are filtered to reduce phonetic information. Within this same age range, infants are also able to use stress patterns to isolate words from sentences, but more so if the words reflect their language's dominant stress pattern. For example, American 7-month-olds recognize words like *doc*tor and *can*dle (trochaic) after hearing these in sentences, but they do not recognize words like gui*tar* (iambic), suggesting that infants use the strong syllable (the one with the primary stress) as the start of a word. Of course, as infants get older, they become more adept at extracting words from sentences with any given stress pattern, including weak syllables, but this is a harder perceptual feat and no doubt requires more language experience.

There is evidence that 2–3-day-old infants can use prosodic cues to help mark the onset of phrase and clause boundaries in continuous speech. These cues are helpful to newborns because they highlight certain units of language and allow for further processing (they can focus on phrase-level vs. sentence-level strings). Likewise, 6-month-olds listen longer to IDS sentences in which natural clauses are bounded by short pauses compared to sentences in which pauses have been artificially inserted, suggesting

that even silence can act as a perceptual cue to phonological boundaries. Interestingly, this same pattern is seen in older infants with words in that they prefer pauses between words rather than within them, but only when the words are not filtered. This is important because the finding that this preference does not emerge when the word-level information is not available demonstrates that as infants grow older and gain more experience with language, they progressively integrate both prosodic (e.g., pauses) and phonological (e.g., specific consonants and vowels) cues for speech segmentation.

Infants may also integrate across prosodic and phonological levels in their speech preferences given the results of several recent experiments in our laboratory. We have found that American 6-month-olds prefer Australian female IDS over American female IDS (even when the same sentences are being spoken), but not if the speech is low-pass filtered (the words are no longer available). In other experiments, we also found that 10-month-olds preferred native utterances (i.e., American) over non-native utterances (e.g., Mandarin), but only within IDS; when using ADS, no preferences were found. It is possible that when listening to ADS, infants did not attend as much to the phonological information in order to recognize utterances as native speech. In sum, the prosodic aspects of language are readily perceived by infants during the entire first postnatal year, and appear to provide important cues to native language structure and to breaking into the speech stream in order to learn about its lexical elements. Next we consider infants' perception at this more elemental level.

Perception of Phonology

Phonemes are the basic sound units in any given language that have become incorporated into formal language systems. For many of the worlds' languages, phonemes consist of various combinations of consonants (C) and vowels (V). For other languages, a phoneme can also be defined as a CV+tone combination. For example, in Thai, ma(rising pitch) is a different phoneme from ma (falling pitch). Phonemes can be differentiated at many levels, such as: (1) their place and/or manner of articulation (e.g., whether the lips are closed or open during production), (2) their voicing properties (e.g., whether activity in the larynx begins prior to full production), and (3) degree of aspiration (or airflow) during production.

From the newborn period onward, infants from all language cultures appear capable of discriminating phonemes (notice a change from one to another), with two features of early phoneme perception being especially noteworthy. First, infants (like adults) perceive phonemes categorically. That is, they discriminate the phonemes /ba/ and /pa/, because they come from two distinct categories (according to an acoustic feature called voice onset time).

However, they do not discriminate two versions of 'pa' [pa_1 vs. pa_2] or two versions of ba [ba_1 vs. ba_2] even though acoustically these pairs are just as distinct as the ba/pa contrast, yet they do not cross category boundaries.

The second interesting aspect of phoneme perception is that younger infants respond categorically to speech contrasts that are present in their native language, and also to those that are not present in their native language (i.e., non-native phonemes they have not previously heard). This is true for both consonants and vowels, suggesting that early phonetic perception derives from more general auditory competencies. However, with age and experience, infants continue to discriminate native phonemes, but have more difficulty discriminating non-native speech sounds. This has generally been referred to as perceptual attunement, resulting from infants' increasing attention to and encoding of native language information.

Interestingly, this pattern of initial perceptual openness followed by progressive narrowing across infancy is seen in other domains. For example, younger infants discriminate between pairs of human faces as well as primate faces, but older infants only maintain discrimination of human faces, even if the primate faces are accompanied by distinct vocalizations. Most recently, infants have even shown discrimination of video presentations of both native and non-native phonemes (with no sound track) at younger ages, but not at older ages. In the older group, only discrimination of native visual phonemes was evident.

Neurophysiological studies support these general behavioral patterns (categorical perception and perceptual attunement). Newborns and slightly older infants show distinct ERPs to categorical changes in consonants, especially those involving voice-onset-time differences. Such category-specific ERPs have been observed over several cortical areas, some involving the right or left hemisphere, and some involving both. Interestingly, distinct ERPs occur in infants when listening to phonemes with place-of-articulation differences but these effects are observed primarily over the left temporal areas (a more adult-like pattern). Discrimination of changes in phoneme categories (both consonants and vowels) has also been observed using MMN measures. For example, newborns show a distinct MMN pattern when presented with two Finnish vowels. MMN has also been observed in English 8-month-olds to the CV pairs /da/ and /ta/. In a similar study, MMN was recorded from Finnish infants at 6 and 12 months of age in a longitudinal design, and from Estonian 12-month-old infants. Both groups of infants were tested for their discrimination of changes in Finnish and in Estonian vowels. The results showed a significant MMN response in the 6-month-olds to both native (Finnish) and non-native (Estonian) vowels, and also in the 12-month-old Estonian infants to their native vowels. However, all infants at 12 months showed diminished MMN to non-native vowels.

Likewise, in a longitudinal ERP study, American infants at 7 and 11 months of age were presented with native and non-native speech contrasts. The results showed no difference in ERP latency or magnitude in speech-related components to either native or non-native contrasts at 7 months of age, but only the native contrasts elicited these same ERP patterns at 11 months of age. This is consistent with the behavioral data reported with non-native speech discrimination. We might expect, then, that the underlying biological substrates that subserve language processing are the same across infants and adults. Infants between 13- and 17-months of age also show larger amplitude ERP responses to known than to unknown words, with this difference evident in both hemispheres in the frontal, parietal and temporal lobes. By 20 months of age, however, this ERP enhancement is restricted to the left hemisphere over the temporal and parietal lobes only, indicating a gradual specialization of the neural systems for processing words (and much more akin to the pattern seen in adults). These results were further corroborated in a study with 14- and 20-month-olds in which they heard known words, unknown words that were phonetically similar to the known words, and unknown words that were phonetically dissimilar from the known words. Both age groups showed higher amplitude ERP responses to known than to unknown words. However, the 14-month-olds' ERP responses were similar in amplitude for known words and phonetically similar unknown words which imply that these words were confusing. In contrast, ERP responses in the 20-month-olds to the phonetically similar unknown words were the same as those to the unknown words. These findings show that the older infants improved processing of phonetic detail with experience compared to the younger infants.

Thus, young infants show consistent brain-related responses to different speech sounds (supporting the behavioral evidence) but their brain-localization patterns in response to different phonemes appears to depend (at least to some extent) on the nature of the information in the speech sounds that make them distinct. Vocal-timing differences appear to be represented more diffusely in the infant brain whereas place/manner of articulation takes on a more adult-like representation (left-temporal localization). This could be due to less cortical specificity for timing in general (because timing is a process involved in many domains of perceptual functioning) and/or because there are multiple pathways available for speech processing in the developing nervous system, given that the infant is less experienced with speech in general. This latter possibility may help to explain one study which examined infants' processing of their native language compared to a non-native language and to backwards speech. The results showed that areas of cortex in infants' brains that are activated by the native language are not completely confined to the primary auditory areas but include those similar to adults in their localization (temporal region) and lateralization (left hemisphere). This early lack of specificity has also been found using ERP methods with 6-month-olds, in which same-component ERPs to words are equally large over temporal and occipital (typically referred to as visual cortex) brain regions. Interestingly, between 6 and 36 months of age, there is a gradual decrease in the ERP amplitude to vocal words (i.e., decreased processing) over occipital areas but the amplitude remains unchanged over temporal areas.

Such findings point to a common process of perceptual attunement to culturally relevant information throughout the first postnatal year. In terms of language development, infants begin building linguistic representations of phonemes so that their subsequent perception is guided by the fit between an incoming speech sound and these phonemic representations. We have also seen that prosodic information appears to assist infants in this focusing on important elements of speech (prosody bootstraps the discovery of phonemic detail). But what happens if the speech stream that infants' hear is prosodically attenuated, as is more likely the case when the caregiver seeks to soothe and calm a distressed infant. Such soothing speech is more likely to be lower in pitch, pitch variance, amplitude, and slow. Therefore, are infants not as perceptually attuned to language in these instances? Would infants not learn language if only an ADS style of speaking was available to them?

Perception of Conditional Probability

These questions can be addressed by studies examining another process that appears to facilitate infants' segmentation of words, called statistical learning. Statistical learning occurs when perceivers are sensitive to the conditional probabilities of the occurrence of adjacent events, over time. When applied to speech, statistical learning refers to the conditional probability that one phoneme will follow another. For example, if the probability of 'mas' being followed by 'cot' is high (let's say close to 90%), then a listener might anticipate the sequence 'mascot'. Such sensitivity to conditional probabilities leads to the perceptual grouping of high probability strings (or phoneme clusters), allowing listeners to parse units (e.g., words) from the speech stream relatively rapidly and efficiently. Recently, 8-month-old infants were played continuous strings of speech sounds with no prosodic cues present (e.g., pagotiku...pagotikitula) in which the conditional probabilities of some phonemes (pagoti) were higher than others. In a subsequent test, infants showed different amounts of attention to 'words' such as 'pagoti' compared to nonwords such as 'dotapa' (the conditional probability of this string was very low). So even in the absence of prosodic cues, infants can use other information to help find words in speech. Nonetheless, other

recent studies have found that when infants have a choice between prosodic and conditional probability cues for segmentation, they tend to rely on prosody first.

In sum, the speech that is characteristically available during interactions between adults and infants appears to be organized in a way that facilitates language processing. In fact, even adults who are learning words from a non-native language benefit from this same kind of speaking style. These benefits derive from the structure of the input itself, especially that the prosodic and phonotactic characteristics are exaggerated in ways that make speech information more perceptually available. Overall, the evidence from neurophysiological studies supports those using only behavioral measures of infants' speech processing abilities (e.g., phoneme discrimination; discrimination of linguistic stress). However, the correspondence between adults and infants regarding cortical patterns of localization for speech is less clear. Some level of cortical organization for speech is apparent, but the precise patterning of area-specific increases in activation is dependent on method and/or speech information. Clearly, this is an area of concern for future infant speech research, and will no doubt benefit from continued improvements in technologies as well as infant-specific cortical models.

Relating Research from the Laboratory to Infants' Language-Learning Ecology

To this point, we have considered the nature of speech to infants and how it appears to be ideally suited to maximize attention and highlight information that needs to be culled from the speech stream in order to learn language. We have also seen that to some extent, early language perception is subserved by patterns of cortical organization that promote language processing (e.g., specialization of the left hemisphere for speech). In this last section, we turn to a slightly different issue in considering the context in which language learning takes place, and whether the current literature on infants' perception of speech can address issues of ecological validity. Ideally, language learning takes place in a quiet environment, one in which the speech signal can easily be attended to and identified, processed and stored for later use. In contrast, most infants face more challenging learning situations in their daily lives. Infants acquire language in homes filled with sources of multisensory information (sounds, sights, smells, textures), that can include multiple caregiver and siblings, and an endless list of potential distractors and competitors for attention. In the laboratory, most of this complexity is substantially reduced to make the perceptual task more accessible to the infant, and to increase the likelihood that learning will occur, but this is done at the risk of potentially misrepresenting the natural context for language learning, and so may reduce external validity. We will review the results of studies that have brought some of this natural complexity into the laboratory in interesting ways, and then we will also make suggestions for how future studies can be designed to more accurately model the language learning ecology during infancy.

Given that most natural language learning situations contain more than one sound source at any point in time, infants must be able to separate speech from background distraction, a process known as streaming. Compared to adults, infants appear to be at a disadvantage for streaming because they have: (1) higher auditory detection thresholds (sounds, including speech, need to be louder before they can be detected), (2) higher auditory discrimination thresholds (sounds, including speech, in both quiet and noise, need to be more discrepant before a change from one to another can be detected), and (3) more difficulty localizing sound in space. Also, unlike adults, infants do not listen more selectively to the frequency band within which most speech sounds occur, which means they are attending to other areas of auditory space that are not necessary for perceiving language.

Nonetheless, infants do perceive speech and learn much about their native language in spite of noisy environments and limitations in their perceptual skills. Once again, it may be IDS that helps to facilitate speech perception under demanding conditions. A series of experiments have found that infants can successfully match a voice track with its complementary video of a female speaker when a distracting male voice has been superimposed on her speech, if she is using IDS; if she is using ADS, no such matching occurs. Similarly, infants are able to learn words being repeated by a female IDS speaker even when a male distractor voice is superimposed on hers. However, they do not learn words if these voices are reversed (i.e., the words are delivered by a male ADS speaker with a female IDS distractor voice superimposed on his). Infants show this same kind of enhanced attention when the speaker's voice is someone they know (e.g., their own mother) compared to an unknown female. Thus, the combination of IDS and familiarity appears to help infants focus on both speakers and what is being said.

The ability of familiarity to aid infants' speech perception was shown in a similar study in which infants listened longer to a female speaker when she uttered the infant's own name compared to when she uttered the names of other infants, even when several background female voices were superimposed on the target voice. Importantly, infants' recognition of familiar words in the speech stream (e.g., their own names) also seems to increase the saliency of adjacent words, allowing infants to better process them. It is thought that frequency of sound patterns that are heard repetitively early in the first year are the first steps in building a lexicon. Around 6 months of age, infants respond more to utterances that contain their names than to those containing other

infants' names (matched for syllable structure). Capitalizing on this finding, researchers familiarized 6-month-olds with utterances containing the infants own names or others' names, along with target words directly before and after the embedded name. They found that the infants were more likely to recognize isolated target words in a subsequent test when they had occurred adjacent to the infant's own name.

There are many cognitive processes associated with an infant's ability to comprehend speech in noise that are relevant to language learning. Speech stream segregation involves infant discrimination of speech from other sources of information (particularly other acoustics), perceptual identification of speech and cues occurring from a specific speaker, and selective attention to that speaker. If there is a deficiency in any of these cognitive processes, an infant's ability to hear speech in noise will be impaired. Further, it has been suggested that if an infant does have difficulty discriminating speech in a noisy environment it may have underpinnings for later language development, as poorer ability to segregate streams of speech could potentially lead to slower language acquisition. This variability in infant performance has yet to be fully explored.

Finally, most existing studies on infants' language learning have employed methods that rely primarily on the presentation of language (whether phonemes, words, or utterances) either in the absence of a face and/or in the presence of an arbitrary visual event (e.g., a checkerboard). However, language learning often takes place in face-to-face interactions between infants and caregivers, and there is often concurrent information about how the sound looks as it is articulated, the timing of the sound with its visual movement in the face, whether or not it is exaggerated in its production (both vocally and facially), and the ways in which speech is complemented by gestures. An important demonstration of the power of face+voice information on infants' perception of consonants is provided by studies involving the McGurk Effect. For example, 4.5-month-old infants were familiarized with a female speaker who was mouthing the phoneme /ga/ but the video was accompanied by her voice saying /ba/. When adults view this video, they perceive a blended phoneme of either /da/ or /tha/. When the infants were tested after familiarization, they only paid attention to the phoneme /ba/, suggesting that they perceived this phoneme as novel even though it is actually the one they heard during familiarization. So, the infants most likely perceived the blended phoneme, like adults, rather than the actual phoneme. This demonstrates the power of the face to influence infants' perception of speech, but this aspect of language learning has largely been ignored in previous research.

Taken together, it is clear that the field of infant speech perception has made great strides toward our understanding of one of the most interesting and important feats in development. With our focus on new and exciting questions, coupled with our continued creativity in designing laboratory tasks that capture the essence of the natural context in which language is learned, this field of research will continue to contribute to our ability to fully characterize language acquisition, and all of its inherent complexities.

See also: Auditory Development and Hearing Disorders; Bilingualism; Down Syndrome; Grammar; Habituation and Novelty; Language Acquisition Theories; Language Development: Overview; Language Acquisition Theories; Learning; Literacy; Music Perception; Perceptual Development; Pragmatic Development; Semantic Development; Speech Perception.

Suggested Readings

Aslin RN, Jusczyk PW, and Pisoni DB (1998) Speech and auditory processing during infancy. In: Kuhn D and Siegler RS (eds.) *Handbook of Child Psychology: Vol. 2. Cognition, Perception, and Language*, pp. 199–254. New York: Wiley.

Jusczyk PW (1997) *The Discovery of Spoken Language.* Cambridge, MA: MIT Press.

Kitamura C and Burnham DK (2003) Pitch and communicative intent in mother's speech: Adjustments for age and sex in the first year. *Infancy* 4: 85–110.

Lavelli M and Fogel A (2005) Developmental changes in the relationship between the infant's attention and emotion during early face-to-face communication: the 2-month transition. *Developmental Psychology* 41: 265–280.

Mehler J (1995) Maturation and learning of language in the first year of life. In: Gazzaniga MS (ed.) *The Cognitive Neurosciences*, pp. 943–954. 943–954. Cambridge, MA: MIT Press.

Sagisaga Y (1990) Speech synthesis from text. *IEEE Communications Magazine* 28: 35–41.

Werker JF and Curtin S (2005) PRIMIR: A developmental framework of infant speech processing. *Language Learning and Development* 1: 197–234.

Werker JF and Desjardins RN (1995) Listening to speech in the first year of life: Experiential influences on phoneme perception. *Current Directions in Psychological Sciences* 4: 76–81.

Werker JF and McLeod PJ (1989) Infant preference for both male and female infant-directed talk: A developmental study of attentional and affective responsiveness. *Canadian Journal of Psychology* 43: 230–246.

Werker JF and Vouloumanos A (2001) Speech and language processing in infancy: A neurocognitive approach. In: Nelson CA and Luciana M (eds.) *Handbook of Developmental Cognitive Neuroscience*, pp. 269–280. Cambridge, MA: MIT Press.